Prepare for Class "Read the Book"

Feature	Description	Benefit	Page
Every chapter begins with....			
Chapter Opening Article & Project	Each chapter begins with a current article and ends with a related project.	The Article describes a real situation. The Project lets you apply what you learned to solve a related problem.	246, 347
Internet-based Projects 	The projects allow for the integration of spreadsheet technology that students will need to be a productive member of the workforce.	The projects allow the opportunity for students to collaborate and use mathematics to deal with issues that come up in their lives.	246, 347
Every section begins with....			
Learning Objectives 1	Each section begins with a list of objectives. Objectives also appear in the text where the objective is covered.	These focus your studying by emphasizing what's most important and where to find it.	267
Most sections contain...			
PREPARING FOR THIS SECTION	Most sections begin with a list of key concepts to review with page numbers.	Ever forget what you've learned? This feature highlights previously learned material to be used in this section. Review it, and you'll always be prepared to move forward.	267
Now Work the 'Are You Prepared?' Problems	Problems that assess whether you have the prerequisite knowledge for the upcoming section.	Not sure you need the Preparing for This Section review? Work the 'Are You Prepared?' problems. If you get one wrong, you'll know exactly what you need to review and where to review it!	267, 278
"Now Work" PROBLEMS	These follow most examples and direct you to a related exercise.	We learn best by doing. You'll solidify your understanding of examples if you try a similar problem right away, to be sure you understand what you've just read.	274, 276
WARNING	Warnings are provided in the text.	These point out common mistakes and help you to avoid them.	299, 300
Explorations and **Seeing the Concept**	These represent graphing utility activities to foreshadow a concept or solidify a concept just presented.	You will obtain a deeper and more intuitive understanding of theorems and definitions.	91, 272
In Words	These provide alternative descriptions of select definitions and theorems.	Does math ever look foreign to you? This feature translates math into plain English.	276
Calculus Icon	These appear next to information essential for the study of calculus.	Pay attention – if you spend extra time now, you'll do better later!	275
NEW! Showcase **EXAMPLES**	These examples provide "how-to" instruction by offering a guided, step-by-step approach to solving a problem.	With each step presented on the left and the mathematics displayed on the right, students can immediately see how each step is employed.	178–179
NEW! **Model It!** Examples and Problems	Marked with ⬤. These are examples and problems that require you to build a mathematical model from either a verbal description or data. The homework Model It! problems are marked by purple descriptions.	It is rare for a problem to come in the form, "Solve the following equation". Rather, the equation must be developed based on an explanation of the problem. These problems require you to develop models that will allow you to describe the problem mathematically and suggest a solution to the problem.	166, 197–206

Practice "Work the Problems"

Feature	Description	Benefit	Page
"Assess Your Understanding" contains a variety of problems at the end of each section.			
'Are You Prepared?' Problems	These assess your retention of the prerequisite material you'll need. Answers are given at the end of the section exercises. This feature is related to the Preparing for This Section feature.	Do you always remember what you've learned? Working these problems is the best way to find out. If you get one wrong, you'll know exactly what you need to review and where to review it!	267, 278
Concepts and Vocabulary	These short-answer questions, mainly Fill-in-the-Blank and True/False items, assess your understanding of key definitions and concepts in the current section.	It is difficult to learn math without knowing the language of mathematics. These problems test your understanding of the formulas and vocabulary.	278
Skill Building	Correlated to section examples, these problems provide straightforward practice.	It's important to dig in and develop your skills. These problems provide you with ample practice to do so.	278–280
NEW! Mixed Practice	These problems offer comprehensive assessment of the skills learned in the section by asking problems that relate to more than one concept or objective. These problems may also require you to utilize skills learned in previous sections.	Learning mathematics is a building process. Many concepts are interrelated. These problems help you see how mathematics builds on itself and also see how the concepts tie together.	280–281
Applications and Extensions	These problems allow you to apply your skills to real-world problems. These problems also allow you to extend concepts learned in the section.	You will see that the material learned within the section has many uses in everyday life.	281–283
Explaining Concepts: Discussion and Writing	"Discussion and Writing" problems are colored red. These support class discussion, verbalization of mathematical ideas, and writing and research projects.	To verbalize an idea, or to describe it clearly in writing, shows real understanding. These problems nurture that understanding. Many are challenging but you'll get out what you put in.	283
NEW! Interactive Exercises	In selected exercise sets, applets are provided to give a "hands-on" experience.	The applets allow students to interact with mathematics in an active learning environment. By exploring a variety of scenarios, the student is able to visualize the mathematics and develop a deeper conceptual understanding of the material.	103
"Now Work" PROBLEMS	Many examples refer you to a related homework problem. These related problems are marked by a pencil and yellow numbers.	If you get stuck while working problems, look for the closest Now Work problem and refer back to the related example to see if it helps.	267, 278
Graphing Calculator	These optional problems require the use of a graphing utility, and are marked by a special icon and green numbers.	Your instructor will usually provide guidance on whether or not to do these problems. If so, these problems help to verify and visualize your analytical results.	273

Review "Study for Quizzes and Tests"

Feature	Description	Benefit	Page
Chapter Reviews at the end of each chapter contain...			
"Things to Know"	A detailed list of important theorems, formulas, and definitions from the chapter.	Review these and you'll know the most important material in the chapter!	340–341
"You Should Be Able to..."	Contains a complete list of objectives by section, examples that illustrate the objective, and practice exercises that test your understanding of the objective.	Do the recommended exercises and you'll have mastery over the key material. If you get something wrong, review the suggested page numbers and try again.	341–342
Review Exercises	These provide comprehensive review and practice of key skills, matched to the Learning Objectives for each section.	Practice makes perfect. These problems combine exercises from all sections, giving you a comprehensive review in one place.	342–345
CHAPTER TEST	About 15–20 problems that can be taken as a Chapter Test. Be sure to take the Chapter Test under test conditions—no notes!	Be prepared. Take the sample practice test under test conditions. This will get you ready for your instructor's test. If you get a problem wrong, watch the Chapter Test Prep video.	346
CUMULATIVE REVIEW	These problem sets appear at the end of each chapter, beginning with Chapter 2. They combine problems from previous chapters, providing an ongoing cumulative review.	These are really important. They will ensure that you are not forgetting anything as you go. These will go a long way toward keeping you constantly primed for the final exam.	346–347
CHAPTER PROJECTS	The Chapter Project applies what you've learned in the chapter. Additional projects are available on the Instructor's Resource Center (IRC).	The Project gives you an opportunity to apply what you've learned in the chapter to solve a problem related to the opening article. If your instructor allows, these make excellent opportunities to work in a group, which is often the best way of learning math.	347–348
NEW! Internet-based Projects	In selected chapters, a web-based project is given.	The projects allow the opportunity for students to collaborate and use mathematics to deal with issues that come up in their lives.	347–348

To the Student

As you begin, you may feel anxious about the number of theorems, definitions, procedures, and equations. You may wonder if you can learn it all in time. Don't worry, your concerns are normal. This textbook was written with you in mind. If you attend class, work hard, and read and study this book, you will build the knowledge and skills you need to be successful. Here's how you can use the book to your benefit.

Read Carefully

When you get busy, it's easy to skip reading and go right to the problems. Don't... the book has a large number of examples and clear explanations to help you break down the mathematics into easy-to-understand steps. Reading will provide you with a clearer understanding, beyond simple memorization. Read before class (not after) so you can ask questions about anything you didn't understand. You'll be amazed at how much more you'll get out of class if you do this.

Use the Features

I use many different methods in the classroom to communicate. Those methods, when incorporated into the book, are called "features." The features serve many purposes, from providing timely review of material you learned before (just when you need it), to providing organized review sessions to help you prepare for quizzes and tests. Take advantage of the features and you will master the material.

To make this easier, I've provided a brief guide to getting the most from this book. Refer to the "Prepare for Class," "Practice," and "Review" pages on the inside front cover of this book. Spend fifteen minutes reviewing the guide and familiarizing yourself with the features by flipping to the page numbers provided. Then, as you read, use them. This is the best way to make the most of your textbook.

Please do not hesitate to contact me, through Pearson Education, with any questions, suggestions, or comments that would improve this text. I look forward to hearing from you, and good luck with all of your studies.

Best Wishes!

Michael Sullivan

STUDY SMARTER

Step-by-step solutions on video for all chapter test exercises from the text

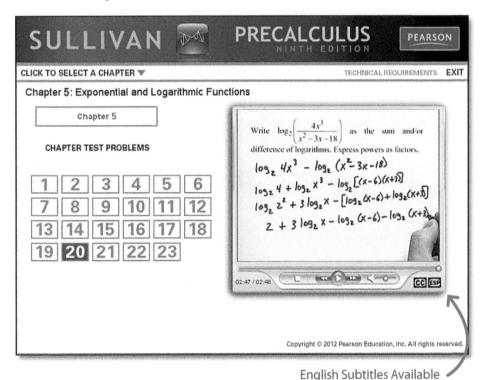

English Subtitles Available

CHAPTER TEST PREP VIDEOS ARE ACCESSIBLE THROUGH THE FOLLOWING:

*To the Memory of
My Mother and Father*

Michael Sullivan

Precalculus
Second Edition

Second Custom Edition for DePaul University

Taken from:
Precalculus, Ninth Edition
by Michael Sullivan

Cover Art: Courtesy of PhotoDisc/Getty Images.

Taken from:

Precalculus, Ninth Edition
by Michael Sullivan
Copyright © 2012, 2008, 2005, 2002 by Pearson Education, Inc.
Published by Prentice Hall
Upper Saddle River, New Jersey 07458

This special edition published in cooperation with Pearson Learning Solutions.

Pearson Learning Solutions, 501 Boylston Street, Suite 900, Boston, MA 02116
A Pearson Education Company
www.pearsoned.com

Printed in the United States of America

1 2 3 4 5 6 7 8 9 10 V092 16 15 14 13 12 11

000200010270747241

SD

ISBN 10: 1-256-34603-9
ISBN 13: 978-1-256-34603-6

Table of Contents

Three Distinct Series

Students have different goals, learning styles, and levels of preparation. Instructors have different teaching philosophies, styles, and techniques. Rather than write one series to fit all, the Sullivans have written three distinct series. All share the same goal—to develop a high level of mathematical understanding and an appreciation for the way mathematics can describe the world around us. The manner of reaching that goal, however, differs from series to series.

Contemporary Series, Ninth Edition

The Contemporary Series is the most traditional in approach yet modern in its treatment of precalculus mathematics. Graphing utility coverage is optional and can be included or excluded at the discretion of the instructor: *College Algebra, Algebra & Trigonometry, Trigonometry, Precalculus.*

Enhanced with Graphing Utilities Series, Fifth Edition

This series provides a more thorough integration of graphing utilities into topics, allowing students to explore mathematical concepts and foreshadow ideas usually studied in later courses. Using technology, the approach to solving certain problems differs from the Contemporary Series, while the emphasis on understanding concepts and building strong skills does not: *College Algebra, Algebra & Trigonometry, Trigonometry, Precalculus.*

Concepts through Functions Series, Second Edition

This series differs from the others, utilizing a functions approach that serves as the organizing principle tying concepts together. Functions are introduced early in various formats. This approach supports the Rule of Four, which states that functions are represented symbolically, numerically, graphically, and verbally. Each chapter introduces a new type of function and then develops all concepts pertaining to that particular function. The solutions of equations and inequalities, instead of being developed as stand-alone topics, are developed in the context of the underlying functions. Graphing utility coverage is optional and can be included or excluded at the discretion of the instructor: *College Algebra; Precalculus, with a Unit Circle Approach to Trigonometry; Precalculus, with a Right Triangle Approach to Trigonometry.*

Preface to the Instructor

As a professor of mathematics at an urban public university for 35 years, I understand the varied needs of students taking precalculus. Students range from being underprepared, with little mathematical background and a fear of mathematics, to being highly prepared and motivated. For some, this is their final course in mathematics. For others, it is preparation for future mathematics courses. I have written this text with both groups in mind.

A tremendous benefit of authoring a successful series is the broad-based feedback I receive from teachers and students who have used previous editions. I am sincerely grateful for their support. Virtually every change to this edition is the result of their thoughtful comments and suggestions. I hope that I have been able to take their ideas and, building upon a successful foundation of the eighth edition, make this series an even better learning and teaching tool for students and teachers.

Features in the Ninth Edition

Rather than provide a list of features here, that information can be found on the endpapers in the front of this book.

This places the features in their proper context, as building blocks of an overall learning system that has been carefully crafted over the years to help students get the most out of the time they put into studying. Please take the time to review this and to discuss it with your students at the beginning of your course. My experience has been that when students utilize these features, they are more successful in the course.

New to the Ninth Edition

- **Chapter Projects**, which apply the concepts of each chapter to a real-world situation, have been enhanced to give students an up-to-the-minute experience. Many projects are new and Internet-based, requiring the student to research information online in order to solve problems.

- **Author Solves It MathXL Video Clips**—author Michael Sullivan works by section through MathXL exercises typically requested by students for more explanation or tutoring. These videos are a result of Sullivan's experiences in teaching online.

- **Showcase Examples** are used to present examples in a guided, step-by-step format. Students can immediately see how each of the steps in a problem are employed. The "How To" examples have a two-column format in which the left column describes the step in solving the problem and the right column displays the algebra complete with annotations.

- **Model It** examples and exercises are clearly marked with a ⊕ icon. These examples and exercises are meant to develop the student's ability to build models from both verbal descriptions and data. Many of the problems involving data require the students to first determine the appropriate model (linear, quadratic, and so on) to fit to the data and justify their choice.

- **Exercise Sets** at the end of each section remain classified according to purpose. The "*Are You Prepared?*" exercises have been expanded to better serve the student who needs a just-in-time review of concepts utilized in the section. The *Concepts and Vocabulary* exercises have been updated. These fill-in-the-blank and True/False problems have been written to serve as reading quizzes. *Mixed Practice* exercises have been added where appropriate. These problems offer a comprehensive assessment of the skills learned in the section by asking problems that relate to more than one objective. Sometimes these require information from previous sections so students must utilize skills learned throughout the course. *Applications and Extension* problems have been updated and many new problems involving sourced information and data have been added to bring relevance and timeliness to the exercises. The *Explaining Concepts: Discussion and Writing* exercises have been updated and reworded to stimulate discussion of concepts in online discussion forums. These can also be used to spark classroom discussion. In selected exercise sets, *Interactive Exercises* are presented. These applets provide a "hands-on" experience allowing students to interact with Mathematics in an active learning environment. Finally, in the **Annotated Instructor's Edition,** I have preselected problems that can serve as sample homework assignments. These are indicated by a blue underline, and they are assignable in MyMathLab® if desired.

- The **Chapter Review** now identifies Examples to review for each objective in the chapter.

Changes in the Ninth Edition

- **CONTENT**
  - **Chapter 2, Section 3** A new objective "Use a graph to locate the absolute maximum and the absolute minimum" has been added. The Extreme Value Theorem is also cited here.
  - **Chapter 3, Section 3** A new objective "Find a quadratic function given its vertex and one point" has been added.
  - **Chapter 4, Section 1** A new objective "Build cubic models from data" has been added.

○ **Chapter 4, Section 5** Descartes' Rule of Signs has been removed as its value is redundant to the information collected from other sources.

○ **Chapter 5, Section 3** The definition of an exponential function has been broadened.

○ **Chapter 9, Section 5** More applications of decomposing vectors have been added.

• **ORGANIZATION**

○ **Appendix A, Section A.3** The objective "Complete the Square" has been relocated to here from Section A.6.

○ **Chapter 7** The two sections on trigonometric equations, *Trigonometric Equations (I)* and *Trigonometric Equations (II)*, have been consolidated into a new section in Chapter 7, Section 3, entitled *Trigonometric Equations*. In addition, trigonometric equations that utilize specific identities have been woven into the appropriate sections throughout the remainder of Chapter 7.

○ **Chapter 9** The material on applications of vectors that was formerly in Section 5 on the Dot Product has been moved to Section 4 to emphasize the applications of the resultant vector.

Using the Ninth Edition Effectively with Your Syllabus

To meet the varied needs of diverse syllabi, this book contains more content than is likely to be covered in a *Precalculus* course. As the chart illustrates, this book has been organized with flexibility of use in mind. Within a given chapter, certain sections are optional (see the detail following the flow chart) and can be omitted without loss of continuity.

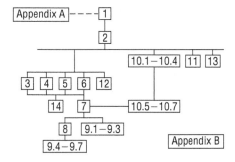

Appendix A   Review
This chapter consists of review material. It may be used as the first part of the course or later as a just-in-time review when the content is required. Specific references to this chapter occur throughout the book to assist in the review process.

Chapter 1   Graphs
This chapter lays the foundation for functions.

Chapter 2   Functions and Their Graphs
Perhaps the most important chapter. Section 2.6 is optional.

Chapter 3   Linear and Quadratic Functions
Topic selection depends on your syllabus. Sections 3.2 and 3.4 may be omitted without a loss of continuity.

Chapter 4   Polynomial and Rational Functions
Topic selection depends on your syllabus.

Chapter 5   Exponential and Logarithmic Functions
Sections 5.1–5.6 follow in sequence. Sections 5.7, 5.8, and 5.9 are optional.

Chapter 6   Trigonometric Functions
Section 6.6 may be omitted in a brief course.

Chapter 7   Analytic Trigonometry
Section 7.7 may be omitted in a brief course.

Chapter 8   Applications of Trigonometric Functions
Sections 8.4 and 8.5 may be omitted in a brief course.

Chapter 9   Polar Coordinates; Vectors
Sections 9.1–9.3 and Sections 9.4–9.7 are independent and may be covered separately.

Acknowledgments

Textbooks are written by authors, but evolve from an idea to final form through the efforts of many people. It was Don Dellen who first suggested this book and series to me. Don is remembered for his extensive contributions to publishing and mathematics.

Thanks are due to the following people for their assistance and encouragement to the preparation of this edition:

- From Pearson Education: Anne Kelly for her substantial contributions, ideas, and enthusiasm; Peggy Lucas, who is a huge fan and supporter; Dawn Murrin, for her unmatched talent at getting the details right; Sherry Berg of Nesbitt Graphics, Inc., for her superb organizational skills in directing production; Peggy McMahon for her leadership in overseeing production; Chris Hoag for her continued support and genuine interest; Greg Tobin for his leadership and commitment to excellence; and the Pearson Math and Science Sales team, for their continued confidence and personal support of our books.

- As this book went to production, Bob Walters, Production Manager, passed away after a long and valiant battle fighting lung disease. He was an old and dear friend — a true professional in every sense of the word.

- Accuracy checkers: C. Brad Davis, who read the entire manuscript and accuracy checked answers. His attention to detail is amazing; Timothy Britt, for creating the Solutions Manuals and accuracy checking answers.

- *Reviewers*: Larissa Williamson, University of Florida; Richard Nadel, Florida International University; Robin Steinberg, Puma CC; Mike Rosenthal, Florida International University; Gerardo Aladro, Florida International University; Tammy Muhs, Universty of Central Florida; Val Mohanakumar, Hillsborough CC.

Finally, I offer my grateful thanks to the dedicated users and reviewers of my books, whose collective insights form the backbone of each textbook revision.

My list of indebtedness just grows and grows. And, if I've forgotten anyone, please accept my apology. Thank you all.

James Africh, College of DuPage
Steve Agronsky, Cal Poly State University
Grant Alexander, Joliet Junior College
Dave Anderson, South Suburban College
Richard Andrews, Florida A&M University
Joby Milo Anthony, University of Central Florida
James E. Arnold, University of Wisconsin-Milwaukee
Adel Arshaghi, Center for Educational Merit
Carolyn Autray, University of West Georgia
Agnes Azzolino, Middlesex County College
Wilson P Banks, Illinois State University
Sudeshna Basu, Howard University
Dale R. Bedgood, East Texas State University
Beth Beno, South Suburban College
Carolyn Bernath, Tallahassee Community College
Rebecca Berthiaume, Edison State College
William H. Beyer, University of Akron
Annette Blackwelder, Florida State University
Richelle Blair, Lakeland Community College
Kevin Bodden, Lewis and Clark College
Barry Booten, Florida Atlantic University
Larry Bouldin, Roane State Community College
Bob Bradshaw, Ohlone College
Trudy Bratten, Grossmont College
Tim Bremer, Broome Community College
Tim Britt, Jackson State Community College
Michael Brook, University of Delaware
Joanne Brunner, Joliet Junior College
Warren Burch, Brevard Community College
Mary Butler, Lincoln Public Schools
Melanie Butler, West Virginia University
Jim Butterbach, Joliet Junior College
William J. Cable, University of Wisconsin-Stevens Point
Lois Calamia, Brookdale Community College
Jim Campbell, Lincoln Public Schools

Roger Carlsen, Moraine Valley Community College
Elena Catoiu, Joliet Junior College
Mathews Chakkanakuzhi, Palomar College
Tim Chappell, Penn Valley Community College
John Collado, South Suburban College
Alicia Collins, Mesa Community College
Nelson Collins, Joliet Junior College
Jim Cooper, Joliet Junior College
Denise Corbett, East Carolina University
Carlos C. Corona, San Antonio College
Theodore C. Coskey, South Seattle Community College
Donna Costello, Plano Senior High School
Paul Crittenden, University of Nebraska at Lincoln
John Davenport, East Texas State University
Faye Dang, Joliet Junior College
Antonio David, Del Mar College
Stephanie Deacon, Liberty University
Duane E. Deal, Ball State University
Jerry DeGroot, Purdue North Central
Timothy Deis, University of Wisconsin-Platteville
Joanna DelMonaco, Middlesex Community College
Vivian Dennis, Eastfield College
Deborah Dillon, R. L. Turner High School
Guesna Dohrman, Tallahassee Community College
Cheryl Doolittle, Iowa State University
Karen R. Dougan, University of Florida
Jerrett Dumouchel, Florida Community College
   at Jacksonville
Louise Dyson, Clark College
Paul D. East, Lexington Community College
Don Edmondson, University of Texas-Austin
Erica Egizio, Joliet Junior College
Jason Eltrevoog, Joliet Junior College
Christopher Ennis, University of Minnesota
Kathy Eppler, Salt Lake Community College

Ralph Esparza, Jr., Richland College
Garret J. Etgen, University of Houston
Scott Fallstrom, Shoreline Community College
Pete Falzone, Pensacola Junior College
W.A. Ferguson, University of Illinois-Urbana/Champaign
Iris B. Fetta, Clemson University
Mason Flake, student at Edison Community College
Timothy W. Flood, Pittsburgh State University
Robert Frank, Westmoreland County
    Community College
Merle Friel, Humboldt State University
Richard A. Fritz, Moraine Valley
    Community College
Dewey Furness, Ricke College
Randy Gallaher, Lewis and Clark College
Tina Garn, University of Arizona
Dawit Getachew, Chicago State University
Wayne Gibson, Rancho Santiago College
Robert Gill, University of Minnesota Duluth
Nina Girard, University of Pittsburgh at Johnstown
Sudhir Kumar Goel, Valdosta State University
Adrienne Goldstein, Miami Dade College,
    Kendall Campus
Joan Goliday, Sante Fe Community College
Lourdes Gonzalez, Miami Dade College, Kendall Campus
Frederic Gooding, Goucher College
Donald Goral, Northern Virginia Community College
Sue Graupner, Lincoln Public Schools
Mary Beth Grayson, Liberty University
Jennifer L. Grimsley, University of Charleston
Ken Gurganus, University of North Carolina
James E. Hall, University of Wisconsin-Madison
Judy Hall, West Virginia University
Edward R. Hancock, DeVry Institute of Technology
Julia Hassett, DeVry Institute-Dupage
Christopher Hay-Jahans, University of South Dakota
Michah Heibel, Lincoln Public Schools
LaRae Helliwell, San Jose City College
Celeste Hernandez, Richland College
Gloria P. Hernandez, Louisiana State University
    at Eunice
Brother Herron, Brother Rice High School
Robert Hoburg, Western Connecticut State University
Lynda Hollingsworth, Northwest Missouri State
    University
Charla Holzbog, Denison High School
Lee Hruby, Naperville North High School
Miles Hubbard, St. Cloud State University
Kim Hughes, California State College-San Bernardino
Ron Jamison, Brigham Young University
Richard A. Jensen, Manatee Community College
Glenn Johnson, Middlesex Community College
Sandra G. Johnson, St. Cloud State University
Tuesday Johnson, New Mexico State University
Susitha Karunaratne, Purdue University
    North Central
Moana H. Karsteter, Tallahassee Community College
Donna Katula, Joliet Junior College

Arthur Kaufman, College of Staten Island
Thomas Kearns, North Kentucky University
Jack Keating, Massasoit Community College
Shelia Kellenbarger, Lincoln Public Schools
Rachael Kenney, North Carolina State University
Debra Kopcso, Louisiana State University
Lynne Kowski, Raritan Valley Community College
Yelena Kravchuk, University of Alabama at
    Birmingham
Keith Kuchar, Manatee Community College
Tor Kwembe, Chicago State University
Linda J. Kyle, Tarrant Country Jr. College
H.E. Lacey, Texas A & M University
Harriet Lamm, Coastal Bend College
James Lapp, Fort Lewis College
Matt Larson, Lincoln Public Schools
Christopher Lattin, Oakton Community College
Julia Ledet, Lousiana State University
Adele LeGere, Oakton Community College
Kevin Leith, University of Houston
JoAnn Lewin, Edison College
Jeff Lewis, Johnson County Community College
Janice C. Lyon, Tallahassee Community College
Jean McArthur, Joliet Junior College
Virginia McCarthy, Iowa State University
Karla McCavit, Albion College
Michael McClendon, University of Central Oklahoma
Tom McCollow, DeVry Institute of Technology
Marilyn McCollum, North Carolina State University
Jill McGowan, Howard University
Will McGowant, Howard University
Angela McNulty, Joliet Junior College
Laurence Maher, North Texas State University
Jay A. Malmstrom, Oklahoma City
    Community College
Rebecca Mann, Apollo High School
Lynn Marecek, Santa Ana College
Sherry Martina, Naperville North High School
Alec Matheson, Lamar University
Nancy Matthews, University of Oklahoma
James Maxwell, Oklahoma State University-Stillwater
Marsha May, Midwestern State University
James McLaughlin, West Chester University
Judy Meckley, Joliet Junior College
David Meel, Bowling Green State University
Carolyn Meitler, Concordia University
Samia Metwali, Erie Community College
Rich Meyers, Joliet Junior College
Eldon Miller, University of Mississippi
James Miller, West Virginia University
Michael Miller, Iowa State University
Kathleen Miranda, SUNY at Old Westbury
Chris Mirbaha, The Community College
    of Baltimore County
Val Mohanakumar, Hillsborough Community College
Thomas Monaghan, Naperville North High School
Miguel Montanez, Miami Dade College,
    Wolfson Campus

Maria Montoya, Our Lady of the Lake University
Susan Moosai, Florida Atlantic University
Craig Morse, Naperville North High School
Samad Mortabit, Metropolitan State University
Pat Mower, Washburn University
A. Muhundan, Manatee Community College
Jane Murphy, Middlesex Community College
Richard Nadel, Florida International University
Gabriel Nagy, Kansas State University
Bill Naegele, South Suburban College
Karla Neal, Lousiana State University
Lawrence E. Newman, Holyoke Community College
Dwight Newsome, Pasco-Hernando Community College
Denise Nunley, Maricopa Community Colleges
James Nymann, University of Texas-El Paso
Mark Omodt, Anoka-Ramsey Community College
Seth F. Oppenheimer, Mississippi State University
Leticia Oropesa, University of Miami
Linda Padilla, Joliet Junior College
E. James Peake, Iowa State University
Kelly Pearson, Murray State University
Dashamir Petrela, Florida Atlantic University
Philip Pina, Florida Atlantic University
Michael Prophet, University of Northern Iowa
Laura Pyzdrowski, West Virginia University
Neal C. Raber, University of Akron
Thomas Radin, San Joaquin Delta College
Aibeng Serene Radulovic, Florida Atlantic University
Ken A. Rager, Metropolitan State College
Kenneth D. Reeves, San Antonio College
Elsi Reinhardt, Truckee Meadows Community College
Jose Remesar, Miami Dade College, Wolfson Campus
Jane Ringwald, Iowa State University
Stephen Rodi, Austin Community College
William Rogge, Lincoln Northeast High School
Howard L. Rolf, Baylor University
Mike Rosenthal, Florida International University
Phoebe Rouse, Lousiana State University
Edward Rozema, University of Tennessee at Chattanooga
Dennis C. Runde, Manatee Community College
Alan Saleski, Loyola University of Chicago
Susan Sandmeyer, Jamestown Community College
Brenda Santistevan, Salt Lake Community College
Linda Schmidt, Greenville Technical College
Ingrid Scott, Montgomery College
A.K. Shamma, University of West Florida
Martin Sherry, Lower Columbia College
Carmen Shershin, Florida International University
Tatrana Shubin, San Jose State University
Anita Sikes, Delgado Community College
Timothy Sipka, Alma College

Charlotte Smedberg, University of Tampa
Lori Smellegar, Manatee Community College
Gayle Smith, Loyola Blakefield
Leslie Soltis, Mercyhurst College
John Spellman, Southwest Texas State University
Karen Spike, University of North Carolina
Rajalakshmi Sriram, Okaloosa-Walton Community College
Katrina Staley, North Carolina Agricultural and Technical State University
Becky Stamper, Western Kentucky University
Judy Staver, Florida Community College-South
Neil Stephens, Hinsdale South High School
Sonya Stephens, Florida A&M University
Patrick Stevens, Joliet Junior College
John Sumner, University of Tampa
Matthew TenHuisen, University of North Carolina, Wilmington
Christopher Terry, Augusta State University
Diane Tesar, South Suburban College
Tommy Thompson, Brookhaven College
Martha K. Tietze, Shawnee Mission Northwest High School
Richard J. Tondra, Iowa State University
Suzanne Topp, Salt Lake Community College
Marilyn Toscano, University of Wisconsin, Superior
Marvel Townsend, University of Florida
Jim Trudnowski, Carroll College
Robert Tuskey, Joliet Junior College
Mihaela Vajiac, Chapman University-Orange
Richard G. Vinson, University of South Alabama
Jorge Viola-Prioli, Florida Atlantic University
Mary Voxman, University of Idaho
Jennifer Walsh, Daytona Beach Community College
Donna Wandke, Naperville North High School
Timothy L. Warkentin, Cloud County Community College
Hayat Weiss, Middlesex Community College
Kathryn Wetzel, Amarillo College
Darlene Whitkenack, Northern Illinois University
Suzanne Williams, Central Piedmont Community College
Larissa Williamson, University of Florida
Christine Wilson, West Virginia University
Brad Wind, Florida International University
Anna Wiodarczyk, Florida International University
Mary Wolyniak, Broome Community College
Canton Woods, Auburn University
Tamara S. Worner, Wayne State College
Terri Wright, New Hampshire Community Technical College, Manchester
George Zazi, Chicago State University
Steve Zuro, Joliet Junior College

Michael Sullivan
Chicago State University

Available to students are the following supplements:

- *Student Solutions Manual (ISBN 10: 0321717635; ISBN 13: 9780321717634)*
  Fully worked solutions to odd-numbered exercises.

- *Algebra Review (ISBN 10: 0131480065; ISBN 13: 9780131480063)*
  Four chapters of Intermediate Algebra Review. Perfect for a slower-paced course or for individual review.

- *Videos on DVD with Chapter Test Prep for Precalculus 9e (ISBN 10: 0321717546; ISBN 13: 9780321717542)*
  The Videos on DVD contain short video clips of Michael Sullivan III working key book examples. Chapter Test Prep Videos (also included) provide fully worked solutions to the Chapter Test exercises. The Chapter Test Prep Videos are also available within MyMathLab® or on YouTube™ (go to http://www.youtube.com/SullivanPrecalc9e). Videos have optional subtitles.

MathXL® Online Course (access code required)

MathXL® is a powerful online homework, tutorial, and assessment system that accompanies Pearson Education's textbooks in mathematics or statistics. With MathXL, instructors can:

- Create, edit, and assign online homework and tests using algorithmically generated exercises correlated at the objective level to the textbook.
- Create and assign their own online exercises and import TestGen tests for added flexibility.
- Maintain records of all student work tracked in MathXL's online gradebook.

With MathXL, students can:

- Take chapter tests in MathXL and receive personalized study plans based on their test results.
- Use the study plan to link directly to tutorial exercises for the objectives they need to study and retest.
- Access supplemental animations and video clips directly from selected exercises.

MathXL is available to qualified adopters. For more information, visit our website at **www.mathxl.com**, or contact your Pearson sales representative.

MyMathLab® Online Course (access code required)

MyMathLab® is a text-specific, easily customizable online course that integrates interactive multimedia instruction with textbook content. MyMathLab gives you the tools you need to deliver all or a portion of your course online, whether your students are in a lab setting or working from home.

- **Interactive homework exercises**, correlated to your textbook at the objective level, are algorithmically generated for unlimited practice and mastery. Most exercises are free-response and provide guided solutions, sample problems, and tutorial learning aids for extra help.
- **Personalized homework** assignments that you can design to meet the needs of your class. MyMathLab tailors the assignment for each student based on their test or quiz scores. Each student receives a homework assignment that contains only the problems they still need to master.
- **Personalized Study Plan,** generated when students complete a test or quiz or homework, indicates which topics have been mastered and links to tutorial exercises for topics students have not mastered. You can customize the Study Plan so that the topics available match your course content.
- **Multimedia learning aids**, such as video lectures and podcasts, animations, and a complete multimedia textbook, help students independently improve their understanding and performance. You can assign these multimedia learning aids as homework to help your students grasp the concepts.
- **Homework and Test Manager** lets you assign homework, quizzes, and tests that are automatically graded. Select just the right mix of questions from the MyMathLab exercise bank, instructor-created custom exercises, and/or TestGen® test items.
- **Gradebook,** designed specifically for mathematics and statistics, automatically tracks students' results, lets you stay on top of student performance, and gives you control over how to calculate final grades. You can also add offline (paper-and-pencil) grades to the gradebook.
- **MathXL Exercise Builder** allows you to create static and algorithmic exercises for your online assignments. You can use the library of sample exercises as an easy starting point, or you can edit any course-related exercise.

- **Pearson Tutor Center** (**www.pearsontutorservices.com**) access is automatically included with MyMathLab. The Tutor Center is staffed by qualified math instructors who provide textbook-specific tutoring for students via toll-free phone, fax, email, and interactive Web sessions.

- **NEW Resources for Sullivan, Precalculus, 9e**

  ○ **Author Solves It videos** feature Mike Sullivan III working by section through MathXL exercises typically requested by students for more explanation or tutoring. These videos are a result of Sullivan's experiences in teaching online.

  ○ **Sample homework assignments**, preselected by the author, are indicated by a blue underline within the end-of-section exercise sets in the Annotated Instructor's Edition and are assignable in MyMathLab.

  ○ **Chapter Project MathXL Exercises** allow instructors to assign problems based on the new Internet-based Chapter Projects.

Students do their assignments in the Flash®-based MathXL Player, which is compatible with almost any browser (Firefox®, Safari™, or Internet Explorer®) on almost any platform (Macintosh® or Windows®). MyMathLab is powered by CourseCompass™, Pearson Education's online teaching and learning environment, and by MathXL®, our online homework, tutorial, and assessment system. MyMathLab is available to qualified adopters. For more information, visit www.mymathlab.com or contact your Pearson representative.

Applications Index

Acoustics
amplifying sound, 344
loudness of sound, 295
loudspeaker, 548
tuning fork, 548–49
whispering galleries, 648–49, 693

Aerodynamics
modeling aircraft motion, 630

Aeronautics
Challenger disaster, 331

Agriculture
crop allocation, 788
farm management, 783
field enclosure, 768
grazing area for cow, 539–40
minimizing cost, 783
removing stump, 602–3

Air travel
bearing of aircraft, 515, 526
frequent flyer miles, 526
holding pattern, 462
parking at O'Hare International
    Airport, 88
revising a flight plan, 533
speed and direction of aircraft, 597–98,
    601–2, 628

Archaeology
age of ancient tools, 324–25
age of fossil, 330
age of tree, 330
date of prehistoric man's death, 344

Architecture
brick staircase, 808, 832
Burj Khalifa building, A15
floor design, 806–7, 832
football stadium seating, 808
mosaic design, 808, 832
Norman window, 153, A21
parabolic arch, 153
racetrack design, 651
special window, 153, 161
stadium construction, 808
window design, 153

Area
of Bermuda Triangle, 539
under a curve, 447–48
of isosceles triangle, 493

of sector of circle, 360
of segment of circle, 551

Art
fine decorative pieces, 378

Astronomy
angle of elevation of Sun, 514
distances of planets from Sun, 802
planetary orbits, 648
    Earth, 651
    Jupiter, 651
    Mars, 651
    Mercury, 678
    Neptune, 695
    Pluto, 651, 695

Aviation
modeling aircraft motion, 630
orbital launches, 709
speed of plane, A71

Biology
alcohol and driving, 291, 296
bacterial growth, 323–24, 336–37
    E-coli, 79, 119
blood types, 840–41
bone length, 161–62
cricket chirp rate and temperature, 155
healing of wounds, 281, 295
maternal age versus Down
    syndrome, 134
yeast biomass as function of time,
    335–36

Business
advertising, 133, 162
automobile production, 253–54, 726
blending coffee, A69
car rentals, 125
checkout lines, 859
cigarette exports, 337
clothing store, 861
commissions, 161
cookie orders, 788
cost
    of can, 210, 213
    of commodity, 254
    of manufacturing, 186, 219, 776–77,
        A13, A69
    marginal, 145, 161
    minimizing, 161, 783
    of production, 79, 254, 752, 789
    of transporting goods, 89
cost equation, 32

cost function, 126
    average, 63
demand
    for jeans, 133
    for PCs, 337
demand equation, 161, 244
depreciation, 246
discounts, 254
drive-thru rate
    at Burger King, 277
    at Citibank, 281, 295
    at McDonald's, 281
equipment depreciation, 818
expense computation, A70
Jiffy Lube's car arrival rate, 281, 295
managing a meat market, 783
mixing candy, A69
mixing nuts, A69
new-car markup, A81
orange juice production, 726
precision ball bearings, A13
price *vs.* quantity demanded, 127,
    337–38
product design, 784
production scheduling, 783
product promotion, 33
profit, 752
    cigar company, 102
    on figurines, 790
    maximizing, 781–82, 783–84
profit function, 59
rate of return on, 320
restaurant management, 710
revenue, 145, 158–59, A69
    advertising and, 133
    airline, 784
    of clothing store, 741
    daily, 145
    from digital music, 102
    instantaneous rate of change of, 891,
        892, 901
    maximizing, 145, 152
    monthly, 145
    theater, 711
RV rental, 163
salary, 808
    gross, 58
    increases in, 818, 832
sales
    commission on, A80
    of movie theater ticket, 697, 702, 709
    net, 8
    profit from, A71
salvage value, 344
straight-line depreciation, 122–23, 126
supply and demand, 123–24, 126
tax, 219
toy truck manufacturing, 776–77

Photo Credits

Graphs

1

Outline

The First Modern Olympics: Athens, 1896

The birth of the modern Olympic Games

By John Gettings—"I hereby proclaim the opening of the first International Olympic Games at Athens." With these words on April 6, 1896, King George I of Greece welcomed the crowd that had gathered in the newly reconstructed Panathenean Stadium to the modern-day Olympic Summer Games.

The event was the idea of Baron Pierre de Coubertin of France who traveled the world to gather support for his dream to have nations come together and overcome national disputes, all in the name of sport.

The program for the Games included track and field, fencing, weightlifting, rifle and pistol shooting, tennis, cycling, swimming, gymnastics, and wrestling. Although 14 nations participated, most of the athletes were Greek.

The Games reached their high point on Day 5 with the first modern-day marathon. The idea to hold an event to commemorate the Ancient Olympic games was suggested by a friend of de Coubertin and was met with great anticipation. The race was run from Marathon to Athens (estimated at 22–26 miles), watched by more than 100,000 people, and won by a Greek runner, Spiridon Louis.   *Gettings, The First Modern Olympics: Athens, 1986, © 2000–2010 Pearson Education, publishing as Infoplease. Reprinted with permission.*

 —See the Internet-based Chapter Project—

◁ **A Look Back** In Appendix A, we review algebra essentials, geometry essentials, and equations in one variable.

A Look Ahead ▷ Here we connect algebra and geometry using the rectangular coordinate system to graph equations in two variables. The idea of using a system of rectangular coordinates dates back to ancient times, when such a system was used for surveying and city planning. Apollonius of Perga, in 200 BC, used a form of rectangular coordinates in his work on conics, although this use does not stand out as clearly as it does in modern treatments. Sporadic use of rectangular coordinates continued until the 1600s. By that time, algebra had developed sufficiently so that René Descartes (1596–1650) and Pierre de Fermat (1601–1665) could take the crucial step, which was the use of rectangular coordinates to translate geometry problems into algebra problems, and vice versa. This step was important for two reasons. First, it allowed both geometers and algebraists to gain new insights into their subjects, which previously had been regarded as separate, but now were seen to be connected in many important ways. Second, these insights made the development of calculus possible, which greatly enlarged the number of areas in which mathematics could be applied and made possible a much deeper understanding of these areas.

1.1 The Distance and Midpoint Formulas

PREPARING FOR THIS SECTION *Before getting started, review the following:*

- Algebra Essentials (Appendix A, Section A.1, pp. A1–A10)
- Geometry Essentials (Appendix A, Section A.2, pp. A14–A19)

Now Work the 'Are You Prepared?' problems on page 6.

OBJECTIVES **1** Use the Distance Formula (p. 3)
            2 Use the Midpoint Formula (p. 5)

Rectangular Coordinates

We locate a point on the real number line by assigning it a single real number, called the *coordinate of the point*. For work in a two-dimensional plane, we locate points by using two numbers.

Figure 1

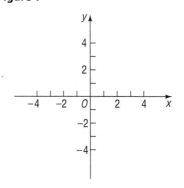

We begin with two real number lines located in the same plane: one horizontal and the other vertical. The horizontal line is called the **x-axis,** the vertical line the **y-axis,** and the point of intersection the **origin O.** See Figure 1. We assign coordinates to every point on these number lines using a convenient scale. We usually use the same scale on each axis, but in applications, different scales appropriate to the application may be used.

The origin *O* has a value of 0 on both the *x*-axis and *y*-axis. Points on the *x*-axis to the right of *O* are associated with positive real numbers, and those to the left of *O* are associated with negative real numbers. Points on the *y*-axis above *O* are associated with positive real numbers, and those below *O* are associated with negative real numbers. In Figure 1, the *x*-axis and *y*-axis are labeled as *x* and *y*, respectively, and we have used an arrow at the end of each axis to denote the positive direction.

The coordinate system described here is called a **rectangular** or **Cartesian*** **coordinate system.** The plane formed by the *x*-axis and *y*-axis is sometimes called the **xy-plane,** and the *x*-axis and *y*-axis are referred to as the **coordinate axes.**

Figure 2

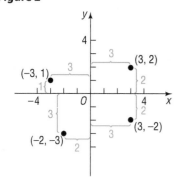

Any point *P* in the *xy*-plane can be located by using an **ordered pair** (x, y) of real numbers. Let *x* denote the signed distance of *P* from the *y*-axis (*signed* means that, if *P* is to the right of the *y*-axis, then $x > 0$, and if *P* is to the left of the *y*-axis, then $x < 0$); and let *y* denote the signed distance of *P* from the *x*-axis. The ordered pair (x, y), also called the **coordinates** of *P*, then gives us enough information to locate the point *P* in the plane.

For example, to locate the point whose coordinates are $(-3, 1)$, go 3 units along the *x*-axis to the left of *O* and then go straight up 1 unit. We **plot** this point by placing a dot at this location. See Figure 2, in which the points with coordinates $(-3, 1)$, $(-2, -3)$, $(3, -2)$, and $(3, 2)$ are plotted.

The origin has coordinates $(0, 0)$. Any point on the *x*-axis has coordinates of the form $(x, 0)$, and any point on the *y*-axis has coordinates of the form $(0, y)$.

If (x, y) are the coordinates of a point *P*, then *x* is called the **x-coordinate,** or **abscissa,** of *P* and *y* is the **y-coordinate,** or **ordinate,** of *P*. We identify the point *P* by its coordinates (x, y) by writing $P = (x, y)$. Usually, we will simply say "the point (x, y)" rather than "the point whose coordinates are (x, y)."

The coordinate axes divide the *xy*-plane into four sections called **quadrants,** as shown in Figure 3. In quadrant I, both the *x*-coordinate and the *y*-coordinate of all points are positive; in quadrant II, *x* is negative and *y* is positive; in quadrant III, both *x* and *y* are negative; and in quadrant IV, *x* is positive and *y* is negative. Points on the coordinate axes belong to no quadrant.

Figure 3

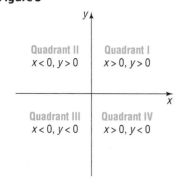

Now Work PROBLEM 13

*Named after René Descartes (1596–1650), a French mathematician, philosopher, and theologian.

COMMENT On a graphing calculator, you can set the scale on each axis. Once this has been done, you obtain the **viewing rectangle.** See Figure 4 for a typical viewing rectangle. You should now read Section B.1, *The Viewing Rectangle*, in Appendix B.

Figure 4

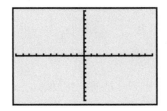

1 Use the Distance Formula

If the same units of measurement, such as inches, centimeters, and so on, are used for both the *x*-axis and *y*-axis, then all distances in the *xy*-plane can be measured using this unit of measurement.

EXAMPLE 1

Finding the Distance between Two Points

Find the distance *d* between the points $(1, 3)$ and $(5, 6)$.

Solution

First plot the points $(1, 3)$ and $(5, 6)$ and connect them with a straight line. See Figure 5(a). We are looking for the length *d*. We begin by drawing a horizontal line from $(1, 3)$ to $(5, 3)$ and a vertical line from $(5, 3)$ to $(5, 6)$, forming a right triangle, as shown in Figure 5(b). One leg of the triangle is of length 4 (since $|5 - 1| = 4$), and the other is of length 3 (since $|6 - 3| = 3$). By the Pythagorean Theorem, the square of the distance *d* that we seek is

$$d^2 = 4^2 + 3^2 = 16 + 9 = 25$$
$$d = \sqrt{25} = 5$$

Figure 5

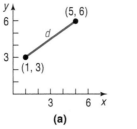   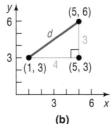

(a)   (b)

The **distance formula** provides a straightforward method for computing the distance between two points.

THEOREM

Distance Formula

The distance between two points $P_1 = (x_1, y_1)$ and $P_2 = (x_2, y_2)$, denoted by $d(P_1, P_2)$, is

$$d(P_1, P_2) = \sqrt{(x_2 - x_1)^2 + (y_2 - y_1)^2} \qquad \textbf{(1)}$$

In Words
To compute the distance between two points, find the difference of the x-coordinates, square it, and add this to the square of the difference of the y-coordinates. The square root of this sum is the distance.

Proof of the Distance Formula   Let (x_1, y_1) denote the coordinates of point P_1 and let (x_2, y_2) denote the coordinates of point P_2. Assume that the line joining P_1 and P_2 is neither horizontal nor vertical. Refer to Figure 6(a) on page 4. The coordinates of P_3 are (x_2, y_1). The horizontal distance from P_1 to P_3 is the absolute value of the difference of the x-coordinates, $|x_2 - x_1|$. The vertical distance from P_3 to P_2 is the absolute value of the difference of the y-coordinates, $|y_2 - y_1|$. See Figure 6(b). The distance $d(P_1, P_2)$ that we seek is the length of the hypotenuse of the right triangle, so, by the Pythagorean Theorem, it follows that

$$[d(P_1, P_2)]^2 = |x_2 - x_1|^2 + |y_2 - y_1|^2$$
$$= (x_2 - x_1)^2 + (y_2 - y_1)^2$$
$$d(P_1, P_2) = \sqrt{(x_2 - x_1)^2 + (y_2 - y_1)^2}$$

Figure 6

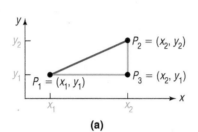

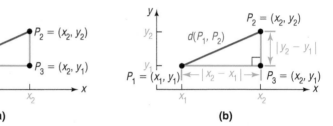

(a)   (b)

Now, if the line joining P_1 and P_2 is horizontal, then the y-coordinate of P_1 equals the y-coordinate of P_2; that is, $y_1 = y_2$. Refer to Figure 7(a). In this case, the distance formula (1) still works, because, for $y_1 = y_2$, it reduces to

$$d(P_1, P_2) = \sqrt{(x_2 - x_1)^2 + 0^2} = \sqrt{(x_2 - x_1)^2} = |x_2 - x_1|$$

Figure 7

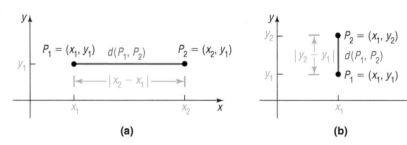

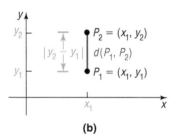

(a)   (b)

A similar argument holds if the line joining P_1 and P_2 is vertical. See Figure 7(b).   ∎

EXAMPLE 2   **Using the Distance Formula**

Find the distance d between the points $(-4, 5)$ and $(3, 2)$.

Solution   Using the distance formula, equation (1), the distance d is

$$d = \sqrt{[3 - (-4)]^2 + (2 - 5)^2} = \sqrt{7^2 + (-3)^2}$$
$$= \sqrt{49 + 9} = \sqrt{58} \approx 7.62$$

─ **Now Work** PROBLEMS **17** AND **21**

The distance between two points $P_1 = (x_1, y_1)$ and $P_2 = (x_2, y_2)$ is never a negative number. Furthermore, the distance between two points is 0 only when the points are identical, that is, when $x_1 = x_2$ and $y_1 = y_2$. Also, because $(x_2 - x_1)^2 = (x_1 - x_2)^2$ and $(y_2 - y_1)^2 = (y_1 - y_2)^2$, it makes no difference whether the distance is computed from P_1 to P_2 or from P_2 to P_1; that is, $d(P_1, P_2) = d(P_2, P_1)$.

The introduction to this chapter mentioned that rectangular coordinates enable us to translate geometry problems into algebra problems, and vice versa. The next example shows how algebra (the distance formula) can be used to solve geometry problems.

EXAMPLE 3	**Using Algebra to Solve Geometry Problems**

Consider the three points $A = (-2, 1)$, $B = (2, 3)$, and $C = (3, 1)$.

(a) Plot each point and form the triangle ABC.
(b) Find the length of each side of the triangle.
(c) Verify that the triangle is a right triangle.
(d) Find the area of the triangle.

Solution
(a) Figure 8 shows the points A, B, C and the triangle ABC.
(b) To find the length of each side of the triangle, use the distance formula, equation (1).

$$d(A, B) = \sqrt{[2 - (-2)]^2 + (3 - 1)^2} = \sqrt{16 + 4} = \sqrt{20} = 2\sqrt{5}$$
$$d(B, C) = \sqrt{(3 - 2)^2 + (1 - 3)^2} = \sqrt{1 + 4} = \sqrt{5}$$
$$d(A, C) = \sqrt{[3 - (-2)]^2 + (1 - 1)^2} = \sqrt{25 + 0} = 5$$

Figure 8

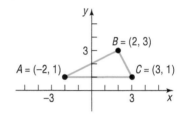

(c) To show that the triangle is a right triangle, we need to show that the sum of the squares of the lengths of two of the sides equals the square of the length of the third side. (Why is this sufficient?) Looking at Figure 8, it seems reasonable to conjecture that the right angle is at vertex B. We shall check to see whether

$$[d(A, B)]^2 + [d(B, C)]^2 = [d(A, C)]^2$$

Using the results in part (b),

$$[d(A, B)]^2 + [d(B, C)]^2 = \left(2\sqrt{5}\right)^2 + \left(\sqrt{5}\right)^2$$
$$= 20 + 5 = 25 = [d(A, C)]^2$$

It follows from the converse of the Pythagorean Theorem that triangle ABC is a right triangle.

(d) Because the right angle is at vertex B, the sides AB and BC form the base and height of the triangle. Its area is

$$\text{Area} = \frac{1}{2}(\text{Base})(\text{Height}) = \frac{1}{2}\left(2\sqrt{5}\right)\left(\sqrt{5}\right) = 5 \text{ square units}$$

Now Work PROBLEM 29

2 Use the Midpoint Formula

Figure 9

We now derive a formula for the coordinates of the **midpoint of a line segment.** Let $P_1 = (x_1, y_1)$ and $P_2 = (x_2, y_2)$ be the endpoints of a line segment, and let $M = (x, y)$ be the point on the line segment that is the same distance from P_1 as it is from P_2. See Figure 9. The triangles P_1AM and MBP_2 are congruent. Do you see why? $d(P_1, M) = d(M, P_2)$ is given; $\angle AP_1M = \angle BMP_2$* and $\angle P_1MA = \angle MP_2B$. So, we have angle–side–angle. Because triangles P_1AM and MBP_2 are congruent, corresponding sides are equal in length. That is,

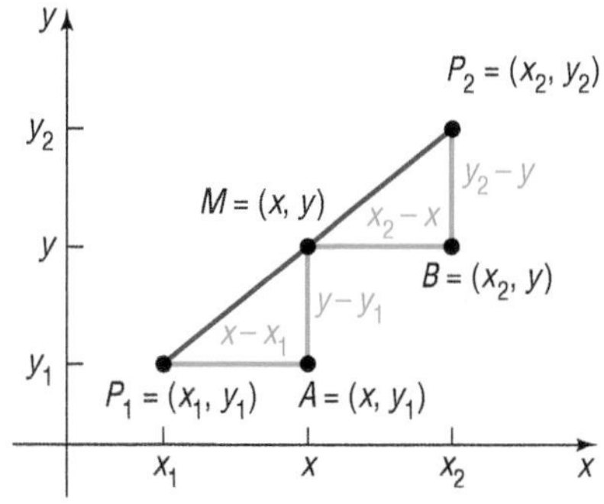

$$x - x_1 = x_2 - x \quad \text{and} \quad y - y_1 = y_2 - y$$
$$2x = x_1 + x_2 \qquad\qquad 2y = y_1 + y_2$$
$$x = \frac{x_1 + x_2}{2} \qquad\qquad y = \frac{y_1 + y_2}{2}$$

*A postulate from geometry states that the transversal $\overline{P_1P_2}$ forms congruent corresponding angles with the parallel line segments $\overline{P_1A}$ and $\overline{MB}$.

<table>
<tr><td>**THEOREM**</td><td>**Midpoint Formula**</td></tr>
</table>

The midpoint $M = (x, y)$ of the line segment from $P_1 = (x_1, y_1)$ to $P_2 = (x_2, y_2)$ is

> **In Words**
> To find the midpoint of a line segment, average the x-coordinates and average the y-coordinates of the endpoints.

$$M = (x, y) = \left(\frac{x_1 + x_2}{2}, \frac{y_1 + y_2}{2} \right)$$

(2)

EXAMPLE 4   **Finding the Midpoint of a Line Segment**

Find the midpoint of the line segment from $P_1 = (-5, 5)$ to $P_2 = (3, 1)$. Plot the points P_1 and P_2 and their midpoint.

Solution   Apply the midpoint formula (2) using $x_1 = -5$, $y_1 = 5$, $x_2 = 3$, and $y_2 = 1$. Then the coordinates (x, y) of the midpoint M are

Figure 10

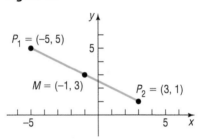

$$x = \frac{x_1 + x_2}{2} = \frac{-5 + 3}{2} = -1 \quad \text{and} \quad y = \frac{y_1 + y_2}{2} = \frac{5 + 1}{2} = 3$$

That is, $M = (-1, 3)$. See Figure 10.

→ **Now Work** PROBLEM 35

1.1   Assess Your Understanding

'Are You Prepared?'   *Answers are given at the end of these exercises. If you get a wrong answer, read the pages listed in red.*

1. On the real number line the origin is assigned the number _____. (p. A4)

2. If -3 and 5 are the coordinates of two points on the real number line, the distance between these points is _____. (pp. A5–A6)

3. If 3 and 4 are the legs of a right triangle, the hypotenuse is _____. (p. A14)

4. Use the converse of the Pythagorean Theorem to show that a triangle whose sides are of lengths 11, 60, and 61 is a right triangle. (pp. A14–A15)

5. The area A of a triangle whose base is b and whose altitude is h is $A = $ _____. (p. A15)

6. *True or False*   Two triangles are congruent if two angles and the included side of one equals two angles and the included side of the other. (pp. A16–A17)

Concepts and Vocabulary

7. If (x, y) are the coordinates of a point P in the xy-plane, then x is called the _____ of P and y is the _____ of P.

8. The coordinate axes divide the xy-plane into four sections called _____.

9. If three distinct points P, Q, and R all lie on a line and if $d(P, Q) = d(Q, R)$, then Q is called the _____ of the line segment from P to R.

10. *True or False*   The distance between two points is sometimes a negative number.

11. *True or False*   The point $(-1, 4)$ lies in quadrant IV of the Cartesian plane.

12. *True or False*   The midpoint of a line segment is found by averaging the x-coordinates and averaging the y-coordinates of the endpoints.

Skill Building

In Problems 13 and 14, plot each point in the xy-plane. Tell in which quadrant or on what coordinate axis each point lies.

13. (a) $A = (-3, 2)$
    (b) $B = (6, 0)$
    (c) $C = (-2, -2)$
    (d) $D = (6, 5)$
    (e) $E = (0, -3)$
    (f) $F = (6, -3)$

14. (a) $A = (1, 4)$
    (b) $B = (-3, -4)$
    (c) $C = (-3, 4)$
    (d) $D = (4, 1)$
    (e) $E = (0, 1)$
    (f) $F = (-3, 0)$

15. Plot the points $(2, 0)$, $(2, -3)$, $(2, 4)$, $(2, 1)$, and $(2, -1)$. Describe the set of all points of the form $(2, y)$, where y is a real number.

16. Plot the points $(0, 3)$, $(1, 3)$, $(-2, 3)$, $(5, 3)$, and $(-4, 3)$. Describe the set of all points of the form $(x, 3)$, where x is a real number.

In Problems 17–28, find the distance $d(P_1, P_2)$ between the points P_1 and P_2.

17.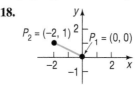

18.

19.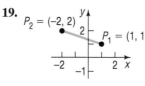

20.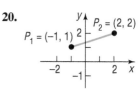

21. $P_1 = (3, -4)$; $P_2 = (5, 4)$

22. $P_1 = (-1, 0)$; $P_2 = (2, 4)$

23. $P_1 = (-3, 2)$; $P_2 = (6, 0)$

24. $P_1 = (2, -3)$; $P_2 = (4, 2)$

25. $P_1 = (4, -3)$; $P_2 = (6, 4)$

26. $P_1 = (-4, -3)$; $P_2 = (6, 2)$

27. $P_1 = (a, b)$; $P_2 = (0, 0)$

28. $P_1 = (a, a)$; $P_2 = (0, 0)$

In Problems 29–34, plot each point and form the triangle ABC. Verify that the triangle is a right triangle. Find its area.

29. $A = (-2, 5)$; $B = (1, 3)$; $C = (-1, 0)$

30. $A = (-2, 5)$; $B = (12, 3)$; $C = (10, -11)$

31. $A = (-5, 3)$; $B = (6, 0)$; $C = (5, 5)$

32. $A = (-6, 3)$; $B = (3, -5)$; $C = (-1, 5)$

33. $A = (4, -3)$; $B = (0, -3)$; $C = (4, 2)$

34. $A = (4, -3)$; $B = (4, 1)$; $C = (2, 1)$

In Problems 35–42, find the midpoint of the line segment joining the points P_1 and P_2.

35. $P_1 = (3, -4)$; $P_2 = (5, 4)$

36. $P_1 = (-2, 0)$; $P_2 = (2, 4)$

37. $P_1 = (-3, 2)$; $P_2 = (6, 0)$

38. $P_1 = (2, -3)$; $P_2 = (4, 2)$

39. $P_1 = (4, -3)$; $P_2 = (6, 1)$

40. $P_1 = (-4, -3)$; $P_2 = (2, 2)$

41. $P_1 = (a, b)$; $P_2 = (0, 0)$

42. $P_1 = (a, a)$; $P_2 = (0, 0)$

Applications and Extensions

43. If the point $(2, 5)$ is shifted 3 units to the right and 2 units down, what are its new coordinates?

44. If the point $(-1, 6)$ is shifted 2 units to the left and 4 units up, what are its new coordinates?

45. Find all points having an x-coordinate of 3 whose distance from the point $(-2, -1)$ is 13.
(a) By using the Pythagorean Theorem.
(b) By using the distance formula.

46. Find all points having a y-coordinate of -6 whose distance from the point $(1, 2)$ is 17.
(a) By using the Pythagorean Theorem.
(b) By using the distance formula.

47. Find all points on the x-axis that are 6 units from the point $(4, -3)$.

48. Find all points on the y-axis that are 6 units from the point $(4, -3)$.

49. The midpoint of the line segment from P_1 to P_2 is $(-1, 4)$. If $P_1 = (-3, 6)$, what is P_2?

50. The midpoint of the line segment from P_1 to P_2 is $(5, -4)$. If $P_2 = (7, -2)$, what is P_1?

51. Geometry The **medians** of a triangle are the line segments from each vertex to the midpoint of the opposite side (see the figure). Find the lengths of the medians of the triangle with vertices at $A = (0, 0)$, $B = (6, 0)$, and $C = (4, 4)$.

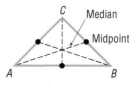

52. Geometry An **equilateral triangle** is one in which all three sides are of equal length. If two vertices of an equilateral triangle are $(0, 4)$ and $(0, 0)$, find the third vertex. How many of these triangles are possible?

53. Geometry Find the midpoint of each diagonal of a square with side of length s. Draw the conclusion that the diagonals of a square intersect at their midpoints.

[Hint: Use $(0, 0)$, $(0, s)$, $(s, 0)$, and (s, s) as the vertices of the square.**]**

54. Geometry Verify that the points $(0, 0)$, $(a, 0)$, and $\left(\dfrac{a}{2}, \dfrac{\sqrt{3}a}{2} \right)$ are the vertices of an equilateral triangle. Then show that the midpoints of the three sides are the vertices of a second equilateral triangle (refer to Problem 52).

*In Problems 55–58, find the length of each side of the triangle determined by the three points P_1, P_2, and P_3. State whether the triangle is an isosceles triangle, a right triangle, neither of these, or both. (An **isosceles triangle** is one in which at least two of the sides are of equal length.)*

55. $P_1 = (2, 1)$; $P_2 = (-4, 1)$; $P_3 = (-4, -3)$

56. $P_1 = (-1, 4)$; $P_2 = (6, 2)$; $P_3 = (4, -5)$

57. $P_1 = (-2, -1)$; $P_2 = (0, 7)$; $P_3 = (3, 2)$

58. $P_1 = (7, 2)$; $P_2 = (-4, 0)$; $P_3 = (4, 6)$

59. Baseball A major league baseball "diamond" is actually a square, 90 feet on a side (see the figure). What is the distance directly from home plate to second base (the diagonal of the square)?

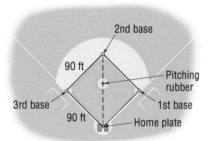

60. Little League Baseball The layout of a Little League playing field is a square, 60 feet on a side. How far is it directly from home plate to second base (the diagonal of the square)?

Source: Little League Baseball, Official Regulations and Playing Rules, 2010.

61. Baseball Refer to Problem 59. Overlay a rectangular coordinate system on a major league baseball diamond so that the origin is at home plate, the positive *x*-axis lies in the direction from home plate to first base, and the positive *y*-axis lies in the direction from home plate to third base.

(a) What are the coordinates of first base, second base, and third base? Use feet as the unit of measurement.

(b) If the right fielder is located at $(310, 15)$, how far is it from the right fielder to second base?

(c) If the center fielder is located at $(300, 300)$, how far is it from the center fielder to third base?

62. Little League Baseball Refer to Problem 60. Overlay a rectangular coordinate system on a Little League baseball diamond so that the origin is at home plate, the positive *x*-axis lies in the direction from home plate to first base, and the positive *y*-axis lies in the direction from home plate to third base.

(a) What are the coordinates of first base, second base, and third base? Use feet as the unit of measurement.

(b) If the right fielder is located at $(180, 20)$, how far is it from the right fielder to second base?

(c) If the center fielder is located at $(220, 220)$, how far is it from the center fielder to third base?

63. Distance between Moving Objects A Dodge Neon and a Mack truck leave an intersection at the same time. The Neon heads east at an average speed of 30 miles per hour, while the truck heads south at an average speed of 40 miles per hour. Find an expression for their distance apart *d* (in miles) at the end of *t* hours.

64. Distance of a Moving Object from a Fixed Point A hot-air balloon, headed due east at an average speed of 15 miles per hour and at a constant altitude of 100 feet, passes over an intersection (see the figure). Find an expression for the distance *d* (measured in feet) from the balloon to the intersection *t* seconds later.

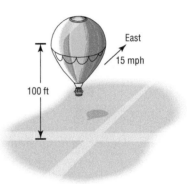

65. Drafting Error When a draftsman draws three lines that are to intersect at one point, the lines may not intersect as intended and subsequently will form an **error triangle.** If this error triangle is long and thin, one estimate for the location of the desired point is the midpoint of the shortest side. The figure shows one such error triangle.

Source: www.uwgb.edu/dutchs/STRUCTGE/sl00.htm

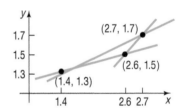

(a) Find an estimate for the desired intersection point.

(b) Find the length of the median for the midpoint found in part (a). See Problem 51.

66. Net Sales The figure illustrates how net sales of Wal-Mart Stores, Inc., have grown from 2002 through 2008. Use the midpoint formula to estimate the net sales of Wal-Mart Stores, Inc., in 2005. How does your result compare to the reported value of $282 billion?

Source: Wal-Mart Stores, Inc., 2008 Annual Report

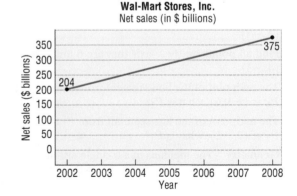

67. Poverty Threshold   Poverty thresholds are determined by the U.S. Census Bureau. A poverty threshold represents the minimum annual household income for a family not to be considered poor. In 1998, the poverty threshold for a family of four with two children under the age of 18 years was $16,530. In 2008, the poverty threshold for a family of four with two children under the age of 18 years was $21,834.

Assuming poverty thresholds increase in a straight-line fashion, use the midpoint formula to estimate the poverty threshold of a family of four with two children under the age of 18 in 2003. How does your result compare to the actual poverty threshold in 2003 of $18,660?
Source: U.S. Census Bureau

Explaining Concepts: Discussion and Writing

68. Write a paragraph that describes a Cartesian plane. Then write a second paragraph that describes how to plot points in the Cartesian plane. Your paragraphs should include the terms "coordinate axes," "ordered pair," "coordinates," "plot," "*x*-coordinate," and "*y*-coordinate."

'Are You Prepared?' Answers

1. 0   **2.** 8   **3.** 5   **4.** $11^2 + 60^2 = 121 + 3600 = 3721 = 61^2$ **5.** $A = \frac{1}{2}bh$ **6.** True

1.2 Graphs of Equations in Two Variables; Intercepts; Symmetry

PREPARING FOR THIS SECTION   *Before getting started, review the following:*

• Solving Equations (Appendix A, Section A.6, pp. A44–A48)

Now Work the 'Are You Prepared?' problems on page 16.

OBJECTIVES   **1** Graph Equations by Plotting Points (p. 9)
     2 Find Intercepts from a Graph (p. 11)
     3 Find Intercepts from an Equation (p. 12)
     4 Test an Equation for Symmetry with Respect to the *x*-Axis, the *y*-Axis, and the Origin (p. 12)
     5 Know How to Graph Key Equations (p. 15)

1 Graph Equations by Plotting Points

An **equation in two variables,** say x and y, is a statement in which two expressions involving x and y are equal. The expressions are called the **sides** of the equation. Since an equation is a statement, it may be true or false, depending on the value of the variables. Any values of x and y that result in a true statement are said to **satisfy** the equation.

For example, the following are all equations in two variables x and y:

$$x^2 + y^2 = 5 \qquad 2x - y = 6 \qquad y = 2x + 5 \qquad x^2 = y$$

The first of these, $x^2 + y^2 = 5$, is satisfied for $x = 1, y = 2$, since $1^2 + 2^2 = 1 + 4 = 5$. Other choices of x and y, such as $x = -1$, $y = -2$, also satisfy this equation. It is not satisfied for $x = 2$ and $y = 3$, since $2^2 + 3^2 = 4 + 9 = 13 \neq 5$.

The **graph of an equation in two variables** x and y consists of the set of points in the xy-plane whose coordinates (x, y) satisfy the equation.

Graphs play an important role in helping us to visualize the relationships that exist between two variables or quantities. Figure 11 on page 10 shows the relation between the level of risk in a stock portfolio and the average annual rate of return. From the graph, we can see that, when 30% of a portfolio of stocks is invested in foreign companies, risk is minimized.

Figure 11
Source: T. Rowe Price

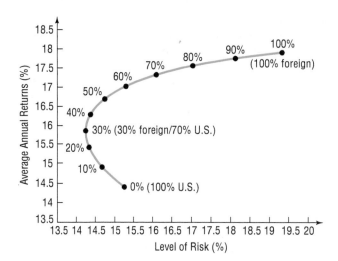

EXAMPLE 1

Determining Whether a Point Is on the Graph of an Equation

Determine if the following points are on the graph of the equation $2x - y = 6$.

(a) $(2, 3)$ (b) $(2, -2)$

Solution

(a) For the point $(2, 3)$, check to see if $x = 2, y = 3$ satisfies the equation $2x - y = 6$.

$$2x - y = 2(2) - 3 = 4 - 3 = 1 \neq 6$$

The equation is not satisfied, so the point $(2, 3)$ is not on the graph of $2x - y = 6$.

(b) For the point $(2, -2)$,

$$2x - y = 2(2) - (-2) = 4 + 2 = 6$$

The equation is satisfied, so the point $(2, -2)$ is on the graph of $2x - y = 6$.

━━━━━**Now Work** PROBLEM 11

EXAMPLE 2

Graphing an Equation by Plotting Points

Graph the equation: $y = 2x + 5$

Solution

We want to find all points (x, y) that satisfy the equation. To locate some of these points (and get an idea of the pattern of the graph), assign some numbers to x and find corresponding values for y.

Figure 12

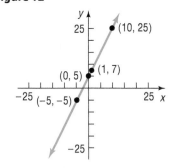

If	Then	Point on Graph
$x = 0$	$y = 2(0) + 5 = 5$	$(0, 5)$
$x = 1$	$y = 2(1) + 5 = 7$	$(1, 7)$
$x = -5$	$y = 2(-5) + 5 = -5$	$(-5, -5)$
$x = 10$	$y = 2(10) + 5 = 25$	$(10, 25)$

By plotting these points and then connecting them, we obtain the graph of the equation (a *line*), as shown in Figure 12.

EXAMPLE 3

Graphing an Equation by Plotting Points

Graph the equation: $y = x^2$

Solution

Table 1 provides several points on the graph. In Figure 13 we plot these points and connect them with a smooth curve to obtain the graph (a *parabola*).

Table 1

x	$y = x^2$	(x, y)
-4	16	$(-4, 16)$
-3	9	$(-3, 9)$
-2	4	$(-2, 4)$
-1	1	$(-1, 1)$
0	0	$(0, 0)$
1	1	$(1, 1)$
2	4	$(2, 4)$
3	9	$(3, 9)$
4	16	$(4, 16)$

Figure 13

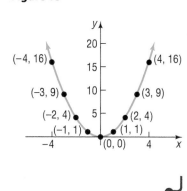

The graphs of the equations shown in Figures 12 and 13 do not show all points. For example, in Figure 12, the point $(20, 45)$ is a part of the graph of $y = 2x + 5$, but it is not shown. Since the graph of $y = 2x + 5$ could be extended out as far as we please, we use arrows to indicate that the pattern shown continues. It is important when illustrating a graph to present enough of the graph so that any viewer of the illustration will "see" the rest of it as an obvious continuation of what is actually there. This is referred to as a **complete graph.**

One way to obtain a complete graph of an equation is to plot a sufficient number of points on the graph until a pattern becomes evident. Then these points are connected with a smooth curve following the suggested pattern. But how many points are sufficient? Sometimes knowledge about the equation tells us. For example, we will learn in the next section that, if an equation is of the form $y = mx + b$, then its graph is a line. In this case, only two points are needed to obtain the graph.

COMMENT Another way to obtain the graph of an equation is to use a graphing utility. Read Section B.2, *Using a Graphing Utility to Graph Equations,* in Appendix B. ▪

One purpose of this book is to investigate the properties of equations in order to decide whether a graph is complete. Sometimes we shall graph equations by plotting points. Shortly, we shall investigate various techniques that will enable us to graph an equation without plotting so many points.

Two techniques that sometimes reduce the number of points required to graph an equation involve finding *intercepts* and checking for *symmetry*.

2   Find Intercepts from a Graph

Figure 14

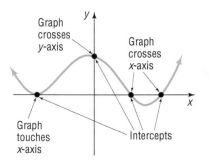

The points, if any, at which a graph crosses or touches the coordinate axes are called the **intercepts.** See Figure 14. The x-coordinate of a point at which the graph crosses or touches the x-axis is an **x-intercept,** and the y-coordinate of a point at which the graph crosses or touches the y-axis is a **y-intercept.** For a graph to be complete, all its intercepts must be displayed.

EXAMPLE 4

Finding Intercepts from a Graph

Find the intercepts of the graph in Figure 15. What are its x-intercepts? What are its y-intercepts?

Solution   The intercepts of the graph are the points

$$(-3, 0), \quad (0, 3), \quad \left(\frac{3}{2}, 0\right), \quad \left(0, -\frac{4}{3}\right), \quad (0, -3.5), \quad (4.5, 0)$$

The x-intercepts are $-3, \dfrac{3}{2}$, and 4.5; the y-intercepts are $-3.5, -\dfrac{4}{3}$, and 3.

Figure 15

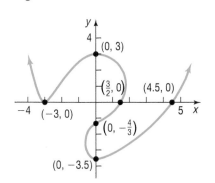

In Example 4, you should notice the following usage: If we do not specify the type of intercept (x- versus y-), then report the intercept as an ordered pair. However, if the type of intercept is specified, then report the coordinate of the specified intercept. For x-intercepts, report the x-coordinate of the intercept; for y-intercepts, report the y-coordinate of the intercept.

⟜**Now Work** PROBLEM 39(a)

3 Find Intercepts from an Equation

The intercepts of a graph can be found from its equation by using the fact that points on the x-axis have y-coordinates equal to 0 and points on the y-axis have x-coordinates equal to 0.

COMMENT For many equations, finding intercepts may not be so easy. In such cases, a graphing utility can be used. Read the first part of Section B.3, *Using a Graphing Utility to Locate Intercepts and Check for Symmetry*, in Appendix B, to find out how to locate intercepts using a graphing utility. ■

Procedure for Finding Intercepts

1. To find the x-intercept(s), if any, of the graph of an equation, let $y = 0$ in the equation and solve for x, where x is a real number.
2. To find the y-intercept(s), if any, of the graph of an equation, let $x = 0$ in the equation and solve for y, where y is a real number.

EXAMPLE 5 **Finding Intercepts from an Equation**

Find the x-intercept(s) and the y-intercept(s) of the graph of $y = x^2 - 4$. Then graph $y = x^2 - 4$ by plotting points.

Solution To find the x-intercept(s), let $y = 0$ and obtain the equation

$$x^2 - 4 = 0 \quad \text{\small $y = x^2 - 4$ with $y = 0$}$$
$$(x + 2)(x - 2) = 0 \quad \text{\small Factor.}$$
$$x + 2 = 0 \quad \text{or} \quad x - 2 = 0 \quad \text{\small Zero-Product Property}$$
$$x = -2 \quad \text{or} \quad x = 2 \quad \text{\small Solve.}$$

The equation has two solutions, -2 and 2. The x-intercepts are -2 and 2.
  To find the y-intercept(s), let $x = 0$ in the equation.

$$y = x^2 - 4$$
$$= 0^2 - 4 = -4$$

The y-intercept is -4.
  Since $x^2 \geq 0$ for all x, we deduce from the equation $y = x^2 - 4$ that $y \geq -4$ for all x. This information, the intercepts, and the points from Table 2 enable us to graph $y = x^2 - 4$. See Figure 16.

Table 2

x	$y = x^2 - 4$	(x, y)
-3	5	$(-3, 5)$
-1	-3	$(-1, -3)$
1	-3	$(1, -3)$
3	5	$(3, 5)$

Figure 16

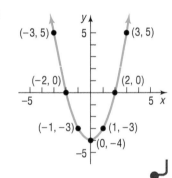

Now Work PROBLEM 21

4 Test an Equation for Symmetry with Respect to the *x*-Axis, the *y*-Axis, and the Origin

We just saw the role that intercepts play in obtaining key points on the graph of an equation. Another helpful tool for graphing equations involves symmetry, particularly symmetry with respect to the x-axis, the y-axis, and the origin.

DEFINITION A graph is said to be **symmetric with respect to the *x*-axis** if, for every point (x, y) on the graph, the point $(x, -y)$ is also on the graph.

Figure 17 illustrates the definition. When a graph is symmetric with respect to the *x*-axis, notice that the part of the graph above the *x*-axis is a reflection or mirror image of the part below it, and vice versa.

Figure 17
Symmetry with respect to the *x*-axis

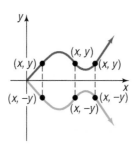

| EXAMPLE 6 | **Points Symmetric with Respect to the *x*-Axis** |

If a graph is symmetric with respect to the *x*-axis and the point $(3, 2)$ is on the graph, then the point $(3, -2)$ is also on the graph. ↵

DEFINITION

Figure 18
Symmetry with respect to the *y*-axis

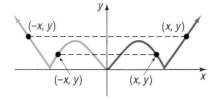

A graph is said to be **symmetric with respect to the *y*-axis** if, for every point (x, y) on the graph, the point $(-x, y)$ is also on the graph. ⌐

Figure 18 illustrates the definition. When a graph is symmetric with respect to the *y*-axis, notice that the part of the graph to the right of the *y*-axis is a reflection of the part to the left of it, and vice versa.

| EXAMPLE 7 | **Points Symmetric with Respect to the *y*-Axis** |

If a graph is symmetric with respect to the *y*-axis and the point $(5, 8)$ is on the graph, then the point $(-5, 8)$ is also on the graph. ↵

DEFINITION

A graph is said to be **symmetric with respect to the origin** if, for every point (x, y) on the graph, the point $(-x, -y)$ is also on the graph. ⌐

Figure 19
Symmetry with respect to the origin

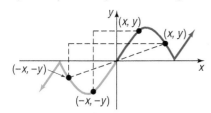

Figure 19 illustrates the definition. Notice that symmetry with respect to the origin may be viewed in three ways:

1. As a reflection about the *y*-axis, followed by a reflection about the *x*-axis
2. As a projection along a line through the origin so that the distances from the origin are equal
3. As half of a complete revolution about the origin

| EXAMPLE 8 | **Points Symmetric with Respect to the Origin** |

If a graph is symmetric with respect to the origin and the point $(4, 2)$ is on the graph, then the point $(-4, -2)$ is also on the graph. ↵

─────**Now Work** PROBLEMS 29 AND 39(b)

When the graph of an equation is symmetric with respect to a coordinate axis or the origin, the number of points that you need to plot in order to see the pattern is reduced. For example, if the graph of an equation is symmetric with respect to the *y*-axis, then, once points to the right of the *y*-axis are plotted, an equal number of points on the graph can be obtained by reflecting them about the *y*-axis. Because of this, before we graph an equation, we first want to determine whether it has any symmetry. The following tests are used for this purpose.

Tests for Symmetry

To test the graph of an equation for symmetry with respect to the

x-Axis   Replace y by $-y$ in the equation and simplify. If an equivalent equation results, the graph of the equation is symmetric with respect to the x-axis.

y-Axis   Replace x by $-x$ in the equation and simplify. If an equivalent equation results, the graph of the equation is symmetric with respect to the y-axis.

Origin   Replace x by $-x$ and y by $-y$ in the equation and simplify. If an equivalent equation results, the graph of the equation is symmetric with respect to the origin.

EXAMPLE 9   **Testing an Equation for Symmetry**

Test $y = \dfrac{4x^2}{x^2 + 1}$ for symmetry.

Solution   *x-Axis:*   To test for symmetry with respect to the x-axis, replace y by $-y$. Since $-y = \dfrac{4x^2}{x^2 + 1}$ is not equivalent to $y = \dfrac{4x^2}{x^2 + 1}$, the graph of the equation is not symmetric with respect to the x-axis.

y-Axis: To test for symmetry with respect to the y-axis, replace x by $-x$. Since $y = \dfrac{4(-x)^2}{(-x)^2 + 1} = \dfrac{4x^2}{x^2 + 1}$ is equivalent to $y = \dfrac{4x^2}{x^2 + 1}$, the graph of the equation is symmetric with respect to the y-axis.

Origin: To test for symmetry with respect to the origin, replace x by $-x$ and y by $-y$.

$$-y = \frac{4(-x)^2}{(-x)^2 + 1} \qquad \text{Replace } x \text{ by } -x \text{ and } y \text{ by } -y.$$

$$-y = \frac{4x^2}{x^2 + 1} \qquad \text{Simplify.}$$

$$y = -\frac{4x^2}{x^2 + 1} \qquad \text{Multiply both sides by } -1.$$

Since the result is not equivalent to the original equation, the graph of the equation $y = \dfrac{4x^2}{x^2 + 1}$ is not symmetric with respect to the origin. ♩

Seeing the Concept

Figure 20 shows the graph of $y = \dfrac{4x^2}{x^2 + 1}$ using a graphing utility. Do you see the symmetry with respect to the y-axis?

Figure 20

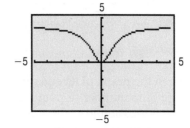

5 Know How to Graph Key Equations

The next three examples use intercepts, symmetry, and point plotting to obtain the graphs of key equations. It is important to know the graphs of these key equations because we use them later. The first of these is $y = x^3$.

EXAMPLE 10   **Graphing the Equation $y = x^3$ by Finding Intercepts, Checking for Symmetry, and Plotting Points**

Graph the equation $y = x^3$ by plotting points. Find any intercepts and check for symmetry first.

Solution   First, find the intercepts. When $x = 0$, then $y = 0$; and when $y = 0$, then $x = 0$. The origin $(0, 0)$ is the only intercept. Now test for symmetry.

x-Axis: Replace y by $-y$. Since $-y = x^3$ is not equivalent to $y = x^3$, the graph is not symmetric with respect to the x-axis.

y-Axis: Replace x by $-x$. Since $y = (-x)^3 = -x^3$ is not equivalent to $y = x^3$, the graph is not symmetric with respect to the y-axis.

Origin: Replace x by $-x$ and y by $-y$. Since $-y = (-x)^3 = -x^3$ is equivalent to $y = x^3$ (multiply both sides by -1), the graph is symmetric with respect to the origin.

To graph $y = x^3$, we use the equation to obtain several points on the graph. Because of the symmetry, we only need to locate points on the graph for which $x \geq 0$. See Table 3. Since $(1, 1)$ is on the graph, and the graph is symmetric with respect to the origin, the point $(-1, -1)$ is also on the graph. Plot the points from Table 3 and use the symmetry. Figure 21 shows the graph.

Figure 21

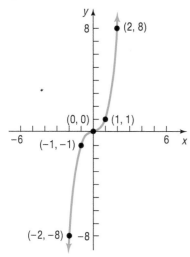

Table 3

x	$y = x^3$	(x, y)
0	0	$(0, 0)$
1	1	$(1, 1)$
2	8	$(2, 8)$
3	27	$(3, 27)$

EXAMPLE 11   **Graphing the Equation $x = y^2$**

(a) Graph the equation $x = y^2$. Find any intercepts and check for symmetry first.
(b) Graph $x = y^2$, $y \geq 0$.

Solution   (a) The lone intercept is $(0, 0)$. The graph is symmetric with respect to the x-axis. (Do you see why? Replace y by $-y$.) Figure 22 shows the graph.

(b) If we restrict y so that $y \geq 0$, the equation $x = y^2$, $y \geq 0$, may be written equivalently as $y = \sqrt{x}$. The portion of the graph of $x = y^2$ in quadrant I is therefore the graph of $y = \sqrt{x}$. See Figure 23.

Figure 24

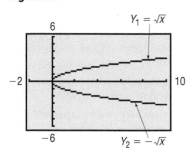

Figure 22
$x = y^2$

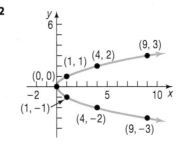

Figure 23
$y = \sqrt{x}$

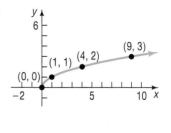

 COMMENT To see the graph of the equation $x = y^2$ on a graphing calculator, you will need to graph two equations: $Y_1 = \sqrt{x}$ and $Y_2 = -\sqrt{x}$. We discuss why in Chapter 2. See Figure 24. ∎

EXAMPLE 12

Graphing the Equation $y = \dfrac{1}{x}$

Graph the equation $y = \dfrac{1}{x}$. Find any intercepts and check for symmetry first.

Table 4

x	$y = \dfrac{1}{x}$	(x, y)
$\dfrac{1}{10}$	10	$\left(\dfrac{1}{10}, 10\right)$
$\dfrac{1}{3}$	3	$\left(\dfrac{1}{3}, 3\right)$
$\dfrac{1}{2}$	2	$\left(\dfrac{1}{2}, 2\right)$
1	1	$(1, 1)$
2	$\dfrac{1}{2}$	$\left(2, \dfrac{1}{2}\right)$
3	$\dfrac{1}{3}$	$\left(3, \dfrac{1}{3}\right)$
10	$\dfrac{1}{10}$	$\left(10, \dfrac{1}{10}\right)$

Figure 25

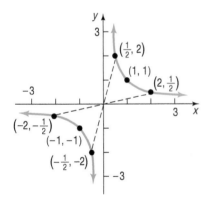

Solution Check for intercepts first. If we let $x = 0$, we obtain 0 in the denominator, which makes y undefined. We conclude that there is no y-intercept. If we let $y = 0$, we get the equation $\dfrac{1}{x} = 0$, which has no solution. We conclude that there is no x-intercept. The graph of $y = \dfrac{1}{x}$ does not cross or touch the coordinate axes.

Next check for symmetry:

x-Axis: Replacing y by $-y$ yields $-y = \dfrac{1}{x}$, which is not equivalent to $y = \dfrac{1}{x}$.

y-Axis: Replacing x by $-x$ yields $y = \dfrac{1}{-x} = -\dfrac{1}{x}$, which is not equivalent to $y = \dfrac{1}{x}$.

Origin: Replacing x by $-x$ and y by $-y$ yields $-y = -\dfrac{1}{x}$, which is equivalent to $y = \dfrac{1}{x}$. The graph is symmetric with respect to the origin.

Now, set up Table 4, listing several points on the graph. Because of the symmetry with respect to the origin, we use only positive values of x. From Table 4 we infer that if x is a large and positive number, then $y = \dfrac{1}{x}$ is a positive number close to 0. We also infer that if x is a positive number close to 0, then $y = \dfrac{1}{x}$ is a large and positive number. Armed with this information, we can graph the equation.

Figure 25 illustrates some of these points and the graph of $y = \dfrac{1}{x}$. Observe how the absence of intercepts and the existence of symmetry with respect to the origin were utilized.

COMMENT Refer to Example 2 in Appendix B, Section B.3, for the graph of $y = \dfrac{1}{x}$ using a graphing utility.

1.2 Assess Your Understanding

'Are You Prepared?' *Answers are given at the end of these exercises. If you get a wrong answer, read the pages listed in red.*

1. Solve the equation $2(x + 3) - 1 = -7$. (pp. A44–A48)

2. Solve the equation $x^2 - 9 = 0$. (pp. A44–A48)

Concepts and Vocabulary

3. The points, if any, at which a graph crosses or touches the coordinate axes are called _____.

4. The x-intercepts of the graph of an equation are those x-values for which _____.

5. If for every point (x, y) on the graph of an equation the point $(-x, y)$ is also on the graph, then the graph is symmetric with respect to the _____.

6. If the graph of an equation is symmetric with respect to the y-axis and -4 is an x-intercept of this graph, then _____ is also an x-intercept.

7. If the graph of an equation is symmetric with respect to the origin and $(3, -4)$ is a point on the graph, then _____ is also a point on the graph.

8. *True or False* To find the y-intercepts of the graph of an equation, let $x = 0$ and solve for y.

9. *True or False* The y-coordinate of a point at which the graph crosses or touches the x-axis is an x-intercept.

10. *True or False* If a graph is symmetric with respect to the x-axis, then it cannot be symmetric with respect to the y-axis.

Skill Building

In Problems 11–16, determine which of the given points are on the graph of the equation.

11. Equation: $y = x^4 - \sqrt{x}$
Points: $(0, 0)$; $(1, 1)$; $(-1, 0)$

12. Equation: $y = x^3 - 2\sqrt{x}$
Points: $(0, 0)$; $(1, 1)$; $(1, -1)$

13. Equation: $y^2 = x^2 + 9$
Points: $(0, 3)$; $(3, 0)$; $(-3, 0)$

14. Equation: $y^3 = x + 1$
Points: $(1, 2)$; $(0, 1)$; $(-1, 0)$

15. Equation: $x^2 + y^2 = 4$
Points: $(0, 2)$; $(-2, 2)$; $\left(\sqrt{2}, \sqrt{2}\right)$

16. Equation: $x^2 + 4y^2 = 4$
Points: $(0, 1)$; $(2, 0)$; $\left(2, \dfrac{1}{2}\right)$

In Problems 17–28, find the intercepts and graph each equation by plotting points. Be sure to label the intercepts.

17. $y = x + 2$

18. $y = x - 6$

19. $y = 2x + 8$

20. $y = 3x - 9$

21. $y = x^2 - 1$

22. $y = x^2 - 9$

23. $y = -x^2 + 4$

24. $y = -x^2 + 1$

25. $2x + 3y = 6$

26. $5x + 2y = 10$

27. $9x^2 + 4y = 36$

28. $4x^2 + y = 4$

In Problems 29–38, plot each point. Then plot the point that is symmetric to it with respect to (a) the x-axis; (b) the y-axis; (c) the origin.

29. $(3, 4)$

30. $(5, 3)$

31. $(-2, 1)$

32. $(4, -2)$

33. $(5, -2)$

34. $(-1, -1)$

35. $(-3, -4)$

36. $(4, 0)$

37. $(0, -3)$

38. $(-3, 0)$

In Problems 39–50, the graph of an equation is given. (a) Find the intercepts. (b) Indicate whether the graph is symmetric with respect to the x-axis, the y-axis, or the origin.

39.
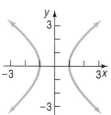

40.
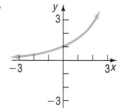

41.
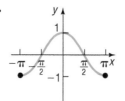

42.
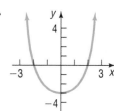

43.
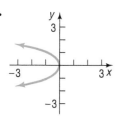

44.
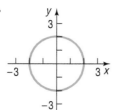

45.
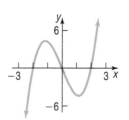

46.
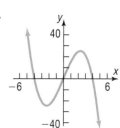

47.
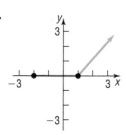

48.
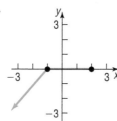

49.
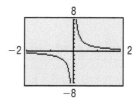

50.
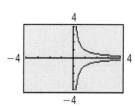

In Problems 51–54, draw a complete graph so that it has the type of symmetry indicated.

51. *y*-axis
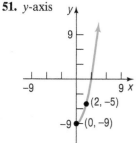

52. *x*-axis
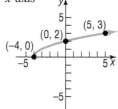

53. Origin
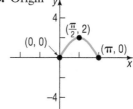

54. *y*-axis
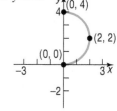

In Problems 55–70, list the intercepts and test for symmetry.

55. $y^2 = x + 4$ **56.** $y^2 = x + 9$ **57.** $y = \sqrt[3]{x}$ **58.** $y = \sqrt[5]{x}$

59. $x^2 + y - 9 = 0$ **60.** $x^2 - y - 4 = 0$ **61.** $9x^2 + 4y^2 = 36$ **62.** $4x^2 + y^2 = 4$

63. $y = x^3 - 27$ **64.** $y = x^4 - 1$ **65.** $y = x^2 - 3x - 4$ **66.** $y = x^2 + 4$

67. $y = \dfrac{3x}{x^2 + 9}$ **68.** $y = \dfrac{x^2 - 4}{2x}$ **69.** $y = \dfrac{-x^3}{x^2 - 9}$ **70.** $y = \dfrac{x^4 + 1}{2x^5}$

In Problems 71–74, draw a quick sketch of each equation.

71. $y = x^3$ **72.** $x = y^2$ **73.** $y = \sqrt{x}$ **74.** $y = \dfrac{1}{x}$

75. If $(3, b)$ is a point on the graph of $y = 4x + 1$, what is b?   **76.** If $(-2, b)$ is a point on the graph of $2x + 3y = 2$, what is b?

77. If $(a, 4)$ is a point on the graph of $y = x^2 + 3x$, what is a?   **78.** If $(a, -5)$ is a point on the graph of $y = x^2 + 6x$, what is a?

Applications and Extensions

79. Given that the point $(1, 2)$ is on the graph of an equation that is symmetric with respect to the origin, what other point is on the graph?

80. If the graph of an equation is symmetric with respect to the y-axis and 6 is an x-intercept of this graph, name another x-intercept.

81. If the graph of an equation is symmetric with respect to the origin and -4 is an x-intercept of this graph, name another x-intercept.

82. If the graph of an equation is symmetric with respect to the x-axis and 2 is a y-intercept, name another y-intercept.

83. Microphones In studios and on stages, cardioid microphones are often preferred for the richness they add to voices and for their ability to reduce the level of sound from the sides and rear of the microphone. Suppose one such cardioid pattern is given by the equation $(x^2 + y^2 - x)^2 = x^2 + y^2$.
(a) Find the intercepts of the graph of the equation.
(b) Test for symmetry with respect to the x-axis, y-axis, and origin.
Source: www.notaviva.com

84. Solar Energy The solar electric generating systems at Kramer Junction, California, use parabolic troughs to heat a heat-transfer fluid to a high temperature. This fluid is used to generate steam that drives a power conversion system to produce electricity. For troughs 7.5 feet wide, an equation for the cross-section is $16y^2 = 120x - 225$.

(a) Find the intercepts of the graph of the equation.
(b) Test for symmetry with respect to the x-axis, y-axis, and origin.
Source: U.S. Department of Energy

Explaining Concepts: Discussion and Writing

85. (a) Graph $y = \sqrt{x^2}$, $y = x$, $y = |x|$, and $y = (\sqrt{x})^2$, noting which graphs are the same.
(b) Explain why the graphs of $y = \sqrt{x^2}$ and $y = |x|$ are the same.
(c) Explain why the graphs of $y = x$ and $y = (\sqrt{x})^2$ are not the same.
(d) Explain why the graphs of $y = \sqrt{x^2}$ and $y = x$ are not the same.

86. Explain what is meant by a complete graph.

87. Draw a graph of an equation that contains two x-intercepts; at one the graph crosses the x-axis, and at the other the graph touches the x-axis.

88. Make up an equation with the intercepts $(2, 0)$, $(4, 0)$, and $(0, 1)$. Compare your equation with a friend's equation. Comment on any similarities.

89. Draw a graph that contains the points $(-2, -1)$, $(0, 1)$, $(1, 3)$, and $(3, 5)$. Compare your graph with those of other students. Are most of the graphs almost straight lines? How many are "curved"? Discuss the various ways that these points might be connected.

90. An equation is being tested for symmetry with respect to the x-axis, the y-axis, and the origin. Explain why, if two of these symmetries are present, the remaining one must also be present.

91. Draw a graph that contains the points $(-2, 5)$, $(-1, 3)$, and $(0, 2)$ that is symmetric with respect to the y-axis. Compare your graph with those of other students; comment on any similarities. Can a graph contain these points and be symmetric with respect to the x-axis? the origin? Why or why not?

Interactive Exercises

Ask your instructor if the applets below are of interest to you.

92. y-axis Symmetry *Open the y-axis symmetry applet.* Move point A around the Cartesian plane with your mouse. How are the coordinates of point A and the coordinates of point B related?

93. x-axis Symmetry *Open the x-axis symmetry applet.* Move point A around the Cartesian plane with your mouse. How

are the coordinates of point A and the coordinates of point B related?

94. Origin Symmetry *Open the origin symmetry applet.* Move point A around the Cartesian plane with your mouse. How are the coordinates of point A and the coordinates of point B related?

'Are You Prepared?' Answers

1. $\{-6\}$ **2.** $\{-3, 3\}$

1.3 Lines

OBJECTIVES
1 Calculate and Interpret the Slope of a Line (p. 19)
2 Graph Lines Given a Point and the Slope (p. 22)
3 Find the Equation of a Vertical Line (p. 22)
4 Use the Point–Slope Form of a Line; Identify Horizontal Lines (p. 23)
5 Find the Equation of a Line Given Two Points (p. 24)
6 Write the Equation of a Line in Slope–Intercept Form (p. 24)
7 Identify the Slope and y-Intercept of a Line from Its Equation (p. 25)
8 Graph Lines Written in General Form Using Intercepts (p. 26)
9 Find Equations of Parallel Lines (p. 27)
10 Find Equations of Perpendicular Lines (p. 28)

In this section we study a certain type of equation that contains two variables, called a *linear equation,* and its graph, a *line.*

Figure 26

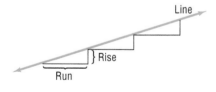

1 Calculate and Interpret the Slope of a Line

Consider the staircase illustrated in Figure 26. Each step contains exactly the same horizontal **run** and the same vertical **rise.** The ratio of the rise to the run, called the *slope,* is a numerical measure of the steepness of the staircase. For example, if the run is increased and the rise remains the same, the staircase becomes less steep. If the run is kept the same, but the rise is increased, the staircase becomes more steep. This important characteristic of a line is best defined using rectangular coordinates.

DEFINITION

Let $P = (x_1, y_1)$ and $Q = (x_2, y_2)$ be two distinct points. If $x_1 \neq x_2$, the **slope m** of the nonvertical line L containing P and Q is defined by the formula

$$m = \frac{y_2 - y_1}{x_2 - x_1} \qquad x_1 \neq x_2 \tag{1}$$

If $x_1 = x_2$, L is a **vertical line** and the slope m of L is **undefined** (since this results in division by 0).

Figure 27(a) on page 20 provides an illustration of the slope of a nonvertical line; Figure 27(b) illustrates a vertical line.

Figure 27

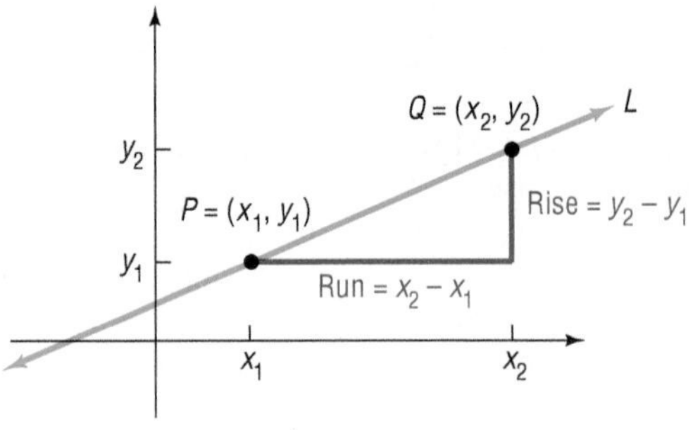

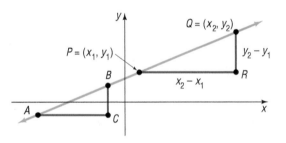

(a) Slope of L is $m = \dfrac{y_2 - y_1}{x_2 - x_1}$

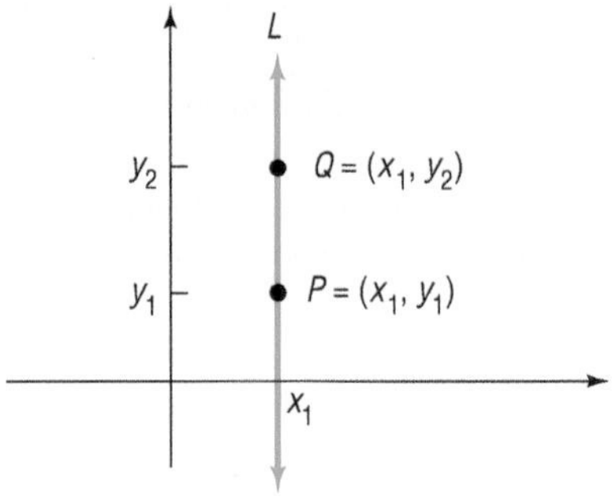

(b) Slope is undefined; L is vertical

As Figure 27(a) illustrates, the slope m of a nonvertical line may be viewed as

$$m = \frac{y_2 - y_1}{x_2 - x_1} = \frac{\text{Rise}}{\text{Run}} \quad \text{or} \quad m = \frac{y_2 - y_1}{x_2 - x_1} = \frac{\text{Change in } y}{\text{Change in } x} = \frac{\Delta y}{\Delta x}$$

That is, the slope m of a nonvertical line measures the amount y changes when x changes from x_1 to x_2. The expression $\dfrac{\Delta y}{\Delta x}$ is called the **average rate of change** of y, with respect to x.

Two comments about computing the slope of a nonvertical line may prove helpful:

1. Any two distinct points on the line can be used to compute the slope of the line. (See Figure 28 for justification.)

Figure 28
Triangles ABC and PQR are similar (equal angles), so ratios of corresponding sides are proportional. Then

Slope using P and $Q = \dfrac{y_2 - y_1}{x_2 - x_1} =$

$\dfrac{d(B, C)}{d(A, C)} = $ Slope using A and B

Since any two distinct points can be used to compute the slope of a line, the average rate of change of a line is always the same number.

2. The slope of a line may be computed from $P = (x_1, y_1)$ to $Q = (x_2, y_2)$ or from Q to P because

$$\frac{y_2 - y_1}{x_2 - x_1} = \frac{y_1 - y_2}{x_1 - x_2}$$

EXAMPLE 1 **Finding and Interpreting the Slope of a Line Given Two Points**

The slope m of the line containing the points $(1, 2)$ and $(5, -3)$ may be computed as

$$m = \frac{-3 - 2}{5 - 1} = \frac{-5}{4} = -\frac{5}{4} \quad \text{or as} \quad m = \frac{2 - (-3)}{1 - 5} = \frac{5}{-4} = -\frac{5}{4}$$

For every 4-unit change in x, y will change by -5 units. That is, if x increases by 4 units, then y will decrease by 5 units. The average rate of change of y with respect to x is $-\dfrac{5}{4}$.

Now Work PROBLEMS 11 AND 17

EXAMPLE 2

Finding the Slopes of Various Lines Containing the Same Point (2, 3)

Compute the slopes of the lines L_1, L_2, L_3, and L_4 containing the following pairs of points. Graph all four lines on the same set of coordinate axes.

$$L_1: \quad P = (2, 3) \qquad Q_1 = (-1, -2)$$
$$L_2: \quad P = (2, 3) \qquad Q_2 = (3, -1)$$
$$L_3: \quad P = (2, 3) \qquad Q_3 = (5, 3)$$
$$L_4: \quad P = (2, 3) \qquad Q_4 = (2, 5)$$

Solution   Let m_1, m_2, m_3, and m_4 denote the slopes of the lines L_1, L_2, L_3, and L_4, respectively. Then

Figure 29

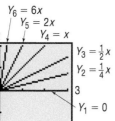

$$m_1 = \frac{-2 - 3}{-1 - 2} = \frac{-5}{-3} = \frac{5}{3} \qquad \text{A rise of 5 divided by a run of 3}$$

$$m_2 = \frac{-1 - 3}{3 - 2} = \frac{-4}{1} = -4$$

$$m_3 = \frac{3 - 3}{5 - 2} = \frac{0}{3} = 0$$

m_4 is undefined because $x_1 = x_2 = 2$

The graphs of these lines are given in Figure 29.

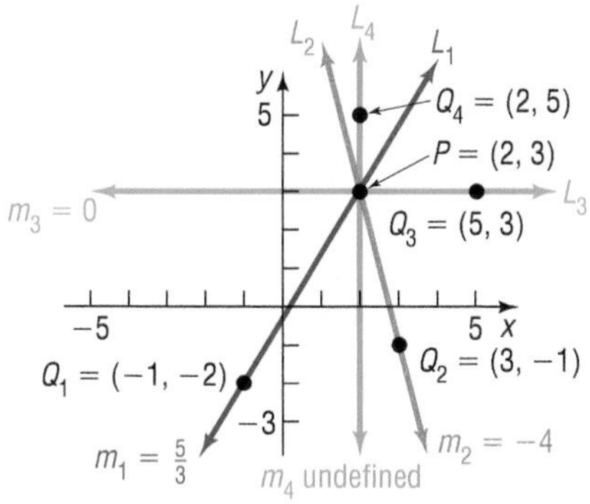

Figure 29 illustrates the following facts:

1. When the slope of a line is positive, the line slants upward from left to right (L_1).
2. When the slope of a line is negative, the line slants downward from left to right (L_2).
3. When the slope is 0, the line is horizontal (L_3).
4. When the slope is undefined, the line is vertical (L_4).

Seeing the Concept

On the same screen, graph the following equations:

Figure 30

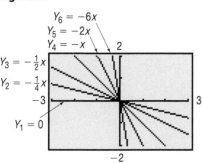

$Y_1 = 0$	Slope of line is 0.
$Y_2 = \dfrac{1}{4}x$	Slope of line is $\dfrac{1}{4}$.
$Y_3 = \dfrac{1}{2}x$	Slope of line is $\dfrac{1}{2}$.
$Y_4 = x$	Slope of line is 1.
$Y_5 = 2x$	Slope of line is 2.
$Y_6 = 6x$	Slope of line is 6.

See Figure 30.

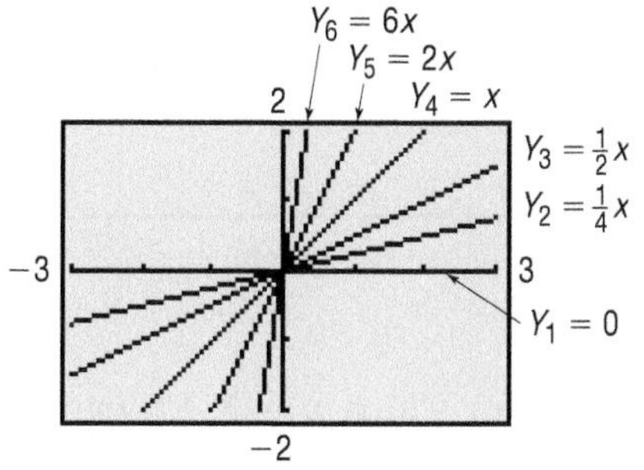

Seeing the Concept

On the same screen, graph the following equations:

Figure 31

$Y_1 = 0$	Slope of line is 0.
$Y_2 = -\dfrac{1}{4}x$	Slope of line is $-\dfrac{1}{4}$.
$Y_3 = -\dfrac{1}{2}x$	Slope of line is $-\dfrac{1}{2}$.
$Y_4 = -x$	Slope of line is -1.
$Y_5 = -2x$	Slope of line is -2.
$Y_6 = -6x$	Slope of line is -6.

See Figure 31.

Figures 30 and 31 on page 21 illustrate that the closer the line is to the vertical position, the greater the magnitude of the slope.

2 Graph Lines Given a Point and the Slope

EXAMPLE 3   **Graphing a Line Given a Point and a Slope**

Draw a graph of the line that contains the point $(3, 2)$ and has a slope of:

(a) $\dfrac{3}{4}$ (b) $-\dfrac{4}{5}$

Solution   (a) Slope $= \dfrac{\text{Rise}}{\text{Run}}$. The fact that the slope is $\dfrac{3}{4}$ means that for every horizontal movement (run) of 4 units to the right there will be a vertical movement (rise) of 3 units. Look at Figure 32. If we start at the given point $(3, 2)$ and move 4 units to the right and 3 units up, we reach the point $(7, 5)$. By drawing the line through this point and the point $(3, 2)$, we have the graph.

Figure 32

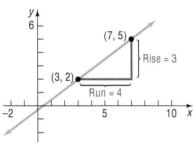

(b) The fact that the slope is

$$-\frac{4}{5} = \frac{-4}{5} = \frac{\text{Rise}}{\text{Run}}$$

Figure 33

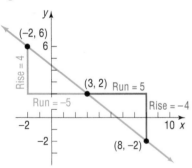

means that for every horizontal movement of 5 units to the right there will be a corresponding vertical movement of -4 units (a downward movement). If we start at the given point $(3, 2)$ and move 5 units to the right and then 4 units down, we arrive at the point $(8, -2)$. By drawing the line through these points, we have the graph. See Figure 33.

Alternatively, we can set

$$-\frac{4}{5} = \frac{4}{-5} = \frac{\text{Rise}}{\text{Run}}$$

so that for every horizontal movement of -5 units (a movement to the left) there will be a corresponding vertical movement of 4 units (upward). This approach brings us to the point $(-2, 6)$, which is also on the graph shown in Figure 33.

Now Work   PROBLEM 23

3 Find the Equation of a Vertical Line

EXAMPLE 4   **Graphing a Line**

Graph the equation: $x = 3$

Solution   To graph $x = 3$, we find all points (x, y) in the plane for which $x = 3$. No matter what y-coordinate is used, the corresponding x-coordinate always equals 3. Consequently, the graph of the equation $x = 3$ is a vertical line with x-intercept 3 and undefined slope. See Figure 34.

Figure 34

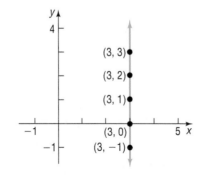

As suggested by Example 4, we have the following result:

THEOREM **Equation of a Vertical Line**

A vertical line is given by an equation of the form

$$x = a$$

where a is the x-intercept.

 COMMENT To graph an equation using a graphing utility, we need to express the equation in the form y = {expression in x}. But x = 3 cannot be put in this form. To overcome this, most graphing utilities have special commands for drawing vertical lines. DRAW, LINE, PLOT, and VERT are among the more common ones. Consult your manual to determine the correct methodology for your graphing utility. ∎

Figure 35

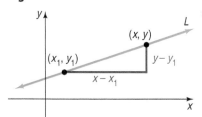

4 Use the Point–Slope Form of a Line; Identify Horizontal Lines

Let L be a nonvertical line with slope m and containing the point (x_1, y_1). See Figure 35. For any other point (x, y) on L, we have

$$m = \frac{y - y_1}{x - x_1} \quad \text{or} \quad y - y_1 = m(x - x_1)$$

THEOREM **Point–Slope Form of an Equation of a Line**

An equation of a nonvertical line with slope m that contains the point (x_1, y_1) is

$$y - y_1 = m(x - x_1) \qquad (2)$$

EXAMPLE 5 **Using the Point–Slope Form of a Line**

Figure 36

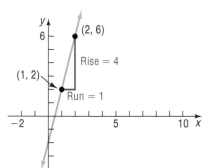

An equation of the line with slope 4 and containing the point $(1, 2)$ can be found by using the point–slope form with $m = 4$, $x_1 = 1$, and $y_1 = 2$.

$$y - y_1 = m(x - x_1)$$
$$y - 2 = 4(x - 1) \qquad m = 4, x_1 = 1, y_1 = 2$$
$$y = 4x - 2 \qquad \text{Solve for } y.$$

See Figure 36 for the graph.

━━━━━Now Work PROBLEM 45

EXAMPLE 6 **Finding the Equation of a Horizontal Line**

Find an equation of the horizontal line containing the point $(3, 2)$.

Solution Because all the y-values are equal on a horizontal line, the slope of a horizontal line is 0. To get an equation, we use the point–slope form with $m = 0$, $x_1 = 3$, and $y_1 = 2$.

Figure 37

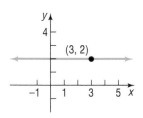

$$y - y_1 = m(x - x_1)$$
$$y - 2 = 0 \cdot (x - 3) \qquad m = 0, x_1 = 3, \text{ and } y_1 = 2$$
$$y - 2 = 0$$
$$y = 2$$

See Figure 37 for the graph.

As suggested by Example 6, we have the following result:

THEOREM   **Equation of a Horizontal Line**

A horizontal line is given by an equation of the form

$$y = b$$

where b is the y-intercept.

5 Find the Equation of a Line Given Two Points

EXAMPLE 7   **Finding an Equation of a Line Given Two Points**

Find an equation of the line containing the points $(2, 3)$ and $(-4, 5)$. Graph the line.

Solution   First compute the slope of the line.

$$m = \frac{5 - 3}{-4 - 2} = \frac{2}{-6} = -\frac{1}{3}$$

Figure 38

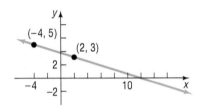

Use the point $(2, 3)$ and the slope $m = -\dfrac{1}{3}$ to get the point–slope form of the equation of the line.

$$y - 3 = -\frac{1}{3}(x - 2)$$

See Figure 38 for the graph.

In the solution to Example 7, we could have used the other point, $(-4, 5)$, instead of the point $(2, 3)$. The equation that results, although it looks different, is equivalent to the equation that we obtained in the example. (Try it for yourself.)

➤**Now Work** PROBLEM 37

6 Write the Equation of a Line in Slope–Intercept Form

Another useful equation of a line is obtained when the slope m and y-intercept b are known. In this event, we know both the slope m of the line and a point $(0, b)$ on the line; then we use the point–slope form, equation (2), to obtain the following equation:

$$y - b = m(x - 0) \quad \text{or} \quad y = mx + b$$

THEOREM   **Slope–Intercept Form of an Equation of a Line**

An equation of a line with slope m and y-intercept b is

$$y = mx + b \tag{3}$$

➤**Now Work** PROBLEM 51 (EXPRESS ANSWER
IN SLOPE–INTERCEPT FORM)

Figure 39 $y = mx + 2$

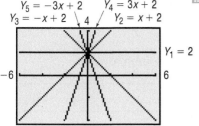

$Y_5 = -3x + 2$ $Y_4 = 3x + 2$
$Y_3 = -x + 2$ $Y_2 = x + 2$

$Y_1 = 2$

Seeing the Concept

To see the role that the slope m plays, graph the following lines on the same screen.

$$Y_1 = 2$$
$$Y_2 = x + 2$$
$$Y_3 = -x + 2$$
$$Y_4 = 3x + 2$$
$$Y_5 = -3x + 2$$

See Figure 39. What do you conclude about the lines $y = mx + 2$?

Figure 40 $y = 2x + b$

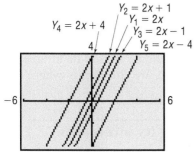

$Y_4 = 2x + 4$ $Y_2 = 2x + 1$
$Y_1 = 2x$
$Y_3 = 2x - 1$
$Y_5 = 2x - 4$

Seeing the Concept

To see the role of the y-intercept b, graph the following lines on the same screen.

$$Y_1 = 2x$$
$$Y_2 = 2x + 1$$
$$Y_3 = 2x - 1$$
$$Y_4 = 2x + 4$$
$$Y_5 = 2x - 4$$

See Figure 40. What do you conclude about the lines $y = 2x + b$?

7 Identify the Slope and y-Intercept of a Line from Its Equation

When the equation of a line is written in slope–intercept form, it is easy to find the slope m and y-intercept b of the line. For example, suppose that the equation of a line is

$$y = -2x + 7$$

Compare it to $y = mx + b$.

$$y = -2x + 7$$
$$y = \quad mx + b$$

The slope of this line is -2 and its y-intercept is 7.

Now Work PROBLEM 71

EXAMPLE 8   **Finding the Slope and y-Intercept**

Find the slope m and y-intercept b of the equation $2x + 4y = 8$. Graph the equation.

Solution   To obtain the slope and y-intercept, write the equation in slope–intercept form by solving for y.

$$2x + 4y = 8$$
$$4y = -2x + 8$$
$$y = -\frac{1}{2}x + 2 \quad y = mx + b$$

Figure 41

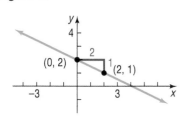

(0, 2)   2   1   (2, 1)

The coefficient of x, $-\dfrac{1}{2}$, is the slope, and the y-intercept is 2. Graph the line using the fact that the y-intercept is 2 and the slope is $-\dfrac{1}{2}$. Then, starting at the point $(0, 2)$, go to the right 2 units and then down 1 unit to the point $(2, 1)$. See Figure 41.

Now Work PROBLEM 77

8 Graph Lines Written in General Form Using Intercepts

Refer to Example 8. The form of the equation of the line $2x + 4y = 8$ is called the *general form*.

DEFINITION

The equation of a line is in **general form*** when it is written as

$$Ax + By = C \qquad (4)$$

where A, B, and C are real numbers and A and B are not both 0.

If $B = 0$ in (4), then $A \neq 0$ and the graph of the equation is a vertical line: $x = \dfrac{C}{A}$. If $B \neq 0$ in (4), then we can solve the equation for y and write the equation in slope–intercept form as we did in Example 8.

Another approach to graphing the equation (4) would be to find its intercepts. Remember, the intercepts of the graph of an equation are the points where the graph crosses or touches a coordinate axis.

EXAMPLE 9

Graphing an Equation in General Form Using Its Intercepts

Graph the equation $2x + 4y = 8$ by finding its intercepts.

Solution   To obtain the x-intercept, let $y = 0$ in the equation and solve for x.

$$2x + 4y = 8$$
$$2x + 4(0) = 8 \quad \text{Let } y = 0.$$
$$2x = 8$$
$$x = 4 \quad \text{Divide both sides by 2.}$$

The x-intercept is 4 and the point $(4, 0)$ is on the graph of the equation.
To obtain the y-intercept, let $x = 0$ in the equation and solve for y.

$$2x + 4y = 8$$
$$2(0) + 4y = 8 \quad \text{Let } x = 0.$$
$$4y = 8$$
$$y = 2 \quad \text{Divide both sides by 4.}$$

Figure 42

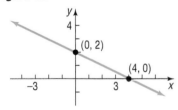

The y-intercept is 2 and the point $(0, 2)$ is on the graph of the equation.
Plot the points $(4, 0)$ and $(0, 2)$ and draw the line through the points. See Figure 42.

Now Work PROBLEM 91

Every line has an equation that is equivalent to an equation written in general form. For example, a vertical line whose equation is

$$x = a$$

can be written in the general form

$$1 \cdot x + 0 \cdot y = a \quad A = 1, B = 0, C = a$$

A horizontal line whose equation is

$$y = b$$

can be written in the general form

$$0 \cdot x + 1 \cdot y = b \quad A = 0, B = 1, C = b$$

*Some books use the term **standard form**.

Lines that are neither vertical nor horizontal have general equations of the form

$$Ax + By = C \quad A \neq 0 \text{ and } B \neq 0$$

Because the equation of every line can be written in general form, any equation equivalent to equation (4) is called a **linear equation.**

9 Find Equations of Parallel Lines

Figure 43

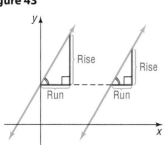

When two lines (in the plane) do not intersect (that is, they have no points in common), they are said to be **parallel.** Look at Figure 43. There we have drawn two parallel lines and have constructed two right triangles by drawing sides parallel to the coordinate axes. The right triangles are similar. (Do you see why? Two angles are equal.) Because the triangles are similar, the ratios of corresponding sides are equal.

THEOREM   Criterion for Parallel Lines

Two nonvertical lines are parallel if and only if their slopes are equal and they have different y-intercepts.

The use of the words "if and only if" in the preceding theorem means that actually two statements are being made, one the converse of the other.

If two nonvertical lines are parallel, then their slopes are equal and they have different y-intercepts.
If two nonvertical lines have equal slopes and they have different y-intercepts, then they are parallel.

EXAMPLE 10   **Showing That Two Lines Are Parallel**

Show that the lines given by the following equations are parallel:

$$L_1: \quad 2x + 3y = 6, \qquad L_2: \quad 4x + 6y = 0$$

Solution   To determine whether these lines have equal slopes and different y-intercepts, write each equation in slope–intercept form:

Figure 44

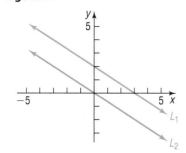

$$
\begin{array}{ll}
L_1: \quad 2x + 3y = 6 & L_2: \quad 4x + 6y = 0 \\
\qquad\quad 3y = -2x + 6 & \qquad\quad 6y = -4x \\
\qquad\quad y = -\dfrac{2}{3}x + 2 & \qquad\quad y = -\dfrac{2}{3}x
\end{array}
$$

$$\text{Slope} = -\frac{2}{3}; \; y\text{-intercept} = 2 \qquad \text{Slope} = -\frac{2}{3}; \; y\text{-intercept} = 0$$

Because these lines have the same slope, $-\dfrac{2}{3}$, but different y-intercepts, the lines are parallel. See Figure 44.

EXAMPLE 11   **Finding a Line That Is Parallel to a Given Line**

Find an equation for the line that contains the point $(2, -3)$ and is parallel to the line $2x + y = 6$.

Solution   Since the two lines are to be parallel, the slope of the line that we seek equals the slope of the line $2x + y = 6$. Begin by writing the equation of the line $2x + y = 6$ in slope–intercept form.

$$2x + y = 6$$
$$y = -2x + 6$$

Figure 45

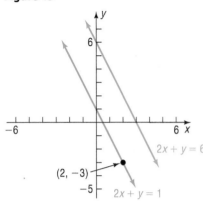

The slope is -2. Since the line that we seek also has slope -2 and contains the point $(2, -3)$, use the point–slope form to obtain its equation.

$$y - y_1 = m(x - x_1) \quad \text{Point–slope form}$$
$$y - (-3) = -2(x - 2) \quad m = -2, x_1 = 2, y_1 = -3$$
$$y + 3 = -2x + 4 \quad \text{Simplify.}$$
$$y = -2x + 1 \quad \text{Slope–intercept form}$$
$$2x + y = 1 \quad \text{General form}$$

This line is parallel to the line $2x + y = 6$ and contains the point $(2, -3)$. See Figure 45.

⟶**Now Work** PROBLEM 59

Figure 46

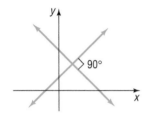

10 Find Equations of Perpendicular Lines

When two lines intersect at a right angle (90°), they are said to be **perpendicular.** See Figure 46.

The following result gives a condition, in terms of their slopes, for two lines to be perpendicular.

THEOREM

Criterion for Perpendicular Lines

Two nonvertical lines are perpendicular if and only if the product of their slopes is -1.

Here we shall prove the "only if" part of the statement:

If two nonvertical lines are perpendicular, then the product of their slopes is -1.

In Problem 128 you are asked to prove the "if" part of the theorem; that is:

If two nonvertical lines have slopes whose product is -1, then the lines are perpendicular.

Figure 47

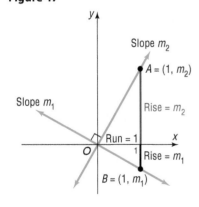

Proof Let m_1 and m_2 denote the slopes of the two lines. There is no loss in generality (that is, neither the angle nor the slopes are affected) if we situate the lines so that they meet at the origin. See Figure 47. The point $A = (1, m_2)$ is on the line having slope m_2, and the point $B = (1, m_1)$ is on the line having slope m_1. (Do you see why this must be true?)

Suppose that the lines are perpendicular. Then triangle OAB is a right triangle. As a result of the Pythagorean Theorem, it follows that

$$[d(O, A)]^2 + [d(O, B)]^2 = [d(A, B)]^2 \tag{5}$$

Using the distance formula, the squares of these distances are

$$[d(O, A)]^2 = (1 - 0)^2 + (m_2 - 0)^2 = 1 + m_2^2$$
$$[d(O, B)]^2 = (1 - 0)^2 + (m_1 - 0)^2 = 1 + m_1^2$$
$$[d(A, B)]^2 = (1 - 1)^2 + (m_2 - m_1)^2 = m_2^2 - 2m_1m_2 + m_1^2$$

Using these facts in equation (5), we get

$$\left(1 + m_2^2\right) + \left(1 + m_1^2\right) = m_2^2 - 2m_1m_2 + m_1^2$$

which, upon simplification, can be written as

$$m_1m_2 = -1$$

If the lines are perpendicular, the product of their slopes is -1. ∎

You may find it easier to remember the condition for two nonvertical lines to be perpendicular by observing that the equality $m_1m_2 = -1$ means that m_1 and m_2 are negative reciprocals of each other; that is, either $m_1 = -\dfrac{1}{m_2}$ or $m_2 = -\dfrac{1}{m_1}$.

EXAMPLE 12 **Finding the Slope of a Line Perpendicular to Another Line**

If a line has slope $\dfrac{3}{2}$, any line having slope $-\dfrac{2}{3}$ is perpendicular to it. ↵

EXAMPLE 13 **Finding the Equation of a Line Perpendicular to a Given Line**

Find an equation of the line that contains the point $(1, -2)$ and is perpendicular to the line $x + 3y = 6$. Graph the two lines.

Solution First write the equation of the given line in slope–intercept form to find its slope.

$$x + 3y = 6$$
$$3y = -x + 6 \qquad \text{Proceed to solve for } y.$$
$$y = -\frac{1}{3}x + 2 \qquad \text{Place in the form } y = mx + b.$$

The given line has slope $-\dfrac{1}{3}$. Any line perpendicular to this line will have slope 3.

Because we require the point $(1, -2)$ to be on this line with slope 3, use the point–slope form of the equation of a line.

$$y - y_1 = m(x - x_1) \qquad \text{Point–slope form}$$
$$y - (-2) = 3(x - 1) \qquad m = 3, x_1 = 1, y_1 = -2$$

To obtain other forms of the equation, proceed as follows:

$$y + 2 = 3x - 3 \qquad \text{Simplify.}$$
$$y = 3x - 5 \qquad \text{Slope–intercept form}$$
$$3x - y = 5 \qquad \text{General form}$$

Figure 48 shows the graphs.

Figure 48

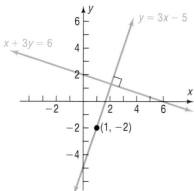

— **Now Work** PROBLEM 65

WARNING Be sure to use a square screen when you graph perpendicular lines. Otherwise, the angle between the two lines will appear distorted. A discussion of square screens is given in Section B.5 of Appendix B. ∎

1.3 Assess Your Understanding

Concepts and Vocabulary

1. The slope of a vertical line is _____; the slope of a horizontal line is _____.

2. For the line $2x + 3y = 6$, the x-intercept is _____ and the y-intercept is _____.

3. A horizontal line is given by an equation of the form _____, where b is the _____.

4. *True or False* Vertical lines have an undefined slope.

5. *True or False* The slope of the line $2y = 3x + 5$ is 3.

6. *True or False* The point $(1, 2)$ is on the line $2x + y = 4$.

7. Two nonvertical lines have slopes m_1 and m_2, respectively. The lines are parallel if _____ and the _____ are unequal; the lines are perpendicular if _____.

8. The lines $y = 2x + 3$ and $y = ax + 5$ are parallel if $a =$ _____.

9. The lines $y = 2x - 1$ and $y = ax + 2$ are perpendicular if $a =$ _____.

10. *True or False* Perpendicular lines have slopes that are reciprocals of one another.

Skill Building

In Problems 11–14, (a) find the slope of the line and (b) interpret the slope.

11.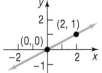

12.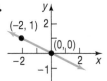

13.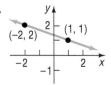

14.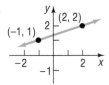

In Problems 15–22, plot each pair of points and determine the slope of the line containing them. Graph the line.

15. $(2, 3); (4, 0)$

16. $(4, 2); (3, 4)$

17. $(-2, 3); (2, 1)$

18. $(-1, 1); (2, 3)$

19. $(-3, -1); (2, -1)$

20. $(4, 2); (-5, 2)$

21. $(-1, 2); (-1, -2)$

22. $(2, 0); (2, 2)$

In Problems 23–30, graph the line containing the point P and having slope m.

23. $P = (1, 2); m = 3$

24. $P = (2, 1); m = 4$

25. $P = (2, 4); m = -\dfrac{3}{4}$

26. $P = (1, 3); m = -\dfrac{2}{5}$

27. $P = (-1, 3); m = 0$

28. $P = (2, -4); m = 0$

29. $P = (0, 3);$ slope undefined

30. $P = (-2, 0);$ slope undefined

In Problems 31–36, the slope and a point on a line are given. Use this information to locate three additional points on the line. Answers may vary.

[**Hint:** *It is not necessary to find the equation of the line. See Example 3.*]

31. Slope 4; point $(1, 2)$

32. Slope 2; point $(-2, 3)$

33. Slope $-\dfrac{3}{2}$; point $(2, -4)$

34. Slope $\dfrac{4}{3}$; point $(-3, 2)$

35. Slope -2; point $(-2, -3)$

36. Slope -1; point $(4, 1)$

In Problems 37–44, find an equation of the line L.

37.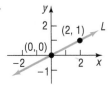

38.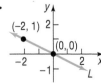

39.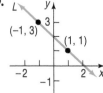

40.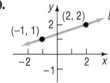

41.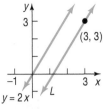

$y = 2x$

L is parallel to $y = 2x$

42.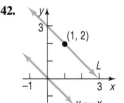

$y = -x$

L is parallel to $y = -x$

43.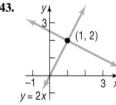

$y = 2x$

L is perpendicular to $y = 2x$

44.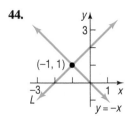

$y = -x$

L is perpendicular to $y = -x$

In Problems 45–70, find an equation for the line with the given properties. Express your answer using either the general form or the slope–intercept form of the equation of a line, whichever you prefer.

45. Slope = 3; containing the point $(-2, 3)$

46. Slope = 2; containing the point $(4, -3)$

47. Slope = $-\dfrac{2}{3}$; containing the point $(1, -1)$

48. Slope = $\dfrac{1}{2}$; containing the point $(3, 1)$

49. Containing the points $(1, 3)$ and $(-1, 2)$

50. Containing the points $(-3, 4)$ and $(2, 5)$

51. Slope = -3; y-intercept = 3

52. Slope = -2; y-intercept = -2

53. x-intercept = 2; y-intercept = -1

54. x-intercept = -4; y-intercept = 4

55. Slope undefined; containing the point $(2, 4)$

56. Slope undefined; containing the point $(3, 8)$

57. Horizontal; containing the point $(-3, 2)$

58. Vertical; containing the point $(4, -5)$

59. Parallel to the line $y = 2x$; containing the point $(-1, 2)$

60. Parallel to the line $y = -3x$; containing the point $(-1, 2)$

61. Parallel to the line $2x - y = -2$; containing the point $(0, 0)$

62. Parallel to the line $x - 2y = -5$; containing the point $(0, 0)$

63. Parallel to the line $x = 5$; containing the point $(4, 2)$

64. Parallel to the line $y = 5$; containing the point $(4, 2)$

65. Perpendicular to the line $y = \dfrac{1}{2}x + 4$; containing the point $(1, -2)$

66. Perpendicular to the line $y = 2x - 3$; containing the point $(1, -2)$

67. Perpendicular to the line $2x + y = 2$; containing the point $(-3, 0)$

68. Perpendicular to the line $x - 2y = -5$; containing the point $(0, 4)$

69. Perpendicular to the line $x = 8$; containing the point $(3, 4)$

70. Perpendicular to the line $y = 8$; containing the point $(3, 4)$

In Problems 71–90, find the slope and y-intercept of each line. Graph the line.

71. $y = 2x + 3$

72. $y = -3x + 4$

73. $\dfrac{1}{2}y = x - 1$

74. $\dfrac{1}{3}x + y = 2$

75. $y = \dfrac{1}{2}x + 2$

76. $y = 2x + \dfrac{1}{2}$

77. $x + 2y = 4$

78. $-x + 3y = 6$

79. $2x - 3y = 6$

80. $3x + 2y = 6$

81. $x + y = 1$

82. $x - y = 2$

83. $x = -4$

84. $y = -1$

85. $y = 5$

86. $x = 2$

87. $y - x = 0$

88. $x + y = 0$

89. $2y - 3x = 0$

90. $3x + 2y = 0$

In Problems 91–100, (a) find the intercepts of the graph of each equation and (b) graph the equation.

91. $2x + 3y = 6$

92. $3x - 2y = 6$

93. $-4x + 5y = 40$

94. $6x - 4y = 24$

95. $7x + 2y = 21$

96. $5x + 3y = 18$

97. $\dfrac{1}{2}x + \dfrac{1}{3}y = 1$

98. $x - \dfrac{2}{3}y = 4$

99. $0.2x - 0.5y = 1$

100. $-0.3x + 0.4y = 1.2$

101. Find an equation of the x-axis.

102. Find an equation of the y-axis.

In Problems 103–106, the equations of two lines are given. Determine if the lines are parallel, perpendicular, or neither.

103. $y = 2x - 3$
$y = 2x + 4$

104. $y = \dfrac{1}{2}x - 3$
$y = -2x + 4$

105. $y = 4x + 5$
$y = -4x + 2$

106. $y = -2x + 3$
$y = -\dfrac{1}{2}x + 2$

In Problems 107–110, write an equation of each line. Express your answer using either the general form or the slope–intercept form of the equation of a line, whichever you prefer.

107.

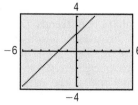

108.

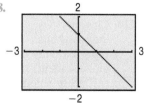

109.

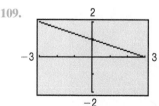

110.

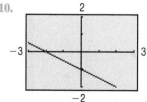

Applications and Extensions

111. Geometry Use slopes to show that the triangle whose vertices are $(-2, 5)$, $(1, 3)$, and $(-1, 0)$ is a right triangle.

112. Geometry Use slopes to show that the quadrilateral whose vertices are $(1, -1)$, $(4, 1)$, $(2, 2)$, and $(5, 4)$ is a parallelogram.

113. Geometry Use slopes to show that the quadrilateral whose vertices are $(-1, 0)$, $(2, 3)$, $(1, -2)$, and $(4, 1)$ is a rectangle.

114. Geometry Use slopes and the distance formula to show that the quadrilateral whose vertices are $(0, 0)$, $(1, 3)$, $(4, 2)$, and $(3, -1)$ is a square.

115. Truck Rentals A truck rental company rents a moving  truck for one day by charging $29 plus $0.20 per mile. Write a linear equation that relates the cost C, in dollars, of renting the truck to the number x of miles driven. What is the cost of renting the truck if the truck is driven 110 miles? 230 miles?

116. Cost Equation The **fixed costs** of operating a business are the costs incurred regardless of the level of production. Fixed costs include rent, fixed salaries, and costs of leasing machinery. The **variable costs** of operating a business are the costs that change with the level of output. Variable costs include raw materials, hourly wages, and electricity. Suppose that a manufacturer of jeans has fixed daily costs of $500 and variable costs of $8 for each pair of jeans manufactured. Write a linear equation that relates the daily cost C, in dollars, of manufacturing the jeans to the number x of jeans manufactured. What is the cost of manufacturing 400 pairs of jeans? 740 pairs?

117. Cost of Driving a Car The annual fixed costs for owning a small sedan are $1289, assuming the car is completely paid for. The cost to drive the car is approximately $0.15 per mile. Write a linear equation that relates the cost C and the number x of miles driven annually.

Source: www.pacebus.com

118. Wages of a Car Salesperson Dan receives $375 per week for selling new and used cars at a car dealership in Oak Lawn, Illinois. In addition, he receives 5% of the profit on any sales that he generates. Write a linear equation that represents Dan's weekly salary S when he has sales that generate a profit of x dollars.

119. Electricity Rates in Illinois Commonwealth Edison Company supplies electricity to residential customers for a monthly customer charge of $10.55 plus 9.44 cents per kilowatt-hour for up to 600 kilowatt-hours.

(a) Write a linear equation that relates the monthly charge C, in dollars, to the number x of kilowatt-hours used in a month, $0 \le x \le 600$.
(b) Graph this equation.
(c) What is the monthly charge for using 200 kilowatt-hours?
(d) What is the monthly charge for using 500 kilowatt-hours?
(e) Interpret the slope of the line.

Source: Commonwealth Edison Company, January, 2010.

120. Electricity Rates in Florida Florida Power & Light Company supplies electricity to residential customers for a monthly customer charge of $5.69 plus 8.48 cents per kilowatt-hour for up to 1000 kilowatt-hours.

(a) Write a linear equation that relates the monthly charge C, in dollars, to the number x of kilowatt-hours used in a month, $0 \le x \le 1000$.
(b) Graph this equation.
(c) What is the monthly charge for using 200 kilowatt-hours?
(d) What is the monthly charge for using 500 kilowatt-hours?
(e) Interpret the slope of the line.

Source: Florida Power & Light Company, February, 2010.

121. Measuring Temperature The relationship between Celsius (°C) and Fahrenheit (°F) degrees of measuring temperature is linear. Find a linear equation relating °C and °F if 0°C corresponds to 32°F and 100°C corresponds to 212°F. Use the equation to find the Celsius measure of 70°F.

122. Measuring Temperature The Kelvin (K) scale for measuring temperature is obtained by adding 273 to the Celsius temperature.

(a) Write a linear equation relating K and °C.
(b) Write a linear equation relating K and °F (see Problem 121).

123. Access Ramp A wooden access ramp is being built to reach a platform that sits 30 inches above the floor. The ramp drops 2 inches for every 25-inch run.

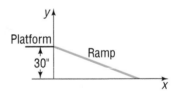

(a) Write a linear equation that relates the height y of the ramp above the floor to the horizontal distance x from the platform.
(b) Find and interpret the x-intercept of the graph of your equation.
(c) Design requirements stipulate that the maximum run be 30 feet and that the maximum slope be a drop of 1 inch for each 12 inches of run. Will this ramp meet the requirements? Explain.
(d) What slopes could be used to obtain the 30-inch rise and still meet design requirements?

Source: www.adaptiveaccess.com/wood_ramps.php

124. Cigarette Use A report in the Child Trends DataBase indicated that, in 1996, 22.2% of twelfth grade students reported daily use of cigarettes. In 2006, 12.2% of twelfth grade students reported daily use of cigarettes.

(a) Write a linear equation that relates the percent y of twelfth grade students who smoke cigarettes daily to the number x of years after 1996.

(b) Find the intercepts of the graph of your equation.

(c) Do the intercepts have any meaningful interpretation?

(d) Use your equation to predict the percent for the year 2016. Is this result reasonable?

Source: www.childtrendsdatabank.org

125. Product Promotion   A cereal company finds that the number of people who will buy one of its products in the first month that it is introduced is linearly related to the amount of money it spends on advertising. If it spends $40,000 on advertising, then 100,000 boxes of cereal will be sold, and if it spends $60,000, then 200,000 boxes will be sold.

(a) Write a linear equation that relates the amount A spent on advertising to the number x of boxes the company aims to sell.

(b) How much advertising is needed to sell 300,000 boxes of cereal?

(c) Interpret the slope.

126. Show that the line containing the points (a, b) and (b, a), $a \neq b$, is perpendicular to the line $y = x$. Also show that the midpoint of (a, b) and (b, a) lies on the line $y = x$.

127. The equation $2x - y = C$ defines a **family of lines,** one line for each value of C. On one set of coordinate axes, graph the members of the family when $C = -4$, $C = 0$, and $C = 2$. Can you draw a conclusion from the graph about each member of the family?

128. Prove that if two nonvertical lines have slopes whose product is -1 then the lines are perpendicular. [**Hint:** Refer to Figure 47 and use the converse of the Pythagorean Theorem.]

Explaining Concepts: Discussion and Writing

129. Which of the following equations might have the graph shown? (More than one answer is possible.)

(a) $2x + 3y = 6$

(b) $-2x + 3y = 6$

(c) $3x - 4y = -12$

(d) $x - y = 1$

(e) $x - y = -1$

(f) $y = 3x - 5$

(g) $y = 2x + 3$

(h) $y = -3x + 3$

130. Which of the following equations might have the graph shown? (More than one answer is possible.)

(a) $2x + 3y = 6$

(b) $2x - 3y = 6$

(c) $3x + 4y = 12$

(d) $x - y = 1$

(e) $x - y = -1$

(f) $y = -2x - 1$

(g) $y = -\dfrac{1}{2}x + 10$

(h) $y = x + 4$

131. The figure shows the graph of two parallel lines. Which of the following pairs of equations might have such a graph?

(a) $x - 2y = 3$
  $x + 2y = 7$

(b) $x + y = 2$
  $x + y = -1$

(c) $x - y = -2$
  $x - y = 1$

(d) $x - y = -2$
  $2x - 2y = -4$

(e) $x + 2y = 2$
  $x + 2y = -1$

132. The figure shows the graph of two perpendicular lines. Which of the following pairs of equations might have such a graph?

(a) $y - 2x = 2$
  $y + 2x = -1$

(b) $y - 2x = 0$
  $2y + x = 0$

(c) $2y - x = 2$
  $2y + x = -2$

(d) $y - 2x = 2$
  $x + 2y = -1$

(e) $2x + y = -2$
  $2y + x = -2$

133. *m* is for Slope   The accepted symbol used to denote the slope of a line is the letter m. Investigate the origin of this symbolism. Begin by consulting a French dictionary and looking up the French word *monter*. Write a brief essay on your findings.

134. Grade of a Road   The term *grade* is used to describe the inclination of a road. How does this term relate to the notion of slope of a line? Is a 4% grade very steep? Investigate the grades of some mountainous roads and determine their slopes. Write a brief essay on your findings.

135. Carpentry   Carpenters use the term *pitch* to describe the steepness of staircases and roofs. How does pitch relate to slope? Investigate typical pitches used for stairs and for roofs. Write a brief essay on your findings.

136. Can the equation of every line be written in slope–intercept form? Why?

137. Does every line have exactly one x-intercept and one y-intercept? Are there any lines that have no intercepts?

138. What can you say about two lines that have equal slopes and equal y-intercepts?

139. What can you say about two lines with the same x-intercept and the same y-intercept? Assume that the x-intercept is not 0.

140. If two distinct lines have the same slope, but different x-intercepts, can they have the same y-intercept?

141. If two distinct lines have the same y-intercept, but different slopes, can they have the same x-intercept?

142. Which form of the equation of a line do you prefer to use? Justify your position with an example that shows that your choice is better than another. Have reasons.

143. What Went Wrong?   A student is asked to find the slope of the line joining $(-3, 2)$ and $(1, -4)$. He states that the slope is $\dfrac{3}{2}$. Is he correct? If not, what went wrong?

Interactive Exercises

Ask your instructor if the applet below is of interest to you.

144. Slope *Open the slope applet.* Move point B around the Cartesian plane with your mouse.

(a) Move B to the point whose coordinates are $(2, 7)$. What is the slope of the line?
(b) Move B to the point whose coordinates are $(3, 6)$. What is the slope of the line?
(c) Move B to the point whose coordinates are $(4, 5)$. What is the slope of the line?
(d) Move B to the point whose coordinates are $(4, 4)$. What is the slope of the line?
(e) Move B to the point whose coordinates are $(4, 1)$. What is the slope of the line?
(f) Move B to the point whose coordinates are $(3, -2)$. What is the slope of the line?
(g) Slowly move B to a point whose x-coordinate is 1. What happens to the value of the slope as the x-coordinate approaches 1?
(h) What can be said about a line whose slope is positive? What can be said about a line whose slope is negative? What can be said about a line whose slope is 0?
(i) Consider the results of parts (a)–(c). What can be said about the steepness of a line with positive slope as its slope increases?
(j) Move B to the point whose coordinates are $(3, 5)$. What is the slope of the line? Move B to the point whose coordinates are $(5, 6)$. What is the slope of the line? Move B to the point whose coordinates are $(-1, 3)$. What is the slope of the line?

1.4 Circles

PREPARING FOR THIS SECTION *Before getting started, review the following:*

- Completing the Square (Appendix A, Section A.3, pp. A29–A30)
- Square Root Method (Appendix A, Section A.6, p. A48)

Now Work the *'Are You Prepared?'* problems on page 37.

OBJECTIVES **1** Write the Standard Form of the Equation of a Circle (p. 34)
2 Graph a Circle (p. 35)
3 Work with the General Form of the Equation of a Circle (p. 36)

1 Write the Standard Form of the Equation of a Circle

One advantage of a coordinate system is that it enables us to translate a geometric statement into an algebraic statement, and vice versa. Consider, for example, the following geometric statement that defines a circle.

DEFINITION

A **circle** is a set of points in the xy-plane that are a fixed distance r from a fixed point (h, k). The fixed distance r is called the **radius,** and the fixed point (h, k) is called the **center** of the circle.

Figure 49

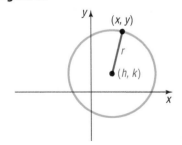

Figure 49 shows the graph of a circle. To find the equation, let (x, y) represent the coordinates of any point on a circle with radius r and center (h, k). Then the distance between the points (x, y) and (h, k) must always equal r. That is, by the distance formula

$$\sqrt{(x - h)^2 + (y - k)^2} = r$$

or, equivalently,

$$(x - h)^2 + (y - k)^2 = r^2$$

DEFINITION

The **standard form of an equation of a circle** with radius r and center (h, k) is

$$(x - h)^2 + (y - k)^2 = r^2 \qquad (1)$$

THEOREM   The standard form of an equation of a circle of radius r with center at the origin $(0, 0)$ is

$$x^2 + y^2 = r^2$$

DEFINITION   If the radius $r = 1$, the circle whose center is at the origin is called the **unit circle** and has the equation

$$x^2 + y^2 = 1$$

See Figure 50. Notice that the graph of the unit circle is symmetric with respect to the x-axis, the y-axis, and the origin.

Figure 50
Unit circle $x^2 + y^2 = 1$

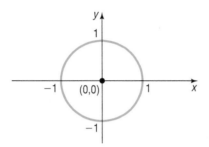

EXAMPLE 1   **Writing the Standard Form of the Equation of a Circle**

Write the standard form of the equation of the circle with radius 5 and center $(-3, 6)$.

Solution   Using equation (1) and substituting the values $r = 5$, $h = -3$, and $k = 6$, we have

$$(x - h)^2 + (y - k)^2 = r^2$$
$$(x + 3)^2 + (y - 6)^2 = 25$$

━━━━━**Now Work** PROBLEM 7

2 Graph a Circle

EXAMPLE 2   **Graphing a Circle**

Graph the equation: $(x + 3)^2 + (y - 2)^2 = 16$

Solution   Since the equation is in the form of equation (1), its graph is a circle. To graph the equation, compare the given equation to the standard form of the equation of a circle. The comparison yields information about the circle.

$$(x + 3)^2 + (y - 2)^2 = 16$$
$$(x - (-3))^2 + (y - 2)^2 = 4^2$$
$$(x - h)^2 + (y - k)^2 = r^2$$

We see that $h = -3$, $k = 2$, and $r = 4$. The circle has center $(-3, 2)$ and a radius of 4 units. To graph this circle, first plot the center $(-3, 2)$. Since the radius is 4, we can locate four points on the circle by plotting points 4 units to the left, to the right, up, and down from the center. These four points can then be used as guides to obtain the graph. See Figure 51.

Figure 51

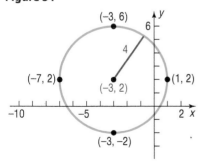

━━━━━**Now Work** PROBLEMS 23(a) AND (b)

EXAMPLE 3	**Finding the Intercepts of a Circle**

For the circle $(x + 3)^2 + (y - 2)^2 = 16$, find the intercepts, if any, of its graph.

Solution This is the equation discussed and graphed in Example 2. To find the x-intercepts, if any, let $y = 0$. Then

$$(x + 3)^2 + (y - 2)^2 = 16$$
$$(x + 3)^2 + (0 - 2)^2 = 16 \qquad y = 0$$
$$(x + 3)^2 + 4 = 16 \qquad \text{Simplify.}$$
$$(x + 3)^2 = 12 \qquad \text{Simplify.}$$
$$x + 3 = \pm\sqrt{12} \qquad \text{Apply the Square Root Method.}$$
$$x = -3 \pm 2\sqrt{3} \qquad \text{Solve for } x.$$

The x-intercepts are $-3 - 2\sqrt{3} \approx -6.46$ and $-3 + 2\sqrt{3} \approx 0.46$.
To find the y-intercepts, if any, let $x = 0$. Then

$$(x + 3)^2 + (y - 2)^2 = 16$$
$$(0 + 3)^2 + (y - 2)^2 = 16$$
$$9 + (y - 2)^2 = 16$$
$$(y - 2)^2 = 7$$
$$y - 2 = \pm\sqrt{7}$$
$$y = 2 \pm \sqrt{7}$$

The y-intercepts are $2 - \sqrt{7} \approx -0.65$ and $2 + \sqrt{7} \approx 4.65$.
Look back at Figure 51 to verify the approximate locations of the intercepts.

> **Now Work** PROBLEM 23(c)

3 Work with the General Form of the Equation of a Circle

If we eliminate the parentheses from the standard form of the equation of the circle given in Example 2, we get

$$(x + 3)^2 + (y - 2)^2 = 16$$
$$x^2 + 6x + 9 + y^2 - 4y + 4 = 16$$

which, upon simplifying, is equivalent to

$$x^2 + y^2 + 6x - 4y - 3 = 0 \qquad (2)$$

It can be shown that any equation of the form

$$x^2 + y^2 + ax + by + c = 0$$

has a graph that is a circle, or a point, or has no graph at all. For example, the graph of the equation $x^2 + y^2 = 0$ is the single point $(0, 0)$. The equation $x^2 + y^2 + 5 = 0$, or $x^2 + y^2 = -5$, has no graph, because sums of squares of real numbers are never negative.

DEFINITION When its graph is a circle, the equation

$$x^2 + y^2 + ax + by + c = 0$$

is referred to as the **general form of the equation of a circle.**

> **Now Work** PROBLEM 13

If an equation of a circle is in the general form, we use the method of completing the square to put the equation in standard form so that we can identify its center and radius.

EXAMPLE 4 **Graphing a Circle Whose Equation Is in General Form**

Graph the equation $x^2 + y^2 + 4x - 6y + 12 = 0$

Solution Group the terms involving x, group the terms involving y, and put the constant on the right side of the equation. The result is

$$(x^2 + 4x) + (y^2 - 6y) = -12$$

Next, complete the square of each expression in parentheses. Remember that any number added on the left side of the equation must also be added on the right.

$$(x^2 + 4x + 4) + (y^2 - 6y + 9) = -12 + 4 + 9$$

$$\left(\frac{4}{2}\right)^2 = 4 \qquad \left(\frac{-6}{2}\right)^2 = 9$$

$$(x + 2)^2 + (y - 3)^2 = 1 \qquad \text{Factor.}$$

This equation is the standard form of the equation of a circle with radius 1 and center $(-2, 3)$.

To graph the equation use the center $(-2, 3)$ and the radius 1. See Figure 52.

Figure 52

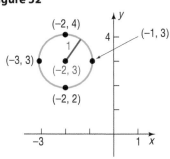

-Now Work PROBLEM 27

 EXAMPLE 5 **Using a Graphing Utility to Graph a Circle**

Graph the equation: $x^2 + y^2 = 4$

Figure 53

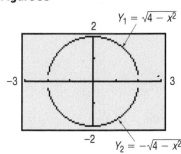

Solution This is the equation of a circle with center at the origin and radius 2. To graph this equation, solve for y.

$$x^2 + y^2 = 4$$
$$y^2 = 4 - x^2 \qquad \text{Subtract } x^2 \text{ from each side.}$$
$$y = \pm\sqrt{4 - x^2} \qquad \text{Apply the Square Root Method to solve for } y.$$

There are two equations to graph: first graph $Y_1 = \sqrt{4 - x^2}$ and then graph $Y_2 = -\sqrt{4 - x^2}$ on the same square screen. (Your circle will appear oval if you do not use a square screen.) See Figure 53.

1.4 Assess Your Understanding

Are You Prepared? *Answers are given at the end of these exercises. If you get a wrong answer, read the pages listed in* red.

1. To complete the square of $x^2 + 10x$, you would (*add/subtract*) the number _____. (pp. A29–A30)

2. Use the Square Root Method to solve the equation $(x - 2)^2 = 9$. (p. A48)

Concepts and Vocabulary

3. *True or False* Every equation of the form

$$x^2 + y^2 + ax + by + c = 0$$

has a circle as its graph.

4. For a circle, the _____ is the distance from the center to any point on the circle.

5. *True or False* The radius of the circle $x^2 + y^2 = 9$ is 3.

6. *True or False* The center of the circle

$$(x + 3)^2 + (y - 2)^2 = 13$$

is $(3, -2)$.

Skill Building

In Problems 7–10, find the center and radius of each circle. Write the standard form of the equation.

7.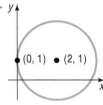

8.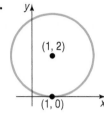

9.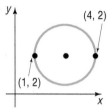

10.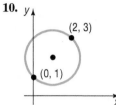

In Problems 11–20, write the standard form of the equation and the general form of the equation of each circle of radius r and center (h, k). Graph each circle.

11. $r = 2$; $(h, k) = (0, 0)$

12. $r = 3$; $(h, k) = (0, 0)$

13. $r = 2$; $(h, k) = (0, 2)$

14. $r = 3$; $(h, k) = (1, 0)$

15. $r = 5$; $(h, k) = (4, -3)$

16. $r = 4$; $(h, k) = (2, -3)$

17. $r = 4$; $(h, k) = (-2, 1)$

18. $r = 7$; $(h, k) = (-5, -2)$

19. $r = \dfrac{1}{2}$; $(h, k) = \left(\dfrac{1}{2}, 0\right)$

20. $r = \dfrac{1}{2}$; $(h, k) = \left(0, -\dfrac{1}{2}\right)$

In Problems 21–34, (a) find the center (h, k) and radius r of each circle; (b) graph each circle; (c) find the intercepts, if any.

21. $x^2 + y^2 = 4$

22. $x^2 + (y - 1)^2 = 1$

23. $2(x - 3)^2 + 2y^2 = 8$

24. $3(x + 1)^2 + 3(y - 1)^2 = 6$

25. $x^2 + y^2 - 2x - 4y - 4 = 0$

26. $x^2 + y^2 + 4x + 2y - 20 = 0$

27. $x^2 + y^2 + 4x - 4y - 1 = 0$

28. $x^2 + y^2 - 6x + 2y + 9 = 0$

29. $x^2 + y^2 - x + 2y + 1 = 0$

30. $x^2 + y^2 + x + y - \dfrac{1}{2} = 0$

31. $2x^2 + 2y^2 - 12x + 8y - 24 = 0$

32. $2x^2 + 2y^2 + 8x + 7 = 0$

33. $2x^2 + 8x + 2y^2 = 0$

34. $3x^2 + 3y^2 - 12y = 0$

In Problems 35–42, find the standard form of the equation of each circle.

35. Center at the origin and containing the point $(-2, 3)$

36. Center $(1, 0)$ and containing the point $(-3, 2)$

37. Center $(2, 3)$ and tangent to the x-axis

38. Center $(-3, 1)$ and tangent to the y-axis

39. With endpoints of a diameter at $(1, 4)$ and $(-3, 2)$

40. With endpoints of a diameter at $(4, 3)$ and $(0, 1)$

41. Center $(-1, 3)$ and tangent to the line $y = 2$

42. Center $(4, -2)$ and tangent to the line $x = 1$

In Problems 43–46, match each graph with the correct equation.

(a) $(x - 3)^2 + (y + 3)^2 = 9$
(b) $(x + 1)^2 + (y - 2)^2 = 4$
(c) $(x - 1)^2 + (y + 2)^2 = 4$
(d) $(x + 3)^2 + (y - 3)^2 = 9$

43.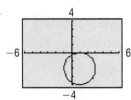

44.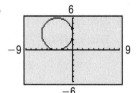

45.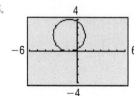

46.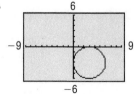

Applications and Extensions

47. Find the area of the square in the figure.

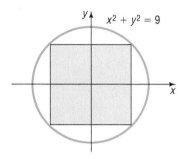

$$x^2 + y^2 = 9$$

48. Find the area of the blue shaded region in the figure, assuming the quadrilateral inside the circle is a square.

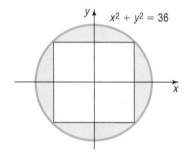

$$x^2 + y^2 = 36$$

49. Ferris Wheel The original Ferris wheel was built in 1893 by Pittsburgh, Pennsylvania, bridge builder George W. Ferris. The Ferris wheel was originally built for the 1893 World's Fair in Chicago, but was also later reconstructed for the 1904 World's Fair in St. Louis. It had a maximum height of 264 feet and a wheel diameter of 250 feet. Find an equation for the wheel if the center of the wheel is on the y-axis.

Source: inventors.about.com

50. Ferris Wheel In 2008, the Singapore Flyer opened as the world's largest Ferris wheel. It has a maximum height of 165 meters and a diameter of 150 meters, with one full rotation taking approximately 30 minutes. Find an equation for the wheel if the center of the wheel is on the y-axis.

Source: Wikipedia

51. Weather Satellites Earth is represented on a map of a portion of the solar system so that its surface is the circle with equation $x^2 + y^2 + 2x + 4y - 4091 = 0$. A weather satellite circles 0.6 unit above Earth with the center of its circular orbit at the center of Earth. Find the equation for the orbit of the satellite on this map.

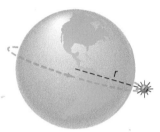

52. The **tangent line** to a circle may be defined as the line that intersects the circle in a single point, called the **point of tangency.** See the figure.

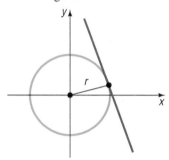

If the equation of the circle is $x^2 + y^2 = r^2$ and the equation of the tangent line is $y = mx + b$, show that:

(a) $r^2(1 + m^2) = b^2$

   [**Hint:** The quadratic equation $x^2 + (mx + b)^2 = r^2$ has exactly one solution.]

(b) The point of tangency is $\left(\dfrac{-r^2 m}{b}, \dfrac{r^2}{b}\right)$.

(c) The tangent line is perpendicular to the line containing the center of the circle and the point of tangency.

53. The Greek Method The Greek method for finding the equation of the tangent line to a circle uses the fact that at any point on a circle the lines containing the center and the tangent line are perpendicular (see Problem 52). Use this method to find an equation of the tangent line to the circle $x^2 + y^2 = 9$ at the point $(1, 2\sqrt{2})$.

54. Use the Greek method described in Problem 53 to find an equation of the tangent line to the circle $x^2 + y^2 - 4x + 6y + 4 = 0$ at the point $(3, 2\sqrt{2} - 3)$.

55. Refer to Problem 52. The line $x - 2y + 4 = 0$ is tangent to a circle at $(0, 2)$. The line $y = 2x - 7$ is tangent to the same circle at $(3, -1)$. Find the center of the circle.

56. Find an equation of the line containing the centers of the two circles

$$x^2 + y^2 - 4x + 6y + 4 = 0$$

and

$$x^2 + y^2 + 6x + 4y + 9 = 0$$

57. If a circle of radius 2 is made to roll along the x-axis, what is an equation for the path of the center of the circle?

58. If the circumference of a circle is 6π, what is its radius?

59. Which of the following equations might have the graph shown? (More than one answer is possible.)

(a) $(x - 2)^2 + (y + 3)^2 = 13$
(b) $(x - 2)^2 + (y - 2)^2 = 8$
(c) $(x - 2)^2 + (y - 3)^2 = 13$
(d) $(x + 2)^2 + (y - 2)^2 = 8$
(e) $x^2 + y^2 - 4x - 9y = 0$
(f) $x^2 + y^2 + 4x - 2y = 0$
(g) $x^2 + y^2 - 9x - 4y = 0$
(h) $x^2 + y^2 - 4x - 4y = 4$

60. Which of the following equations might have the graph shown? (More than one answer is possible.)

(a) $(x - 2)^2 + y^2 = 3$
(b) $(x + 2)^2 + y^2 = 3$
(c) $x^2 + (y - 2)^2 = 3$
(d) $(x + 2)^2 + y^2 = 4$
(e) $x^2 + y^2 + 10x + 16 = 0$
(f) $x^2 + y^2 + 10x - 2y = 1$
(g) $x^2 + y^2 + 9x + 10 = 0$
(h) $x^2 + y^2 - 9x - 10 = 0$

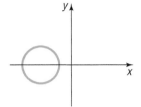

Explaining Concepts: Discussion and Writing

61. Explain how the center and radius of a circle can be used to graph the circle.

62. **What Went Wrong?** A student stated that the center and radius of the graph whose equation is $(x + 3)^2 + (y - 2)^2 = 16$ are $(3, -2)$ and 4, respectively. Why is this incorrect?

63. Suppose that you have a rectangular field that requires watering. Your watering system consists of an arm of variable length that rotates so that the watering pattern is a circle. Decide where to position the arm and what length it should be so that the entire field is watered most efficiently. When does it become desirable to use more than one arm?

[**Hint:** Use a rectangular coordinate system positioned as shown in the figures. Write equations for the circle(s) swept out by the watering arm(s).]

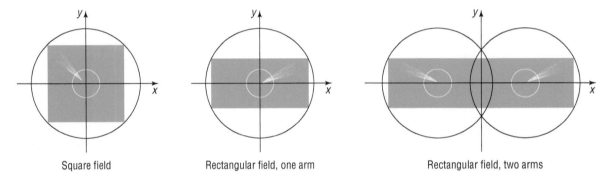

| Square field | Rectangular field, one arm | Rectangular field, two arms |

Interactive Exercises

Ask your instructor if the applets below are of interest to you.

64. Center of a Circle *Open the "Circle: the role of the center" applet.* Place the cursor on the center of the circle and hold the mouse button. Drag the center around the Cartesian plane and note how the equation of the circle changes.

(a) What is the radius of the circle?

(b) Draw a circle whose center is at $(1, 3)$. What is the equation of the circle?

(c) Draw a circle whose center is at $(-1, 3)$. What is the equation of the circle?

(d) Draw a circle whose center is at $(-1, -3)$. What is the equation of the circle?

(e) Draw a circle whose center is at $(1, -3)$. What is the equation of the circle?

(f) Write a few sentences explaining the role the center of the circle plays in the equation of the circle.

65. Radius of a Circle *Open the "Circle: the role of the radius" applet.* Place the cursor on point B, press and hold the mouse button. Drag B around the Cartesian plane.

(a) What is the center of the circle?

(b) Move B to a point in the Cartesian plane directly above the center such that the radius of the circle is 5.

(c) Move B to a point in the Cartesian plane such that the radius of the circle is 4.

(d) Move B to a point in the Cartesian plane such that the radius of the circle is 3.

(e) Find the coordinates of two points with integer coordinates in the fourth quadrant on the circle that result in a circle of radius 5 with center equal to that found in part (a).

(f) Use the concept of symmetry about the center, vertical line through the center of the circle, and horizontal line through the center of the circle to find three other points with integer coordinates in the other three quadrants that lie on the circle of radius five with center equal to that found in part (a).

'Are You Prepared?' Answers

1. add; 25   **2.** $\{-1, 5\}$

CHAPTER REVIEW

Things to Know

Formulas

Distance formula (p. 3)	$d = \sqrt{(x_2 - x_1)^2 + (y_2 - y_1)^2}$
Midpoint formula (p. 6)	$(x, y) = \left(\dfrac{x_1 + x_2}{2}, \dfrac{y_1 + y_2}{2} \right)$
Slope (p. 19)	$m = \dfrac{y_2 - y_1}{x_2 - x_1}$ if $x_1 \neq x_2$; undefined if $x_1 = x_2$
Parallel lines (p. 27)	Equal slopes ($m_1 = m_2$) and different y-intercepts ($b_1 \neq b_2$)
Perpendicular lines (p. 28)	Product of slopes is -1 ($m_1 \cdot m_2 = -1$)

Equations of Lines and Circles

Vertical line (p. 23)	$x = a$; a is the x-intercept
Horizontal line (p. 24)	$y = b$; b is the y-intercept
Point–slope form of the equation of a line (p. 23)	$y - y_1 = m(x - x_1)$; m is the slope of the line, (x_1, y_1) is a point on the line
Slope–intercept form of the equation of a line (p. 24)	$y = mx + b$; m is the slope of the line, b is the y-intercept
General form of the equation of a line (p. 26)	$Ax + By = C$; A, B not both 0
Standard form of the equation of a circle (p. 34)	$(x - h)^2 + (y - k)^2 = r^2$; r is the radius of the circle, (h, k) is the center of the circle
Equation of the unit circle (p. 35)	$x^2 + y^2 = 1$
General form of the equation of a circle (p. 36)	$x^2 + y^2 + ax + by + c = 0$, with restrictions on a, b, and c

Objectives

Section		You should be able to ...	Examples	Review Exercises
1.1	1	Use the distance formula (p. 3)	1–3	1(a)–6(a), 48, 49(a), 50
	2	Use the midpoint formula (p. 5)	4	1(b)–6(b), 50
1.2	1	Graph equations by plotting points (p. 9)	1–3	7
	2	Find intercepts from a graph (p. 11)	4	8
	3	Find intercepts from an equation (p. 12)	5	9–16
	4	Test an equation for symmetry with respect to the x-axis, the y-axis, and the origin (p. 12)	6–9	9–16
	5	Know how to graph key equations (p. 15)	10–12	45, 46
1.3	1	Calculate and interpret the slope of a line (p. 19)	1, 2	1(c)–6(c), 1(d)–6(d), 49(b), 51
	2	Graph lines given a point and the slope (p. 22)	3	47
	3	Find the equation of a vertical line (p. 22)	4	29
	4	Use the point–slope form of a line; identify horizontal lines (p. 23)	5, 6	27, 28
	5	Find the equation of a line given two points (p. 24)	7	30–32
	6	Write the equation of a line in slope–intercept form (p. 24)	8	27, 28, 30–36
	7	Identify the slope and y-intercept of a line from its equation (p. 25)	8	37–40
	8	Graph lines written in general form using intercepts (p. 26)	9	41–44
	9	Find equations of parallel lines (p. 27)	10, 11	33, 34
	10	Find equations of perpendicular lines (p. 28)	12, 13	35, 36
1.4	1	Write the standard form of the equation of a circle (p. 34)	1	17–20, 50
	2	Graph a circle (p. 35)	2, 3	21–26
	3	Work with the general form of the equation of a circle (p. 36)	4	23–26

Review Exercises

In Problems 1–6, find the following for each pair of points:

  (a) The distance between the points
  (b) The midpoint of the line segment connecting the points
  (c) The slope of the line containing the points
  (d) Interpret the slope found in part (c)

1. $(0, 0); (4, 2)$ **2.** $(0, 0); (-4, 6)$

3. $(1, -1); (-2, 3)$ **4.** $(-2, 2); (1, 4)$

5. $(4, -4); (4, 8)$ **6.** $(-3, 4); (2, 4)$

7. Graph $y = x^2 + 4$ by plotting points.

8. List the intercepts of the graph below.

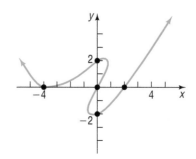

In Problems 9–16, list the intercepts and test for symmetry with respect to the x-axis, the y-axis, and the origin.

9. $2x = 3y^2$ **10.** $y = 5x$ **11.** $x^2 + 4y^2 = 16$ **12.** $9x^2 - y^2 = 9$

13. $y = x^4 + 2x^2 + 1$ **14.** $y = x^3 - x$ **15.** $x^2 + x + y^2 + 2y = 0$ **16.** $x^2 + 4x + y^2 - 2y = 0$

In Problems 17–20, find the standard form of the equation of the circle whose center and radius are given.

17. $(h, k) = (-2, 3); r = 4$ **18.** $(h, k) = (3, 4); r = 4$ **19.** $(h, k) = (-1, -2); r = 1$ **20.** $(h, k) = (2, -4); r = 3$

In Problems 21–26, find the center and radius of each circle. Graph each circle. Find the intercepts, if any, of each circle.

21. $x^2 + (y - 1)^2 = 4$ **22.** $(x + 2)^2 + y^2 = 9$ **23.** $x^2 + y^2 - 2x + 4y - 4 = 0$

24. $x^2 + y^2 + 4x - 4y - 1 = 0$ **25.** $3x^2 + 3y^2 - 6x + 12y = 0$ **26.** $2x^2 + 2y^2 - 4x = 0$

In Problems 27–36, find an equation of the line having the given characteristics. Express your answer using either the general form or the slope–intercept form of the equation of a line, whichever you prefer.

27. Slope $= -2$;   containing the point $(3, -1)$ **28.** Slope $= 0$;   containing the point $(-5, 4)$

29. Vertical;   containing the point $(-3, 4)$ **30.** x-intercept $= 2$;   containing the point $(4, -5)$

31. y-intercept $= -2$;   containing the point $(5, -3)$ **32.** Containing the points $(3, -4)$ and $(2, 1)$

33. Parallel to the line $2x - 3y = -4$;   containing the point $(-5, 3)$

34. Parallel to the line $x + y = 2$;   containing the point $(1, -3)$

35. Perpendicular to the line $x + y = 2$;   containing the point $(4, -3)$

36. Perpendicular to the line $3x - y = -4$;   containing the point $(-2, 4)$

In Problems 37–40, find the slope and y-intercept of each line. Graph the line, labeling any intercepts.

37. $4x - 5y = -20$ **38.** $3x + 4y = 12$ **39.** $\dfrac{1}{2}x - \dfrac{1}{3}y = -\dfrac{1}{6}$ **40.** $-\dfrac{3}{4}x + \dfrac{1}{2}y = 0$

In Problems 41–44, find the intercepts and graph each line.

41. $2x - 3y = 12$ **42.** $x - 2y = 8$ **43.** $\dfrac{1}{2}x + \dfrac{1}{3}y = 2$ **44.** $\dfrac{1}{3}x - \dfrac{1}{4}y = 1$

45. Sketch a graph of $y = x^3$.

46. Sketch a graph of $y = \sqrt{x}$.

47. Graph the line with slope $\dfrac{2}{3}$ containing the point $(1, 2)$.

48. Show that the points $A = (3, 4)$, $B = (1, 1)$, and $C = (-2, 3)$ are the vertices of an isosceles triangle.

49. Show that the points $A = (-2, 0)$, $B = (-4, 4)$, and $C = (8, 5)$ are the vertices of a right triangle in two ways:
(a) By using the converse of the Pythagorean Theorem
(b) By using the slopes of the lines joining the vertices

50. The endpoints of the diameter of a circle are $(-3, 2)$ and $(5, -6)$. Find the center and radius of the circle. Write the standard equation of this circle.

51. Show that the points $A = (2, 5)$, $B = (6, 1)$, and $C = (8, -1)$ lie on a line by using slopes.

52. Create four problems that you might be asked to do given the two points $(-3, 4)$ and $(6, 1)$. Each problem should involve a different concept. Be sure that your directions are clearly stated.

53. Describe each of the following graphs in the xy-plane. Give justification.
(a) $x = 0$ (b) $y = 0$
(c) $x + y = 0$ (d) $xy = 0$
(e) $x^2 + y^2 = 0$

CHAPTER TEST

The Chapter Test Prep Videos are step-by-step test solutions available in the Video Resources DVD, in MyMathLab, or on this text's You Tube Channel. Flip back to the Student Resources page to see the exact web address for this text's YouTube channel.

In Problems 1–3, use $P_1 = (-1, 3)$ and $P_2 = (5, -1)$.

1. Find the distance from P_1 to P_2.

2. Find the midpoint of the line segment joining P_1 and P_2.

3. (a) Find the slope of the line containing P_1 and P_2.
(b) Interpret this slope.

4. Graph $y = x^2 - 9$ by plotting points.

5. Sketch the graph of $y^2 = x$.

6. List the intercepts and test for symmetry: $x^2 + y = 9$.

7. Write the slope–intercept form of the line with slope -2 containing the point $(3, -4)$. Graph the line.

8. Write the general form of the circle with center $(4, -3)$ and radius 5.

9. Find the center and radius of the circle $x^2 + y^2 + 4x - 2y - 4 = 0$. Graph this circle.

10. For the line $2x + 3y = 6$, find a line parallel to it containing the point $(1, -1)$. Also find a line perpendicular to it containing the point $(0, 3)$.

CHAPTER PROJECT

Year	Men	Women
1984	2.16	2.41
1988	2.18	2.43
1992	2.22	2.54
1996	2.21	2.43
2000	2.17	2.39

Source: www.hickoksports.com/history/olmtandf.shtml

Internet-based Project

Predicting Olympic Performance Measurements of human performance over time sometimes follow a strong linear relationship for reasonably short periods. In 2004 the Summer Olympic Games returned to Greece, the home of both the ancient Olympics and the first modern Olympics. The following data represent the winning times (in hours) for men and women in the Olympic marathon.

1. Treating year as the independent variable and the winning value as the dependent variable, find linear equations relating these variables (separately for men and women) using the data for the years 1992 and 1996. Compare the equations and comment on any similarities or differences.

2. Interpret the slopes in your equations from part 1. Do the y-intercepts have a reasonable interpretation? Why or why not?

3. Use your equations to predict the winning time in the 2004 Olympics. Compare your predictions to the actual results (2.18 hours for men and 2.44 hours for women). How well did your equations do in predicting the winning times?

4. Repeat parts 1 to 3 using the data for the years 1996 and 2000. How do your results compare?

5. Would your equations be useful in predicting the winning marathon times in the 2104 Summer Olympics? Why or why not?

6. Pick your favorite Winter Olympics event and find the winning value (that is, distance, time, or the like) in two Winter Olympics prior to 2006. Repeat parts 1 to 3 using your selected event and years and compare to the actual results of the 2006 Winter Olympics in Torino, Italy.

Functions and Their Graphs

2

Outline

Choosing a Cellular Telephone Plan

Most consumers choose a cellular telephone provider first, and then select an appropriate plan from that provider. The choice as to the type of plan selected depends upon your use of the phone. For example, is text messaging important? How many minutes do you plan to use the phone? Do you desire a data plan to browse the Web? The mathematics learned in this chapter can help you decide the plan best-suited for your particular needs.

 —See the Internet-based Chapter Project—

◁ **A Look Back** So far, our discussion has focused on techniques for graphing equations containing two variables.

A Look Ahead ▷ In this chapter, we look at a special type of equation involving two variables called a *function*. This chapter deals with what a function is, how to graph functions, properties of functions, and how functions are used in applications. The word function apparently was introduced by René Descartes in 1637. For him, a function simply meant any positive integral power of a variable *x*. Gottfried Wilhelm Leibniz (1646–1716), who always emphasized the geometric side of mathematics, used the word function to denote any quantity associated with a curve, such as the coordinates of a point on the curve. Leonhard Euler (1707–1783) employed the word to mean any equation or formula involving variables and constants. His idea of a function is similar to the one most often seen in courses that precede calculus. Later, the use of functions in investigating heat flow equations led to a very broad definition, due to Lejeune Dirichlet (1805–1859), which describes a function as a correspondence between two sets. It is his definition that we use here.

2.1 Functions

PREPARING FOR THIS SECTION *Before getting started, review the following:*

- Interval Notation (Appendix A, Section A.9, pp. A72–A73)
- Solving Inequalities (Appendix A, Section A.9, pp. A75–A78)
- Evaluating Algebraic Expressions, Domain of a Variable (Appendix A, Section A.1, pp. A6–A7)

Now Work the *'Are You Prepared?'* problems on page 56.

OBJECTIVES   **1** Determine Whether a Relation Represents a Function (p. 46)
2 Find the Value of a Function (p. 49)
3 Find the Domain of a Function Defined by an Equation (p. 52)
4 Form the Sum, Difference, Product, and Quotient of Two Functions (p. 54)

1 Determine Whether a Relation Represents a Function

Figure 1

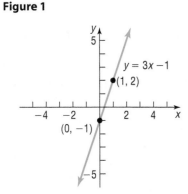

Often there are situations where one variable is somehow linked to the value of another variable. For example, an individual's level of education is linked to annual income. Engine size is linked to gas mileage. When the value of one variable is related to the value of a second variable, we have a *relation*. A **relation** is a correspondence between two sets. If x and y are two elements in these sets and if a relation exists between x and y, then we say that x **corresponds** to y or that y **depends on** x, and we write $x \rightarrow y$.

There are a number of ways to express relations between two sets. For example, the equation $y = 3x - 1$ shows a relation between x and y. It says that if we take some number x, multiply it by 3, and then subtract 1 we obtain the corresponding value of y. In this sense, x serves as the **input** to the relation and y is the **output** of the relation. We can also express this relation as a graph as shown in Figure 1.

Not only can a relation be expressed through an equation or graph, but we can also express a relation through a technique called *mapping*. A **map** illustrates a relation by using a set of inputs and drawing arrows to the corresponding element in the set of outputs. **Ordered pairs** can be used to represent $x \rightarrow y$ as (x, y).

EXAMPLE 1   **Maps and Ordered Pairs as Relations**

Figure 2 shows a relation between states and the number of representatives each state has in the House of Representatives. The relation might be named "number of representatives."

Figure 2

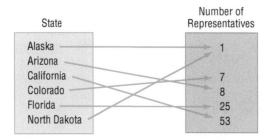

In this relation, Alaska corresponds to 1, Arizona corresponds to 8, and so on. Using ordered pairs, this relation would be expressed as

{(Alaska, 1), (Arizona, 8), (California, 53), (Colorado, 7), (Florida, 25), (North Dakota, 1)}

One of the most important concepts in algebra is the *function*. A function is a special type of relation. To understand the idea behind a function, let's revisit the relation presented in Example 1. If we were to ask, "How many representatives does Alaska have?," you would respond "1." In fact, each input *state* corresponds to a single output *number of representatives*.

Figure 3

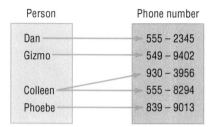

Let's consider a second relation where we have a correspondence between four people and their phone numbers. See Figure 3. Notice that Colleen has two telephone numbers. If asked, "What is Colleen's phone number?," you cannot assign a single number to her.

Let's look at one more relation. Figure 4 is a relation that shows a correspondence between *animals* and *life expectancy*. If asked to determine the life expectancy of a dog, we would all respond "11 years." If asked to determine the life expectancy of a rabbit, we would all respond "7 years."

Figure 4

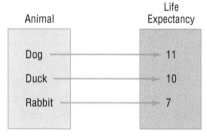

Notice that the relations presented in Figures 2 and 4 have something in common. What is it? The common link between these two relations is that each input corresponds to exactly one output. This leads to the definition of a *function*.

Figure 5

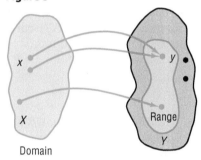

Domain

DEFINITION

Let X and Y be two nonempty sets.* A **function** from X into Y is a relation that associates with each element of X exactly one element of Y.

The set X is called the **domain** of the function. For each element x in X, the corresponding element y in Y is called the **value** of the function at x, or the **image** of x. The set of all images of the elements in the domain is called the **range** of the function. See Figure 5.

Since there may be some elements in Y that are not the image of some x in X, it follows that the range of a function may be a subset of Y, as shown in Figure 5.

Not all relations between two sets are functions. The next example shows how to determine whether a relation is a function.

EXAMPLE 2

Determining Whether a Relation Represents a Function

Determine which of the following relations represent a function. If the relation is a function, then state its domain and range.

(a) See Figure 6. For this relation, the domain represents the number of calories in a sandwich from a fast-food restaurant and the range represents the fat content (in grams).

Figure 6
Source: Each company's Web site

---

* The sets X and Y will usually be sets of real numbers, in which case a (real) function results. The two sets can also be sets of complex numbers, and then we have defined a complex function. In the broad definition (due to Lejeune Dirichlet), X and Y can be any two sets.

(b) See Figure 7. For this relation, the domain represents gasoline stations in Collier County, Florida, and the range represents the price per gallon of unleaded regular in July 2010.

(c) See Figure 8. For this relation, the domain represents the weight (in carats) of pear-cut diamonds and the range represents the price (in dollars).

Figure 7

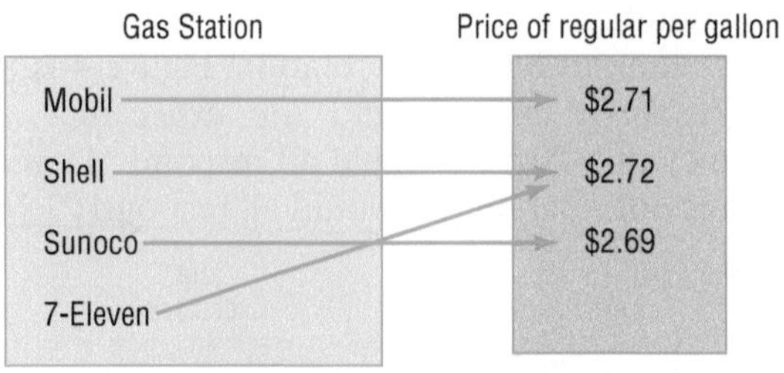

Gas Station   Price of regular per gallon

Mobil $2.71

Shell $2.72

Sunoco $2.69

7-Eleven

Figure 8

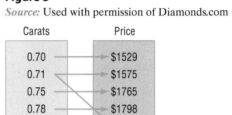

Source: Used with permission of Diamonds.com

Carats   Price

0.70 $1529

0.71 $1575

0.75 $1765

0.78 $1798

              $1952

Solution

(a) The relation in Figure 6 is a function because each element in the domain corresponds to exactly one element in the range. The domain of the function is $\{470, 670, 630, 540, 360\}$, and the range of the function is $\{31, 40, 39, 29, 16\}$.

(b) The relation in Figure 7 is a function because each element in the domain corresponds to exactly one element in the range. The domain of the function is $\{$Mobil, Shell, Sunoco, 7-Eleven$\}$. The range of the function is $\{2.69, 2.71, 2.72\}$. Notice that it is okay for more than one element in the domain to correspond to the same element in the range (Shell and 7-Eleven each sell gas for $2.72 a gallon).

(c) The relation in Figure 8 is not a function because each element in the domain does not correspond to exactly one element in the range. If a 0.71-carat diamond is chosen from the domain, a single price cannot be assigned to it. ⏎

Now Work PROBLEM 15

The idea behind a function is its predictability. If the input is known, we can use the function to determine the output. With "nonfunctions," we don't have this predictability. Look back at Figure 7. The inputs are $\{$Mobil, Shell, Sunoco, 7-Eleven$\}$ The correspondence is "sells regular gas for," and the outputs are $\{$$2.69, $2.71, 2.72\}$. If asked, "How much does Shell sell regular gas for?," we can use the correspondence to answer "$2.72." Now consider Figure 8. If asked, "What is the price of a 0.71-carat diamond?," we could not give a single response because two outputs result from the single input "0.71." For this reason, the relation in Figure 8 is not a function.

We may also think of a function as a set of ordered pairs (x, y) in which no ordered pairs have the same first element and different second elements. The set of all first elements x is the domain of the function, and the set of all second elements y is its range. Each element x in the domain corresponds to exactly one element y in the range.

> **In Words**
> For a function, no input has more than one output. The domain of a function is the set of all inputs; the range is the set of all outputs.

| EXAMPLE 3 |

Determining Whether a Relation Represents a Function

Determine whether each relation represents a function. If it is a function, state the domain and range.

(a) $\{(1, 4), (2, 5), (3, 6), (4, 7)\}$

(b) $\{(1, 4), (2, 4), (3, 5), (6, 10)\}$

(c) $\{(-3, 9), (-2, 4), (0, 0), (1, 1), (-3, 8)\}$

Solution
(a) This relation is a function because there are no ordered pairs with the same first element and different second elements. The domain of this function is $\{1, 2, 3, 4\}$, and its range is $\{4, 5, 6, 7\}$.

(b) This relation is a function because there are no ordered pairs with the same first element and different second elements. The domain of this function is $\{1, 2, 3, 6\}$, and its range is $\{4, 5, 10\}$.

(c) This relation is not a function because there are two ordered pairs, $(-3, 9)$ and $(-3, 8)$, that have the same first element and different second elements.

In Example 3(b), notice that 1 and 2 in the domain each have the same image in the range. This does not violate the definition of a function; two different first elements can have the same second element. A violation of the definition occurs when two ordered pairs have the same first element and different second elements, as in Example 3(c).

Now Work PROBLEM 19

Up to now we have shown how to identify when a relation is a function for relations defined by mappings (Example 2) and ordered pairs (Example 3). But relations can also be expressed as equations. We discuss next the circumstances under which equations are functions.

To determine whether an equation, where y depends on x, is a function, it is often easiest to solve the equation for y. If any value of x in the domain corresponds to more than one y, the equation does not define a function; otherwise, it does define a function.

EXAMPLE 4   **Determining Whether an Equation Is a Function**

Determine if the equation $y = 2x - 5$ defines y as a function of x.

Solution
The equation tells us to take an input x, multiply it by 2, and then subtract 5. For any input x, these operations yield only one output y. For example, if $x = 1$, then $y = 2(1) - 5 = -3$. If $x = 3$, then $y = 2(3) - 5 = 1$. For this reason, the equation is a function.

EXAMPLE 5   **Determining Whether an Equation Is a Function**

Determine if the equation $x^2 + y^2 = 1$ defines y as a function of x.

Solution
To determine whether the equation $x^2 + y^2 = 1$, which defines the unit circle, is a function, solve the equation for y.

$$x^2 + y^2 = 1$$
$$y^2 = 1 - x^2$$
$$y = \pm\sqrt{1 - x^2}$$

For values of x between -1 and 1, two values of y result. For example, if $x = 0$, then $y = \pm 1$, so two different outputs result from the same input. This means that the equation $x^2 + y^2 = 1$ does not define a function.

Now Work PROBLEM 33

2 Find the Value of a Function

Functions are often denoted by letters such as f, F, g, G, and others. If f is a function, then for each number x in its domain the corresponding image in the range is designated by the symbol $f(x)$, read as "f of x" or as "f at x." We refer to $f(x)$ as the **value of f at the number x**; $f(x)$ is the number that results when x is given and the function f is applied; $f(x)$ is the output corresponding to x or the image of x; $f(x)$

does *not* mean "*f* times *x*." For example, the function given in Example 4 may be written as $y = f(x) = 2x - 5$. Then $f\left(\dfrac{3}{2}\right) = -2$.

Figure 9 illustrates some other functions. Notice that, in every function, for each *x* in the domain there is one value in the range.

Figure 9

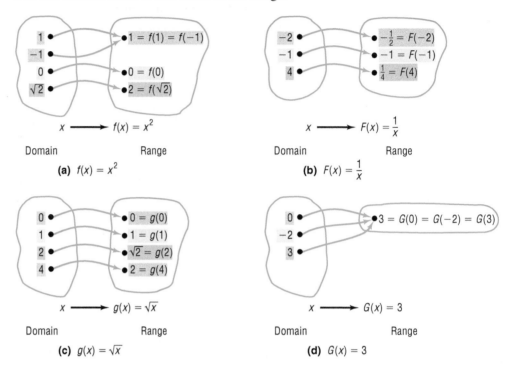

(a) $f(x) = x^2$

(b) $F(x) = \dfrac{1}{x}$

(c) $g(x) = \sqrt{x}$

(d) $G(x) = 3$

Figure 10

Input *x*

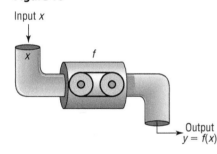

Output
$y = f(x)$

Sometimes it is helpful to think of a function *f* as a machine that receives as input a number from the domain, manipulates it, and outputs a value. See Figure 10.

The restrictions on this input/output machine are as follows:

1. It only accepts numbers from the domain of the function.
2. For each input, there is exactly one output (which may be repeated for different inputs).

For a function $y = f(x)$, the variable *x* is called the **independent variable,** because it can be assigned any of the permissible numbers from the domain. The variable *y* is called the **dependent variable,** because its value depends on *x*.

Any symbols can be used to represent the independent and dependent variables. For example, if *f* is the *cube function*, then *f* can be given by $f(x) = x^3$ or $f(t) = t^3$ or $f(z) = z^3$. All three functions are the same. Each tells us to cube the independent variable to get the output. In practice, the symbols used for the independent and dependent variables are based on common usage, such as using *C* for cost in business.

The independent variable is also called the **argument** of the function. Thinking of the independent variable as an argument can sometimes make it easier to find the value of a function. For example, if *f* is the function defined by $f(x) = x^3$, then *f* tells us to cube the argument. Thus, $f(2)$ means to cube 2, $f(a)$ means to cube the number *a*, and $f(x + h)$ means to cube the quantity $x + h$.

EXAMPLE 6 **Finding Values of a Function**

For the function *f* defined by $f(x) = 2x^2 - 3x$, evaluate

(a) $f(3)$ (b) $f(x) + f(3)$ (c) $3f(x)$ (d) $f(-x)$

(e) $-f(x)$ (f) $f(3x)$ (g) $f(x + 3)$ (h) $\dfrac{f(x + h) - f(x)}{h}$ $h \neq 0$

Solution (a) Substitute 3 for x in the equation for f, $f(x) = 2x^2 - 3x$, to get

$$f(3) = 2(3)^2 - 3(3) = 18 - 9 = 9$$

The image of 3 is 9.

(b) $f(x) + f(3) = (2x^2 - 3x) + (9) = 2x^2 - 3x + 9$

(c) Multiply the equation for f by 3.

$$3f(x) = 3(2x^2 - 3x) = 6x^2 - 9x$$

(d) Substitute $-x$ for x in the equation for f and simplify.

$$f(-x) = 2(-x)^2 - 3(-x) = 2x^2 + 3x \quad \text{Notice the use of parentheses here.}$$

(e) $-f(x) = -(2x^2 - 3x) = -2x^2 + 3x$

(f) Substitute $3x$ for x in the equation for f and simplify.

$$f(3x) = 2(3x)^2 - 3(3x) = 2(9x^2) - 9x = 18x^2 - 9x$$

(g) Substitute $x + 3$ for x in the equation for f and simplify.

$$
\begin{aligned}
f(x + 3) &= 2(x + 3)^2 - 3(x + 3) \\
&= 2(x^2 + 6x + 9) - 3x - 9 \\
&= 2x^2 + 12x + 18 - 3x - 9 \\
&= 2x^2 + 9x + 9
\end{aligned}
$$

(h) $\dfrac{f(x + h) - f(x)}{h} = \dfrac{[2(x + h)^2 - 3(x + h)] - [2x^2 - 3x]}{h}$

$\uparrow$
$f(x + h) = 2(x + h)^2 - 3(x + h)$

$$
\begin{aligned}
&= \frac{2(x^2 + 2xh + h^2) - 3x - 3h - 2x^2 + 3x}{h} && \text{Simplify.} \\
&= \frac{2x^2 + 4xh + 2h^2 - 3h - 2x^2}{h} && \text{Distribute and combine like terms.} \\
&= \frac{4xh + 2h^2 - 3h}{h} && \text{Combine like terms.} \\
&= \frac{h(4x + 2h - 3)}{h} && \text{Factor out } h. \\
&= 4x + 2h - 3 && \text{Divide out the } h\text{'s.}
\end{aligned}
$$

Notice in this example that $f(x + 3) \neq f(x) + f(3)$, $f(-x) \neq -f(x)$, and $3f(x) \neq f(3x)$.

The expression in part (h) is called the **difference quotient** of f, an important expression in calculus.

──**Now Work** PROBLEMS 39 AND 75

Most calculators have special keys that allow you to find the value of certain commonly used functions. For example, you should be able to find the square function $f(x) = x^2$, the square root function $f(x) = \sqrt{x}$, the reciprocal function $f(x) = \dfrac{1}{x} = x^{-1}$, and many others that will be discussed later in this book (such as $\ln x$ and $\log x$). Verify the results of Example 7, which follows, on your calculator.

EXAMPLE 7 **Finding Values of a Function on a Calculator**

(a) $f(x) = x^2$ $\quad f(1.234) = 1.234^2 = 1.522756$

(b) $F(x) = \dfrac{1}{x}$ $\quad F(1.234) = \dfrac{1}{1.234} \approx 0.8103727715$

(c) $g(x) = \sqrt{x}$ $\quad g(1.234) = \sqrt{1.234} \approx 1.110855526$

 COMMENT Graphing calculators can be used to evaluate any function that you wish. Figure 11 shows the result obtained in Example 6(a) on a TI-84 Plus graphing calculator with the function to be evaluated, $f(x) = 2x^2 - 3x$, in Y_1.

Figure 11

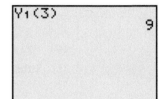

Implicit Form of a Function

 COMMENT The explicit form of a function is the form required by a graphing calculator. ∎

In general, when a function f is defined by an equation in x and y, we say that the function f is given **implicitly.** If it is possible to solve the equation for y in terms of x, then we write $y = f(x)$ and say that the function is given **explicitly.** For example,

Implicit Form	**Explicit Form**
$3x + y = 5$	$y = f(x) = -3x + 5$
$x^2 - y = 6$	$y = f(x) = x^2 - 6$
$xy = 4$	$y = f(x) = \dfrac{4}{x}$

SUMMARY   Important Facts about Functions

(a) For each x in the domain of a function f, there is exactly one image $f(x)$ in the range; however, an element in the range can result from more than one x in the domain.

(b) f is the symbol that we use to denote the function. It is symbolic of the equation (rule) that we use to get from an x in the domain to $f(x)$ in the range.

(c) If $y = f(x)$, then x is called the independent variable or argument of f, and y is called the dependent variable or the value of f at x.

---

3 Find the Domain of a Function Defined by an Equation

Often the domain of a function f is not specified; instead, only the equation defining the function is given. In such cases, we agree that the **domain of f** is the largest set of real numbers for which the value $f(x)$ is a real number. The domain of a function f is the same as the domain of the variable x in the expression $f(x)$.

EXAMPLE 8 **Finding the Domain of a Function**

Find the domain of each of the following functions:

(a) $f(x) = x^2 + 5x$

(b) $g(x) = \dfrac{3x}{x^2 - 4}$

(c) $h(t) = \sqrt{4 - 3t}$

(d) $F(x) = \dfrac{\sqrt{3x + 12}}{x - 5}$

Solution

(a) The function tells us to square a number and then add five times the number. Since these operations can be performed on any real number, we conclude that the domain of f is the set of all real numbers.

In Words

The domain of g found in Example 8(b) is $\{x \mid x \neq -2, x \neq 2\}$. This notation is read, "The domain of the function g is the set of all real numbers x such that x does not equal -2 and x does not equal 2."

(b) The function g tells us to divide $3x$ by $x^2 - 4$. Since division by 0 is not defined, the denominator $x^2 - 4$ can never be 0, so x can never equal -2 or 2. The domain of the function g is $\{x \mid x \neq -2, x \neq 2\}$.

(c) The function h tells us to take the square root of $4 - 3t$. But only nonnegative numbers have real square roots, so the expression under the square root (the radicand) must be nonnegative (greater than or equal to zero). This requires that

$$4 - 3t \geq 0$$
$$-3t \geq -4$$
$$t \leq \frac{4}{3}$$

The domain of h is $\left\{ t \,\middle|\, t \leq \frac{4}{3} \right\}$ or the interval $\left(-\infty, \frac{4}{3} \right]$.

(d) The function F tells us to take the square root of $3x + 12$ and divide this result by $x - 5$. This requires that $3x + 12 \geq 0$, so $x \geq -4$, and also that $x - 5 \neq 0$, so $x \neq 5$. Combining these two restrictions, the domain of F is $\{x \mid x \geq -4, x \neq 5\}$.

For the functions that we will encounter in this book, the following steps may prove helpful for finding the domain of a function that is defined by an equation and whose domain is a subset of the real numbers.

Finding the Domain of a Function Defined by an Equation

1. Start with the domain as the set of real numbers.
2. If the equation has a denominator, exclude any numbers that give a zero denominator.
3. If the equation has a radical of even index, exclude any numbers that cause the expression inside the radical to be negative.

Now Work PROBLEM 51

If x is in the domain of a function f, we shall say that f **is defined at x,** or **$f(x)$ exists.** If x is not in the domain of f, we say that f **is not defined at x,** or **$f(x)$ does not exist.** For example, if $f(x) = \dfrac{x}{x^2 - 1}$, then $f(0)$ exists, but $f(1)$ and $f(-1)$ do not exist. (Do you see why?)

We have not said much about finding the range of a function. We will say more about finding the range when we look at the graph of a function in the next section. When a function is defined by an equation, it can be difficult to find the range. Therefore, we shall usually be content to find just the domain of a function when the function is defined by an equation. We shall express the domain of a function using inequalities, interval notation, set notation, or words, whichever is most convenient.

When we use functions in applications, the domain may be restricted by physical or geometric considerations. For example, the domain of the function f defined by $f(x) = x^2$ is the set of all real numbers. However, if f is used to obtain the area of a square when the length x of a side is known, then we must restrict the domain of f to the positive real numbers, since the length of a side can never be 0 or negative.

EXAMPLE 9

Finding the Domain in an Application

Express the area of a circle as a function of its radius. Find the domain.

Solution

See Figure 12. The formula for the area A of a circle of radius r is $A = \pi r^2$. If we use r to represent the independent variable and A to represent the dependent variable, the function expressing this relationship is

Figure 12

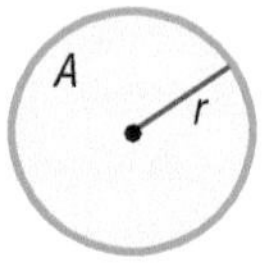

$$A(r) = \pi r^2$$

In this setting, the domain is $\{r | r > 0\}$. (Do you see why?)

Observe in the solution to Example 9 that the symbol A is used in two ways: It is used to name the function, and it is used to symbolize the dependent variable. This double use is common in applications and should not cause any difficulty.

Now Work PROBLEM 89

4 Form the Sum, Difference, Product, and Quotient of Two Functions

Next we introduce some operations on functions. We shall see that functions, like numbers, can be added, subtracted, multiplied, and divided. For example, if $f(x) = x^2 + 9$ and $g(x) = 3x + 5$, then

$$f(x) + g(x) = (x^2 + 9) + (3x + 5) = x^2 + 3x + 14$$

The new function $y = x^2 + 3x + 14$ is called the *sum function $f + g$*. Similarly,

$$f(x) \cdot g(x) = (x^2 + 9)(3x + 5) = 3x^3 + 5x^2 + 27x + 45$$

The new function $y = 3x^3 + 5x^2 + 27x + 45$ is called the *product function $f \cdot g$*. The general definitions are given next.

DEFINITION

If f and g are functions:
The **sum $f + g$** is the function defined by

$$(f + g)(x) = f(x) + g(x)$$

REMEMBER The symbol $\cap$ stands for intersection. It means you should find the elements that are common to two sets. ∎

The domain of $f + g$ consists of the numbers x that are in the domains of both f and g. That is, domain of $f + g = $ domain of $f \cap$ domain of g.

DEFINITION

The **difference $f - g$** is the function defined by

$$(f - g)(x) = f(x) - g(x)$$

The domain of $f - g$ consists of the numbers x that are in the domains of both f and g. That is, domain of $f - g = $ domain of $f \cap$ domain of g.

DEFINITION

The **product $f \cdot g$** is the function defined by

$$(f \cdot g)(x) = f(x) \cdot g(x)$$

The domain of $f \cdot g$ consists of the numbers x that are in the domains of both f and g. That is, domain of $f \cdot g = $ domain of $f \cap$ domain of g.

DEFINITION

The **quotient** $\dfrac{f}{g}$ is the function defined by

$$\left(\frac{f}{g}\right)(x) = \frac{f(x)}{g(x)} \qquad g(x) \neq 0$$

The domain of $\dfrac{f}{g}$ consists of the numbers x for which $g(x) \neq 0$ and that are in the domains of both f and g. That is,

$$\text{domain of } \frac{f}{g} = \{x \mid g(x) \neq 0\} \cap \text{ domain of } f \cap \text{ domain of } g$$

EXAMPLE 10

Operations on Functions

Let f and g be two functions defined as

$$f(x) = \frac{1}{x + 2} \quad \text{and} \quad g(x) = \frac{x}{x - 1}$$

Find the following, and determine the domain in each case.

(a) $(f + g)(x)$ (b) $(f - g)(x)$ (c) $(f \cdot g)(x)$ (d) $\left(\dfrac{f}{g}\right)(x)$

Solution

The domain of f is $\{x \mid x \neq -2\}$ and the domain of g is $\{x \mid x \neq 1\}$.

(a) $(f + g)(x) = f(x) + g(x) = \dfrac{1}{x + 2} + \dfrac{x}{x - 1}$

$$= \frac{x - 1}{(x + 2)(x - 1)} + \frac{x(x + 2)}{(x + 2)(x - 1)} = \frac{x^2 + 3x - 1}{(x + 2)(x - 1)}$$

The domain of $f + g$ consists of those numbers x that are in the domains of both f and g. Therefore, the domain of $f + g$ is $\{x \mid x \neq -2, x \neq 1\}$.

(b) $(f - g)(x) = f(x) - g(x) = \dfrac{1}{x + 2} - \dfrac{x}{x - 1}$

$$= \frac{x - 1}{(x + 2)(x - 1)} - \frac{x(x + 2)}{(x + 2)(x - 1)} = \frac{-(x^2 + x + 1)}{(x + 2)(x - 1)}$$

The domain of $f - g$ consists of those numbers x that are in the domains of both f and g. Therefore, the domain of $f - g$ is $\{x \mid x \neq -2, x \neq 1\}$.

(c) $(f \cdot g)(x) = f(x) \cdot g(x) = \dfrac{1}{x + 2} \cdot \dfrac{x}{x - 1} = \dfrac{x}{(x + 2)(x - 1)}$

The domain of $f \cdot g$ consists of those numbers x that are in the domains of both f and g. Therefore, the domain of $f \cdot g$ is $\{x \mid x \neq -2, x \neq 1\}$.

(d) $\left(\dfrac{f}{g}\right)(x) = \dfrac{f(x)}{g(x)} = \dfrac{\dfrac{1}{x + 2}}{\dfrac{x}{x - 1}} = \dfrac{1}{x + 2} \cdot \dfrac{x - 1}{x} = \dfrac{x - 1}{x(x + 2)}$

The domain of $\dfrac{f}{g}$ consists of the numbers x for which $g(x) \neq 0$ and that are in the domains of both f and g. Since $g(x) = 0$ when $x = 0$, we exclude 0 as well as -2 and 1 from the domain. The domain of $\dfrac{f}{g}$ is $\{x \mid x \neq -2, x \neq 0, x \neq 1\}$.

—**Now Work** PROBLEM 63

In calculus, it is sometimes helpful to view a complicated function as the sum, difference, product, or quotient of simpler functions. For example,

$$F(x) = x^2 + \sqrt{x} \text{ is the sum of } f(x) = x^2 \text{ and } g(x) = \sqrt{x}.$$

$$H(x) = \frac{x^2 - 1}{x^2 + 1} \text{ is the quotient of } f(x) = x^2 - 1 \text{ and } g(x) = x^2 + 1.$$

SUMMARY

Function
A relation between two sets of real numbers so that each number x in the first set, the domain, has corresponding to it exactly one number y in the second set.

A set of ordered pairs (x, y) or $(x, f(x))$ in which no first element is paired with two different second elements.

The range is the set of y values of the function that are the images of the x values in the domain.

A function f may be defined implicitly by an equation involving x and y or explicitly by writing $y = f(x)$.

Unspecified domain
If a function f is defined by an equation and no domain is specified, then the domain will be taken to be the largest set of real numbers for which the equation defines a real number.

Function notation
$y = f(x)$
f is a symbol for the function.
x is the independent variable or argument.
y is the dependent variable.
$f(x)$ is the value of the function at x, or the image of x.

2.1 Assess Your Understanding

'Are You Prepared?' *Answers are given at the end of these exercises. If you get a wrong answer, read the pages listed in red.*

1. The inequality $-1 < x < 3$ can be written in interval notation as _____. (pp. A72–A73)

2. If $x = -2$, the value of the expression $3x^2 - 5x + \dfrac{1}{x}$ is _____. (pp. A6–A7)

3. The domain of the variable in the expression $\dfrac{x - 3}{x + 4}$ is _____. (pp. A6–A7)

4. Solve the inequality: $3 - 2x > 5$. Graph the solution set. (pp. A75–A78)

Concepts and Vocabulary

5. If f is a function defined by the equation $y = f(x)$, then x is called the _____ variable and y is the _____ variable.

6. The set of all images of the elements in the domain of a function is called the _____.

7. If the domain of f is all real numbers in the interval $[0, 7]$ and the domain of g is all real numbers in the interval $[-2, 5]$, the domain of $f + g$ is all real numbers in the interval _____.

8. The domain of $\dfrac{f}{g}$ consists of numbers x for which $g(x)$ ____ 0 that are in the domains of both ____ and ____.

9. If $f(x) = x + 1$ and $g(x) = x^3$, then _____ $= x^3 - (x + 1)$.

10. **True or False** Every relation is a function.

11. **True or False** The domain of $(f \cdot g)(x)$ consists of the numbers x that are in the domains of both f and g.

12. **True or False** The independent variable is sometimes referred to as the argument of the function.

13. **True or False** If no domain is specified for a function f, then the domain of f is taken to be the set of real numbers.

14. **True or False** The domain of the function $f(x) = \dfrac{x^2 - 4}{x}$ is $\{x | x \neq \pm 2\}$.

Skill Building

In Problems 15–26, determine whether each relation represents a function. For each function, state the domain and range.

15.

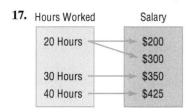

16.

17.

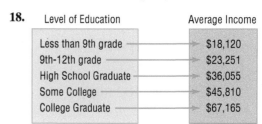

18.

19. $\{(2, 6), (-3, 6), (4, 9), (2, 10)\}$

20. $\{(-2, 5), (-1, 3), (3, 7), (4, 12)\}$

21. $\{(1, 3), (2, 3), (3, 3), (4, 3)\}$

22. $\{(0, -2), (1, 3), (2, 3), (3, 7)\}$

23. $\{(-2, 4), (-2, 6), (0, 3), (3, 7)\}$

24. $\{(-4, 4), (-3, 3), (-2, 2), (-1, 1), (-4, 0)\}$

25. $\{(-2, 4), (-1, 1), (0, 0), (1, 1)\}$

26. $\{(-2, 16), (-1, 4), (0, 3), (1, 4)\}$

In Problems 27–38, determine whether the equation defines y as a function of x.

27. $y = x^2$

28. $y = x^3$

29. $y = \dfrac{1}{x}$

30. $y = |x|$

31. $y^2 = 4 - x^2$

32. $y = \pm\sqrt{1 - 2x}$

33. $x = y^2$

34. $x + y^2 = 1$

35. $y = 2x^2 - 3x + 4$

36. $y = \dfrac{3x - 1}{x + 2}$

37. $2x^2 + 3y^2 = 1$

38. $x^2 - 4y^2 = 1$

In Problems 39–46, find the following for each function:

(a) $f(0)$　　(b) $f(1)$　　(c) $f(-1)$　　(d) $f(-x)$　　(e) $-f(x)$　　(f) $f(x + 1)$　　(g) $f(2x)$　　(h) $f(x + h)$

39. $f(x) = 3x^2 + 2x - 4$

40. $f(x) = -2x^2 + x - 1$

41. $f(x) = \dfrac{x}{x^2 + 1}$

42. $f(x) = \dfrac{x^2 - 1}{x + 4}$

43. $f(x) = |x| + 4$

44. $f(x) = \sqrt{x^2 + x}$

45. $f(x) = \dfrac{2x + 1}{3x - 5}$

46. $f(x) = 1 - \dfrac{1}{(x + 2)^2}$

In Problems 47–62, find the domain of each function.

47. $f(x) = -5x + 4$

48. $f(x) = x^2 + 2$

49. $f(x) = \dfrac{x}{x^2 + 1}$

50. $f(x) = \dfrac{x^2}{x^2 + 1}$

51. $g(x) = \dfrac{x}{x^2 - 16}$

52. $h(x) = \dfrac{2x}{x^2 - 4}$

53. $F(x) = \dfrac{x - 2}{x^3 + x}$

54. $G(x) = \dfrac{x + 4}{x^3 - 4x}$

55. $h(x) = \sqrt{3x - 12}$

56. $G(x) = \sqrt{1 - x}$

57. $f(x) = \dfrac{4}{\sqrt{x - 9}}$

58. $f(x) = \dfrac{x}{\sqrt{x - 4}}$

59. $p(x) = \sqrt{\dfrac{2}{x - 1}}$

60. $q(x) = \sqrt{-x - 2}$

61. $P(t) = \dfrac{\sqrt{t - 4}}{3t - 21}$

62. $h(z) = \dfrac{\sqrt{z + 3}}{z - 2}$

In Problems 63–72, for the given functions f and g, find the following. For parts (a)–(d), also find the domain.

(a) $(f + g)(x)$　　(b) $(f - g)(x)$　　(c) $(f \cdot g)(x)$　　(d) $\left(\dfrac{f}{g}\right)(x)$

(e) $(f + g)(3)$　　(f) $(f - g)(4)$　　(g) $(f \cdot g)(2)$　　(h) $\left(\dfrac{f}{g}\right)(1)$

63. $f(x) = 3x + 4$;　$g(x) = 2x - 3$

64. $f(x) = 2x + 1$;　$g(x) = 3x - 2$

65. $f(x) = x - 1$;　$g(x) = 2x^2$

66. $f(x) = 2x^2 + 3$;　$g(x) = 4x^3 + 1$

67. $f(x) = \sqrt{x};\quad g(x) = 3x - 5$

68. $f(x) = |x|;\quad g(x) = x$

69. $f(x) = 1 + \dfrac{1}{x};\quad g(x) = \dfrac{1}{x}$

70. $f(x) = \sqrt{x - 1};\quad g(x) = \sqrt{4 - x}$

71. $f(x) = \dfrac{2x + 3}{3x - 2};\quad g(x) = \dfrac{4x}{3x - 2}$

72. $f(x) = \sqrt{x + 1};\quad g(x) = \dfrac{2}{x}$

73. Given $f(x) = 3x + 1$ and $(f + g)(x) = 6 - \dfrac{1}{2}x$, find the function g.

74. Given $f(x) = \dfrac{1}{x}$ and $\left(\dfrac{f}{g}\right)(x) = \dfrac{x + 1}{x^2 - x}$, find the function g.

In Problems 75–82, find the difference quotient of f; that is, find $\dfrac{f(x + h) - f(x)}{h}$, $h \neq 0$, for each function. Be sure to simplify.

75. $f(x) = 4x + 3$

76. $f(x) = -3x + 1$

77. $f(x) = x^2 - x + 4$

78. $f(x) = 3x^2 - 2x + 6$

79. $f(x) = \dfrac{1}{x^2}$

80. $f(x) = \dfrac{1}{x + 3}$

81. $f(x) = \sqrt{x}$
[**Hint:** Rationalize the numerator.]

82. $f(x) = \sqrt{x + 1}$

Applications and Extensions

83. If $f(x) = 2x^3 + Ax^2 + 4x - 5$ and $f(2) = 5$, what is the value of A?

84. If $f(x) = 3x^2 - Bx + 4$ and $f(-1) = 12$, what is the value of B?

85. If $f(x) = \dfrac{3x + 8}{2x - A}$ and $f(0) = 2$, what is the value of A?

86. If $f(x) = \dfrac{2x - B}{3x + 4}$ and $f(2) = \dfrac{1}{2}$, what is the value of B?

87. If $f(x) = \dfrac{2x - A}{x - 3}$ and $f(4) = 0$, what is the value of A? Where is f not defined?

88. If $f(x) = \dfrac{x - B}{x - A}$, $f(2) = 0$ and $f(1)$ is undefined, what are the values of A and B?

89. Geometry Express the area A of a rectangle as a function of the length x if the length of the rectangle is twice its width.

90. Geometry Express the area A of an isosceles right triangle as a function of the length x of one of the two equal sides.

91. Constructing Functions Express the gross salary G of a person who earns \$10 per hour as a function of the number x of hours worked.

92. Constructing Functions Tiffany, a commissioned salesperson, earns \$100 base pay plus \$10 per item sold. Express her gross salary G as a function of the number x of items sold.

93. Population as a Function of Age The function

$$P(a) = 0.015a^2 - 4.962a + 290.580$$

represents the population P (in millions) of Americans that are a years of age or older.

(a) Identify the dependent and independent variables.
(b) Evaluate $P(20)$. Provide a verbal explanation of the meaning of $P(20)$.
(c) Evaluate $P(0)$. Provide a verbal explanation of the meaning of $P(0)$.

94. Number of Rooms The function

$$N(r) = -1.44r^2 + 14.52r - 14.96$$

represents the number N of housing units (in millions) that have r rooms, where r is an integer and $2 \leq r \leq 9$.

(a) Identify the dependent and independent variables.
(b) Evaluate $N(3)$. Provide a verbal explanation of the meaning of $N(3)$.

95. Effect of Gravity on Earth If a rock falls from a height of 20 meters on Earth, the height H (in meters) after x seconds is approximately

$$H(x) = 20 - 4.9x^2$$

(a) What is the height of the rock when $x = 1$ second? $x = 1.1$ seconds? $x = 1.2$ seconds? $x = 1.3$ seconds?
(b) When is the height of the rock 15 meters? When is it 10 meters? When is it 5 meters?
(c) When does the rock strike the ground?

96. Effect of Gravity on Jupiter If a rock falls from a height of 20 meters on the planet Jupiter, its height H (in meters) after x seconds is approximately

$$H(x) = 20 - 13x^2$$

(a) What is the height of the rock when $x = 1$ second? $x = 1.1$ seconds? $x = 1.2$ seconds?
(b) When is the height of the rock 15 meters? When is it 10 meters? When is it 5 meters?
(c) When does the rock strike the ground?

97. Cost of Trans-Atlantic Travel A Boeing 747 crosses the Atlantic Ocean (3000 miles) with an airspeed of 500 miles per hour. The cost C (in dollars) per passenger is given by

$$C(x) = 100 + \frac{x}{10} + \frac{36{,}000}{x}$$

where x is the ground speed (airspeed $\pm$ wind).
(a) What is the cost per passenger for quiescent (no wind) conditions?
(b) What is the cost per passenger with a head wind of 50 miles per hour?
(c) What is the cost per passenger with a tail wind of 100 miles per hour?
(d) What is the cost per passenger with a head wind of 100 miles per hour?

98. Cross-sectional Area The cross-sectional area of a beam cut from a log with radius 1 foot is given by the function $A(x) = 4x\sqrt{1 - x^2}$, where x represents the length, in feet, of half the base of the beam. See the figure. Determine the cross-sectional area of the beam if the length of half the base of the beam is as follows:
(a) One-third of a foot
(b) One-half of a foot
(c) Two-thirds of a foot

$A(x) = 4x\sqrt{1 - x^2}$

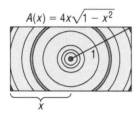

99. Economics The **participation rate** is the number of people in the labor force divided by the civilian population (excludes military). Let $L(x)$ represent the size of the labor force in year x and $P(x)$ represent the civilian population in year x. Determine a function that represents the participation rate R as a function of x.

100. Crimes Suppose that $V(x)$ represents the number of violent crimes committed in year x and $P(x)$ represents the number of property crimes committed in year x. Determine a function T that represents the combined total of violent crimes and property crimes in year x.

101. Health Care Suppose that $P(x)$ represents the percentage of income spent on health care in year x and $I(x)$ represents income in year x. Determine a function H that represents total health care expenditures in year x.

102. Income Tax Suppose that $I(x)$ represents the income of an individual in year x before taxes and $T(x)$ represents the individual's tax bill in year x. Determine a function N that represents the individual's net income (income after taxes) in year x.

103. Profit Function Suppose that the revenue R, in dollars, from selling x cell phones, in hundreds, is $R(x) = -1.2x^2 + 220x$. The cost C, in dollars, of selling x cell phones is $C(x) = 0.05x^3 - 2x^2 + 65x + 500$.
(a) Find the profit function, $P(x) = R(x) - C(x)$.
(b) Find the profit if $x = 15$ hundred cell phones are sold.
(c) Interpret $P(15)$.

104. Profit Function Suppose that the revenue R, in dollars, from selling x clocks is $R(x) = 30x$. The cost C, in dollars, of selling x clocks is $C(x) = 0.1x^2 + 7x + 400$.
(a) Find the profit function, $P(x) = R(x) - C(x)$.
(b) Find the profit if $x = 30$ clocks are sold.
(c) Interpret $P(30)$.

105. Some functions f have the property that $f(a + b) = f(a) + f(b)$ for all real numbers a and b. Which of the following functions have this property?
(a) $h(x) = 2x$ (b) $g(x) = x^2$
(c) $F(x) = 5x - 2$ (d) $G(x) = \dfrac{1}{x}$

Explaining Concepts: Discussion and Writing

106. Are the functions $f(x) = x - 1$ and $g(x) = \dfrac{x^2 - 1}{x + 1}$ the same? Explain.

107. Investigate when, historically, the use of the function notation $y = f(x)$ first appeared.

108. Find a function H that multiplies a number x by 3, then subtracts the cube of x and divides the result by your age.

'Are You Prepared?' Answers

1. $(-1, 3)$ **2.** 21.5   **3.** $\{x \mid x \neq -4\}$ **4.** $\{x \mid x < -1\}$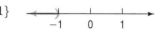

2.2 The Graph of a Function

PREPARING FOR THIS SECTION *Before getting started, review the following:*

- Graphs of Equations (Section 1.2, pp. 9–11)
- Intercepts (Section 1.2, pp. 11–12)

Now Work the *'Are You Prepared?'* problems on page 64.

OBJECTIVES **1** Identify the Graph of a Function (p. 60)
2 Obtain Information from or about the Graph of a Function (p. 61)

In applications, a graph often demonstrates more clearly the relationship between two variables than, say, an equation or table would. For example, Table 1 shows the average price of gasoline at a particular gas station in Texas (for the years 1980–2009 adjusted for inflation, based on 2008 dollars). If we plot these data and then connect the points, we obtain Figure 13.

Table 1

Year	Price	Year	Price	Year	Price
1980	3.41	1990	2.25	2000	1.85
1981	3.26	1991	1.90	2001	1.40
1982	3.15	1992	1.82	2002	1.86
1983	2.51	1993	1.70	2003	1.79
1984	2.51	1994	1.85	2004	2.13
1985	2.46	1995	1.68	2005	2.60
1986	1.63	1996	1.87	2006	2.62
1987	1.90	1997	1.65	2007	3.29
1988	1.77	1998	1.50	2008	2.10
1989	1.83	1999	1.73	2009	2.45

Source: http://www.randomuseless.info/gasprice/gasprice.html

Figure 13
Average retail price of gasoline (2008 dollars)

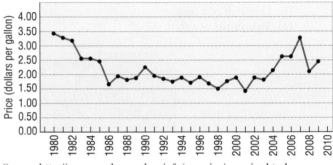

Source: http://www.randomuseless.info/gasprice/gasprice.html

We can see from the graph that the price of gasoline (adjusted for inflation) fell from 1980 to 1986 and rose rapidly from 2003 to 2007. The graph also shows that the lowest price occurred in 2001. To learn information such as this from an equation requires that some calculations be made.

Look again at Figure 13. The graph shows that for each date on the horizontal axis there is only one price on the vertical axis. The graph represents a function, although the exact rule for getting from date to price is not given.

When a function is defined by an equation in x and y, the **graph of the function** is the graph of the equation, that is, the set of points (x, y) in the xy-plane that satisfies the equation.

1 Identify the Graph of a Function

Not every collection of points in the xy-plane represents the graph of a function. Remember, for a function, each number x in the domain has exactly one image y in the range. This means that the graph of a function cannot contain two points with the same x-coordinate and different y-coordinates. Therefore, the graph of a function must satisfy the following **vertical-line test.**

In Words
If any vertical line intersects a graph at more than one point, the graph is not the graph of a function.

THEOREM **Vertical-line Test**

A set of points in the xy-plane is the graph of a function if and only if every vertical line intersects the graph in at most one point.

EXAMPLE 1   **Identifying the Graph of a Function**

Which of the graphs in Figure 14 are graphs of functions?

Figure 14

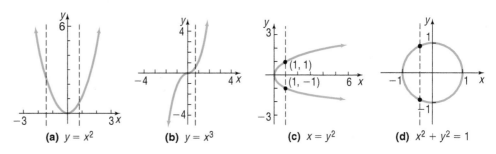

(a) $y = x^2$ (b) $y = x^3$ (c) $x = y^2$ (d) $x^2 + y^2 = 1$

Solution   The graphs in Figures 14(a) and 14(b) are graphs of functions, because every vertical line intersects each graph in at most one point. The graphs in Figures 14(c) and 14(d) are not graphs of functions, because there is a vertical line that intersects each graph in more than one point. Notice in Figure 14(c) that the input 1 corresponds to two outputs, -1 and 1. This is why the graph does not represent a function.

Now Work PROBLEM 15

2 Obtain Information from or about the Graph of a Function

If (x, y) is a point on the graph of a function f, then y is the value of f at x; that is, $y = f(x)$. Also if $y = f(x)$, then (x, y) is a point on the graph of f. For example, if $(-2, 7)$ is on the graph of f, then $f(-2) = 7$, and if $f(5) = 8$, then the point $(5, 8)$ is on the graph of $y = f(x)$. The next example illustrates how to obtain information about a function if its graph is given.

EXAMPLE 2   **Obtaining Information from the Graph of a Function**

Figure 15

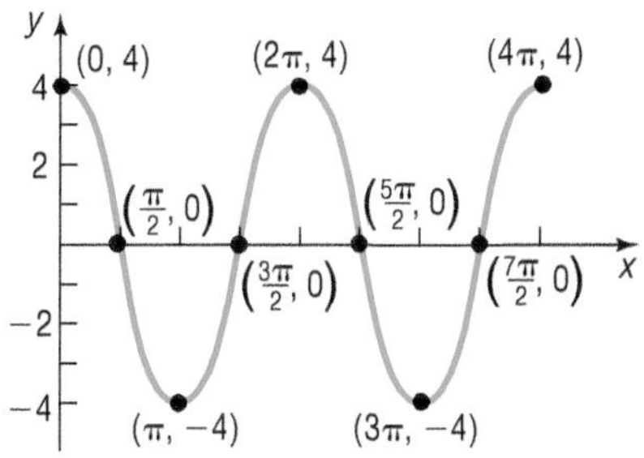

Let f be the function whose graph is given in Figure 15. (The graph of f might represent the distance y that the bob of a pendulum is from its *at-rest* position at time x. Negative values of y mean that the pendulum is to the left of the at-rest position, and positive values of y mean that the pendulum is to the right of the at-rest position.)

(a) What are $f(0)$, $f\left(\dfrac{3\pi}{2}\right)$, and $f(3\pi)$?

(b) What is the domain of f?

(c) What is the range of f?

(d) List the intercepts. (Recall that these are the points, if any, where the graph crosses or touches the coordinate axes.)

(e) How many times does the line $y = 2$ intersect the graph?

(f) For what values of x does $f(x) = -4$?

(g) For what values of x is $f(x) > 0$?

Solution   (a) Since $(0, 4)$ is on the graph of f, the y-coordinate 4 is the value of f at the x-coordinate 0; that is, $f(0) = 4$. In a similar way, we find that when $x = \dfrac{3\pi}{2}$, then $y = 0$, so $f\left(\dfrac{3\pi}{2}\right) = 0$. When $x = 3\pi$, then $y = -4$, so $f(3\pi) = -4$.

(b) To determine the domain of f, we notice that the points on the graph of f have x-coordinates between 0 and 4π, inclusive; and for each number x between 0 and 4π, there is a point $(x, f(x))$ on the graph. The domain of f is $\{x | 0 \le x \le 4\pi\}$ or the interval $[0, 4\pi]$.

(c) The points on the graph all have y-coordinates between -4 and 4, inclusive; and for each such number y, there is at least one number x in the domain. The range of f is $\{y | -4 \le y \le 4\}$ or the interval $[-4, 4]$.

(d) The intercepts are the points

$$(0, 4), \left(\frac{\pi}{2}, 0\right), \left(\frac{3\pi}{2}, 0\right), \left(\frac{5\pi}{2}, 0\right), \quad \text{and} \quad \left(\frac{7\pi}{2}, 0\right)$$

(e) If we draw the horizontal line $y = 2$ on the graph in Figure 15, we find that it intersects the graph four times.

(f) Since $(\pi, -4)$ and $(3\pi, -4)$ are the only points on the graph for which $y = f(x) = -4$, we have $f(x) = -4$ when $x = \pi$ and $x = 3\pi$.

(g) To determine where $f(x) > 0$, look at Figure 15 and determine the x-values from 0 to 4π for which the y-coordinate is positive. This occurs on $\left[0, \frac{\pi}{2}\right) \cup \left(\frac{3\pi}{2}, \frac{5\pi}{2}\right) \cup \left(\frac{7\pi}{2}, 4\pi\right]$. Using inequality notation, $f(x) > 0$ for

$$0 \le x < \frac{\pi}{2} \text{ or } \frac{3\pi}{2} < x < \frac{5\pi}{2} \quad \text{or} \quad \frac{7\pi}{2} < x \le 4\pi.$$

When the graph of a function is given, its domain may be viewed as the shadow created by the graph on the x-axis by vertical beams of light. Its range can be viewed as the shadow created by the graph on the y-axis by horizontal beams of light. Try this technique with the graph given in Figure 15.

Now Work PROBLEMS 9 AND 13

EXAMPLE 3 **Obtaining Information about the Graph of a Function**

Consider the function: $f(x) = \dfrac{x + 1}{x + 2}$

(a) Find the domain of f.

(b) Is the point $\left(1, \dfrac{1}{2}\right)$ on the graph of f?

(c) If $x = 2$, what is $f(x)$? What point is on the graph of f?

(d) If $f(x) = 2$, what is x? What point is on the graph of f?

(e) What are the x-intercepts of the graph of f (if any)? What point(s) are on the graph of f?

Solution
(a) The domain of f is $\{x | x \ne -2\}$.

(b) When $x = 1$, then

$$f(x) = \frac{x + 1}{x + 2}$$

$$f(1) = \frac{1 + 1}{1 + 2} = \frac{2}{3}$$

The point $\left(1, \dfrac{2}{3}\right)$ is on the graph of f; the point $\left(1, \dfrac{1}{2}\right)$ is not.

(c) If $x = 2$, then

$$f(x) = \frac{x + 1}{x + 2}$$

$$f(2) = \frac{2 + 1}{2 + 2} = \frac{3}{4}$$

The point $\left(2, \dfrac{3}{4}\right)$ is on the graph of f.

(d) If $f(x) = 2$, then

$$f(x) = 2$$

$$\frac{x + 1}{x + 2} = 2$$

$$x + 1 = 2(x + 2) \qquad \text{Multiply both sides by } x + 2.$$
$$x + 1 = 2x + 4 \qquad \text{Remove parentheses.}$$
$$x = -3 \qquad \text{Solve for } x.$$

If $f(x) = 2$, then $x = -3$. The point $(-3, 2)$ is on the graph of f.

(e) The x-intercepts of the graph of f are the real solutions of the equation $f(x) = 0$ that are in the domain of f. The only real solution of the equation $f(x) = \dfrac{x + 1}{x + 2} = 0$, is $x = -1$, so -1 is the only x-intercept. Since $f(-1) = 0$, the point $(-1, 0)$ is on the graph of f.

━━ Now Work PROBLEM 25

EXAMPLE 4

Average Cost Function

The average cost $\overline{C}$ of manufacturing x computers per day is given by the function

$$\overline{C}(x) = 0.56x^2 - 34.39x + 1212.57 + \frac{20{,}000}{x}$$

Determine the average cost of manufacturing:

(a) 30 computers in a day

(b) 40 computers in a day

(c) 50 computers in a day

(d) Graph the function $\overline{C} = \overline{C}(x)$, $0 < x \le 80$.

(e) Create a TABLE with TblStart $= 1$ and ΔTbl $= 1$. Which value of x minimizes the average cost?

Solution

(a) The average cost of manufacturing $x = 30$ computers is

$$\overline{C}(30) = 0.56(30)^2 - 34.39(30) + 1212.57 + \frac{20{,}000}{30} = \$1351.54$$

(b) The average cost of manufacturing $x = 40$ computers is

$$\overline{C}(40) = 0.56(40)^2 - 34.39(40) + 1212.57 + \frac{20{,}000}{40} = \$1232.97$$

(c) The average cost of manufacturing $x = 50$ computers is

$$\overline{C}(50) = 0.56(50)^2 - 34.39(50) + 1212.57 + \frac{20{,}000}{50} = \$1293.07$$

(d) See Figure 16 for the graph of $\overline{C} = \overline{C}(x)$.

(e) With the function $\overline{C} = \overline{C}(x)$ in Y_1, we create Table 2. We scroll down until we find a value of x for which Y_1 is smallest. Table 3 shows that manufacturing $x = 41$ computers minimizes the average cost at $\$1231.74$ per computer.

Figure 16

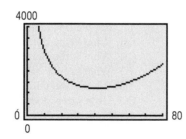

Table 2

Table 3

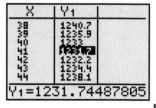

━━ Now Work PROBLEM 31

> ## SUMMARY
>
> **Graph of a Function** The collection of points (x, y) that satisfies the equation $y = f(x)$.
>
> **Vertical Line Test** A collection of points is the graph of a function provided that every vertical line intersects the graph in at most one point.

2.2 Assess Your Understanding

'Are You Prepared?' *Answers are given at the end of these exercises. If you get a wrong answer, read the pages listed in red.*

1. The intercepts of the equation $x^2 + 4y^2 = 16$ are _____. (pp. 11–12)

2. *True or False* The point $(-2, -6)$ is on the graph of the equation $x = 2y - 2$. (pp. 9–11)

Concepts and Vocabulary

3. A set of points in the xy-plane is the graph of a function if and only if every _____ line intersects the graph in at most one point.

4. If the point $(5, -3)$ is a point on the graph of f, then $f(\underline{}) = \underline{}$.

5. Find a so that the point $(-1, 2)$ is on the graph of $f(x) = ax^2 + 4$.

6. *True or False* A function can have more than one y-intercept.

7. *True or False* The graph of a function $y = f(x)$ always crosses the y-axis.

8. *True or False* The y-intercept of the graph of the function $y = f(x)$, whose domain is all real numbers, is $f(0)$.

Skill Building

9. Use the given graph of the function f to answer parts (a)–(n).

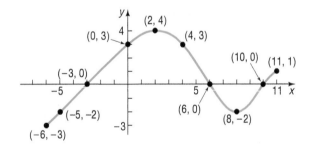

(a) Find $f(0)$ and $f(-6)$.
(b) Find $f(6)$ and $f(11)$.
(c) Is $f(3)$ positive or negative?
(d) Is $f(-4)$ positive or negative?
(e) For what values of x is $f(x) = 0$?
(f) For what values of x is $f(x) > 0$?
(g) What is the domain of f?
(h) What is the range of f?
(i) What are the x-intercepts?
(j) What is the y-intercept?
(k) How often does the line $y = \dfrac{1}{2}$ intersect the graph?
(l) How often does the line $x = 5$ intersect the graph?
(m) For what values of x does $f(x) = 3$?
(n) For what values of x does $f(x) = -2$?

10. Use the given graph of the function f to answer parts (a)–(n).

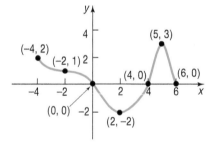

(a) Find $f(0)$ and $f(6)$.
(b) Find $f(2)$ and $f(-2)$.
(c) Is $f(3)$ positive or negative?
(d) Is $f(-1)$ positive or negative?
(e) For what values of x is $f(x) = 0$?
(f) For what values of x is $f(x) < 0$?
(g) What is the domain of f?
(h) What is the range of f?
(i) What are the x-intercepts?
(j) What is the y-intercept?
(k) How often does the line $y = -1$ intersect the graph?
(l) How often does the line $x = 1$ intersect the graph?
(m) For what value of x does $f(x) = 3$?
(n) For what value of x does $f(x) = -2$?

In Problems 11–22, determine whether the graph is that of a function by using the vertical-line test. If it is, use the graph to find:

(a) *The domain and range*
(b) *The intercepts, if any*
(c) *Any symmetry with respect to the x-axis, the y-axis, or the origin*

11.
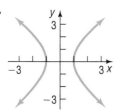

12.
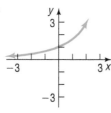

13.
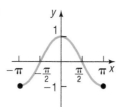

14.
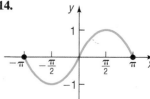

15.
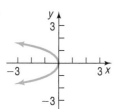

16.
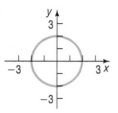

17.
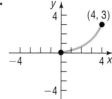

18.
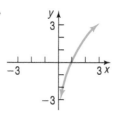

19.
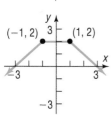

20.
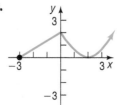

21.
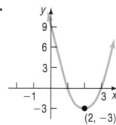

22.
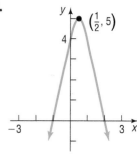

In Problems 23–28, answer the questions about the given function.

23. $f(x) = 2x^2 - x - 1$
 (a) Is the point $(-1, 2)$ on the graph of f?
 (b) If $x = -2$, what is $f(x)$? What point is on the graph of f?
 (c) If $f(x) = -1$, what is x? What point(s) are on the graph of f?
 (d) What is the domain of f?
 (e) List the x-intercepts, if any, of the graph of f.
 (f) List the y-intercept, if there is one, of the graph of f.

24. $f(x) = -3x^2 + 5x$
 (a) Is the point $(-1, 2)$ on the graph of f?
 (b) If $x = -2$, what is $f(x)$? What point is on the graph of f?
 (c) If $f(x) = -2$, what is x? What point(s) are on the graph of f?
 (d) What is the domain of f?
 (e) List the x-intercepts, if any, of the graph of f.
 (f) List the y-intercept, if there is one, of the graph of f.

25. $f(x) = \dfrac{x + 2}{x - 6}$
 (a) Is the point $(3, 14)$ on the graph of f?
 (b) If $x = 4$, what is $f(x)$? What point is on the graph of f?
 (c) If $f(x) = 2$, what is x? What point(s) are on the graph of f?
 (d) What is the domain of f?
 (e) List the x-intercepts, if any, of the graph of f.
 (f) List the y-intercept, if there is one, of the graph of f.

26. $f(x) = \dfrac{x^2 + 2}{x + 4}$
 (a) Is the point $\left(1, \dfrac{3}{5}\right)$ on the graph of f?

 (b) If $x = 0$, what is $f(x)$? What point is on the graph of f?
 (c) If $f(x) = \dfrac{1}{2}$, what is x? What point(s) are on the graph of f?
 (d) What is the domain of f?
 (e) List the x-intercepts, if any, of the graph of f.
 (f) List the y-intercept, if there is one, of the graph of f.

27. $f(x) = \dfrac{2x^2}{x^4 + 1}$
 (a) Is the point $(-1, 1)$ on the graph of f?
 (b) If $x = 2$, what is $f(x)$? What point is on the graph of f?
 (c) If $f(x) = 1$, what is x? What point(s) are on the graph of f?
 (d) What is the domain of f?
 (e) List the x-intercepts, if any, of the graph of f.
 (f) List the y-intercept, if there is one, of the graph of f.

28. $f(x) = \dfrac{2x}{x - 2}$
 (a) Is the point $\left(\dfrac{1}{2}, -\dfrac{2}{3}\right)$ on the graph of f?
 (b) If $x = 4$, what is $f(x)$? What point is on the graph of f?
 (c) If $f(x) = 1$, what is x? What point(s) are on the graph of f?
 (d) What is the domain of f?
 (e) List the x-intercepts, if any, of the graph of f.
 (f) List the y-intercept, if there is one, of the graph of f.

Applications and Extensions

29. Free-throw Shots According to physicist Peter Brancazio, the key to a successful foul shot in basketball lies in the arc of the shot. Brancazio determined the optimal angle of the arc from the free-throw line to be 45 degrees. The arc also depends on the velocity with which the ball is shot. If a player shoots a foul shot, releasing the ball at a 45-degree angle from a position 6 feet above the floor, then the path of the ball can be modeled by the function

$$h(x) = -\frac{44x^2}{v^2} + x + 6$$

where h is the height of the ball above the floor, x is the forward distance of the ball in front of the foul line, and v is the initial velocity with which the ball is shot in feet per second. Suppose a player shoots a ball with an initial velocity of 28 feet per second.

(a) Determine the height of the ball after it has traveled 8 feet in front of the foul line.
(b) Determine the height of the ball after it has traveled 12 feet in front of the foul line.
(c) Find additional points and graph the path of the basketball.
(d) The center of the hoop is 10 feet above the floor and 15 feet in front of the foul line. Will the ball go through the hoop? Why or why not? If not, with what initial velocity must the ball be shot in order for the ball to go through the hoop?

Source: The Physics of Foul Shots, Discover, Vol. 21, No. 10, October 2000

30. Granny Shots The last player in the NBA to use an underhand foul shot (a "granny" shot) was Hall of Fame forward Rick Barry who retired in 1980. Barry believes that current NBA players could increase their free-throw percentage if they were to use an underhand shot. Since underhand shots are released from a lower position, the angle of the shot must be increased. If a player shoots an underhand foul shot, releasing the ball at a 70-degree angle from a position 3.5 feet above the floor, then the path of the ball can be modeled by the function $h(x) = -\frac{136x^2}{v^2} + 2.7x + 3.5$, where h is the height of the ball above the floor, x is the forward distance of the ball in front of the foul line, and v is the initial velocity with which the ball is shot in feet per second.

(a) The center of the hoop is 10 feet above the floor and 15 feet in front of the foul line. Determine the initial velocity with which the ball must be shot in order for the ball to go through the hoop.
(b) Write the function for the path of the ball using the velocity found in part (a).
(c) Determine the height of the ball after it has traveled 9 feet in front of the foul line.
(d) Find additional points and graph the path of the basketball.

Source: The Physics of Foul Shots, Discover, Vol. 21, No. 10, October 2000

31. Motion of a Golf Ball A golf ball is hit with an initial velocity of 130 feet per second at an inclination of 45° to the horizontal. In physics, it is established that the height h

of the golf ball is given by the function

$$h(x) = \frac{-32x^2}{130^2} + x$$

where x is the horizontal distance that the golf ball has traveled.

(a) Determine the height of the golf ball after it has traveled 100 feet.
(b) What is the height after it has traveled 300 feet?
(c) What is the height after it has traveled 500 feet?
(d) How far was the golf ball hit?
(e) Use a graphing utility to graph the function $h = h(x)$.
(f) Use a graphing utility to determine the distance that the ball has traveled when the height of the ball is 90 feet.
(g) Create a TABLE with TblStart = 0 and ΔTbl = 25. To the nearest 25 feet, how far does the ball travel before it reaches a maximum height? What is the maximum height?
(h) Adjust the value of ΔTbl until you determine the distance, to within 1 foot, that the ball travels before it reaches a maximum height.

32. Cross-sectional Area The cross-sectional area of a beam cut from a log with radius 1 foot is given by the function $A(x) = 4x\sqrt{1 - x^2}$, where x represents the length, in feet, of half the base of the beam. See the figure.

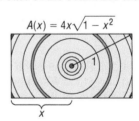

$A(x) = 4x\sqrt{1 - x^2}$

(a) Find the domain of A.
(b) Use a graphing utility to graph the function $A = A(x)$.
(c) Create a TABLE with TblStart = 0 and ΔTbl = 0.1 for $0 \le x \le 1$. Which value of x maximizes the cross-sectional area? What should be the length of the base of the beam to maximize the cross-sectional area?

33. **Cost of Trans-Atlantic Travel**   A Boeing 747 crosses the Atlantic Ocean (3000 miles) with an airspeed of 500 miles per hour. The cost C (in dollars) per passenger is given by

$$C(x) = 100 + \frac{x}{10} + \frac{36,000}{x}$$

where x is the ground speed (airspeed ± wind).
   (a) Use a graphing utility to graph the function $C = C(x)$.
   (b) Create a TABLE with TblStart = 0 and ΔTbl = 50.
   (c) To the nearest 50 miles per hour, what ground speed minimizes the cost per passenger?

34. **Effect of Elevation on Weight**   If an object weighs m pounds at sea level, then its weight W (in pounds) at a height of h miles above sea level is given approximately by

$$W(h) = m\left(\frac{4000}{4000 + h}\right)^2$$

   (a) If Amy weighs 120 pounds at sea level, how much will she weigh on Pike's Peak, which is 14,110 feet above sea level?
   (b) Use a graphing utility to graph the function $W = W(h)$. Use $m = 120$ pounds.

   (c) Create a Table with TblStart = 0 and ΔTbl = 0.5 to see how the weight W varies as h changes from 0 to 5 miles.
   (d) At what height will Amy weigh 119.95 pounds?
   (e) Does your answer to part (d) seem reasonable? Explain.

35. The graph of two functions, f and g, is illustrated. Use the graph to answer parts (a)–(f).

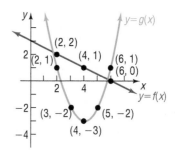

   (a) $(f + g)(2)$ (b) $(f + g)(4)$
   (c) $(f - g)(6)$ (d) $(g - f)(6)$
   (e) $(f \cdot g)(2)$ (f) $\left(\dfrac{f}{g}\right)(4)$

Explaining Concepts: Discussion and Writing

36. Describe how you would proceed to find the domain and range of a function if you were given its graph. How would your strategy change if you were given the equation defining the function instead of its graph?

37. How many x-intercepts can the graph of a function have? How many y-intercepts can the graph of a function have?

38. Is a graph that consists of a single point the graph of a function? Can you write the equation of such a function?

39. Match each of the following functions with the graph that best describes the situation.
   (a) The cost of building a house as a function of its square footage
   (b) The height of an egg dropped from a 300-foot building as a function of time
   (c) The height of a human as a function of time
   (d) The demand for Big Macs as a function of price
   (e) The height of a child on a swing as a function of time

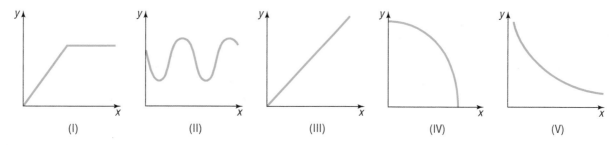

40. Match each of the following functions with the graph that best describes the situation.
   (a) The temperature of a bowl of soup as a function of time
   (b) The number of hours of daylight per day over a 2-year period
   (c) The population of Florida as a function of time
   (d) The distance traveled by a car going at a constant velocity as a function of time
   (e) The height of a golf ball hit with a 7-iron as a function of time

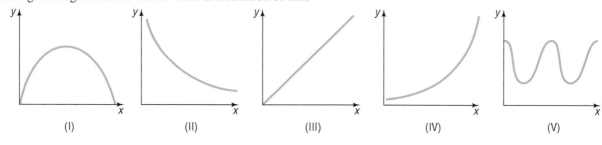

41. Consider the following scenario: Barbara decides to take a walk. She leaves home, walks 2 blocks in 5 minutes at a constant speed, and realizes that she forgot to lock the door. So Barbara runs home in 1 minute. While at her doorstep, it takes her 1 minute to find her keys and lock the door. Barbara walks 5 blocks in 15 minutes and then decides to jog home. It takes her 7 minutes to get home. Draw a graph of Barbara's distance from home (in blocks) as a function of time.

42. Consider the following scenario: Jayne enjoys riding her bicycle through the woods. At the forest preserve, she gets on her bicycle and rides up a 2000-foot incline in 10 minutes. She then travels down the incline in 3 minutes. The next 5000 feet is level terrain and she covers the distance in 20 minutes. She rests for 15 minutes. Jayne then travels 10,000 feet in 30 minutes. Draw a graph of Jayne's distance traveled (in feet) as a function of time.

43. The following sketch represents the distance d (in miles) that Kevin was from home as a function of time t (in hours). Answer the questions based on the graph. In parts (a)–(g), how many hours elapsed and how far was Kevin from home during this time?

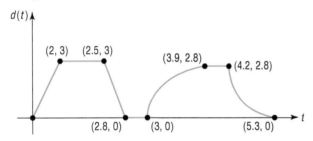

(a) From $t = 0$ to $t = 2$
(b) From $t = 2$ to $t = 2.5$

(c) From $t = 2.5$ to $t = 2.8$
(d) From $t = 2.8$ to $t = 3$
(e) From $t = 3$ to $t = 3.9$
(f) From $t = 3.9$ to $t = 4.2$
(g) From $t = 4.2$ to $t = 5.3$
(h) What is the farthest distance that Kevin was from home?
(i) How many times did Kevin return home?

44. The following sketch represents the speed v (in miles per hour) of Michael's car as a function of time t (in minutes).

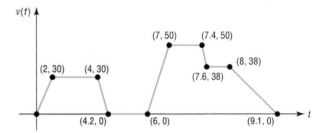

(a) Over what interval of time was Michael traveling fastest?
(b) Over what interval(s) of time was Michael's speed zero?
(c) What was Michael's speed between 0 and 2 minutes?
(d) What was Michael's speed between 4.2 and 6 minutes?
(e) What was Michael's speed between 7 and 7.4 minutes?
(f) When was Michael's speed constant?

45. Draw the graph of a function whose domain is $\{x \mid -3 \le x \le 8, \ x \ne 5\}$ and whose range is $\{y \mid -1 \le y \le 2, \ y \ne 0\}$. What point(s) in the rectangle $-3 \le x \le 8, -1 \le y \le 2$ cannot be on the graph? Compare your graph with those of other students. What differences do you see?

46. Is there a function whose graph is symmetric with respect to the x-axis? Explain.

'Are You Prepared?' Answers

1. $(-4, 0), (4, 0), (0, -2), (0, 2)$ **2.** False

2.3 Properties of Functions

PREPARING FOR THIS SECTION *Before getting started, review the following:*

- Interval Notation (Appendix A, Section A.9, pp. A72–A73)
- Intercepts (Section 1.2, pp. 11–12)

- Slope of a Line (Section 1.3, pp. 19–21)
- Point–Slope Form of a Line (Section 1.3, p. 23)
- Symmetry (Section 1.2, pp. 12–14)

 Now Work the *'Are You Prepared?'* problems on page 76.

OBJECTIVES   1 Determine Even and Odd Functions from a Graph (p. 69)

2 Identify Even and Odd Functions from the Equation (p. 70)

3 Use a Graph to Determine Where a Function Is Increasing, Decreasing, or Constant (p. 70)

4 Use a Graph to Locate Local Maxima and Local Minima (p. 71)

5 Use a Graph to Locate the Absolute Maximum and the Absolute Minimum (p. 72)

6 Use a Graphing Utility to Approximate Local Maxima and Local Minima and to Determine Where a Function Is Increasing or Decreasing (p. 74)

7 Find the Average Rate of Change of a Function (p. 74)

To obtain the graph of a function $y = f(x)$, it is often helpful to know certain properties that the function has and the impact of these properties on the way that the graph will look.

1 Determine Even and Odd Functions from a Graph

The words *even* and *odd,* when applied to a function f, describe the symmetry that exists for the graph of the function.

A function f is even, if and only if, whenever the point (x, y) is on the graph of f then the point $(-x, y)$ is also on the graph. Using function notation, we define an even function as follows:

DEFINITION   A function f is **even** if, for every number x in its domain, the number $-x$ is also in the domain and

$$f(-x) = f(x)$$

A function f is odd, if and only if, whenever the point (x, y) is on the graph of f then the point $(-x, -y)$ is also on the graph. Using function notation, we define an odd function as follows:

DEFINITION   A function f is **odd** if, for every number x in its domain, the number $-x$ is also in the domain and

$$f(-x) = -f(x)$$

Refer to page 14, where the tests for symmetry are listed. The following results are then evident.

THEOREM   A function is even if and only if its graph is symmetric with respect to the y-axis. A function is odd if and only if its graph is symmetric with respect to the origin.

EXAMPLE 1   **Determining Even and Odd Functions from the Graph**

Determine whether each graph given in Figure 17 is the graph of an even function, an odd function, or a function that is neither even nor odd.

Figure 17

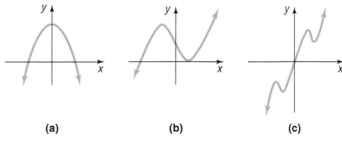

(a)   (b)   (c)

Solution   (a) The graph in Figure 17(a) is that of an even function, because the graph is symmetric with respect to the y-axis.

(b) The function whose graph is given in Figure 17(b) is neither even nor odd, because the graph is neither symmetric with respect to the y-axis nor symmetric with respect to the origin.

(c) The function whose graph is given in Figure 17(c) is odd, because its graph is symmetric with respect to the origin.

Now Work PROBLEMS 21(a), (b), AND (d)

2 Identify Even and Odd Functions from the Equation

EXAMPLE 2

Identifying Even and Odd Functions Algebraically

Determine whether each of the following functions is even, odd, or neither. Then determine whether the graph is symmetric with respect to the y-axis, or with respect to the origin.

(a) $f(x) = x^2 - 5$ (b) $g(x) = x^3 - 1$

(c) $h(x) = 5x^3 - x$ (d) $F(x) = |x|$

Solution

(a) To determine whether f is even, odd, or neither, replace x by $-x$ in $f(x) = x^2 - 5$. Then

$$f(-x) = (-x)^2 - 5 = x^2 - 5 = f(x)$$

Since $f(-x) = f(x)$, we conclude that f is an even function, and the graph of f is symmetric with respect to the y-axis.

(b) Replace x by $-x$ in $g(x) = x^3 - 1$. Then

$$g(-x) = (-x)^3 - 1 = -x^3 - 1$$

Since $g(-x) \neq g(x)$ and $g(-x) \neq -g(x) = -(x^3 - 1) = -x^3 + 1$, we conclude that g is neither even nor odd. The graph of g is not symmetric with respect to the y-axis nor is it symmetric with respect to the origin.

(c) Replace x by $-x$ in $h(x) = 5x^3 - x$. Then

$$h(-x) = 5(-x)^3 - (-x) = -5x^3 + x = -(5x^3 - x) = -h(x)$$

Since $h(-x) = -h(x)$, h is an odd function, and the graph of h is symmetric with respect to the origin.

(d) Replace x by $-x$ in $F(x) = |x|$. Then

$$F(-x) = |-x| = |-1| \cdot |x| = |x| = F(x)$$

Since $F(-x) = F(x)$, F is an even function, and the graph of F is symmetric with respect to the y-axis.

↲

━━━━━**Now Work** PROBLEM 33

3 Use a Graph to Determine Where a Function Is Increasing, Decreasing, or Constant

Consider the graph given in Figure 18. If you look from left to right along the graph of the function, you will notice that parts of the graph are going up, parts are going down, and parts are horizontal. In such cases, the function is described as *increasing, decreasing,* or *constant,* respectively.

Figure 18

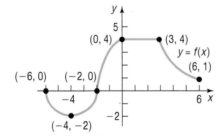

EXAMPLE 3

Determining Where a Function Is Increasing, Decreasing, or Constant from Its Graph

Where is the function in Figure 18 increasing? Where is it decreasing? Where is it constant?

Solution

WARNING We describe the behavior of a graph in terms of its x-values. Do not say the graph in Figure 18 is increasing from the point $(-4, 2)$ to the point $(0, 4)$. Rather, say it is increasing on the interval $(-4, 0)$. ∎

To answer the question of where a function is increasing, where it is decreasing, and where it is constant, we use strict inequalities involving the independent variable x, or we use open intervals* of x-coordinates. The function whose graph is given in Figure 18 is increasing on the open interval $(-4, 0)$ or for $-4 < x < 0$. The function is decreasing on the open intervals $(-6, -4)$ and $(3, 6)$ or for $-6 < x < -4$ and $3 < x < 6$. The function is constant on the open interval $(0, 3)$ or for $0 < x < 3$. ⌐•

More precise definitions follow:

DEFINITIONS

A function f is **increasing** on an open interval I if, for any choice of x_1 and x_2 in I, with $x_1 < x_2$, we have $f(x_1) < f(x_2)$.

A function f is **decreasing** on an open interval I if, for any choice of x_1 and x_2 in I, with $x_1 < x_2$, we have $f(x_1) > f(x_2)$.

A function f is **constant** on an open interval I if, for all choices of x in I, the values $f(x)$ are equal.

Figure 19 illustrates the definitions. The graph of an increasing function goes up from left to right, the graph of a decreasing function goes down from left to right, and the graph of a constant function remains at a fixed height.

Figure 19

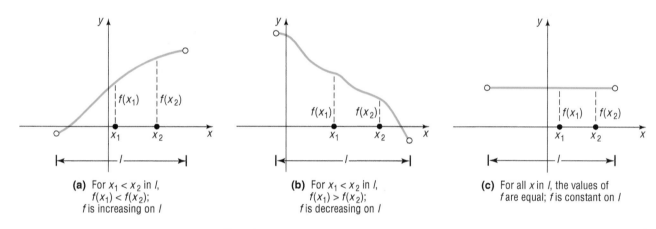

(a) For $x_1 < x_2$ in I, $f(x_1) < f(x_2)$; f is increasing on I

(b) For $x_1 < x_2$ in I, $f(x_1) > f(x_2)$; f is decreasing on I

(c) For all x in I, the values of f are equal; f is constant on I

━━▬ **Now Work** PROBLEMS **11, 13, 15, AND 21(c)**

4 Use a Graph to Locate Local Maxima and Local Minima

Suppose f is a function defined on an open interval containing c. If the value of f at c is greater than or equal to the values of f on I, then f has a *local maximum* at c[†]. See Figure 20(a).

If the value of f at c is less than or equal to the values of f on I, then f has a *local minimum* at c. See Figure 20(b).

Figure 20

f has a local maximum at c.

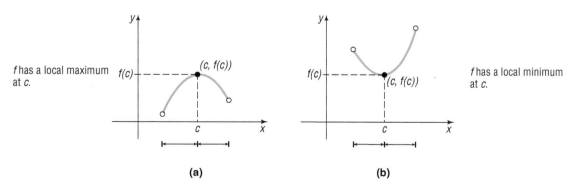

f has a local minimum at c.

(a)　　　　**(b)**

* The open interval (a, b) consists of all real numbers x for which $a < x < b$.
[†] Some texts use the term *relative* instead of *local*.

DEFINITIONS

A function f has a **local maximum** at c if there is an open interval I containing c so that for all x in $I, f(x) \leq f(c)$. We call $f(c)$ a **local maximum value of f**.

A function f has a **local minimum** at c if there is an open interval I containing c so that, for all x in $I, f(x) \geq f(c)$. We call $f(c)$ a **local minimum value of f**.

If f has a local maximum at c, then the value of f at c is greater than or equal to the values of f near c. If f has a local minimum at c, then the value of f at c is less than or equal to the values of f near c. The word *local* is used to suggest that it is only near c, that is, in some open interval containing c, that the value $f(c)$ has these properties.

EXAMPLE 4

Finding Local Maxima and Local Minima from the Graph of a Function and Determining Where the Function Is Increasing, Decreasing, or Constant

Figure 21 shows the graph of a function f.

(a) At what value(s) of x, if any, does f have a local maximum? List the local maximum values.

(b) At what value(s) of x, if any, does f have a local minimum? List the local minimum values.

(c) Find the intervals on which f is increasing. Find the intervals on which f is decreasing.

Figure 21

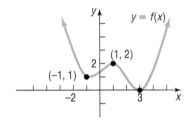

Solution

The domain of f is the set of real numbers.

(a) f has a local maximum at 1, since for all x close to 1, we have $f(x) \leq f(1)$. The local maximum value is $f(1) = 2$.

(b) f has local minima at -1 and at 3. The local minima values are $f(-1) = 1$ and $f(3) = 0$.

(c) The function whose graph is given in Figure 21 is increasing for all values of x between -1 and 1 and for all values of x greater than 3. That is, the function is increasing on the intervals $(-1, 1)$ and $(3, \infty)$ or for $-1 < x < 1$ and $x > 3$. The function is decreasing for all values of x less than -1 and for all values of x between 1 and 3. That is, the function is decreasing on the intervals $(-\infty, -1)$ and $(1, 3)$ or for $x < -1$ and $1 < x < 3$.

WARNING The y-value is the local maximum value or local minimum value and it occurs at some x-value. For example, in Figure 21, we say f has a local maximum at 1 and the local maximum value is 2. ∎

─────── **Now Work** PROBLEMS **17** AND **19**

Figure 22

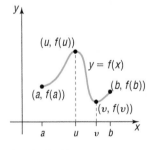

domain: [a, b]
for all x in [a, b], f(x) ≤ f(u)
for all x in [a, b], f(x) ≥ f(v)
absolute maximum: f(u)
absolute minimum: f(v)

5 Use a Graph to Locate the Absolute Maximum and the Absolute Minimum

Look at the graph of the function f given in Figure 22. The domain of f is the closed interval $[a, b]$. Also, the largest value of f is $f(u)$ and the smallest value of f is $f(v)$. These are called, respectively, the *absolute maximum* and the *absolute minimum* of f on $[a, b]$.

DEFINITION Let f denote a function defined on some interval I. If there is a number u in I for which $f(x) \leq f(u)$ for all x in I, then $f(u)$ is the **absolute maximum of f** on I and we say **the absolute maximum of f occurs at u**.

If there is a number v in I for which $f(x) \geq f(v)$ for all x in I, then $f(v)$ is the **absolute minimum of f** on I and we say **the absolute minimum of f occurs at v**.

The absolute maximum and absolute minimum of a function f are sometimes called the **extreme values** of f on I.

The absolute maximum or absolute minimum of a function f may not exist. Let's look at some examples.

EXAMPLE 5

Finding the Absolute Maximum and the Absolute Minimum from the Graph of a Function

For each graph of a function $y = f(x)$ in Figure 23, find the absolute maximum and the absolute minimum, if they exist.

Figure 23

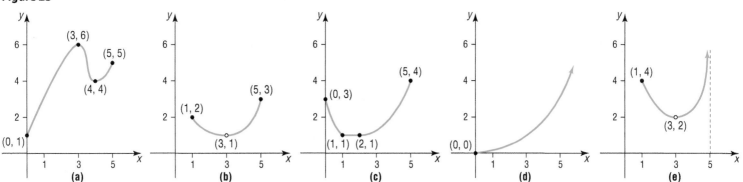

Solution

(a) The function f whose graph is given in Figure 23(a) has the closed interval $[0, 5]$ as its domain. The largest value of f is $f(3) = 6$, the absolute maximum. The smallest value of f is $f(0) = 1$, the absolute minimum.

(b) The function f whose graph is given in Figure 23(b) has the domain $\{x | 1 \le x \le 5, x \ne 3\}$. Note that we exclude 3 from the domain because of the "hole" at $(3, 1)$. The largest value of f on its domain is $f(5) = 3$, the absolute maximum. There is no absolute minimum. Do you see why? As you trace the graph, getting closer to the point $(3, 1)$, there is no single smallest value. [As soon as you claim a smallest value, we can trace closer to $(3, 1)$ and get a smaller value!]

(c) The function f whose graph is given in Figure 23(c) has the interval $[0, 5]$ as its domain. The absolute maximum of f is $f(5) = 4$. The absolute minimum is 1. Notice that the absolute minimum 1 occurs at any number in the interval $[1, 2]$.

(d) The graph of the function f given in Figure 23(d) has the interval $[0, \infty)$ as its domain. The function has no absolute maximum; the absolute minimum is $f(0) = 0$.

(e) The graph of the function f in Figure 23(e) has the domain $\{x | 1 \le x < 5, x \ne 3\}$. The function f has no absolute maximum and no absolute minimum. Do you see why?

In calculus, there is a theorem with conditions that guarantee a function will have an absolute maximum and an absolute minimum.

THEOREM

Extreme Value Theorem

If f is a continuous function* whose domain is a closed interval $[a, b]$, then f has an absolute maximum and an absolute minimum on $[a, b]$.

Now Work PROBLEM 45

---

* Although it requires calculus for a precise definition, we'll agree for now that a continuous function is one whose graph has no gaps or holes and can be traced without lifting the pencil from the paper.

6 Use a Graphing Utility to Approximate Local Maxima and Local Minima and to Determine Where a Function Is Increasing or Decreasing

To locate the exact value at which a function f has a local maximum or a local minimum usually requires calculus. However, a graphing utility may be used to approximate these values by using the MAXIMUM and MINIMUM features.

EXAMPLE 6   **Using a Graphing Utility to Approximate Local Maxima and Minima and to Determine Where a Function Is Increasing or Decreasing**

(a) Use a graphing utility to graph $f(x) = 6x^3 - 12x + 5$ for $-2 < x < 2$. Approximate where f has a local maximum and where f has a local minimum.

(b) Determine where f is increasing and where it is decreasing.

Solution   (a) Graphing utilities have a feature that finds the maximum or minimum point of a graph within a given interval. Graph the function f for $-2 < x < 2$. The MAXIMUM and MINIMUM commands require us to first determine the open interval I. The graphing utility will then approximate the maximum or minimum value in the interval. Using MAXIMUM we find that the local maximum value is 11.53 and it occurs at $x = -0.82$, rounded to two decimal places. See Figure 24(a). Using MINIMUM, we find that the local minimum value is -1.53 and it occurs at $x = 0.82$, rounded to two decimal places. See Figure 24(b).

Figure 24

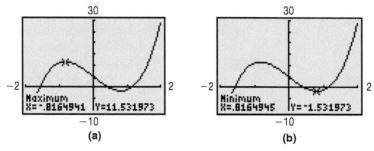

(a)   (b)

(b) Looking at Figures 24(a) and (b), we see that the graph of f is increasing from $x = -2$ to $x = -0.82$ and from $x = 0.82$ to $x = 2$, so f is increasing on the intervals $(-2, -0.82)$ and $(0.82, 2)$ or for $-2 < x < -0.82$ and $0.82 < x < 2$. The graph is decreasing from $x = -0.82$ to $x = 0.82$, so f is decreasing on the interval $(-0.82, 0.82)$ or for $-0.82 < x < 0.82$.

━━━━━Now Work   PROBLEM 53

7 Find the Average Rate of Change of a Function

In Section 1.3, we said that the slope of a line could be interpreted as the average rate of change. To find the average rate of change of a function between any two points on its graph, calculate the slope of the line containing the two points.

DEFINITION   If a and b, $a \neq b$, are in the domain of a function $y = f(x)$, the **average rate of change of f** from a to b is defined as

$$\text{Average rate of change} = \frac{\Delta y}{\Delta x} = \frac{f(b) - f(a)}{b - a} \qquad a \neq b \qquad (1)$$

The symbol Δy in (1) is the "change in y," and Δx is the "change in x." The average rate of change of f is the change in y divided by the change in x.

EXAMPLE 7 | Finding the Average Rate of Change

Find the average rate of change of $f(x) = 3x^2$:

(a) From 1 to 3   (b) From 1 to 5   (c) From 1 to 7

Solution   (a) The average rate of change of $f(x) = 3x^2$ from 1 to 3 is

$$\frac{\Delta y}{\Delta x} = \frac{f(3) - f(1)}{3 - 1} = \frac{27 - 3}{3 - 1} = \frac{24}{2} = 12$$

(b) The average rate of change of $f(x) = 3x^2$ from 1 to 5 is

$$\frac{\Delta y}{\Delta x} = \frac{f(5) - f(1)}{5 - 1} = \frac{75 - 3}{5 - 1} = \frac{72}{4} = 18$$

(c) The average rate of change of $f(x) = 3x^2$ from 1 to 7 is

$$\frac{\Delta y}{\Delta x} = \frac{f(7) - f(1)}{7 - 1} = \frac{147 - 3}{7 - 1} = \frac{144}{6} = 24$$

Figure 25

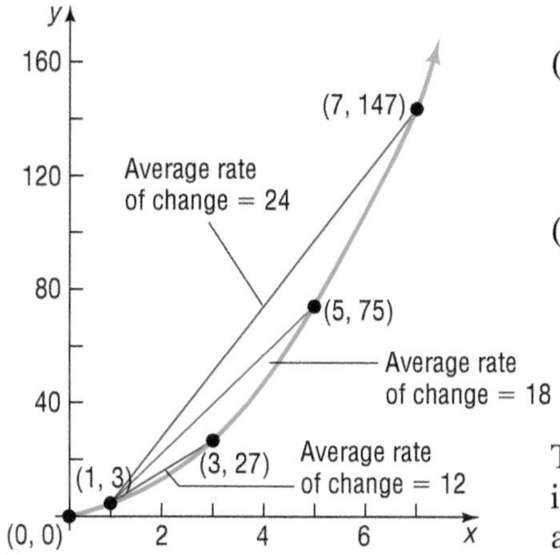

See Figure 25 for a graph of $f(x) = 3x^2$. The function f is increasing for $x > 0$. The fact that the average rate of change is positive for any $x_1, x_2, x_1 \neq x_2$ in the interval $(1, 7)$ indicates that the graph is increasing on $1 < x < 7$. Further, the average rate of change is consistently getting larger for $1 < x < 7$, indicating that the graph is increasing at an increasing rate.

Now Work PROBLEM 61

The Secant Line

The average rate of change of a function has an important geometric interpretation. Look at the graph of $y = f(x)$ in Figure 26. We have labeled two points on the graph: $(a, f(a))$ and $(b, f(b))$. The line containing these two points is called the **secant line;** its slope is

$$m_{\text{sec}} = \frac{f(b) - f(a)}{b - a}$$

Figure 26

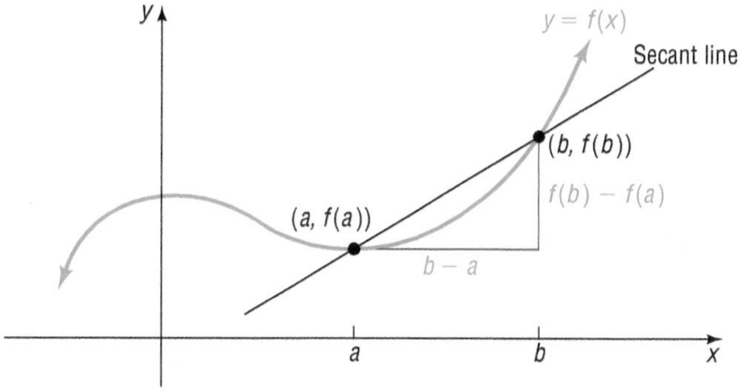

THEOREM | Slope of the Secant Line

The average rate of change of a function from a to b equals the slope of the secant line containing the two points $(a, f(a))$ and $(b, f(b))$ on its graph.

EXAMPLE 8 | Finding the Equation of a Secant Line

Suppose that $g(x) = 3x^2 - 2x + 3$.

(a) Find the average rate of change of g from -2 to 1.
(b) Find an equation of the secant line containing $(-2, g(-2))$ and $(1, g(1))$.
 (c) Using a graphing utility, draw the graph of g and the secant line obtained in part (b) on the same screen.

Solution   (a) The average rate of change of $g(x) = 3x^2 - 2x + 3$ from -2 to 1 is

$$\text{Average rate of change} = \frac{g(1) - g(-2)}{1 - (-2)}$$

$$= \frac{4 - 19}{3} \qquad g(1) = 3(1)^2 - 2(1) + 3 = 4$$
$$\qquad\qquad\qquad g(-2) = 3(-2)^2 - 2(-2) + 3 = 19$$

$$= -\frac{15}{3} = -5$$

(b) The slope of the secant line containing $(-2, g(-2)) = (-2, 19)$ and $(1, g(1)) = (1, 4)$ is $m_{sec} = -5$. Use the point–slope form to find an equation of the secant line.

Figure 27

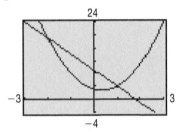

$$y - y_1 = m_{sec}(x - x_1) \qquad \text{Point–slope form of the secant line}$$
$$y - 19 = -5(x - (-2)) \qquad x_1 = -2, y_1 = g(-2) = 19, m_{sec} = -5$$
$$y - 19 = -5x - 10 \qquad \text{Simplify.}$$
$$y = -5x + 9 \qquad \text{Slope–intercept form of the secant line}$$

(c) Figure 27 shows the graph of g along with the secant line $y = -5x + 9$.

Now Work PROBLEM 67

2.3 Assess Your Understanding

'Are You Prepared?' *Answers are given at the end of these exercises. If you get a wrong answer, read the pages listed in red.*

1. The interval $(2, 5)$ can be written as the inequality _____. (pp. A72–A73)

2. The slope of the line containing the points $(-2, 3)$ and $(3, 8)$ is ____. (pp. 19–21)

3. Test the equation $y = 5x^2 - 1$ for symmetry with respect to the x-axis, the y-axis, and the origin. (pp. 12–14)

4. Write the point–slope form of the line with slope 5 containing the point $(3, -2)$. (p. 23)

5. The intercepts of the equation $y = x^2 - 9$ are _____. (pp. 11–12)

Concepts and Vocabulary

6. A function f is _____ on an open interval I if, for any choice of x_1 and x_2 in I, with $x_1 < x_2$, we have $f(x_1) < f(x_2)$.

7. A(n) _____ function f is one for which $f(-x) = f(x)$ for every x in the domain of f; a(n) _____ function f is one for which $f(-x) = -f(x)$ for every x in the domain of f.

8. **True or False** A function f is decreasing on an open interval I if, for any choice of x_1 and x_2 in I, with $x_1 < x_2$, we have $f(x_1) > f(x_2)$.

9. **True or False** A function f has a local maximum at c if there is an open interval I containing c so that for all x in I, $f(x) \le f(c)$.

10. **True or False** Even functions have graphs that are symmetric with respect to the origin.

Skill Building

In Problems 11–20, use the graph of the function f given.

11. Is f increasing on the interval $(-8, -2)$?

12. Is f decreasing on the interval $(-8, -4)$?

13. Is f increasing on the interval $(2, 10)$?

14. Is f decreasing on the interval $(2, 5)$?

15. List the interval(s) on which f is increasing.

16. List the interval(s) on which f is decreasing.

17. Is there a local maximum value at 2? If yes, what is it?

18. Is there a local maximum value at 5? If yes, what is it?

19. List the number(s) at which f has a local maximum. What are the local maximum values?

20. List the number(s) at which f has a local minimum. What are the local minimum values?

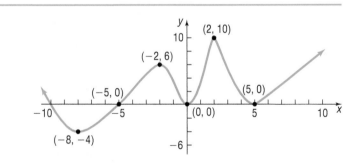

In Problems 21–28, the graph of a function is given. Use the graph to find:
 (a) *The intercepts, if any*
 (b) *The domain and range*
 (c) *The intervals on which it is increasing, decreasing, or constant*
 (d) *Whether it is even, odd, or neither*

21.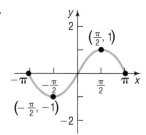

22.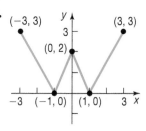

23.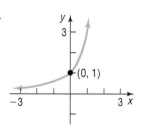

24.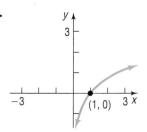

25.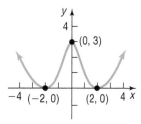

26.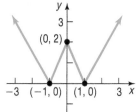

27.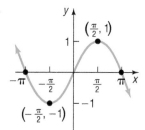

28.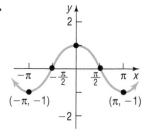

In Problems 29–32, the graph of a function f is given. Use the graph to find:
 (a) *The numbers, if any, at which f has a local maximum value. What are the local maximum values?*
 (b) *The numbers, if any, at which f has a local minimum value. What are the local minimum values?*

29.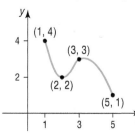

30.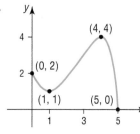

31.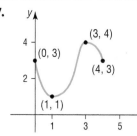

32.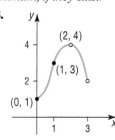

In Problems 33–44, determine algebraically whether each function is even, odd, or neither.

33. $f(x) = 4x^3$

34. $f(x) = 2x^4 - x^2$

35. $g(x) = -3x^2 - 5$

36. $h(x) = 3x^3 + 5$

37. $F(x) = \sqrt[3]{x}$

38. $G(x) = \sqrt{x}$

39. $f(x) = x + |x|$

40. $f(x) = \sqrt[3]{2x^2 + 1}$

41. $g(x) = \dfrac{1}{x^2}$

42. $h(x) = \dfrac{x}{x^2 - 1}$

43. $h(x) = \dfrac{-x^3}{3x^2 - 9}$

44. $F(x) = \dfrac{2x}{|x|}$

In Problems 45–52, for each graph of a function $y = f(x)$, find the absolute maximum and the absolute minimum, if they exist.

45.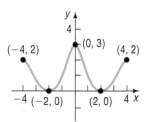

46.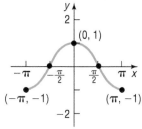

47.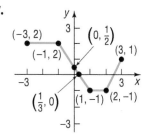

48.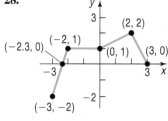

49.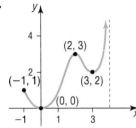

50.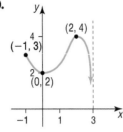

51.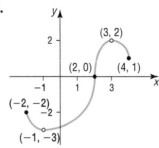

52.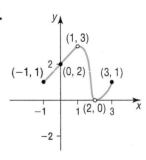

In Problems 53–60, use a graphing utility to graph each function over the indicated interval and approximate any local maximum values and local minimum values. Determine where the function is increasing and where it is decreasing. Round answers to two decimal places.

53. $f(x) = x^3 - 3x + 2$ $(-2, 2)$

54. $f(x) = x^3 - 3x^2 + 5$ $(-1, 3)$

55. $f(x) = x^5 - x^3$ $(-2, 2)$

56. $f(x) = x^4 - x^2$ $(-2, 2)$

57. $f(x) = -0.2x^3 - 0.6x^2 + 4x - 6$ $(-6, 4)$

58. $f(x) = -0.4x^3 + 0.6x^2 + 3x - 2$ $(-4, 5)$

59. $f(x) = 0.25x^4 + 0.3x^3 - 0.9x^2 + 3$ $(-3, 2)$

60. $f(x) = -0.4x^4 - 0.5x^3 + 0.8x^2 - 2$ $(-3, 2)$

---

61. Find the average rate of change of $f(x) = -2x^2 + 4$
  (a) From 0 to 2
  (b) From 1 to 3
  (c) From 1 to 4

62. Find the average rate of change of $f(x) = -x^3 + 1$
  (a) From 0 to 2
  (b) From 1 to 3
  (c) From −1 to 1

63. Find the average rate of change of $g(x) = x^3 - 2x + 1$
  (a) From −3 to −2
  (b) From −1 to 1
  (c) From 1 to 3

64. Find the average rate of change of $h(x) = x^2 - 2x + 3$
  (a) From −1 to 1
  (b) From 0 to 2
  (c) From 2 to 5

65. $f(x) = 5x - 2$
  (a) Find the average rate of change from 1 to 3.
  (b) Find an equation of the secant line containing $(1, f(1))$ and $(3, f(3))$.

66. $f(x) = -4x + 1$
  (a) Find the average rate of change from 2 to 5.
  (b) Find an equation of the secant line containing $(2, f(2))$ and $(5, f(5))$.

67. $g(x) = x^2 - 2$
  (a) Find the average rate of change from −2 to 1.
  (b) Find an equation of the secant line containing $(-2, g(-2))$ and $(1, g(1))$.

68. $g(x) = x^2 + 1$
  (a) Find the average rate of change from −1 to 2.
  (b) Find an equation of the secant line containing $(-1, g(-1))$ and $(2, g(2))$.

69. $h(x) = x^2 - 2x$
  (a) Find the average rate of change from 2 to 4.
  (b) Find an equation of the secant line containing $(2, h(2))$ and $(4, h(4))$.

70. $h(x) = -2x^2 + x$
  (a) Find the average rate of change from 0 to 3.
  (b) Find an equation of the secant line containing $(0, h(0))$ and $(3, h(3))$.

Mixed Practice

71. $g(x) = x^3 - 27x$
  (a) Determine whether g is even, odd, or neither.
  (b) There is a local minimum value of −54 at 3. Determine the local maximum value.

72. $f(x) = -x^3 + 12x$
  (a) Determine whether f is even, odd, or neither.
  (b) There is a local maximum value of 16 at 2. Determine the local minimum value.

73. $F(x) = -x^4 + 8x^2 + 8$
  (a) Determine whether F is even, odd, or neither.
  (b) There is a local maximum value of 24 at $x = 2$. Determine a second local maximum value.

  (c) Suppose the area under the graph of F between $x = 0$ and $x = 3$ that is bounded below by the x-axis is 47.4 square units. Using the result from part (a), determine the area under the graph of F between $x = -3$ and $x = 0$ bounded below by the x-axis.

74. $G(x) = -x^4 + 32x^2 + 144$
  (a) Determine whether G is even, odd, or neither.
  (b) There is a local maximum value of 400 at $x = 4$. Determine a second local maximum value.

  (c) Suppose the area under the graph of G between $x = 0$ and $x = 6$ that is bounded below by the x-axis is 1612.8 square units. Using the result from part (a), determine the area under the graph of G between $x = -6$ and $x = 0$ bounded below by the x-axis.

Applications and Extensions

75. Minimum Average Cost The average cost per hour in dollars, $\overline{C}$, of producing x riding lawn mowers can be modeled by the function

$$\overline{C}(x) = 0.3x^2 + 21x - 251 + \frac{2500}{x}$$

(a) Use a graphing utility to graph $\overline{C} = \overline{C}(x)$.
(b) Determine the number of riding lawn mowers to produce in order to minimize average cost.
(c) What is the minimum average cost?

76. Medicine Concentration The concentration C of a medication in the bloodstream t hours after being administered is modeled by the function

$$C(t) = -0.002x^4 + 0.039t^3 - 0.285t^2 + 0.766t + 0.085$$

(a) After how many hours will the concentration be highest?
(b) A woman nursing a child must wait until the concentration is below 0.5 before she can feed him. After taking the medication, how long must she wait before feeding her child?

77. E-coli Growth A strain of E-coli Beu 397-recA441 is placed into a nutrient broth at 30° Celsius and allowed to grow. The data shown in the table are collected. The population is measured in grams and the time in hours. Since population P depends on time t and each input corresponds to exactly one output, we can say that population is a function of time; so $P(t)$ represents the population at time t.

(a) Find the average rate of change of the population from 0 to 2.5 hours.
(b) Find the average rate of change of the population from 4.5 to 6 hours.
(c) What is happening to the average rate of change as time passes?

Time (hours), t	Population (grams), P
0	0.09
2.5	0.18
3.5	0.26
4.5	0.35
6	0.50

78. e-Filing Tax Returns The Internal Revenue Service Restructuring and Reform Act (RRA) was signed into law by President Bill Clinton in 1998. A major objective of the RRA was to promote electronic filing of tax returns. The data in the table that follows show the percentage of individual income tax returns filed electronically for filing years 2000–2008. Since the percentage P of returns filed electronically depends on the filing year y and each input corresponds to exactly one output, the percentage of returns filed electronically is a function of the filing year; so $P(y)$ represents the percentage of returns filed electronically for filing year y.

(a) Find the average rate of change of the percentage of e-filed returns from 2000 to 2002.
(b) Find the average rate of change of the percentage of e-filed returns from 2004 to 2006.
(c) Find the average rate of change of the percentage of e-filed returns from 2006 to 2008.
(d) What is happening to the average rate of change as time passes?

Year	Percentage of returns e-filed
2000	27.9
2001	31.1
2002	35.9
2003	40.6
2004	47.0
2005	51.8
2006	54.5
2007	58.0
2008	59.8

SOURCE: Internal Revenue Service

79. For the function $f(x) = x^2$, compute each average rate of change:
(a) From 0 to 1
(b) From 0 to 0.5
(c) From 0 to 0.1
(d) From 0 to 0.01
(e) From 0 to 0.001
(f) Use a graphing utility to graph each of the secant lines along with f.
(g) What do you think is happening to the secant lines?
(h) What is happening to the slopes of the secant lines? Is there some number that they are getting closer to? What is that number?

80. For the function $f(x) = x^2$, compute each average rate of change:
(a) From 1 to 2
(b) From 1 to 1.5
(c) From 1 to 1.1
(d) From 1 to 1.01
(e) From 1 to 1.001
(f) Use a graphing utility to graph each of the secant lines along with f.
(g) What do you think is happening to the secant lines?
(h) What is happening to the slopes of the secant lines? Is there some number that they are getting closer to? What is that number?

Problems 81–88 require the following discussion of a secant line. The slope of the secant line containing the two points $(x, f(x))$ and $(x + h, f(x + h))$ on the graph of a function $y = f(x)$ may be given as

$$m_{\text{sec}} = \frac{f(x + h) - f(x)}{(x + h) - x} = \frac{f(x + h) - f(x)}{h} \qquad h \neq 0$$

In calculus, this expression is called the **difference quotient of f.**

(a) Express the slope of the secant line of each function in terms of x and h. Be sure to simplify your answer.
(b) Find m_{sec} for $h = 0.5, 0.1$, and 0.01 at $x = 1$. What value does m_{sec} approach as h approaches 0?
(c) Find the equation for the secant line at $x = 1$ with $h = 0.01$.
(d) Use a graphing utility to graph f and the secant line found in part (c) on the same viewing window.

81. $f(x) = 2x + 5$
82. $f(x) = -3x + 2$
83. $f(x) = x^2 + 2x$
84. $f(x) = 2x^2 + x$

85. $f(x) = 2x^2 - 3x + 1$
86. $f(x) = -x^2 + 3x - 2$
87. $f(x) = \dfrac{1}{x}$
88. $f(x) = \dfrac{1}{x^2}$

Explaining Concepts: Discussion and Writing

89. Draw the graph of a function that has the following properties: domain: all real numbers; range: all real numbers; intercepts: $(0, -3)$ and $(3, 0)$; a local maximum value of -2 is at -1; a local minimum value of -6 is at 2. Compare your graph with those of others. Comment on any differences.

90. Redo Problem 89 with the following additional information: increasing on $(-\infty, -1), (2, \infty)$; decreasing on $(-1, 2)$. Again compare your graph with others and comment on any differences.

91. How many x-intercepts can a function defined on an interval have if it is increasing on that interval? Explain.

92. Suppose that a friend of yours does not understand the idea of increasing and decreasing functions. Provide an explanation, complete with graphs, that clarifies the idea.

93. Can a function be both even and odd? Explain.

94. Using a graphing utility, graph $y = 5$ on the interval $(-3, 3)$. Use MAXIMUM to find the local maximum values on $(-3, 3)$. Comment on the result provided by the calculator.

95. A function f has a positive average rate of change on the interval $[2, 5]$. Is f increasing on $[2, 5]$? Explain.

96. Show that a constant function $f(x) = b$ has an average rate of change of 0. Compute the average rate of change of $y = \sqrt{4 - x^2}$ on the interval $[-2, 2]$. Explain how this can happen.

'Are You Prepared?' Answers

1. $2 < x < 5$ **2.** 1 **3.** symmetric with respect to the y-axis **4.** $y + 2 = 5(x - 3)$ **5.** $(-3, 0), (3, 0), (0, -9)$

2.4 Library of Functions; Piecewise-defined Functions

PREPARING FOR THIS SECTION *Before getting started, review the following:*

- Intercepts (Section 1.2, pp. 11–12)
- Graphs of Key Equations (Section 1.2: Example 3, p. 10; Example 10, p. 15; Example 11, p. 15; Example 12, p. 16)

Now Work the 'Are You Prepared?' problems on page 87.

OBJECTIVES **1** Graph the Functions Listed in the Library of Functions (p. 80)
2 Graph Piecewise-defined Functions (p. 85)

1 Graph the Functions Listed in the Library of Functions

First we introduce a few more functions, beginning with the *square root function*.
On page 15, we graphed the equation $y = \sqrt{x}$. Figure 28 shows a graph of the function $f(x) = \sqrt{x}$. Based on the graph, we have the following properties:

Figure 28

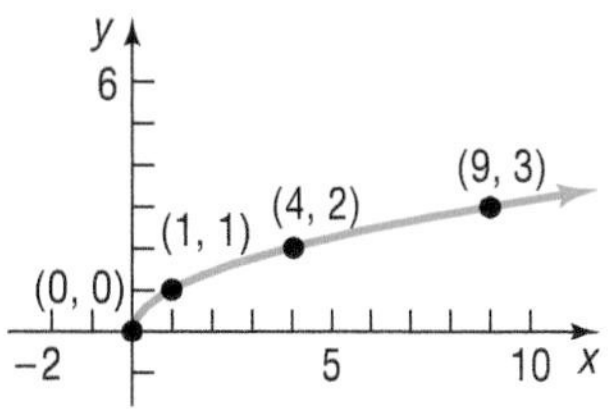

Properties of f(x) = $\sqrt{x}$

1. The domain and the range are the set of nonnegative real numbers.
2. The x-intercept of the graph of $f(x) = \sqrt{x}$ is 0. The y-intercept of the graph of $f(x) = \sqrt{x}$ is also 0.
3. The function is neither even nor odd.
4. The function is increasing on the interval $(0, \infty)$.
5. The function has an absolute minimum of 0 at $x = 0$.

EXAMPLE 1

Graphing the Cube Root Function

(a) Determine whether $f(x) = \sqrt[3]{x}$ is even, odd, or neither. State whether the graph of f is symmetric with respect to the y-axis or symmetric with respect to the origin.

(b) Determine the intercepts, if any, of the graph of $f(x) = \sqrt[3]{x}$.

(c) Graph $f(x) = \sqrt[3]{x}$.

Solution

(a) Because

$$f(-x) = \sqrt[3]{-x} = -\sqrt[3]{x} = -f(x)$$

the function is odd. The graph of f is symmetric with respect to the origin.

(b) The y-intercept is $f(0) = \sqrt[3]{0} = 0$. The x-intercept is found by solving the equation $f(x) = 0$.

$$f(x) = 0$$
$$\sqrt[3]{x} = 0 \quad \text{f(x)} = \sqrt[3]{x}$$
$$x = 0 \quad \text{Cube both sides of the equation.}$$

The x-intercept is also 0.

(c) Use the function to form Table 4 and obtain some points on the graph. Because of the symmetry with respect to the origin, we find only points (x, y) for which $x \geq 0$. Figure 29 shows the graph of $f(x) = \sqrt[3]{x}$.

Table 4

x	$y = f(x) = \sqrt[3]{x}$	(x, y)
0	0	$(0, 0)$
$\dfrac{1}{8}$	$\dfrac{1}{2}$	$\left(\dfrac{1}{8}, \dfrac{1}{2}\right)$
1	1	$(1, 1)$
2	$\sqrt[3]{2} \approx 1.26$	$(2, \sqrt[3]{2})$
8	2	$(8, 2)$

Figure 29

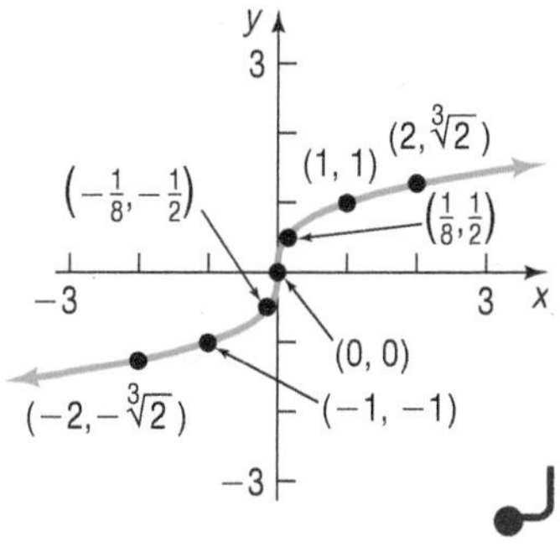

From the results of Example 1 and Figure 29, we have the following properties of the cube root function.

Properties of f(x) = $\sqrt[3]{x}$

1. The domain and the range are the set of all real numbers.
2. The x-intercept of the graph of $f(x) = \sqrt[3]{x}$ is 0. The y-intercept of the graph of $f(x) = \sqrt[3]{x}$ is also 0.
3. The graph is symmetric with respect to the origin. The function is odd.
4. The function is increasing on the interval $(-\infty, \infty)$.
5. The function does not have any local minima or any local maxima.

EXAMPLE 2

Graphing the Absolute Value Function

(a) Determine whether $f(x) = |x|$ is even, odd, or neither. State whether the graph of f is symmetric with respect to the y-axis or symmetric with respect to the origin.

(b) Determine the intercepts, if any, of the graph of $f(x) = |x|$.

(c) Graph $f(x) = |x|$.

Solution

(a) Because

$$f(-x) = |-x|$$
$$= |x| = f(x)$$

the function is even. The graph of f is symmetric with respect to the y-axis.

(b) The y-intercept is $f(0) = |0| = 0$. The x-intercept is found by solving the equation $f(x) = 0$ or $|x| = 0$. So the x-intercept is 0.

(c) Use the function to form Table 5 and obtain some points on the graph. Because of the symmetry with respect to the y-axis, we need to find only points (x, y) for which $x \geq 0$. Figure 30 shows the graph of $f(x) = |x|$.

Table 5

x	y = f(x) = |x|	(x, y)
0	0	(0, 0)
1	1	(1, 1)
2	2	(2, 2)
3	3	(3, 3)

Figure 30

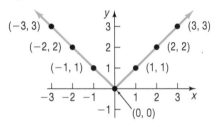

From the results of Example 2 and Figure 30, we have the following properties of the absolute value function.

Properties of $f(x) = |x|$

1. The domain is the set of all real numbers. The range of f is $\{y|y \geq 0\}$.

2. The x-intercept of the graph of $f(x) = |x|$ is 0. The y-intercept of the graph of $f(x) = |x|$ is also 0.

3. The graph is symmetric with respect to the y-axis. The function is even.

4. The function is decreasing on the interval $(-\infty, 0)$. It is increasing on the interval $(0, \infty)$.

5. The function has an absolute minimum of 0 at $x = 0$.

 Seeing the Concept

Graph $y = |x|$ on a square screen and compare what you see with Figure 30. Note that some graphing calculators use abs(x) for absolute value.

Below is a list of the key functions that we have discussed. In going through this list, pay special attention to the properties of each function, particularly to the shape of each graph. Knowing these graphs along with key points on each graph will lay the foundation for further graphing techniques.

Figure 31 Constant Function

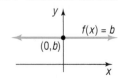

Constant Function

$$f(x) = b \qquad b \text{ is a real number}$$

See Figure 31.

The domain of a **constant function** is the set of all real numbers; its range is the set consisting of a single number b. Its graph is a horizontal line whose y-intercept is b. The constant function is an even function.

Identity Function

$$f(x) = x$$

See Figure 32.

The domain and the range of the **identity function** are the set of all real numbers. Its graph is a line whose slope is 1 and whose y-intercept is 0. The line consists of all points for which the x-coordinate equals the y-coordinate. The identity function is an odd function that is increasing over its domain. Note that the graph bisects quadrants I and III.

Figure 32 Identity Function

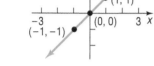

Square Function

$$f(x) = x^2$$

See Figure 33.

The domain of the **square function** f is the set of all real numbers; its range is the set of nonnegative real numbers. The graph of this function is a parabola whose intercept is at $(0, 0)$. The square function is an even function that is decreasing on the interval $(-\infty, 0)$ and increasing on the interval $(0, \infty)$.

Figure 33 Square Function

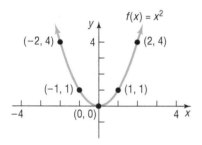

Cube Function

$$f(x) = x^3$$

See Figure 34.

The domain and the range of the **cube function** are the set of all real numbers. The intercept of the graph is at $(0, 0)$. The cube function is odd and is increasing on the interval $(-\infty, \infty)$.

Figure 34 Cube Function

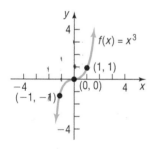

Square Root Function

$$f(x) = \sqrt{x}$$

See Figure 35.

The domain and the range of the **square root function** are the set of nonnegative real numbers. The intercept of the graph is at $(0, 0)$. The square root function is neither even nor odd and is increasing on the interval $(0, \infty)$.

Figure 35 Square Root Function

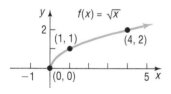

Cube Root Function

$$f(x) = \sqrt[3]{x}$$

See Figure 36.

The domain and the range of the **cube root function** are the set of all real numbers. The intercept of the graph is at $(0, 0)$. The cube root function is an odd function that is increasing on the interval $(-\infty, \infty)$.

Figure 36 Cube Root Function

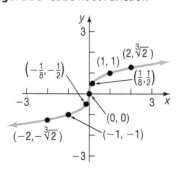

Reciprocal Function

$$f(x) = \frac{1}{x}$$

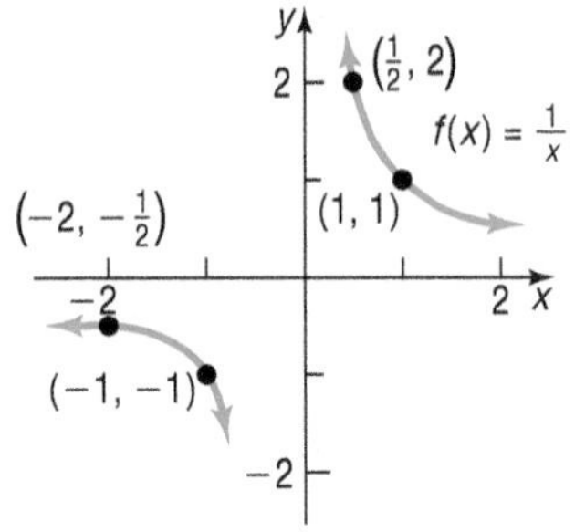

Figure 37 Reciprocal Function

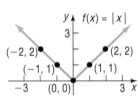

Refer to Example 12, page 16, for a discussion of the equation $y = \frac{1}{x}$. See Figure 37.

The domain and the range of the **reciprocal function** are the set of all nonzero real numbers. The graph has no intercepts. The reciprocal function is decreasing on the intervals $(-\infty, 0)$ and $(0, \infty)$ and is an odd function.

Absolute Value Function

$$f(x) = |x|$$

Figure 38 Absolute Value Function

See Figure 38.

The domain of the **absolute value function** is the set of all real numbers; its range is the set of nonnegative real numbers. The intercept of the graph is at $(0, 0)$. If $x \geq 0$, then $f(x) = x$, and the graph of f is part of the line $y = x$; if $x < 0$, then $f(x) = -x$, and the graph of f is part of the line $y = -x$. The absolute value function is an even function; it is decreasing on the interval $(-\infty, 0)$ and increasing on the interval $(0, \infty)$.

The notation $\text{int}(x)$ stands for the largest integer less than or equal to x. For example,

$$\text{int}(1) = 1, \quad \text{int}(2.5) = 2, \quad \text{int}\left(\frac{1}{2}\right) = 0, \quad \text{int}\left(-\frac{3}{4}\right) = -1, \quad \text{int}(\pi) = 3$$

This type of correspondence occurs frequently enough in mathematics that we give it a name.

DEFINITION

Greatest Integer Function

$$f(x) = \text{int}(x)^* = \text{greatest integer less than or equal to } x$$

We obtain the graph of $f(x) = \text{int}(x)$ by plotting several points. See Table 6. For values of x, $-1 \leq x < 0$, the value of $f(x) = \text{int}(x)$ is -1; for values of x, $0 \leq x < 1$, the value of f is 0. See Figure 39 for the graph.

Figure 39 Greatest Integer Function

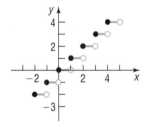

Table 6

x	y = f(x) = int(x)	(x, y)
-1	-1	$(-1, -1)$
$-\frac{1}{2}$	-1	$\left(-\frac{1}{2}, -1\right)$
$-\frac{1}{4}$	-1	$\left(-\frac{1}{4}, -1\right)$
0	0	$(0, 0)$
$\frac{1}{4}$	0	$\left(\frac{1}{4}, 0\right)$
$\frac{1}{2}$	0	$\left(\frac{1}{2}, 0\right)$
$\frac{3}{4}$	0	$\left(\frac{3}{4}, 0\right)$

The domain of the **greatest integer function** is the set of all real numbers; its range is the set of integers. The y-intercept of the graph is 0. The x-intercepts lie in the interval $[0, 1)$. The greatest integer function is neither even nor odd. It is constant on every interval of the form $[k, k + 1)$, for k an integer. In Figure 39, we use a solid dot to indicate, for example, that at $x = 1$ the value of f is $f(1) = 1$; we use an open circle to illustrate that the function does not assume the value of 0 at $x = 1$.

* Some books use the notation $f(x) = [x]$ instead of $\text{int}(x)$.

Figure 40 $f(x) = \text{int}(x)$

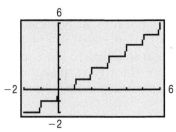

(a) Connected mode

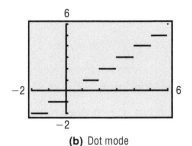

(b) Dot mode

 Although a precise definition requires the idea of a limit, discussed in calculus, in a rough sense, a function is said to be **continuous** if its graph has no gaps or holes and can be drawn without lifting a pencil from the paper on which the graph is drawn. We contrast this with a *discontinuous* function. A function is **discontinuous** if its graph has gaps or holes so that its graph cannot be drawn without lifting a pencil from the paper.

From the graph of the greatest integer function, we can see why it is also called a **step function.** At $x = 0$, $x = \pm 1$, $x = \pm 2$, and so on, this function is discontinuous because, at integer values, the graph suddenly "steps" from one value to another without taking on any of the intermediate values. For example, to the immediate left of $x = 3$, the y-coordinates of the points on the graph are 2, and at $x = 3$ and to the immediate right of $x = 3$, the y-coordinates of the points on the graph are 3. So, the graph has gaps in it.

COMMENT When graphing a function using a graphing utility, you can choose either the **connected mode,** in which points plotted on the screen are connected, making the graph appear without any breaks, or the **dot mode,** in which only the points plotted appear. When graphing the greatest integer function with a graphing utility, it may be necessary to be in the dot mode. This is to prevent the utility from "connecting the dots" when f(x) changes from one integer value to the next. See Figure 40. ∎

The functions discussed so far are basic. Whenever you encounter one of them, you should see a mental picture of its graph. For example, if you encounter the function $f(x) = x^2$, you should see in your mind's eye a picture like Figure 33.

━━━**Now Work** PROBLEMS 9 THROUGH 16

2 Graph Piecewise-defined Functions

Sometimes a function is defined using different equations on different parts of its domain. For example, the absolute value function $f(x) = |x|$ is actually defined by two equations: $f(x) = x$ if $x \geq 0$ and $f(x) = -x$ if $x < 0$. For convenience, these equations are generally combined into one expression as

$$f(x) = |x| = \begin{cases} x & \text{if } x \geq 0 \\ -x & \text{if } x < 0 \end{cases}$$

When a function is defined by different equations on different parts of its domain, it is called a **piecewise-defined** function.

EXAMPLE 3

Analyzing a Piecewise-defined Function

The function f is defined as

$$f(x) = \begin{cases} -2x + 1 & \text{if } -3 \leq x < 1 \\ 2 & \text{if } x = 1 \\ x^2 & \text{if } x > 1 \end{cases}$$

(a) Find $f(-2)$, $f(1)$, and $f(2)$.　　　　(b) Determine the domain of f.
(c) Locate any intercepts.　　　　　　　　(d) Graph f.
(e) Use the graph to find the range of f.　(f) Is f continuous on its domain?

Solution　(a) To find $f(-2)$, observe that when $x = -2$ the equation for f is given by $f(x) = -2x + 1$. So

$$f(-2) = -2(-2) + 1 = 5$$

When $x = 1$, the equation for f is $f(x) = 2$. That is,

$$f(1) = 2$$

When $x = 2$, the equation for f is $f(x) = x^2$. So

$$f(2) = 2^2 = 4$$

(b) To find the domain of f, look at its definition. Since f is defined for all x greater than or equal to -3, the domain of f is $\{x | x \geq -3\}$, or the interval $[-3, \infty)$.

(c) The y-intercept of the graph of the function is $f(0)$. Because the equation for f when $x = 0$ is $f(x) = -2x + 1$, the y-intercept is $f(0) = -2(0) + 1 = 1$. The x-intercepts of the graph of a function f are the real solutions to the equation $f(x) = 0$. To find the x-intercepts of f, solve $f(x) = 0$ for each "piece" of the function and then determine if the values of x, if any, satisfy the condition that defines the piece.

$$f(x) = 0 \qquad\qquad f(x) = 0 \qquad\qquad f(x) = 0$$
$$-2x + 1 = 0 \quad -3 \leq x < 1 \qquad 2 = 0 \quad x = 1 \qquad x^2 = 0 \quad x > 1$$
$$-2x = -1 \qquad\qquad\quad \text{No solution} \qquad\qquad x = 0$$
$$x = \frac{1}{2}$$

The first potential x-intercept, $x = \dfrac{1}{2}$, satisfies the condition $-3 \leq x < 1$, so $x = \dfrac{1}{2}$ is an x-intercept. The second potential x-intercept, $x = 0$, does not satisfy the condition $x > 1$, so $x = 0$ is not an x-intercept. The only x-intercept is $\dfrac{1}{2}$. The intercepts are $(0, 1)$ and $\left(\dfrac{1}{2}, 0\right)$.

(d) To graph f, graph "each piece." First graph the line $y = -2x + 1$ and keep only the part for which $-3 \leq x < 1$. Then plot the point $(1, 2)$ because, when $x = 1, f(x) = 2$. Finally, graph the parabola $y = x^2$ and keep only the part for which $x > 1$. See Figure 41.

(e) From the graph, we conclude that the range of f is $\{y | y > -1\}$, or the interval $(-1, \infty)$.

(f) The function f is not continuous because there is a "jump" in the graph at $x = 1$.

Figure 41

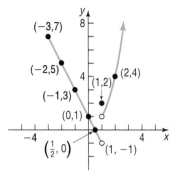

—**Now Work** PROBLEM 29

EXAMPLE 4

Cost of Electricity

In the summer of 2009, Duke Energy supplied electricity to residences of Ohio for a monthly customer charge of $4.50 plus 4.2345¢ per kilowatt-hour (kWhr) for the first 1000 kWhr supplied in the month and 5.3622¢ per kWhr for all usage over 1000 kWhr in the month.

(a) What is the charge for using 300 kWhr in a month?

(b) What is the charge for using 1500 kWhr in a month?

(c) If C is the monthly charge for x kWhr, develop a model relating the monthly charge and kilowatt-hours used. That is, express C as a function of x.

Source: Duke Energy, 2009.

Solution

(a) For 300 kWhr, the charge is $4.50 plus 4.2345¢ = $0.042345 per kWhr. That is,

$$\text{Charge} = \$4.50 + \$0.042345(300) = \$17.20$$

(b) For 1500 kWhr, the charge is $4.50 plus 4.2345¢ per kWhr for the first 1000 kWhr plus 5.3622¢ per kWhr for the 500 kWhr in excess of 1000. That is,

$$\text{Charge} = \$4.50 + \$0.042345(1000) + \$0.053622(500) = \$73.66$$

(c) Let x represent the number of kilowatt-hours used. If $0 \leq x \leq 1000$, the monthly charge C (in dollars) can be found by multiplying x times $0.042345 and adding the monthly customer charge of $4.50. So, if $0 \leq x \leq 1000$, then $C(x) = 0.042345x + 4.50$.

For $x > 1000$, the charge is $0.042345(1000) + 4.50 + 0.053622(x - 1000)$, since $x - 1000$ equals the usage in excess of 1000 kWhr, which costs \$0.053622 per kWhr. That is, if $x > 1000$, then

$$C(x) = 0.042345(1000) + 4.50 + 0.053622(x - 1000)$$
$$= 46.845 + 0.053622(x - 1000)$$
$$= 0.053622x - 6.777$$

The rule for computing C follows two equations:

Figure 42

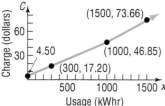

$$C(x) = \begin{cases} 0.042345x + 4.50 & \text{if } 0 \le x \le 1000 \\ 0.053622x - 6.777 & \text{if } x > 1000 \end{cases} \qquad \textit{The Model}$$

See Figure 42 for the graph.

2.4 Assess Your Understanding

'Are You Prepared?' *Answers are given at the end of these exercises. If you get a wrong answer, read the pages listed in red.*

1. Sketch the graph of $y = \sqrt{x}$. (p. 15)

2. Sketch the graph of $y = \dfrac{1}{x}$. (p. 16)

3. List the intercepts of the equation $y = x^3 - 8$. (pp. 11–12)

Concepts and Vocabulary

4. The function $f(x) = x^2$ is decreasing on the interval _____.

5. When functions are defined by more than one equation, they are called _____ functions.

6. *True or False* The cube function is odd and is increasing on the interval $(-\infty, \infty)$.

7. *True or False* The cube root function is odd and is decreasing on the interval $(-\infty, \infty)$.

8. *True or False* The domain and the range of the reciprocal function are the set of all real numbers.

Skill Building

In Problems 9–16, match each graph to its function.

A. *Constant function*
E. *Square root function*

B. *Identity function*
F. *Reciprocal function*

C. *Square function*
G. *Absolute value function*

D. *Cube function*
H. *Cube root function*

9.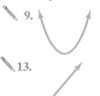

10.

11.

12.

13.

14.

15.

16.

In Problems 17–24, sketch the graph of each function. Be sure to label three points on the graph.

17. $f(x) = x$

18. $f(x) = x^2$

19. $f(x) = x^3$

20. $f(x) = \sqrt{x}$

21. $f(x) = \dfrac{1}{x}$

22. $f(x) = |x|$

23. $f(x) = \sqrt[3]{x}$

24. $f(x) = 3$

25. If $f(x) = \begin{cases} x^2 & \text{if } x < 0 \\ 2 & \text{if } x = 0 \\ 2x + 1 & \text{if } x > 0 \end{cases}$

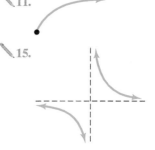

find: (a) $f(-2)$ (b) $f(0)$ (c) $f(2)$

26. If $f(x) = \begin{cases} -3x & \text{if } x < -1 \\ 0 & \text{if } x = -1 \\ 2x^2 + 1 & \text{if } x > -1 \end{cases}$

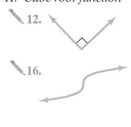

find: (a) $f(-2)$ (b) $f(-1)$ (c) $f(0)$

27. If $f(x) = \begin{cases} 2x - 4 & \text{if } -1 \le x \le 2 \\ x^3 - 2 & \text{if } 2 < x \le 3 \end{cases}$

find: (a) $f(0)$ (b) $f(1)$ (c) $f(2)$ (d) $f(3)$

28. If $f(x) = \begin{cases} x^3 & \text{if } -2 \le x < 1 \\ 3x + 2 & \text{if } 1 \le x \le 4 \end{cases}$

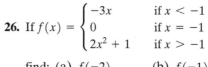

find: (a) $f(-1)$ (b) $f(0)$ (c) $f(1)$ (d) $f(3)$

In Problems 29–40:

  (a) Find the domain of each function.   *(b) Locate any intercepts.*   *(c) Graph each function.*

  (d) Based on the graph, find the range.   *(e) Is f continuous on its domain?*

29. $f(x) = \begin{cases} 2x & \text{if } x \neq 0 \\ 1 & \text{if } x = 0 \end{cases}$

30. $f(x) = \begin{cases} 3x & \text{if } x \neq 0 \\ 4 & \text{if } x = 0 \end{cases}$

31. $f(x) = \begin{cases} -2x + 3 & \text{if } x < 1 \\ 3x - 2 & \text{if } x \geq 1 \end{cases}$

32. $f(x) = \begin{cases} x + 3 & \text{if } x < -2 \\ -2x - 3 & \text{if } x \geq -2 \end{cases}$

33. $f(x) = \begin{cases} x + 3 & \text{if } -2 \leq x < 1 \\ 5 & \text{if } x = 1 \\ -x + 2 & \text{if } x > 1 \end{cases}$

34. $f(x) = \begin{cases} 2x + 5 & \text{if } -3 \leq x < 0 \\ -3 & \text{if } x = 0 \\ -5x & \text{if } x > 0 \end{cases}$

35. $f(x) = \begin{cases} 1 + x & \text{if } x < 0 \\ x^2 & \text{if } x \geq 0 \end{cases}$

36. $f(x) = \begin{cases} \dfrac{1}{x} & \text{if } x < 0 \\ \sqrt[3]{x} & \text{if } x \geq 0 \end{cases}$

37. $f(x) = \begin{cases} |x| & \text{if } -2 \leq x < 0 \\ x^3 & \text{if } x > 0 \end{cases}$

38. $f(x) = \begin{cases} 2 - x & \text{if } -3 \leq x < 1 \\ \sqrt{x} & \text{if } x > 1 \end{cases}$

39. $f(x) = 2\,\text{int}(x)$

40. $f(x) = \text{int}(2x)$

In Problems 41–44, the graph of a piecewise-defined function is given. Write a definition for each function.

41.

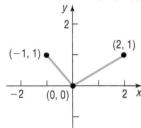

42.

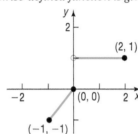

43.

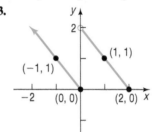

44.

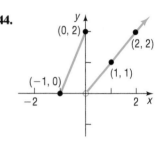

45. If $f(x) = \text{int}(2x)$, find

  (a) $f(1.2)$ (b) $f(1.6)$ (c) $f(-1.8)$

46. If $f(x) = \text{int}\left(\dfrac{x}{2}\right)$, find

  (a) $f(1.2)$ (b) $f(1.6)$ (c) $f(-1.8)$

Applications and Extensions

47. Cell Phone Service Sprint PCS offers a monthly cellular phone plan for $39.99. It includes 450 anytime minutes and charges $0.45 per minute for additional minutes. The following function is used to compute the monthly cost for a subscriber:

$$C(x) = \begin{cases} 39.99 & \text{if } 0 \leq x \leq 450 \\ 0.45x - 162.51 & \text{if } x > 450 \end{cases}$$

where x is the number of anytime minutes used. Compute the monthly cost of the cellular phone for use of the following number of anytime minutes:

  (a) 200   (b) 465   (c) 451

Source: Sprint PCS

48. Parking at O'Hare International Airport The short-term (no more than 24 hours) parking fee F (in dollars) for parking x hours at O'Hare International Airport's main parking garage can be modeled by the function

$$F(x) = \begin{cases} 3 & \text{if } 0 < x \leq 3 \\ 5\,\text{int}(x + 1) + 1 & \text{if } 3 < x < 9 \\ 50 & \text{if } 9 \leq x \leq 24 \end{cases}$$

Determine the fee for parking in the short-term parking garage for

  (a) 2 hours   (b) 7 hours   (c) 15 hours

  (d) 8 hours and 24 minutes

Source: O'Hare International Airport

49. Cost of Natural Gas In April 2009, Peoples Energy had the following rate schedule for natural gas usage in single-family residences:

Monthly service charge	$15.95
Per therm service charge	
1st 50 therms	$0.33606/therm
Over 50 therms	$0.10580/therm
Gas charge	$0.3940/therm

  (a) What is the charge for using 50 therms in a month?

  (b) What is the charge for using 500 therms in a month?

  (c) Develop a model that relates the monthly charge C for x therms of gas.

  (d) Graph the function found in part (c).

Source: Peoples Energy, Chicago, Illinois, 2009

50. Cost of Natural Gas In April 2009, Nicor Gas had the following rate schedule for natural gas usage in single-family residences:

Monthly customer charge	$8.40
Distribution charge	
1st 20 therms	$0.1473/therm
Next 30 therms	$0.0579/therm
Over 50 therms	$0.0519/therm
Gas supply charge	$0.43/therm

  (a) What is the charge for using 40 therms in a month?

  (b) What is the charge for using 150 therms in a month?

  (c) Develop a model that gives the monthly charge C for x therms of gas.

  (d) Graph the function found in part (c).

Source: Nicor Gas, Aurora, Illinois, 2009

51. Federal Income Tax   Two 2009 Tax Rate Schedules are given in the accompanying table. If x equals taxable income and y equals the tax due, construct a function $y = f(x)$ for Schedule X.

REVISED 2009 TAX RATE SCHEDULES											
Schedule X—Single						**Schedule Y-1—Married Filing Jointly or qualifying Widow(er)**					
If Taxable Income Is Over	**But Not Over**	**The Tax Is This Amount**		**Plus This %**	**Of the Excess Over**	**If Taxable Income Is Over**	**But Not Over**	**The Tax Is This Amount**		**Plus This %**	**Of The Excess Over**
$0	$8,350	–	+	10%	$0	$0	$16,700	–	+	10%	$0
8,350	33,950	$835.00	+	15%	8,350	16,700	67,900	$1,670.00	+	15%	16,700
33,950	82,250	4,675.00	+	25%	33,950	67,900	137,050	9,350.00	+	25%	67,900
82,250	171,550	16,750.00	+	28%	82,250	137,050	208,850	26,637.50	+	28%	137,050
171,550	372,950	41,754.00	+	33%	171,550	208,850	372,950	46,741.50	+	33%	208,850
372,950	–	108,216.00	+	35%	372,950	372,950	–	100,894.50	+	35%	372,950

Source: Internal Revenue Service

52. Federal Income Tax   Refer to the revised 2009 tax rate schedules. If x equals taxable income and y equals the tax due, construct a function $y = f(x)$ for Schedule Y-1.

53. Cost of Transporting Goods   A trucking company transports goods between Chicago and New York, a distance of 960 miles. The company's policy is to charge, for each pound, $0.50 per mile for the first 100 miles, $0.40 per mile for the next 300 miles, $0.25 per mile for the next 400 miles, and no charge for the remaining 160 miles.
   (a) Graph the relationship between the cost of transportation in dollars and mileage over the entire 960-mile route.
   (b) Find the cost as a function of mileage for hauls between 100 and 400 miles from Chicago.
   (c) Find the cost as a function of mileage for hauls between 400 and 800 miles from Chicago.

54. Car Rental Costs   An economy car rented in Florida from National Car Rental® on a weekly basis costs $95 per week. Extra days cost $24 per day until the day rate exceeds the weekly rate, in which case the weekly rate applies. Also, any part of a day used counts as a full day. Find the cost C of renting an economy car as a function of the number x of days used, where $7 \leq x \leq 14$. Graph this function.

55. Minimum Payments for Credit Cards   Holders of credit cards issued by banks, department stores, oil companies, and so on, receive bills each month that state minimum amounts that must be paid by a certain due date. The minimum due depends on the total amount owed. One such credit card company uses the following rules: For a bill of less than $10, the entire amount is due. For a bill of at least $10 but less than $500, the minimum due is $10. A minimum of $30 is due on a bill of at least $500 but less than $1000, a minimum of $50 is due on a bill of at least $1000 but less than $1500, and a minimum of $70 is due on bills of $1500 or more. Find the function f that describes the minimum payment due on a bill of x dollars. Graph f.

56. Interest Payments for Credit Cards   Refer to Problem 55. The card holder may pay any amount between the minimum due and the total owed. The organization issuing the card charges the card holder interest of 1.5% per month for the first $1000 owed and 1% per month on any unpaid balance over $1000. Find the function g that gives the amount of interest charged per month on a balance of x dollars. Graph g.

57. Wind Chill   The wind chill factor represents the equivalent air temperature at a standard wind speed that would produce the same heat loss as the given temperature and wind speed. One formula for computing the equivalent temperature is

$$W = \begin{cases} t & 0 \leq v < 1.79 \\ 33 - \dfrac{(10.45 + 10\sqrt{v} - v)(33 - t)}{22.04} & 1.79 \leq v \leq 20 \\ 33 - 1.5958(33 - t) & v > 20 \end{cases}$$

where v represents the wind speed (in meters per second) and t represents the air temperature (°C). Compute the wind chill for the following:
   (a) An air temperature of 10°C and a wind speed of 1 meter per second (m/sec)
   (b) An air temperature of 10°C and a wind speed of 5 m/sec
   (c) An air temperature of 10°C and a wind speed of 15 m/sec
   (d) An air temperature of 10°C and a wind speed of 25 m/sec
   (e) Explain the physical meaning of the equation corresponding to $0 \leq v < 1.79$.
   (f) Explain the physical meaning of the equation corresponding to $v > 20$.

58. Wind Chill   Redo Problem 57(a)–(d) for an air temperature of −10°C.

59. First-class Mail   In 2009 the U.S. Postal Service charged $1.17 postage for first-class mail retail flats (such as an 8.5″ by 11″ envelope) weighing up to 1 ounce, plus $0.17 for each additional ounce up to 13 ounces. First-class rates do not apply to flats weighing more than 13 ounces. Develop a model that relates C, the first-class postage charged, for a flat weighing x ounces. Graph the function.

Source: United States Postal Service

Explaining Concepts: Discussion and Writing

In Problems 60–67, use a graphing utility.

60. Exploration Graph $y = x^2$. Then on the same screen graph $y = x^2 + 2$, followed by $y = x^2 + 4$, followed by $y = x^2 - 2$. What pattern do you observe? Can you predict the graph of $y = x^2 - 4$? Of $y = x^2 + 5$?

61. Exploration Graph $y = x^2$. Then on the same screen graph $y = (x - 2)^2$, followed by $y = (x - 4)^2$, followed by $y = (x + 2)^2$. What pattern do you observe? Can you predict the graph of $y = (x + 4)^2$? Of $y = (x - 5)^2$?

62. Exploration Graph $y = |x|$. Then on the same screen graph $y = 2|x|$, followed by $y = 4|x|$, followed by $y = \frac{1}{2}|x|$. What pattern do you observe? Can you predict the graph of $y = \frac{1}{4}|x|$? Of $y = 5|x|$?

63. Exploration Graph $y = x^2$. Then on the same screen graph $y = -x^2$. What pattern do you observe? Now try $y = |x|$ and $y = -|x|$. What do you conclude?

64. Exploration Graph $y = \sqrt{x}$. Then on the same screen graph $y = \sqrt{-x}$. What pattern do you observe? Now try $y = 2x + 1$ and $y = 2(-x) + 1$. What do you conclude?

65. Exploration Graph $y = x^3$. Then on the same screen graph $y = (x - 1)^3 + 2$. Could you have predicted the result?

66. Exploration Graph $y = x^2$, $y = x^4$, and $y = x^6$ on the same screen. What do you notice is the same about each graph? What do you notice that is different?

67. Exploration Graph $y = x^3$, $y = x^5$, and $y = x^7$ on the same screen. What do you notice is the same about each graph? What do you notice that is different?

68. Consider the equation

$$y = \begin{cases} 1 & \text{if } x \text{ is rational} \\ 0 & \text{if } x \text{ is irrational} \end{cases}$$

Is this a function? What is its domain? What is its range? What is its y-intercept, if any? What are its x-intercepts, if any? Is it even, odd, or neither? How would you describe its graph?

69. Define some functions that pass through $(0, 0)$ and $(1, 1)$ and are increasing for $x \geq 0$. Begin your list with $y = \sqrt{x}$, $y = x$, and $y = x^2$. Can you propose a general result about such functions?

'Are You Prepared?' Answers

1.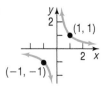

2.

3. $(0, -8)$, $(2, 0)$

2.5 Graphing Techniques: Transformations

OBJECTIVES **1** Graph Functions Using Vertical and Horizontal Shifts (p. 90)

2 Graph Functions Using Compressions and Stretches (p. 93)

3 Graph Functions Using Reflections about the x-Axis and the y-Axis (p. 96)

At this stage, if you were asked to graph any of the functions defined by $y = x$, $y = x^2$, $y = x^3$, $y = \sqrt{x}$, $y = \sqrt[3]{x}$, $y = \dfrac{1}{x}$, or $y = |x|$, your response should be, "Yes, I recognize these functions and know the general shapes of their graphs." (If this is not your answer, review the previous section, Figures 32 through 38.)

Sometimes we are asked to graph a function that is "almost" like one that we already know how to graph. In this section, we develop techniques for graphing such functions. Collectively, these techniques are referred to as **transformations.**

1 Graph Functions Using Vertical and Horizontal Shifts

EXAMPLE 1 **Vertical Shift Up**

Use the graph of $f(x) = x^2$ to obtain the graph of $g(x) = x^2 + 3$.

Solution Begin by obtaining some points on the graphs of f and g. For example, when $x = 0$, then $y = f(0) = 0$ and $y = g(0) = 3$. When $x = 1$, then $y = f(1) = 1$ and

$y = g(1) = 4$. Table 7 lists these and a few other points on each graph. Notice that each y-coordinate of a point on the graph of g is 3 units larger than the y-coordinate of the corresponding point on the graph of f. We conclude that the graph of g is identical to that of f, except that it is shifted vertically up 3 units. See Figure 43.

Figure 43

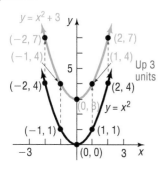

Table 7

	$y = f(x)$	$y = g(x)$
x	$= x^2$	$= x^2 + 3$
-2	4	7
-1	1	4
0	0	3
1	1	4
2	4	7

EXAMPLE 2

Vertical Shift Down

Use the graph of $f(x) = x^2$ to obtain the graph of $g(x) = x^2 - 4$.

Solution

Table 8 lists some points on the graphs of f and g. Notice that each y-coordinate of g is 4 units less than the corresponding y-coordinate of f.

To obtain the graph of g from the graph of f, subtract 4 from each y-coordinate on the graph of f. So the graph of g is identical to that of f, except that it is shifted down 4 units. See Figure 44.

Figure 44

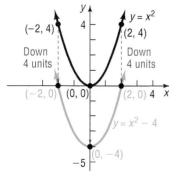

Table 8

	$y = f(x)$	$y = g(x)$
x	$= x^2$	$= x^2 - 4$
-2	4	0
-1	1	-3
0	0	-4
1	1	-3
2	4	0

Figure 45

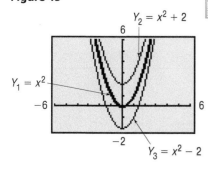

Exploration

On the same screen, graph each of the following functions:

$$Y_1 = x^2$$
$$Y_2 = x^2 + 2$$
$$Y_3 = x^2 - 2$$

Figure 45 illustrates the graphs. You should have observed a general pattern. With $Y_1 = x^2$ on the screen, the graph of $Y_2 = x^2 + 2$ is identical to that of $Y_1 = x^2$, except that it is shifted vertically up 2 units. The graph of $Y_3 = x^2 - 2$ is identical to that of $Y_1 = x^2$, except that it is shifted vertically down 2 units.

We are led to the following conclusions:

> If a positive real number k is added to the output of a function $y = f(x)$, the graph of the new function $y = f(x) + k$ is the graph of f **shifted vertically up** k units.

> If a positive real number k is subtracted from the output of a function $y = f(x)$, the graph of the new function $y = f(x) - k$ is the graph of f **shifted vertically down** k units.

━━━**Now Work** PROBLEM 39

EXAMPLE 3 | **Horizontal Shift to the Right**

Use the graph of $f(x) = x^2$ to obtain the graph of $g(x) = (x - 2)^2$.

Solution

The function $g(x) = (x - 2)^2$ is basically a square function. Table 9 lists some points on the graphs of f and g. Note that when $f(x) = 0$ then $x = 0$, and when $g(x) = 0$, then $x = 2$. Also, when $f(x) = 4$, then $x = -2$ or 2, and when $g(x) = 4$, then $x = 0$ or 4. Notice that the x-coordinates on the graph of g are two units larger than the corresponding x-coordinates on the graph of f for any given y-coordinate. We conclude that the graph of g is identical to that of f, except that it is shifted horizontally 2 units to the right. See Figure 46.

Figure 46

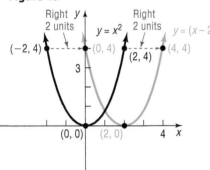

Table 9

x	$y = f(x)$ $= x^2$	$y = g(x)$ $= (x - 2)^2$
-2	4	16
0	0	4
2	4	0
4	16	4

Figure 47

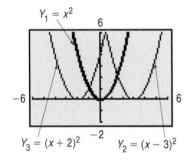

$Y_3 = (x + 2)^2$ $Y_2 = (x - 3)^2$

 Exploration

On the same screen, graph each of the following functions:

$$Y_1 = x^2$$
$$Y_2 = (x - 3)^2$$
$$Y_3 = (x + 2)^2$$

Figure 47 illustrates the graphs.

You should have observed the following pattern. With the graph of $Y_1 = x^2$ on the screen, the graph of $Y_2 = (x - 3)^2$ is identical to that of $Y_1 = x^2$, except that it is shifted horizontally to the right 3 units. The graph of $Y_3 = (x + 2)^2$ is identical to that of $Y_1 = x^2$, except that it is shifted horizontally to the left 2 units.

We are led to the following conclusion.

> ⌒ **In Other Words**
> ⌒ If a positive number h is
> ⌒ subtracted from x in $y = f(x)$,
> ⌒ the graph of the new function
> ⌒ $y = f(x - h)$ is the graph of
> ⌒ $y = f(x)$ shifted horizontally
> ⌒ right h units. If h is added to x,
> ⌒ shift horizontally left h units.

If the argument x of a function f is replaced by $x - h$, $h > 0$, the graph of the new function $y = f(x - h)$ is the graph of f **shifted horizontally right h units.** If the argument x of a function f is replaced by $x + h$, $h > 0$, the graph of the new function $y = f(x + h)$ is the graph of f **shifted horizontally left h units.**

EXAMPLE 4 | **Horizontal Shift to the Left**

Use the graph of $f(x) = x^2$ to obtain the graph of $g(x) = (x + 4)^2$.

Solution

Again, the function $g(x) = (x + 4)^2$ is basically a square function. Its graph is the same as that of f, except that it is shifted horizontally 4 units to the left. See Figure 48.

Figure 48

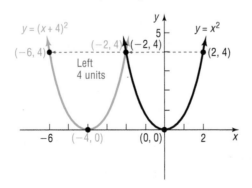

Now Work PROBLEM 43

Notice the distinction between vertical and horizontal shifts. The graph of $f(x) = \sqrt{x} + 3$ is obtained by shifting the graph of $y = \sqrt{x}$ *up* 3 units, because we evaluate the square root function first and then add 3. The graph of $g(x) = \sqrt{x + 3}$ is obtained by shifting the graph of $y = \sqrt{x}$ *left* 3 units, because we add 3 to x before we evaluate the square root function.

Vertical and horizontal shifts are sometimes combined.

EXAMPLE 5

Combining Vertical and Horizontal Shifts

Graph the function: $f(x) = (x + 3)^2 - 5$

Solution

We graph f in steps. First, notice that the rule for f is basically a square function, so begin with the graph of $y = x^2$ as shown in Figure 49(a). Next, to get the graph of $y = (x + 3)^2$, shift the graph of $y = x^2$ horizontally 3 units to the left. See Figure 49(b). Finally, to get the graph of $y = (x + 3)^2 - 5$, shift the graph of $y = (x + 3)^2$ vertically down 5 units. See Figure 49(c). Note the points plotted on each graph. Using key points can be helpful in keeping track of the transformation that has taken place.

Figure 49

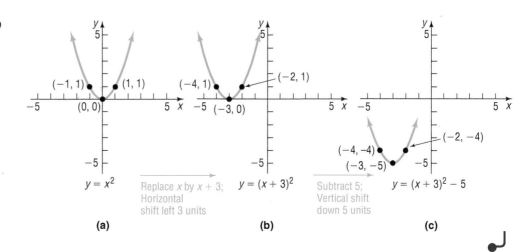

(a)   (b)   (c)

 ✔**Check:** Graph $Y_1 = f(x) = (x + 3)^2 - 5$ and compare the graph to Figure 49(c).

In Example 5, if the vertical shift had been done first, followed by the horizontal shift, the final graph would have been the same. Try it for yourself.

‑**Now Work** PROBLEM 45

---

2 Graph Functions Using Compressions and Stretches

EXAMPLE 6

Vertical Stretch

Use the graph of $f(x) = |x|$ to obtain the graph of $g(x) = 2|x|$.

Solution

To see the relationship between the graphs of f and g, form Table 10, listing points on each graph. For each x, the y-coordinate of a point on the graph of g is 2 times as large as the corresponding y-coordinate on the graph of f. The graph of $f(x) = |x|$ is vertically stretched by a factor of 2 to obtain the graph of $g(x) = 2|x|$ [for example, $(1, 1)$ is on the graph of f, but $(1, 2)$ is on the graph of g]. See Figure 50 on the next page.

Table 10

x	$y = f(x)$ $= \lvert x \rvert$	$y = g(x)$ $= 2\lvert x \rvert$
−2	2	4
−1	1	2
0	0	0
1	1	2
2	2	4

Figure 50

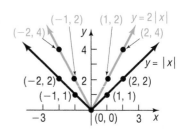

EXAMPLE 7

Vertical Compression

Use the graph of $f(x) = \lvert x \rvert$ to obtain the graph of $g(x) = \frac{1}{2}\lvert x \rvert$.

Solution

For each x, the y-coordinate of a point on the graph of g is $\frac{1}{2}$ as large as the corresponding y-coordinate on the graph of f. The graph of $f(x) = \lvert x \rvert$ is vertically compressed by a factor of $\frac{1}{2}$ to obtain the graph of $g(x) = \frac{1}{2}\lvert x \rvert$ [for example, $(2, 2)$ is on the graph of f, but $(2, 1)$ is on the graph of g]. See Table 11 and Figure 51.

Table 11

x	$y = f(x)$ $= \lvert x \rvert$	$y = g(x)$ $= \frac{1}{2}\lvert x \rvert$
−2	2	1
−1	1	$\frac{1}{2}$
0	0	0
1	1	$\frac{1}{2}$
2	2	1

Figure 51

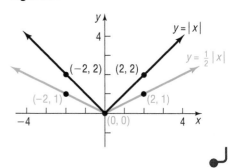

When the right side of a function $y = f(x)$ is multiplied by a positive number a, the graph of the new function $y = af(x)$ is obtained by multiplying each y-coordinate on the graph of $y = f(x)$ by a. The new graph is a **vertically compressed** (if $0 < a < 1$) or a **vertically stretched** (if $a > 1$) version of the graph of $y = f(x)$.

Now Work PROBLEM 47

What happens if the argument x of a function $y = f(x)$ is multiplied by a positive number a, creating a new function $y = f(ax)$? To find the answer, look at the following Exploration.

Exploration

On the same screen, graph each of the following functions:

$$Y_1 = f(x) = \sqrt{x} \qquad Y_2 = f(2x) = \sqrt{2x} \qquad Y_3 = f\left(\frac{1}{2}x\right) = \sqrt{\frac{1}{2}x} = \sqrt{\frac{x}{2}}$$

Create a table of values to explore the relation between the x- and y-coordinates of each function.

Result You should have obtained the graphs in Figure 52. Look at Table 12(a). Notice that $(1, 1)$, $(4, 2)$, and $(9, 3)$ are points on the graph of $Y_1 = \sqrt{x}$. Also, $(0.5, 1)$, $(2, 2)$, and $(4.5, 3)$ are points on the graph of $Y_2 = \sqrt{2x}$. For a given y-coordinate, the x-coordinate on the graph of Y_2 is $\frac{1}{2}$ of the x-coordinate on Y_1.

Figure 52

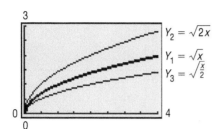

$Y_2 = \sqrt{2x}$

$Y_1 = \sqrt{x}$

$Y_3 = \sqrt{\dfrac{x}{2}}$

Table 12

X	Y₁	Y₂
0	0	0
.5	.70711	1
1	1	1.4142
2	1.4142	2
4	2	2.8284
4.5	2.1213	3
9	3	4.2426

Y₂⊟√(2X)

(a)

X	Y₁	Y₃
0	0	0
1	1	.70711
2	1.4142	1
4	2	1.4142
8	2.8284	2
9	3	2.1213
18	4.2426	3

Y₃⊟√(X/2)

(b)

We conclude that the graph of $Y_2 = \sqrt{2x}$ is obtained by multiplying the x-coordinate of each point on the graph of $Y_1 = \sqrt{x}$ by $\dfrac{1}{2}$. The graph of $Y_2 = \sqrt{2x}$ is the graph of $Y_1 = \sqrt{x}$ *compressed* horizontally.

Look at Table 12(b). Notice that (1, 1), (4, 2), and (9, 3) are points on the graph of $Y_1 = \sqrt{x}$. Also notice that (2, 1), (8, 2), and (18, 3) are points on the graph of $Y_3 = \sqrt{\dfrac{x}{2}}$. For a given y-coordinate, the x-coordinate on the graph of Y_3 is 2 times the x-coordinate on Y_1. We conclude that the graph of $Y_3 = \sqrt{\dfrac{x}{2}}$ is obtained by multiplying the x-coordinate of each point on the graph of $Y_1 = \sqrt{x}$ by 2. The graph of $Y_3 = \sqrt{\dfrac{x}{2}}$ is the graph of $Y_1 = \sqrt{x}$ *stretched* horizontally.

Based on the results of the Exploration, we have the following result:

If the argument x of a function $y = f(x)$ is multiplied by a positive number a, the graph of the new function $y = f(ax)$ is obtained by multiplying each x-coordinate of $y = f(x)$ by $\dfrac{1}{a}$. A **horizontal compression** results if $a > 1$, and a **horizontal stretch** occurs if $0 < a < 1$.

EXAMPLE 8

Graphing Using Stretches and Compressions

The graph of $y = f(x)$ is given in Figure 53. Use this graph to find the graphs of

(a) $y = 2f(x)$ (b) $y = f(3x)$

Solution   (a) The graph of $y = 2f(x)$ is obtained by multiplying each y-coordinate of $y = f(x)$ by 2. See Figure 54.

(b) The graph of $y = f(3x)$ is obtained from the graph of $y = f(x)$ by multiplying each x-coordinate of $y = f(x)$ by $\dfrac{1}{3}$. See Figure 55.

Figure 53

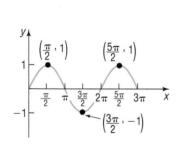

$y = f(x)$

Figure 54

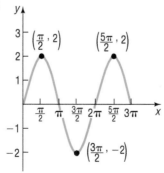

$y = 2f(x)$

Figure 55

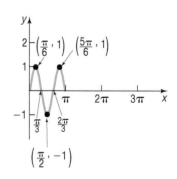

$y = f(3x)$

━━ **Now Work** PROBLEMS 63(e) AND (g)

3 Graph Functions Using Reflections about the *x*-Axis and the *y*-Axis

---

EXAMPLE 9

Reflection about the *x*-Axis

Graph the function: $f(x) = -x^2$

Solution

Begin with the graph of $y = x^2$, as shown in black in Figure 56. For each point (x, y) on the graph of $y = x^2$, the point $(x, -y)$ is on the graph of $y = -x^2$, as indicated in Table 13. Draw the graph of $y = -x^2$ by reflecting the graph of $y = x^2$ about the *x*-axis. See Figure 56.

Figure 56

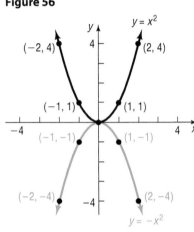

Table 13

x	$y = x^2$	$y = -x^2$
−2	4	−4
−1	1	−1
0	0	0
1	1	−1
2	4	−4

> When the right side of the function $y = f(x)$ is multiplied by -1, the graph of the new function $y = -f(x)$ is the **reflection about the *x*-axis** of the graph of the function $y = f(x)$.

──── **Now Work** PROBLEM 49

EXAMPLE 10

Reflection about the *y*-Axis

Graph the function: $f(x) = \sqrt{-x}$

Solution

First, notice that the domain of f consists of all real numbers x for which $-x \geq 0$ or, equivalently, $x \leq 0$. To get the graph of $f(x) = \sqrt{-x}$, begin with the graph of $y = \sqrt{x}$, as shown in Figure 57. For each point (x, y) on the graph of $y = \sqrt{x}$, the point $(-x, y)$ is on the graph of $y = \sqrt{-x}$. Obtain the graph of $y = \sqrt{-x}$ by reflecting the graph of $y = \sqrt{x}$ about the *y*-axis. See Figure 57.

Figure 57

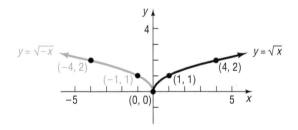

> When the graph of the function $y = f(x)$ is known, the graph of the new function $y = f(-x)$ is the **reflection about the *y*-axis** of the graph of the function $y = f(x)$.

SUMMARY OF GRAPHING TECHNIQUES

To Graph:	Draw the Graph of f and:	Functional Change to f(x)

Vertical shifts

$y = f(x) + k, \quad k > 0$ Raise the graph of f by k units. Add k to $f(x)$.
$y = f(x) - k, \quad k > 0$ Lower the graph of f by k units. Subtract k from $f(x)$.

Horizontal shifts

$y = f(x + h), \quad h > 0$ Shift the graph of f to the left h units. Replace x by $x + h$.
$y = f(x - h), \quad h > 0$ Shift the graph of f to the right h units. Replace x by $x - h$.

Compressing or stretching

$y = af(x), \quad a > 0$ Multiply each y-coordinate of $y = f(x)$ by a. Multiply $f(x)$ by a.
Stretch the graph of f vertically if $a > 1$.
Compress the graph of f vertically if $0 < a < 1$.

$y = f(ax), \quad a > 0$ Multiply each x-coordinate of $y = f(x)$ by $\frac{1}{a}$. Replace x by ax.

Stretch the graph of f horizontally if $0 < a < 1$.
Compress the graph of f horizontally if $a > 1$.

Reflection about the x-axis

$y = -f(x)$ Reflect the graph of f about the x-axis. Multiply $f(x)$ by -1.

Reflection about the y-axis

$y = f(-x)$ Reflect the graph of f about the y-axis. Replace x by $-x$.

EXAMPLE 11 **Determining the Function Obtained from a Series of Transformations**

Find the function that is finally graphed after the following three transformations are applied to the graph of $y = |x|$.

1. Shift left 2 units
2. Shift up 3 units
3. Reflect about the y-axis

Solution
1. Shift left 2 units: Replace x by $x + 2$. $y = |x + 2|$
2. Shift up 3 units: Add 3. $y = |x + 2| + 3$
3. Reflect about the y-axis: Replace x by $-x$. $y = |-x + 2| + 3$

Now Work PROBLEM 27

EXAMPLE 12   **Combining Graphing Procedures**

Graph the function $f(x) = \dfrac{3}{x - 2} + 1$. Find the domain and the range of f.

Solution   It is helpful to write f as $f(x) = 3\left(\dfrac{1}{x - 2}\right) + 1$. Now use the following steps to obtain the graph of f:

STEP 1: $y = \dfrac{1}{x}$ Reciprocal function

STEP 2: $y = 3 \cdot \left(\dfrac{1}{x}\right) = \dfrac{3}{x}$ Multiply by 3; vertical stretch of the graph of $y = \dfrac{1}{x}$ by a factor of 3.

STEP 3: $y = \dfrac{3}{x - 2}$ Replace x by x − 2; horizontal shift to the right 2 units.

STEP 4: $y = \dfrac{3}{x - 2} + 1$ Add 1; vertical shift up 1 unit.

See Figure 58.

Figure 58

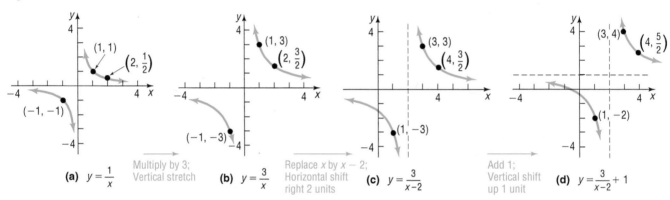

(a) $y = \dfrac{1}{x}$ Multiply by 3; Vertical stretch   (b) $y = \dfrac{3}{x}$ Replace x by x − 2; Horizontal shift right 2 units   (c) $y = \dfrac{3}{x-2}$ Add 1; Vertical shift up 1 unit   (d) $y = \dfrac{3}{x-2} + 1$

The domain of $y = \dfrac{1}{x}$ is $\{x \mid x \neq 0\}$ and its range is $\{y \mid y \neq 0\}$. Because we shifted right 2 units and up 1 unit to obtain f, the domain of f is $\{x \mid x \neq 2\}$ and its range is $\{y \mid y \neq 1\}$.

Other orderings of the steps shown in Example 12 would also result in the graph of f. For example, try this one:

STEP 1: $y = \dfrac{1}{x}$ Reciprocal function

STEP 2: $y = \dfrac{1}{x - 2}$ Replace x by x − 2; horizontal shift to the right 2 units.

STEP 3: $y = \dfrac{3}{x - 2}$ Multiply by 3; vertical stretch of the graph of $y = \dfrac{1}{x - 2}$ by a factor of 3.

STEP 4: $y = \dfrac{3}{x - 2} + 1$ Add 1; vertical shift up 1 unit.

Hint: Although the order in which transformations are performed can be altered, you may consider using the following order for consistency:

1. Reflections
2. Compressions and stretches
3. Shifts

EXAMPLE 13   **Combining Graphing Procedures**

Graph the function $f(x) = \sqrt{1-x} + 2$. Find the domain and the range of f.

Solution   Because horizontal shifts require the form $x - h$, we begin by rewriting $f(x)$ as
$f(x) = \sqrt{1-x} + 2 = \sqrt{-(x-1)} + 2$. Now use the following steps:

STEP 1: $y = \sqrt{x}$ Square root function

STEP 2: $y = \sqrt{-x}$ Replace x by −x; reflect about the y-axis.

STEP 3: $y = \sqrt{-(x-1)} = \sqrt{1-x}$ Replace x by x − 1; horizontal shift to the right 1 unit.

STEP 4: $y = \sqrt{1-x} + 2$ Add 2; vertical shift up 2 units.

See Figure 59.

Figure 59

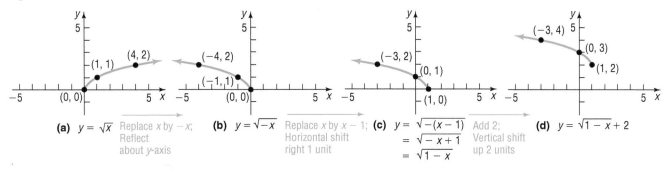

(a) $y = \sqrt{x}$ Replace x by −x; Reflect about y-axis

(b) $y = \sqrt{-x}$ Replace x by x − 1; Horizontal shift right 1 unit

(c) $y = \sqrt{-(x-1)}$ $= \sqrt{-x+1}$ $= \sqrt{1-x}$ Add 2; Vertical shift up 2 units

(d) $y = \sqrt{1-x} + 2$

The domain of f is $(-\infty, 1]$ and the range is $[2, \infty)$.

Now Work PROBLEM 55

2.5 Assess Your Understanding

Concepts and Vocabulary

1. Suppose that the graph of a function f is known. Then the graph of $y = f(x - 2)$ may be obtained by a(n) _____ shift of the graph of f to the _____ a distance of 2 units.

2. Suppose that the graph of a function f is known. Then the graph of $y = f(-x)$ may be obtained by a reflection about the _____-axis of the graph of the function $y = f(x)$.

3. Suppose that the graph of a function g is known. The graph of $y = g(x) + 2$ may be obtained by a _____ shift of the graph of g _____ a distance of 2 units.

4. *True or False* The graph of $y = -f(x)$ is the reflection about the x-axis of the graph of $y = f(x)$.

5. *True or False* To obtain the graph of $f(x) = \sqrt{x+2}$, shift the graph of $y = \sqrt{x}$ horizontally to the right 2 units.

6. *True or False* To obtain the graph of $f(x) = x^3 + 5$, shift the graph of $y = x^3$ vertically up 5 units.

Skill Building

In Problems 7–18, match each graph to one of the following functions:

A. $y = x^2 + 2$ B. $y = -x^2 + 2$ C. $y = |x| + 2$ D. $y = -|x| + 2$

E. $y = (x-2)^2$ F. $y = -(x+2)^2$ G. $y = |x - 2|$ H. $y = -|x + 2|$

I. $y = 2x^2$ J. $y = -2x^2$ K. $y = 2|x|$ L. $y = -2|x|$

7.
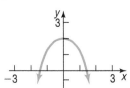

8.
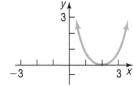

9.
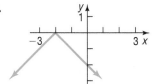

10.
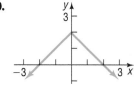

11.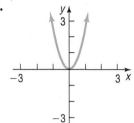

12.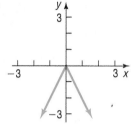

13.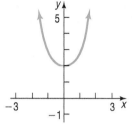

14.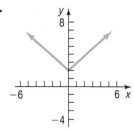

15.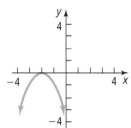

16.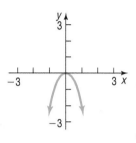

17.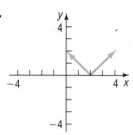

18.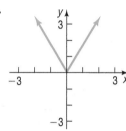

In Problems 19–26, write the function whose graph is the graph of $y = x^3$, but is:

19. Shifted to the right 4 units

20. Shifted to the left 4 units

21. Shifted up 4 units

22. Shifted down 4 units

23. Reflected about the y-axis

24. Reflected about the x-axis

25. Vertically stretched by a factor of 4

26. Horizontally stretched by a factor of 4

In Problems 27–30, find the function that is finally graphed after each of the following transformations is applied to the graph of $y = \sqrt{x}$ in the order stated.

27. (1) Shift up 2 units
(2) Reflect about the x-axis
(3) Reflect about the y-axis

28. (1) Reflect about the x-axis
(2) Shift right 3 units
(3) Shift down 2 units

29. (1) Reflect about the x-axis
(2) Shift up 2 units
(3) Shift left 3 units

30. (1) Shift up 2 units
(2) Reflect about the y-axis
(3) Shift left 3 units

31. If $(3, 6)$ is a point on the graph of $y = f(x)$, which of the following points must be on the graph of $y = -f(x)$?
(a) $(6, 3)$ (b) $(6, -3)$
(c) $(3, -6)$ (d) $(-3, 6)$

32. If $(3, 6)$ is a point on the graph of $y = f(x)$, which of the following points must be on the graph of $y = f(-x)$?
(a) $(6, 3)$ (b) $(6, -3)$
(c) $(3, -6)$ (d) $(-3, 6)$

33. If $(1, 3)$ is a point on the graph of $y = f(x)$, which of the following points must be on the graph of $y = 2f(x)$?
(a) $\left(1, \dfrac{3}{2}\right)$ (b) $(2, 3)$

(c) $(1, 6)$ (d) $\left(\dfrac{1}{2}, 3\right)$

34. If $(4, 2)$ is a point on the graph of $y = f(x)$, which of the following points must be on the graph of $y = f(2x)$?
(a) $(4, 1)$ (b) $(8, 2)$
(c) $(2, 2)$ (d) $(4, 4)$

35. Suppose that the x-intercepts of the graph of $y = f(x)$ are -5 and 3.
(a) What are the x-intercepts of the graph of $y = f(x + 2)$?
(b) What are the x-intercepts of the graph of $y = f(x - 2)$?
(c) What are the x-intercepts of the graph of $y = 4f(x)$?
(d) What are the x-intercepts of the graph of $y = f(-x)$?

36. Suppose that the x-intercepts of the graph of $y = f(x)$ are -8 and 1.
(a) What are the x-intercepts of the graph of $y = f(x + 4)$?
(b) What are the x-intercepts of the graph of $y = f(x - 3)$?
(c) What are the x-intercepts of the graph of $y = 2f(x)$?
(d) What are the x-intercepts of the graph of $y = f(-x)$?

37. Suppose that the function $y = f(x)$ is increasing on the interval $(-1, 5)$.
(a) Over what interval is the graph of $y = f(x + 2)$ increasing?
(b) Over what interval is the graph of $y = f(x - 5)$ increasing?
(c) What can be said about the graph of $y = -f(x)$?
(d) What can be said about the graph of $y = f(-x)$?

38. Suppose that the function $y = f(x)$ is decreasing on the interval $(-2, 7)$.
(a) Over what interval is the graph of $y = f(x + 2)$ decreasing?
(b) Over what interval is the graph of $y = f(x - 5)$ decreasing?
(c) What can be said about the graph of $y = -f(x)$?
(d) What can be said about the graph of $y = f(-x)$?

In Problems 39–62, graph each function using the techniques of shifting, compressing, stretching, and/or reflecting. Start with the graph of the basic function (for example, $y = x^2$) and show all stages. Be sure to show at least three key points. Find the domain and the range of each function.

39. $f(x) = x^2 - 1$

40. $f(x) = x^2 + 4$

41. $g(x) = x^3 + 1$

42. $g(x) = x^3 - 1$

43. $h(x) = \sqrt{x - 2}$

44. $h(x) = \sqrt{x + 1}$

45. $f(x) = (x - 1)^3 + 2$

46. $f(x) = (x + 2)^3 - 3$

47. $g(x) = 4\sqrt{x}$

48. $g(x) = \frac{1}{2}\sqrt{x}$

49. $f(x) = -\sqrt[3]{x}$

50. $f(x) = -\sqrt{x}$

51. $f(x) = 2(x + 1)^2 - 3$

52. $f(x) = 3(x - 2)^2 + 1$

53. $g(x) = 2\sqrt{x - 2} + 1$

54. $g(x) = 3|x + 1| - 3$

55. $h(x) = \sqrt{-x} - 2$

56. $h(x) = \frac{4}{x} + 2$

57. $f(x) = -(x + 1)^3 - 1$

58. $f(x) = -4\sqrt{x - 1}$

59. $g(x) = 2|1 - x|$

60. $g(x) = 4\sqrt{2 - x}$

61. $h(x) = 2 \operatorname{int}(x - 1)$

62. $h(x) = \operatorname{int}(-x)$

In Problems 63–66, the graph of a function f is illustrated. Use the graph of f as the first step toward graphing each of the following functions:

(a) $F(x) = f(x) + 3$

(b) $G(x) = f(x + 2)$

(c) $P(x) = -f(x)$

(d) $H(x) = f(x + 1) - 2$

(e) $Q(x) = \frac{1}{2}f(x)$

(f) $g(x) = f(-x)$

(g) $h(x) = f(2x)$

63.

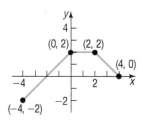

64.

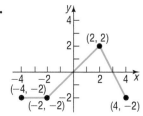

65.

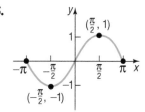

66.

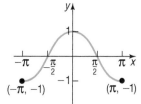

Mixed Practice

In Problems 67–74, complete the square of each quadratic expression. Then graph each function using the technique of shifting. (If necessary, refer to Appendix A, Section A.3 to review completing the square.)

67. $f(x) = x^2 + 2x$

68. $f(x) = x^2 - 6x$

69. $f(x) = x^2 - 8x + 1$

70. $f(x) = x^2 + 4x + 2$

71. $f(x) = 2x^2 - 12x + 19$

72. $f(x) = 3x^2 + 6x + 1$

73. $f(x) = -3x^2 - 12x - 17$

74. $f(x) = -2x^2 - 12x - 13$

Applications and Extensions

75. The equation $y = (x - c)^2$ defines a *family of parabolas,* one parabola for each value of c. On one set of coordinate axes, graph the members of the family for $c = 0$, $c = 3$, and $c = -2$.

76. Repeat Problem 75 for the family of parabolas $y = x^2 + c$.

77. Thermostat Control   Energy conservation experts estimate that homeowners can save 5% to 10% on winter heating bills by programming their thermostats 5 to 10 degrees lower while sleeping. In the given graph, the temperature T (in degrees Fahrenheit) of a home is given as a function of time t (in hours after midnight) over a 24-hour period.

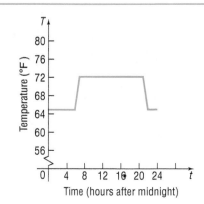

(a) At what temperature is the thermostat set during daytime hours? At what temperature is the thermostat set overnight?

(b) The homeowner reprograms the thermostat to $y = T(t) - 2$. Explain how this affects the temperature in the house. Graph this new function.

(c) The homeowner reprograms the thermostat to $y = T(t + 1)$. Explain how this affects the temperature in the house. Graph this new function.

Source: Roger Albright, 547 Ways to Be Fuel Smart, 2000

78. **Digital Music Revenues** The total projected worldwide digital music revenues R, in millions of dollars, for the years 2005 through 2010 can be estimated by the function

$$R(x) = 170.7x^2 + 1373x + 1080$$

where x is the number of years after 2005.

(a) Find $R(0)$, $R(3)$, and $R(5)$ and explain what each value represents.

(b) Find $r = R(x - 5)$.

(c) Find $r(5)$, $r(8)$, and $r(10)$ and explain what each value represents.

(d) In the model r, what does x represent?

(e) Would there be an advantage in using the model r when estimating the projected revenues for a given year instead of the model R?

Source: eMarketer.com, May 2006

79. **Temperature Measurements** The relationship between the Celsius (°C) and Fahrenheit (°F) scales for measuring temperature is given by the equation

$$F = \frac{9}{5}C + 32$$

The relationship between the Celsius (°C) and Kelvin (K) scales is $K = C + 273$. Graph the equation $F = \frac{9}{5}C + 32$ using degrees Fahrenheit on the y-axis and degrees Celsius on the x-axis. Use the techniques introduced in this section to obtain the graph showing the relationship between Kelvin and Fahrenheit temperatures.

80. **Period of a Pendulum** The period T (in seconds) of a simple pendulum is a function of its length l (in feet) defined by the equation

$$T = 2\pi\sqrt{\frac{l}{g}}$$

where $g \approx 32.2$ feet per second per second is the acceleration of gravity.

(a) Use a graphing utility to graph the function $T = T(l)$.

(b) Now graph the functions $T = T(l + 1)$, $T = T(l + 2)$, and $T = T(l + 3)$.

(c) Discuss how adding to the length l changes the period T.

(d) Now graph the functions $T = T(2l)$, $T = T(3l)$, and $T = T(4l)$.

(e) Discuss how multiplying the length l by factors of 2, 3, and 4 changes the period T.

81. **Cigar Company Profits** The daily profits of a cigar company from selling x cigars are given by

$$p(x) = -0.05x^2 + 100x - 2000$$

The government wishes to impose a tax on cigars (sometimes called a *sin tax*) that gives the company the option of either paying a flat tax of \$10,000 per day or a tax of 10% on profits. As chief financial officer (CFO) of the company, you need to decide which tax is the better option for the company.

(a) On the same screen, graph $Y_1 = p(x) - 10,000$ and $Y_2 = (1 - 0.10)p(x)$.

(b) Based on the graph, which option would you select? Why?

(c) Using the terminology learned in this section, describe each graph in terms of the graph of $p(x)$.

(d) Suppose that the government offered the options of a flat tax of \$4800 or a tax of 10% on profits. Which would you select? Why?

82. The graph of a function f is illustrated in the figure.
(a) Draw the graph of $y = |f(x)|$.
(b) Draw the graph of $y = f(|x|)$.

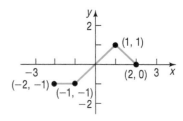

83. The graph of a function f is illustrated in the figure.
(a) Draw the graph of $y = |f(x)|$.
(b) Draw the graph of $y = f(|x|)$.

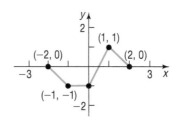

84. Suppose $(1, 3)$ is a point on the graph of $y = f(x)$.
(a) What point is on the graph of $y = f(x + 3) - 5$?
(b) What point is on the graph of $y = -2f(x - 2) + 1$?
(c) What point is on the graph of $y = f(2x + 3)$?

85. Suppose $(-3, 5)$ is a point on the graph of $y = g(x)$.
(a) What point is on the graph of $y = g(x + 1) - 3$?
(b) What point is on the graph of $y = -3g(x - 4) + 3$?
(c) What point is on the graph of $y = g(3x + 9)$?

Explaining Concepts: Discussion and Writing

86. Suppose that the graph of a function f is known. Explain how the graph of $y = 4f(x)$ differs from the graph of $y = f(4x)$.

87. Suppose that the graph of a function f is known. Explain how the graph of $y = f(x) - 2$ differs from the graph of $y = f(x - 2)$.

88. The area under the curve $y = \sqrt{x}$ bounded below by the x-axis and on the right by $x = 4$ is $\dfrac{16}{3}$ square units. Using the ideas presented in this section, what do you think is the area under the curve of $y = \sqrt{-x}$ bounded below by the x-axis and on the left by $x = -4$? Justify your answer.

Interactive Exercises: Exploring Transformations

Ask your instructor if the applets below are of interest to you.

89. Vertical Shifts *Open the vertical shift applet.* Use your mouse to grab the slider and change the value of k. Note the role k plays in the graph of $g(x) = f(x) + k$, where $f(x) = x^2$.

90. Horizontal Shifts *Open the horizontal shift applet.* Use your mouse to grab the slider and change the value of h. Note the role h plays in the graph of $g(x) = f(x - h)$, where $f(x) = x^2$.

91. Vertical Stretches *Open the vertical stretch applet.* Use your mouse to grab the slider and change the value of a. Note the role a plays in the graph of $g(x) = af(x)$, where $f(x) = |x|$.

92. Horizontal Stretches *Open the horizontal stretch applet.*
(a) Use your mouse to grab the slider and change the value of a. Note the role a plays in the graph of $g(x) = f(ax) = \sqrt{ax}$, where $f(x) = \sqrt{x}$. What happens to the points on the graph of g when $0 < a < 1$? What happens to the points on the graph when $a > 1$?
(b) To further understand the concept of horizontal compressions, fill in the spreadsheet to the right of the graph as follows:
(i) What x-coordinate is required on the graph of $g(x) = \sqrt{2x}$, if the y-coordinate is to be 1?

(ii) What x-coordinate is required on the graph of $g(x) = \sqrt{2x}$, if the y-coordinate is to be 2?
(iii) What x-coordinate is required on the graph of $g(x) = \sqrt{2x}$, if the y-coordinate is to be 3?
(iv) What x-coordinate is required on the graph of $g(x) = \sqrt{\dfrac{1}{2}x}$, if the y-coordinate is to be 1?
(v) What x-coordinate is required on the graph of $g(x) = \sqrt{\dfrac{1}{2}x}$, if the y-coordinate is to be 2?
(vi) What x-coordinate is required on the graph of $g(x) = \sqrt{\dfrac{1}{2}x}$, if the y-coordinate is to be 3?

93. Reflection about the y-axis *Open the reflection about the y-axis applet.* Move your mouse to grab the slide and change the value of a from 1 to -1.

94. Reflection about the x-axis *Open the reflection about the x-axis applet.* Move your mouse to grab the slide and change the value of a from 1 to -1.

2.6 Mathematical Models: Building Functions

OBJECTIVE 1 Build and Analyze Functions (p. 103)

1 Build and Analyze Functions

Real-world problems often result in mathematical models that involve functions. These functions need to be constructed or built based on the information given. In building functions, we must be able to translate the verbal description into the language of mathematics. We do this by assigning symbols to represent the independent and dependent variables and then by finding the function or rule that relates these variables.

EXAMPLE 1   **Finding the Distance from the Origin to a Point on a Graph**

Let $P = (x, y)$ be a point on the graph of $y = x^2 - 1$.

(a) Express the distance d from P to the origin O as a function of x.
(b) What is d if $x = 0$?
(c) What is d if $x = 1$?
(d) What is d if $x = \dfrac{\sqrt{2}}{2}$?

(e) Use a graphing utility to graph the function $d = d(x)$, $x \geq 0$. Rounded to two decimal places, find the value(s) of x at which d has a local minimum. [This gives the point(s) on the graph of $y = x^2 - 1$ closest to the origin.]

Figure 60

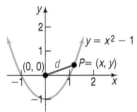

Solution

(a) Figure 60 illustrates the graph of $y = x^2 - 1$. The distance d from P to O is

$$d = \sqrt{(x - 0)^2 + (y - 0)^2} = \sqrt{x^2 + y^2}$$

Since P is a point on the graph of $y = x^2 - 1$, substitute $x^2 - 1$ for y. Then

$$d(x) = \sqrt{x^2 + (x^2 - 1)^2} = \sqrt{x^4 - x^2 + 1}$$

The distance d is expressed as a function of x.

(b) If $x = 0$, the distance d is

$$d(0) = \sqrt{0^4 - 0^2 + 1} = \sqrt{1} = 1$$

(c) If $x = 1$, the distance d is

$$d(1) = \sqrt{1^4 - 1^2 + 1} = 1$$

(d) If $x = \dfrac{\sqrt{2}}{2}$, the distance d is

Figure 61

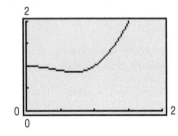

$$d\left(\frac{\sqrt{2}}{2}\right) = \sqrt{\left(\frac{\sqrt{2}}{2}\right)^4 - \left(\frac{\sqrt{2}}{2}\right)^2 + 1} = \sqrt{\frac{1}{4} - \frac{1}{2} + 1} = \frac{\sqrt{3}}{2}$$

(e) Figure 61 shows the graph of $Y_1 = \sqrt{x^4 - x^2 + 1}$. Using the MINIMUM feature on a graphing utility, we find that when $x \approx 0.71$ the value of d is smallest. The local minimum value is $d \approx 0.87$ rounded to two decimal places. Since $d(x)$ is even, by symmetry, it follows that when $x \approx -0.71$ the value of d is also a local minimum value. Since $(\pm 0.71)^2 - 1 \approx -0.50$, the points $(-0.71, -0.50)$ and $(0.71, -0.50)$ on the graph of $y = x^2 - 1$ are closest to the origin.

—Now Work PROBLEM 1

| EXAMPLE 2 | **Area of a Rectangle** |

Figure 62

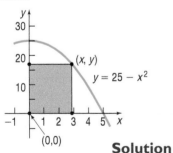

A rectangle has one corner in quadrant I on the graph of $y = 25 - x^2$, another at the origin, a third on the positive y-axis, and the fourth on the positive x-axis. See Figure 62.

(a) Express the area A of the rectangle as a function of x.
(b) What is the domain of A?
(c) Graph $A = A(x)$.
(d) For what value of x is the area largest?

Solution

(a) The area A of the rectangle is $A = xy$, where $y = 25 - x^2$. Substituting this expression for y, we obtain $A(x) = x(25 - x^2) = 25x - x^3$.

(b) Since (x, y) is in quadrant I, we have $x > 0$. Also, $y = 25 - x^2 > 0$, which implies that $x^2 < 25$, so $-5 < x < 5$. Combining these restrictions, we have the domain of A as $\{x | 0 < x < 5\}$, or $(0, 5)$ using interval notation.

(c) See Figure 63 for the graph of $A = A(x)$.

(d) Using MAXIMUM, we find that the maximum area is 48.11 square units at $x = 2.89$ units, each rounded to two decimal places. See Figure 64.

Figure 63

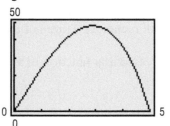

Figure 64

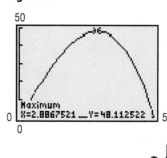

━━━**Now Work** PROBLEM 7

EXAMPLE 3

Making a Playpen*

A manufacturer of children's playpens makes a square model that can be opened at one corner and attached at right angles to a wall or, perhaps, the side of a house. If each side is 3 feet in length, the open configuration doubles the available area in which the child can play from 9 square feet to 18 square feet. See Figure 65.

Now suppose that we place hinges at the outer corners to allow for a configuration like the one shown in Figure 66.

Figure 65

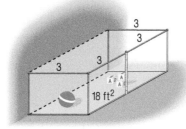

Figure 66

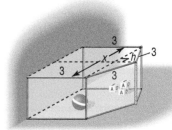

(a) Build a model that expresses the area A of the configuration shown in Figure 66 as a function of the distance x between the two parallel sides.

(b) Find the domain of A.

(c) Find A if $x = 5$.

 (d) Graph $A = A(x)$. For what value of x is the area largest? What is the maximum area?

Solution

(a) Refer to Figure 66. The area A we seek consists of the area of a rectangle (with width 3 and length x) and the area of an isosceles triangle (with base x and two equal sides of length 3). The height h of the triangle may be found using the Pythagorean Theorem.

$$h^2 + \left(\frac{x}{2}\right)^2 = 3^2$$

$$h^2 = 3^2 - \left(\frac{x}{2}\right)^2 = 9 - \frac{x^2}{4} = \frac{36 - x^2}{4}$$

$$h = \frac{1}{2}\sqrt{36 - x^2}$$

---

* Adapted from *Proceedings, Summer Conference for College Teachers on Applied Mathematics* (University of Missouri, Rolla), 1971.

The area A enclosed by the playpen is

$$A = \text{area of rectangle} + \text{area of triangle} = 3x + \frac{1}{2}x\left(\frac{1}{2}\sqrt{36 - x^2}\right)$$

The area A expressed as a function of x is

$$A(x) = 3x + \frac{x\sqrt{36 - x^2}}{4} \qquad \textit{The Model}$$

(b) To find the domain of A, notice that $x > 0$, since x is a length. Also, the expression under the square root must be positive, so

$$36 - x^2 > 0$$
$$x^2 < 36$$
$$-6 < x < 6$$

Figure 67

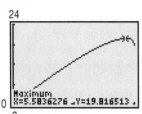

Combining these restrictions, the domain of A is $0 < x < 6$, or $(0, 6)$ using interval notation.

(c) If $x = 5$, the area is

$$A(5) = 3(5) + \frac{5}{4}\sqrt{36 - (5)^2} \approx 19.15 \text{ square feet}$$

If the length of the playpen is 5 feet, its area is 19.15 square feet.

 (d) See Figure 67. The maximum area is about 19.82 square feet, obtained when x is about 5.58 feet.

2.6 Assess Your Understanding

Applications and Extensions

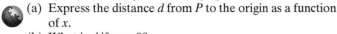

1. Let $P = (x, y)$ be a point on the graph of $y = x^2 - 8$.
   (a) Express the distance d from P to the origin as a function of x.
   (b) What is d if $x = 0$?
   (c) What is d if $x = 1$?
   (d) Use a graphing utility to graph $d = d(x)$.
   (e) For what values of x is d smallest?

2. Let $P = (x, y)$ be a point on the graph of $y = x^2 - 8$.
   (a) Express the distance d from P to the point $(0, -1)$ as a function of x.
   (b) What is d if $x = 0$?
   (c) What is d if $x = -1$?
   (d) Use a graphing utility to graph $d = d(x)$.
   (e) For what values of x is d smallest?

3. Let $P = (x, y)$ be a point on the graph of $y = \sqrt{x}$.
   (a) Express the distance d from P to the point $(1, 0)$ as a function of x.
   (b) Use a graphing utility to graph $d = d(x)$.
   (c) For what values of x is d smallest?

4. Let $P = (x, y)$ be a point on the graph of $y = \dfrac{1}{x}$.
   (a) Express the distance d from P to the origin as a function of x.
   (b) Use a graphing utility to graph $d = d(x)$.
   (c) For what values of x is d smallest?

5. A right triangle has one vertex on the graph of $y = x^3$, $x > 0$, at (x, y), another at the origin, and the third on the positive y-axis at $(0, y)$, as shown in the figure. Express the area A of the triangle as a function of x.

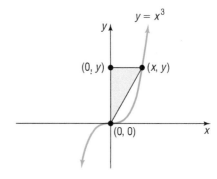

6. A right triangle has one vertex on the graph of $y = 9 - x^2$, $x > 0$, at (x, y), another at the origin, and the third on the positive x-axis at $(x, 0)$. Express the area A of the triangle as a function of x.

7. A rectangle has one corner in quadrant I on the graph of $y = 16 - x^2$, another at the origin, a third on the positive y-axis, and the fourth on the positive x-axis. See the figure.

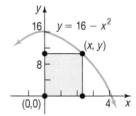

(a) Express the area A of the rectangle as a function of x.
(b) What is the domain of A?
(c) Graph $A = A(x)$. For what value of x is A largest?

8. A rectangle is inscribed in a semicircle of radius 2. See the figure. Let $P = (x, y)$ be the point in quadrant I that is a vertex of the rectangle and is on the circle.

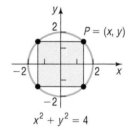

(a) Express the area A of the rectangle as a function of x.
(b) Express the perimeter p of the rectangle as a function of x.
(c) Graph $A = A(x)$. For what value of x is A largest?
(d) Graph $p = p(x)$. For what value of x is p largest?

9. A rectangle is inscribed in a circle of radius 2. See the figure. Let $P = (x, y)$ be the point in quadrant I that is a vertex of the rectangle and is on the circle.

$$x^2 + y^2 = 4$$

(a) Express the area A of the rectangle as a function of x.
(b) Express the perimeter p of the rectangle as a function of x.
(c) Graph $A = A(x)$. For what value of x is A largest?
(d) Graph $p = p(x)$. For what value of x is p largest?

10. A circle of radius r is inscribed in a square. See the figure.

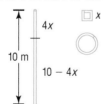

(a) Express the area A of the square as a function of the radius r of the circle.
(b) Express the perimeter p of the square as a function of r.

11. **Geometry** A wire 10 meters long is to be cut into two pieces. One piece will be shaped as a square, and the other piece will be shaped as a circle. See the figure.

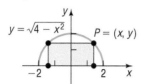

(a) Express the total area A enclosed by the pieces of wire as a function of the length x of a side of the square.
(b) What is the domain of A?
(c) Graph $A = A(x)$. For what value of x is A smallest?

12. **Geometry** A wire 10 meters long is to be cut into two pieces. One piece will be shaped as an equilateral triangle, and the other piece will be shaped as a circle.
(a) Express the total area A enclosed by the pieces of wire as a function of the length x of a side of the equilateral triangle.
(b) What is the domain of A?
(c) Graph $A = A(x)$. For what value of x is A smallest?

13. A wire of length x is bent into the shape of a circle.
(a) Express the circumference C of the circle as a function of x.
(b) Express the area A of the circle as a function of x.

14. A wire of length x is bent into the shape of a square.
(a) Express the perimeter p of the square as a function of x.
(b) Express the area A of the square as a function of x.

15. **Geometry** A semicircle of radius r is inscribed in a rectangle so that the diameter of the semicircle is the length of the rectangle. See the figure.

(a) Express the area A of the rectangle as a function of the radius r of the semicircle.
(b) Express the perimeter p of the rectangle as a function of r.

16. **Geometry** An equilateral triangle is inscribed in a circle of radius r. See the figure. Express the circumference C of the circle as a function of the length x of a side of the triangle.

[**Hint:** First show that $r^2 = \dfrac{x^2}{3}$.]

17. **Geometry** An equilateral triangle is inscribed in a circle of radius r. See the figure in Problem 16. Express the area A within the circle, but outside the triangle, as a function of the length x of a side of the triangle.

18. **Uniform Motion** Two cars leave an intersection at the same time. One is headed south at a constant speed of 30 miles per hour, and the other is headed west at a constant speed of 40 miles per hour (see the figure). Build a model that expresses the distance d between the cars as a function of the time t.

[**Hint:** At $t = 0$, the cars leave the intersection.]

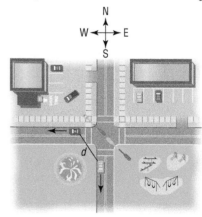

19. Uniform Motion Two cars are approaching an intersection. One is 2 miles south of the intersection and is moving at a constant speed of 30 miles per hour. At the same time, the other car is 3 miles east of the intersection and is moving at a constant speed of 40 miles per hour.

(a) Build a model that expresses the distance d between the cars as a function of time t.

  [**Hint:** At $t = 0$, the cars are 2 miles south and 3 miles east of the intersection, respectively.]

(b) Use a graphing utility to graph $d = d(t)$. For what value of t is d smallest?

20. Inscribing a Cylinder in a Sphere Inscribe a right circular cylinder of height h and radius r in a sphere of fixed radius R. See the illustration. Express the volume V of the cylinder as a function of h.

[**Hint:** $V = \pi r^2 h$. Note also the right triangle.]

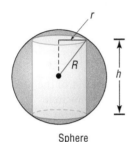

Sphere

21. Inscribing a Cylinder in a Cone Inscribe a right circular cylinder of height h and radius r in a cone of fixed radius R and fixed height H. See the illustration. Express the volume V of the cylinder as a function of r.

[**Hint:** $V = \pi r^2 h$. Note also the similar triangles.]

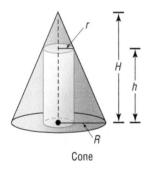

Cone

22. Installing Cable TV MetroMedia Cable is asked to provide service to a customer whose house is located 2 miles from the road along which the cable is buried. The nearest connection box for the cable is located 5 miles down the road. See the figure.

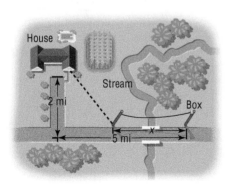

(a) If the installation cost is $500 per mile along the road and $700 per mile off the road, build a model that expresses the total cost C of installation as a function of the distance x (in miles) from the connection box to the point where the cable installation turns off the road. Give the domain.

(b) Compute the cost if $x = 1$ mile.

(c) Compute the cost if $x = 3$ miles.

(d) Graph the function $C = C(x)$. Use TRACE to see how the cost C varies as x changes from 0 to 5.

(e) What value of x results in the least cost?

23. Time Required to Go from an Island to a Town An island is 2 miles from the nearest point P on a straight shoreline. A town is 12 miles down the shore from P. See the illustration.

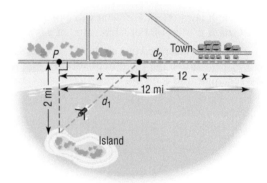

(a) If a person can row a boat at an average speed of 3 miles per hour and the same person can walk 5 miles per hour, build a model that expresses the time T that it takes to go from the island to town as a function of the distance x from P to where the person lands the boat.

(b) What is the domain of T?

(c) How long will it take to travel from the island to town if the person lands the boat 4 miles from P?

(d) How long will it take if the person lands the boat 8 miles from P?

24. Filling a Conical Tank Water is poured into a container in the shape of a right circular cone with radius 4 feet and height 16 feet. See the figure. Express the volume V of the water in the cone as a function of the height h of the water.

[**Hint:** The volume V of a cone of radius r and height h is $V = \dfrac{1}{3}\pi r^2 h$.]

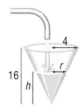

25. Constructing an Open Box An open box with a square base is to be made from a square piece of cardboard 24 inches on a side by cutting out a square from each corner and turning up the sides. See the figure.

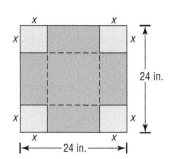

(a) Express the volume V of the box as a function of the length x of the side of the square cut from each corner.

(b) What is the volume if a 3-inch square is cut out?

(c) What is the volume if a 10-inch square is cut out?

(d) Graph $V = V(x)$. For what value of x is V largest?

26. Constructing an Open Box An open box with a square base is required to have a volume of 10 cubic feet.

(a) Express the amount A of material used to make such a box as a function of the length x of a side of the square base.

(b) How much material is required for a base 1 foot by 1 foot?

(c) How much material is required for a base 2 feet by 2 feet?

(d) Use a graphing utility to graph $A = A(x)$. For what value of x is A smallest?

CHAPTER REVIEW

Library of Functions

Constant function (p. 82)

$$f(x) = b$$

The graph is a horizontal line with y-intercept b.

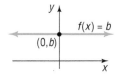

Identity function (p. 83)

$$f(x) = x$$

The graph is a line with slope 1 and y-intercept 0.

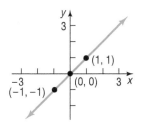

Square function (p. 83)

$$f(x) = x^2$$

The graph is a parabola with intercept at $(0, 0)$.

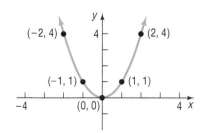

Cube function (p. 83)

$$f(x) = x^3$$

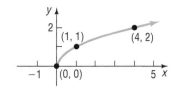

Square root function (p. 83)

$$f(x) = \sqrt{x}$$

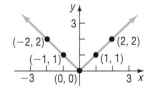

Cube root function (p. 83)

$$f(x) = \sqrt[3]{x}$$

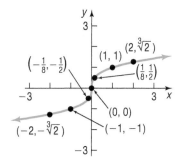

Reciprocal function (p. 84)

$$f(x) = \frac{1}{x}$$

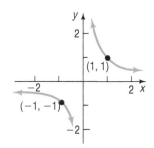

Absolute value function (p. 84)

$$f(x) = |x|$$

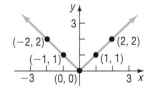

Greatest integer function (p. 84)

$$f(x) = \text{int}(x)$$

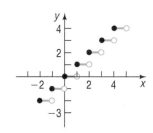

Things to Know

Function (pp. 47–49)	A relation between two sets so that each element x in the first set, the domain, has corresponding to it exactly one element y in the second set. The range is the set of y values of the function for the x values in the domain.
	A function can also be characterized as a set of ordered pairs (x, y) in which no first element is paired with two different second elements.
Function notation (pp. 49–52)	$y = f(x)$
	f is a symbol for the function.
	x is the argument, or independent variable.
	y is the dependent variable.
	$f(x)$ is the value of the function at x, or the image of x.
	A function f may be defined implicitly by an equation involving x and y or explicitly by writing $y = f(x)$.
Difference quotient of f (pp. 51 and 80)	$\dfrac{f(x + h) - f(x)}{h} \quad h \neq 0$
Domain (pp. 52–54)	If unspecified, the domain of a function f defined by an equation is the largest set of real numbers for which $f(x)$ is a real number.
Vertical-line test (p. 60)	A set of points in the plane is the graph of a function if and only if every vertical line intersects the graph in at most one point.
Even function f (p. 69)	$f(-x) = f(x)$ for every x in the domain ($-x$ must also be in the domain).
Odd function f (p. 69)	$f(-x) = -f(x)$ for every x in the domain ($-x$ must also be in the domain).
Increasing function (p. 71)	A function f is increasing on an open interval I if, for any choice of x_1 and x_2 in I, with $x_1 < x_2$, we have $f(x_1) < f(x_2)$.
Decreasing function (p. 71)	A function f is decreasing on an open interval I if, for any choice of x_1 and x_2 in I, with $x_1 < x_2$, we have $f(x_1) > f(x_2)$.
Constant function (p. 71)	A function f is constant on an open interval I if, for all choices of x in I, the values of $f(x)$ are equal.
Local maximum (p. 72)	A function f has a local maximum at c if there is an open interval I containing c so that, for all x in I, $f(x) \leq f(c)$.
Local minimum (p. 72)	A function f has a local minimum at c if there is an open interval I containing c so that, for all x in I, $f(x) \geq f(c)$.
Absolute maximum and Absolute minimum (p. 72)	Let f denote a function defined on some interval I. If there is a number u in I for which $f(x) \leq f(u)$ for all x in I, then $f(u)$ is the absolute maximum of f on I and we say the absolute maximum of f occurs at u. If there is a number v in I for which $f(x) \geq f(v)$, for all x in I, then $f(v)$ is the absolute minimum of f on I and we say the absolute minimum of f occurs at v.
Average rate of change of a function (p. 74)	The average rate of change of f from a to b is $$\frac{\Delta y}{\Delta x} = \frac{f(b) - f(a)}{b - a} \quad a \neq b$$

Objectives

Section		You should be able to . . .	Examples	Review Exercises
2.1	1	Determine whether a relation represents a function (p. 46)	1–5	1, 2
	2	Find the value of a function (p. 49)	6, 7	3–8, 23, 24, 71, 72
	3	Find the domain of a function defined by an equation (p. 52)	8, 9	9–16
	4	Form the sum, difference, product, and quotient of two functions (p. 54)	10	17–22
2.2	1	Identify the graph of a function (p. 60)	1	47–50
	2	Obtain information from or about the graph of a function (p. 61)	2–4	25(a)–(f), 26(a)–(f), 27(a), 27(e), 27(g), 28(a), 28(e), 28(g)
2.3	1	Determine even and odd functions from a graph (p. 69)	1	27(f), 28(f)
	2	Identify even and odd functions from the equation (p. 70)	2	29–36
	3	Use a graph to determine where a function is increasing, decreasing, or constant (p. 70)	3	27(b), 28(b)

Section	You should be able to . . .	Examples	Review Exercises
	4 Use a graph to locate local maxima and local minima (p. 71)	4	27(c), 28(c)
	5 Use a graph to locate the absolute maximum and the absolute minimum (p. 72)	5	27(d), 28(d)
	📱 6 Use a graphing utility to approximate local maxima and local minima and to determine where a function is increasing or decreasing (p. 74)	6	37–40, 74(d), 75(b)
	7 Find the average rate of change of a function (p. 74)	7, 8	41–46
2.4	1 Graph the functions listed in the library of functions (p. 80)	1, 2	51–54
	2 Graph piecewise-defined functions (p. 85)	3, 4	67–70
2.5	1 Graph functions using vertical and horizontal shifts (p. 90)	1–5	25(f), 26(f), 26(g) 55, 56, 59–66
	2 Graph functions using compressions and stretches (p. 93)	6–8	25(g), 26(h), 57, 58, 65, 66
	3 Graph functions using reflections about the x-axis or y-axis (p. 96)	9–10	25(h), 57, 61, 62, 66
2.6	1 Build and analyze functions (p. 103)	1–3	73–75

Review Exercises

In Problems 1 and 2, determine whether each relation represents a function. For each function, state the domain and range.

1. $\{(-1, 0), (2, 3), (4, 0)\}$

2. $\{(4, -1), (2, 1), (4, 2)\}$

In Problems 3–8, find the following for each function:

(a) $f(2)$ (b) $f(-2)$ (c) $f(-x)$ (d) $-f(x)$ (e) $f(x - 2)$ (f) $f(2x)$

3. $f(x) = \dfrac{3x}{x^2 - 1}$

4. $f(x) = \dfrac{x^2}{x + 1}$

5. $f(x) = \sqrt{x^2 - 4}$

6. $f(x) = |x^2 - 4|$

7. $f(x) = \dfrac{x^2 - 4}{x^2}$

8. $f(x) = \dfrac{x^3}{x^2 - 9}$

In Problems 9–16, find the domain of each function.

9. $f(x) = \dfrac{x}{x^2 - 9}$

10. $f(x) = \dfrac{3x^2}{x - 2}$

11. $f(x) = \sqrt{2 - x}$

12. $f(x) = \sqrt{x + 2}$

13. $h(x) = \dfrac{\sqrt{x}}{|x|}$

14. $g(x) = \dfrac{|x|}{x}$

15. $f(x) = \dfrac{x}{x^2 + 2x - 3}$

16. $F(x) = \dfrac{1}{x^2 - 3x - 4}$

In Problems 17–22, find $f + g$, $f - g$, $f \cdot g$, and $\dfrac{f}{g}$ for each pair of functions. State the domain of each of these functions.

17. $f(x) = 2 - x;\ \ g(x) = 3x + 1$

18. $f(x) = 2x - 1;\ \ g(x) = 2x + 1$

19. $f(x) = 3x^2 + x + 1;\ \ g(x) = 3x$

20. $f(x) = 3x;\ \ g(x) = 1 + x + x^2$

21. $f(x) = \dfrac{x + 1}{x - 1};\ \ g(x) = \dfrac{1}{x}$

22. $f(x) = \dfrac{1}{x - 3};\ \ g(x) = \dfrac{3}{x}$

In Problems 23 and 24, find the difference quotient of each function f; that is, find

$$\frac{f(x + h) - f(x)}{h} \qquad h \neq 0$$

23. $f(x) = -2x^2 + x + 1$

24. $f(x) = 3x^2 - 2x + 4$

25. Using the graph of the function f shown:

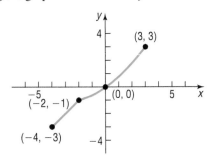

(a) Find the domain and the range of f.
(b) List the intercepts.
(c) Find $f(-2)$.
(d) For what value of x does $f(x) = -3$?
(e) Solve $f(x) > 0$.
(f) Graph $y = f(x - 3)$.
(g) Graph $y = f\left(\dfrac{1}{2}x\right)$.
(h) Graph $y = -f(x)$.

26. Using the graph of the function g shown:

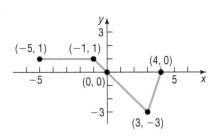

(a) Find the domain and the range of g.
(b) Find $g(-1)$.
(c) List the intercepts.
(d) For what value of x does $g(x) = -3$?
(e) Solve $g(x) > 0$.
(f) Graph $y = g(x - 2)$.
(g) Graph $y = g(x) + 1$.
(h) Graph $y = 2g(x)$.

In Problems 27 and 28, use the graph of the function f to find:

(a) The domain and the range of f.
(b) The intervals on which f is increasing, decreasing, or constant.
(c) The local minimum values and local maximum values.
(d) The absolute maximum and absolute minimum.
(e) Whether the graph is symmetric with respect to the x-axis, the y-axis, or the origin.
(f) Whether the function is even, odd, or neither.
(g) The intercepts, if any.

27.

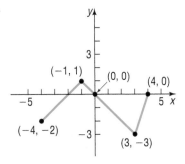

28.

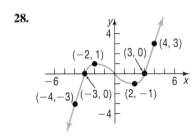

In Problems 29–36, determine (algebraically) whether the given function is even, odd, or neither.

29. $f(x) = x^3 - 4x$

30. $g(x) = \dfrac{4 + x^2}{1 + x^4}$

31. $h(x) = \dfrac{1}{x^4} + \dfrac{1}{x^2} + 1$

32. $F(x) = \sqrt{1 - x^3}$

33. $G(x) = 1 - x + x^3$

34. $H(x) = 1 + x + x^2$

35. $f(x) = \dfrac{x}{1 + x^2}$

36. $g(x) = \dfrac{1 + x^2}{x^3}$

In Problems 37–40, use a graphing utility to graph each function over the indicated interval. Approximate any local maximum values and local minimum values. Determine where the function is increasing and where it is decreasing.

37. $f(x) = 2x^3 - 5x + 1$ $(-3, 3)$

38. $f(x) = -x^3 + 3x - 5$ $(-3, 3)$

39. $f(x) = 2x^4 - 5x^3 + 2x + 1$ $(-2, 3)$

40. $f(x) = -x^4 + 3x^3 - 4x + 3$ $(-2, 3)$

In Problems 41 and 42, find the average rate of change of f:

(a) From 1 to 2   *(b) From 0 to 1*   *(c) From 2 to 4*

41. $f(x) = 8x^2 - x$

42. $f(x) = 2x^3 + x$

In Problems 43–46, find the average rate of change from 2 to 3 for each function f. Be sure to simplify.

43. $f(x) = 2 - 5x$ **44.** $f(x) = 2x^2 + 7$ **45.** $f(x) = 3x - 4x^2$ **46.** $f(x) = x^2 - 3x + 2$

In Problems 47–50, is the graph shown the graph of a function?

47.

48.

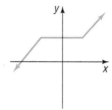

49.

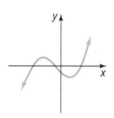

50.

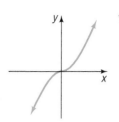

In Problems 51–54, sketch the graph of each function. Be sure to label at least three points.

51. $f(x) = |x|$

52. $f(x) = \sqrt[3]{x}$

53. $f(x) = \sqrt{x}$

54. $f(x) = \dfrac{1}{x}$

In Problems 55–66, graph each function using the techniques of shifting, compressing or stretching, and reflections. Identify any intercepts on the graph. State the domain and, based on the graph, find the range.

55. $F(x) = |x| - 4$

56. $f(x) = |x| + 4$

57. $g(x) = -2|x|$

58. $g(x) = \dfrac{1}{2}|x|$

59. $h(x) = \sqrt{x - 1}$

60. $h(x) = \sqrt{x} - 1$

61. $f(x) = \sqrt{1 - x}$

62. $f(x) = -\sqrt{x + 3}$

63. $h(x) = (x - 1)^2 + 2$

64. $h(x) = (x + 2)^2 - 3$

65. $g(x) = 3(x - 1)^3 + 1$

66. $g(x) = -2(x + 2)^3 - 8$

In Problems 67–70,

(a) *Find the domain of each function.*
(b) *Locate any intercepts.*
(c) *Graph each function.*
(d) *Based on the graph, find the range.*
(e) *Is f continuous on its domain?*

67. $f(x) = \begin{cases} 3x & \text{if } -2 < x \le 1 \\ x + 1 & \text{if } x > 1 \end{cases}$

68. $f(x) = \begin{cases} x - 1 & \text{if } -3 < x < 0 \\ 3x - 1 & \text{if } x \ge 0 \end{cases}$

69. $f(x) = \begin{cases} x & \text{if } -4 \le x < 0 \\ 1 & \text{if } x = 0 \\ 3x & \text{if } x > 0 \end{cases}$

70. $f(x) = \begin{cases} x^2 & \text{if } -2 \le x \le 2 \\ 2x - 1 & \text{if } x > 2 \end{cases}$

71. A function f is defined by

$$f(x) = \frac{Ax + 5}{6x - 2}$$

If $f(1) = 4$, find A.

72. A function g is defined by

$$g(x) = \frac{A}{x} + \frac{8}{x^2}$$

If $g(-1) = 0$, find A.

---

73. Page Design A page with dimensions of $8\dfrac{1}{2}$ inches by 11 inches has a border of uniform width x surrounding the printed matter of the page, as shown in the figure.
(a) Develop a model that expresses the area A of the printed part of the page as a function of the width x of the border.
(b) Give the domain and the range of A.
(c) Find the area of the printed page for borders of widths 1 inch, 1.2 inches, and 1.5 inches.
(d) Graph the function $A = A(x)$.

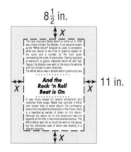

$8\frac{1}{2}$ in.

11 in.

And the
Rock 'n Roll
Beat is On

74. Constructing a Closed Box A closed box with a square base is required to have a volume of 10 cubic feet.
(a) Build a model that expresses the amount A of material used to make such a box as a function of the length x of a side of the square base.
(b) How much material is required for a base 1 foot by 1 foot?
(c) How much material is required for a base 2 feet by 2 feet?
(d) Graph $A = A(x)$. For what value of x is A smallest?

75. A rectangle has one vertex in quadrant I on the graph of $y = 10 - x^2$, another at the origin, one on the positive x-axis, and one on the positive y-axis.
(a) Express the area A of the rectangle as a function of x.
(b) Find the largest area A that can be enclosed by the rectangle.

CHAPTER TEST

CHAPTER
Test Prep
VIDEOS

The Chapter Test Prep Videos are step-by-step test solutions available in the Video Resources DVD, in *MyMathLab*, or on this text's You Tube Channel. Flip back to the Student Resources page to see the exact web address for this text's YouTube channel.

1. Determine whether each relation represents a function. For each function, state the domain and the range.
   (a) $\{(2, 5), (4, 6), (6, 7), (8, 8)\}$
   (b) $\{(1, 3), (4, -2), (-3, 5), (1, 7)\}$
   (c)

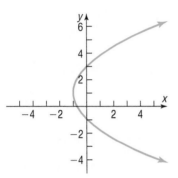

   (d)

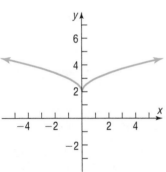

In Problems 2–4, find the domain of each function and evaluate each function at $x = -1$.

2. $f(x) = \sqrt{4 - 5x}$

3. $g(x) = \dfrac{x + 2}{|x + 2|}$

4. $h(x) = \dfrac{x - 4}{x^2 + 5x - 36}$

5. Using the graph of the function f:

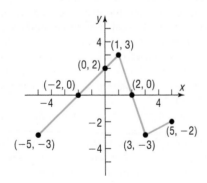

   (a) Find the domain and the range of f.
   (b) List the intercepts.
   (c) Find $f(1)$.
   (d) For what value(s) of x does $f(x) = -3$?
   (e) Solve $f(x) < 0$.

6. Use a graphing utility to graph the function $f(x) = -x^4 + 2x^3 + 4x^2 - 2$ on the interval $(-5, 5)$. Approximate any local maximum values and local minimum values rounded to two decimal places. Determine where the function is increasing and where it is decreasing.

7. Consider the function $g(x) = \begin{cases} 2x + 1 & \text{if } x < -1 \\ x - 4 & \text{if } x \geq -1 \end{cases}$
   (a) Graph the function.
   (b) List the intercepts.
   (c) Find $g(-5)$.
   (d) Find $g(2)$.

8. For the function $f(x) = 3x^2 - 2x + 4$, find the average rate of change of f from 3 to 4.

9. For the functions $f(x) = 2x^2 + 1$ and $g(x) = 3x - 2$, find the following and simplify:
   (a) $f - g$
   (b) $f \cdot g$
   (c) $f(x + h) - f(x)$

10. Graph each function using the techniques of shifting, compressing or stretching, and reflections. Start with the graph of the basic function and show all stages.
    (a) $h(x) = -2(x + 1)^3 + 3$
    (b) $g(x) = |x + 4| + 2$

11. The variable interest rate on a student loan changes each July 1 based on the bank prime loan rate. For the years 1992–2007, this rate can be approximated by the model $r(x) = -0.115x^2 + 1.183x + 5.623$, where x is the number of years since 1992 and r is the interest rate as a percent.
    (a) Use a graphing utility to estimate the highest rate during this time period. During which year was the interest rate the highest?
    (b) Use the model to estimate the rate in 2010. Does this value seem reasonable?

    Source: U.S. Federal Reserve

12. A community skating rink is in the shape of a rectangle with semicircles attached at the ends. The length of the rectangle is 20 feet less than twice the width. The thickness of the ice is 0.75 inch.
    (a) Build a model that expresses the ice volume, V, as a function of the width, x.
    (b) How much ice is in the rink if the width is 90 feet?

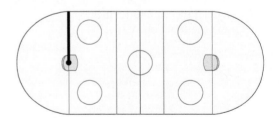

CUMULATIVE REVIEW

In Problems 1–6, find the real solutions of each equation.

1. $3x - 8 = 10$

2. $3x^2 - x = 0$

3. $x^2 - 8x - 9 = 0$

4. $6x^2 - 5x + 1 = 0$

5. $|2x + 3| = 4$

6. $\sqrt{2x + 3} = 2$

In Problems 7–9, solve each inequality. Graph the solution set.

7. $2 - 3x > 6$

8. $|2x - 5| < 3$

9. $|4x + 1| \geq 7$

10. (a) Find the distance from $P_1 = (-2, -3)$ to $P_2 = (3, -5)$.
(b) What is the midpoint of the line segment from P_1 to P_2?
(c) What is the slope of the line containing the points P_1 and P_2?

In Problems 11–14, graph each equation.

11. $3x - 2y = 12$

12. $x = y^2$

13. $x^2 + (y - 3)^2 = 16$

14. $y = \sqrt{x}$

15. For the equation $3x^2 - 4y = 12$, find the intercepts and check for symmetry.

16. Find the slope–intercept form of the equation of the line containing the points $(-2, 4)$ and $(6, 8)$.

In Problems 17–19, graph each function.

17. $f(x) = (x + 2)^2 - 3$

18. $f(x) = \dfrac{1}{x}$

19. $f(x) = \begin{cases} 2 - x & \text{if } x \leq 2 \\ |x| & \text{if } x > 2 \end{cases}$

CHAPTER PROJECTS

 Internet-based Project

I. Choosing a Cellular Telephone Plan Collect information from your family, friends, or consumer agencies such as Consumer Reports. Then decide on a cellular telephone provider, choosing the company that you feel offers the best service. Once you have selected a service provider, research the various types of individual plans offered by the company by visiting the provider's website.

1. Suppose you expect to use 400 anytime minutes without a texting or data plan. What would be the monthly cost of each plan you are considering?

2. Suppose you expect to use 600 anytime minutes with unlimited texting, but no data plan. What would be the monthly cost of each plan you are considering?

3. Suppose you expect to use 500 anytime minutes with unlimited texting and an unlimited data plan. What would be the monthly cost of each plan you are considering?

4. Suppose you expect to use 500 anytime minutes with unlimited texting and 20 MB of data. What would be the monthly cost of each plan you are considering?

5. Build a model that describes the monthly cost C as a function of the number of anytime minutes used m assuming unlimited texting and 20 MB of data each month for each plan you are considering.

6. Graph each function from Problem 5.

7. Based on your particular usage, which plan is best for you?

8. Now, develop an Excel spreadsheet to analyze the various plans you are considering. Suppose you want a plan that offers 700 anytime minutes with additional minutes costing $0.40 per minute that costs $39.99 per month. In addition, you want unlimited texting, which costs an additional $20 per month, and a data plan that offers up to 25 MB of data each month, with each additional MB costing $0.20. Because cellular telephone plans cost structure is based on piecewise-defined functions, we need "if-then" statements within Excel to analyze the cost of the plan. Use the Excel spreadsheet below as a guide in developing your worksheet. Enter into your spreadsheet a variety of possible minutes and data used to help arrive at a decision regarding which plan is best for you.

9. Write a paragraph supporting the choice in plans that best meets your needs.

10. How are "if/then" loops similar to a piecewise-defined function?

	A	B	C	D
1				
2	Monthly Fee	$ 39.99		
3	Alloted number of anytime minutes	700		
4	Number of anytime minutes used:	700		
5	Cost per additional minute	$ 0.40		
6	Monthly cost of text messaging:	$ 20.00		
7	Monthly cost of data plan	$ 9.99		
8	Alloted data per month (MB)	25		
9	Data used	30		
10	Cost per additional MB of data	$ 0.20		
11				
12	Cost of phone minutes	=IF(B4<B3,B2,B2+B5*(B4-B3))		
13	Cost of data	=IF(B9<B8,B7,B7+B10*(B9-B8))		
14				
15	Total Cost	=B6+B12+B13		
16				

The following projects are available on the Instructor's Resource Center (IRC):

II. Project at Motorola: *Wireless Internet Service* Use functions and their graphs to analyze the total cost of various wireless Internet service plans.

III. Cost of Cable When government regulations and customer preference influence the path of a new cable line, the Pythagorean Theorem can be used to assess the cost of installation.

IV. Oil Spill Functions are used to analyze the size and spread of an oil spill from a leaking tanker.

Citation: Excel © 2010 Microsoft Corporation. Used with permission from Microsoft.

Linear and Quadratic Functions

3

Outline

The Beta of a Stock

Investing in the stock market can be rewarding and fun, but how does one go about selecting which stocks to purchase? Financial investment firms hire thousands of analysts who track individual stocks (equities) and assess the value of the underlying company. One measure the analysts consider is the *beta* of the stock. **Beta** measures the relative risk of an individual company's equity to that of a market basket of stocks, such as the Standard & Poor's 500. But how is beta computed?

 —*See the Internet-based Chapter Project*—

◁ **A Look Back** Up to now, our discussion has focused on graphs of equations and functions. We learned how to graph equations using the point-plotting method, intercepts, and the tests for symmetry. In addition, we learned what a function is and how to identify whether a relation represents a function. We also discussed properties of functions, such as domain/range, increasing/decreasing, even/odd, and average rate of change.

A Look Ahead ▷ Going forward, we look at classes of functions. In this chapter, we focus on linear and quadratic functions, their properties, and applications.

3.1 Linear Functions and Their Properties

PREPARING FOR THIS SECTION *Before getting started, review the following:*

- Lines (Section 1.3, pp. 19–27)
- Graphs of Equations in Two Variables; Intercepts; Symmetry (Section 1.2, pp. 9–16)
- Solving Equations (Appendix A, Section A.6, pp. A44–A51)

- Functions (Section 2.1, pp. 46–54)
- The Graph of a Function (Section 2.2, pp. 60–63)
- Properties of Functions (Section 2.3, pp. 68–76)

Now Work the *'Are You Prepared?'* problems on page 124.

OBJECTIVES 1 Graph Linear Functions (p. 118)
      2 Use Average Rate of Change to Identify Linear Functions (p. 118)
      3 Determine Whether a Linear Function Is Increasing, Decreasing, or Constant (p. 121)
      4 Build Linear Models from Verbal Descriptions (p. 122)

1 Graph Linear Functions

In Section 1.3 we discussed lines. In particular, for nonvertical lines we developed the slope–intercept form of the equation of a line $y = mx + b$. When we write the slope–intercept form of a line using function notation, we have a *linear function*.

DEFINITION

A **linear function** is a function of the form

$$f(x) = mx + b$$

The graph of a linear function is a line with slope m and y-intercept b. Its domain is the set of all real numbers.

Functions that are not linear are said to be **nonlinear.**

EXAMPLE 1

Graphing a Linear Function

Graph the linear function: $f(x) = -3x + 7$

Figure 1

Solution This is a linear function with slope $m = -3$ and y-intercept $b = 7$. To graph this function, we plot the point $(0, 7)$, the y-intercept, and use the slope to find an additional point by moving right 1 unit and down 3 units. See Figure 1.

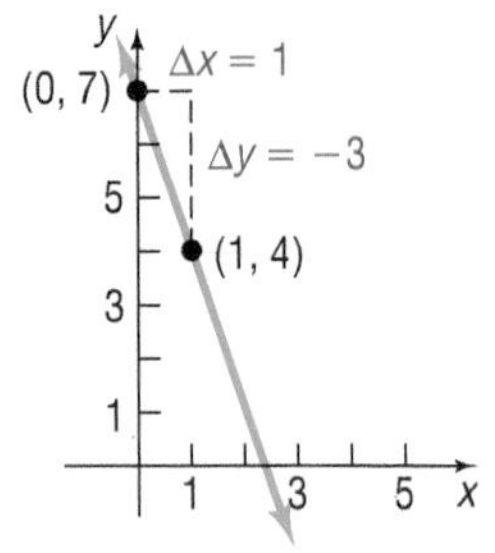

Alternatively, we could have found an additional point by evaluating the function at some $x \neq 0$. For $x = 1$, we find $f(1) = -3(1) + 7 = 4$ and obtain the point $(1, 4)$ on the graph.

Now Work PROBLEMS 13(a) AND (b)

2 Use Average Rate of Change to Identify Linear Functions

Look at Table 1, which shows certain values of the independent variable x and corresponding values of the dependent variable y for the function $f(x) = -3x + 7$. Notice that as the value of the independent variable, x, increases by 1 the value of the dependent variable y decreases by 3. That is, the average rate of change of y with respect to x is a constant, -3.

Table 1

x	$y = f(x) = -3x + 7$	Average Rate of Change $= \dfrac{\Delta y}{\Delta x}$
−2	13	
		$\dfrac{10 - 13}{-1 - (-2)} = \dfrac{-3}{1} = -3$
−1	10	
		$\dfrac{7 - 10}{0 - (-1)} = \dfrac{-3}{1} = -3$
0	7	
		−3
1	4	
		−3
2	1	
		−3
3	−2	

It is not a coincidence that the average rate of change of the linear function $f(x) = -3x + 7$ is the slope of the linear function. That is, $\dfrac{\Delta y}{\Delta x} = m = -3$. The following theorem states this fact.

THEOREM

Average Rate of Change of a Linear Function

Linear functions have a constant average rate of change. That is, the average rate of change of a linear function $f(x) = mx + b$ is

$$\frac{\Delta y}{\Delta x} = m$$

Proof   The average rate of change of $f(x) = mx + b$ from x_1 to x_2, $x_1 \neq x_2$, is

$$\frac{\Delta y}{\Delta x} = \frac{f(x_2) - f(x_1)}{x_2 - x_1} = \frac{(mx_2 + b) - (mx_1 + b)}{x_2 - x_1}$$

$$= \frac{mx_2 - mx_1}{x_2 - x_1} = \frac{m(x_2 - x_1)}{x_2 - x_1} = m \qquad ▪$$

Based on the theorem just proved, the average rate of change of the function $g(x) = -\dfrac{2}{5}x + 5$ is $-\dfrac{2}{5}$.

━━━━ **Now Work** PROBLEM 13(c)

As it turns out, only linear functions have a constant average rate of change. Because of this, we can use the average rate of change to determine whether a function is linear or not. This is especially useful if the function is defined by a data set.

EXAMPLE 2

Using the Average Rate of Change to Identify Linear Functions

(a) A strain of E-coli Beu 397-recA441 is placed into a Petri dish at 30° Celsius and allowed to grow. The data shown in Table 2 on page 120 are collected. The population is measured in grams and the time in hours. Plot the ordered pairs (x, y) in the Cartesian plane and use the average rate of change to determine whether the function is linear.

(b) The data in Table 3 represent the maximum number of heartbeats that a healthy individual should have during a 15-second interval of time while exercising for different ages. Plot the ordered pairs (x, y) in the Cartesian plane and use the average rate of change to determine whether the function is linear.

Table 2

Time (hours), x	Population (grams), y	(x, y)
0	0.09	(0, 0.09)
1	0.12	(1, 0.12)
2	0.16	(2, 0.16)
3	0.22	(3, 0.22)
4	0.29	(4, 0.29)
5	0.39	(5, 0.39)

Table 3

Age, x	Maximum Number of Heartbeats, y	(x, y)
20	50	(20, 50)
30	47.5	(30, 47.5)
40	45	(40, 45)
50	42.5	(50, 42.5)
60	40	(60, 40)
70	37.5	(70, 37.5)

Source: American Heart Association

Solution Compute the average rate of change of each function. If the average rate of change is constant, the function is linear. If the average rate of change is not constant, the function is nonlinear.

(a) Figure 2 shows the points listed in Table 2 plotted in the Cartesian plane. Notice that it is impossible to draw a straight line that contains all the points. Table 4 displays the average rate of change of the population.

Figure 2

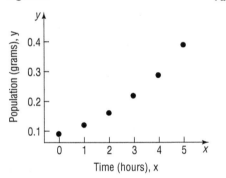

Population (grams), y vs. Time (hours), x

Table 4

Time (hours), x	Population (grams), y	Average Rate of Change $= \dfrac{\Delta y}{\Delta x}$
0	0.09	
		$\dfrac{0.12 - 0.09}{1 - 0} = 0.03$
1	0.12	
		0.04
2	0.16	
		0.06
3	0.22	
		0.07
4	0.29	
		0.10
5	0.39	

Because the average rate of change is not constant, we know that the function is not linear. In fact, because the average rate of change is increasing as the value of the independent variable increases, the function is increasing at an increasing rate. So not only is the population increasing over time, but it is also growing more rapidly as time passes.

(b) Figure 3 shows the points listed in Table 3 plotted in the Cartesian plane. We can see that the data in Figure 3 lie on a straight line. Table 5 contains the average rate of change of the maximum number of heartbeats. The average rate of change of the heartbeat data is constant, -0.25 beat per year, so the function is linear.

Figure 3

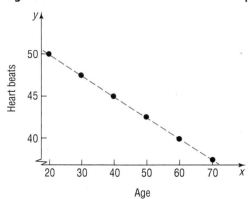

Table 5

Age, x	Maximum Number of Heartbeats, y	Average Rate of Change $= \dfrac{\Delta y}{\Delta x}$
20	50	
30	47.5	$\dfrac{47.5 - 50}{30 - 20} = -0.25$
40	45	-0.25
50	42.5	-0.25
60	40	-0.25
70	37.5	-0.25

Now Work PROBLEM 21

3 Determine Whether a Linear Function Is Increasing, Decreasing, or Constant

Look back at the Seeing the Concept on page 21. When the slope m of a linear function is positive $(m > 0)$, the line slants upward from left to right. When the slope m of a linear function is negative $(m < 0)$, the line slants downward from left to right. When the slope m of a linear function is zero $(m = 0)$, the line is horizontal.

THEOREM

Increasing, Decreasing, and Constant Linear Functions

A linear function $f(x) = mx + b$ is increasing over its domain if its slope, m, is positive. It is decreasing over its domain if its slope, m, is negative. It is constant over its domain if its slope, m, is zero.

EXAMPLE 3

Determining Whether a Linear Function Is Increasing, Decreasing, or Constant

Determine whether the following linear functions are increasing, decreasing, or constant.

(a) $f(x) = 5x - 2$ (b) $g(x) = -2x + 8$

(c) $s(t) = \dfrac{3}{4}t - 4$ (d) $h(z) = 7$

Solution

(a) For the linear function $f(x) = 5x - 2$, the slope is 5, which is positive. The function f is increasing on the interval $(-\infty, \infty)$.

(b) For the linear function $g(x) = -2x + 8$, the slope is -2, which is negative. The function g is decreasing on the interval $(-\infty, \infty)$.

(c) For the linear function $s(t) = \dfrac{3}{4}t - 4$, the slope is $\dfrac{3}{4}$, which is positive. The function s is increasing on the interval $(-\infty, \infty)$.

(d) We can write the linear function h as $h(z) = 0z + 7$. Because the slope is 0, the function h is constant on the interval $(-\infty, \infty)$.

Now Work PROBLEM 13 (d)

4 Build Linear Models from Verbal Descriptions

When the average rate of change of a function is constant, we can use a linear function to model the relation between the two variables. For example, if your phone company charges you $0.07 per minute to talk regardless of the number of minutes used, we can model the relation between the cost C and minutes used x as the linear function $C(x) = 0.07x$, with slope $m = \dfrac{0.07 \, \text{dollar}}{1 \, \text{minute}}$.

Modeling with a Linear Function

If the average rate of change of a function is a constant m, a linear function f can be used to model the relation between the two variables as follows:

$$f(x) = mx + b$$

where b is the value of f at 0; that is, $b = f(0)$.

EXAMPLE 4

Straight-line Depreciation

Book value is the value of an asset that a company uses to create its balance sheet. Some companies depreciate their assets using straight-line depreciation so that the value of the asset declines by a fixed amount each year. The amount of the decline depends on the useful life that the company places on the asset. Suppose that a company just purchased a fleet of new cars for its sales force at a cost of $28,000 per car. The company chooses to depreciate each vehicle using the straight-line method over 7 years. This means that each car will depreciate by $\dfrac{\$28,000}{7} = \$4000$ per year.

(a) Write a linear function that expresses the book value V of each car as a function of its age, x.
(b) Graph the linear function.
(c) What is the book value of each car after 3 years?
(d) Interpret the slope.
(e) When will the book value of each car be $8000?
  [**Hint:** Solve the equation $V(x) = 8000$.]

Solution

(a) If we let $V(x)$ represent the value of each car after x years, then $V(0)$ represents the original value of each car, so $V(0) = \$28,000$. The y-intercept of the linear function is $28,000. Because each car depreciates by $4000 per year, the slope of the linear function is -4000. The linear function that represents the book value V of each car after x years is

$$V(x) = -4000x + 28,000$$

(b) Figure 4 shows the graph of V.
(c) The book value of each car after 3 years is

$$V(3) = -4000(3) + 28,000$$
$$= \$16,000$$

(d) Since the slope of $V(x) = -4000x + 28,000$ is -4000, the average rate of change of book value is $-\$4000$/year. So for each additional year that passes the book value of the car decreases by $4000.

Figure 4

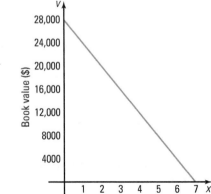

Age of vehicle (years)

(e) To find when the book value will be $8000, solve the equation

$$V(x) = 8000$$
$$-4000x + 28{,}000 = 8000$$
$$-4000x = -20{,}000 \qquad \text{Subtract 28,000 from each side.}$$
$$x = \frac{-20{,}000}{-4000} = 5 \qquad \text{Divide by } -4000.$$

The car will have a book value of $8000 when it is 5 years old.

Now Work PROBLEM 45

EXAMPLE 5

Supply and Demand

The **quantity supplied** of a good is the amount of a product that a company is willing to make available for sale at a given price. The **quantity demanded** of a good is the amount of a product that consumers are willing to purchase at a given price. Suppose that the quantity supplied, S, and quantity demanded, D, of cellular telephones each month are given by the following functions:

$$S(p) = 60p - 900$$
$$D(p) = -15p + 2850$$

where p is the price (in dollars) of the telephone.

(a) The **equilibrium price** of a product is defined as the price at which quantity supplied equals quantity demanded. That is, the equilibrium price is the price at which $S(p) = D(p)$. Find the equilibrium price of cellular telephones. What is the **equilibrium quantity,** the amount demanded (or supplied) at the equilibrium price?

(b) Determine the prices for which quantity supplied is greater than quantity demanded. That is, solve the inequality $S(p) > D(p)$.

(c) Graph $S = S(p), D = D(p)$ and label the equilibrium price.

Solution

(a) To find the equilibrium price, solve the equation $S(p) = D(p)$.

$$60p - 900 = -15p + 2850 \qquad \begin{array}{l} S(p) = 60p - 900; \\ D(p) = -15p + 2850 \end{array}$$
$$60p = -15p + 3750 \qquad \text{Add 900 to each side.}$$
$$75p = 3750 \qquad \text{Add 15p to each side.}$$
$$p = 50 \qquad \text{Divide each side by 75.}$$

The equilibrium price is $50 per cellular phone. To find the equilibrium quantity, evaluate either $S(p)$ or $D(p)$ at $p = 50$.

$$S(50) = 60(50) - 900 = 2100$$

The equilibrium quantity is 2100 cellular phones. At a price of $50 per phone, the company will produce and sell 2100 phones each month and have no shortages or excess inventory.

(b) The inequality $S(p) > D(p)$ is

$$60p - 900 > -15p + 2850 \qquad S(p) > D(p)$$
$$60p > -15p + 3750 \qquad \text{Add 900 to each side.}$$
$$75p > 3750 \qquad \text{Add 15p to each side.}$$
$$p > 50 \qquad \text{Divide each side by 75.}$$

If the company charges more than $50 per phone, quantity supplied will exceed quantity demanded. In this case the company will have excess phones in inventory.

(c) Figure 5 shows the graphs of $S = S(p)$ and $D = D(p)$ with the equilibrium point labeled.

Figure 5

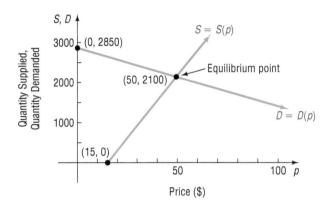

Now Work PROBLEM 39

3.1 Assess Your Understanding

'Are You Prepared?' *Answers are given at the end of these exercises. If you get a wrong answer, read the pages listed in red.*

1. Graph $y = 2x - 3$. (pp. 9–16)

2. Find the slope of the line joining the points $(2, 5)$ and $(-1, 3)$. (pp. 19–27)

3. Find the average rate of change of $f(x) = 3x^2 - 2$, from 2 to 4. (pp. 68–76)

4. Solve: $60x - 900 = -15x + 2850$. (pp. A44–A51)

5. If $f(x) = x^2 - 4$, find $f(-2)$. (pp. 46–54)

6. *True or False* The graph of the function $f(x) = x^2$ is increasing on the interval $(0, \infty)$. (pp. 68–76)

Concepts and Vocabulary

7. For the graph of the linear function $f(x) = mx + b$, m is the _____ and b is the _____.

8. For the graph of the linear function $H(z) = -4z + 3$, the slope is _____ and the y-intercept is _____.

9. If the slope m of the graph of a linear function is _____, the function is increasing over its domain.

10. *True or False* The slope of a nonvertical line is the average rate of change of the linear function.

11. *True or False* If the average rate of change of a linear function is $\frac{2}{3}$, then if y increases by 3, x will increase by 2.

12. *True or False* The average rate of change of $f(x) = 2x + 8$ is 8.

Skill Building

In Problems 13–20, a linear function is given.

(a) *Determine the slope and y-intercept of each function.*
(b) *Use the slope and y-intercept to graph the linear function.*
(c) *Determine the average rate of change of each function.*
(d) *Determine whether the linear function is increasing, decreasing, or constant.*

13. $f(x) = 2x + 3$

14. $g(x) = 5x - 4$

15. $h(x) = -3x + 4$

16. $p(x) = -x + 6$

17. $f(x) = \dfrac{1}{4}x - 3$

18. $h(x) = -\dfrac{2}{3}x + 4$

19. $F(x) = 4$

20. $G(x) = -2$

In Problems 21–28, determine whether the given function is linear or nonlinear. If it is linear, determine the slope.

21.

x	y = f(x)
-2	4
-1	1
0	-2
1	-5
2	-8

22.

x	y = f(x)
-2	1/4
-1	1/2
0	1
1	2
2	4

23.

x	y = f(x)
-2	-8
-1	-3
0	0
1	1
2	0

24.

x	y = f(x)
-2	-4
-1	0
0	4
1	8
2	12

25.

x	y = f(x)
−2	−26
−1	−4
0	2
1	−2
2	−10

26.

x	y = f(x)
−2	−4
−1	−3.5
0	−3
1	−2.5
2	−2

27.

x	y = f(x)
−2	8
−1	8
0	8
1	8
2	8

28.

x	y = f(x)
−2	0
−1	1
0	4
1	9
2	16

Applications and Extensions

29. Suppose that $f(x) = 4x - 1$ and $g(x) = -2x + 5$.
(a) Solve $f(x) = 0$. (b) Solve $f(x) > 0$.
(c) Solve $f(x) = g(x)$. (d) Solve $f(x) \leq g(x)$.
(e) Graph $y = f(x)$ and $y = g(x)$ and label the point that represents the solution to the equation $f(x) = g(x)$.

30. Suppose that $f(x) = 3x + 5$ and $g(x) = -2x + 15$.
(a) Solve $f(x) = 0$. (b) Solve $f(x) < 0$.
(c) Solve $f(x) = g(x)$. (d) Solve $f(x) \geq g(x)$.
(e) Graph $y = f(x)$ and $y = g(x)$ and label the point that represents the solution to the equation $f(x) = g(x)$.

31. In parts (a)–(f), use the following figure.

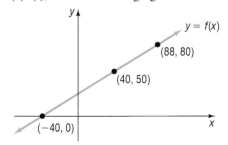

(a) Solve $f(x) = 50$. (b) Solve $f(x) = 80$.
(c) Solve $f(x) = 0$. (d) Solve $f(x) > 50$.
(e) Solve $f(x) \leq 80$. (f) Solve $0 < f(x) < 80$.

32. In parts (a)–(f), use the following figure.

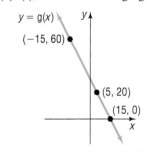

(a) Solve $g(x) = 20$. (b) Solve $g(x) = 60$.
(c) Solve $g(x) = 0$. (d) Solve $g(x) > 20$.
(e) Solve $g(x) \leq 60$. (f) Solve $0 < g(x) < 60$.

33. In parts (a) and (b) use the following figure.

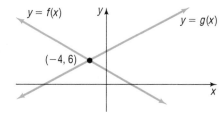

(a) Solve the equation: $f(x) = g(x)$.
(b) Solve the inequality: $f(x) > g(x)$.

34. In parts (a) and (b), use the following figure.

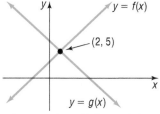

(a) Solve the equation: $f(x) = g(x)$.
(b) Solve the inequality: $f(x) \leq g(x)$.

35. In parts (a) and (b), use the following figure.

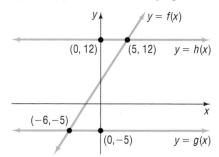

(a) Solve the equation: $f(x) = g(x)$.
(b) Solve the inequality: $g(x) \leq f(x) < h(x)$.

36. In parts (a) and (b), use the following figure.

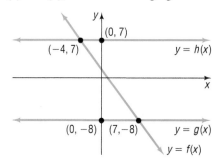

(a) Solve the equation: $f(x) = g(x)$.
(b) Solve the inequality: $g(x) < f(x) \leq h(x)$.

37. Car Rentals The cost C, in dollars, of renting a moving truck for a day is modeled by the function $C(x) = 0.25x + 35$, where x is the number of miles driven.
(a) What is the cost if you drive $x = 40$ miles?
(b) If the cost of renting the moving truck is $80, how many miles did you drive?
(c) Suppose that you want the cost to be no more than $100. What is the maximum number of miles that you can drive?
(d) What is the implied domain of C?

38. Phone Charges The monthly cost C, in dollars, for international calls on a certain cellular phone plan is modeled by the function $C(x) = 0.38x + 5$, where x is the number of minutes used.
(a) What is the cost if you talk on the phone for $x = 50$ minutes?
(b) Suppose that your monthly bill is $29.32. How many minutes did you use the phone?
(c) Suppose that you budget yourself $60 per month for the phone. What is the maximum number of minutes that you can talk?
(d) What is the implied domain of C if there are 30 days in the month?

39. Supply and Demand Suppose that the quantity supplied S and quantity demanded D of T-shirts at a concert are given by the following functions:

$$S(p) = -200 + 50p$$
$$D(p) = 1000 - 25p$$

where p is the price of a T-shirt.
(a) Find the equilibrium price for T-shirts at this concert. What is the equilibrium quantity?
(b) Determine the prices for which quantity demanded is greater than quantity supplied.
(c) What do you think will eventually happen to the price of T-shirts if quantity demanded is greater than quantity supplied?

40. Supply and Demand Suppose that the quantity supplied S and quantity demanded D of hot dogs at a baseball game are given by the following functions:

$$S(p) = -2000 + 3000p$$
$$D(p) = 10,000 - 1000p$$

where p is the price of a hot dog.
(a) Find the equilibrium price for hot dogs at the baseball game. What is the equilibrium quantity?
(b) Determine the prices for which quantity demanded is less than quantity supplied.
(c) What do you think will eventually happen to the price of hot dogs if quantity demanded is less than quantity supplied?

41. Taxes The function $T(x) = 0.15(x - 8350) + 835$ represents the tax bill T of a single person whose adjusted gross income is x dollars for income between $8350 and $33,950, inclusive, in 2009.
Source: Internal Revenue Service
(a) What is the domain of this linear function?
(b) What is a single filer's tax bill if adjusted gross income is $20,000?
(c) Which variable is independent and which is dependent?
(d) Graph the linear function over the domain specified in part (a).
(e) What is a single filer's adjusted gross income if the tax bill is $3707.50?

42. Luxury Tax In 2002, major league baseball signed a labor agreement with the players. In this agreement, any team whose payroll exceeded $136.5 million in 2006 had to pay a luxury tax of 40% (for second offenses). The linear function $T(p) = 0.40(p - 136.5)$ describes the luxury tax T of a team whose payroll was p (in millions of dollars).
Source: Major League Baseball

(a) What is the implied domain of this linear function?
(b) What was the luxury tax for the New York Yankees whose 2006 payroll was $171.1 million?
(c) Graph the linear function.
(d) What is the payroll of a team that pays a luxury tax of $11.7 million?

*The point at which a company's profits equal zero is called the company's **break-even point**. For Problems 43 and 44, let R represent a company's revenue, let C represent the company's costs, and let x represent the number of units produced and sold each day.*
(a) Find the firm's break-even point; that is, find x so that R = C.
(b) Find the values of x such that R(x) > C(x). This represents the number of units that the company must sell to earn a profit.

43. $R(x) = 8x$
$C(x) = 4.5x + 17,500$

44. $R(x) = 12x$
$C(x) = 10x + 15,000$

45. Straight-line Depreciation Suppose that a company has just purchased a new computer for $3000. The company chooses to depreciate the computer using the straight-line method over 3 years.
(a) Write a linear model that expresses the book value V of the computer as a function of its age x.
(b) What is the implied domain of the function found in part (a)?
(c) Graph the linear function.
(d) What is the book value of the computer after 2 years?
(e) When will the computer have a book value of $2000?

46. Straight-line Depreciation Suppose that a company has just purchased a new machine for its manufacturing facility for $120,000. The company chooses to depreciate the machine using the straight-line method over 10 years.
(a) Write a linear model that expresses the book value V of the machine as a function of its age x.
(b) What is the implied domain of the function found in part (a)?
(c) Graph the linear function.
(d) What is the book value of the machine after 4 years?
(e) When will the machine have a book value of $72,000?

47. Cost Function The simplest cost function is the linear cost function, $C(x) = mx + b$, where the y-intercept b represents the fixed costs of operating a business and the slope m represents the cost of each item produced. Suppose that a small bicycle manufacturer has daily fixed costs of $1800 and each bicycle costs $90 to manufacture.
(a) Write a linear model that expresses the cost C of manufacturing x bicycles in a day.
(b) Graph the model.
(c) What is the cost of manufacturing 14 bicycles in a day?
(d) How many bicycles could be manufactured for $3780?

48. Cost Function Refer to Problem 47. Suppose that the landlord of the building increases the bicycle manufacturer's rent by $100 per month.
(a) Assuming that the manufacturer is open for business 20 days per month, what are the new daily fixed costs?
(b) Write a linear model that expresses the cost C of manufacturing x bicycles in a day with the higher rent.
(c) Graph the model.
(d) What is the cost of manufacturing 14 bicycles in a day?
(e) How many bicycles can be manufactured for $3780?

49. Truck Rentals A truck rental company rents a truck for one day by charging $29 plus $0.07 per mile.
(a) Write a linear model that relates the cost C, in dollars, of renting the truck to the number x of miles driven.
(b) What is the cost of renting the truck if the truck is driven 110 miles? 230 miles?

50. Long Distance A phone company offers a domestic long distance package by charging $5 plus $0.05 per minute.
(a) Write a linear model that relates the cost C, in dollars, of talking x minutes.
(b) What is the cost of talking 105 minutes? 180 minutes?

Mixed Practice

51. Developing a Linear Model from Data The following data represent the price p and quantity demanded per day q of 24" LCD monitor.

Price, p (in dollars)	Quantity Demanded, q
150	100
200	80
250	60
300	40

(a) Plot the ordered pairs (p, q) in a Cartesian plane.
(b) Show that quantity demanded q is a linear function of the price p.
(c) Determine the linear function that describes the relation between p and q.
(d) What is the implied domain of the linear function?
(e) Graph the linear function in the Cartesian plane drawn in part (a).
(f) Interpret the slope.
(g) Interpret the values of the intercepts.

52. Developing a Linear Model from Data The following data represent the various combinations of soda and hot dogs that Yolanda can buy at a baseball game with $60.

Soda, s	Hot Dogs, h
20	0
15	3
10	6
5	9

(a) Plot the ordered pairs (s, h) in a Cartesian plane.
(b) Show that the number of hot dogs purchased h is a linear function of the number of sodas purchased s.
(c) Determine the linear function that describes the relation between s and h.
(d) What is the implied domain of the linear function?
(e) Graph the linear function in the Cartesian plane drawn in part (a).
(f) Interpret the slope.
(g) Interpret the values of the intercepts.

Explaining Concepts: Discussion and Writing

53. Which of the following functions might have the graph shown? (More than one answer is possible.)
(a) $f(x) = 2x - 7$
(b) $g(x) = -3x + 4$
(c) $H(x) = 5$
(d) $F(x) = 3x + 4$
(e) $G(x) = \dfrac{1}{2}x + 2$

54. Which of the following functions might have the graph shown? (More than one answer is possible.)
(a) $f(x) = 3x + 1$
(b) $g(x) = -2x + 3$
(c) $H(x) = 3$
(d) $F(x) = -4x - 1$
(e) $G(x) = -\dfrac{2}{3}x + 3$

55. Under what circumstances is a linear function $f(x) = mx + b$ odd? Can a linear function ever be even?

56. Explain how the graph of $f(x) = mx + b$ can be used to solve $mx + b > 0$.

'Are You Prepared?' Answers

1.

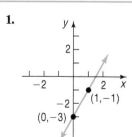

2. $\dfrac{2}{3}$ **3.** 18   **4.** $\{50\}$ **5.** 0   **6.** True

3.2 Linear Models: Building Linear Functions from Data

PREPARING FOR THIS SECTION *Before getting started, review the following:*

- Rectangular Coordinates (Section 1.1, pp. 2–3)
- Functions (Section 2.1, pp. 46–54)

- Lines (Section 1.3, pp. 19–27)

Now Work the 'Are You Prepared?' problems on page 131.

OBJECTIVES 1 Draw and Interpret Scatter Diagrams (p. 128)
2 Distinguish between Linear and Nonlinear Relations (p. 129)
 3 Use a Graphing Utility to Find the Line of Best Fit (p. 130)

1 Draw and Interpret Scatter Diagrams

In Section 3.1, we built linear models from verbal descriptions. Linear models can also be constructed by fitting a linear function to data. The first step is to plot the ordered pairs using rectangular coordinates. The resulting graph is called a **scatter diagram.**

EXAMPLE 1 **Drawing and Interpreting a Scatter Diagram**

In baseball, the on-base percentage for a team represents the percentage of time that the players safely reach base. The data given in Table 6 represent the number of runs scored *y* and the on-base percentage *x* for teams in the National League during the 2008 baseball season.

Table 6

Team	On-Base Percentage, x	Runs Scored, y	(x, y)
Atlanta	34.5	753	(34.5, 753)
St. Louis	35.0	779	(35.0, 779)
Colorado	33.6	747	(33.6, 747)
Houston	32.3	712	(32.3, 712)
Philadelphia	33.2	799	(33.2, 799)
San Francisco	32.1	640	(32.1, 640)
Pittsburgh	32.0	735	(32.0, 735)
Florida	32.6	770	(32.6, 770)
Chicago Cubs	35.4	855	(35.4, 855)
Arizona	32.7	720	(32.7, 720)
Milwaukee	32.5	750	(32.5, 750)
Washington	32.3	641	(32.3, 641)
Cincinnati	32.1	704	(32.1, 704)
San Diego	31.7	637	(31.7, 637)
NY Mets	34.0	799	(34.0, 799)
Los Angeles	33.3	700	(33.3, 700)

Source: Based on data from http://www.baseball-reference.com.
A Sports Reference, LLC, web site.

(a) Draw a scatter diagram of the data, treating on-base percentage as the independent variable.
 (b) Use a graphing utility to draw a scatter diagram.
(c) Describe what happens to runs scored as the on-base percentage increases.

Solution   (a) To draw a scatter diagram, plot the ordered pairs listed in Table 6, with the on-base percentage as the *x*-coordinate and the runs scored as the *y*-coordinate. See Figure 6(a). Notice that the points in the scatter diagram are not connected.

(b) Figure 6(b) shows a scatter diagram using a TI-84 Plus graphing calculator.

(c) We see from the scatter diagrams that, as the on-base percentage increases, the trend is that the number of runs scored also increases.

Figure 6

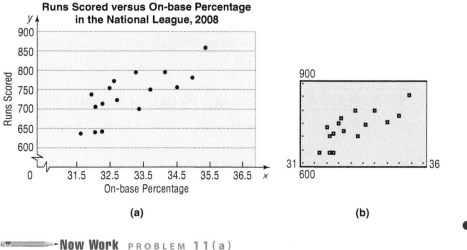

(a)   (b)

──**Now Work**   PROBLEM 11(a)

2 Distinguish between Linear and Nonlinear Relations

Notice that the points in Figure 6 do not follow a perfect linear relation (as they do in Figure 3 in Section 3.1). However, the data do exhibit a linear pattern. There are numerous explanations as to why the data are not perfectly linear, but one easy explanation is the fact that other variables besides on-base percentage play a role in determining runs scored, such as number of home runs hit.

Scatter diagrams are used to help us to see the type of relation that exists between two variables. In this text, we will discuss a variety of different relations that may exist between two variables. For now, we concentrate on distinguishing between linear and nonlinear relations. See Figure 7.

Figure 7

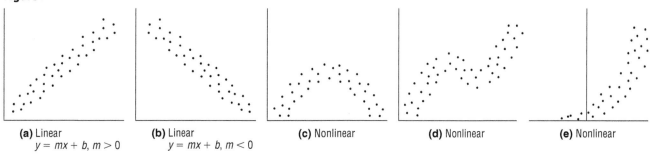

(a) Linear
$y = mx + b, m > 0$

(b) Linear
$y = mx + b, m < 0$

(c) Nonlinear

(d) Nonlinear

(e) Nonlinear

⎯⎯

EXAMPLE 2   **Distinguishing between Linear and Nonlinear Relations**

Determine whether the relation between the two variables in Figure 8 is linear or nonlinear.

Figure 8

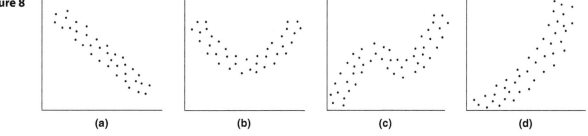

(a)   (b)   (c)   (d)

Solution   (a) Linear   (b) Nonlinear   (c) Nonlinear   (d) Nonlinear

—**Now Work** PROBLEM 5

In this section we study data whose scatter diagrams imply that a linear relation exists between the two variables.

Suppose that the scatter diagram of a set of data appears to be linearly related as in Figure 7(a) or (b). We might want to model the data by finding an equation of a line that relates the two variables. One way to obtain a model for such data is to draw a line through two points on the scatter diagram and determine the equation of the line.

EXAMPLE 3   **Finding a Model for Linearly Related Data**

Use the data in Table 6 from Example 1 to:

(a) Select two points and find an equation of the line containing the points.
(b) Graph the line on the scatter diagram obtained in Example 1(a).

Solution   (a) Select two points, say $(32.7, 720)$ and $(35.4, 855)$. The slope of the line joining the points $(32.7, 720)$ and $(35.4, 855)$ is

$$m = \frac{855 - 720}{35.4 - 32.7} = \frac{135}{2.7} = 50$$

The equation of the line with slope 50 and passing through $(32.7, 720)$ is found using the point–slope form with $m = 50$, $x_1 = 32.7$, and $y_1 = 720$.

$$y - y_1 = m(x - x_1) \quad \text{Point–slope form of a line}$$
$$y - 720 = 50(x - 32.7) \quad x_1 = 32.7,\ y_1 = 720,\ m = 50$$
$$y - 720 = 50x - 1635$$
$$y = 50x - 915 \quad \text{The Model}$$

(b) Figure 9 shows the scatter diagram with the graph of the line found in part (a).

Figure 9

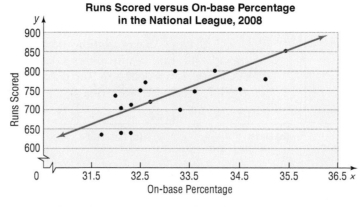

Runs Scored versus On-base Percentage in the National League, 2008

Select two other points and complete the solution. Graph the line on the scatter diagram obtained in Figure 6.

—**Now Work** PROBLEMS 11(b) AND (c)

3 Use a Graphing Utility to Find the Line of Best Fit

The model obtained in Example 3 depends on the selection of points, which will vary from person to person. So the model that we found might be different from the model you found. Although the model in Example 3 appears to fit the data well, there may be a model that "fits it better." Do you think your model fits the data better? Is there a *line of best fit*? As it turns out, there is a method for finding a model that best fits linearly related data (called the **line of best fit**).*

EXAMPLE 4 | **Finding a Model for Linearly Related Data**

Use the data in Table 6 from Example 1.

(a) Use a graphing utility to find the line of best fit that models the relation between on-base percentage and runs scored.
(b) Graph the line of best fit on the scatter diagram obtained in Example 1(b).
(c) Interpret the slope.
(d) Use the line of best fit to predict the number of runs a team will score if their on-base percentage is 34.1.

Solution
(a) Graphing utilities contain built-in programs that find the line of best fit for a collection of points in a scatter diagram. Upon executing the LINear REGression program, we obtain the results shown in Figure 10. The output that the utility provides shows us the equation $y = ax + b$, where a is the slope of the line and b is the y-intercept. The line of best fit that relates on-base percentage to runs scored may be expressed as the line

Figure 10

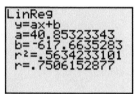

$$y = 40.85x - 617.66 \quad \text{The Model}$$

(b) Figure 11 shows the graph of the line of best fit, along with the scatter diagram.

Figure 11

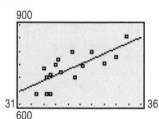

(c) The slope of the line of best fit is 40.85, which means that, for every 1 percent increase in the on-base percentage, runs scored increase 40.85, on average.
(d) Letting $x = 34.1$ in the equation of the line of best fit, we obtain $y = 40.85(34.1) - 617.66 \approx 775$ runs.

Now Work PROBLEMS **11(d)** AND **(e)**

Does the line of best fit appear to be a good fit? In other words, does the line appear to accurately describe the relation between on-base percentage and runs scored?

And just how "good" is this line of best fit? Look again at Figure 10. The last line of output is $r = 0.751$. This number, called the **correlation coefficient**, r, $-1 \leq r \leq 1$, is a measure of the strength of the linear relation that exists between two variables. The closer that $|r|$ is to 1, the more perfect the linear relationship is. If r is close to 0, there is little or no linear relationship between the variables. A negative value of r, $r < 0$, indicates that as x increases y decreases; a positive value of r, $r > 0$, indicates that as x increases y does also. The data given in Table 6, having a correlation coefficient of 0.751, are indicative of a linear relationship with positive slope.

3.2 Assess Your Understanding

'Are You Prepared?' *Answers are given at the end of these exercises. If you get a wrong answer, read the pages listed in red.*

1. Plot the points $(1, 5)$, $(2, 6)$, $(3, 9)$, $(1, 12)$ in the Cartesian plane. Is the relation $\{(1, 5), (2, 6), (3, 9), (1, 12)\}$ a function? Why? (pp. 2 and 46–54)

2. Find an equation of the line containing the points $(1, 4)$ and $(3, 8)$. (pp. 19–27)

Concepts and Vocabulary

3. A _____ is used to help us to see the type of relation, if any, that may exist between two variables.

4. *True or False* The correlation coefficient is a measure of the strength of a linear relation between two variables and must lie between -1 and 1, inclusive.

---

* We shall not discuss the underlying mathematics of lines of best fit in this book.

Skill Building

In Problems 5–10, examine the scatter diagram and determine whether the type of relation is linear or nonlinear.

5.
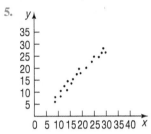

6.
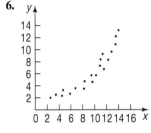

7.
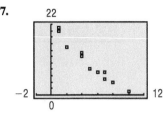

8.
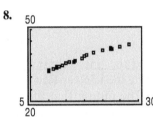

9.
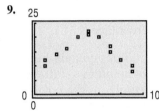

10.
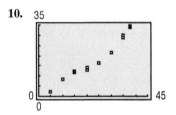

In Problems 11–16,

    (a) Draw a scatter diagram.
    (b) Select two points from the scatter diagram and find the equation of the line containing the points selected.
    (c) Graph the line found in part (b) on the scatter diagram.
    (d) Use a graphing utility to find the line of best fit.
    (e) Use a graphing utility to draw the scatter diagram and graph the line of best fit on it.

11.

x	3	4	5	6	7	8	9
y	4	6	7	10	12	14	16

12.

x	3	5	7	9	11	13
y	0	2	3	6	9	11

13.

x	-2	-1	0	1	2
y	-4	0	1	4	5

14.

x	-2	-1	0	1	2
y	7	6	3	2	0

15.

x	-20	-17	-15	-14	-10
y	100	120	118	130	140

16.

x	-30	-27	-25	-20	-14
y	10	12	13	13	18

Applications and Extensions

17. **Candy** The following data represent the weight (in grams) of various candy bars and the corresponding number of calories.

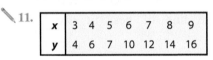

Candy Bar	Weight, x	Calories, y
Hershey's Milk Chocolate®	44.28	230
Nestle's Crunch®	44.84	230
Butterfinger®	61.30	270
Baby Ruth®	66.45	280
Almond Joy®	47.33	220
Twix® (with Caramel)	58.00	280
Snickers®	61.12	280
Heath®	39.52	210

Source: Megan Pocius, Student at Joliet Junior College

    (a) Draw a scatter diagram of the data treating weight as the independent variable.
    (b) What type of relation appears to exist between the weight of a candy bar and the number of calories?
    (c) Select two points and find a linear model that contains the points.

    (d) Graph the line on the scatter diagram drawn in part (a).
    (e) Use the linear model to predict the number of calories in a candy bar that weighs 62.3 grams.
    (f) Interpret the slope of the line found in part (c).

18. **Raisins** The following data represent the weight (in grams) of a box of raisins and the number of raisins in the box.

Weight (in grams), w	Number of Raisins, N
42.3	87
42.7	91
42.8	93
42.4	87
42.6	89
42.4	90
42.3	82
42.5	86
42.7	86
42.5	86

Source: Jennifer Maxwell, Student at Joliet Junior College

(a) Draw a scatter diagram of the data treating weight as the independent variable.
(b) What type of relation appears to exist between the weight of a box of raisins and the number of raisins?
(c) Select two points and find a linear model that contains the points.
(d) Graph the line on the scatter diagram drawn in part (b).
(e) Use the linear model to predict the number of raisins in a box that weighs 42.5 grams.
(f) Interpret the slope of the line found in part (c).

19. Video Games and Grade-Point Average Professor Grant Alexander wanted to find a linear model that relates the number of hours a student plays video games each week, h, to the cumulative grade-point average, G, of the student. He obtained a random sample of 10 full-time students at his college and asked each student to disclose the number of hours spent playing video games and the student's cumulative grade-point average.

Hours of Video Games per Week, h	Grade-point Average, G
0	3.49
0	3.05
2	3.24
3	2.82
3	3.19
5	2.78
8	2.31
8	2.54
10	2.03
12	2.51

(a) Explain why the number of hours spent playing video games is the independent variable and cumulative grade-point average is the dependent variable.
(b) Use a graphing utility to draw a scatter diagram.
(c) Use a graphing utility to find the line of best fit that models the relation between number of hours of video game playing each week and grade-point average. Express the model using function notation.
(d) Interpret the slope.
(e) Predict the grade-point average of a student who plays video games for 8 hours each week.
(f) How many hours of video game playing do you think a student plays whose grade-point average is 2.40?

20. Height versus Head Circumference A pediatrician wanted to find a linear model that relates a child's height, H, to head circumference, C. She randomly selects nine children from her practice, measures their height and head circumference, and obtains the data shown. Let H represent the independent variable and C the dependent variable.
(a) Use a graphing utility to draw a scatter diagram.
(b) Use a graphing utility to find the line of best fit that models the relation between height and head circumference. Express the model using function notation.
(c) Interpret the slope.
(d) Predict the head circumference of a child that is 26 inches tall.

(e) What is the height of a child whose head circumference is 17.4 inches?

Height, H (inches)	Head Circumference, C (inches)
25.25	16.4
25.75	16.9
25	16.9
27.75	17.6
26.5	17.3
27	17.5
26.75	17.3
26.75	17.5
27.5	17.5

Source: Denise Slucki, Student at Joliet Junior College

21. Demand for Jeans The marketing manager at Levi-Strauss wishes to find a function that relates the demand D for men's jeans and p, the price of the jeans. The following data were obtained based on a price history of the jeans.

Price ($/Pair), p	Demand (Pairs of Jeans Sold per Day), D
20	60
22	57
23	56
23	53
27	52
29	49
30	44

(a) Does the relation defined by the set of ordered pairs (p, D) represent a function?
(b) Draw a scatter diagram of the data.
(c) Using a graphing utility, find the line of best fit that models the relation between price and quantity demanded.
(d) Interpret the slope.
(e) Express the relationship found in part (c) using function notation.
(f) What is the domain of the function?
(g) How many jeans will be demanded if the price is $28 a pair?

22. Advertising and Sales Revenue A marketing firm wishes to find a function that relates the sales S of a product and A, the amount spent on advertising the product. The data are obtained from past experience. Advertising and sales are measured in thousands of dollars.

Advertising Expenditures, A	Sales, S
20	335
22	339
22.5	338
24	343
24	341
27	350
28.3	351

(a) Does the relation defined by the set of ordered pairs (A, S) represent a function?

(b) Draw a scatter diagram of the data.

(c) Using a graphing utility, find the line of best fit that models the relation between advertising expenditures and sales.

(d) Interpret the slope.

(e) Express the relationship found in part (c) using function notation.

(f) What is the domain of the function?

(g) Predict sales if advertising expenditures are $25,000.

Explaining Concepts: Discussion and Writing

23. **Maternal Age versus Down Syndrome** A biologist would like to know how the age of the mother affects the incidence rate of Down syndrome. The data to the right represent the age of the mother and the incidence rate of Down syndrome per 1000 pregnancies.

    Draw a scatter diagram treating age of the mother as the independent variable. Would it make sense to find the line of best fit for these data? Why or why not?

24. Find the line of best fit for the ordered pairs $(1, 5)$ and $(3, 8)$. What is the correlation coefficient for these data? Why is this result reasonable?

25. What does a correlation coefficient of 0 imply?

26. Explain why it does not make sense to interpret the y-intercept in Problem 17.

27. Refer to Problem 19. Solve $G(h) = 0$. Provide an interpretation of this result. Find $G(0)$. Provide an interpretation of this result.

Age of Mother, x	Incidence of Down Syndrome, y
33	2.4
34	3.1
35	4
36	5
37	6.7
38	8.3
39	10
40	13.3
41	16.7
42	22.2
43	28.6
44	33.3
45	50

Source: Hook, E.B., *Journal of the American Medical Association*, 249, 2034-2038, 1983.

'Are You Prepared?' Answers

1.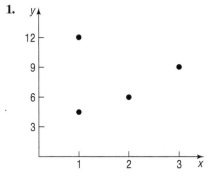

No, because the input, 1, corresponds to two different outputs.

2. $y = 2x + 2$

3.3 Quadratic Functions and Their Properties

PREPARING FOR THIS SECTION *Before getting started, review the following:*

- Intercepts (Section 1.2, pp. 11–12)
- Graphing Techniques: Transformations (Section 2.5, pp. 90–99)
- Completing the Square (Appendix A, Section A.3, pp. A29–A30)
- Quadratic Equations (Appendix A, Section A.6, pp. A47–A51)

Now Work the 'Are You Prepared?' problems on page 143.

OBJECTIVES
1 Graph a Quadratic Function Using Transformations (p. 136)
2 Identify the Vertex and Axis of Symmetry of a Quadratic Function (p. 138)
3 Graph a Quadratic Function Using Its Vertex, Axis, and Intercepts (p. 138)
4 Find a Quadratic Function Given Its Vertex and One Other Point (p. 141)
5 Find the Maximum or Minimum Value of a Quadratic Function (p. 142)

Quadratic Functions

Here are some examples of quadratic functions.

$$F(x) = 3x^2 - 5x + 1 \qquad g(x) = -6x^2 + 1 \qquad H(x) = \frac{1}{2}x^2 + \frac{2}{3}x$$

DEFINITION

A **quadratic function** is a function of the form

$$f(x) = ax^2 + bx + c$$

where a, b, and c are real numbers and $a \neq 0$. The domain of a quadratic function is the set of all real numbers.

In Words

A quadratic function is a function defined by a second-degree polynomial in one variable.

Many applications require a knowledge of quadratic functions. For example, suppose that Texas Instruments collects the data shown in Table 7, which relate the number of calculators sold to the price p (in dollars) per calculator. Since the price of a product determines the quantity that will be purchased, we treat price as the independent variable. The relationship between the number x of calculators sold and the price p per calculator is given by the linear equation

$$x = 21{,}000 - 150p$$

Table 7

Price per Calculator, p (Dollars)	Number of Calculators, x
60	12,000
65	11,250
70	10,500
75	9,750
80	9,000
85	8,250
90	7,500

Then the revenue R derived from selling x calculators at the price p per calculator is equal to the unit selling price p of the calculator times the number x of units actually sold. That is,

$$R = xp$$
$$R(p) = (21{,}000 - 150p)p \qquad {\scriptstyle x = 21{,}000 - 150p}$$
$$= -150p^2 + 21{,}000p$$

So the revenue R is a quadratic function of the price p. Figure 12 illustrates the graph of this revenue function, whose domain is $0 \le p \le 140$, since both x and p must be nonnegative.

Figure 12

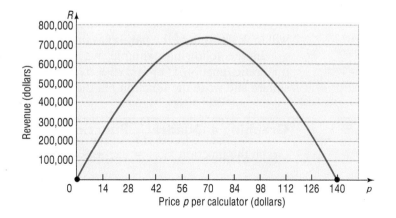

Figure 13
Path of a cannonball

A second situation in which a quadratic function appears involves the motion of a projectile. Based on Newton's Second Law of Motion (force equals mass times acceleration, $F = ma$), it can be shown that, ignoring air resistance, the path of a projectile propelled upward at an inclination to the horizontal is the graph of a quadratic function. See Figure 13 for an illustration.

1 Graph a Quadratic Function Using Transformations

We know how to graph the square function $f(x) = x^2$. Figure 14 shows the graph of three functions of the form $f(x) = ax^2, a > 0$, for $a = 1, a = \dfrac{1}{2}$, and $a = 3$. Notice that the larger the value of a, the "narrower" the graph is, and the smaller the value of a, the "wider" the graph is.

Figure 15 shows the graphs of $f(x) = ax^2$ for $a < 0$. Notice that these graphs are reflections about the x-axis of the graphs in Figure 14. Based on the results of these two figures, we can draw some general conclusions about the graph of $f(x) = ax^2$. First, as $|a|$ increases, the graph becomes "taller" (a vertical stretch), and as $|a|$ gets closer to zero, the graph gets "shorter" (a vertical compression). Second, if a is positive, the graph opens "up," and if a is negative, the graph opens "down."

Figure 14   **Figure 15**

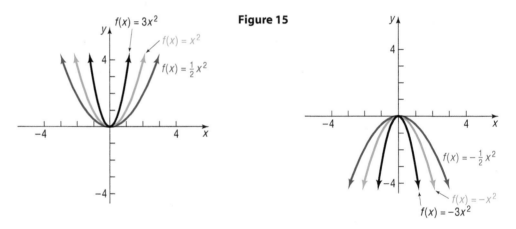

The graphs in Figures 14 and 15 are typical of the graphs of all quadratic functions, which we call **parabolas.*** Refer to Figure 16, where two parabolas are pictured. The one on the left **opens up** and has a lowest point; the one on the right **opens down** and has a highest point. The lowest or highest point of a parabola is called the **vertex.** The vertical line passing through the vertex in each parabola in Figure 16 is called the **axis of symmetry** (usually abbreviated to **axis**) of the parabola. Because the parabola is symmetric about its axis, the axis of symmetry of a parabola can be used to find additional points on the parabola.

Figure 16
Graphs of a quadratic function,
$f(x) = ax^2 + bx + c, a \neq 0$

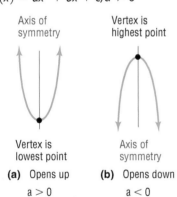

The parabolas shown in Figure 16 are the graphs of a quadratic function $f(x) = ax^2 + bx + c, a \neq 0$. Notice that the coordinate axes are not included in the figure. Depending on the values of a, b, and c, the axes could be placed anywhere. The important fact is that the shape of the graph of a quadratic function will look like one of the parabolas in Figure 16.

In the following example, we use techniques from Section 2.5 to graph a quadratic function $f(x) = ax^2 + bx + c, a \neq 0$. In so doing, we shall complete the square and write the function f in the form $f(x) = a(x - h)^2 + k$.

EXAMPLE 1   **Graphing a Quadratic Function Using Transformations**

Graph the function $f(x) = 2x^2 + 8x + 5$. Find the vertex and axis of symmetry.

* We shall study parabolas using a geometric definition later in this book.

Solution Begin by completing the square on the right side.

$$f(x) = 2x^2 + 8x + 5$$

$$= 2(x^2 + 4x) + 5 \qquad \text{Factor out the 2 from } 2x^2 + 8x.$$

$$= 2(x^2 + 4x + 4) + 5 - 8 \qquad \text{Complete the square of } x^2 + 4x \text{ by adding 4.}$$
$$\qquad\qquad\qquad\qquad\qquad\qquad \text{Notice that the factor of 2 requires that 8 be}$$
$$= 2(x + 2)^2 - 3 \qquad\qquad\qquad \text{added and subtracted.}$$

The graph of f can be obtained from the graph of $y = x^2$ in three stages, as shown in Figure 17. Now compare this graph to the graph in Figure 16(a). The graph of $f(x) = 2x^2 + 8x + 5$ is a parabola that opens up and has its vertex (lowest point) at $(-2, -3)$. Its axis of symmetry is the line $x = -2$.

Figure 17

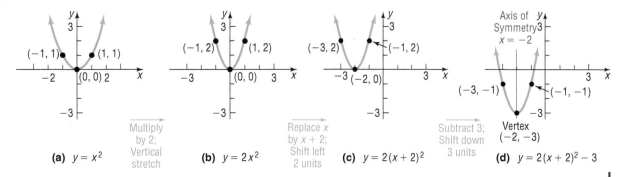

(a) $y = x^2$ — Multiply by 2; Vertical stretch

(b) $y = 2x^2$ — Replace x by $x + 2$; Shift left 2 units

(c) $y = 2(x + 2)^2$ — Subtract 3; Shift down 3 units

(d) $y = 2(x + 2)^2 - 3$ — Vertex $(-2, -3)$

Now Work PROBLEM 23

The method used in Example 1 can be used to graph any quadratic function $f(x) = ax^2 + bx + c, a \neq 0$, as follows:

$$f(x) = ax^2 + bx + c$$

$$= a\left(x^2 + \frac{b}{a}x\right) + c \qquad \text{Factor out } a \text{ from } ax^2 + bx.$$

$$= a\left(x^2 + \frac{b}{a}x + \frac{b^2}{4a^2}\right) + c - a\left(\frac{b^2}{4a^2}\right) \qquad \text{Complete the square by adding } \frac{b^2}{4a^2}.$$
$$\qquad\qquad\qquad\qquad\qquad\qquad\qquad\qquad \text{Look closely at this step!}$$

$$= a\left(x + \frac{b}{2a}\right)^2 + c - \frac{b^2}{4a} \qquad \text{Factor.}$$

$$= a\left(x + \frac{b}{2a}\right)^2 + \frac{4ac - b^2}{4a} \qquad c - \frac{b^2}{4a} = c \cdot \frac{4a}{4a} - \frac{b^2}{4a} = \frac{4ac - b^2}{4a}$$

Based on these results, we conclude the following:

$$\text{If } h = -\frac{b}{2a} \quad \text{and} \quad k = \frac{4ac - b^2}{4a}, \quad \text{then}$$

$$f(x) = ax^2 + bx + c = a(x - h)^2 + k \qquad\qquad \textbf{(1)}$$

The graph of $f(x) = a(x - h)^2 + k$ is the parabola $y = ax^2$ shifted horizontally h units (replace x by $x - h$) and vertically k units (add k). As a result, the vertex is at (h, k), and the graph opens up if $a > 0$ and down if $a < 0$. The axis of symmetry is the vertical line $x = h$.

For example, compare equation (1) with the solution given in Example 1.

$$f(x) = 2(x + 2)^2 - 3$$
$$= 2(x - (-2))^2 + (-3)$$
$$= a(x - h)^2 + k$$

We conclude that $a = 2$, so the graph opens up. Also, we find that $h = -2$ and $k = -3$, so its vertex is at $(-2, -3)$.

2 Identify the Vertex and Axis of Symmetry of a Quadratic Function

We do not need to complete the square to obtain the vertex. In almost every case, it is easier to obtain the vertex of a quadratic function f by remembering that its x-coordinate is $h = -\dfrac{b}{2a}$. The y-coordinate k can then be found by evaluating f at $-\dfrac{b}{2a}$. That is, $k = f\left(-\dfrac{b}{2a}\right)$.

Properties of the Graph of a Quadratic Function

$$f(x) = ax^2 + bx + c \qquad a \neq 0$$

$$\text{Vertex} = \left(-\frac{b}{2a}, f\left(-\frac{b}{2a}\right)\right) \quad \text{Axis of symmetry: the line } x = -\frac{b}{2a} \quad \textbf{(2)}$$

Parabola opens up if $a > 0$; the vertex is a minimum point.
Parabola opens down if $a < 0$; the vertex is a maximum point.

EXAMPLE 2

Locating the Vertex without Graphing

Without graphing, locate the vertex and axis of symmetry of the parabola defined by $f(x) = -3x^2 + 6x + 1$. Does it open up or down?

Solution

For this quadratic function, $a = -3, b = 6$, and $c = 1$. The x-coordinate of the vertex is

$$h = -\frac{b}{2a} = -\frac{6}{-6} = 1$$

The y-coordinate of the vertex is

$$k = f\left(-\frac{b}{2a}\right) = f(1) = -3 + 6 + 1 = 4$$

The vertex is located at the point $(1, 4)$. The axis of symmetry is the line $x = 1$. Because $a = -3 < 0$, the parabola opens down.

3 Graph a Quadratic Function Using Its Vertex, Axis, and Intercepts

The location of the vertex and intercepts of a quadratic function, $f(x) = ax^2 + bx + c, a \neq 0$, along with knowledge as to whether the graph opens up or down, usually provides enough information to graph it.

The y-intercept is the value of f at $x = 0$; that is, the y-intercept is $f(0) = c$.

The x-intercepts, if there are any, are found by solving the quadratic equation

$$ax^2 + bx + c = 0$$

This equation has two, one, or no real solutions, depending on whether the discriminant $b^2 - 4ac$ is positive, 0, or negative. Depending on the value of the discriminant, the graph of f has x-intercepts, as follows:

The x-Intercepts of a Quadratic Function

1. If the discriminant $b^2 - 4ac > 0$, the graph of $f(x) = ax^2 + bx + c$ has two distinct x-intercepts so it crosses the x-axis in two places.
2. If the discriminant $b^2 - 4ac = 0$, the graph of $f(x) = ax^2 + bx + c$ has one x-intercept so it touches the x-axis at its vertex.
3. If the discriminant $b^2 - 4ac < 0$, the graph of $f(x) = ax^2 + bx + c$ has no x-intercepts so it does not cross or touch the x-axis.

Figure 18 illustrates these possibilities for parabolas that open up.

Figure 18
$f(x) = ax^2 + bx + c,\ a > 0$

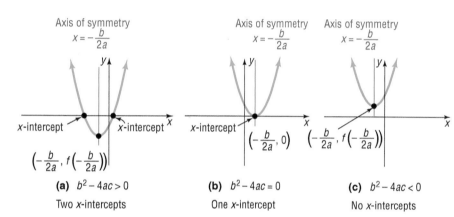

(a) $b^2 - 4ac > 0$
Two x-intercepts

(b) $b^2 - 4ac = 0$
One x-intercept

(c) $b^2 - 4ac < 0$
No x-intercepts

| EXAMPLE 3 | **Graphing a Quadratic Function Using Its Vertex, Axis, and Intercepts** |

(a) Use the information from Example 2 and the locations of the intercepts to graph $f(x) = -3x^2 + 6x + 1$.
(b) Determine the domain and the range of f.
(c) Determine where f is increasing and where it is decreasing.

Solution

(a) In Example 2, we found the vertex to be at $(1, 4)$ and the axis of symmetry to be $x = 1$. The y-intercept is found by letting $x = 0$. The y-intercept is $f(0) = 1$. The x-intercepts are found by solving the equation $f(x) = 0$. This results in the equation

$$-3x^2 + 6x + 1 = 0 \qquad a = -3, b = 6, c = 1$$

The discriminant $b^2 - 4ac = (6)^2 - 4(-3)(1) = 36 + 12 = 48 > 0$, so the equation has two real solutions and the graph has two x-intercepts. Using the quadratic formula, we find that

$$x = \frac{-b + \sqrt{b^2 - 4ac}}{2a} = \frac{-6 + \sqrt{48}}{-6} = \frac{-6 + 4\sqrt{3}}{-6} \approx -0.15$$

and

$$x = \frac{-b - \sqrt{b^2 - 4ac}}{2a} = \frac{-6 - \sqrt{48}}{-6} = \frac{-6 - 4\sqrt{3}}{-6} \approx 2.15$$

The x-intercepts are approximately -0.15 and 2.15.

The graph is illustrated in Figure 19. Notice how we used the y-intercept and the axis of symmetry, $x = 1$, to obtain the additional point $(2, 1)$ on the graph.

Figure 19

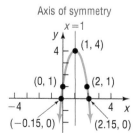

(b) The domain of f is the set of all real numbers. Based on the graph, the range of f is the interval $(-\infty, 4]$.

(c) The function f is increasing on the interval $(-\infty, 1)$ and decreasing on the interval $(1, \infty)$.

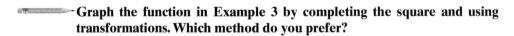 Graph the function in Example 3 by completing the square and using transformations. Which method do you prefer?

Now Work PROBLEM 31

If the graph of a quadratic function has only one x-intercept or no x-intercepts, it is usually necessary to plot an additional point to obtain the graph.

EXAMPLE 4   **Graphing a Quadratic Function Using Its Vertex, Axis, and Intercepts**

(a) Graph $f(x) = x^2 - 6x + 9$ by determining whether the graph opens up or down and by finding its vertex, axis of symmetry, y-intercept, and x-intercepts, if any.

(b) Determine the domain and the range of f.

(c) Determine where f is increasing and where it is decreasing.

Solution   (a) For $f(x) = x^2 - 6x + 9$, we have $a = 1$, $b = -6$, and $c = 9$. Since $a = 1 > 0$, the parabola opens up. The x-coordinate of the vertex is

Figure 20

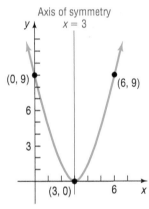

Axis of symmetry
$x = 3$

$(0, 9)$ $(6, 9)$

$(3, 0)$

$$h = -\frac{b}{2a} = -\frac{-6}{2(1)} = 3$$

The y-coordinate of the vertex is

$$k = f(3) = (3)^2 - 6(3) + 9 = 0$$

So the vertex is at $(3, 0)$. The axis of symmetry is the line $x = 3$. The y-intercept is $f(0) = 9$. Since the vertex $(3, 0)$ lies on the x-axis, the graph touches the x-axis at the x-intercept. By using the axis of symmetry and the y-intercept at $(0, 9)$, we can locate the additional point $(6, 9)$ on the graph. See Figure 20.

(b) The domain of f is the set of all real numbers. Based on the graph, the range of f is the interval $[0, \infty)$.

(c) The function f is decreasing on the interval $(-\infty, 3)$ and increasing on the interval $(3, \infty)$.

Now Work PROBLEM 37

EXAMPLE 5   **Graphing a Quadratic Function Using Its Vertex, Axis, and Intercepts**

(a) Graph $f(x) = 2x^2 + x + 1$ by determining whether the graph opens up or down and by finding its vertex, axis of symmetry, y-intercept, and x-intercepts, if any.

(b) Determine the domain and the range of f.

(c) Determine where f is increasing and where it is decreasing.

Solution   (a) For $f(x) = 2x^2 + x + 1$, we have $a = 2$, $b = 1$, and $c = 1$. Since $a = 2 > 0$, the parabola opens up. The x-coordinate of the vertex is

$$h = -\frac{b}{2a} = -\frac{1}{4}$$

NOTE In Example 5, since the vertex is above the x-axis and the parabola opens up, we can conclude that the graph of the quadratic function will have no x-intercepts. ∎

The y-coordinate of the vertex is

$$k = f\left(-\frac{1}{4}\right) = 2\left(\frac{1}{16}\right) + \left(-\frac{1}{4}\right) + 1 = \frac{7}{8}$$

So the vertex is at $\left(-\frac{1}{4}, \frac{7}{8}\right)$. The axis of symmetry is the line $x = -\frac{1}{4}$. The y-intercept is $f(0) = 1$. The x-intercept(s), if any, obey the equation $2x^2 + x + 1 = 0$. Since the discriminant $b^2 - 4ac = (1)^2 - 4(2)(1) = -7 < 0$, this equation has no real solutions, and therefore the graph has no x-intercepts.

We use the point $(0, 1)$ and the axis of symmetry $x = -\frac{1}{4}$ to locate the additional point $\left(-\frac{1}{2}, 1\right)$ on the graph. See Figure 21.

Figure 21

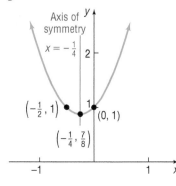

(b) The domain of f is the set of all real numbers. Based on the graph, the range of f is the interval $\left[\frac{7}{8}, \infty\right)$.

(c) The function f is decreasing on the interval $\left(-\infty, -\frac{1}{4}\right)$ and is increasing on the interval $\left(-\frac{1}{4}, \infty\right)$.

—**Now Work** PROBLEM 41

4 Find a Quadratic Function Given Its Vertex and One Other Point

Given the vertex (h, k) and one additional point on the graph of a quadratic function $f(x) = ax^2 + bx + c, a \neq 0$, we can use

$$f(x) = a(x - h)^2 + k \qquad \textbf{(3)}$$

to obtain the quadratic function.

EXAMPLE 6

Finding the Quadratic Function Given Its Vertex and One Other Point

Determine the quadratic function whose vertex is $(1, -5)$ and whose y-intercept is -3. The graph of the parabola is shown in Figure 22.

Solution

The vertex is $(1, -5)$, so $h = 1$ and $k = -5$. Substitute these values into equation (3).

$$f(x) = a(x - h)^2 + k \quad \text{Equation (3)}$$
$$f(x) = a(x - 1)^2 - 5 \quad h = 1, k = -5$$

Figure 22

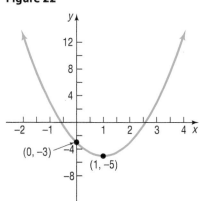

To determine the value of a, we use the fact that $f(0) = -3$ (the y-intercept).

$$f(x) = a(x - 1)^2 - 5$$
$$-3 = a(0 - 1)^2 - 5 \quad x = 0, y = f(0) = -3$$
$$-3 = a - 5$$
$$a = 2$$

The quadratic function whose graph is shown in Figure 22 is

$$f(x) = a(x - h)^2 + k = 2(x - 1)^2 - 5 = 2x^2 - 4x - 3$$

—**Now Work** PROBLEM 47

5 Find the Maximum or Minimum Value of a Quadratic Function

The graph of a quadratic function

$$f(x) = ax^2 + bx + c \qquad a \neq 0$$

is a parabola with vertex at $\left(-\dfrac{b}{2a}, f\left(-\dfrac{b}{2a}\right)\right)$. This vertex is the highest point on the graph if $a < 0$ and the lowest point on the graph if $a > 0$. If the vertex is the highest point $(a < 0)$, then $f\left(-\dfrac{b}{2a}\right)$ is the **maximum value** of f. If the vertex is the lowest point $(a > 0)$, then $f\left(-\dfrac{b}{2a}\right)$ is the **minimum value** of f.

EXAMPLE 7	**Finding the Maximum or Minimum Value of a Quadratic Function**

Determine whether the quadratic function

$$f(x) = x^2 - 4x - 5$$

has a maximum or minimum value. Then find the maximum or minimum value.

Solution Compare $f(x) = x^2 - 4x - 5$ to $f(x) = ax^2 + bx + c$. Then $a = 1$, $b = -4$, and $c = -5$. Since $a > 0$, the graph of f opens up, so the vertex is a minimum point. The minimum value occurs at

$$x = -\frac{b}{2a} = -\frac{-4}{2(1)} = \frac{4}{2} = 2$$

$$\uparrow$$
$$a = 1, b = -4$$

The minimum value is

$$f\left(-\frac{b}{2a}\right) = f(2) = 2^2 - 4(2) - 5 = 4 - 8 - 5 = -9$$

➙ **Now Work** PROBLEM 55

SUMMARY   Steps for Graphing a Quadratic Function $f(x) = ax^2 + bx + c, a \neq 0$

Option 1

STEP 1: Complete the square in x to write the quadratic function in the form $f(x) = a(x - h)^2 + k$.

STEP 2: Graph the function in stages using transformations.

Option 2

STEP 1: Determine whether the parabola opens up $(a > 0)$ or down $(a < 0)$.

STEP 2: Determine the vertex $\left(-\dfrac{b}{2a}, f\left(-\dfrac{b}{2a}\right)\right)$.

STEP 3: Determine the axis of symmetry, $x = -\dfrac{b}{2a}$.

STEP 4: Determine the y-intercept, $f(0)$, and the x-intercepts, if any.
(a) If $b^2 - 4ac > 0$, the graph of the quadratic function has two x-intercepts, which are found by solving the equation $ax^2 + bx + c = 0$.
(b) If $b^2 - 4ac = 0$, the vertex is the x-intercept.
(c) If $b^2 - 4ac < 0$, there are no x-intercepts.

STEP 5: Determine an additional point by using the y-intercept and the axis of symmetry.

STEP 6: Plot the points and draw the graph.

3.3 Assess Your Understanding

'Are You Prepared?' *Answers are given at the end of these exercises. If you get a wrong answer, read the pages listed in red.*

1. List the intercepts of the equation $y = x^2 - 9$. (pp. 11–12)
2. Find the real solutions of the equation $2x^2 + 7x - 4 = 0$. (pp. A47–A51)
3. To complete the square of $x^2 - 5x$, you add the number _____ . (pp. A29–A30)
4. To graph $y = (x - 4)^2$, you shift the graph of $y = x^2$ to the _____ a distance of _____ units. (pp. 90–99)

Concepts and Vocabulary

5. The graph of a quadratic function is called a(n) _____ .
6. The vertical line passing through the vertex of a parabola is called the _____ .
7. The x-coordinate of the vertex of $f(x) = ax^2 + bx + c$, $a \neq 0$, is _____ .
8. **True or False** The graph of $f(x) = 2x^2 + 3x - 4$ opens up.
9. **True or False** The y-coordinate of the vertex of $f(x) = -x^2 + 4x + 5$ is $f(2)$.
10. **True or False** If the discriminant $b^2 - 4ac = 0$, the graph of $f(x) = ax^2 + bx + c$, $a \neq 0$, will touch the x-axis at its vertex.

Skill Building

In Problems 11–18, match each graph to one the following functions.

11. $f(x) = x^2 - 1$
12. $f(x) = -x^2 - 1$
13. $f(x) = x^2 - 2x + 1$
14. $f(x) = x^2 + 2x + 1$
15. $f(x) = x^2 - 2x + 2$
16. $f(x) = x^2 + 2x$
17. $f(x) = x^2 - 2x$
18. $f(x) = x^2 + 2x + 2$

A
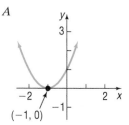

B
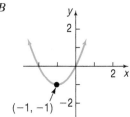

C
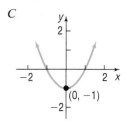

D
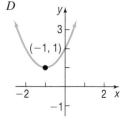

E
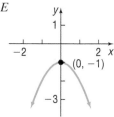

F
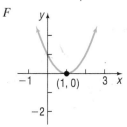

G
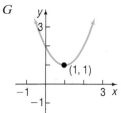

H
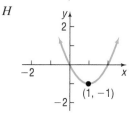

In Problems 19–30, graph the function f by starting with the graph of $y = x^2$ and using transformations (shifting, compressing, stretching, and/or reflection).

[**Hint:** If necessary, write f in the form $f(x) = a(x - h)^2 + k$.]

19. $f(x) = \dfrac{1}{4}x^2$
20. $f(x) = 2x^2 + 4$
21. $f(x) = (x + 2)^2 - 2$
22. $f(x) = (x - 3)^2 - 10$

23. $f(x) = x^2 + 4x + 2$
24. $f(x) = x^2 - 6x - 1$
25. $f(x) = 2x^2 - 4x + 1$
26. $f(x) = 3x^2 + 6x$

27. $f(x) = -x^2 - 2x$
28. $f(x) = -2x^2 + 6x + 2$
29. $f(x) = \dfrac{1}{2}x^2 + x - 1$
30. $f(x) = \dfrac{2}{3}x^2 + \dfrac{4}{3}x - 1$

In Problems 31–46, (a) graph each quadratic function by determining whether its graph opens up or down and by finding its vertex, axis of symmetry, y-intercept, and x-intercepts, if any. (b) Determine the domain and the range of the function. (c) Determine where the function is increasing and where it is decreasing.

31. $f(x) = x^2 + 2x$
32. $f(x) = x^2 - 4x$
33. $f(x) = -x^2 - 6x$
34. $f(x) = -x^2 + 4x$

35. $f(x) = x^2 + 2x - 8$
36. $f(x) = x^2 - 2x - 3$
37. $f(x) = x^2 + 2x + 1$
38. $f(x) = x^2 + 6x + 9$

39. $f(x) = 2x^2 - x + 2$
40. $f(x) = 4x^2 - 2x + 1$
41. $f(x) = -2x^2 + 2x - 3$
42. $f(x) = -3x^2 + 3x - 2$

43. $f(x) = 3x^2 + 6x + 2$
44. $f(x) = 2x^2 + 5x + 3$
45. $f(x) = -4x^2 - 6x + 2$
46. $f(x) = 3x^2 - 8x + 2$

In Problems 47–52, determine the quadratic function whose graph is given.

47.

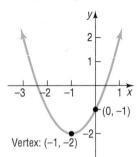

48.

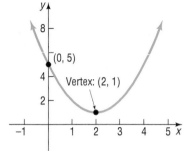

49.

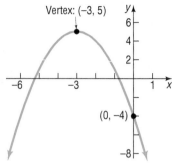

50.

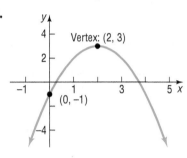

51.

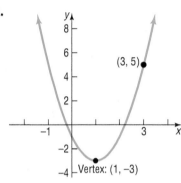

52.

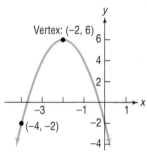

In Problems 53–60, determine, without graphing, whether the given quadratic function has a maximum value or a minimum value and then find the value.

53. $f(x) = 2x^2 + 12x$

54. $f(x) = -2x^2 + 12x$

55. $f(x) = 2x^2 + 12x - 3$

56. $f(x) = 4x^2 - 8x + 3$

57. $f(x) = -x^2 + 10x - 4$

58. $f(x) = -2x^2 + 8x + 3$

59. $f(x) = -3x^2 + 12x + 1$

60. $f(x) = 4x^2 - 4x$

Applications and Extensions

61. The graph of the function $f(x) = ax^2 + bx + c$ has vertex at $(0, 2)$ and passes through the point $(1, 8)$. Find a, b, and c.

62. The graph of the function $f(x) = ax^2 + bx + c$ has vertex at $(1, 4)$ and passes through the point $(-1, -8)$. Find a, b, and c.

In Problems 63–68, for the given functions f and g,
(a) Graph f and g on the same Cartesian plane.
(b) Solve $f(x) = g(x)$.
(c) Use the result of part (b) to label the points of intersection of the graphs of f and g.
(d) Shade the region for which $f(x) > g(x)$, that is, the region below f and above g.

63. $f(x) = 2x - 1$; $g(x) = x^2 - 4$

64. $f(x) = -2x - 1$; $g(x) = x^2 - 9$

65. $f(x) = -x^2 + 4$; $g(x) = -2x + 1$

66. $f(x) = -x^2 + 9$; $g(x) = 2x + 1$

67. $f(x) = -x^2 + 5x$; $g(x) = x^2 + 3x - 4$

68. $f(x) = -x^2 + 7x - 6$; $g(x) = x^2 + x - 6$

Answer Problems 69 and 70 using the following: A quadratic function of the form $f(x) = ax^2 + bx + c$ with $b^2 - 4ac > 0$ may also be written in the form $f(x) = a(x - r_1)(x - r_2)$, where r_1 and r_2 are the x-intercepts of the graph of the quadratic function.

69. (a) Find a quadratic function whose x-intercepts are -3 and 1 with $a = 1$; $a = 2$; $a = -2$; $a = 5$.
   (b) How does the value of a affect the intercepts?
   (c) How does the value of a affect the axis of symmetry?
   (d) How does the value of a affect the vertex?
   (e) Compare the x-coordinate of the vertex with the midpoint of the x-intercepts. What might you conclude?

70. (a) Find a quadratic function whose x-intercepts are -5 and 3 with $a = 1$; $a = 2$; $a = -2$; $a = 5$.
   (b) How does the value of a affect the intercepts?
   (c) How does the value of a affect the axis of symmetry?
   (d) How does the value of a affect the vertex?
   (e) Compare the x-coordinate of the vertex with the midpoint of the x-intercepts. What might you conclude?

71. Suppose that $f(x) = x^2 + 4x - 21$
   (a) What is the vertex of f?
   (b) What are the x-intercepts of the graph of f?
   (c) Solve $f(x) = -21$ for x. What points are on the graph of f?
   (d) Use the information obtained in parts (a)–(c) to graph $f(x) = x^2 + 4x - 21$.

72. Suppose that $f(x) = x^2 + 2x - 8$
   (a) What is the vertex of f?
   (b) What are the x-intercepts of the graph of f?
   (c) Solve $f(x) = -8$ for x. What points are on the graph of f?
   (d) Use the information obtained in parts (a)–(c) to graph $f(x) = x^2 + 2x - 8$.

73. Find the point on the line $y = x$ that is closest to the point $(3, 1)$.

[**Hint:** Express the distance d from the point to the line as a function of x, and then find the minimum value of $[d(x)]^2$.

74. Find the point on the line $y = x + 1$ that is closest to the point $(4, 1)$.

75. Maximizing Revenue Suppose that the manufacturer of a gas clothes dryer has found that, when the unit price is p dollars, the revenue R (in dollars) is

$$R(p) = -4p^2 + 4000p$$

What unit price should be established for the dryer to maximize revenue? What is the maximum revenue?

76. Maximizing Revenue The John Deere company has found that the revenue, in dollars, from sales of riding mowers is a function of the unit price p, in dollars, that it charges. If the revenue R is

$$R(p) = -\frac{1}{2}p^2 + 1900p$$

what unit price p should be charged to maximize revenue? What is the maximum revenue?

77. Minimizing Marginal Cost The **marginal cost** of a product can be thought of as the cost of producing one additional unit of output. For example, if the marginal cost of producing the 50th product is $6.20, it cost $6.20 to increase production from 49 to 50 units of output. Suppose the marginal cost C (in dollars) to produce x thousand mp3 players is given by the function

$$C(x) = x^2 - 140x + 7400$$

(a) How many players should be produced to minimize the marginal cost?

(b) What is the minimum marginal cost?

78. Minimizing Marginal Cost (See Problem 77.) The marginal cost C (in dollars) of manufacturing x cell phones (in thousands) is given by

$$C(x) = 5x^2 - 200x + 4000$$

(a) How many cell phones should be manufactured to minimize the marginal cost?

(b) What is the minimum marginal cost?

79. Business The monthly revenue R achieved by selling x wristwatches is figured to be $R(x) = 75x - 0.2x^2$. The monthly cost C of selling x wristwatches is $C(x) = 32x + 1750$.

(a) How many wristwatches must the firm sell to maximize revenue? What is the maximum revenue?

(b) Profit is given as $P(x) = R(x) - C(x)$. What is the profit function?

(c) How many wristwatches must the firm sell to maximize profit? What is the maximum profit?

(d) Provide a reasonable explanation as to why the answers found in parts (a) and (c) differ. Explain why a quadratic function is a reasonable model for revenue.

80. Business The daily revenue R achieved by selling x boxes of candy is figured to be $R(x) = 9.5x - 0.04x^2$. The daily cost C of selling x boxes of candy is $C(x) = 1.25x + 250$.

(a) How many boxes of candy must the firm sell to maximize revenue? What is the maximum revenue?

(b) Profit is given as $P(x) = R(x) - C(x)$. What is the profit function?

(c) How many boxes of candy must the firm sell to maximize profit? What is the maximum profit?

(d) Provide a reasonable explanation as to why the answers found in parts (a) and (c) differ. Explain why a quadratic function is a reasonable model for revenue.

81. Stopping Distance An accepted relationship between stopping distance, d (in feet), and the speed of a car, v (in mph), is $d = 1.1v + 0.06v^2$ on dry, level concrete.

(a) How many feet will it take a car traveling 45 mph to stop on dry, level concrete?

(b) If an accident occurs 200 feet ahead of you, what is the maximum speed you can be traveling to avoid being involved?

(c) What might the term $1.1v$ represent?

Source: www2.nsta.org/Energy/fn_braking.html

82. Birthrate of Unmarried Women In the United States, the birthrate B of unmarried women (births per 1000 unmarried women) for women whose age is a is modeled by the function $B(a) = -0.27a^2 + 14.23a - 120.16$.

(a) What is the age of unmarried women with the highest birthrate?

(b) What is the highest birthrate of unmarried women?

(c) Evaluate and interpret $B(40)$.

Source: United States Statistical Abstract, 2009

83. Find a quadratic function whose x-intercepts are -4 and 2 and whose range is $[-18, \infty)$.

84. Find a quadratic function whose x-intercepts are -1 and 5 and whose range is $(-\infty, 9]$.

85. Let $f(x) = ax^2 + bx + c$, where a, b, and c are odd integers. If x is an integer, show that $f(x)$ must be an odd integer.

[**Hint:** x is either an even integer or an odd integer.]

Explaining Concepts: Discussion and Writing

86. Make up a quadratic function that opens down and has only one x-intercept. Compare yours with others in the class. What are the similarities? What are the differences?

87. On one set of coordinate axes, graph the family of parabolas $f(x) = x^2 + 2x + c$ for $c = -3$, $c = 0$, and $c = 1$. Describe the characteristics of a member of this family.

88. On one set of coordinate axes, graph the family of parabolas $f(x) = x^2 + bx + 1$ for $b = -4$, $b = 0$, and $b = 4$. Describe the general characteristics of this family.

89. State the circumstances that cause the graph of a quadratic function $f(x) = ax^2 + bx + c$ to have no x-intercepts.

90. Why does the graph of a quadratic function open up if $a > 0$ and down if $a < 0$?

91. Can a quadratic function have a range of $(-\infty, \infty)$? Justify your answer.

92. What are the possibilities for the number of times the graphs of two different quadratic functions intersect?

'Are You Prepared?' Answers

1. $(0, -9)$, $(-3, 0)$, $(3, 0)$ **2.** $\left\{-4, \frac{1}{2}\right\}$ **3.** $\frac{25}{4}$ **4.** right; 4

3.4 Build Quadratic Models from Verbal Descriptions and from Data

PREPARING FOR THIS SECTION *Before getting started, review the following:*

- Problem Solving (Appendix A, Section A.8, pp. A62–A63)
- Linear Models: Building Linear Functions from Data (Section 3.2, pp. 128–131)

Now Work the *'Are You Prepared?'* problems on page 151.

> **OBJECTIVES** 1 Build Quadratic Models from Verbal Descriptions (p. 146)
> 2 Build Quadratic Models from Data (p. 150)

In this section we first discuss models in the form of a quadratic function when a verbal description of the problem is given. We end the section by fitting a quadratic function to data, which is another form of modeling.

When a mathematical model is in the form of a quadratic function, the properties of the graph of the quadratic function can provide important information about the model. In particular, we can use the quadratic function to determine the maximum or minimum value of the function. The fact that the graph of a quadratic function has a maximum or minimum value enables us to answer questions involving **optimization,** that is, finding the maximum or minimum values in models.

1 Build Quadratic Models from Verbal Descriptions

In economics, revenue R, in dollars, is defined as the amount of money received from the sale of an item and is equal to the unit selling price p, in dollars, of the item times the number x of units actually sold. That is,

$$R = xp$$

The Law of Demand states that p and x are related: As one increases, the other decreases. The equation that relates p and x is called the **demand equation.** When the demand equation is linear, the revenue model is a quadratic function.

EXAMPLE 1

Maximizing Revenue

The marketing department at Texas Instruments has found that, when certain calculators are sold at a price of p dollars per unit, the number x of calculators sold is given by the demand equation

$$x = 21,000 - 150p$$

(a) Find a model that expresses the revenue R as a function of the price p.

(b) What is the domain of R?

(c) What unit price should be used to maximize revenue?

(d) If this price is charged, what is the maximum revenue?

(e) How many units are sold at this price?

(f) Graph R.

(g) What price should Texas Instruments charge to collect at least $675,000 in revenue?

Solution

(a) The revenue R is $R = xp$, where $x = 21,000 - 150p$.

$$R = xp = (21,000 - 150p)p = -150p^2 + 21,000p \quad \text{The Model}$$

(b) Because x represents the number of calculators sold, we have $x \geq 0$, so $21,000 - 150p \geq 0$. Solving this linear inequality, we find that $p \leq 140$. In addition, Texas Instruments will only charge a positive price for the calculator, so $p > 0$. Combining these inequalities, the domain of R is $\{p \,|\, 0 < p \leq 140\}$.

(c) The function R is a quadratic function with $a = -150, b = 21,000$, and $c = 0$. Because $a < 0$, the vertex is the highest point on the parabola. The revenue R is a maximum when the price p is

$$p = -\frac{b}{2a} = -\frac{21,000}{2(-150)} = -\frac{21,000}{-300} = \$70.00$$

$$a = -150, b = 21,000$$

(d) The maximum revenue R is

$$R(70) = -150(70)^2 + 21,000(70) = \$735,000$$

(e) The number of calculators sold is given by the demand equation $x = 21,000 - 150p$. At a price of $p = \$70$,

$$x = 21,000 - 150(70) = 10,500$$

calculators are sold.

(f) To graph R, plot the intercept $(140, 0)$ and the vertex $(70, 735,000)$. See Figure 23 for the graph.

Figure 23

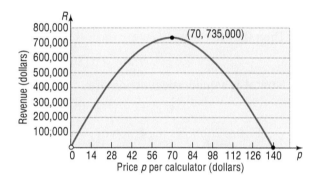

(g) Graph $R = 675,000$ and $R(p) = -150p^2 + 21,000p$ on the same Cartesian plane. See Figure 24. We find where the graphs intersect by solving

$$675,000 = -150p^2 + 21,000p$$
$$150p^2 - 21,000p + 675,000 = 0 \qquad \text{Add } 150p^2 - 21,000p \text{ to both sides.}$$
$$p^2 - 140p + 4500 = 0 \qquad \text{Divide both sides by 150.}$$
$$(p - 50)(p - 90) = 0 \qquad \text{Factor.}$$
$$p = 50 \text{ or } p = 90 \qquad \text{Use the Zero-Product Property.}$$

Figure 24

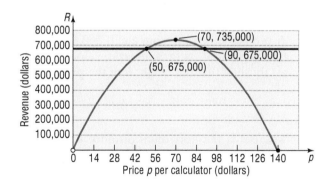

The graphs intersect at $(50, 675,000)$ and $(90, 675,000)$. Based on the graph in Figure 24, Texas Instruments should charge between $50 and $90 to earn at least $675,000 in revenue.

Now Work PROBLEM 3

| EXAMPLE 2 | **Maximizing the Area Enclosed by a Fence** |

A farmer has 2000 yards of fence to enclose a rectangular field. What are the dimensions of the rectangle that encloses the most area?

Figure 25

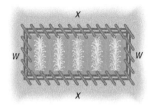

Solution Figure 25 illustrates the situation. The available fence represents the perimeter of the rectangle. If x is the length and w is the width, then

$$2x + 2w = 2000 \qquad\qquad (1)$$

The area A of the rectangle is

$$A = xw$$

To express A in terms of a single variable, solve equation (1) for w and substitute the result in $A = xw$. Then A involves only the variable x. [You could also solve equation (1) for x and express A in terms of w alone. Try it!]

$$2x + 2w = 2000$$
$$2w = 2000 - 2x$$
$$w = \frac{2000 - 2x}{2} = 1000 - x$$

Then the area A is

$$A = xw = x(1000 - x) = -x^2 + 1000x$$

Now, A is a quadratic function of x.

$$A(x) = -x^2 + 1000x \qquad a = -1, b = 1000, c = 0$$

Figure 26

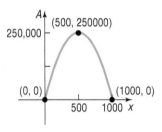

Figure 26 shows the graph of $A(x) = -x^2 + 1000x$. Since $a < 0$, the vertex is a maximum point on the graph of A. The maximum value occurs at

$$x = -\frac{b}{2a} = -\frac{1000}{2(-1)} = 500$$

The maximum value of A is

$$A\left(-\frac{b}{2a}\right) = A(500) = -500^2 + 1000(500) = -250{,}000 + 500{,}000 = 250{,}000$$

The largest rectangle that can be enclosed by 2000 yards of fence has an area of 250,000 square yards. Its dimensions are 500 yards by 500 yards.

━━━━ **Now Work** PROBLEM 7

| EXAMPLE 3 | **Analyzing the Motion of a Projectile** |

A projectile is fired from a cliff 500 feet above the water at an inclination of 45° to the horizontal, with a muzzle velocity of 400 feet per second. In physics, it is established that the height h of the projectile above the water can be modeled by

$$h(x) = \frac{-32x^2}{(400)^2} + x + 500$$

where x is the horizontal distance of the projectile from the base of the cliff. See Figure 27.

Figure 27

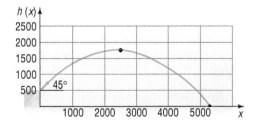

(a) Find the maximum height of the projectile.

(b) How far from the base of the cliff will the projectile strike the water?

Solution (a) The height of the projectile is given by a quadratic function.

$$h(x) = \frac{-32x^2}{(400)^2} + x + 500 = \frac{-1}{5000}x^2 + x + 500$$

We are looking for the maximum value of h. Since $a < 0$, the maximum value is obtained at the vertex, whose x-coordinate is

$$x = -\frac{b}{2a} = -\frac{1}{2\left(-\dfrac{1}{5000}\right)} = \frac{5000}{2} = 2500$$

The maximum height of the projectile is

$$h(2500) = \frac{-1}{5000}(2500)^2 + 2500 + 500 = -1250 + 2500 + 500 = 1750 \text{ ft}$$

(b) The projectile will strike the water when the height is zero. To find the distance x traveled, solve the equation

$$h(x) = \frac{-1}{5000}x^2 + x + 500 = 0$$

The discriminant of this quadratic equation is

$$b^2 - 4ac = 1^2 - 4\left(\frac{-1}{5000}\right)(500) = 1.4$$

Then

$$x = \frac{-b \pm \sqrt{b^2 - 4ac}}{2a} = \frac{-1 \pm \sqrt{1.4}}{2\left(-\dfrac{1}{5000}\right)} \approx \begin{cases} -458 \\ 5458 \end{cases}$$

Discard the negative solution. The projectile will strike the water at a distance of about 5458 feet from the base of the cliff.

Seeing the Concept

Graph

$$h(x) = \frac{-1}{5000}x^2 + x + 500$$

$$0 \le x \le 5500$$

Use MAXIMUM to find the maximum height of the projectile, and use ROOT or ZERO to find the distance from the base of the cliff to where it strikes the water. Compare your results with those obtained in Example 3.

Now Work PROBLEM 11

EXAMPLE 4

The Golden Gate Bridge

The Golden Gate Bridge, a suspension bridge, spans the entrance to San Francisco Bay. Its 746-foot-tall towers are 4200 feet apart. The bridge is suspended from two huge cables more than 3 feet in diameter; the 90-foot-wide roadway is 220 feet above the water. The cables are parabolic in shape* and touch the road surface at the center of the bridge. Find the height of the cable above the road at a distance of 1000 feet from the center.

Solution See Figure 28 on page 150. Begin by choosing the placement of the coordinate axes so that the x-axis coincides with the road surface and the origin coincides with the center of the bridge. As a result, the twin towers will be vertical (height $746 - 220 = 526$ feet above the road) and located 2100 feet from the center. Also, the cable, which has the shape of a parabola, will extend from the towers, open up, and have its vertex at $(0, 0)$. The choice of placement of the axes enables us to identify the equation of the parabola as $y = ax^2, a > 0$. Notice that the points $(-2100, 526)$ and $(2100, 526)$ are on the graph.

* A cable suspended from two towers is in the shape of a **catenary,** but when a horizontal roadway is suspended from the cable, the cable takes the shape of a parabola.

Figure 28

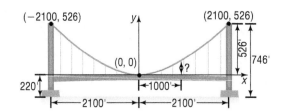

Based on these facts, we can find the value of a in $y = ax^2$.

$$y = ax^2$$
$$526 = a(2100)^2 \quad \text{x = 2100, y = 526}$$
$$a = \frac{526}{(2100)^2}$$

The equation of the parabola is

$$y = \frac{526}{(2100)^2}x^2$$

The height of the cable when $x = 1000$ is

$$y = \frac{526}{(2100)^2}(1000)^2 \approx 119.3 \text{ feet}$$

The cable is 119.3 feet above the road at a distance of 1000 feet from the center of the bridge.

Now Work PROBLEM 13

2 Build Quadratic Models from Data

In Section 3.2, we found the line of best fit for data that appeared to be linearly related. It was noted that data may also follow a nonlinear relation. Figures 29(a) and (b) show scatter diagrams of data that follow a quadratic relation.

Figure 29

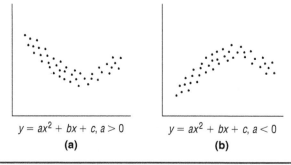

$y = ax^2 + bx + c, a > 0$

(a)

$y = ax^2 + bx + c, a < 0$

(b)

EXAMPLE 5

Fitting a Quadratic Function to Data

The data in Table 8 represent the percentage D of the population that is divorced for various ages x in 2007.

(a) Draw a scatter diagram of the data treating age as the independent variable. Comment on the type of relation that may exist between age and percentage of the population divorced.

(b) Use a graphing utility to find the quadratic function of best fit that models the relation between age and percentage of the population divorced.

(c) Use the model found in part (b) to approximate the age at which the percentage of the population divorced is greatest.

(d) Use the model found in part (b) to approximate the highest percentage of the population that is divorced.

(e) Use a graphing utility to draw the quadratic function of best fit on the scatter diagram.

Table 8

Age, x	Percentage Divorced, D
22	0.8
27	2.8
32	6.4
37	8.7
42	12.3
50	14.5
60	13.8
70	9.6
80	4.9

Source: United States Statistical Abstract, 2009

Solution

(a) Figure 30 shows the scatter diagram, from which it appears the data follow a quadratic relation, with $a < 0$.

Figure 30

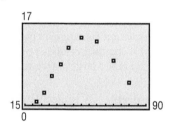

(b) Upon executing the QUADratic REGression program, we obtain the results shown in Figure 31. The output of the utility shows us the equation $y = ax^2 + bx + c$. The quadratic function of best fit that models the relation between age and percentage divorced is

$$D(x) = -0.0136x^2 + 1.4794x - 26.3412 \quad \text{The Model}$$

where a represents age and D represents the percentage divorced.

(c) Based on the quadratic function of best fit, the age with the greatest percentage divorced is

$$-\frac{b}{2a} = -\frac{1.4794}{2(-0.0136)} \approx 54 \text{ years}$$

Figure 31

(d) Evaluate the function $D(x)$ at $x = 54$.

$$D(54) = -0.0136(54)^2 + 1.4794(54) - 26.3412 \approx 13.9 \text{ percent}$$

According to the model, 54-year-olds have the highest percentage divorced at 13.9 percent.

(e) Figure 32 shows the graph of the quadratic function found in part (b) drawn on the scatter diagram.

Figure 32

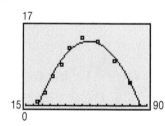

Look again at Figure 31. Notice that the output given by the graphing calculator does not include r, the correlation coefficient. Recall that the correlation coefficient is a measure of the strength of a linear relation that exists between two variables. The graphing calculator does not provide an indication of how well the function fits the data in terms of r since a quadratic function cannot be expressed as a linear function.

═══►**Now Work** PROBLEM 25

3.4 Assess Your Understanding

'Are You Prepared?' *Answers are given at the end of these exercises. If you get a wrong answer, read the pages listed in* red.

1. Translate the following sentence into a mathematical equation: The total revenue R from selling x hot dogs is $3 times the number of hot dogs sold. (pp. A62–A63)

2. Use a graphing utility to find the line of best fit for the following data: (pp. 128–131)

x	3	5	5	6	7	8
y	10	13	12	15	16	19

Applications and Extensions

3. **Maximizing Revenue** The price p (in dollars) and the quantity x sold of a certain product obey the demand equation

$$p = -\frac{1}{6}x + 100$$

(a) Find a model that expresses the revenue R as a function of x. (Remember, $R = xp$.)
(b) What is the domain of R?
(c) What is the revenue if 200 units are sold?
(d) What quantity x maximizes revenue? What is the maximum revenue?
(e) What price should the company charge to maximize revenue?

4. **Maximizing Revenue** The price p (in dollars) and the quantity x sold of a certain product obey the demand equation

$$p = -\frac{1}{3}x + 100$$

(a) Find a model that expresses the revenue R as a function of x.
(b) What is the domain of R?
(c) What is the revenue if 100 units are sold?
(d) What quantity x maximizes revenue? What is the maximum revenue?
(e) What price should the company charge to maximize revenue?

5. **Maximizing Revenue** The price p (in dollars) and the quantity x sold of a certain product obey the demand equation

$$x = -5p + 100 \qquad 0 < p \leq 20$$

(a) Express the revenue R as a function of x.
(b) What is the revenue if 15 units are sold?
(c) What quantity x maximizes revenue? What is the maximum revenue?
(d) What price should the company charge to maximize revenue?
(e) What price should the company charge to earn at least $480 in revenue?

6. **Maximizing Revenue** The price p (in dollars) and the quantity x sold of a certain product obey the demand equation

$$x = -20p + 500 \qquad 0 < p \leq 25$$

(a) Express the revenue R as a function of x.
(b) What is the revenue if 20 units are sold?
(c) What quantity x maximizes revenue? What is the maximum revenue?
(d) What price should the company charge to maximize revenue?
(e) What price should the company charge to earn at least $3000 in revenue?

7. **Enclosing a Rectangular Field** David has 400 yards of fencing and wishes to enclose a rectangular area.
(a) Express the area A of the rectangle as a function of the width w of the rectangle.
(b) For what value of w is the area largest?
(c) What is the maximum area?

8. **Enclosing a Rectangular Field** Beth has 3000 feet of fencing available to enclose a rectangular field.
(a) Express the area A of the rectangle as a function of x, where x is the length of the rectangle.
(b) For what value of x is the area largest?
(c) What is the maximum area?

9. **Enclosing the Most Area with a Fence** A farmer with 4000 meters of fencing wants to enclose a rectangular plot that borders on a river. If the farmer does not fence the side along the river, what is the largest area that can be enclosed? (See the figure.)

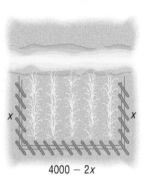

4000 − 2x

10. **Enclosing the Most Area with a Fence** A farmer with 2000 meters of fencing wants to enclose a rectangular plot that borders on a straight highway. If the farmer does not fence the side along the highway, what is the largest area that can be enclosed?

11. **Analyzing the Motion of a Projectile** A projectile is fired from a cliff 200 feet above the water at an inclination of 45° to the horizontal, with a muzzle velocity of 50 feet per second. The height h of the projectile above the water is modeled by

$$h(x) = \frac{-32x^2}{(50)^2} + x + 200$$

where x is the horizontal distance of the projectile from the face of the cliff.
(a) At what horizontal distance from the face of the cliff is the height of the projectile a maximum?
(b) Find the maximum height of the projectile.
(c) At what horizontal distance from the face of the cliff will the projectile strike the water?
(d) Using a graphing utility, graph the function h, $0 \leq x \leq 200$.
(e) Use a graphing utility to verify the solutions found in parts (b) and (c).
(f) When the height of the projectile is 100 feet above the water, how far is it from the cliff?

12. **Analyzing the Motion of a Projectile** A projectile is fired at an inclination of 45° to the horizontal, with a muzzle velocity of 100 feet per second. The height h of the projectile is modeled by

$$h(x) = \frac{-32x^2}{(100)^2} + x$$

where x is the horizontal distance of the projectile from the firing point.
(a) At what horizontal distance from the firing point is the height of the projectile a maximum?
(b) Find the maximum height of the projectile.
(c) At what horizontal distance from the firing point will the projectile strike the ground?
(d) Using a graphing utility, graph the function h, $0 \leq x \leq 350$.

(e) Use a graphing utility to verify the results obtained in parts (b) and (c).

(f) When the height of the projectile is 50 feet above the ground, how far has it traveled horizontally?

13. **Suspension Bridge** A suspension bridge with weight uniformly distributed along its length has twin towers that extend 75 meters above the road surface and are 400 meters apart. The cables are parabolic in shape and are suspended from the tops of the towers. The cables touch the road surface at the center of the bridge. Find the height of the cables at a point 100 meters from the center. (Assume that the road is level.)

14. **Architecture** A parabolic arch has a span of 120 feet and a maximum height of 25 feet. Choose suitable rectangular coordinate axes and find the equation of the parabola. Then calculate the height of the arch at points 10 feet, 20 feet, and 40 feet from the center.

15. **Constructing Rain Gutters** A rain gutter is to be made of aluminum sheets that are 12 inches wide by turning up the edges 90°. See the illustration.

(a) What depth will provide maximum cross-sectional area and hence allow the most water to flow?

(b) What depths will allow at least 16 square inches of water to flow?

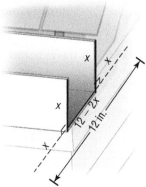

16. **Norman Windows** A **Norman window** has the shape of a rectangle surmounted by a semicircle of diameter equal to the width of the rectangle. See the figure. If the perimeter of the window is 20 feet, what dimensions will admit the most light (maximize the area)?

[**Hint:** Circumference of a circle $= 2\pi r$; area of a circle $= \pi r^2$, where r is the radius of the circle.]

17. **Constructing a Stadium** A track and field playing area is in the shape of a rectangle with semicircles at each end. See the figure. The inside perimeter of the track is to be 1500 meters. What should the dimensions of the rectangle be so that the area of the rectangle is a maximum?

18. **Architecture** A special window has the shape of a rectangle surmounted by an equilateral triangle. See the figure. If the perimeter of the window is 16 feet, what dimensions will admit the most light?

[**Hint:** Area of an equilateral triangle $= \left(\dfrac{\sqrt{3}}{4}\right)x^2$, where x is the length of a side of the triangle.]

19. **Chemical Reactions** A self-catalytic chemical reaction results in the formation of a compound that causes the formation ratio to increase. If the reaction rate V is modeled by

$$V(x) = kx(a - x), \qquad 0 \le x \le a$$

where k is a positive constant, a is the initial amount of the compound, and x is the variable amount of the compound, for what value of x is the reaction rate a maximum?

20. **Calculus: Simpson's Rule** The figure shows the graph of $y = ax^2 + bx + c$. Suppose that the points $(-h, y_0)$, $(0, y_1)$, and (h, y_2) are on the graph. It can be shown that the area enclosed by the parabola, the x-axis, and the lines $x = -h$ and $x = h$ is

$$\text{Area} = \frac{h}{3}(2ah^2 + 6c)$$

Show that this area may also be given by

$$\text{Area} = \frac{h}{3}(y_0 + 4y_1 + y_2)$$

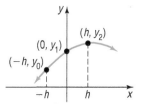

21. Use the result obtained in Problem 20 to find the area enclosed by $f(x) = -5x^2 + 8$, the x-axis, and the lines $x = -1$ and $x = 1$.

22. Use the result obtained in Problem 20 to find the area enclosed by $f(x) = 2x^2 + 8$, the x-axis, and the lines $x = -2$ and $x = 2$.

23. Use the result obtained in Problem 20 to find the area enclosed by $f(x) = x^2 + 3x + 5$, the x-axis, and the lines $x = -4$ and $x = 4$.

24. Use the result obtained in Problem 20 to find the area enclosed by $f(x) = -x^2 + x + 4$, the x-axis, and the lines $x = -1$ and $x = 1$.

25. Life Cycle Hypothesis An individual's income varies with his or her age. The following table shows the median income I of males of different age groups within the United States for 2006. For each age group, let the class midpoint represent the independent variable, x. For the class "65 years and older," we will assume that the class midpoint is 69.5.

Age	Class Midpoint, x	Median Income, I
15–24 years	19.5	$10,964
25–34 years	29.5	$32,131
35–44 years	39.5	$42,637
45–54 years	49.5	$45,693
55–64 years	59.5	$41,477
65 years and older	69.5	$23,500

Source: U.S. Census Bureau

(a) Use a graphing utility to draw a scatter diagram of the data. Comment on the type of relation that may exist between the two variables.
(b) Use a graphing utility to find the quadratic function of best fit that models the relation between age and median income.
(c) Use the function found in part (b) to determine the age at which an individual can expect to earn the most income.
(d) Use the function found in part (b) to predict the peak income earned.
(e) With a graphing utility, graph the quadratic function of best fit on the scatter diagram.

26. Height of a Ball A shot-putter throws a ball at an inclination of 45° to the horizontal. The following data represent the height of the ball h at the instant that it has traveled x feet horizontally.

Distance, x	Height, h
20	25
40	40
60	55
80	65
100	71
120	77
140	77
160	75
180	71
200	64

(a) Use a graphing utility to draw a scatter diagram of the data. Comment on the type of relation that may exist between the two variables.
(b) Use a graphing utility to find the quadratic function of best fit that models the relation between distance and height.
(c) Use the function found in part (b) to determine how far the ball will travel before it reaches its maximum height.
(d) Use the function found in part (b) to find the maximum height of the ball.
(e) With a graphing utility, graph the quadratic function of best fit on the scatter diagram.

Mixed Practice

27. Which Model? The following data represent the square footage and rents (dollars per month) for apartments in the Del Mar area of San Diego, California.

Square Footage, x	Rent per Month, R
686	1600
770	1665
817	1750
800	1685
809	1700
901	1770
803	1725

Source: apartments.com

(a) Using a graphing utility, draw a scatter diagram of the data treating square footage as the independent variable. What type of relation appears to exist between square footage and rent?
(b) Based on your response to part (a), find either a linear or quadratic model that describes the relation between square footage and rent.
(c) Use your model to predict the rent of an apartment in San Diego that is 850 square feet.

28. Which Model? An engineer collects the following data showing the speed s of a Toyota Camry and its average miles per gallon, M.

Speed, s	Miles per Gallon, M
30	18
35	20
40	23
40	25
45	25
50	28
55	30
60	29
65	26
65	25
70	25

(a) Using a graphing utility, draw a scatter diagram of the data treating speed as the independent variable. What type of relation appears to exist between speed and miles per gallon?

(b) Based on your response to part (a), find either a linear or quadratic model that describes the relation between speed and miles per gallon.

(c) Use your model to predict the miles per gallon for a Camry that is traveling 63 miles per hour.

29. Which Model? The following data represent the percentage of the U.S. population whose age is *x* who do not have a high school diploma as of March 2005.

Age, *a*	Percentage without a High School Diploma, *P*
30	13.3
40	11.6
50	10.9
60	13.7
70	22.3
80	30.2

Source: U.S. Census Bureau

(a) Using a graphing utility, draw a scatter diagram of the data treating age as the independent variable. What type of relation appears to exist between age and percentage of the population without a high school diploma?

(b) Based on your response to part (a), find either a linear or quadratic model that describes the relation between age and percentage of the population that do not have a high school diploma.

(c) Use your model to predict the percentage of 35-year-olds that do not have a high school diploma.

30. Which Model? A cricket makes a chirping noise by sliding its wings together rapidly. Perhaps you have noticed that the number of chirps seems to increase with the temperature. The following data list the temperature (in degrees Fahrenheit) and the number of chirps per second for the striped ground cricket.

Temperature, *x*	Chirps per Second, *C*
88.6	20.0
93.3	19.8
80.6	17.1
69.7	14.7
69.4	15.4
79.6	15.0
80.6	16.0
76.3	14.4
75.2	15.5

Source: Pierce, George W. *The Songs of Insects.* Cambridge, MA Harvard University Press, 1949, pp. 12–21

(a) Using a graphing utility, draw a scatter diagram of the data treating temperature as the independent variable. What type of relation appears to exist between temperature and chirps per second?

(b) Based on your response to part (a), find either a linear or quadratic model that best describes the relation between temperature and chirps per second.

(c) Use your model to predict the chirps per second if the temperature is 80°F.

Explaining Concepts: Discussion and Writing

31. Refer to Example 1 on page 146. Notice that if the price charged for the calculators is $0 or $140 the revenue is $0. It is easy to explain why revenue would be $0 if the price charged is $0, but how can revenue be $0 if the price charged is $140?

'Are You Prepared?' Answers

1. $R = 3x$ **2.** $y = 1.7826x + 4.0652$

3.5 Inequalities Involving Quadratic Functions

PREPARING FOR THIS SECTION *Before getting started, review the following:*

- Solve Inequalities (Appendix A, Section A.9, pp. A75–A78)

- Interval Notation (Appendix A, Section A.9, pp. A72–A73)

Now Work the 'Are You Prepared?' problems on page 158.

OBJECTIVE 1 Solve Inequalities Involving a Quadratic Function (p. 155)

1 Solve Inequalities Involving a Quadratic Function

In this section we solve inequalities that involve quadratic functions. We will accomplish this by using their graphs. For example, to solve the inequality

$$ax^2 + bx + c > 0 \qquad a \neq 0$$

graph the function $f(x) = ax^2 + bx + c$ and, from the graph, determine where it is above the x-axis, that is, where $f(x) > 0$. To solve the inequality $ax^2 + bx + c < 0, a \neq 0$, graph the function $f(x) = ax^2 + bx + c$ and determine where the graph is below the x-axis. If the inequality is not strict, include the x-intercepts, if any, in the solution.

EXAMPLE 1

Solving an Inequality

Solve the inequality $x^2 - 4x - 12 \leq 0$ and graph the solution set.

Solution

Figure 33

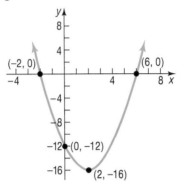

Graph the function $f(x) = x^2 - 4x - 12$. The intercepts are

y-intercept:	$f(0) = -12$	Evaluate f at 0.
x-intercepts (if any):	$x^2 - 4x - 12 = 0$	Solve $f(x) = 0$.
	$(x - 6)(x + 2) = 0$	Factor.
	$x - 6 = 0$ or $x + 2 = 0$	Apply the Zero-Product Property.
	$x = 6$ or $x = -2$	

The y-intercept is -12; the x-intercepts are -2 and 6.

The vertex is at $x = -\dfrac{b}{2a} = -\dfrac{-4}{2} = 2$. Since $f(2) = -16$, the vertex is $(2, -16)$.

See Figure 33 for the graph.

The graph is below the x-axis for $-2 < x < 6$. Since the original inequality is not strict, include the x-intercepts. The solution set is $\{x | -2 \leq x \leq 6\}$ or, using interval notation, $[-2, 6]$. See Figure 34 for the graph of the solution set.

Figure 34

════ **Now Work** PROBLEM 9

EXAMPLE 2

Solving an Inequality

Solve the inequality $2x^2 < x + 10$ and graph the solution set.

Solution

Method 1   Rearrange the inequality so that 0 is on the right side.

$$2x^2 < x + 10$$
$$2x^2 - x - 10 < 0 \qquad \text{Subtract } x + 10 \text{ from both sides.}$$

This inequality is equivalent to the one that we want to solve.

Next graph the function $f(x) = 2x^2 - x - 10$ to find where $f(x) < 0$. The intercepts are

Figure 35

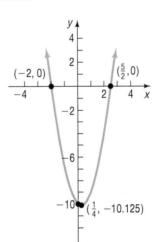

y-intercept:	$f(0) = -10$	Evaluate f at 0.
x-intercepts (if any):	$2x^2 - x - 10 = 0$	Solve $f(x) = 0$.
	$(2x - 5)(x + 2) = 0$	Factor.
	$2x - 5 = 0$ or $x + 2 = 0$	Apply the Zero-Product Property.
	$x = \dfrac{5}{2}$ or $x = -2$	

The y-intercept is -10; the x-intercepts are -2 and $\dfrac{5}{2}$.

The vertex is at $x = -\dfrac{b}{2a} = -\dfrac{-1}{4} = \dfrac{1}{4}$. Since $f\left(\dfrac{1}{4}\right) = -10.125$, the vertex is $\left(\dfrac{1}{4}, -10.125\right)$. See Figure 35 for the graph.

The graph is below the x-axis ($f(x) < 0$) between $x = -2$ and $x = \dfrac{5}{2}$. Since the inequality is strict, the solution set is $\left\{ x \middle| -2 < x < \dfrac{5}{2} \right\}$ or, using interval notation, $\left(-2, \dfrac{5}{2} \right)$.

Method 2 If $f(x) = 2x^2$ and $g(x) = x + 10$, the inequality that we want to solve is $f(x) < g(x)$. Graph the functions $f(x) = 2x^2$ and $g(x) = x + 10$. See Figure 36. The graphs intersect where $f(x) = g(x)$. Then

$$2x^2 = x + 10 \qquad\qquad f(x) = g(x)$$
$$2x^2 - x - 10 = 0$$
$$(2x - 5)(x + 2) = 0 \qquad\qquad \text{Factor.}$$
$$2x - 5 = 0 \quad \text{or} \quad x + 2 = 0 \qquad \text{Apply the Zero-Product Property.}$$
$$x = \frac{5}{2} \quad \text{or} \qquad x = -2$$

Figure 36

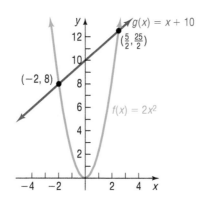

The graphs intersect at the points $(-2, 8)$ and $\left(\dfrac{5}{2}, \dfrac{25}{2} \right)$. To solve $f(x) < g(x)$, we need to find where the graph of f is below the graph of g. This happens between the points of intersection. Since the inequality is strict, the solution set is $\left\{ x \middle| -2 < x < \dfrac{5}{2} \right\}$ or, using interval notation, $\left(-2, \dfrac{5}{2} \right)$.

Figure 37

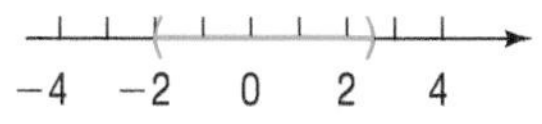

See Figure 37 for the graph of the solution set. ⤶

━━━ **Now Work** PROBLEMS **5** AND **13**

EXAMPLE 3 **Solving an Inequality**

Solve the inequality $x^2 + x + 1 > 0$ and graph the solution set.

Figure 38

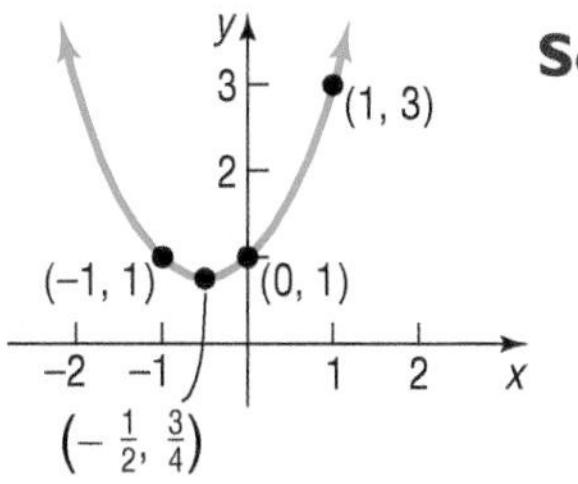

Solution Graph the function $f(x) = x^2 + x + 1$. The y-intercept is 1; there are no x-intercepts (Do you see why? Check the discriminants). The vertex is at $x = -\dfrac{b}{2a} = -\dfrac{1}{2}$. Since $f\left(-\dfrac{1}{2} \right) = \dfrac{3}{4}$, the vertex is at $\left(-\dfrac{1}{2}, \dfrac{3}{4} \right)$. The points $(1, 3)$ and $(-1, 1)$ are also on the graph. See Figure 38.

The graph of f lies above the x-axis for all x. The solution set is the set of all real numbers. See Figure 39. ⤶

Figure 39

━━━ **Now Work** PROBLEM **17**

3.5 Assess Your Understanding

'Are You Prepared?' *Answers are given at the end of these exercises. If you get a wrong answer, read the pages listed in* red.

1. Solve the inequality $-3x - 2 < 7$. (pp. A75–A78)

2. Write the interval $(-2, 7]$ using inequality notation. (pp. A72–A73)

Skill Building

In Problems 3–6, use the figure to solve each inequality.

3.
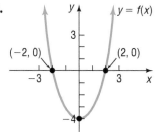

4.
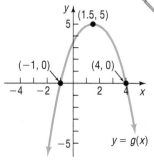

5.
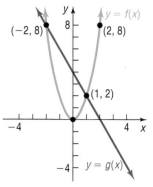

6.
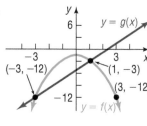

(a) $f(x) > 0$
(b) $f(x) \leq 0$

(a) $g(x) < 0$
(b) $g(x) \geq 0$

(a) $g(x) \geq f(x)$
(b) $f(x) > g(x)$

(a) $f(x) < g(x)$
(b) $f(x) \geq g(x)$

In Problems 7–22, solve each inequality.

7. $x^2 - 3x - 10 < 0$

8. $x^2 + 3x - 10 > 0$

9. $x^2 - 4x > 0$

10. $x^2 + 8x > 0$

11. $x^2 - 9 < 0$

12. $x^2 - 1 < 0$

13. $x^2 + x > 12$

14. $x^2 + 7x < -12$

15. $2x^2 < 5x + 3$

16. $6x^2 < 6 + 5x$

17. $x^2 - x + 1 \leq 0$

18. $x^2 + 2x + 4 > 0$

19. $4x^2 + 9 < 6x$

20. $25x^2 + 16 < 40x$

21. $6(x^2 - 1) > 5x$

22. $2(2x^2 - 3x) > -9$

Mixed Practice

23. What is the domain of the function $f(x) = \sqrt{x^2 - 16}$?

24. What is the domain of the function $f(x) = \sqrt{x - 3x^2}$?

In Problems 25–32, use the given functions f and g.

(a) *Solve* $f(x) = 0$.
(b) *Solve* $g(x) = 0$.
(c) *Solve* $f(x) = g(x)$.
(d) *Solve* $f(x) > 0$.
(e) *Solve* $g(x) \leq 0$.
(f) *Solve* $f(x) > g(x)$.
(g) *Solve* $f(x) \geq 1$.

25. $f(x) = x^2 - 1$
$g(x) = 3x + 3$

26. $f(x) = -x^2 + 3$
$g(x) = -3x + 3$

27. $f(x) = -x^2 + 1$
$g(x) = 4x + 1$

28. $f(x) = -x^2 + 4$
$g(x) = -x - 2$

29. $f(x) = x^2 - 4$
$g(x) = -x^2 + 4$

30. $f(x) = x^2 - 2x + 1$
$g(x) = -x^2 + 1$

31. $f(x) = x^2 - x - 2$
$g(x) = x^2 + x - 2$

32. $f(x) = -x^2 - x + 1$
$g(x) = -x^2 + x + 6$

Applications and Extensions

33. Physics A ball is thrown vertically upward with an initial velocity of 80 feet per second. The distance s

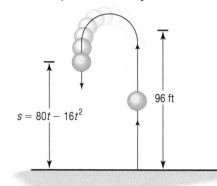

$s = 80t - 16t^2$

96 ft

(in feet) of the ball from the ground after t seconds is $s(t) = 80t - 16t^2$.
(a) At what time t will the ball strike the ground?
(b) For what time t is the ball more than 96 feet above the ground?

34. Physics A ball is thrown vertically upward with an initial velocity of 96 feet per second. The distance s (in feet) of the ball from the ground after t seconds is $s(t) = 96t - 16t^2$.
(a) At what time t will the ball strike the ground?
(b) For what time t is the ball more than 128 feet above the ground?

35. Revenue Suppose that the manufacturer of a gas clothes dryer has found that, when the unit price is p dollars, the revenue R (in dollars) is

$$R(p) = -4p^2 + 4000p$$

(a) At what prices p is revenue zero?

(b) For what range of prices will revenue exceed $800,000?

36. **Revenue** The John Deere company has found that the revenue from sales of heavy-duty tractors is a function of the unit price p, in dollars, that it charges. If the revenue R, in dollars, is

$$R(p) = -\frac{1}{2}p^2 + 1900p$$

(a) At what prices p is revenue zero?

(b) For what range of prices will revenue exceed $1,200,000?

37. **Artillery** A projectile fired from the point $(0,0)$ at an angle to the positive x-axis has a trajectory given by

$$y = cx - (1 + c^2)\left(\frac{g}{2}\right)\left(\frac{x}{v}\right)^2$$

where

x = horizontal distance in meters

y = height in meters

v = initial muzzle velocity in meters per second (m/sec)

g = acceleration due to gravity = 9.81 meters per second squared (m/sec^2)

$c > 0$ is a constant determined by the angle of elevation.

A howitzer fires an artillery round with a muzzle velocity of 897 m/sec.

(a) If the round must clear a hill 200 meters high at a distance of 2000 meters in front of the howitzer, what c values are permitted in the trajectory equation?

(b) If the goal in part (a) is to hit a target on the ground 75 kilometers away, is it possible to do so? If so, for what values of c? If not, what is the maximum distance the round will travel?

Source: www.answers.com

38. **Runaway Car** Using Hooke's Law, we can show that the *work* done in compressing a spring a distance of x feet from its at-rest position is $W = \frac{1}{2}kx^2$, where k is a stiffness constant depending on the spring. It can also be shown that the work done by a body in motion before it comes to rest is given by $\tilde{W} = \frac{w}{2g}v^2$, where w = weight of the object (lb), g = acceleration due to gravity (32.2 ft/sec^2), and v = object's velocity (in ft/sec). A parking garage has a spring shock absorber at the end of a ramp to stop runaway cars. The spring has a stiffness constant k = 9450 lb/ft and must be able to stop a 4000-lb car traveling at 25 mph. What is the least compression required of the spring? Express your answer using feet to the nearest tenth.

[**Hint:** Solve $W > \tilde{W}$, $x \geq 0$.]

Source: www.sciforums.com

Explaining Concepts: Discussion and Writing

39. Show that the inequality $(x - 4)^2 \leq 0$ has exactly one solution.

40. Show that the inequality $(x - 2)^2 > 0$ has one real number that is not a solution.

41. Explain why the inequality $x^2 + x + 1 > 0$ has all real numbers as the solution set.

42. Explain why the inequality $x^2 - x + 1 < 0$ has the empty set as solution set.

43. Explain the circumstances under which the x-intercepts of the graph of a quadratic function are included in the solution set of a quadratic inequality.

'Are You Prepared?' Answers

1. $\{x | x > -3\}$ or $(-3, \infty)$

2. $-2 < x \leq 7$

CHAPTER REVIEW

Things to Know

Linear function (p. 118)

$f(x) = mx + b$

Average rate of change = m

The graph is a line with slope m and y-intercept b.

Quadratic function (pp. 135–139)

$f(x) = ax^2 + bx + c, a \neq 0$

The graph is a parabola that opens up if $a > 0$ and opens down if $a < 0$.

Vertex: $\left(-\frac{b}{2a}, f\left(-\frac{b}{2a}\right)\right)$

Axis of symmetry: $x = -\frac{b}{2a}$

y-intercept: $f(0) = c$

x-intercept(s): If any, found by finding the real solutions of the equation $ax^2 + bx + c = 0$

Objectives

Section		You should be able to ...	Examples	Review Exercises
3.1	1	Graph linear functions (p. 118)	1	1(a)–6(a), 1(b)–6(b)
	2	Use average rate of change to identify linear functions (p. 118)	2	7, 8
	3	Determine whether a linear function is increasing, decreasing, or constant (p. 121)	3	1(d)–6(d)
	4	Build linear models from verbal descriptions (p. 122)	4, 5	37, 38
3.2	1	Draw and interpret scatter diagrams (p. 128)	1	46(a), 47(a)
	2	Distinguish between linear and nonlinear relations (p. 129)	2	46(b), 47(a)
	3	Use a graphing utility to find the line of best fit (p. 130)	4	46(c)
3.3	1	Graph a quadratic function using transformations (p. 136)	1	9–14
	2	Identify the vertex and axis of symmetry of a quadratic function (p. 138)	2	15–24
	3	Graph a quadratic function using its vertex, axis, and intercepts (p. 138)	3–5	15–24
	4	Find a quadratic function given its vertex and one other point (p. 141)	6	35, 36
	5	Find the maximum or minimum value of a quadratic function (p. 142)	7	25–30, 39–44
3.4	1	Build quadratic models from verbal descriptions (p. 146)	1–4	39–45
	2	Build quadratic models from data (p. 150)	5	47
3.5	1	Solve inequalities involving a quadratic function (p. 155)	1–3	31–34

Review Exercises

In Problems 1–6:

(a) *Determine the slope and y-intercept of each linear function.*
(b) *Find the average rate of change of each function.*
(c) *Graph each function. Label the intercepts.*
(d) *Determine whether the function is increasing, decreasing, or constant.*

1. $f(x) = 2x - 5$ **2.** $g(x) = -4x + 7$ **3.** $h(x) = \dfrac{4}{5}x - 6$

4. $F(x) = -\dfrac{1}{3}x + 1$ **5.** $G(x) = 4$ **6.** $H(x) = -3$

In Problems 7 and 8, determine whether the function is linear or nonlinear. If the function is linear, state its slope.

7.

x	y = f(x)
−1	−2
0	3
1	8
2	13
3	18

8.

x	y = g(x)
−1	−3
0	4
1	7
2	6
3	1

In Problems 9–14, graph each quadratic function using transformations (shifting, compressing, stretching, and/or reflecting).

9. $f(x) = (x - 2)^2 + 2$ **10.** $f(x) = (x + 1)^2 - 4$ **11.** $f(x) = -(x - 4)^2$

12. $f(x) = (x - 1)^2 - 3$ **13.** $f(x) = 2(x + 1)^2 + 4$ **14.** $f(x) = -3(x + 2)^2 + 1$

In Problems 15–24, (a) graph each quadratic function by determining whether its graph opens up or down and by finding its vertex, axis of symmetry, y-intercept, and x-intercepts, if any. (b) Determine the domain and the range of the function. (c) Determine where the function is increasing and where it is decreasing.

15. $f(x) = (x - 2)^2 + 2$ **16.** $f(x) = (x + 1)^2 - 4$ **17.** $f(x) = \dfrac{1}{4}x^2 - 16$ **18.** $f(x) = -\dfrac{1}{2}x^2 + 2$

19. $f(x) = -4x^2 + 4x$ **20.** $f(x) = 9x^2 - 6x + 3$ **21.** $f(x) = \dfrac{9}{2}x^2 + 3x + 1$ **22.** $f(x) = -x^2 + x + \dfrac{1}{2}$

23. $f(x) = 3x^2 + 4x - 1$ **24.** $f(x) = -2x^2 - x + 4$

In Problems 25–30, determine whether the given quadratic function has a maximum value or a minimum value, and then find the value.

25. $f(x) = 3x^2 - 6x + 4$ **26.** $f(x) = 2x^2 + 8x + 5$ **27.** $f(x) = -x^2 + 8x - 4$

28. $f(x) = -x^2 - 10x - 3$ **29.** $f(x) = -3x^2 + 12x + 4$ **30.** $f(x) = -2x^2 + 4$

In Problems 31–34, solve each quadratic inequality.

31. $x^2 + 6x - 16 < 0$ **32.** $3x^2 - 2x - 1 \geq 0$ **33.** $3x^2 \geq 14x + 5$ **34.** $4x^2 < 13x - 3$

In Problems 35 and 36, find the quadratic function for which:

35. Vertex is $(-1, 2)$; contains the point $(1, 6)$

36. Vertex is $(3, -4)$; contains the point $(4, 2)$

37. Comparing Phone Companies Marissa must decide between one of two companies as her long-distance phone provider. Company A charges a monthly fee of $7.00 plus $0.06 per minute, while Company B does not have a monthly fee, but charges $0.08 per minute.
  (a) Find a linear function that relates cost, C, to total minutes on the phone, x, for each company.
  (b) Determine the number of minutes x for which the bill from Company A will equal the bill from Company B.
  (c) Over what interval of minutes x will the bill from Company B be less than the bill from Company A?

38. Sales Commissions Bill was just offered a sales position for a computer company. His salary would be $15,000 per year plus 1% of his total annual sales.
  (a) Find a linear function that relates Bill's annual salary, S, to his total annual sales, x.
  (b) In 2010, Bill had total annual sales of $1,000,000. What was Bill's salary?
  (c) What would Bill have to sell to earn $100,000?
  (d) Determine the sales required of Bill for his salary to exceed $150,000.

39. Demand Equation The price p (in dollars) and the quantity x sold of a certain product obey the demand equation

$$p = -\frac{1}{10}x + 150 \qquad 0 \leq x \leq 1500$$

  (a) Express the revenue R as a function of x.
  (b) What is the revenue if 100 units are sold?
  (c) What quantity x maximizes revenue? What is the maximum revenue?
  (d) What price should the company charge to maximize revenue?

40. Landscaping A landscape engineer has 200 feet of border to enclose a rectangular pond. What dimensions will result in the largest pond?

41. Enclosing the Most Area with a Fence A farmer with 10,000 meters of fencing wants to enclose a rectangular field and then divide it into two plots with a fence parallel to one of

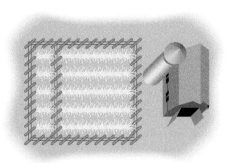

the sides. See the figure. What is the largest area that can be enclosed?

42. Architecture A special window in the shape of a rectangle with semicircles at each end is to be constructed so that the outside dimensions are 100 feet in length. See the illustration. Find the dimensions of the rectangle that maximizes its area.

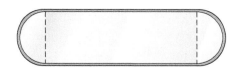

43. Minimizing Marginal Cost Callaway Golf Company has determined that the marginal cost C of manufacturing x Big Bertha golf clubs may be expressed by the quadratic function

$$C(x) = 4.9x^2 - 617.4x + 19,600$$

  (a) How many clubs should be manufactured to minimize the marginal cost?
  (b) At this level of production, what is the marginal cost?

44. A rectangle has one vertex on the line $y = 10 - x$, $x > 0$, another at the origin, one on the positive x-axis, and one on the positive y-axis. Express the area A of the rectangle as a function of x. Find the largest area A that can be enclosed by the rectangle.

45. Parabolic Arch Bridge A horizontal bridge is in the shape of a parabolic arch. Given the information shown in the figure, what is the height h of the arch 2 feet from shore?

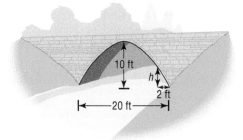

46. Bone Length Research performed at NASA, led by Dr. Emily R. Morey-Holton, measured the lengths of the right humerus and right tibia in 11 rats that were sent to space on Spacelab Life Sciences 2. The data on page 162 were collected.
  (a) Draw a scatter diagram of the data treating length of the right humerus as the independent variable.
  (b) Based on the scatter diagram, do you think that there is a linear relation between the length of the right humerus and the length of the right tibia?
  (c) Use a graphing utility to find the line of best fit relating length of the right humerus and length of the right tibia.

(d) Predict the length of the right tibia on a rat whose right humerus is 26.5 millimeters (mm).

Right Humerus (mm), x	Right Tibia (mm), y
24.80	36.05
24.59	35.57
24.59	35.57
24.29	34.58
23.81	34.20
24.87	34.73
25.90	37.38
26.11	37.96
26.63	37.46
26.31	37.75
26.84	38.50

Source: NASA Life Sciences Data Archive

47. Advertising A small manufacturing firm collected the following data on advertising expenditures A (in thousands of dollars) and total revenue R (in thousands of dollars).
 (a) Draw a scatter diagram of the data. Comment on the type of relation that may exist between the two variables.

Advertising	Total Revenue
20	$6101
22	$6222
25	$6350
25	$6378
27	$6453
28	$6423
29	$6360
31	$6231

(b) The quadratic function of best fit to these data is
$$R(A) = -7.76A^2 + 411.88A + 942.72$$
Use this function to determine the optimal level of advertising.
(c) Use the function to predict the total revenue when the optimal level of advertising is spent.
(d) Use a graphing utility to verify that the function given in part (b) is the quadratic function of best fit.
(e) Use a graphing utility to draw a scatter diagram of the data and then graph the quadratic function of best fit on the scatter diagram.

CHAPTER TEST CHAPTER **Test Prep** VIDEOS

The Chapter Test Prep Videos are step-by-step test solutions available in the Video Resources DVD, in *MyMathLab*, or on this text's You Tube™ Channel. Flip back to the Student Resources page to see the exact web address for this text's YouTube channel.

1. For the linear function $f(x) = -4x + 3$,
 (a) Find the slope and y-intercept.
 (b) What is the average rate of change of f?
 (c) Determine whether f is increasing, decreasing, or constant.
 (d) Graph f.

In Problems 2 and 3, find the intercepts of each quadratic function.

2. $f(x) = 3x^2 - 2x - 8$

3. $G(x) = -2x^2 + 4x + 1$

4. Given that $f(x) = x^2 + 3x$ and $g(x) = 5x + 3$, solve $f(x) = g(x)$. Graph each function and label the points of intersection.

5. Graph $f(x) = (x - 3)^2 - 2$ using transformations.

6. For the quadratic function $f(x) = 3x^2 - 12x + 4$,
 (a) Determine whether the graph opens up or down.
 (b) Determine the vertex.
 (c) Determine the axis of symmetry.
 (d) Determine the intercepts.
 (e) Use the information from parts (a)–(d) to graph f.

7. Determine whether $f(x) = -2x^2 + 12x + 3$ has a maximum or minimum value. Then find the maximum or minimum value.

8. Solve $x^2 - 10x + 24 \geq 0$.

9. **RV Rental**   The weekly rental cost of a 20-foot recreational vehicle is $129.50 plus $0.15 per mile.
   (a) Find a linear function that expresses the cost C as a function of miles driven m.
   (b) What is the rental cost if 860 miles are driven?
   (c) How many miles were driven if the rental cost is $213.80?

CUMULATIVE REVIEW

1. Find the distance between the points $P = (-1, 3)$ and $Q = (4, -2)$. Find the midpoint of the line segment P to Q.

2. Which of the following points are on the graph of $y = x^3 - 3x + 1$?
   (a) $(-2, -1)$
   (b) $(2, 3)$
   (c) $(3, 1)$

3. Solve the inequality $5x + 3 \geq 0$ and graph the solution set.

4. Find the equation of the line containing the points $(-1, 4)$ and $(2, -2)$. Express your answer in slope–intercept form and graph the line.

5. Find the equation of the line perpendicular to the line $y = 2x + 1$ and containing the point $(3, 5)$. Express your answer in slope–intercept form and graph the line.

6. Graph the equation $x^2 + y^2 - 4x + 8y - 5 = 0$.

7. Does the following relation represent a function? $\{(-3, 8), (1, 3), (2, 5), (3, 8)\}$.

8. For the function f defined by $f(x) = x^2 - 4x + 1$, find:
   (a) $f(2)$
   (b) $f(x) + f(2)$
   (c) $f(-x)$
   (d) $-f(x)$
   (e) $f(x + 2)$
   (f) $\dfrac{f(x + h) - f(x)}{h}$ $h \neq 0$

9. Find the domain of $h(z) = \dfrac{3z - 1}{6z - 7}$.

10. Is the following graph the graph of a function?

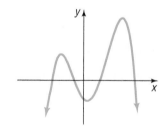

11. Consider the function $f(x) = \dfrac{x}{x + 4}$.
    (a) Is the point $\left(1, \dfrac{1}{4}\right)$ on the graph of f?
    (b) If $x = -2$, what is $f(x)$? What point is on the graph of f?
    (c) If $f(x) = 2$, what is x? What point is on the graph of f?

12. Is the function $f(x) = \dfrac{x^2}{2x + 1}$ even, odd, or neither?

13. Approximate the local maximum values and local minimum values of $f(x) = x^3 - 5x + 1$ on $(-4, 4)$. Determine where the function is increasing and where it is decreasing.

14. If $f(x) = 3x + 5$ and $g(x) = 2x + 1$,
    (a) Solve $f(x) = g(x)$.   (b) Solve $f(x) > g(x)$.

15. For the graph of the function f,

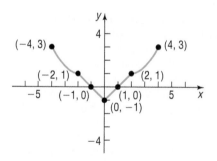

    (a) Find the domain and the range of f.
    (b) Find the intercepts.
    (c) Is the graph of f symmetric with respect to the x-axis, the y-axis, or the origin?
    (d) Find $f(2)$.
    (e) For what value(s) of x is $f(x) = 3$?
    (f) Solve $f(x) < 0$.
    (g) Graph $y = f(x) + 2$
    (h) Graph $y = f(-x)$.
    (i) Graph $y = 2f(x)$.
    (j) Is f even, odd, or neither?
    (k) Find the interval(s) on which f is increasing.

CHAPTER PROJECTS

the percentage change in the stock you chose as the dependent variable. The easiest way to draw a scatter diagram in Excel is to place the two columns of data next to each other (for example, have the percentage change in the S&P500 in column F and the percentage change in the stock you chose in column G). Then highlight the data and select the Scatter Diagram icon under Insert. Comment on the type of relation that appears to exist between the two variables.

3. **Finding beta.** To find beta requires that we find the line of best fit using least-squares regression. The easiest approach is to click inside the scatter diagram. Across the top of the screen you will see an option entitled "Chart Layouts." Select the option with a line drawn on the scatter diagram and *fx* labeled on the graph. The line of best fit appears on the scatter diagram. See below.

Internet-based Project

I. The Beta of a Stock You want to invest in the stock market but are not sure which stock to purchase. Information is the key to making an informed investment decision. One piece of information that many stock analysts use is the beta of the stock. Go to Wikipedia (*http://en.wikipedia.org/wiki/ Beta_%28finance%29*) and research what beta measures and what it represents.

1. **Approximating the beta of a stock.** Choose a well-known company such as Google or Coca-Cola. Go to a website such as Yahoo! Finance (*http://finance.yahoo.com/*) and find the weekly closing price of the company's stock for the past year. Then find the closing price of the Standard & Poor's 500 (S&P500) for the same time period. To get the historical prices in Yahoo! Finance click the price graph, choose Basic Chart, then scroll down and select Historical Prices. Choose the appropriate time period and select Weekly. Finally, select Download to Spreadsheet. Repeat this for the S&P500 and copy the data into the same spreadsheet. Finally, rearrange the data in chronological order. Be sure to expand the selection to sort all the data. Now, using the adjusted close price, compute the percentage change in price for each week using the formula% change $= \dfrac{P_1 - P_o}{P_o}$. For example, if week 1 price is in cell D1 and week 2 price is in cell D2, then % change $= \dfrac{D2 - D1}{D1}$. Repeat this for the S&P500 data.

2. **Using Excel to draw a scatter diagram.** Treat the percentage change in the S&P500 as the independent variable and

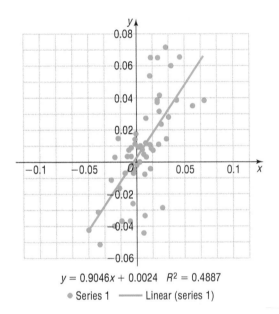

$y = 0.9046x + 0.0024$ $R^2 = 0.4887$

● Series 1 —— Linear (series 1)

The line of best fit for these data is $y = 0.9046x + 0.0024$. You may click on Chart Title or either axis title and insert the appropriate names. The beta is the slope of the line of best fit, 0.9046. We interpret this by saying if the S&P500 increases by 1%, this stock will increase by 0.9%, on average. Find the beta of your stock and provide an interpretation. NOTE: Another way to use Excel to find the line of best fit requires using the Data Analysis Tool Pack under add-ins.

The following projects are available on the Instructor's Resource Center (IRC):

II. Cannons A battery commander uses the weight of a missile, its initial velocity, and the position of its gun to determine where the missile will travel.

III. First and Second Differences Finite differences provide a numerical method that is used to estimate the graph of an unknown function.

IV. CBL Experiment Computer simulation is used to study the physical properties of a bouncing ball.

Polynomial and Rational Functions

Outline

Day Length

Day length refers to the time each day from the moment the upper limb of the sun's disk appears above the horizon during sunrise to the moment when the upper limb disappears below the horizon during sunset. The length of a day depends upon the day of the year as well as the latitude of the location. Latitude gives the location of a point on Earth north or south of the equator. In the Internet Project at the end of this chapter, we use information from the chapter to investigate the relation between the length of day and latitude for a specific day of the year.

 —*See the Internet-based Chapter Project I*—

◁ **A Look Back** In Chapter 2, we began our discussion of functions. We defined domain, range, and independent and dependent variables, found the value of a function, and graphed functions. We continued our study of functions by listing the properties that a function might have, such as being even or odd, and created a library of functions, naming key functions and listing their properties, including their graphs.

In Chapter 3, we discussed linear functions and quadratic functions, which belong to the class of *polynomial functions*.

A Look Ahead ▷ In this chapter, we look at two general classes of functions, polynomial functions and rational functions, and examine their properties. Polynomial functions are arguably the simplest expressions in algebra. For this reason, they are often used to approximate other, more complicated functions. Rational functions are ratios of polynomial functions.

4.1 Polynomial Functions and Models

PREPARING FOR THIS SECTION *Before getting started, review the following:*

- Polynomials (Appendix A, Section A.3, pp. A22–A29)
- Using a Graphing Utility to Approximate Local Maxima and Local Minima (Section 2.3, p. 74)
- Intercepts of a Function (Section 2.2, pp. 61–63)

- Graphing Techniques: Transformations (Section 2.5, pp. 90–99)
- Intercepts (Section 1.2, pp. 11–12)

Now Work the 'Are You Prepared?' problems on page 183.

OBJECTIVES 1 Identify Polynomial Functions and Their Degree (p. 166)
2 Graph Polynomial Functions Using Transformations (p. 170)
3 Identify the Real Zeros of a Polynomial Function and Their Multiplicity (p. 171)
4 Analyze the Graph of a Polynomial Function (p. 178)
5 Build Cubic Models from Data (p. 182)

1 Identify Polynomial Functions and Their Degree

In Chapter 3, we studied the linear function $f(x) = mx + b$, which can be written as

$$f(x) = a_1x + a_0$$

and the quadratic function $f(x) = ax^2 + bx + c, a \neq 0$, which can be written as

$$f(x) = a_2x^2 + a_1x + a_0 \qquad a_2 \neq 0$$

Each of these functions is an example of a *polynomial function*.

DEFINITION

A **polynomial function** is a function of the form

$$f(x) = a_nx^n + a_{n-1}x^{n-1} + \cdots + a_1x + a_0 \tag{1}$$

In Words

A polynomial function is a sum of monomials.

where $a_n, a_{n-1}, \ldots, a_1, a_0$ are real numbers and n is a nonnegative integer. The domain of a polynomial function is the set of all real numbers.

A polynomial function is a function whose rule is given by a polynomial in one variable. The **degree** of a polynomial function is the largest power of x that appears. The zero polynomial function $f(x) = 0 + 0x + 0x^2 + \cdots + 0x^n$ is not assigned a degree.

Polynomial functions are among the simplest expressions in algebra. They are easy to evaluate: only addition and repeated multiplication are required. Because of this, they are often used to approximate other, more complicated functions. In this section, we investigate properties of this important class of functions.

EXAMPLE 1 **Identifying Polynomial Functions**

Determine which of the following are polynomial functions. For those that are, state the degree; for those that are not, tell why not.

(a) $f(x) = 2 - 3x^4$ (b) $g(x) = \sqrt{x}$ (c) $h(x) = \dfrac{x^2 - 2}{x^3 - 1}$

(d) $F(x) = 0$ (e) $G(x) = 8$ (f) $H(x) = -2x^3(x - 1)^2$

Solution   (a) f is a polynomial function of degree 4.

(b) g is not a polynomial function because $g(x) = \sqrt{x} = x^{\frac{1}{2}}$, so the variable x is raised to the $\dfrac{1}{2}$ power, which is not a nonnegative integer.

(c) h is not a polynomial function. It is the ratio of two distinct polynomials, and the polynomial in the denominator is of positive degree.

(d) F is the zero polynomial function; it is not assigned a degree.

(e) G is a nonzero constant function. It is a polynomial function of degree 0 since $G(x) = 8 = 8x^0$.

(f) $H(x) = -2x^3(x - 1)^2 = -2x^3(x^2 - 2x + 1) = -2x^5 + 4x^4 - 2x^3$. So H is a polynomial function of degree 5. Do you see a way to find the degree of H without multiplying out?

═══════-**Now Work**   PROBLEMS 15 AND 19

We have already discussed in detail polynomial functions of degrees 0, 1, and 2. See Table 1 for a summary of the properties of the graphs of these polynomial functions.

Table 1

Degree	Form	Name	Graph
No degree	$f(x) = 0$	Zero function	The x-axis
0	$f(x) = a_0, \quad a_0 \neq 0$	Constant function	Horizontal line with y-intercept a_0
1	$f(x) = a_1 x + a_0, \quad a_1 \neq 0$	Linear function	Nonvertical, nonhorizontal line with slope a_1 and y-intercept a_0
2	$f(x) = a_2 x^2 + a_1 x + a_0, \quad a_2 \neq 0$	Quadratic function	Parabola: graph opens up if $a_2 > 0$; graph opens down if $a_2 < 0$

One objective of this section is to analyze the graph of a polynomial function. If you take a course in calculus, you will learn that the graph of every polynomial function is both smooth and continuous. By **smooth,** we mean that the graph contains no sharp corners or cusps; by **continuous,** we mean that the graph has no gaps or holes and can be drawn without lifting pencil from paper. See Figures 1(a) and (b).

Figure 1

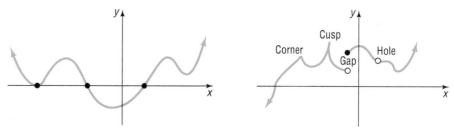

(a) Graph of a polynomial function: smooth, continuous

(b) Cannot be the graph of a polynomial function

Power Functions

We begin the analysis of the graph of a polynomial function by discussing *power functions,* a special kind of polynomial function.

DEFINITION

A **power function of degree n** is a monomial function of the form

$$f(x) = ax^n \tag{2}$$

where a is a real number, $a \neq 0$, and $n > 0$ is an integer.

In Words
A power function is defined by a single monomial.

Examples of power functions are

$$f(x) = 3x \qquad f(x) = -5x^2 \qquad f(x) = 8x^3 \qquad f(x) = -5x^4$$
$$\text{degree 1} \qquad \text{degree 2} \qquad \text{degree 3} \qquad \text{degree 4}$$

The graph of a power function of degree 1, $f(x) = ax$, is a straight line, with slope a, that passes through the origin. The graph of a power function of degree 2, $f(x) = ax^2$, is a parabola, with vertex at the origin, that opens up if $a > 0$ and down if $a < 0$.

If we know how to graph a power function of the form $f(x) = x^n$, a compression or stretch and, perhaps, a reflection about the x-axis will enable us to obtain the graph of $g(x) = ax^n$. Consequently, we shall concentrate on graphing power functions of the form $f(x) = x^n$.

We begin with power functions of even degree of the form $f(x) = x^n$, $n \geq 2$ and n even. The domain of f is the set of all real numbers, and the range is the set of nonnegative real numbers. Such a power function is an even function (do you see why?), so its graph is symmetric with respect to the y-axis. Its graph always contains the origin and the points $(-1, 1)$ and $(1, 1)$.

If $n = 2$, the graph is the familiar parabola $y = x^2$ that opens up, with vertex at the origin. If $n \geq 4$, the graph of $f(x) = x^n$, n even, will be closer to the x-axis than the parabola $y = x^2$ if $-1 < x < 1$, $x \neq 0$, and farther from the x-axis than the parabola $y = x^2$ if $x < -1$ or if $x > 1$. Figure 2(a) illustrates this conclusion. Figure 2(b) shows the graphs of $y = x^4$ and $y = x^8$ for comparison.

Figure 2

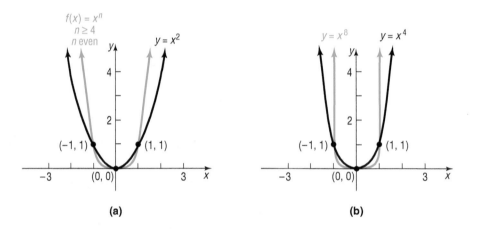

(a)   (b)

From Figure 2, we can see that as n increases the graph of $f(x) = x^n$, $n \geq 2$ and n even, tends to flatten out near the origin and to increase very rapidly when x is far from 0. For large n, it may appear that the graph coincides with the x-axis near the origin, but it does not; the graph actually touches the x-axis only at the origin (see Table 2). Also, for large n, it may appear that for $x < -1$ or for $x > 1$ the graph is vertical, but it is not; it is only increasing very rapidly in these intervals. If the graphs were enlarged many times, these distinctions would be clear.

Table 2

	$x = 0.1$	$x = 0.3$	$x = 0.5$
$f(x) = x^8$	10^{-8}	0.0000656	0.0039063
$f(x) = x^{20}$	10^{-20}	$3.487 \cdot 10^{-11}$	0.000001
$f(x) = x^{40}$	10^{-40}	$1.216 \cdot 10^{-21}$	$9.095 \cdot 10^{-13}$

Seeing the Concept

Graph $Y_1 = x^4$, $Y_2 = x^8$, and $Y_3 = x^{12}$ using the viewing rectangle $-2 \leq x \leq 2$, $-4 \leq y \leq 16$. Then graph each again using the viewing rectangle $-1 \leq x \leq 1$, $0 \leq y \leq 1$. See Figure 3. TRACE along one of the graphs to confirm that for x close to 0 the graph is above the x-axis and that for $x > 0$ the graph is increasing.

Figure 3

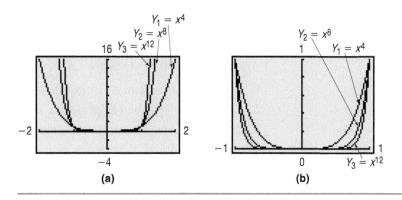

(a)   (b)

Properties of Power Functions, $f(x) = x^n$, n Is a Positive Even Integer

1. f is an even function, so its graph is symmetric with respect to the y-axis.
2. The domain is the set of all real numbers. The range is the set of nonnegative real numbers.
3. The graph always contains the points $(-1, 1)$, $(0, 0)$, and $(1, 1)$.
4. As the exponent n increases in magnitude, the function increases more rapidly when $x < -1$ or $x > 1$; but for x near the origin, the graph tends to flatten out and lie closer to the x-axis.

Figure 4

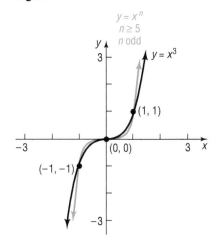

Now we consider power functions of odd degree of the form $f(x) = x^n$, $n \geq 3$ and n odd. The domain and the range of f are the set of real numbers. Such a power function is an odd function (do you see why?), so its graph is symmetric with respect to the origin. Its graph always contains the origin and the points $(-1, -1)$ and $(1, 1)$.

The graph of $f(x) = x^n$ when $n = 3$ has been shown several times and is repeated in Figure 4. If $n \geq 5$, the graph of $f(x) = x^n$, n odd, will be closer to the x-axis than that of $y = x^3$ if $-1 < x < 1$ and farther from the x-axis than that of $y = x^3$ if $x < -1$ or if $x > 1$. Figure 4 also illustrates this conclusion.

Figure 5 shows the graph of $y = x^5$ and the graph of $y = x^9$ for further comparison.

Figure 5

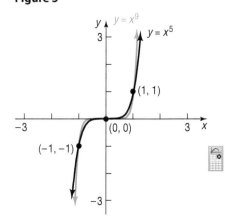

It appears that each graph coincides with the x-axis near the origin, but it does not; each graph actually crosses the x-axis at the origin. Also, it appears that as x increases the graph becomes vertical, but it does not; each graph is increasing very rapidly.

Seeing the Concept

Graph $Y_1 = x^3$, $Y_2 = x^7$, and $Y_3 = x^{11}$ using the viewing rectangle $-2 \leq x \leq 2$, $-16 \leq y \leq 16$. Then graph each again using the viewing rectangle $-1 \leq x \leq 1$, $-1 \leq y \leq 1$. See Figure 6. TRACE along one of the graphs to confirm that the graph is increasing and crosses the x-axis at the origin.

Figure 6

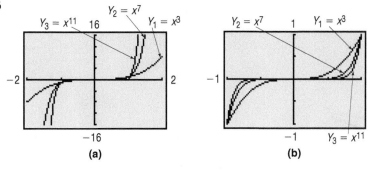

(a)   (b)

To summarize:

Properties of Power Functions, $f(x) = x^n$, n Is a Positive Odd Integer

1. f is an odd function, so its graph is symmetric with respect to the origin.
2. The domain and the range are the set of all real numbers.
3. The graph always contains the points $(-1, -1)$, $(0, 0)$, and $(1, 1)$.
4. As the exponent n increases in magnitude, the function increases more rapidly when $x < -1$ or $x > 1$; but for x near the origin, the graph tends to flatten out and lie closer to the x-axis.

---

2 Graph Polynomial Functions Using Transformations

The methods of shifting, compression, stretching, and reflection studied in Section 2.5, when used with the facts just presented, will enable us to graph polynomial functions that are transformations of power functions.

EXAMPLE 2

Graphing a Polynomial Function Using Transformations

Graph: $f(x) = 1 - x^5$

Solution It is helpful to rewrite f as $f(x) = -x^5 + 1$. Figure 7 shows the required stages.

Figure 7

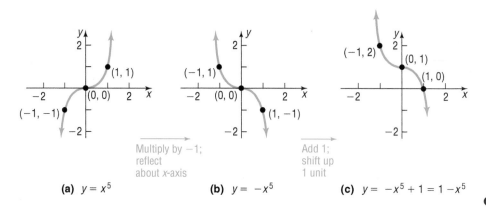

(a) $y = x^5$ **(b)** $y = -x^5$ **(c)** $y = -x^5 + 1 = 1 - x^5$

EXAMPLE 3

Graphing a Polynomial Function Using Transformations

Graph: $f(x) = \dfrac{1}{2}(x - 1)^4$

Solution Figure 8 shows the required stages.

Figure 8

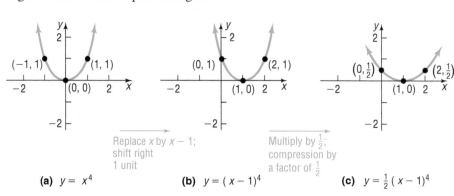

(a) $y = x^4$ **(b)** $y = (x - 1)^4$ **(c)** $y = \dfrac{1}{2}(x - 1)^4$

-**Now Work** PROBLEMS 27 AND 33

3 Identify the Real Zeros of a Polynomial Function and Their Multiplicity

Figure 9 shows the graph of a polynomial function with four x-intercepts. Notice that at the x-intercepts the graph must either cross the x-axis or touch the x-axis. Consequently, between consecutive x-intercepts the graph is either above the x-axis or below the x-axis.

Figure 9

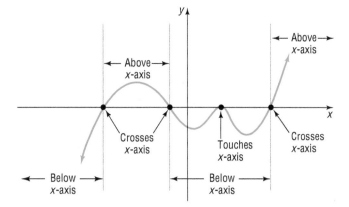

If a polynomial function f is factored completely, it is easy to locate the x-intercepts of the graph by solving the equation $f(x) = 0$ and using the Zero-Product Property. For example, if $f(x) = (x - 1)^2(x + 3)$, then the solutions of the equation

$$f(x) = (x - 1)^2(x + 3) = 0$$

are identified as 1 and -3. That is, $f(1) = 0$ and $f(-3) = 0$.

DEFINITION

If f is a function and r is a real number for which $f(r) = 0$, then r is called a **real zero** of f.

As a consequence of this definition, the following statements are equivalent.

1. r is a real zero of a polynomial function f.
2. r is an x-intercept of the graph of f.
3. $x - r$ is a factor of f.
4. r is a solution to the equation $f(x) = 0$.

So the real zeros of a polynomial function are the x-intercepts of its graph, and they are found by solving the equation $f(x) = 0$.

EXAMPLE 4   **Finding a Polynomial Function from Its Zeros**

(a) Find a polynomial function of degree 3 whose zeros are -3, 2, and 5.

 (b) Use a graphing utility to graph the polynomial found in part (a) to verify your result.

Solution   (a) If r is a real zero of a polynomial function f, then $x - r$ is a factor of f. This means that $x - (-3) = x + 3$, $x - 2$, and $x - 5$ are factors of f. As a result, any polynomial function of the form

$$f(x) = a(x + 3)(x - 2)(x - 5)$$

where a is a nonzero real number, qualifies. The value of a causes a stretch, compression, or reflection, but does not affect the x-intercepts of the graph. Do you know why?

Figure 10

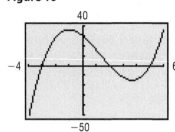

 (b) We choose to graph f with $a = 1$. Then

$$f(x) = (x + 3)(x - 2)(x - 5) = x^3 - 4x^2 - 11x + 30$$

Figure 10 shows the graph of f. Notice that the x-intercepts are $-3, 2,$ and 5.

Seeing the Concept

Graph the function found in Example 4 for $a = 2$ and $a = -1$. Does the value of a affect the zeros of f? How does the value of a affect the graph of f?

━━━━**Now Work** PROBLEM 41

If the same factor $x - r$ occurs more than once, r is called a **repeated,** or **multiple, zero of f.** More precisely, we have the following definition.

DEFINITION

If $(x - r)^m$ is a factor of a polynomial f and $(x - r)^{m+1}$ is not a factor of f, then r is called a **zero of multiplicity m of f.***

━━━━━━━━━━━━━━━━━━━━━━━━

EXAMPLE 5

Identifying Zeros and Their Multiplicities

For the polynomial

$$f(x) = 5(x - 2)(x + 3)^2\left(x - \frac{1}{2}\right)^4$$

2 is a zero of multiplicity 1 because the exponent on the factor $x - 2$ is 1.

-3 is a zero of multiplicity 2 because the exponent on the factor $x + 3$ is 2.

$\dfrac{1}{2}$ is a zero of multiplicity 4 because the exponent on the factor $x - \dfrac{1}{2}$ is 4.

━━━━**Now Work** PROBLEM 49(a)

Suppose that it is possible to factor completely a polynomial function and, as a result, locate all the x-intercepts of its graph (the real zeros of the function). These x-intercepts then divide the x-axis into open intervals and, on each such interval, the graph of the polynomial will be either above or below the x-axis. Let's look at an example.

━━━━━━━━━━━━━━━━━━━━━━━━

EXAMPLE 6

Graphing a Polynomial Using Its x-Intercepts

For the polynomial: $f(x) = x^2(x - 2)$

(a) Find the x- and y-intercepts of the graph of f.

(b) Use the x-intercepts to find the intervals on which the graph of f is above the x-axis and the intervals on which the graph of f is below the x-axis.

(c) Locate other points on the graph and connect all the points plotted with a smooth, continuous curve.

Solution

(a) The y-intercept is $f(0) = 0^2(0 - 2) = 0$. The x-intercepts satisfy the equation

$$f(x) = x^2(x - 2) = 0$$

from which we find

$$x^2 = 0 \quad \text{or} \quad x - 2 = 0$$
$$x = 0 \quad \text{or} \qquad x = 2$$

The x-intercepts are 0 and 2.

*Some books use the terms **multiple root** and **root of multiplicity m.**

(b) The two x-intercepts divide the x-axis into three intervals:

$$(-\infty, 0) \qquad (0, 2) \qquad (2, \infty)$$

Since the graph of f crosses or touches the x-axis only at $x = 0$ and $x = 2$, it follows that the graph of f is either above the x-axis $[f(x) > 0]$ or below the x-axis $[f(x) < 0]$ on each of these three intervals. To see where the graph lies, we only need to pick one number in each interval, evaluate f there, and see whether the value is positive (above the x-axis) or negative (below the x-axis). See Table 3.

(c) In constructing Table 3, we obtained three additional points on the graph: $(-1, -3)$, $(1, -1)$, and $(3, 9)$. Figure 11 illustrates these points, the intercepts, and a smooth, continuous curve (the graph of f) connecting them.

Figure 11

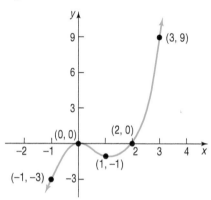

Table 3

Interval	$(-\infty, 0)$	$(0, 2)$	$(2, \infty)$
Number chosen	-1	1	3
Value of f	$f(-1) = -3$	$f(1) = -1$	$f(3) = 9$
Location of graph	Below x-axis	Below x-axis	Above x-axis
Point on graph	$(-1, -3)$	$(1, -1)$	$(3, 9)$

Look again at Table 3. Since the graph of $f(x) = x^2(x - 2)$ is below the x-axis on both sides of 0, the graph of f *touches* the x-axis at $x = 0$, a *zero of multiplicity 2*. Since the graph of f is below the x-axis for $x < 2$ and above the x-axis for $x > 2$, the graph of f *crosses* the x-axis at $x = 2$, a *zero of multiplicity 1*.

This suggests the following results:

If *r* Is a Zero of Even Multiplicity

The sign of $f(x)$ does not change from one side to the other side of r.

The graph of f **touches** the x-axis at r.

If *r* Is a Zero of Odd Multiplicity

The sign of $f(x)$ changes from one side to the other side of r.

The graph of f **crosses** the x-axis at r.

—**Now Work** PROBLEM 49(b)

Behavior Near a Zero

The multiplicity of a zero can be used to determine whether the graph of a function touches or crosses the x-axis at the zero. However, we can learn more about the behavior of the graph near its zeros than just whether the graph crosses or touches the x-axis. Consider the function $f(x) = x^2(x - 2)$ whose graph is drawn in Figure 11. The zeros of f are 0 and 2. Table 4 on page 174 shows the values of $f(x) = x^2(x - 2)$ and $y = -2x^2$ for x near 0. Figure 12 shows the points $(-0.1, -0.021)$, $(-0.05, -0.0051)$, and so on, that are on the graph of $f(x) = x^2(x - 2)$ along with the graph of $y = -2x^2$ on the same Cartesian plane. From the table and graph, we can see that the points on the graph of $f(x) = x^2(x - 2)$ and the points on the

Table 4

x	$f(x) = x^2(x-2)$	$y = -2x^2$
−0.1	−0.021	−0.02
−0.05	−0.005125	−0.005
−0.03	−0.001827	−0.0018
−0.01	−0.000201	−0.0002
0	0	0
0.01	−0.000199	−0.0002
0.03	−0.001773	−0.0018
0.05	−0.004875	−0.005
0.1	−0.019	−0.02

Figure 12

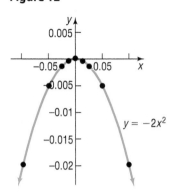

graph of $y = -2x^2$ are indistinguishable near $x = 0$. So $y = -2x^2$ describes the behavior of the graph of $f(x) = x^2(x-2)$ near $x = 0$.

But how did we know that the function $f(x) = x^2(x-2)$ behaves like $y = -2x^2$ when x is close to 0? In other words, where did $y = -2x^2$ come from? Because the zero, 0, comes from the factor x^2, we evaluate all factors in the function f at 0 with the exception of x^2.

$$f(x) = x^2(x-2) \quad \text{The factor } x^2 \text{ gives rise to the zero, so we keep}$$
$$\approx x^2(0-2) \quad \text{the factor } x^2 \text{ and let } x = 0 \text{ in the remaining}$$
$$= -2x^2 \quad \text{factors to find the behavior near } 0.$$

This tells us that the graph of $f(x) = x^2(x-2)$ will behave like the graph of $y = -2x^2$ near $x = 0$.

Now let's discuss the behavior of $f(x) = x^2(x-2)$ near $x = 2$, the other zero. Because the zero, 2, comes from the factor $x-2$, we evaluate all factors of the function f at 2 with the exception of $x-2$.

$$f(x) = x^2(x-2) \quad \text{The factor } x-2 \text{ gives rise to the zero, so we}$$
$$\approx 2^2(x-2) \quad \text{keep the factor } x-2 \text{ and let } x = 2 \text{ in the}$$
$$= 4(x-2) \quad \text{remaining factors to find the behavior near 2.}$$

So the graph of $f(x) = x^2(x-2)$ will behave like the graph of $y = 4(x-2)$ near $x = 2$. Table 5 verifies that $f(x) = x^2(x-2)$ and $y = 4(x-2)$ have similar values for x near 2. Figure 13 shows the points $(1.9, -0.361)$, $(1.99, -0.0396)$, and so on, that are on the graph of $f(x) = x^2(x-2)$ along with the graph of $y = 4(x-2)$ on the same Cartesian plane. We can see that the points on the graph of $f(x) = x^2(x-2)$ and the points on the graph of $y = 4(x-2)$ are indistinguishable near $x = 2$. So $y = 4(x-2)$, a line with slope 4, describes the behavior of the graph of $f(x) = x^2(x-2)$ near $x = 2$.

Table 5

x	$f(x) = x^2(x-2)$	$y = 4(x-2)$
1.9	−0.361	−0.4
1.99	−0.0396	−0.04
1.999	−0.003996	−0.004
2	0	0
2.001	0.004004	0.004
2.01	0.0404	0.04
2.1	0.441	0.4

Figure 13

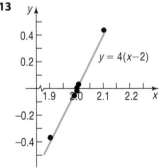

Figure 14

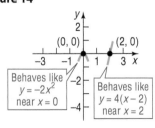

Figure 14 illustrates how we would use this information to begin to graph $f(x) = x^2(x-2)$.

- The multiplicity of a real zero determines whether the graph crosses or touches the *x*-axis at the zero.
- The behavior of the graph near a real zero determines how the graph touches or crosses the *x*-axis.

━━━━━Now Work PROBLEM 49(c)

Turning Points

 Look again at Figure 11 on page 173. We cannot be sure just how low the graph actually goes between $x = 0$ and $x = 2$. But we do know that somewhere in the interval $(0, 2)$ the graph of f must change direction (from decreasing to increasing). The points at which a graph changes direction are called **turning points.** In calculus, techniques for locating them are given. So we shall not ask for the location of turning points in our graphs. Instead, we will use the following result from calculus, which tells us the maximum number of turning points that the graph of a polynomial function can have.

THEOREM

Turning Points

If f is a polynomial function of degree n, then the graph of f has at most $n - 1$ turning points.

If the graph of a polynomial function f has $n - 1$ turning points, the degree of f is at least n.

For example, the graph of $f(x) = x^2(x - 2)$ shown in Figure 11 is the graph of a polynomial function of degree 3 and has $3 - 1 = 2$ turning points: one at $(0, 0)$ and the other somewhere between $x = 0$ and $x = 2$.

Based on the theorem, if the graph of a polynomial function has three turning points, then the degree of the function must be at least 4.

Exploration

A graphing utility can be used to locate the turning points of a graph. Graph $Y_1 = x^2(x - 2)$. Use MINIMUM to find the location of the turning point for $0 < x < 2$. See Figure 15.

Figure 15

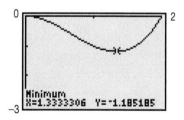

Minimum
X=1.3333306 Y=-1.185185

━━━━━Now Work PROBLEM 49(d)

EXAMPLE 7

Identifying the Graph of a Polynomial Function

Which of the graphs in Figure 16 on the next page could be the graph of a polynomial function? For those that could, list the real zeros and state the least degree the polynomial can have. For those that could not, say why not.

Figure 16

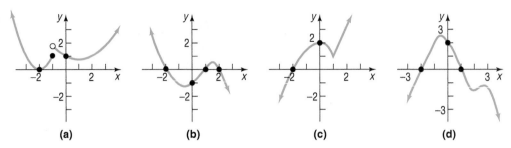

(a)   (b)   (c)   (d)

Solution   (a) The graph in Figure 16(a) cannot be the graph of a polynomial function because of the gap that occurs at $x = -1$. Remember, the graph of a polynomial function is continuous—no gaps or holes.

(b) The graph in Figure 16(b) could be the graph of a polynomial function because the graph is smooth and continuous. It has three real zeros, at -2, at 1, and at 2. Since the graph has two turning points, the degree of the polynomial function must be at least 3.

(c) The graph in Figure 16(c) cannot be the graph of a polynomial function because of the cusp at $x = 1$. Remember, the graph of a polynomial function is smooth.

(d) The graph in Figure 16(d) could be the graph of a polynomial function. It has two real zeros, at -2 and at 1. Since the graph has three turning points, the degree of the polynomial function is at least 4.

━━━━**Now Work** PROBLEM 61

End Behavior

One last remark about Figure 11. For very large values of x, either positive or negative, the graph of $f(x) = x^2(x - 2)$ looks like the graph of $y = x^3$. To see why, we write f in the form

$$f(x) = x^2(x - 2) = x^3 - 2x^2 = x^3\left(1 - \frac{2}{x}\right)$$

Now, for large values of x, either positive or negative, the term $\frac{2}{x}$ is close to 0, so for large values of x

$$f(x) = x^3 - 2x^2 = x^3\left(1 - \frac{2}{x}\right) \approx x^3$$

The behavior of the graph of a function for large values of x, either positive or negative, is referred to as its **end behavior.**

THEOREM

End Behavior

For large values of x, either positive or negative, the graph of the polynomial function

> *In Words*
> The end behavior of a polynomial function resembles that of its leading term.

$$f(x) = a_n x^n + a_{n-1}x^{n-1} + \cdots + a_1 x + a_0$$

resembles the graph of the power function

$$y = a_n x^n$$

For example, if $f(x) = -2x^3 + 5x^2 + x - 4$, then the graph of f will behave like the graph of $y = -2x^3$ for very large values of x, either positive or negative. We can see that the graphs of f and $y = -2x^3$ "behave" the same by considering Table 6 and Figure 17.

Table 6

x	f(x)	$y = -2x^3$
10	$-1,494$	$-2,000$
100	$-1,949,904$	$-2,000,000$
500	$-248,749,504$	$-250,000,000$
1,000	$-1,994,999,004$	$-2,000,000,000$

Figure 17

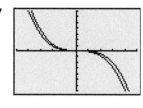

Notice that, as x becomes a larger and larger positive number, the values of f become larger and larger negative numbers. When this happens, we say that f is **unbounded in the negative direction.** Rather than using words to describe the behavior of the graph of the function, we explain its behavior using notation. We can symbolize "the value of f becomes a larger and larger negative number as x becomes a larger and larger positive number" by writing $f(x) \rightarrow -\infty$ as $x \rightarrow \infty$ (read "the values of f approach negative infinity as x approaches infinity"). In calculus, **limits** are used to convey these ideas. There we use the symbolism $\lim\limits_{x \to \infty} f(x) = -\infty$, read "the limit of $f(x)$ as x approaches infinity equals negative infinity," to mean that $f(x) \rightarrow -\infty$ as $x \rightarrow \infty$.

When the value of a limit equals infinity, we mean that the values of the function are unbounded in the positive or negative direction and call the limit an **infinite limit.** When we discuss limits as x becomes unbounded in the negative direction or unbounded in the positive direction, we are discussing **limits at infinity.**

Look back at Figures 2 and 4. Based on the preceding theorem and the previous discussion on power functions, the end behavior of a polynomial function can only be of four types. See Figure 18.

Figure 18

End behavior of $f(x) = a_n x^n + a_{n-1} x^{n-1} + \cdots + a_1 x + a_0$

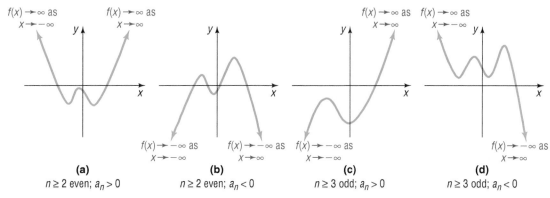

(a) $n \geq 2$ even; $a_n > 0$ (b) $n \geq 2$ even; $a_n < 0$ (c) $n \geq 3$ odd; $a_n > 0$ (d) $n \geq 3$ odd; $a_n < 0$

For example, if $f(x) = -2x^4 + x^3 + 4x^2 - 7x + 1$, the graph of f will resemble the graph of the power function $y = -2x^4$ for large $|x|$. The graph of f will behave like Figure 18(b) for large $|x|$.

Now Work PROBLEM 49(e)

EXAMPLE 8   **Identifying the Graph of a Polynomial Function**

Which of the graphs in Figure 19 could be the graph of

$$f(x) = x^4 + 5x^3 + 5x^2 - 5x - 6?$$

Figure 19

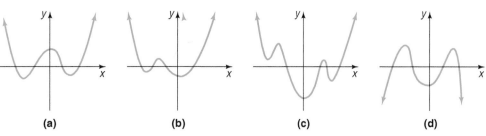

(a)   (b)   (c)   (d)

Solution   The y-intercept of f is $f(0) = -6$. We can eliminate the graph in Figure 19(a), whose y-intercept is positive.

We don't have any methods for finding the x-intercepts of f, so we move on to investigate the turning points of each graph. Since f is of degree 4, the graph of f has at most 3 turning points. We eliminate the graph in Figure 19(c) since that graph has 5 turning points.

Now we look at end behavior. For large values of x, the graph of f will behave like the graph of $y = x^4$. This eliminates the graph in Figure 19(d), whose end behavior is like the graph of $y = -x^4$.

Only the graph in Figure 19(b) could be (and, in fact, is) the graph of $f(x) = x^4 + 5x^3 + 5x^2 - 5x - 6$.

Now Work PROBLEM 65

SUMMARY   Graph of a Polynomial Function $f(x) = a_n x^n + a_{n-1} x^{n-1} + \cdots + a_1 x + a_0$ $a_n \neq 0$

Degree of the polynomial function f: n
Graph is smooth and continuous.
Maximum number of turning points: $n - 1$
At a zero of even multiplicity: The graph of f touches the x-axis.
At a zero of odd multiplicity: The graph of f crosses the x-axis.
Between zeros, the graph of f is either above or below the x-axis.
End behavior: For large $|x|$, the graph of f behaves like the graph of $y = a_n x^n$.

---

4 Analyze the Graph of a Polynomial Function

EXAMPLE 9

How to Analyze the Graph of a Polynomial Function

Analyze the graph of the polynomial function $f(x) = (2x + 1)(x - 3)^2$.

Step-by-Step Solution

Step 1: Determine the end behavior of the graph of the function.

Expand the polynomial to write it in the form

$$f(x) = a_n x^n + a_{n-1} x^{n-1} + \cdots + a_1 x + a_0$$
$$f(x) = (2x + 1)(x - 3)^2$$
$$= (2x + 1)(x^2 - 6x + 9)$$
$$= 2x^3 - 12x^2 + 18x + x^2 - 6x + 9 \qquad \text{Multiply.}$$
$$= 2x^3 - 11x^2 + 12x + 9 \qquad \text{Combine like terms.}$$

The polynomial function f is of degree 3. The graph of f behaves like $y = 2x^3$ for large values of $|x|$.

Step 2: Find the x- and y-intercepts of the graph of the function.

The y-intercept is $f(0) = 9$. To find the x-intercepts, we solve $f(x) = 0$.

$$f(x) = 0$$
$$(2x + 1)(x - 3)^2 = 0$$
$$2x + 1 = 0 \quad \text{or} \quad (x - 3)^2 = 0$$
$$x = -\frac{1}{2} \quad \text{or} \quad x - 3 = 0$$
$$x = 3$$

The x-intercepts are $-\frac{1}{2}$ and 3.

Step 3: Determine the zeros of the function and their multiplicity. Use this information to determine whether the graph crosses or touches the x-axis at each x-intercept.

The zeros of f are $-\dfrac{1}{2}$ and 3. The zero $-\dfrac{1}{2}$ is a zero of multiplicity 1, so the graph of f crosses the x-axis at $x = -\dfrac{1}{2}$. The zero 3 is a zero of multiplicity 2, so the graph of f touches the x-axis at $x = 3$.

Step 4: Determine the maximum number of turning points on the graph of the function.

Because the polynomial function is of degree 3 (Step 1), the graph of the function will have at most $3 - 1 = 2$ turning points.

Step 5: Determine the behavior of the graph of f near each x-intercept.

The two x-intercepts are $-\dfrac{1}{2}$ and 3.

$$\text{Near } -\frac{1}{2}: \quad f(x) = (2x + 1)(x - 3)^2$$

$$\approx (2x + 1)\left(-\frac{1}{2} + 3\right)^2$$

$$= (2x + 1)\left(\frac{25}{4}\right)$$

$$= \frac{25}{2}x + \frac{25}{4} \qquad \text{A line with slope } \frac{25}{2}$$

$$\text{Near } 3: \quad f(x) = (2x + 1)(x - 3)^2$$

$$\approx (2 \cdot 3 + 1)(x - 3)^2$$

$$= 7(x - 3)^2 \qquad \text{A parabola that opens up}$$

Step 6: Put all the information from Steps 1 through 5 together to obtain the graph of f.

Figure 20(a) illustrates the information obtained from Steps 1 through 5. We evaluate f at -1, 1, and 4 to help establish the scale on the y-axis. The graph of f is given in Figure 20(b).

Figure 20

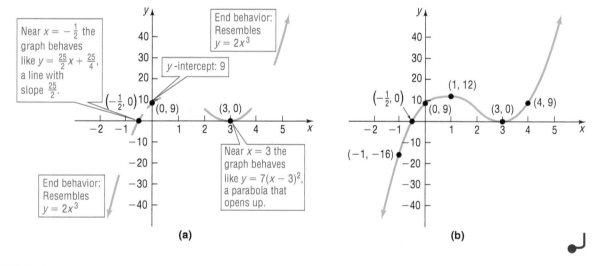

(a)

(b)

SUMMARY Analyzing the Graph of a Polynomial Function

STEP 1: Determine the end behavior of the graph of the function.

STEP 2: Find the x- and y-intercepts of the graph of the function.

STEP 3: Determine the zeros of the function and their multiplicity. Use this information to determine whether the graph crosses or touches the x-axis at each x-intercept.

STEP 4: Determine the maximum number of turning points on the graph of the function.

STEP 5: Determine the behavior of the graph near each x-intercept.

STEP 6: Use the information in Steps 1 through 5 to draw a complete graph of the function.

EXAMPLE 10   **Analyzing the Graph of a Polynomial Function**

Analyze the graph of the polynomial function

$$f(x) = x^2(x - 4)(x + 1)$$

Solution   **STEP 1:** End behavior: the graph of f resembles that of the power function $y = x^4$ for large values of $|x|$.

STEP 2: The y-intercept is $f(0) = 0$. The x-intercepts satisfy the equation

$$f(x) = x^2(x - 4)(x + 1) = 0$$

So

$$x^2 = 0 \quad \text{or} \quad x - 4 = 0 \quad \text{or} \quad x + 1 = 0$$
$$x = 0 \quad \text{or} \qquad x = 4 \quad \text{or} \qquad x = -1$$

The x-intercepts are $-1, 0,$ and 4.

STEP 3: The intercept 0 is a zero of multiplicity 2, so the graph of f will touch the x-axis at 0; 4 and -1 are zeros of multiplicity 1, so the graph of f will cross the x-axis at 4 and -1.

STEP 4: The graph of f will contain at most three turning points.

STEP 5: The three x-intercepts are $-1, 0,$ and 4.

Near -1: $f(x) = x^2(x - 4)(x + 1) \approx (-1)^2(-1 - 4)(x + 1) = -5(x + 1)$ A line with slope -5

Near 0: $f(x) = x^2(x - 4)(x + 1) \approx x^2(0 - 4)(0 + 1) = -4x^2$ A parabola opening down

Near 4: $f(x) = x^2(x - 4)(x + 1) \approx 4^2(x - 4)(4 + 1) = 80(x - 4)$ A line with slope 80

STEP 6: Figure 21(a) illustrates the information obtained from Steps 1–5. The graph of f is given in Figure 21(b). Notice that we evaluated f at $-2, -\dfrac{1}{2}, 2,$ and 5 to help establish the scale on the y-axis.

Figure 21

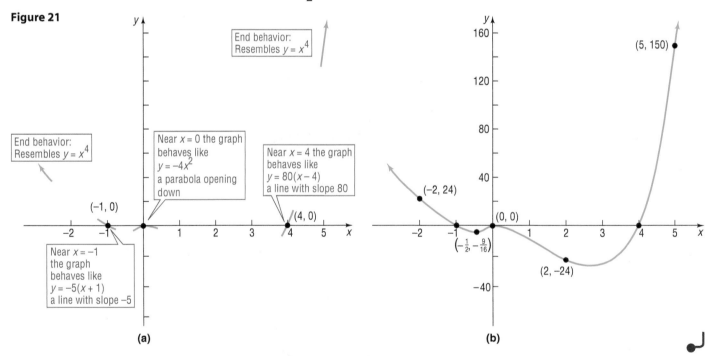

(a)

(b)

Exploration

Graph $Y_1 = x^2(x - 4)(x + 1)$. Compare what you see with Figure 21(b). Use MAXIMUM/MINIMUM to locate the three turning points.

Now Work PROBLEM 69

For polynomial functions that have noninteger coefficients and for polynomials that are not easily factored, we utilize the graphing utility early in the analysis. This is because the amount of information that can be obtained from algebraic analysis is limited.

EXAMPLE 11

How to Use a Graphing Utility to Analyze the Graph of a Polynomial Function

Analyze the graph of the polynomial function

$$f(x) = x^3 + 2.48x^2 - 4.3155x + 2.484406$$

Step-by-Step Solution

Step 1: Determine the end behavior of the graph of the function.

The polynomial function f is of degree 3. The graph of f behaves like $y = x^3$ for large values of $|x|$.

Step 2: Graph the function using a graphing utility.

See Figure 22 for the graph of f.

Figure 22

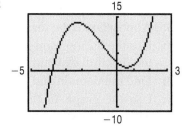

Step 3: Use a graphing utility to approximate the x- and y-intercepts of the graph.

The y-intercept is $f(0) = 2.484406$. In Examples 9 and 10, the polynomial function was factored, so it was easy to find the x-intercepts algebraically. However, it is not readily apparent how to factor f in this example. Therefore, we use a graphing utility's ZERO (or ROOT or SOLVE) feature and find the lone x-intercept to be -3.79, rounded to two decimal places.

Step 4: Use a graphing utility to create a TABLE to find points on the graph around each x-intercept.

Table 7 shows values of x on each side of the x-intercept. The points $(-4, -4.57)$ and $(-2, 13.04)$ are on the graph.

Table 7

X	Y1
-4	-4.574
-2	13.035

Y1◼X^3+2.48X²−4...

Step 5: Approximate the turning points of the graph.

From the graph of f shown in Figure 22, we can see that f has two turning points. Using MAXIMUM, one turning point is at $(-2.28, 13.36)$, rounded to two decimal places. Using MINIMUM, the other turning point is at $(0.63, 1)$, rounded to two decimal places.

Step 6: Use the information in Steps 1 through 5 to draw a complete graph of the function by hand.

Figure 23 shows a graph of f using the information in Steps 1 through 5.

Figure 23

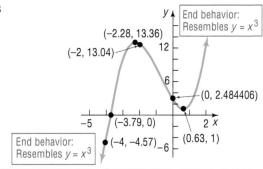

| Step 7: Find the domain and the range of the function. | The domain and the range of f are the set of all real numbers. |

| Step 8: Use the graph to determine where the function is increasing and where it is decreasing. | Based on the graph, f is increasing on the intervals $(-\infty, -2.28)$ and $(0.63, \infty)$. Also, f is decreasing on the interval $(-2.28, 0.63)$. ↵ |

Using a Graphing Utility to Analyze the Graph of a Polynomial Function

STEP 1: Determine the end behavior of the graph of the function.

STEP 2: Graph the function using a graphing utility.

STEP 3: Use a graphing utility to approximate the x- and y-intercepts of the graph.

STEP 4: Use a graphing utility to create a TABLE to find points on the graph around each x-intercept.

STEP 5: Approximate the turning points of the graph.

STEP 6: Use the information in Steps 1 through 5 to draw a complete graph of the function by hand.

STEP 7: Find the domain and the range of the function.

STEP 8: Use the graph to determine where the function is increasing and where it is decreasing.

━━━━━**Now Work** PROBLEM 87

5 Build Cubic Models from Data

In Section 3.2 we found the line of best fit from data, and in Section 3.4 we found the quadratic function of best fit. It is also possible to find polynomial functions of best fit. However, most statisticians do not recommend finding polynomials of best fit of degree higher than 3.

Data that follow a cubic relation should look like Figure 24(a) or (b).

Figure 24

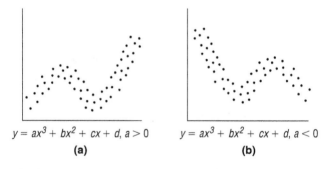

$y = ax^3 + bx^2 + cx + d, a > 0$ $y = ax^3 + bx^2 + cx + d, a < 0$

        (a)   **(b)**

EXAMPLE 12   **A Cubic Function of Best Fit**

The data in Table 8 represent the weekly cost C (in thousands of dollars) of printing x thousand textbooks.

(a) Draw a scatter diagram of the data using x as the independent variable and C as the dependent variable. Comment on the type of relation that may exist between the two variables x and C.

(b) Using a graphing utility, find the cubic function of best fit $C = C(x)$ that models the relation between number of texts and cost.

(c) Graph the cubic function of best fit on your scatter diagram.

(d) Use the function found in part (b) to predict the cost of printing 22 thousand texts per week.

Table 8

Number of Textbooks, x	Cost, C
0	100
5	128.1
10	144
13	153.5
17	161.2
18	162.6
20	166.3
23	178.9
25	190.2
27	221.8

Solution

(a) Figure 25 shows the scatter diagram. A cubic relation may exist between the two variables.

(b) Upon executing the CUBIC REGression program, we obtain the results shown in Figure 26. The output that the utility provides shows us the equation $y = ax^3 + bx^2 + cx + d$. The cubic function of best fit to the data is $C(x) = 0.0155x^3 - 0.5951x^2 + 9.1502x + 98.4327$.

(c) Figure 27 shows the graph of the cubic function of best fit on the scatter diagram. The function fits the data reasonably well.

Figure 25

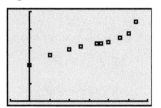

Figure 26

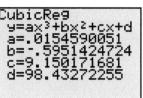

Figure 27

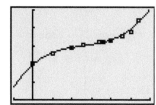

(d) Evaluate the function $C(x)$ at $x = 22$.

$$C(22) = 0.0155(22)^3 - 0.5951(22)^2 + 9.1502(22) + 98.4327 \approx 176.8$$

The model predicts that the cost of printing 22 thousand textbooks in a week will be 176.8 thousand dollars, that is, \$176,800.

4.1 Assess Your Understanding

'Are You Prepared?' *Answers are given at the end of these exercises. If you get a wrong answer, read the pages listed in* red.

1. The intercepts of the equation $9x^2 + 4y = 36$ are _____. (pp. 11–12)

2. Is the expression $4x^3 - 3.6x^2 - \sqrt{2}$ a polynomial? If so, what is its degree? (pp. A22–A29)

3. To graph $y = x^2 - 4$, you would shift the graph of $y = x^2$ _____ a distance of _____ units. (pp. 90–99)

4. Use a graphing utility to approximate (rounded to two decimal places) the local maximum value and local minimum value of $f(x) = x^3 - 2x^2 - 4x + 5$, for $-3 < x < 3$. (p. 74)

5. **True or False** The x-intercepts of the graph of a function $y = f(x)$ are the real solutions of the equation $f(x) = 0$. (pp. 61–63)

6. If $g(5) = 0$, what point is on the graph of g? What is the corresponding x-intercept of the graph of g? (pp. 61–63)

Concepts and Vocabulary

7. The graph of every polynomial function is both _____ and _____.

8. If r is a real zero of even multiplicity of a function f, then the graph of f _____ (crosses/touches) the x-axis at r.

9. The graphs of power functions of the form $f(x) = x^n$, where n is an even integer, always contain the points _____, _____, and _____.

10. If r is a solution to the equation $f(x) = 0$, name three additional statements that can be made about f and r assuming f is a polynomial function.

11. The points at which a graph changes direction (from increasing to decreasing or decreasing to increasing) are called _____.

12. The graph of the function $f(x) = 3x^4 - x^3 + 5x^2 - 2x - 7$ will behave like the graph of _____ for large values of $|x|$.

13. If $f(x) = -2x^5 + x^3 - 5x^2 + 7$, then $\lim\limits_{x \to -\infty} f(x) = $ _____ and $\lim\limits_{x \to \infty} f(x) = $ _____.

14. Explain what the notation $\lim\limits_{x \to \infty} f(x) = -\infty$ means.

Skill Building

In Problems 15–26, determine which functions are polynomial functions. For those that are, state the degree. For those that are not, tell why not.

15. $f(x) = 4x + x^3$

16. $f(x) = 5x^2 + 4x^4$

17. $g(x) = \dfrac{1 - x^2}{2}$

18. $h(x) = 3 - \dfrac{1}{2}x$

19. $f(x) = 1 - \dfrac{1}{x}$

20. $f(x) = x(x - 1)$

21. $g(x) = x^{3/2} - x^2 + 2$

22. $h(x) = \sqrt{x}(\sqrt{x} - 1)$

23. $F(x) = 5x^4 - \pi x^3 + \dfrac{1}{2}$

24. $F(x) = \dfrac{x^2 - 5}{x^3}$

25. $G(x) = 2(x - 1)^2(x^2 + 1)$

26. $G(x) = -3x^2(x + 2)^3$

In Problems 27–40, use transformations of the graph of $y = x^4$ or $y = x^5$ to graph each function.

27. $f(x) = (x + 1)^4$

28. $f(x) = (x - 2)^5$

29. $f(x) = x^5 - 3$

30. $f(x) = x^4 + 2$

31. $f(x) = \dfrac{1}{2}x^4$

32. $f(x) = 3x^5$

33. $f(x) = -x^5$

34. $f(x) = -x^4$

35. $f(x) = (x - 1)^5 + 2$

36. $f(x) = (x + 2)^4 - 3$

37. $f(x) = 2(x + 1)^4 + 1$

38. $f(x) = \dfrac{1}{2}(x - 1)^5 - 2$

39. $f(x) = 4 - (x - 2)^5$

40. $f(x) = 3 - (x + 2)^4$

In Problems 41–48, form a polynomial function whose real zeros and degree are given. Answers will vary depending on the choice of a leading coefficient.

41. Zeros: $-1, 1, 3$; degree 3

42. Zeros: $-2, 2, 3$; degree 3

43. Zeros: $-3, 0, 4$; degree 3

44. Zeros: $-4, 0, 2$; degree 3

45. Zeros: $-4, -1, 2, 3$; degree 4

46. Zeros: $-3, -1, 2, 5$; degree 4

47. Zeros: -1, multiplicity 1; 3, multiplicity 2; degree 3

48. Zeros: -2, multiplicity 2; 4, multiplicity 1; degree 3

In Problems 49–60, for each polynomial function:

(a) List each real zero and its multiplicity.

(b) Determine whether the graph crosses or touches the x-axis at each x-intercept.

(c) Determine the behavior of the graph near each x-intercept (zero).

(d) Determine the maximum number of turning points on the graph.

(e) Determine the end behavior; that is, find the power function that the graph of f resembles for large values of $|x|$.

49. $f(x) = 3(x - 7)(x + 3)^2$

50. $f(x) = 4(x + 4)(x + 3)^3$

51. $f(x) = 4(x^2 + 1)(x - 2)^3$

52. $f(x) = 2(x - 3)(x^2 + 4)^3$

53. $f(x) = -2\left(x + \dfrac{1}{2}\right)^2(x + 4)^3$

54. $f(x) = \left(x - \dfrac{1}{3}\right)^2(x - 1)^3$

55. $f(x) = (x - 5)^3(x + 4)^2$

56. $f(x) = (x + \sqrt{3})^2(x - 2)^4$

57. $f(x) = 3(x^2 + 8)(x^2 + 9)^2$

58. $f(x) = -2(x^2 + 3)^3$

59. $f(x) = -2x^2(x^2 - 2)$

60. $f(x) = 4x(x^2 - 3)$

In Problems 61–64, identify which of the graphs could be the graph of a polynomial function. For those that could, list the real zeros and state the least degree the polynomial can have. For those that could not, say why not.

61.

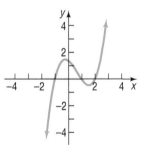

62.

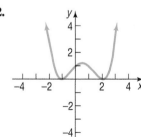

63.

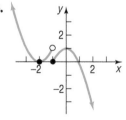

64.

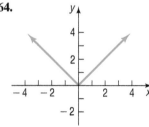

In Problems 65–68, construct a polynomial function that might have the given graph. (More than one answer may be possible.)

65.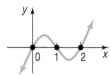

66.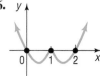

67.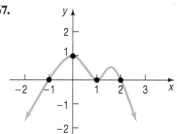

68.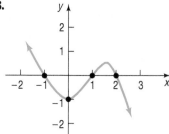

In Problems 69–86, analyze each polynomial function by following Steps 1 through 6 on page 179.

69. $f(x) = x^2(x - 3)$

70. $f(x) = x(x + 2)^2$

71. $f(x) = (x + 4)(x - 2)^2$

72. $f(x) = (x - 1)(x + 3)^2$

73. $f(x) = -2(x + 2)(x - 2)^3$

74. $f(x) = -\dfrac{1}{2}(x + 4)(x - 1)^3$

75. $f(x) = (x + 1)(x - 2)(x + 4)$

76. $f(x) = (x - 1)(x + 4)(x - 3)$

77. $f(x) = x^2(x - 2)(x + 2)$

78. $f(x) = x^2(x - 3)(x + 4)$

79. $f(x) = (x + 1)^2(x - 2)^2$

80. $f(x) = (x + 1)^3(x - 3)$

81. $f(x) = x^2(x - 3)(x + 1)$

82. $f(x) = x^2(x - 3)(x - 1)$

83. $f(x) = (x + 2)^2(x - 4)^2$

84. $f(x) = (x - 2)^2(x + 2)(x + 4)$

85. $f(x) = x^2(x - 2)(x^2 + 3)$

86. $f(x) = x^2(x^2 + 1)(x + 4)$

In Problems 87–94, analyze each polynomial function f by following Steps 1 through 8 on page 182.

87. $f(x) = x^3 + 0.2x^2 - 1.5876x - 0.31752$

88. $f(x) = x^3 - 0.8x^2 - 4.6656x + 3.73248$

89. $f(x) = x^3 + 2.56x^2 - 3.31x + 0.89$

90. $f(x) = x^3 - 2.91x^2 - 7.668x - 3.8151$

91. $f(x) = x^4 - 2.5x^2 + 0.5625$

92. $f(x) = x^4 - 18.5x^2 + 50.2619$

93. $f(x) = 2x^4 - \pi x^3 + \sqrt{5}x - 4$

94. $f(x) = -1.2x^4 + 0.5x^2 - \sqrt{3}x + 2$

Mixed Practice

In Problems 95–102, analyze each polynomial function by following Steps 1 through 6 on page 179.
[**Hint:** You will need to first factor the polynomial].

95. $f(x) = 4x - x^3$

96. $f(x) = x - x^3$

97. $f(x) = x^3 + x^2 - 12x$

98. $f(x) = x^3 + 2x^2 - 8x$

99. $f(x) = 2x^4 + 12x^3 - 8x^2 - 48x$

100. $f(x) = 4x^3 + 10x^2 - 4x - 10$

101. $f(x) = -x^5 - x^4 + x^3 + x^2$

102. $f(x) = -x^5 + 5x^4 + 4x^3 - 20x^2$

In Problems 103–106, construct a polynomial function f with the given characteristics.

103. Zeros: $-3, 1, 4$; degree 3; y-intercept: 36

104. Zeros: $-4, -1, 2$; degree 3; y-intercept: 16

105. Zeros: -5 (multiplicity 2); 2 (multiplicity 1); 4 (multiplicity 1); degree 4; contains the point $(3, 128)$

106. Zeros: -4 (multiplicity 1); 0 (multiplicity 3); 2 (multiplicity 1); degree 5; contains the point $(-2, 64)$

107. $G(x) = (x + 3)^2(x - 2)$
(a) Identify the x-intercepts of the graph of G.
(b) What are the x-intercepts of the graph of $y = G(x + 3)$?

108. $h(x) = (x + 2)(x - 4)^3$
(a) Identify the x-intercepts of the graph of h.
(b) What are the x-intercepts of the graph of $y = h(x - 2)$?

Applications and Extensions

109. Hurricanes In 2005, Hurricane Katrina struck the Gulf Coast of the United States, killing 1289 people and causing an estimated $200 billion in damage. The following data represent the number of major hurricane strikes in the United States (category 3, 4, or 5) each decade from 1921 to 2000.

Decade, x	Major Hurricanes Striking United States, H
1921–1930, 1	5
1931–1940, 2	8
1941–1950, 3	10
1951–1960, 4	8
1961–1970, 5	6
1971–1980, 6	4
1981–1990, 7	5
1991–2000, 8	5

Source: National Oceanic & Atmospheric Administration

(a) Draw a scatter diagram of the data. Comment on the type of relation that may exist between the two variables.
(b) Use a graphing utility to find the cubic function of best fit that models the relation between decade and number of major hurricanes.
(c) Use the model found in part (b) to predict the number of major hurricanes that struck the United States between 1961 and 1970.
(d) With a graphing utility, draw a scatter diagram of the data and then graph the cubic function of best fit on the scatter diagram.
(e) Concern has risen about the increase in the number and intensity of hurricanes, but some scientists believe this is just a natural fluctuation that could last another decade or two. Use your model to predict the number of major hurricanes that will strike the United States between 2001 and 2010. Does your result appear to agree with what these scientists believe?
(f) From 2001 through 2010, 10 major hurricanes struck the United States. Does this support or contradict your prediction in part (e)?

110. Cost of Manufacturing The following data represent the cost C (in thousands of dollars) of manufacturing Chevy Cobalts and the number x of Cobalts produced.
(a) Draw a scatter diagram of the data using x as the independent variable and C as the dependent variable. Comment on the type of relation that may exist between the two variables C and x.
(b) Use a graphing utility to find the cubic function of best fit C = C(x).
(c) Graph the cubic function of best fit on the scatter diagram.
(d) Use the function found in part (b) to predict the cost of manufacturing 11 Cobalts.
(e) Interpret the y-intercept.

Number of Cobalts Produced, x	Cost, C
0	10
1	23
2	31
3	38
4	43
5	50
6	59
7	70
8	85
9	105
10	135

111. Temperature The following data represent the temperature T (°Fahrenheit) in Kansas City, Missouri, x hours after midnight on May 15, 2010.

Hours after Midnight, x	Temperature (°F), T
3	45.0
6	44.1
9	51.1
12	57.9
15	63.0
18	63.0
21	59.0
24	54.0

Source: The Weather Underground

(a) Draw a scatter diagram of the data. Comment on the type of relation that may exist between the two variables.
(b) Find the average rate of change in temperature from 9 AM to 12 noon.
(c) What is the average rate of change in temperature from 3 PM to 6 PM?
(d) Decide on a function of best fit to these data (linear, quadratic, or cubic) and use this function to predict the temperature at 5 PM.
(e) With a graphing utility, draw a scatter diagram of the data and then graph the function of best fit on the scatter diagram.
(f) Interpret the y-intercept.

112. Future Value of Money Suppose that you make deposits of $500 at the beginning of every year into an Individual Retirement Account (IRA) earning interest r. At the beginning of the first year, the value of the account will be $500; at the beginning of the second year, the value of the account, will be

$$\underbrace{\$500 + \$500r}_{\text{Value of 1st deposit}} + \underbrace{\$500}_{\text{Value of 2nd deposit}} = \$500(1 + r) + \$500 = 500r + 1000$$

(a) Verify that the value of the account at the beginning of the third year is $T(r) = 500r^2 + 1500r + 1500$.

(b) The account value at the beginning of the fourth year is $F(r) = 500r^3 + 2000r^2 + 3000r + 2000$. If the annual rate of interest is $5\% = 0.05$, what will be the value of the account at the beginning of the fourth year?

113. **A Geometric Series** In calculus, you will learn that certain functions can be approximated by polynomial functions. We will explore one such function now.

(a) Using a graphing utility, create a table of values with $Y_1 = f(x) = \dfrac{1}{1-x}$ and $Y_2 = g_2(x) = 1 + x + x^2 + x^3$ for $-1 < x < 1$ with $\Delta \text{Tbl} = 0.1$.

(b) Using a graphing utility, create a table of values with $Y_1 = f(x) = \dfrac{1}{1-x}$ and $Y_3 = g_3(x) = 1 + x + x^2 + x^3 + x^4$ for $-1 < x < 1$ with $\Delta \text{Tbl} = 0.1$.

(c) Using a graphing utility, create a table of values with $Y_1 = f(x) = \dfrac{1}{1-x}$ and $Y_4 = g_4(x) = 1 + x + x^2 + x^3 + x^4 + x^5$ for $-1 < x < 1$ with $\Delta \text{Tbl} = 0.1$.

(d) What do you notice about the values of the function as more terms are added to the polynomial? Are there some values of x for which the approximations are better?

Explaining Concepts: Discussion and Writing

114. Can the graph of a polynomial function have no y-intercept? Can it have no x-intercepts? Explain.

115. Write a few paragraphs that provide a general strategy for graphing a polynomial function. Be sure to mention the following: degree, intercepts, end behavior, and turning points.

116. Make up a polynomial that has the following characteristics: crosses the x-axis at -1 and 4, touches the x-axis at 0 and 2, and is above the x-axis between 0 and 2. Give your polynomial to a fellow classmate and ask for a written critique.

117. Make up two polynomials, not of the same degree, with the following characteristics: crosses the x-axis at -2, touches the x-axis at 1, and is above the x-axis between -2 and 1. Give your polynomials to a fellow classmate and ask for a written critique.

118. The graph of a polynomial function is always smooth and continuous. Name a function studied earlier that is smooth and not continuous. Name one that is continuous, but not smooth.

119. Which of the following statements are true regarding the graph of the cubic polynomial $f(x) = x^3 + bx^2 + cx + d$? (Give reasons for your conclusions.)
(a) It intersects the y-axis in one and only one point.
(b) It intersects the x-axis in at most three points.
(c) It intersects the x-axis at least once.
(d) For $|x|$ very large, it behaves like the graph of $y = x^3$.
(e) It is symmetric with respect to the origin.
(f) It passes through the origin.

120. The illustration shows the graph of a polynomial function.

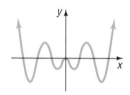

(a) Is the degree of the polynomial even or odd?
(b) Is the leading coefficient positive or negative?
(c) Is the function even, odd, or neither?
(d) Why is x^2 necessarily a factor of the polynomial?
(e) What is the minimum degree of the polynomial?
(f) Formulate five different polynomials whose graphs could look like the one shown. Compare yours to those of other students. What similarities do you see? What differences?

121. Design a polynomial function with the following characteristics: degree 6; four distinct real zeros, one of multiplicity 3; y-intercept 3; behaves like $y = -5x^6$ for large values of $|x|$. Is this polynomial unique? Compare your polynomial with those of other students. What terms will be the same as everyone else's? Add some more characteristics, such as symmetry or naming the real zeros. How does this modify the polynomial?

Interactive Exercises

Ask your instructor if the applet exercise below is of interest to you.

Multiplicity and Turning Points *Open the Multiplicity applet. On the screen you will see the graph of $f(x) = (x + 2)^a x^b (x - 2)^c$ where $a = \{1, 2, 3\}, b = \{1, 2, 3\},$ and $c = \{1, 2, 3, 4\}$.*

1. Grab the slider for the exponent a and move it from 1 to 2 to 3. What happens to the graph as the value of a changes? In particular, describe the behavior of the graph around the zero -2.

2. On the same graph, grab the slider for the exponent a and move it to 1. Grab the slider for the exponent b and move it from 1 to 2 to 3. What happens to the graph as the value of b changes? In particular, describe the behavior of the graph around the zero 0.

3. On the same graph, grab the slider for the exponent b and move it to 1. Grab the slider for the exponent c and move it from 1 to 2 to 3 to 4. What happens to the graph as the value of c changes? In particular, describe the behavior of the graph around the zero 2.

4. Experiment with the graph by adjusting a, b, and c. Based on your experiences conjecture the role the exponent plays in the behavior of the graph around each zero of the function.

5. Obtain a graph of the function for the values of a, b, and c in the following table. Conjecture a relation between the degree of a polynomial and the number of turning points after completing the table. In the table, a can be 1, 2, or 3; b can be 1, 2, or 3; and c can be 1, 2, 3, or 4.

Values of a, b, and c	Degree of Polynomial	Number of Turning Points
$a = 1, b = 1, c = 1$	3	
$a = 1, b = 1, c = 2$	4	
$a = 1, b = 1, c = 3$	5	
$a = 1, b = 1, c = 4$		
$a = 1, b = 2, c = 1$		
$a = 1, b = 2, c = 2$		
$a = 1, b = 2, c = 3$		
$a = 1, b = 2, c = 4$		
$a = 1, b = 3, c = 1$		
$a = 1, b = 3, c = 2$		
$a = 1, b = 3, c = 3$		
$a = 1, b = 3, c = 4$		
$a = 2, b = 1, c = 1$		
$a = 2, b = 1, c = 2$		
$a = 2, b = 1, c = 3$		
$a = 2, b = 1, c = 4$		
$a = 2, b = 2, c = 1$		
$a = 2, b = 2, c = 2$		
$a = 3, b = 3, c = 4$		

'Are You Prepared?' Answers

1. $(-2, 0), (2, 0), (0, 9)$ 2. Yes; 3   3. Down; 4   4. Local maximum value 6.48 at $x = -0.67$; local minimum value -3 at $x = 2$

5. True   6. $(5, 0); 5$

4.2 Properties of Rational Functions

PREPARING FOR THIS SECTION *Before getting started, review the following:*

- Rational Expressions (Appendix A, Section A.5, pp. A36–A42)
- Polynomial Division (Appendix A, Section A.3, pp. A25–A28)
- Graph of $f(x) = \dfrac{1}{x}$ (Section 1.2, Example 12, p. 16)
- Graphing Techniques: Transformations (Section 2.5, pp. 90–99)

Now Work the 'Are You Prepared?' problems on page 196.

OBJECTIVES   **1** Find the Domain of a Rational Function (p. 189)
   2 Find the Vertical Asymptotes of a Rational Function (p. 192)
   3 Find the Horizontal or Oblique Asymptote of a Rational Function (p. 193)

Ratios of integers are called *rational numbers*. Similarly, ratios of polynomial functions are called *rational functions*. Examples of rational functions are

$$R(x) = \frac{x^2 - 4}{x^2 + x + 1} \qquad F(x) = \frac{x^3}{x^2 - 4} \qquad G(x) = \frac{3x^2}{x^4 - 1}$$

DEFINITION

A **rational function** is a function of the form

$$R(x) = \frac{p(x)}{q(x)}$$

where p and q are polynomial functions and q is not the zero polynomial. The domain of a rational function is the set of all real numbers except those for which the denominator q is 0.

1 Find the Domain of a Rational Function

EXAMPLE 1

Finding the Domain of a Rational Function

(a) The domain of $R(x) = \dfrac{2x^2 - 4}{x + 5}$ is the set of all real numbers x except -5; that is, the domain is $\{x | x \neq -5\}$.

(b) The domain of $R(x) = \dfrac{1}{x^2 - 4}$ is the set of all real numbers x except -2 and 2; that is, the domain is $\{x | x \neq -2, x \neq 2\}$.

(c) The domain of $R(x) = \dfrac{x^3}{x^2 + 1}$ is the set of all real numbers.

(d) The domain of $R(x) = \dfrac{x^2 - 1}{x - 1}$ is the set of all real numbers x except 1; that is, the domain is $\{x | x \neq 1\}$.

Although $\dfrac{x^2 - 1}{x - 1}$ reduces to $x + 1$, it is important to observe that the functions

$$R(x) = \frac{x^2 - 1}{x - 1} \quad \text{and} \quad f(x) = x + 1$$

are not equal, since the domain of R is $\{x | x \neq 1\}$ and the domain of f is the set of all real numbers.

━━━━Now Work PROBLEM 15

If $R(x) = \dfrac{p(x)}{q(x)}$ is a rational function and if p and q have no common factors, then the rational function R is said to be in **lowest terms.** For a rational function $R(x) = \dfrac{p(x)}{q(x)}$ in lowest terms, the real zeros, if any, of the numerator in the domain of R are the x-intercepts of the graph of R and so will play a major role in the graph of R. The real zeros of the denominator of R [that is, the numbers x, if any, for which $q(x) = 0$], although not in the domain of R, also play a major role in the graph of R.

We have already discussed the properties of the rational function $y = \dfrac{1}{x}$. (Refer to Example 12, page 16). The next rational function that we take up is

$$H(x) = \frac{1}{x^2}.$$

EXAMPLE 2

Graphing $y = \dfrac{1}{x^2}$

Analyze the graph of $H(x) = \dfrac{1}{x^2}$.

Solution

The domain of $H(x) = \dfrac{1}{x^2}$ is the set of all real numbers x except 0. The graph has no y-intercept, because x can never equal 0. The graph has no x-intercept because the equation $H(x) = 0$ has no solution. Therefore, the graph of H will not cross or touch either of the coordinate axes. Because

$$H(-x) = \frac{1}{(-x)^2} = \frac{1}{x^2} = H(x)$$

H is an even function, so its graph is symmetric with respect to the y-axis.

Table 9 shows the behavior of $H(x) = \dfrac{1}{x^2}$ for selected positive numbers x. (We will use symmetry to obtain the graph of H when $x < 0$.) From the first three rows of Table 9, we see that, as the values of x approach (get closer to) 0, the values of $H(x)$ become larger and larger positive numbers, so H is unbounded in the positive direction. We use limit notation, $\lim\limits_{x \to 0} H(x) = \infty$, read "the limit of $H(x)$ as x approaches zero equals infinity," to mean that $H(x) \to \infty$ as $x \to 0$.

Look at the last four rows of Table 9. As $x \to \infty$, the values of $H(x)$ approach 0 (the end behavior of the graph). In calculus, this is symbolized by writing $\lim\limits_{x \to \infty} H(x) = 0$. Figure 28 shows the graph. Notice the use of red dashed lines to convey the ideas discussed above.

Table 9

x	$H(x) = \dfrac{1}{x^2}$
$\dfrac{1}{2}$	4
$\dfrac{1}{100}$	10,000
$\dfrac{1}{10,000}$	100,000,000
1	1
2	$\dfrac{1}{4}$
100	$\dfrac{1}{10,000}$
10,000	$\dfrac{1}{100,000,000}$

Figure 28

$H(x) = \dfrac{1}{x^2}$

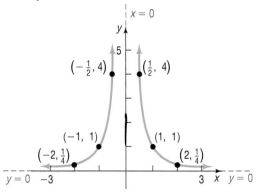

EXAMPLE 3

Using Transformations to Graph a Rational Function

Graph the rational function: $R(x) = \dfrac{1}{(x-2)^2} + 1$

Solution

The domain of R is the set of all real numbers except $x = 2$. To graph R, start with the graph of $y = \dfrac{1}{x^2}$. See Figure 29 for the steps.

Figure 29

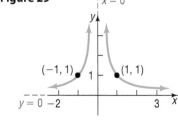

Replace x by $x - 2$; shift right 2 units

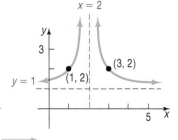

Add 1; shift up 1 unit

(a) $y = \dfrac{1}{x^2}$

(b) $y = \dfrac{1}{(x-2)^2}$

(c) $y = \dfrac{1}{(x-2)^2} + 1$

━━Now Work PROBLEM 33

Asymptotes

Let's investigate the roles of the vertical line $x = 2$ and the horizontal line $y = 1$ in Figure 29(c).

First, we look at the end behavior of $R(x) = \dfrac{1}{(x-2)^2} + 1$. Table 10(a) shows the values of R at $x = 10, 100, 1000, 10,000$. Notice that, as x becomes unbounded in the positive direction, the values of R approach 1, so $\lim\limits_{x \to \infty} R(x) = 1$. From Table 10(b) we see that, as x becomes unbounded in the negative direction, the values of R also approach 1, so $\lim\limits_{x \to -\infty} R(x) = 1$.

Even though $x = 2$ is not in the domain of R, the behavior of the graph of R near $x = 2$ is important. Table 10(c) shows the values of R at $x = 1.5$, $1.9, 1.99, 1.999$, and 1.9999. We see that, as x approaches 2 for $x < 2$, denoted $x \to 2^-$, the values of R are increasing without bound, so $\lim\limits_{x \to 2^-} R(x) = \infty$. From Table 10(d), we see that, as x approaches 2 for $x > 2$, denoted $x \to 2^+$, the values of R are also increasing without bound, so $\lim\limits_{x \to 2^+} R(x) = \infty$.

Table 10

x	R(x)
10	1.0156
100	1.0001
1000	1.000001
10,000	1.00000001

(a)

x	R(x)
−10	1.0069
−100	1.0001
−1000	1.000001
−10,000	1.00000001

(b)

x	R(x)
1.5	5
1.9	101
1.99	10,001
1.999	1,000,001
1.9999	100,000,001

(c)

x	R(x)
2.5	5
2.1	101
2.01	10,001
2.001	1,000,001
2.0001	100,000,001

(d)

The vertical line $x = 2$ and the horizontal line $y = 1$ are called *asymptotes* of the graph of R.

DEFINITION

Let R denote a function.

If, as $x \to -\infty$ or as $x \to \infty$, the values of $R(x)$ approach some fixed number L, then the line $y = L$ is a **horizontal asymptote** of the graph of R. [Refer to Figures 30(a) and (b).]

If, as x approaches some number c, the values $|R(x)| \to \infty [R(x) \to -\infty$ or $R(x) \to \infty]$, then the line $x = c$ is a **vertical asymptote** of the graph of R. [Refer to Figures 30(c) and (d).]

Figure 30

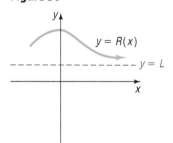

(a) End behavior: As $x \to \infty$, the values of $R(x)$ approach L [$\lim\limits_{x \to \infty} R(x) = L$]. That is, the points on the graph of R are getting closer to the line $y = L$; $y = L$ is a horizontal asymptote.

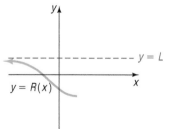

(b) End behavior: As $x \to -\infty$, the values of $R(x)$ approach L [$\lim\limits_{x \to -\infty} R(x) = L$]. That is, the points on the graph of R are getting closer to the line $y = L$; $y = L$ is a horizontal asymptote.

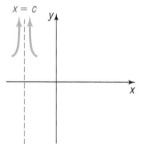

(c) As x approaches c, the values of $|R(x)| \to \infty$ [$\lim\limits_{x \to c^-} R(x) = \infty$; $\lim\limits_{x \to c^+} R(x) = \infty$]. That is, the points on the graph of R are getting closer to the line $x = c$; $x = c$ is a vertical asymptote.

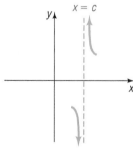

(d) As x approaches c, the values of $|R(x)| \to \infty$ [$\lim\limits_{x \to c^-} R(x) = -\infty$; $\lim\limits_{x \to c^+} R(x) = \infty$]. That is, the points on the graph of R are getting closer to the line $x = c$; $x = c$ is a vertical asymptote.

Figure 31

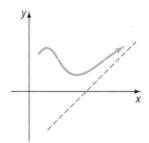

A horizontal asymptote, when it occurs, describes the **end behavior** of the graph as $x \rightarrow \infty$ or as $x \rightarrow -\infty$. **The graph of a function may intersect a horizontal asymptote.**

A vertical asymptote, when it occurs, describes the behavior of the graph when x is close to some number c. **The graph of a rational function will never intersect a vertical asymptote.**

There is a third possibility. If, as $x \rightarrow -\infty$ or as $x \rightarrow \infty$, the value of a rational function $R(x)$ approaches a linear expression $ax + b$, $a \neq 0$, then the line $y = ax + b$, $a \neq 0$, is an **oblique asymptote** of R. Figure 31 shows an oblique asymptote. An oblique asymptote, when it occurs, describes the end behavior of the graph. **The graph of a function may intersect an oblique asymptote.**

➤ **Now Work** PROBLEM 25

2 Find the Vertical Asymptotes of a Rational Function

The vertical asymptotes of a rational function $R(x) = \dfrac{p(x)}{q(x)}$, in lowest terms, are located at the real zeros of the denominator of $q(x)$. Suppose that r is a real zero of q, so $x - r$ is a factor of q. As x approaches r, symbolized as $x \rightarrow r$, the values of $x - r$ approach 0, causing the ratio to become unbounded, that is, $|R(x)| \rightarrow \infty$. Based on the definition, we conclude that the line $x = r$ is a vertical asymptote.

THEOREM

Locating Vertical Asymptotes

A rational function $R(x) = \dfrac{p(x)}{q(x)}$, *in lowest terms*, will have a vertical asymptote $x = r$ if r is a real zero of the *denominator* q. That is, if $x - r$ is a factor of the denominator q of a rational function $R(x) = \dfrac{p(x)}{q(x)}$, in lowest terms, R will have the vertical asymptote $x = r$.

WARNING If a rational function is not in lowest terms, an application of this theorem may result in an incorrect listing of vertical asymptotes. ∎

EXAMPLE 4

Finding Vertical Asymptotes

Find the vertical asymptotes, if any, of the graph of each rational function.

(a) $F(x) = \dfrac{x + 3}{x - 1}$ (b) $R(x) = \dfrac{x}{x^2 - 4}$

(c) $H(x) = \dfrac{x^2}{x^2 + 1}$ (d) $G(x) = \dfrac{x^2 - 9}{x^2 + 4x - 21}$

Solution

(a) F is in lowest terms and the only zero of the denominator is 1. The line $x = 1$ is the vertical asymptote of the graph of F.

WARNING In Example 4(a), the vertical asymptote is x = 1. Do not say that the vertical asymptote is 1. ∎

(b) R is in lowest terms and the zeros of the denominator $x^2 - 4$ are -2 and 2. The lines $x = -2$ and $x = 2$ are the vertical asymptotes of the graph of R.

(c) H is in lowest terms and the denominator has no real zeros, because the equation $x^2 + 1 = 0$ has no real solutions. The graph of H has no vertical asymptotes.

(d) Factor the numerator and denominator of $G(x)$ to determine if it is in lowest terms.

$$G(x) = \frac{x^2 - 9}{x^2 + 4x - 21} = \frac{(x + 3)(x - 3)}{(x + 7)(x - 3)} = \frac{x + 3}{x + 7} \qquad x \neq 3$$

The only zero of the denominator of $G(x)$ in lowest terms is -7. The line $x = -7$ is the only vertical asymptote of the graph of G.

As Example 4 points out, rational functions can have no vertical asymptotes, one vertical asymptote, or more than one vertical asymptote.

Exploration

Graph each of the following rational functions:

$$R(x) = \frac{1}{x - 1} \qquad R(x) = \frac{1}{(x - 1)^2} \qquad R(x) = \frac{1}{(x - 1)^3} \qquad R(x) = \frac{1}{(x - 1)^4}$$

Each has the vertical asymptote $x = 1$. What happens to the value of $R(x)$ as x approaches 1 from the right side of the vertical asymptote; that is, what is $\lim\limits_{x \to 1^+} R(x)$? What happens to the value of $R(x)$ as x approaches 1 from the left side of the vertical asymptote; that is, what is $\lim\limits_{x \to 1^-} R(x)$? How does the multiplicity of the zero in the denominator affect the graph of R?

Now Work PROBLEM 47 (FIND THE VERTICAL ASYMPTOTES, IF ANY.)

3 Find the Horizontal or Oblique Asymptote of a Rational Function

The procedure for finding horizontal and oblique asymptotes is somewhat more involved. To find such asymptotes, we need to know how the values of a function behave as $x \to -\infty$ or as $x \to \infty$. That is, we need to find the end behavior of the rational function.

If a rational function $R(x)$ is **proper,** that is, if the degree of the numerator is less than the degree of the denominator, then as $x \to -\infty$ or as $x \to \infty$ the value of $R(x)$ approaches 0. Consequently, the line $y = 0$ (the x-axis) is a horizontal asymptote of the graph.

THEOREM
> If a rational function is proper, the line $y = 0$ is a horizontal asymptote of its graph.

EXAMPLE 5

Finding a Horizontal Asymptote

Find the horizontal asymptote, if one exists, of the graph of

$$R(x) = \frac{x - 12}{4x^2 + x + 1}$$

Solution
Since the degree of the numerator, 1, is less than the degree of the denominator, 2, the rational function R is proper. The line $y = 0$ is a horizontal asymptote of the graph of R.

To see why $y = 0$ is a horizontal asymptote of the function R in Example 5, we investigate the behavior of R as $x \to -\infty$ and $x \to \infty$. When $|x|$ is very large, the numerator of R, which is $x - 12$, can be approximated by the power function $y = x$, while the denominator of R, which is $4x^2 + x + 1$, can be approximated by the power function $y = 4x^2$. Applying these ideas to $R(x)$, we find

$$R(x) = \frac{x - 12}{4x^2 + x + 1} \underset{\substack{\uparrow \\ \text{For } |x| \text{ very large}}}{\approx} \frac{x}{4x^2} = \frac{1}{4x} \underset{\substack{\uparrow \\ \text{As } x \to -\infty \text{ or } x \to \infty}}{\to 0}$$

This shows that the line $y = 0$ is a horizontal asymptote of the graph of R.

If a rational function $R(x) = \dfrac{p(x)}{q(x)}$ is **improper,** that is, if the degree of the numerator is greater than or equal to the degree of the denominator, we use long division to write the rational function as the sum of a polynomial $f(x)$ (the quotient) plus a proper rational function $\dfrac{r(x)}{q(x)}$ ($r(x)$ is the remainder). That is, we write

$$R(x) = \frac{p(x)}{q(x)} = f(x) + \frac{r(x)}{q(x)}$$

where $f(x)$ is a polynomial and $\dfrac{r(x)}{q(x)}$ is a proper rational function. Since $\dfrac{r(x)}{q(x)}$ is proper, $\dfrac{r(x)}{q(x)} \to 0$ as $x \to -\infty$ or as $x \to \infty$. As a result,

$$R(x) = \frac{p(x)}{q(x)} \to f(x) \qquad \text{as } x \to -\infty \text{ or as } x \to \infty$$

The possibilities are listed next.

1. If $f(x) = b$, a constant, the line $y = b$ is a horizontal asymptote of the graph of R.

2. If $f(x) = ax + b, a \neq 0$, the line $y = ax + b$ is an oblique asymptote of the graph of R.

3. In all other cases, the graph of R approaches the graph of f, and there are no horizontal or oblique asymptotes.

We illustrate each of the possibilities in Examples 6, 7, and 8.

EXAMPLE 6   **Finding a Horizontal or Oblique Asymptote**

Find the horizontal or oblique asymptote, if one exists, of the graph of

$$H(x) = \frac{3x^4 - x^2}{x^3 - x^2 + 1}$$

Solution   Since the degree of the numerator, 4, is greater than the degree of the denominator, 3, the rational function H is improper. To find a horizontal or oblique asymptote, we use long division.

$$
\begin{array}{r}
3x + 3 \\
x^3 - x^2 + 1 \overline{)\,3x^4 - x^2 } \\
\underline{3x^4 - 3x^3 + 3x} \\
3x^3 - x^2 - 3x \\
\underline{3x^3 - 3x^2 + 3} \\
2x^2 - 3x - 3
\end{array}
$$

As a result,

$$H(x) = \frac{3x^4 - x^2}{x^3 - x^2 + 1} = 3x + 3 + \frac{2x^2 - 3x - 3}{x^3 - x^2 + 1}$$

As $x \to -\infty$ or as $x \to \infty$,

$$\frac{2x^2 - 3x - 3}{x^3 - x^2 + 1} \approx \frac{2x^2}{x^3} = \frac{2}{x} \to 0$$

As $x \to -\infty$ or as $x \to \infty$, we have $H(x) \to 3x + 3$. We conclude that the graph of the rational function H has an oblique asymptote $y = 3x + 3$. ♪

EXAMPLE 7   **Finding a Horizontal or Oblique Asymptote**

Find the horizontal or oblique asymptote, if one exists, of the graph of

$$R(x) = \frac{8x^2 - x + 2}{4x^2 - 1}$$

Solution Since the degree of the numerator, 2, equals the degree of the denominator, 2, the rational function R is improper. To find a horizontal or oblique asymptote, we use long division.

$$
\begin{array}{r}
2 \\
4x^2 - 1 \overline{\smash{)}8x^2 - x + 2} \\
\underline{8x^2 - 2} \\
-x + 4
\end{array}
$$

As a result,

$$R(x) = \frac{8x^2 - x + 2}{4x^2 - 1} = 2 + \frac{-x + 4}{4x^2 - 1}$$

Then, as $x \rightarrow -\infty$ or as $x \rightarrow \infty$,

$$\frac{-x + 4}{4x^2 - 1} \approx \frac{-x}{4x^2} = \frac{-1}{4x} \rightarrow 0$$

As $x \rightarrow -\infty$ or as $x \rightarrow \infty$, we have $R(x) \rightarrow 2$. We conclude that $y = 2$ is a horizontal asymptote of the graph. ◞

   In Example 7, notice that the quotient 2 obtained by long division is the quotient of the leading coefficients of the numerator polynomial and the denominator polynomial $\left(\dfrac{8}{4}\right)$. This means that we can avoid the long division process for rational functions where the numerator and denominator *are of the same degree* and conclude that the quotient of the leading coefficients will give us the horizontal asymptote.

══════**Now Work** PROBLEMS 43 AND 45

EXAMPLE 8   **Finding a Horizontal or Oblique Asymptote**

Find the horizontal or oblique asymptote, if one exists, of the graph of

$$G(x) = \frac{2x^5 - x^3 + 2}{x^3 - 1}$$

Solution Since the degree of the numerator, 5, is greater than the degree of the denominator, 3, the rational function G is improper. To find a horizontal or oblique asymptote, we use long division.

$$
\begin{array}{r}
2x^2 - 1 \\
x^3 - 1 \overline{\smash{)}2x^5 - x^3 + 2} \\
\underline{2x^5 - 2x^2} \\
-x^3 + 2x^2 + 2 \\
\underline{-x^3 + 1} \\
2x^2 + 1
\end{array}
$$

As a result,

$$G(x) = \frac{2x^5 - x^3 + 2}{x^3 - 1} = 2x^2 - 1 + \frac{2x^2 + 1}{x^3 - 1}$$

Then, as $x \rightarrow -\infty$ or as $x \rightarrow \infty$,

$$\frac{2x^2 + 1}{x^3 - 1} \approx \frac{2x^2}{x^3} = \frac{2}{x} \rightarrow 0$$

As $x \to -\infty$ or as $x \to \infty$, we have $G(x) \to 2x^2 - 1$. We conclude that, for large values of $|x|$, the graph of G approaches the graph of $y = 2x^2 - 1$. That is, the graph of G will look like the graph of $y = 2x^2 - 1$ as $x \to -\infty$ or $x \to \infty$. Since $y = 2x^2 - 1$ is not a linear function, G has no horizontal or oblique asymptote. ♩

SUMMARY   Finding a Horizontal or Oblique Asymptote of a Rational Function

Consider the rational function

$$R(x) = \frac{p(x)}{q(x)} = \frac{a_n x^n + a_{n-1} x^{n-1} + \cdots + a_1 x + a_0}{b_m x^m + b_{m-1} x^{m-1} + \cdots + b_1 x + b_0}$$

in which the degree of the numerator is n and the degree of the denominator is m.

1. If $n < m$ (the degree of the numerator is less than the degree of the denominator), then R is a proper rational function, and the graph of R will have the horizontal asymptote $y = 0$ (the x-axis).

2. If $n \geq m$ (the degree of the numerator is greater than or equal to the degree of the denominator), then R is improper. Here long division is used.

   (a) If $n = m$ (the degree of the numerator equals the degree of the denominator), the quotient obtained will be the number $\dfrac{a_n}{b_m}$, and the line $y = \dfrac{a_n}{b_m}$ is a horizontal asymptote.

   (b) If $n = m + 1$ (the degree of the numerator is one more than the degree of the denominator), the quotient obtained is of the form $ax + b$ (a polynomial of degree 1), and the line $y = ax + b$ is an oblique asymptote.

   (c) If $n \geq m + 2$ (the degree of the numerator is two or more greater than the degree of the denominator), the quotient obtained is a polynomial of degree 2 or higher, and R has neither a horizontal nor an oblique asymptote. In this case, for very large values of $|x|$, the graph of R will behave like the graph of the quotient.

Note: The graph of a rational function either has one horizontal or one oblique asymptote or else has no horizontal and no oblique asymptote. ∎

4.2 Assess Your Understanding

'Are You Prepared?' *Answers are given at the end of these exercises. If you get a wrong answer, read the pages listed in* red.

1. **True or False** The quotient of two polynomial expressions is a rational expression. (pp. A36–A42)

2. What are the quotient and remainder when $3x^4 - x^2$ is divided by $x^3 - x^2 + 1$. (pp. A25–A28)

3. Graph $y = \dfrac{1}{x}$. (p. 16)

4. Graph $y = 2(x + 1)^2 - 3$ using transformations. (pp. 90–99)

Concepts and Vocabulary

5. **True or False** The domain of every rational function is the set of all real numbers.

6. If, as $x \to -\infty$ or as $x \to \infty$, the values of $R(x)$ approach some fixed number L, then the line $y = L$ is a _____ _____ of the graph of R.

7. If, as x approaches some number c, the values of $|R(x)| \to \infty$, then the line $x = c$ is a _____ _____ of the graph of R.

8. For a rational function R, if the degree of the numerator is less than the degree of the denominator, then R is _____ .

9. **True or False** The graph of a rational function may intersect a horizontal asymptote.

10. **True or False** The graph of a rational function may intersect a vertical asymptote.

11. If a rational function is proper, then _____ is a horizontal asymptote.

12. **True or False** If the degree of the numerator of a rational function equals the degree of the denominator, then the ratio of the leading coefficients gives rise to the horizontal asymptote.

Skill Building

In Problems 13–24, find the domain of each rational function.

13. $R(x) = \dfrac{4x}{x - 3}$

14. $R(x) = \dfrac{5x^2}{3 + x}$

15. $H(x) = \dfrac{-4x^2}{(x - 2)(x + 4)}$

16. $G(x) = \dfrac{6}{(x + 3)(4 - x)}$

17. $F(x) = \dfrac{3x(x - 1)}{2x^2 - 5x - 3}$

18. $Q(x) = \dfrac{-x(1 - x)}{3x^2 + 5x - 2}$

19. $R(x) = \dfrac{x}{x^3 - 8}$

20. $R(x) = \dfrac{x}{x^4 - 1}$

21. $H(x) = \dfrac{3x^2 + x}{x^2 + 4}$

22. $G(x) = \dfrac{x - 3}{x^4 + 1}$

23. $R(x) = \dfrac{3(x^2 - x - 6)}{4(x^2 - 9)}$

24. $F(x) = \dfrac{-2(x^2 - 4)}{3(x^2 + 4x + 4)}$

In Problems 25–30, use the graph shown to find

  (a) The domain and range of each function

  (b) The intercepts, if any

  (c) Horizontal asymptotes, if any

  (d) Vertical asymptotes, if any

  (e) Oblique asymptotes, if any

25.

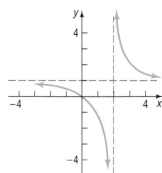

26.

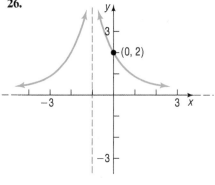

27.

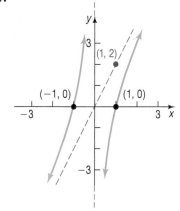

28.

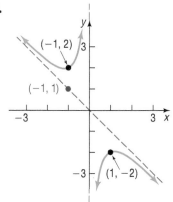

29.

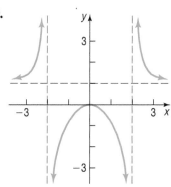

30.

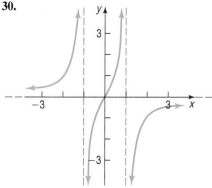

In Problems 31–42, graph each rational function using transformations.

31. $F(x) = 2 + \dfrac{1}{x}$

32. $Q(x) = 3 + \dfrac{1}{x^2}$

33. $R(x) = \dfrac{1}{(x - 1)^2}$

34. $R(x) = \dfrac{3}{x}$

35. $H(x) = \dfrac{-2}{x + 1}$

36. $G(x) = \dfrac{2}{(x + 2)^2}$

37. $R(x) = \dfrac{-1}{x^2 + 4x + 4}$

38. $R(x) = \dfrac{1}{x - 1} + 1$

39. $G(x) = 1 + \dfrac{2}{(x - 3)^2}$

40. $F(x) = 2 - \dfrac{1}{x + 1}$

41. $R(x) = \dfrac{x^2 - 4}{x^2}$

42. $R(x) = \dfrac{x - 4}{x}$

In Problems 43–54, find the vertical, horizontal, and oblique asymptotes, if any, of each rational function.

43. $R(x) = \dfrac{3x}{x + 4}$

44. $R(x) = \dfrac{3x + 5}{x - 6}$

45. $H(x) = \dfrac{x^3 - 8}{x^2 - 5x + 6}$

46. $G(x) = \dfrac{x^3 + 1}{x^2 - 5x - 14}$

47. $T(x) = \dfrac{x^3}{x^4 - 1}$

48. $P(x) = \dfrac{4x^2}{x^3 - 1}$

49. $Q(x) = \dfrac{2x^2 - 5x - 12}{3x^2 - 11x - 4}$

50. $F(x) = \dfrac{x^2 + 6x + 5}{2x^2 + 7x + 5}$

51. $R(x) = \dfrac{6x^2 + 7x - 5}{3x + 5}$

52. $R(x) = \dfrac{8x^2 + 26x - 7}{4x - 1}$

53. $G(x) = \dfrac{x^4 - 1}{x^2 - x}$

54. $F(x) = \dfrac{x^4 - 16}{x^2 - 2x}$

Applications and Extensions

55. Gravity   In physics, it is established that the acceleration due to gravity, g (in m/sec^2), at a height h meters above sea level is given by

$$g(h) = \frac{3.99 \times 10^{14}}{(6.374 \times 10^6 + h)^2}$$

where 6.374×10^6 is the radius of Earth in meters.
   (a) What is the acceleration due to gravity at sea level?
   (b) The Willis Tower in Chicago, Illinois, is 443 meters tall. What is the acceleration due to gravity at the top of the Willis Tower?
   (c) The peak of Mount Everest is 8848 meters above sea level. What is the acceleration due to gravity on the peak of Mount Everest?
   (d) Find the horizontal asymptote of $g(h)$.
   (e) Solve $g(h) = 0$. How do you interpret your answer?

56. Population Model   A rare species of insect was discovered in the Amazon Rain Forest. To protect the species, environmentalists declared the insect endangered and transplanted the insect into a protected area. The population P of the insect t months after being transplanted is

$$P(t) = \frac{50(1 + 0.5t)}{2 + 0.01t}$$

   (a) How many insects were discovered? In other words, what was the population when $t = 0$?
   (b) What will the population be after 5 years?
   (c) Determine the horizontal asymptote of $P(t)$. What is the largest population that the protected area can sustain?

57. Resistance in Parallel Circuits   From Ohm's law for circuits, it follows that the total resistance R_{tot} of two components hooked in parallel is given by the equation

$$R_{tot} = \frac{R_1 R_2}{R_1 + R_2}$$

where R_1 and R_2 are the individual resistances.

   (a) Let $R_1 = 10$ ohms, and graph R_{tot} as a function of R_2.
   (b) Find and interpret any asymptotes of the graph obtained in part (a).
   (c) If $R_2 = 2\sqrt{R_1}$, what value of R_1 will yield an R_{tot} of 17 ohms?

   Source: en.wikipedia.org/wiki/Series_and_parallel_circuits

58. Newton's Method   In calculus you will learn that, if

$$p(x) = a_n x^n + a_{n-1} x^{n-1} + \cdots + a_1 x + a_0$$

is a polynomial function, then the *derivative* of $p(x)$ is

$$p'(x) = na_n x^{n-1} + (n - 1)a_{n-1} x^{n-2} + \cdots + 2a_2 x + a_1$$

Newton's Method is an efficient method for approximating the x-intercepts (or real zeros) of a function, such as $p(x)$. The following steps outline Newton's Method.

STEP 1: Select an initial value x_0 that is somewhat close to the x-intercept being sought.

STEP 2: Find values for x using the relation

$$x_{n+1} = x_n - \frac{p(x_n)}{p'(x_n)} \quad n = 1, 2, \ldots$$

until you get two consecutive values x_n and x_{n+1} that agree to whatever decimal place accuracy you desire.

STEP 3: The approximate zero will be x_{n+1}.

Consider the polynomial $p(x) = x^3 - 7x - 40$.
   (a) Evaluate $p(5)$ and $p(-3)$.
   (b) What might we conclude about a zero of p? Explain.
   (c) Use Newton's Method to approximate an x-intercept, r, $-3 < r < 5$, of $p(x)$ to four decimal places.
   (d) Use a graphing utility to graph $p(x)$ and verify your answer in part (c).
   (e) Using a graphing utility, evaluate $p(r)$ to verify your result.

Explaining Concepts: Discussion and Writing

59. If the graph of a rational function R has the vertical asymptote $x = 4$, the factor $x - 4$ must be present in the denominator of R. Explain why.

60. If the graph of a rational function R has the horizontal asymptote $y = 2$, the degree of the numerator of R equals the degree of the denominator of R. Explain why.

61. Can the graph of a rational function have both a horizontal and an oblique asymptote? Explain.

62. Make up a rational function that has $y = 2x + 1$ as an oblique asymptote. Explain the methodology that you used.

1. True   **2.** Quotient: $3x + 3$; remainder: $2x^2 - 3x - 3$ **3.** 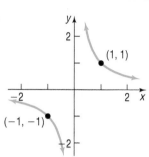   **4.**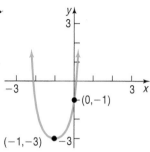

4.3 The Graph of a Rational Function

PREPARING FOR THIS SECTION *Before getting started, review the following:*

- Intercepts (Section 1.2, pp. 11–12)

Now Work the 'Are You Prepared?' problem on page 211.

OBJECTIVES   **1** Analyze the Graph of a Rational Function (p. 199)

   2 Solve Applied Problems Involving Rational Functions (p. 210)

1 Analyze the Graph of a Rational Function

We commented earlier that calculus provides the tools required to graph a polynomial function accurately. The same holds true for rational functions. However, we can gather together quite a bit of information about their graphs to get an idea of the general shape and position of the graph.

EXAMPLE 1

How to Analyze the Graph of a Rational Function

Analyze the graph of the rational function: $R(x) = \dfrac{x - 1}{x^2 - 4}$

Step-by-Step Solution

Step 1: Factor the numerator and denominator of R. Find the domain of the rational function.

$$R(x) = \frac{x - 1}{x^2 - 4} = \frac{x - 1}{(x + 2)(x - 2)}$$

The domain of R is $\{x \mid x \neq -2, x \neq 2\}$.

Step 2: Write R in lowest terms.

Because there are no common factors between the numerator and denominator, R is in lowest terms.

Step 3: Locate the intercepts of the graph. Determine the behavior of the graph of R near each x-intercept using the same procedure as for polynomial functions. Plot each x-intercept and indicate the behavior of the graph near it.

Since 0 is in the domain of R, the y-intercept is $R(0) = \dfrac{1}{4}$. The x-intercepts are found by determining the real zeros of the numerator of R that are in the domain of R. By solving $x - 1 = 0$, the only real zero of the numerator is 1, so the only x-intercept of the graph of R is 1. We analyze the behavior of the graph of R near $x = 1$:

Near 1: $R(x) = \dfrac{x - 1}{(x + 2)(x - 2)} \approx \dfrac{x - 1}{(1 + 2)(1 - 2)} = -\dfrac{1}{3}(x - 1)$

Plot the point $(1, 0)$ and draw a line through $(1, 0)$ with a negative slope. See Figure 32(a) on page 201.

Step 4: Locate the vertical asymptotes. Graph each vertical asymptote using a dashed line.

The vertical asymptotes are the zeros of the denominator with the rational function in lowest terms. With R written in lowest terms, we find that the graph of R has two vertical asymptotes: the lines $x = -2$ and $x = 2$.

Step 5: Locate the horizontal or oblique asymptote, if one exists. Determine points, if any, at which the graph of R intersects this asymptote. Graph the asymptotes using a dashed line. Plot any points at which the graph of R intersects the asymptote.

Because the degree of the numerator is less than the degree of the denominator, R is proper and the line $y = 0$ (the x-axis) is a horizontal asymptote of the graph. To determine if the graph of R intersects the horizontal asymptote, solve the equation $R(x) = 0$:

$$\frac{x - 1}{x^2 - 4} = 0$$

$$x - 1 = 0$$

$$x = 1$$

The only solution is $x = 1$, so the graph of R intersects the horizontal asymptote at $(1, 0)$.

Step 6: Use the zeros of the numerator and denominator of R to divide the x-axis into intervals. Determine where the graph of R is above or below the x-axis by choosing a number in each interval and evaluating R there. Plot the points found.

The zero of the numerator, 1, and the zeros of the denominator, -2 and 2, divide the x-axis into four intervals:

$$(-\infty, -2) \qquad (-2, 1) \qquad (1, 2) \qquad (2, \infty)$$

Now construct Table 11.

Table 11

Interval	$(-\infty, -2)$	$(-2, 1)$	$(1, 2)$	$(2, \infty)$
Number chosen	-3	0	$\dfrac{3}{2}$	3
Value of R	$R(-3) = -0.8$	$R(0) = \dfrac{1}{4}$	$R\left(\dfrac{3}{2}\right) = -\dfrac{2}{7}$	$R(3) = 0.4$
Location of graph	Below x-axis	Above x-axis	Below x-axis	Above x-axis
Point on graph	$(-3, -0.8)$	$\left(0, \dfrac{1}{4}\right)$	$\left(\dfrac{3}{2}, -\dfrac{2}{7}\right)$	$(3, 0.4)$

Figure 32(a) shows the asymptotes, the points from Table 11, the y-intercept, the x-intercept, and the behavior of the graph near the x-intercept, 1.

Step 7: Analyze the behavior of the graph of R near each asymptote and indicate this behavior on the graph.

- Since $y = 0$ (the x-axis) is a horizontal asymptote and the graph lies below the x-axis for $x < -2$, we can sketch a portion of the graph by placing a small arrow to the far left and under the x-axis.
- Since the line $x = -2$ is a vertical asymptote and the graph lies below the x-axis for $x < -2$, we place an arrow well below the x-axis and approaching the line $x = -2$ from the left $\left(\lim_{x \to -2^-} R(x) = -\infty\right)$.
- Since the graph is above the x-axis for $-2 < x < 1$ and $x = -2$ is a vertical asymptote, the graph will continue on the right of $x = -2$ at the top $\left(\lim_{x \to -2^+} R(x) = +\infty\right)$. Similar explanations account for the other arrows shown in Figure 32(b).

Step 8: Use the results obtained in Steps 1 through 7 to graph R.

Figure 32(c) shows the graph of R.

Figure 32

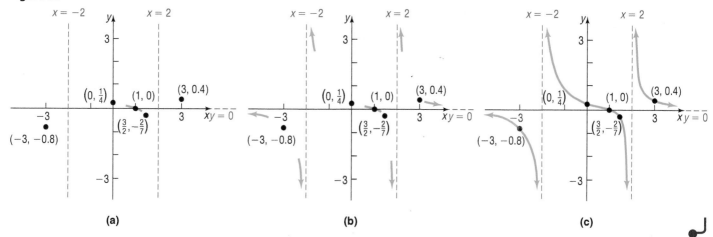

(a)   (b)   (c)

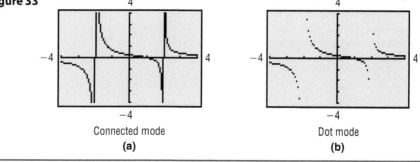

Exploration

Graph $R(x) = \dfrac{x-1}{x^2-4}$

Result The analysis just completed in Example 1 helps us to set the viewing rectangle to obtain a complete graph. Figure 33(a) shows the graph of $R(x) = \dfrac{x-1}{x^2-4}$ in connected mode, and Figure 33(b) shows it in dot mode. Notice in Figure 33(a) that the graph has vertical lines at $x = -2$ and $x = 2$. This is due to the fact that, when the graphing utility is in connected mode, it will connect the dots between consecutive pixels and vertical lines may occur. We know that the graph of R does not cross the lines $x = -2$ and $x = 2$, since R is not defined at $x = -2$ or $x = 2$. So, when graphing rational functions, dot mode should be used to avoid extraneous vertical lines that are not part of the graph. See Figure 33(b).

Figure 33

Connected mode
(a)

Dot mode
(b)

━━ **Now Work** PROBLEM 7

SUMMARY   Analyzing the Graph of a Rational Function R

STEP 1: Factor the numerator and denominator of R. Find the domain of the rational function.

STEP 2: Write R in lowest terms.

STEP 3: Locate the intercepts of the graph. The x-intercepts are the zeros of the numerator of R that are in the domain of R. Determine the behavior of the graph of R near each x-intercept.

STEP 4: Determine the vertical asymptotes. Graph each vertical asymptote using a dashed line.

STEP 5: Determine the horizontal or oblique asymptote, if one exists. Determine points, if any, at which the graph of R intersects this asymptote. Graph the asymptote using a dashed line. Plot any points at which the graph of R intersects the asymptote.

(Continued)

STEP 6: Use the zeros of the numerator and denominator of R to divide the x-axis into intervals. Determine where the graph of R is above or below the x-axis by choosing a number in each interval and evaluating R there. Plot the points found.

STEP 7: Analyze the behavior of the graph of R near each asymptote and indicate this behavior on the graph.

STEP 8: Use the results obtained in Steps 1 through 7 to graph R.

EXAMPLE 2   **Analyzing the Graph of a Rational Function**

Analyze the graph of the rational function: $R(x) = \dfrac{x^2 - 1}{x}$

Solution   **STEP 1:** $R(x) = \dfrac{(x+1)(x-1)}{x}$. The domain of R is $\{x | x \neq 0\}$.

STEP 2: R is in lowest terms.

STEP 3: Because x cannot equal 0, there is no y-intercept. The graph has two x-intercepts: -1 and 1.

$$\text{Near } -1: \quad R(x) = \frac{(x+1)(x-1)}{x} \approx \frac{(x+1)(-1-1)}{-1} = 2(x+1)$$

$$\text{Near } 1: \quad R(x) = \frac{(x+1)(x-1)}{x} \approx \frac{(1+1)(x-1)}{1} = 2(x-1)$$

Plot the point $(-1, 0)$ and indicate a line with positive slope there. Plot the point $(1, 0)$ and indicate a line with positive slope there.

STEP 4: The real zero of the denominator with R in lowest terms is 0, so the graph of R has the line $x = 0$ (the y-axis) as a vertical asymptote. Graph $x = 0$ using a dashed line.

STEP 5: Since the degree of the numerator, 2, is one greater than the degree of the denominator, 1, the rational function will have an oblique asymptote. To find the oblique asymptote, we use long division.

COMMENT Because the denominator of the rational function is a monomial, we can also find the oblique asymptote as follows:

$$\frac{x^2 - 1}{x} = \frac{x^2}{x} - \frac{1}{x} = x - \frac{1}{x}$$

Since $\dfrac{1}{x} \to 0$ as $x \to \infty$, $y = x$ is the oblique asymptote.   ∎

$$\require{enclose}\begin{array}{r} x \\ x\enclose{longdiv}{x^2 - 1} \\ \underline{x^2} \\ -1 \end{array}$$

The quotient is x, so the line $y = x$ is an oblique asymptote of the graph. Graph $y = x$ using a dashed line.

To determine whether the graph of R intersects the asymptote $y = x$, we solve the equation $R(x) = x$.

$$R(x) = \frac{x^2 - 1}{x} = x$$

$$x^2 - 1 = x^2$$

$$-1 = 0 \quad \text{Impossible}$$

We conclude that the equation $\dfrac{x^2 - 1}{x} = x$ has no solution, so the graph of R does not intersect the line $y = x$.

COMMENT Notice that R is an odd function and so its graph is symmetric with respect to the origin. This observation reduces the work involved in graphing R.   ∎

STEP 6: The zeros of the numerator are -1 and 1; the zero of the denominator is 0. Use these values to divide the x-axis into four intervals:

$$(-\infty, -1) \quad (-1, 0) \quad (0, 1) \quad (1, \infty)$$

Now construct Table 12. Plot the points from Table 12. You should now have Figure 34(a).

Table 12

Interval	$(-\infty, -1)$	$(-1, 0)$	$(0, 1)$	$(1, \infty)$
Number chosen	-2	$-\dfrac{1}{2}$	$\dfrac{1}{2}$	2
Value of R	$R(-2) = -\dfrac{3}{2}$	$R\left(-\dfrac{1}{2}\right) = \dfrac{3}{2}$	$R\left(\dfrac{1}{2}\right) = -\dfrac{3}{2}$	$R(2) = \dfrac{3}{2}$
Location of graph	Below x-axis	Above x-axis	Below x-axis	Above x-axis
Point on graph	$\left(-2, -\dfrac{3}{2}\right)$	$\left(-\dfrac{1}{2}, \dfrac{3}{2}\right)$	$\left(\dfrac{1}{2}, -\dfrac{3}{2}\right)$	$\left(2, \dfrac{3}{2}\right)$

STEP 7: Since the graph of R is below the x-axis for $x < -1$ and is above the x-axis for $x > 1$, and since the graph of R does not intersect the oblique asymptote $y = x$, the graph of R will approach the line $y = x$ as shown in Figure 34(b).

Since the graph of R is above the x-axis for $-1 < x < 0$, the graph of R will approach the vertical asymptote $x = 0$ at the top to the left of $x = 0$ $[\lim_{x \to 0^-} R(x) = \infty]$; since the graph of R is below the x-axis for $0 < x < 1$, the graph of R will approach the vertical asymptote $x = 0$ at the bottom to the right of $x = 0$ $[\lim_{x \to 0^+} R(x) = -\infty]$. See Figure 34(b).

STEP 8: The complete graph is given in Figure 34(c).

Figure 34

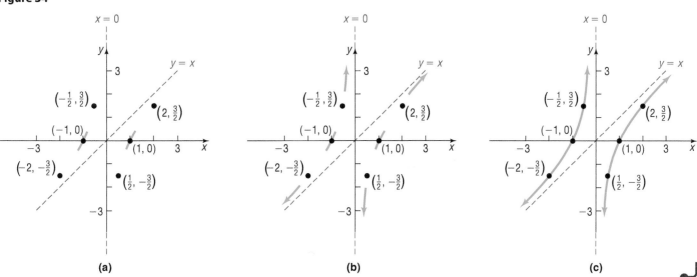

(a)　　　　　　　　　(b)　　　　　　　　　(c)

Seeing the Concept

Graph $R(x) = \dfrac{x^2 - 1}{x}$ and compare what you see with Figure 34(c). Could you have predicted from the graph that $y = x$ is an oblique asymptote? Graph $y = x$ and ZOOM-OUT. What do you observe?

──Now Work PROBLEM 15

EXAMPLE 3　　**Analyzing the Graph of a Rational Function**

Analyze the graph of the rational function:　$R(x) = \dfrac{x^4 + 1}{x^2}$

Solution　　**STEP 1:** R is completely factored. The domain of R is $\{x \mid x \neq 0\}$.

STEP 2: R is in lowest terms.

STEP 3: There is no y-intercept. Since $x^4 + 1 = 0$ has no real solutions, there are no x-intercepts.

STEP 4: R is in lowest terms, so $x = 0$ (the y-axis) is a vertical asymptote of R. Graph the line $x = 0$ using dashes.

STEP 5: Since the degree of the numerator, 4, is two more than the degree of the denominator, 2, the rational function will not have a horizontal or oblique asymptote. We use long division to find the end behavior of R.

$$\begin{array}{r} x^2 \\ x^2 \overline{\smash{)}\, x^4 + 1} \\ \underline{x^4 } \\ 1 \end{array}$$

The quotient is x^2, so the graph of R will approach the graph of $y = x^2$ as $x \to -\infty$ and as $x \to \infty$. The graph of R does not intersect $y = x^2$. Do you know why? Graph $y = x^2$ using dashes.

STEP 6: The numerator has no real zeros, and the denominator has one real zero at 0. We divide the x-axis into the two intervals

$$(-\infty, 0) \qquad (0, \infty)$$

and construct Table 13.

Table 13

	$(-\infty, 0)$	$(0, \infty)$
Interval	$(-\infty, 0)$	$(0, \infty)$
Number chosen	-1	1
Value of R	$R(-1) = 2$	$R(1) = 2$
Location of graph	Above x-axis	Above x-axis
Point on graph	$(-1, 2)$	$(1, 2)$

Plot the points $(-1, 2)$ and $(1, 2)$.

STEP 7: Since the graph of R is above the x-axis and does not intersect $y = x^2$, we place arrows above $y = x^2$ as shown in Figure 35(a). Also, since the graph of R is above the x-axis, it will approach the vertical asymptote $x = 0$ at the top to the left of $x = 0$ and at the top to the right of $x = 0$. See Figure 35(a).

STEP 8: Figure 35(b) shows the complete graph.

COMMENT Notice that R in Example 3 is an even function. Do you see the symmetry about the y-axis in the graph of R? ∎

Figure 35

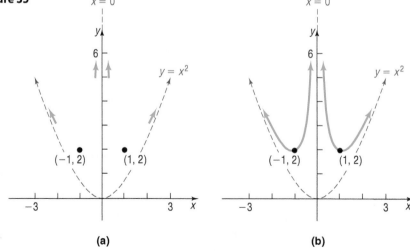

(a)   (b)

> **Seeing the Concept**
>
> Graph $R(x) = \dfrac{x^4 + 1}{x^2}$ and compare what you see with Figure 35(b). Use MINIMUM to find the two
>
> turning points. Enter $Y_2 = x^2$ and ZOOM-OUT. What do you see?

Now Work PROBLEM 13

EXAMPLE 4   **Analyzing the Graph of a Rational Function**

Analyze the graph of the rational function: $R(x) = \dfrac{3x^2 - 3x}{x^2 + x - 12}$

Solution   **STEP 1:** Factor R to get

$$R(x) = \frac{3x(x - 1)}{(x + 4)(x - 3)}$$

The domain of R is $\{x \mid x \neq -4, x \neq 3\}$.

STEP 2: R is in lowest terms.

STEP 3: The y-intercept is $R(0) = 0$. Plot the point $(0, 0)$. Since the real solutions of the equation $3x(x - 1) = 0$ are $x = 0$ and $x = 1$, the graph has two x-intercepts, 0 and 1. We determine the behavior of the graph of R near each x-intercept.

$$\text{Near } 0: \quad R(x) = \frac{3x(x - 1)}{(x + 4)(x - 3)} \approx \frac{3x(0 - 1)}{(0 + 4)(0 - 3)} = \frac{1}{4}x$$

$$\text{Near } 1: \quad R(x) = \frac{3x(x - 1)}{(x + 4)(x - 3)} \approx \frac{3(1)(x - 1)}{(1 + 4)(1 - 3)} = -\frac{3}{10}(x - 1)$$

Plot the point $(0, 0)$ and show a line with positive slope there. Plot the point $(1, 0)$ and show a line with negative slope there.

STEP 4: R is in lowest terms. The real solutions of the equation $(x + 4)(x - 3) = 0$ are $x = -4$ and $x = 3$, so the graph of R has two vertical asymptotes, the lines $x = -4$ and $x = 3$. Graph these lines using dashes.

STEP 5: Since the degree of the numerator equals the degree of the denominator, the graph has a horizontal asymptote. To find it, form the quotient of the leading coefficient of the numerator, 3, and the leading coefficient of the denominator, 1. The graph of R has the horizontal asymptote $y = 3$.

To find out whether the graph of R intersects the asymptote, solve the equation $R(x) = 3$.

$$R(x) = \frac{3x^2 - 3x}{x^2 + x - 12} = 3$$
$$3x^2 - 3x = 3x^2 + 3x - 36$$
$$-6x = -36$$
$$x = 6$$

The graph intersects the line $y = 3$ at $x = 6$, and $(6, 3)$ is a point on the graph of R. Plot the point $(6, 3)$ and graph the line $y = 3$ using dashes.

STEP 6: The real zeros of the numerator, 0 and 1, and the real zeros of the denominator, -4 and 3, divide the x-axis into five intervals:

$$(-\infty, -4) \quad (-4, 0) \quad (0, 1) \quad (1, 3) \quad (3, \infty)$$

Construct Table 14. Plot the points from Table 14. Figure 36(a) shows the graph we have so far.

Table 14

	$(-\infty, -4)$	$(-4, 0)$	$(0, 1)$	$(1, 3)$	$(3, \infty)$
Interval	$(-\infty, -4)$	$(-4, 0)$	$(0, 1)$	$(1, 3)$	$(3, \infty)$
Number chosen	-5	-2	$\dfrac{1}{2}$	2	4
Value of R	$R(-5) = 11.25$	$R(-2) = -1.8$	$R\left(\dfrac{1}{2}\right) = \dfrac{1}{15}$	$R(2) = -1$	$R(4) = 4.5$
Location of graph	Above x-axis	Below x-axis	Above x-axis	Below x-axis	Above x-axis
Point on graph	$(-5, 11.25)$	$(-2, -1.8)$	$\left(\dfrac{1}{2}, \dfrac{1}{15}\right)$	$(2, -1)$	$(4, 4.5)$

STEP 7: • Since the graph of R is above the x-axis for $x < -4$ and only crosses the line $y = 3$ at $(6, 3)$, as x approaches $-\infty$ the graph of R will approach the horizontal asymptote $y = 3$ from above ($\lim\limits_{x \to -\infty} R(x) = 3$).

• The graph of R will approach the vertical asymptote $x = -4$ at the top to the left of $x = -4$ ($\lim\limits_{x \to -4^-} R(x) = +\infty$) and at the bottom to the right of $x = -4$ ($\lim\limits_{x \to -4^+} R(x) = -\infty$).

• The graph of R will approach the vertical asymptote $x = 3$ at the bottom to the left of $x = 3$ ($\lim\limits_{x \to 3^-} R(x) = -\infty$) and at the top to the right of $x = 3$ ($\lim\limits_{x \to 3^+} R(x) = +\infty$).

• We do not know whether the graph of R crosses or touches the line $y = 3$ at $(6, 3)$. To see whether the graph, in fact, crosses or touches the line $y = 3$, we plot an additional point to the right of $(6, 3)$. We use $x = 7$ to find $R(7) = \dfrac{63}{22} < 3$. The graph crosses $y = 3$ at $x = 6$. Because $(6, 3)$ is the only point where the graph of R intersects the asymptote $y = 3$, the graph must approach the line $y = 3$ from below as $x \to \infty$ ($\lim\limits_{x \to \infty} R(x) = 3$). See Figure 36(b).

STEP 8: The complete graph is shown in Figure 36(c).

Figure 36

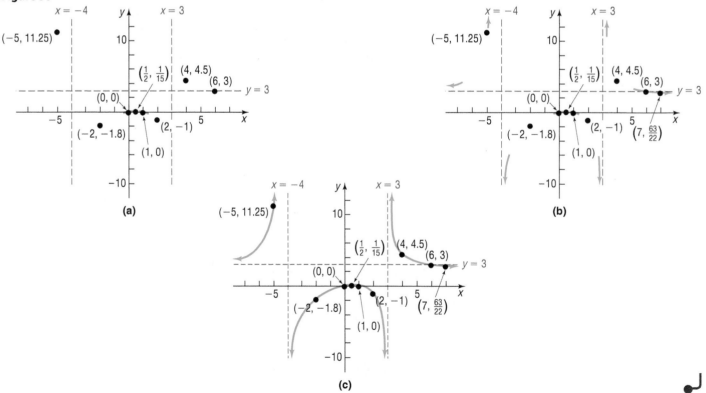

![Exploration icon] Exploration

Graph $R(x) = \dfrac{3x^2 - 3x}{x^2 + x - 12}$

Result Figure 37 shows the graph in connected mode, and Figure 38(a) shows it in dot mode. Neither graph displays clearly the behavior of the function between the two x-intercepts, 0 and 1. Nor do they clearly display the fact that the graph crosses the horizontal asymptote at (6, 3). To see these parts better, we graph R for $-1 \le x \le 2$ [Figure 38(b)] and for $4 \le x \le 60$ [Figure 39(b)].

Figure 37

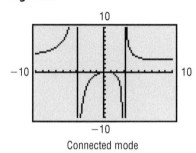

Connected mode

Figure 38

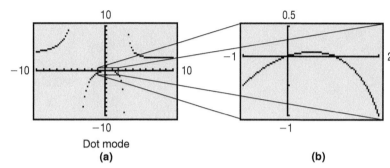

Dot mode
(a)

(b)

Figure 39

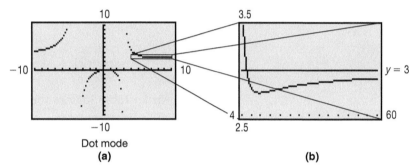

Dot mode
(a)

(b)

The new graphs reflect the behavior produced by the analysis. Furthermore, we observe two turning points, one between 0 and 1 and the other to the right of 6. Rounded to two decimal places, these turning points are (0.52, 0.07) and (11.48, 2.75).

EXAMPLE 5 **Analyzing the Graph of a Rational Function with a Hole**

Analyze the graph of the rational function: $R(x) = \dfrac{2x^2 - 5x + 2}{x^2 - 4}$

Solution **STEP 1:** Factor R and obtain

$$R(x) = \frac{(2x - 1)(x - 2)}{(x + 2)(x - 2)}$$

The domain of R is $\{x \mid x \ne -2, x \ne 2\}$.

STEP 2: In lowest terms,

$$R(x) = \frac{2x - 1}{x + 2} \qquad x \ne -2, x \ne 2$$

STEP 3: The y-intercept is $R(0) = -\dfrac{1}{2}$. Plot the point $\left(0, -\dfrac{1}{2}\right)$.
The graph has one x-intercept: $\dfrac{1}{2}$.

Near $\dfrac{1}{2}$: $R(x) = \dfrac{2x - 1}{x + 2} \approx \dfrac{2x - 1}{\dfrac{1}{2} + 2} = \dfrac{2}{5}(2x - 1)$

Plot the point $\left(\dfrac{1}{2}, 0\right)$ showing a line with positive slope.

STEP 4: Since $x + 2$ is the only factor of the denominator of $R(x)$ *in lowest terms*, the graph has one vertical asymptote, $x = -2$. However, the rational function is undefined at both $x = 2$ and $x = -2$. Graph the line $x = -2$ using dashes.

STEP 5: Since the degree of the numerator equals the degree of the denominator, the graph has a horizontal asymptote. To find it, form the quotient of the leading coefficient of the numerator, 2, and the leading coefficient of the denominator, 1. The graph of R has the horizontal asymptote $y = 2$. Graph the line $y = 2$ using dashes.

To find out whether the graph of R intersects the horizontal asymptote $y = 2$, we solve the equation $R(x) = 2$.

$$R(x) = \frac{2x - 1}{x + 2} = 2$$
$$2x - 1 = 2(x + 2)$$
$$2x - 1 = 2x + 4$$
$$-1 = 4 \qquad \text{Impossible}$$

The graph does not intersect the line $y = 2$.

STEP 6: Look at the factored expression for R in Step 1. The real zeros of the numerator and denominator, $-2, \dfrac{1}{2}$, and 2, divide the x-axis into four intervals:

$$(-\infty, -2) \qquad \left(-2, \frac{1}{2}\right) \qquad \left(\frac{1}{2}, 2\right) \qquad (2, \infty)$$

Construct Table 15. Plot the points in Table 15.

Table 15

	$(-\infty, -2)$	$\left(-2, \dfrac{1}{2}\right)$	$\left(\dfrac{1}{2}, 2\right)$	$(2, \infty)$
Interval	$(-\infty, -2)$	$\left(-2, \dfrac{1}{2}\right)$	$\left(\dfrac{1}{2}, 2\right)$	$(2, \infty)$
Number chosen	-3	-1	1	3
Value of R	$R(-3) = 7$	$R(-1) = -3$	$R(1) = \dfrac{1}{3}$	$R(3) = 1$
Location of graph	Above x-axis	Below x-axis	Above x-axis	Above x-axis
Point on graph	$(-3, 7)$	$(-1, -3)$	$\left(1, \dfrac{1}{3}\right)$	$(3, 1)$

(number line across the top marked at -2, $1/2$, 2 with arrow to x)

STEP 7: • From Table 15 we know that the graph of R is above the x-axis for $x < -2$.

• From Step 5 we know that the graph of R does not intersect the asymptote $y = 2$. Therefore, the graph of R will approach $y = 2$ from above as $x \to -\infty$ and will approach the vertical asymptote $x = -2$ at the top from the left.

• Since the graph of R is below the x-axis for $-2 < x < \dfrac{1}{2}$, the graph of R will approach $x = -2$ at the bottom from the right.

• Finally, since the graph of R is above the x-axis for $x > \dfrac{1}{2}$ and does not intersect the horizontal asymptote $y = 2$, the graph of R will approach $y = 2$ from below as $x \to \infty$. See Figure 40(a).

STEP 8: See Figure 40(b) for the complete graph. Since R is not defined at 2, there is a hole at the point $\left(2, \dfrac{3}{4}\right)$.

COMMENT The coordinates of the hole were obtained by evaluating R in lowest terms at 2. R in lowest terms is $\dfrac{2x - 1}{x + 2}$, which, at $x = 2$, is $\dfrac{2(2) - 1}{2 + 2} = \dfrac{3}{4}$. ∎

Figure 40

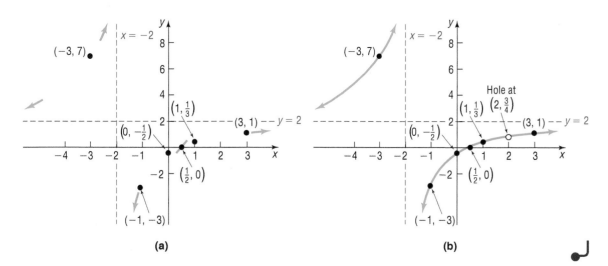

(a)   (b)

Exploration

Graph $R(x) = \dfrac{2x^2 - 5x + 2}{x^2 - 4}$. Do you see the hole at $\left(2, \dfrac{3}{4}\right)$? TRACE along the graph. Did you obtain an ERROR at $x = 2$? Are you convinced that an algebraic analysis of a rational function is required in order to accurately interpret the graph obtained with a graphing utility?

As Example 5 shows, **the zeros of the denominator of a rational function give rise to either vertical asymptotes or holes in the graph.**

Now Work PROBLEM 33

EXAMPLE 6   **Constructing a Rational Function from Its Graph**

Find a rational function that might have the graph shown in Figure 41.

Figure 41

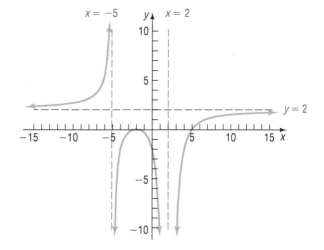

Solution   The numerator of a rational function $R(x) = \dfrac{p(x)}{q(x)}$ in lowest terms determines the x-intercepts of its graph. The graph shown in Figure 41 has x-intercepts -2 (even multiplicity; graph touches the x-axis) and 5 (odd multiplicity; graph crosses the x-axis). So one possibility for the numerator is $p(x) = (x + 2)^2(x - 5)$.

The denominator of a rational function in lowest terms determines the vertical asymptotes of its graph. The vertical asymptotes of the graph are $x = -5$ and $x = 2$. Since $R(x)$ approaches ∞ to the left of $x = -5$ and $R(x)$ approaches $-\infty$ to the right of $x = -5$, we know that $(x + 5)$ is a factor of odd multiplicity in $q(x)$. Also, $R(x)$ approaches $-\infty$ on both sides of $x = 2$, so $(x - 2)$ is a factor of even multiplicity in

$q(x)$. A possibility for the denominator is $q(x) = (x + 5)(x - 2)^2$. So far we have

$$R(x) = \frac{(x + 2)^2(x - 5)}{(x + 5)(x - 2)^2}.$$

The horizontal asymptote of the graph given in Figure 41 is $y = 2$, so we know that the degree of the numerator must equal the degree of the denominator and the quotient of leading coefficients must be $\frac{2}{1}$. This leads to

$$R(x) = \frac{2(x + 2)^2(x - 5)}{(x + 5)(x - 2)^2}$$

Figure 42

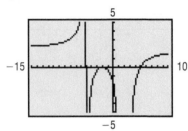

 ✓**Check:** Figure 42 shows the graph of R on a graphing utility. Since Figure 42 looks similar to Figure 41, we have found a rational function R for the graph in Figure 41.

═══**Now Work** PROBLEM 45

2 Solve Applied Problems Involving Rational Functions

EXAMPLE 7 **Finding the Least Cost of a Can**

Reynolds Metal Company manufactures aluminum cans in the shape of a cylinder with a capacity of 500 cubic centimeters $\left(\frac{1}{2} \text{ liter}\right)$. The top and bottom of the can are made of a special aluminum alloy that costs 0.05¢ per square centimeter. The sides of the can are made of material that costs 0.02¢ per square centimeter.

(a) Express the cost of material for the can as a function of the radius r of the can.
(b) Use a graphing utility to graph the function $C = C(r)$.
(c) What value of r will result in the least cost?
(d) What is this least cost?

Solution

(a) Figure 43 illustrates the components of a can in the shape of a right circular cylinder. Notice that the material required to produce a cylindrical can of height h and radius r consists of a rectangle of area $2\pi rh$ and two circles, each of area πr^2. The total cost C (in cents) of manufacturing the can is therefore

Figure 43

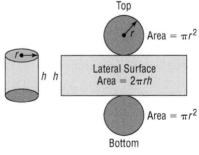

Top

Area = πr^2

Lateral Surface Area = $2\pi rh$

Area = πr^2

Bottom

$$C = \text{Cost of the top and bottom} + \text{Cost of the side}$$
$$= \underbrace{2(\pi r^2)}_{\substack{\text{Total area} \\ \text{of top and} \\ \text{bottom}}} \underbrace{(0.05)}_{\substack{\text{Cost/unit} \\ \text{area}}} + \underbrace{(2\pi rh)}_{\substack{\text{Total} \\ \text{area of} \\ \text{side}}} \underbrace{(0.02)}_{\substack{\text{Cost/unit} \\ \text{area}}}$$
$$= 0.10\pi r^2 + 0.04\pi rh$$

But we have the additional restriction that the height h and radius r must be chosen so that the volume V of the can is 500 cubic centimeters. Since $V = \pi r^2 h$, we have

$$500 = \pi r^2 h \quad \text{so} \quad h = \frac{500}{\pi r^2}$$

Figure 44

Substituting this expression for h, the cost C, in cents, as a function of the radius r is

$$C(r) = 0.10\pi r^2 + 0.04\pi r \cdot \frac{500}{\pi r^2} = 0.10\pi r^2 + \frac{20}{r} = \frac{0.10\pi r^3 + 20}{r}$$

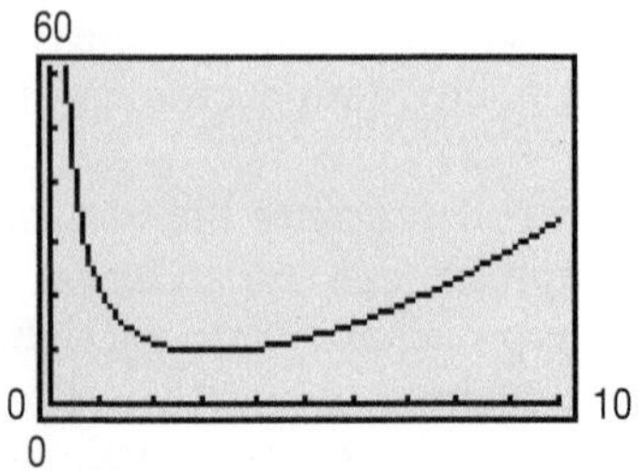

(b) See Figure 44 for the graph of $C = C(r)$.
(c) Using the MINIMUM command, the cost is least for a radius of about 3.17 centimeters.
(d) The least cost is $C(3.17) \approx 9.47$¢.

═══**Now Work** PROBLEM 55

4.3 Assess Your Understanding

'Are You Prepared?' *The answer is given at the end of these exercises. If you get a wrong answer, read the pages listed in red.*

1. Find the intercepts of the graph of the equation $y = \dfrac{x^2 - 1}{x^2 - 4}$. (pp. 11–12)

Concepts and Vocabulary

2. If the numerator and the denominator of a rational function have no common factors, the rational function is ___ _____ _____.

3. The graph of a rational function never intersects a _____ asymptote.

4. *True or False* The graph of a rational function sometimes intersects an oblique asymptote.

5. *True or False* The graph of a rational function sometimes has a hole.

6. $R(x) = \dfrac{x(x - 2)^2}{x - 2}$
   (a) Find the domain of R.
   (b) Find the x-intercepts of R.

Skill Building

In Problems 7–44, follow Steps 1 through 8 on pages 201–202 to analyze the graph of each function.

7. $R(x) = \dfrac{x + 1}{x(x + 4)}$

8. $R(x) = \dfrac{x}{(x - 1)(x + 2)}$

9. $R(x) = \dfrac{3x + 3}{2x + 4}$

10. $R(x) = \dfrac{2x + 4}{x - 1}$

11. $R(x) = \dfrac{3}{x^2 - 4}$

12. $R(x) = \dfrac{6}{x^2 - x - 6}$

13. $P(x) = \dfrac{x^4 + x^2 + 1}{x^2 - 1}$

14. $Q(x) = \dfrac{x^4 - 1}{x^2 - 4}$

15. $H(x) = \dfrac{x^3 - 1}{x^2 - 9}$

16. $G(x) = \dfrac{x^3 + 1}{x^2 + 2x}$

17. $R(x) = \dfrac{x^2}{x^2 + x - 6}$

18. $R(x) = \dfrac{x^2 + x - 12}{x^2 - 4}$

19. $G(x) = \dfrac{x}{x^2 - 4}$

20. $G(x) = \dfrac{3x}{x^2 - 1}$

21. $R(x) = \dfrac{3}{(x - 1)(x^2 - 4)}$

22. $R(x) = \dfrac{-4}{(x + 1)(x^2 - 9)}$

23. $H(x) = \dfrac{x^2 - 1}{x^4 - 16}$

24. $H(x) = \dfrac{x^2 + 4}{x^4 - 1}$

25. $F(x) = \dfrac{x^2 - 3x - 4}{x + 2}$

26. $F(x) = \dfrac{x^2 + 3x + 2}{x - 1}$

27. $R(x) = \dfrac{x^2 + x - 12}{x - 4}$

28. $R(x) = \dfrac{x^2 - x - 12}{x + 5}$

29. $F(x) = \dfrac{x^2 + x - 12}{x + 2}$

30. $G(x) = \dfrac{x^2 - x - 12}{x + 1}$

31. $R(x) = \dfrac{x(x - 1)^2}{(x + 3)^3}$

32. $R(x) = \dfrac{(x - 1)(x + 2)(x - 3)}{x(x - 4)^2}$

33. $R(x) = \dfrac{x^2 + x - 12}{x^2 - x - 6}$

34. $R(x) = \dfrac{x^2 + 3x - 10}{x^2 + 8x + 15}$

35. $R(x) = \dfrac{6x^2 - 7x - 3}{2x^2 - 7x + 6}$

36. $R(x) = \dfrac{8x^2 + 26x + 15}{2x^2 - x - 15}$

37. $R(x) = \dfrac{x^2 + 5x + 6}{x + 3}$

38. $R(x) = \dfrac{x^2 + x - 30}{x + 6}$

39. $f(x) = x + \dfrac{1}{x}$

40. $f(x) = 2x + \dfrac{9}{x}$

41. $f(x) = x^2 + \dfrac{1}{x}$

42. $f(x) = 2x^2 + \dfrac{16}{x}$

43. $f(x) = x + \dfrac{1}{x^3}$

44. $f(x) = 2x + \dfrac{9}{x^3}$

In Problems 45–48, find a rational function that might have the given graph. (More than one answer might be possible.)

45.
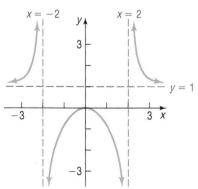

46.
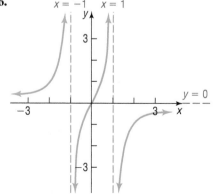

47.

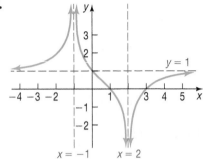

48.

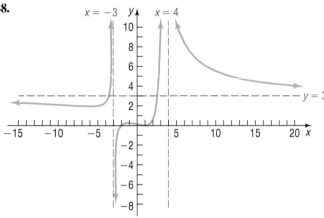

Applications and Extensions

49. Drug Concentration The concentration C of a certain drug in a patient's bloodstream t hours after injection is given by

$$C(t) = \frac{t}{2t^2 + 1}$$

(a) Find the horizontal asymptote of $C(t)$. What happens to the concentration of the drug as t increases?

(b) Using your graphing utility, graph $C = C(t)$.

(c) Determine the time at which the concentration is highest.

50. Drug Concentration The concentration C of a certain drug in a patient's bloodstream t minutes after injection is given by

$$C(t) = \frac{50t}{t^2 + 25}$$

(a) Find the horizontal asymptote of $C(t)$. What happens to the concentration of the drug as t increases?

(b) Using your graphing utility, graph $C = C(t)$.

(c) Determine the time at which the concentration is highest.

51. Minimum Cost A rectangular area adjacent to a river is to be fenced in; no fence is needed on the river side. The enclosed area is to be 1000 square feet. Fencing for the side parallel to the river is $5 per linear foot, and fencing for the other two sides is $8 per linear foot; the four corner posts are $25 apiece. Let x be the length of one of the sides perpendicular to the river.

(a) Write a function $C(x)$ that describes the cost of the project.

(b) What is the domain of C?

(c) Use a graphing utility to graph $C = C(x)$.

(d) Find the dimensions of the cheapest enclosure.

Source: www.uncwil.edu/courses/math111hb/PandR/rational/rational.html

52. Doppler Effect The Doppler effect (named after Christian Doppler) is the change in the pitch (frequency) of the sound

from a source (s) as heard by an observer (o) when one or both are in motion. If we assume both the source and the observer are moving in the same direction, the relationship is

$$f' = f_a\left(\frac{v - v_o}{v - v_s}\right)$$

where
- f' = perceived pitch by the observer
- f_a = actual pitch of the source
- v = speed of sound in air (assume 772.4 mph)
- v_o = speed of the observer
- v_s = speed of the source

Suppose that you are traveling down the road at 45 mph and you hear an ambulance (with siren) coming toward you from the rear. The actual pitch of the siren is 600 hertz (Hz).

(a) Write a function $f'(v_s)$ that describes this scenario.

(b) If $f' = 620$ Hz, find the speed of the ambulance.

(c) Use a graphing utility to graph the function.

(d) Verify your answer from part (b).

Source: www.kettering.edu/~drussell/

53. Minimizing Surface Area United Parcel Service has contracted you to design a closed box with a square base that has a volume of 10,000 cubic inches. See the illustration.

(a) Express the surface area S of the box as a function of x.

(b) Using a graphing utility, graph the function found in part (a).

(c) What is the minimum amount of cardboard that can be used to construct the box?

(d) What are the dimensions of the box that minimize the surface area?

(e) Why might UPS be interested in designing a box that minimizes the surface area?

54. Minimizing Surface Area United Parcel Service has contracted you to design an open box with a square base that has a volume of 5000 cubic inches. See the illustration.

(a) Express the surface area S of the box as a function of x.
(b) Using a graphing utility, graph the function found in part (a).
(c) What is the minimum amount of cardboard that can be used to construct the box?
(d) What are the dimensions of the box that minimize the surface area?
(e) Why might UPS be interested in designing a box that minimizes the surface area?

55. Cost of a Can A can in the shape of a right circular cylinder is required to have a volume of 500 cubic centimeters. The top and bottom are made of material that costs 6¢ per square centimeter, while the sides are made of material that costs 4¢ per square centimeter.
(a) Express the total cost C of the material as a function of the radius r of the cylinder. (Refer to Figure 43.)
(b) Graph $C = C(r)$. For what value of r is the cost C a minimum?

56. Material Needed to Make a Drum A steel drum in the shape of a right circular cylinder is required to have a volume of 100 cubic feet.

(a) Express the amount A of material required to make the drum as a function of the radius r of the cylinder.
(b) How much material is required if the drum's radius is 3 feet?
(c) How much material is required if the drum's radius is 4 feet?
(d) How much material is required if the drum's radius is 5 feet?
(e) Graph $A = A(r)$. For what value of r is A smallest?

Explaining Concepts: Discussion and Writing

57. Graph each of the following functions:

$$y = \frac{x^2 - 1}{x - 1} \qquad y = \frac{x^3 - 1}{x - 1}$$

$$y = \frac{x^4 - 1}{x - 1} \qquad y = \frac{x^5 - 1}{x - 1}$$

Is $x = 1$ a vertical asymptote? Why not? What is happening for $x = 1$? What do you conjecture about $y = \frac{x^n - 1}{x - 1}$, $n \geq 1$ an integer, for $x = 1$?

58. Graph each of the following functions:

$$y = \frac{x^2}{x - 1} \qquad y = \frac{x^4}{x - 1} \qquad y = \frac{x^6}{x - 1} \qquad y = \frac{x^8}{x - 1}$$

What similarities do you see? What differences?

59. Write a few paragraphs that provide a general strategy for graphing a rational function. Be sure to mention the following: proper, improper, intercepts, and asymptotes.

60. Create a rational function that has the following characteristics: crosses the x-axis at 2; touches the x-axis

at -1; one vertical asymptote at $x = -5$ and another at $x = 6$; and one horizontal asymptote, $y = 3$. Compare your function to a fellow classmate's. How do they differ? What are their similarities?

61. Create a rational function that has the following characteristics: crosses the x-axis at 3; touches the x-axis at -2; one vertical asymptote, $x = 1$; and one horizontal asymptote, $y = 2$. Give your rational function to a fellow classmate and ask for a written critique of your rational function.

62. Create a rational function with the following characteristics: three real zeros, one of multiplicity 2; y-intercept 1; vertical asymptotes, $x = -2$ and $x = 3$; oblique asymptote, $y = 2x + 1$. Is this rational function unique? Compare your function with those of other students. What will be the same as everyone else's? Add some more characteristics, such as symmetry or naming the real zeros. How does this modify the rational function?

63. Explain the circumstances under which the graph of a rational function will have a hole.

'Are You Prepared?' Answer

1. $\left(0, \dfrac{1}{4}\right), (1, 0), (-1, 0)$

4.4 Polynomial and Rational Inequalities

PREPARING FOR THIS SECTION *Before getting started, review the following:*

- Solving Inequalities (Appendix A, Section A.9, pp. A75–A78)
- Solving Quadratic Inequalities (Section 3.5, pp. 155–157)

✎ **Now Work** the *'Are You Prepared?'* problems on page 217.

> **OBJECTIVES** 1 Solve Polynomial Inequalities (p. 214)
> 2 Solve Rational Inequalities (p. 215)

1 Solve Polynomial Inequalities

In this section we solve inequalities that involve polynomials of degree 3 and higher, along with inequalities that involve rational functions. To help understand the algebraic procedure for solving such inequalities, we use the information obtained in the previous three sections about the graphs of polynomial and rational functions. The approach follows the same methodology that we used to solve inequalities involving quadratic functions.

EXAMPLE 1 | **Solving a Polynomial Inequality Using Its Graph**

Solve $(x + 3)(x - 1)^2 > 0$ by graphing $f(x) = (x + 3)(x - 1)^2$.

Solution Graph $f(x) = (x + 3)(x - 1)^2$ and determine the intervals of x for which the graph is above the x-axis. These values of x result in $f(x)$ being positive. Using Steps 1 through 6 on page 179, we obtain the graph shown in Figure 45.

Figure 45

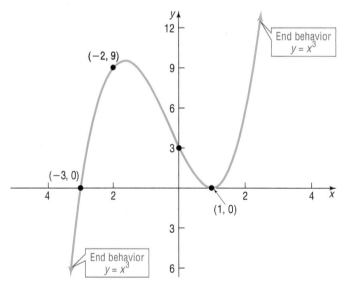

From the graph, we can see that $f(x) > 0$ for $-3 < x < 1$ or $x > 1$. The solution set is $\{x \mid -3 < x < 1 \text{ or } x > 1\}$ or, using interval notation, $(-3, 1) \cup (1, \infty)$. ♩

═══ **Now Work** PROBLEM 9

The results of Example 1 lead to the following approach to solving polynomial and rational inequalities algebraically. Suppose that the polynomial or rational inequality is in one of the forms

$$f(x) < 0 \qquad f(x) > 0 \qquad f(x) \le 0 \qquad f(x) \ge 0$$

Locate the zeros of f if f is a polynomial function, and locate the zeros of the numerator and the denominator if f is a rational function. If we use these zeros to divide the real number line into intervals, we know that on each interval the graph of f is either above the x-axis $[f(x) > 0]$ or below the x-axis $[f(x) < 0]$. In other words, we have found the solution of the inequality.

| EXAMPLE 2 | **How to Solve a Polynomial Inequality Algebraically** |

Solve the inequality $x^4 > x$ algebraically, and graph the solution set.

Step-by-Step Solution

Step 1: Write the inequality so that a polynomial expression f is on the left side and zero is on the right side.

Rearrange the inequality so that 0 is on the right side.

$$x^4 > x$$
$$x^4 - x > 0 \quad \text{Subtract } x \text{ from both sides of the inequality.}$$

This inequality is equivalent to the one we wish to solve.

Step 2: Determine the real zeros (x-intercepts of the graph) of f.

Find the real zeros of $f(x) = x^4 - x$ by solving $x^4 - x = 0$.

$$x^4 - x = 0$$
$$x(x^3 - 1) = 0 \quad \text{Factor out } x.$$
$$x(x - 1)(x^2 + x + 1) = 0 \quad \text{Factor the difference of two cubes.}$$
$$x = 0 \quad \text{or} \quad x - 1 = 0 \quad \text{or} \quad x^2 + x + 1 = 0 \quad \text{Set each factor equal to zero and solve.}$$
$$x = 0 \quad \text{or} \qquad x = 1$$

The equation $x^2 + x + 1 = 0$ has no real solutions. Do you see why?

Step 3: Use the zeros found in Step 2 to divide the real number line into intervals.

Use the real zeros to separate the real number line into three intervals:

$$(-\infty, 0) \qquad (0, 1) \qquad (1, \infty)$$

Step 4: Select a number in each interval, evaluate f at the number, and determine whether f is positive or negative. If f is positive, all values of f in the interval are positive. If f is negative, all values of f in the interval are negative.

Select a test number in each interval found in Step 3 and evaluate $f(x) = x^4 - x$ at each number to determine if $f(x)$ is positive or negative. See Table 16.

Table 16

Interval	$(-\infty, 0)$	$(0, 1)$	$(1, \infty)$
Number chosen	-1	$\dfrac{1}{2}$	2
Value of f	$f(-1) = 2$	$f\left(\dfrac{1}{2}\right) = -\dfrac{7}{16}$	$f(2) = 14$
Conclusion	Positive	Negative	Positive

NOTE If the inequality is not strict ($\leq$ or $\geq$), include the solutions of $f(x) = 0$ in the solution set. ∎

Since we want to know where $f(x)$ is positive, we conclude that $f(x) > 0$ for all numbers x for which $x < 0$ or $x > 1$. Because the original inequality is strict, numbers x that satisfy the equation $x^4 = x$ are not solutions. The solution set of the inequality $x^4 > x$ is $\{x \mid x < 0 \text{ or } x > 1\}$ or, using interval notation, $(-\infty, 0) \cup (1, \infty)$. Figure 46 shows the graph of the solution set.

Figure 46

$-2 -1 \ 0 \ 1 \ 2$

━━━━**Now Work** PROBLEM 21

2 Solve Rational Inequalities

Just as we presented a graphical approach to help us understand the algebraic procedure for solving inequalities involving polynomials, we present a graphical approach to help us understand the algebraic procedure for solving inequalities involving rational expressions.

EXAMPLE 3 — **Solving a Rational Inequality Using Its Graph**

Solve $\dfrac{x-1}{x^2-4} \geq 0$ by graphing $R(x) = \dfrac{x-1}{x^2-4}$.

Solution — Graph $R(x) = \dfrac{x-1}{x^2-4}$ and determine the intervals of x such that the graph is above or on the x-axis. Do you see why? These values of x result in $R(x)$ being positive or zero. We graphed $R(x) = \dfrac{x-1}{x^2-4}$ in Example 1, Section 4.3 (pp. 199–201). We reproduce the graph in Figure 47.

Figure 47

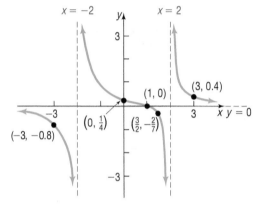

From the graph, we can see that $R(x) \geq 0$ for $-2 < x \leq 1$ or $x > 2$. The solution set is $\{x | -2 < x \leq 1 \text{ or } x > 2\}$ or, using interval notation, $(-2, 1] \cup (2, \infty)$.

Now Work PROBLEM 33

To solve a rational inequality algebraically, we follow the same approach that we used to solve a polynomial inequality algebraically. However, we must also identify the zeros of the denominator of the rational function, because the sign of a rational function may change on either side of a vertical asymptote. Convince yourself of this by looking at Figure 47. Notice that the function values are negative for $x < -2$ and are positive for $x > -2$ (but less than 1).

EXAMPLE 4 — **How to Solve a Rational Inequality Algebraically**

Solve the inequality $\dfrac{4x+5}{x+2} \geq 3$ algebraically, and graph the solution set.

Step-by-Step Solution

Step 1: Write the inequality so that a rational expression f is on the left side and zero is on the right side.

Rearrange the inequality so that 0 is on the right side.

$$\frac{4x+5}{x+2} \geq 3$$

$$\frac{4x+5}{x+2} - 3 \geq 0 \quad \text{Subtract 3 from both sides of the inequality.}$$

$$\frac{4x+5}{x+2} - 3 \cdot \frac{x+2}{x+2} \geq 0 \quad \text{Multiply 3 by } \frac{x+2}{x+2}.$$

$$\frac{4x+5-3x-6}{x+2} \geq 0 \quad \text{Write as a single quotient.}$$

$$\frac{x-1}{x+2} \geq 0 \quad \text{Combine like terms.}$$

Step 2: Determine the real zeros (x-intercepts of the graph) of f and the real numbers for which f is undefined.

The zero of $f(x) = \dfrac{x-1}{x+2}$ is 1. Also, f is undefined for $x = -2$.

Step 3: Use the zeros and undefined values found in Step 2 to divide the real number line into intervals.

Use the zero and undefined value to separate the real number line into three intervals:

$$(-\infty, -2) \qquad (-2, 1) \qquad (1, \infty)$$

Step 4: Select a number in each interval, evaluate f at the number, and determine whether f is positive or negative. If f is positive, all values of f in the interval are positive. If f is negative, all values of f in the interval are negative.

Select a test number in each interval found in Step 3 and evaluate $f(x) = \dfrac{x-1}{x+2}$ at each number to determine if $f(x)$ is positive or negative. See Table 17.

Table 17

	$(-\infty, -2)$	$(-2, 1)$	$(1, \infty)$
Interval	$(-\infty, -2)$	$(-2, 1)$	$(1, \infty)$
Number chosen	-3	0	2
Value of f	$f(-3) = 4$	$f(0) = -\dfrac{1}{2}$	$f(2) = \dfrac{1}{4}$
Conclusion	Positive	Negative	Positive

Since we want to know where $f(x)$ is positive or zero, we conclude that $f(x) \geq 0$ for all numbers x for which $x < -2$ or $x \geq 1$. Notice we do not include -2 in the solution because -2 is not in the domain of f. The solution set of the inequality $\dfrac{4x+5}{x+2} \geq 3$ is $\{x \mid x < -2 \text{ or } x \geq 1\}$ or, using interval notation, $(-\infty, -2) \cup [1, \infty)$. Figure 48 shows the graph of the solution set.

Figure 48

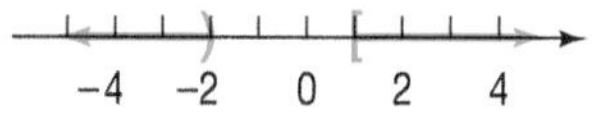

↪ **Now Work** PROBLEM 39

SUMMARY Steps for Solving Polynomial and Rational Inequalities Algebraically

STEP 1: Write the inequality so that a polynomial or rational expression f is on the left side and zero is on the right side in one of the following forms:

$$f(x) > 0 \qquad f(x) \geq 0 \qquad f(x) < 0 \qquad f(x) \leq 0$$

For rational expressions, be sure that the left side is written as a single quotient and find the domain of f.

STEP 2: Determine the real numbers at which the expression f equals zero and, if the expression is rational, the real numbers at which the expression f is undefined.

STEP 3: Use the numbers found in Step 2 to separate the real number line into intervals.

STEP 4: Select a number in each interval and evaluate f at the number.

(a) If the value of f is positive, then $f(x) > 0$ for all numbers x in the interval.

(b) If the value of f is negative, then $f(x) < 0$ for all numbers x in the interval.

If the inequality is not strict ($\geq$ or $\leq$), include the solutions of $f(x) = 0$ that are in the domain of f in the solution set. Be careful to exclude values of x where f is undefined.

4.4 Assess Your Understanding

'Are You Prepared?' Answers are given at the end of these exercises. If you get a wrong answer, read the pages listed in red.

1. Solve the inequality $3 - 4x > 5$. Graph the solution set. (pp. A75–A78)

2. Solve the inequality $x^2 - 5x \leq 24$. Graph the solution set. (pp. 155–157)

Concepts and Vocabulary

3. *True or False* A test number for the interval $-2 < x < 5$ could be 4.

4. *True or False* The graph of $f(x) = \dfrac{x}{x-3}$ is above the x-axis for $x < 0$ or $x > 3$, so the solution set of the inequality $\dfrac{x}{x-3} \geq 0$ is $\{x \mid x \leq 0 \text{ or } x \geq 3\}$.

Skill Building

In Problems 5–8, use the graph of the function f to solve the inequality.

5. (a) $f(x) > 0$
    (b) $f(x) \leq 0$

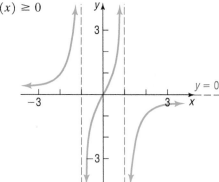

6. (a) $f(x) < 0$
    (b) $f(x) \geq 0$

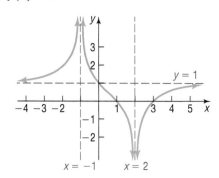

7. (a) $f(x) < 0$
    (b) $f(x) \geq 0$

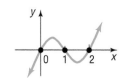

8. (a) $f(x) > 0$
    (b) $f(x) \leq 0$

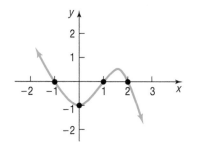

In Problems 9–14, solve the inequality by using the graph of the function.
[**Hint:** The graphs were drawn in Problems 69–74 of Section 4.1.]

9. Solve $f(x) < 0$, where $f(x) = x^2(x-3)$.

10. Solve $f(x) \leq 0$, where $f(x) = x(x+2)^2$.

11. Solve $f(x) \geq 0$, where $f(x) = (x+4)(x-2)^2$.

12. Solve $f(x) > 0$, where $f(x) = (x-1)(x+3)^2$.

13. Solve $f(x) \leq 0$, where $f(x) = -2(x+2)(x-2)^3$.

14. Solve $f(x) < 0$, where $f(x) = -\dfrac{1}{2}(x+4)(x-1)^3$.

In Problems 15–18, solve the inequality by using the graph of the function.
[**Hint:** The graphs were drawn in Problems 7–10 of Section 4.3.]

15. Solve $R(x) > 0$, where $R(x) = \dfrac{x+1}{x(x+4)}$.

16. Solve $R(x) < 0$, where $R(x) = \dfrac{x}{(x-1)(x+2)}$.

17. Solve $R(x) \leq 0$, where $R(x) = \dfrac{3x+3}{2x+4}$.

18. Solve $R(x) \geq 0$, where $R(x) = \dfrac{2x+4}{x-1}$.

In Problems 19–48, solve each inequality algebraically.

19. $(x-5)^2(x+2) < 0$

20. $(x-5)(x+2)^2 > 0$

21. $x^3 - 4x^2 > 0$

22. $x^3 + 8x^2 < 0$

23. $2x^3 > -8x^2$

24. $3x^3 < -15x^2$

25. $(x-1)(x-2)(x-3) \leq 0$

26. $(x+1)(x+2)(x+3) \leq 0$

27. $x^3 - 2x^2 - 3x > 0$

28. $x^3 + 2x^2 - 3x > 0$

29. $x^4 > x^2$

30. $x^4 < 9x^2$

31. $x^4 > 1$

32. $x^3 > 1$

33. $\dfrac{x + 1}{x - 1} > 0$

34. $\dfrac{x - 3}{x + 1} > 0$

35. $\dfrac{(x - 1)(x + 1)}{x} \leq 0$

36. $\dfrac{(x - 3)(x + 2)}{x - 1} \leq 0$

37. $\dfrac{(x - 2)^2}{x^2 - 1} \geq 0$

38. $\dfrac{(x + 5)^2}{x^2 - 4} \geq 0$

39. $\dfrac{x + 4}{x - 2} \leq 1$

40. $\dfrac{x + 2}{x - 4} \geq 1$

41. $\dfrac{3x - 5}{x + 2} \leq 2$

42. $\dfrac{x - 4}{2x + 4} \geq 1$

43. $\dfrac{1}{x - 2} < \dfrac{2}{3x - 9}$

44. $\dfrac{5}{x - 3} > \dfrac{3}{x + 1}$

45. $\dfrac{x^2(3 + x)(x + 4)}{(x + 5)(x - 1)} \geq 0$

46. $\dfrac{x(x^2 + 1)(x - 2)}{(x - 1)(x + 1)} \geq 0$

47. $\dfrac{(3 - x)^3(2x + 1)}{x^3 - 1} < 0$

48. $\dfrac{(2 - x)^3(3x - 2)}{x^3 + 1} < 0$

Mixed Practice

In Problems 49–60, solve each inequality algebraically.

49. $(x + 1)(x - 3)(x - 5) > 0$

50. $(2x - 1)(x + 2)(x + 5) < 0$

51. $7x - 4 \geq -2x^2$

52. $x^2 + 3x \geq 10$

53. $\dfrac{x + 1}{x - 3} \leq 2$

54. $\dfrac{x - 1}{x + 2} \geq -2$

55. $3(x^2 - 2) < 2(x - 1)^2 + x^2$

56. $(x - 3)(x + 2) < x^2 + 3x + 5$

57. $6x - 5 < \dfrac{6}{x}$

58. $x + \dfrac{12}{x} < 7$

59. $x^3 - 9x \leq 0$

60. $x^3 - x \geq 0$

Applications and Extensions

61. For what positive numbers will the cube of a number exceed four times its square?

62. For what positive numbers will the cube of a number be less than the number?

63. What is the domain of the function $f(x) = \sqrt{x^4 - 16}$?

64. What is the domain of the function $f(x) = \sqrt{x^3 - 3x^2}$?

65. What is the domain of the function $f(x) = \sqrt{\dfrac{x - 2}{x + 4}}$?

66. What is the domain of the function $f(x) = \sqrt{\dfrac{x - 1}{x + 4}}$?

In Problems 67–70, determine where the graph of f is below the graph of g by solving the inequality $f(x) \leq g(x)$. Graph f and g together.

67. $f(x) = x^4 - 1$
$g(x) = -2x^2 + 2$

68. $f(x) = x^4 - 1$
$g(x) = x - 1$

69. $f(x) = x^4 - 4$
$g(x) = 3x^2$

70. $f(x) = x^4$
$g(x) = 2 - x^2$

71. Average Cost Suppose that the daily cost C of manufacturing bicycles is given by $C(x) = 80x + 5000$. Then the average daily cost $\overline{C}$ is given by $\overline{C}(x) = \dfrac{80x + 5000}{x}$. How many bicycles must be produced each day for the average cost to be no more than $100?

72. Average Cost See Problem 71. Suppose that the government imposes a $1000 per day tax on the bicycle manufacturer so that the daily cost C of manufacturing x bicycles is now given by $C(x) = 80x + 6000$. Now the average daily cost $\overline{C}$ is given by $\overline{C}(x) = \dfrac{80x + 6000}{x}$. How many bicycles must be produced each day for the average cost to be no more than $100?

73. Bungee Jumping Originating on Pentecost Island in the Pacific, the practice of a person jumping from a high place harnessed to a flexible attachment was introduced to western culture in 1979 by the Oxford University Dangerous Sport Club. One important parameter to know before attempting a bungee jump is the amount the cord will stretch at the bottom of the fall. The stiffness of the cord is related to the amount of stretch by the equation

$$K = \dfrac{2W(S + L)}{S^2}$$

where W = weight of the jumper (pounds)
K = cord's stiffness (pounds per foot)
L = free length of the cord (feet)
S = stretch (feet)

(a) A 150-pound person plans to jump off a ledge attached to a cord of length 42 feet. If the stiffness of the cord is no less than 16 pounds per foot, how much will the cord stretch?

(b) If safety requirements will not permit the jumper to get any closer than 3 feet to the ground, what is the minimum height required for the ledge in part (a)?

Source: American Institute of Physics, Physics News Update, No. 150, November 5, 1993

74. Gravitational Force According to Newton's Law of universal gravitation, the attractive force F between two bodies is given by

$$F = G\frac{m_1 m_2}{r^2}$$

where m_1, m_2 = the masses of the two bodies
r = distance between the two bodies
G = gravitational constant = 6.6742×10^{-11} newtons meter^2 kilogram^{-2}

Suppose an object is traveling directly from Earth to the moon. The mass of Earth is 5.9742×10^{24} kilograms, the mass of the moon is 7.349×10^{22} kilograms, and the mean distance from Earth to the moon is 384,400 kilometers. For an object between Earth and the moon, how far from Earth is the force on the object due to the moon greater than the force on the object due to Earth?

Source: www.solarviews.com;en.wikipedia.org

75. Field Trip Mrs. West has decided to take her fifth grade class to a play. The manager of the theater agreed to discount the regular $40 price of the ticket by $0.20 for each ticket sold. The cost of the bus, $500, will be split equally among each of the students. How many students must attend to keep the cost per student at or below $40?

Explaining Concepts: Discussion and Writing

76. Make up an inequality that has no solution. Make up one that has exactly one solution.

77. The inequality $x^4 + 1 < -5$ has no solution. Explain why.

78. A student attempted to solve the inequality $\dfrac{x+4}{x-3} \le 0$ by multiplying both sides of the inequality by $x - 3$ to get

$x + 4 \le 0$. This led to a solution of $\{x \mid x \le -4\}$. Is the student correct? Explain.

79. Write a rational inequality whose solution set is $\{x \mid -3 < x \le 5\}$.

'Are You Prepared?' Answers

1. $\left\{x \middle| x < -\dfrac{1}{2}\right\}$ or $\left(-\infty, -\dfrac{1}{2}\right)$

2. $\{x \mid -3 \le x \le 8\}$ or $[-3, 8]$

4.5 The Real Zeros of a Polynomial Function

PREPARING FOR THIS SECTION *Before getting started, review the following:*

- Evaluating Functions (Section 2.1, pp. 49–52)
- Factoring Polynomials (Appendix A, Section A.3, pp. A28–A29)
- Synthetic Division (Appendix A, Section A.4, pp. A32–A35)

- Polynomial Division (Appendix A, Section A.3, pp. A25–A28)
- Intercepts of a Quadratic Function (Section 3.3, pp. 138–139)

Now Work the 'Are You Prepared?' problems on page 230.

OBJECTIVES
1 Use the Remainder and Factor Theorems (p. 221)
2 Use the Rational Zeros Theorem to List the Potential Rational Zeros of a Polynomial Function (p. 224)
3 Find the Real Zeros of a Polynomial Function (p. 224)
4 Solve Polynomial Equations (p. 227)
5 Use the Theorem for Bounds on Zeros (p. 227)
6 Use the Intermediate Value Theorem (p. 228)

In Section 4.1, we were able to identify the real zeros of a polynomial function because either the polynomial function was in factored form or it could be easily factored. But how do we find the real zeros of a polynomial function if it is not factored or cannot be easily factored?

Recall that if r is a real zero of a polynomial function f then $f(r) = 0$, r is an x-intercept of the graph of f, $x - r$ is a factor of f, and r is a solution of the equation $f(x) = 0$. For example, if $x - 4$ is a factor of f, then 4 is a real zero of f and 4 is a solution to the equation $f(x) = 0$. For polynomial and rational functions, we have seen the importance of the real zeros for graphing. In most cases, however, the real zeros of a polynomial function are difficult to find using algebraic methods. No nice formulas like the quadratic formula are available to help us find zeros for polynomials of degree 3 or higher. Formulas do exist for solving any third- or fourth-degree polynomial equation, but they are somewhat complicated. No general formulas exist for polynomial equations of degree 5 or higher. Refer to the Historical Feature at the end of this section for more information.

1 Use the Remainder and Factor Theorems

When we divide one polynomial (the dividend) by another (the divisor), we obtain a quotient polynomial and a remainder, the remainder being either the zero polynomial or a polynomial whose degree is less than the degree of the divisor. To check our work, we verify that

$$(\text{Quotient})(\text{Divisor}) + \text{Remainder} = \text{Dividend}$$

This checking routine is the basis for a famous theorem called the **division algorithm*** **for polynomials,** which we now state without proof.

THEOREM

Division Algorithm for Polynomials

If $f(x)$ and $g(x)$ denote polynomial functions and if $g(x)$ is a polynomial whose degree is greater than zero, then there are unique polynomial functions $q(x)$ and $r(x)$ such that

$$\frac{f(x)}{g(x)} = q(x) + \frac{r(x)}{g(x)} \quad \text{or} \quad f(x) = q(x)g(x) + r(x) \qquad \textbf{(1)}$$

$$\underset{\text{dividend}}{\uparrow} \quad \underset{\text{quotient}}{\uparrow} \ \underset{\text{divisor}}{\uparrow} \quad \underset{\text{remainder}}{\uparrow}$$

where $r(x)$ is either the zero polynomial or a polynomial of degree less than that of $g(x)$.

In equation (1), $f(x)$ is the **dividend,** $g(x)$ is the **divisor,** $q(x)$ is the **quotient,** and $r(x)$ is the **remainder.**

If the divisor $g(x)$ is a first-degree polynomial of the form

$$g(x) = x - c \quad c \text{ a real number}$$

then the remainder $r(x)$ is either the zero polynomial or a polynomial of degree 0. As a result, for such divisors, the remainder is some number, say R, and

$$f(x) = (x - c)q(x) + R \qquad \textbf{(2)}$$

This equation is an identity in x and is true for all real numbers x. Suppose that $x = c$. Then equation (2) becomes

$$f(c) = (c - c)q(c) + R$$
$$f(c) = R$$

---

*A systematic process in which certain steps are repeated a finite number of times is called an **algorithm.** For example, long division is an algorithm.

Substitute $f(c)$ for R in equation (2) to obtain

$$f(x) = (x - c)q(x) + f(c) \qquad\qquad (3)$$

We have now proved the **Remainder Theorem.**

REMAINDER THEOREM

Let f be a polynomial function. If $f(x)$ is divided by $x - c$, then the remainder is $f(c)$.

EXAMPLE 1

Using the Remainder Theorem

Find the remainder if $f(x) = x^3 - 4x^2 - 5$ is divided by

(a) $x - 3$ (b) $x + 2$

Solution

(a) We could use long division or synthetic division, but it is easier to use the Remainder Theorem, which says that the remainder is $f(3)$.

$$f(3) = (3)^3 - 4(3)^2 - 5 = 27 - 36 - 5 = -14$$

The remainder is -14.

(b) To find the remainder when $f(x)$ is divided by $x + 2 = x - (-2)$, evaluate $f(-2)$.

$$f(-2) = (-2)^3 - 4(-2)^2 - 5 = -8 - 16 - 5 = -29$$

The remainder is -29.

Compare the method used in Example 1(a) with the method used in Example 1 of Appendix A, Section A.4. Which method do you prefer? Give reasons.

 COMMENT A graphing utility provides another way to find the value of a function using the eVALUEate feature. Consult your manual for details. Then check the results of Example 1. ∎

An important and useful consequence of the Remainder Theorem is the **Factor Theorem.**

FACTOR THEOREM

Let f be a polynomial function. Then $x - c$ is a factor of $f(x)$ if and only if $f(c) = 0$.

The Factor Theorem actually consists of two separate statements:

1. If $f(c) = 0$, then $x - c$ is a factor of $f(x)$.
2. If $x - c$ is a factor of $f(x)$, then $f(c) = 0$.

The proof requires two parts.

Proof

1. Suppose that $f(c) = 0$. Then, by equation (3), we have

$$f(x) = (x - c)q(x)$$

for some polynomial $q(x)$. That is, $x - c$ is a factor of $f(x)$.

2. Suppose that $x - c$ is a factor of $f(x)$. Then there is a polynomial function q such that

$$f(x) = (x - c)q(x)$$

Replacing x by c, we find that

$$f(c) = (c - c)q(c) = 0 \cdot q(c) = 0$$

This completes the proof.   ∎

EXAMPLE 2

Using the Factor Theorem

Use the Factor Theorem to determine whether the function

$$f(x) = 2x^3 - x^2 + 2x - 3$$

has the factor

(a) $x - 1$ (b) $x + 3$

Solution
The Factor Theorem states that if $f(c) = 0$ then $x - c$ is a factor.

(a) Because $x - 1$ is of the form $x - c$ with $c = 1$, we find the value of $f(1)$. We choose to use substitution.

$$f(1) = 2(1)^3 - (1)^2 + 2(1) - 3 = 2 - 1 + 2 - 3 = 0$$

By the Factor Theorem, $x - 1$ is a factor of $f(x)$.

(b) To test the factor $x + 3$, we first need to write it in the form $x - c$. Since $x + 3 = x - (-3)$, we find the value of $f(-3)$. We choose to use synthetic division.

$$
\begin{array}{r|rrrr}
-3 & 2 & -1 & 2 & -3 \\
   &   & -6 & 21 & -69 \\
\hline
   & 2 & -7 & 23 & -72
\end{array}
$$

Because $f(-3) = -72 \neq 0$, we conclude from the Factor Theorem that $x - (-3) = x + 3$ is not a factor of $f(x)$.   ↵

═══──**Now Work** PROBLEM 1 1

In Example 2(a), we found that $x - 1$ is a factor of f. To write f in factored form, use long division or synthetic division. Using synthetic division,

$$
\begin{array}{r|rrrr}
1 & 2 & -1 & 2 & -3 \\
  &   & 2 & 1 & 3 \\
\hline
  & 2 & 1 & 3 & 0
\end{array}
$$

The quotient is $q(x) = 2x^2 + x + 3$ with a remainder of 0, as expected. We can write f in factored form as

$$f(x) = 2x^3 - x^2 + 2x - 3 = (x - 1)(2x^2 + x + 3)$$

The next theorem concerns the number of real zeros that a polynomial function may have. In counting the zeros of a polynomial, we count each zero as many times as its multiplicity.

THEOREM

Number of Real Zeros

A polynomial function cannot have more real zeros than its degree.   ⌐

Proof The proof is based on the Factor Theorem. If r is a real zero of a polynomial function f, then $f(r) = 0$ and, hence, $x - r$ is a factor of $f(x)$. Each real zero corresponds to a factor of degree 1. Because f cannot have more first-degree factors than its degree, the result follows.   ∎

2 Use the Rational Zeros Theorem to List the Potential Rational Zeros of a Polynomial Function

The next result, called the **Rational Zeros Theorem,** provides information about the rational zeros of a polynomial *with integer coefficients.*

THEOREM

Rational Zeros Theorem

Let f be a polynomial function of degree 1 or higher of the form

$$f(x) = a_n x^n + a_{n-1} x^{n-1} + \cdots + a_1 x + a_0 \quad a_n \neq 0, \quad a_0 \neq 0$$

where each coefficient is an integer. If $\dfrac{p}{q}$, in lowest terms, is a rational zero of f, then p must be a factor of a_0 and q must be a factor of a_n.

EXAMPLE 3

Listing Potential Rational Zeros

List the potential rational zeros of

$$f(x) = 2x^3 + 11x^2 - 7x - 6$$

Solution

Because f has integer coefficients, we may use the Rational Zeros Theorem. First, list all the integers p that are factors of the constant term $a_0 = -6$ and all the integers q that are factors of the leading coefficient $a_3 = 2$.

$$p: \quad \pm 1, \pm 2, \pm 3, \pm 6 \quad \text{Factors of } -6$$
$$q: \quad \pm 1, \pm 2 \quad \text{Factors of 2}$$

Now form all possible ratios $\dfrac{p}{q}$.

$$\frac{p}{q}: \quad \pm 1, \pm 2, \pm 3, \pm 6, \pm \frac{1}{2}, \pm \frac{3}{2}$$

If f has a rational zero, it will be found in this list, which contains 12 possibilities.

COMMENT For the polynomial function $f(x) = 2x^3 + 11x^2 - 7x - 6$, we know 5 is not a zero, because 5 is not in the list of potential rational zeros. However, -1 may or may not be a zero. ∎

Now Work PROBLEM 33

Be sure that you understand what the Rational Zeros Theorem says: For a polynomial with integer coefficients, *if* there is a rational zero, it is one of those listed. It may be the case that the function does not have any rational zeros.

Long division, synthetic division, or substitution can be used to test each potential rational zero to determine whether it is indeed a zero. To make the work easier, integers are usually tested first.

3 Find the Real Zeros of a Polynomial Function

EXAMPLE 4

How to Find the Real Zeros of a Polynomial Function

Find the real zeros of the polynomial function $f(x) = 2x^3 + 11x^2 - 7x - 6$. Write f in factored form.

Step-by-Step Solution

Step 1: Use the degree of the polynomial to determine the maximum number of zeros.

Since f is a polynomial of degree 3, there are at most three real zeros.

Step 2: If the polynomial has integer coefficients, use the Rational Zeros Theorem to identify those rational numbers that potentially can be zeros. Use the Factor Theorem to determine if each potential rational zero is a zero. If it is, use synthetic division or long division to factor the polynomial function. Repeat Step 2 until all the zeros of the polynomial function have been identified and the polynomial function is completely factored.

List the potential rational zeros obtained in Example 3:

$$\pm 1, \pm 2, \pm 3, \pm 6, \pm \frac{1}{2}, \pm \frac{3}{2}$$

From our list of potential rational zeros, we will test 6 to determine if it is a zero of f. Because $f(6) = 780 \neq 0$, we know that 6 is not a zero of f. Now, let's test if -6 is a zero. Because $f(-6) = 0$, we know that -6 is a zero and $x - (-6) = x + 6$ is a factor of f. Use long division or synthetic division to factor f. (We will not show the division here, but you are encouraged to verify the results shown.) After dividing f by $x + 6$, the quotient is $2x^2 - x - 1$, so

$$f(x) = 2x^3 + 11x^2 - 7x - 6$$
$$= (x + 6)(2x^2 - x - 1)$$

Now any solution of the equation $2x^2 - x - 1 = 0$ will be a zero of f. We call the equation $2x^2 - x - 1 = 0$ a **depressed equation** of f. Because any solution to the equation $2x^2 - x - 1 = 0$ is a zero of f, we work with the depressed equation to find the remaining zeros of f.

The depressed equation $2x^2 - x - 1 = 0$ is a quadratic equation with discriminant $b^2 - 4ac = (-1)^2 - 4(2)(-1) = 9 > 0$. The equation has two real solutions, which can be found by factoring.

$$2x^2 - x - 1 = (2x + 1)(x - 1) = 0$$
$$2x + 1 = 0 \quad \text{or} \quad x - 1 = 0$$
$$x = -\frac{1}{2} \quad \text{or} \quad x = 1$$

The zeros of f are -6, $-\frac{1}{2}$, and 1.

We completely factor f as follows:

$$f(x) = 2x^3 + 11x^2 - 7x - 6 = (x + 6)(2x^2 - x - 1)$$
$$= (x + 6)(2x + 1)(x - 1)$$

Notice that the three zeros of f are in the list of potential rational zeros.

SUMMARY   Steps for Finding the Real Zeros of a Polynomial Function

STEP 1: Use the degree of the polynomial to determine the maximum number of real zeros.

STEP 2: (a) If the polynomial has integer coefficients, use the Rational Zeros Theorem to identify those rational numbers that potentially could be zeros.

(b) Use substitution, synthetic division, or long division to test each potential rational zero. Each time that a zero (and thus a factor) is found, repeat Step 2 on the depressed equation.

In attempting to find the zeros, remember to use (if possible) the factoring techniques that you already know (special products, factoring by grouping, and so on).

EXAMPLE 5   **Finding the Real Zeros of a Polynomial Function**

Find the real zeros of $f(x) = x^5 - 5x^4 + 12x^3 - 24x^2 + 32x - 16$. Write f in factored form.

Solution   **STEP 1:** There are at most five real zeros.

STEP 2: Because the leading coefficient is $a_5 = 1$, the potential rational zeros are the integers ± 1, ± 2, ± 4, ± 8, and ± 16, the factors of the constant term, 16.

We test the potential rational zero 1 first, using synthetic division.

$$
\begin{array}{r}
1)\overline{1 \quad -5 \quad 12 \quad -24 \quad 32 \quad -16} \\
1 \quad -4 \quad 8 \quad -16 \quad 16 \\
\hline
1 \quad -4 \quad 8 \quad -16 \quad 16 \quad 0
\end{array}
$$

The remainder is $f(1) = 0$, so 1 is a zero and $x - 1$ is a factor of f. Using the entries in the bottom row of the synthetic division, we can begin to factor f.

$$
\begin{aligned}
f(x) &= x^5 - 5x^4 + 12x^3 - 24x^2 + 32x - 16 \\
&= (x - 1)(x^4 - 4x^3 + 8x^2 - 16x + 16)
\end{aligned}
$$

We now work with the first depressed equation:

$$
q_1(x) = x^4 - 4x^3 + 8x^2 - 16x + 16 = 0
$$

REPEAT STEP 2: The potential rational zeros of q_1 are still ± 1, ± 2, ± 4, ± 8, and ± 16. We test 1 first, since it may be a repeated zero of f.

$$
\begin{array}{r}
1)\overline{1 \quad -4 \quad 8 \quad -16 \quad 16} \\
1 \quad -3 \quad 5 \quad -11 \\
\hline
1 \quad -3 \quad 5 \quad -11 \quad 5
\end{array}
$$

Since the remainder is 5, 1 is not a repeated zero. Try 2 next.

$$
\begin{array}{r}
2)\overline{1 \quad -4 \quad 8 \quad -16 \quad 16} \\
2 \quad -4 \quad 8 \quad -16 \\
\hline
1 \quad -2 \quad 4 \quad -8 \quad 0
\end{array}
$$

The remainder is $f(2) = 0$, so 2 is a zero and $x - 2$ is a factor of f. Again using the bottom row, we find

$$
\begin{aligned}
f(x) &= x^5 - 5x^4 + 12x^3 - 24x^2 + 32x - 16 \\
&= (x - 1)(x - 2)(x^3 - 2x^2 + 4x - 8)
\end{aligned}
$$

The remaining zeros satisfy the new depressed equation

$$
q_2(x) = x^3 - 2x^2 + 4x - 8 = 0
$$

Notice that $q_2(x)$ can be factored using grouping. (Alternatively, you could repeat Step 2 and check the potential rational zero 2.) Then

$$
\begin{aligned}
x^3 - 2x^2 + 4x - 8 &= 0 \\
x^2(x - 2) + 4(x - 2) &= 0 \\
(x^2 + 4)(x - 2) &= 0 \\
x^2 + 4 = 0 \quad \text{or} \quad x - 2 &= 0 \\
x &= 2
\end{aligned}
$$

Since $x^2 + 4 = 0$ has no real solutions, the real zeros of f are 1 and 2, with 2 being a zero of multiplicity 2. The factored form of f is

$$
\begin{aligned}
f(x) &= x^5 - 5x^4 + 12x^3 - 24x^2 + 32x - 16 \\
&= (x - 1)(x - 2)^2(x^2 + 4)
\end{aligned}
$$

Now Work PROBLEM 45

4 Solve Polynomial Equations

EXAMPLE 6

Solving a Polynomial Equation

Find the real solutions of the equation: $x^5 - 5x^4 + 12x^3 - 24x^2 + 32x - 16 = 0$

Solution

The real solutions of this equation are the real zeros of the polynomial function

$$f(x) = x^5 - 5x^4 + 12x^3 - 24x^2 + 32x - 16$$

Using the result of Example 5, the real zeros of f are 1 and 2. So, $\{1, 2\}$ is the solution set of the equation

$$x^5 - 5x^4 + 12x^3 - 24x^2 + 32x - 16 = 0$$

⌐⌐⌐⌐⌐**Now Work** PROBLEM 57

In Example 5, the quadratic factor $x^2 + 4$ that appears in the factored form of f is called *irreducible*, because the polynomial $x^2 + 4$ cannot be factored over the real numbers. In general, a quadratic factor $ax^2 + bx + c$ is **irreducible** if it cannot be factored over the real numbers, that is, if it is prime over the real numbers.

Refer to Examples 4 and 5. The polynomial function of Example 4 has three real zeros, and its factored form contains three linear factors. The polynomial function of Example 5 has two distinct real zeros, and its factored form contains two distinct linear factors and one irreducible quadratic factor.

THEOREM

Every polynomial function with real coefficients can be uniquely factored into a product of linear factors and/or irreducible (prime) quadratic factors.

We prove this result in Section 4.6, and, in fact, shall draw several additional conclusions about the zeros of a polynomial function. One conclusion is worth noting now. If a polynomial with real coefficients is of odd degree, it must contain at least one linear factor. (Do you see why? Consider the end behavior of polynomial functions of odd degree.) This means that it must have at least one real zero.

THEOREM

A polynomial function of odd degree that has real coefficients has at least one real zero.

5 Use the Theorem for Bounds on Zeros

The search for the real zeros of a polynomial function can be reduced somewhat if *bounds* on the zeros are found. A number M is a **bound** on the zeros of a polynomial if every zero lies between $-M$ and M, inclusive. That is, M is a bound on the zeros of a polynomial f if

$$-M \leq \text{any real zero of } f \leq M$$

THEOREM

Bounds on Zeros

Let f denote a polynomial function whose leading coefficient is 1.

$$f(x) = x^n + a_{n-1}x^{n-1} + \cdots + a_1 x + a_0$$

A bound M on the real zeros of f is the smaller of the two numbers

$$\boxed{\text{Max}\{1, |a_0| + |a_1| + \cdots + |a_{n-1}|\}, 1 + \text{Max}\{|a_0|, |a_1|, \cdots, |a_{n-1}|\} \quad \textbf{(4)}}$$

where Max $\{\ \}$ means "choose the largest entry in $\{\ \}$."

EXAMPLE 7   **Using the Theorem for Finding Bounds on Zeros**

Find a bound on the real zeros of each polynomial function.

(a) $f(x) = x^5 + 3x^3 - 9x^2 + 5$ (b) $g(x) = 4x^5 - 2x^3 + 2x^2 + 1$

Solution   (a) The leading coefficient of f is 1.

$$f(x) = x^5 + 3x^3 - 9x^2 + 5 \quad a_4 = 0, a_3 = 3, a_2 = -9, a_1 = 0, a_0 = 5$$

Evaluate the two expressions in (4).

$$\text{Max}\{1, |a_0| + |a_1| + \cdots + |a_{n-1}|\} = \text{Max}\{1, |5| + |0| + |-9| + |3| + |0|\}$$
$$= \text{Max}\{1, 17\} = 17$$

$$1 + \text{Max}\{|a_0|, |a_1|, \cdots, |a_{n-1}|\} = 1 + \text{Max}\{|5|, |0|, |-9|, |3|, |0|\}$$
$$= 1 + 9 = 10$$

The smaller of the two numbers, 10, is the bound. Every real zero of f lies between -10 and 10.

(b) First write g so that it is the product of a constant times a polynomial whose leading coefficient is 1 by factoring out the leading coefficient of g, 4.

$$g(x) = 4x^5 - 2x^3 + 2x^2 + 1 = 4\left(x^5 - \frac{1}{2}x^3 + \frac{1}{2}x^2 + \frac{1}{4}\right)$$

Next evaluate the two expressions in (4) with $a_4 = 0$, $a_3 = -\frac{1}{2}$, $a_2 = \frac{1}{2}$, $a_1 = 0$, and $a_0 = \frac{1}{4}$.

$$\text{Max}\{1, |a_0| + |a_1| + \cdots + |a_{n-1}|\} = \text{Max}\left\{1, \left|\frac{1}{4}\right| + |0| + \left|\frac{1}{2}\right| + \left|-\frac{1}{2}\right| + |0|\right\}$$
$$= \text{Max}\left\{1, \frac{5}{4}\right\} = \frac{5}{4}$$

$$1 + \text{Max}\{|a_0|, |a_1|, \ldots, |a_{n-1}|\} = 1 + \text{Max}\left\{\left|\frac{1}{4}\right|, |0|, \left|\frac{1}{2}\right|, \left|-\frac{1}{2}\right|, |0|\right\}$$
$$= 1 + \frac{1}{2} = \frac{3}{2}$$

 COMMENT The bounds on the zeros of a polynomial provide good choices for setting Xmin and Xmax of the viewing rectangle. With these choices, all the x-intercepts of the graph can be seen. ∎

The smaller of the two numbers, $\frac{5}{4}$, is the bound. Every real zero of g lies between $-\frac{5}{4}$ and $\frac{5}{4}$.

─────**Now Work** PROBLEM 69

6 Use the Intermediate Value Theorem

The next result, called the **Intermediate Value Theorem,** is based on the fact that the graph of a polynomial function is continuous; that is, it contains no "holes" or "gaps." Although the proof of this result requires advanced methods in calculus, it is easy to "see" why the result is true. Look at Figure 49.

Figure 49 If $f(a) < 0$ and $f(b) > 0$, there is a zero between a and b.

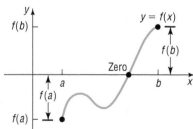

THEOREM   **Intermediate Value Theorem**

Let f denote a polynomial function. If $a < b$ and if $f(a)$ and $f(b)$ are of opposite sign, there is at least one real zero of f between a and b.

EXAMPLE 8

Using the Intermediate Value Theorem to Locate a Real Zero

Show that $f(x) = x^5 - x^3 - 1$ has a zero between 1 and 2.

Solution

Evaluate f at 1 and at 2.

$$f(1) = -1 \quad \text{and} \quad f(2) = 23$$

Because $f(1) < 0$ and $f(2) > 0$, it follows from the Intermediate Value Theorem that the polynomial function f has at least one zero between 1 and 2.

Now Work PROBLEM 77

Let's look at the polynomial f of Example 8 more closely. Based on the Rational Zeros Theorem, ± 1 are the only potential rational zeros. Since $f(1) \neq 0$, we conclude that the zero between 1 and 2 is irrational. We can use the Intermediate Value Theorem to approximate it.

Approximating the Real Zeros of a Polynomial Function

STEP 1: Find two consecutive integers a and $a + 1$ such that f has a zero between them.

STEP 2: Divide the interval $[a, a + 1]$ into 10 equal subintervals.

STEP 3: Evaluate f at each endpoint of the subintervals until the Intermediate Value Theorem applies; this subinterval then contains a zero.

STEP 4: Repeat the process starting at Step 2 until the desired accuracy is achieved.

EXAMPLE 9

Approximating a Real Zero of a Polynomial Function

$f(x) = x^5 - x^3 - 1$ has exactly one zero between 1 and 2. Approximate it correct to two decimal places.

Solution

Divide the interval $[1, 2]$ into 10 equal subintervals: $[1, 1.1]$, $[1.1, 1.2]$, $[1.2, 1.3]$, $[1.3, 1.4]$, $[1.4, 1.5]$, $[1.5, 1.6]$, $[1.6, 1.7]$, $[1.7, 1.8]$, $[1.8, 1.9]$, $[1.9, 2]$. Now find the value of f at each endpoint until the Intermediate Value Theorem applies.

$$f(x) = x^5 - x^3 - 1$$
$$f(1.0) = -1 \qquad f(1.2) = -0.23968$$
$$f(1.1) = -0.72049 \quad f(1.3) = 0.51593$$

COMMENT The TABLE feature of a graphing calculator makes the computations in the solution to Example 9 a lot easier. ■

We can stop here and conclude that the zero is between 1.2 and 1.3. Now divide the interval $[1.2, 1.3]$ into 10 equal subintervals and proceed to evaluate f at each endpoint.

$$f(1.20) = -0.23968 \qquad f(1.23) \approx -0.0455613$$
$$f(1.21) \approx -0.1778185 \quad f(1.24) \approx 0.025001$$
$$f(1.22) \approx -0.1131398$$

Figure 50

We conclude that the zero lies between 1.23 and 1.24, and so, correct to two decimal places, the zero is 1.23.

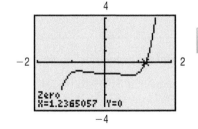

Exploration

We examine the polynomial f given in Example 9. The Theorem on Bounds of Zeros tells us that every zero is between -2 and 2. If we graph f using $-2 \le x \le 2$ (see Figure 50), we see that f has exactly one x-intercept. Using ZERO or ROOT, we find this zero to be 1.24 rounded to two decimal places. Correct to two decimal places, the zero is 1.23.

Now Work PROBLEM 89

There are many other numerical techniques for approximating the zeros of a polynomial. The one outlined in Example 9 (a variation of the *bisection method*) has the advantages that it will always work, it can be programmed rather easily on a computer, and each time it is used another decimal place of accuracy is achieved. See Problem 115 for the bisection method, which places the zero in a succession of intervals, with each new interval being half the length of the preceding one.

Historical Feature

Formulas for the solution of third- and fourth-degree polynomial equations exist, and, while not very practical, they do have an interesting history.

In the 1500s in Italy, mathematical contests were a popular pastime, and persons possessing methods for solving problems kept them secret. (Solutions that were published were already common knowledge.) Niccolo of Brescia (1499–1557), commonly referred to as Tartaglia ("the stammerer"), had the secret for solving cubic (third-degree) equations, which gave him a decided advantage in the contests. Girolamo Cardano (1501–1576) found out that Tartaglia had the secret, and, being interested in cubics, he requested it from Tartaglia. The reluctant Tartaglia hesitated for some time, but finally, swearing Cardano to secrecy with midnight oaths by candlelight, told him the secret. Cardano then published the solution in his book

Ars Magna (1545), giving Tartaglia the credit but rather compromising the secrecy. Tartaglia exploded into bitter recriminations, and each wrote pamphlets that reflected on the other's mathematics, moral character, and ancestry.

The quartic (fourth-degree) equation was solved by Cardano's student Lodovico Ferrari, and this solution also was included, with credit and this time with permission, in the *Ars Magna*.

Attempts were made to solve the fifth-degree equation in similar ways, all of which failed. In the early 1800s, P. Ruffini, Niels Abel, and Evariste Galois all found ways to show that it is not possible to solve fifth-degree equations by formula, but the proofs required the introduction of new methods. Galois's methods eventually developed into a large part of modern algebra.

Historical Problems

Problems 1–8 develop the Tartaglia–Cardano solution of the cubic equation and show why it is not altogether practical.

1. Show that the general cubic equation $y^3 + by^2 + cy + d = 0$ can be transformed into an equation of the form $x^3 + px + q = 0$ by using the substitution $y = x - \dfrac{b}{3}$.

2. In the equation $x^3 + px + q = 0$, replace x by $H + K$. Let $3HK = -p$, and show that $H^3 + K^3 = -q$.

3. Based on Problem 2, we have the two equations

$$3HK = -p \quad \text{and} \quad H^3 + K^3 = -q$$

Solve for K in $3HK = -p$ and substitute into $H^3 + K^3 = -q$. Then show that

$$H = \sqrt[3]{\dfrac{-q}{2} + \sqrt{\dfrac{q^2}{4} + \dfrac{p^3}{27}}}$$

[**Hint:** Look for an equation that is quadratic in form.]

4. Use the solution for H from Problem 3 and the equation $H^3 + K^3 = -q$ to show that

$$K = \sqrt[3]{\dfrac{-q}{2} - \sqrt{\dfrac{q^2}{4} + \dfrac{p^3}{27}}}$$

5. Use the results from Problems 2 to 4 to show that the solution of $x^3 + px + q = 0$ is

$$x = \sqrt[3]{\dfrac{-q}{2} + \sqrt{\dfrac{q^2}{4} + \dfrac{p^3}{27}}} + \sqrt[3]{\dfrac{-q}{2} - \sqrt{\dfrac{q^2}{4} + \dfrac{p^3}{27}}}$$

6. Use the result of Problem 5 to solve the equation $x^3 - 6x - 9 = 0$.

7. Use a calculator and the result of Problem 5 to solve the equation $x^3 + 3x - 14 = 0$.

8. Use the methods of this section to solve the equation $x^3 + 3x - 14 = 0$.

4.5 Assess Your Understanding

'Are You Prepared?' *Answers are given at the end of these exercises. If you get a wrong answer, read the pages listed in* red.

1. Find $f(-1)$ if $f(x) = 2x^2 - x$. (pp. 49–52)

2. Factor the expression $6x^2 + x - 2$. (pp. A28–A29)

3. Find the quotient and remainder if $3x^4 - 5x^3 + 7x - 4$ is divided by $x - 3$. (pp. A25–A28 or A32–A35)

4. Find the intercepts of $f(x) = x^2 + x - 3$. (pp. 138–139)

Concepts and Vocabulary

5. In the process of polynomial division, (Divisor)(Quotient) + _____ = _____ .

6. When a polynomial function f is divided by $x - c$, the remainder is _____ .

7. If a function f, whose domain is all real numbers, is even and if 4 is a zero of f, then _____ is also a zero.

8. *True or False* Every polynomial function of degree 3 with real coefficients has exactly three real zeros.

9. If f is a polynomial function and $x - 4$ is a factor of f, then $f(4) = $ _____ .

10. *True or False* If f is a polynomial function of degree 4 and if $f(2) = 5$, then

$$\frac{f(x)}{x - 2} = p(x) + \frac{5}{x - 2}$$

where $p(x)$ is a polynomial of degree 3.

Skill Building

In Problems 11–20, use the Remainder Theorem to find the remainder when $f(x)$ is divided by $x - c$. Then use the Factor Theorem to determine whether $x - c$ is a factor of $f(x)$.

11. $f(x) = 4x^3 - 3x^2 - 8x + 4;\ x - 2$

12. $f(x) = -4x^3 + 5x^2 + 8;\ \ x + 3$

13. $f(x) = 3x^4 - 6x^3 - 5x + 10;\ x - 2$

14. $f(x) = 4x^4 - 15x^2 - 4;\ x - 2$

15. $f(x) = 3x^6 + 82x^3 + 27;\ x + 3$

16. $f(x) = 2x^6 - 18x^4 + x^2 - 9;\ x + 3$

17. $f(x) = 4x^6 - 64x^4 + x^2 - 15;\ x + 4$

18. $f(x) = x^6 - 16x^4 + x^2 - 16;\ x + 4$

19. $f(x) = 2x^4 - x^3 + 2x - 1;\ x - \dfrac{1}{2}$

20. $f(x) = 3x^4 + x^3 - 3x + 1;\ x + \dfrac{1}{3}$

In Problems 21–32, tell the maximum number of real zeros that each polynomial function may have. Do not attempt to find the zeros.

21. $f(x) = -4x^7 + x^3 - x^2 + 2$

22. $f(x) = 5x^4 + 2x^2 - 6x - 5$

23. $f(x) = 2x^6 - 3x^2 - x + 1$

24. $f(x) = -3x^5 + 4x^4 + 2$

25. $f(x) = 3x^3 - 2x^2 + x + 2$

26. $f(x) = -x^3 - x^2 + x + 1$

27. $f(x) = -x^4 + x^2 - 1$

28. $f(x) = x^4 + 5x^3 - 2$

29. $f(x) = x^5 + x^4 + x^2 + x + 1$

30. $f(x) = x^5 - x^4 + x^3 - x^2 + x - 1$

31. $f(x) = x^6 - 1$

32. $f(x) = x^6 + 1$

In Problems 33–44, list the potential rational zeros of each polynomial function. Do not attempt to find the zeros.

33. $f(x) = 3x^4 - 3x^3 + x^2 - x + 1$

34. $f(x) = x^5 - x^4 + 2x^2 + 3$

35. $f(x) = x^5 - 6x^2 + 9x - 3$

36. $f(x) = 2x^5 - x^4 - x^2 + 1$

37. $f(x) = -4x^3 - x^2 + x + 2$

38. $f(x) = 6x^4 - x^2 + 2$

39. $f(x) = 6x^4 - x^2 + 9$

40. $f(x) = -4x^3 + x^2 + x + 6$

41. $f(x) = 2x^5 - x^3 + 2x^2 + 12$

42. $f(x) = 3x^5 - x^2 + 2x + 18$

43. $f(x) = 6x^4 + 2x^3 - x^2 + 20$

44. $f(x) = -6x^3 - x^2 + x + 10$

In Problems 45–56, use the Rational Zeros Theorem to find all the real zeros of each polynomial function. Use the zeros to factor f over the real numbers.

45. $f(x) = x^3 + 2x^2 - 5x - 6$

46. $f(x) = x^3 + 8x^2 + 11x - 20$

47. $f(x) = 2x^3 - x^2 + 2x - 1$

48. $f(x) = 2x^3 + x^2 + 2x + 1$

49. $f(x) = 2x^3 - 4x^2 - 10x + 20$

50. $f(x) = 3x^3 + 6x^2 - 15x - 30$

51. $f(x) = 2x^4 + x^3 - 7x^2 - 3x + 3$

52. $f(x) = 2x^4 - x^3 - 5x^2 + 2x + 2$

53. $f(x) = x^4 + x^3 - 3x^2 - x + 2$

54. $f(x) = x^4 - x^3 - 6x^2 + 4x + 8$

55. $f(x) = 4x^4 + 5x^3 + 9x^2 + 10x + 2$

56. $f(x) = 3x^4 + 4x^3 + 7x^2 + 8x + 2$

In Problems 57–68, solve each equation in the real number system.

57. $x^4 - x^3 + 2x^2 - 4x - 8 = 0$

58. $2x^3 + 3x^2 + 2x + 3 = 0$

59. $3x^3 + 4x^2 - 7x + 2 = 0$

60. $2x^3 - 3x^2 - 3x - 5 = 0$

61. $3x^3 - x^2 - 15x + 5 = 0$

62. $2x^3 - 11x^2 + 10x + 8 = 0$

63. $x^4 + 4x^3 + 2x^2 - x + 6 = 0$

64. $x^4 - 2x^3 + 10x^2 - 18x + 9 = 0$

65. $x^3 - \dfrac{2}{3}x^2 + \dfrac{8}{3}x + 1 = 0$

66. $x^3 + \dfrac{3}{2}x^2 + 3x - 2 = 0$

67. $2x^4 - 19x^3 + 57x^2 - 64x + 20 = 0$

68. $2x^4 + x^3 - 24x^2 + 20x + 16 = 0$

In Problems 69–76, find bounds on the real zeros of each polynomial function.

69. $f(x) = x^4 - 3x^2 - 4$

70. $f(x) = x^4 - 5x^2 - 36$

71. $f(x) = x^4 + x^3 - x - 1$

72. $f(x) = x^4 - x^3 + x - 1$

73. $f(x) = 3x^4 + 3x^3 - x^2 - 12x - 12$

74. $f(x) = 3x^4 - 3x^3 - 5x^2 + 27x - 36$

75. $f(x) = 4x^5 - x^4 + 2x^3 - 2x^2 + x - 1$

76. $f(x) = 4x^5 + x^4 + x^3 + x^2 - 2x - 2$

In Problems 77–82, use the Intermediate Value Theorem to show that each polynomial function has a zero in the given interval.

77. $f(x) = 8x^4 - 2x^2 + 5x - 1; [0, 1]$

78. $f(x) = x^4 + 8x^3 - x^2 + 2; [-1, 0]$

79. $f(x) = 2x^3 + 6x^2 - 8x + 2; [-5, -4]$

80. $f(x) = 3x^3 - 10x + 9; [-3, -2]$

81. $f(x) = x^5 - x^4 + 7x^3 - 7x^2 - 18x + 18; [1.4, 1.5]$

82. $f(x) = x^5 - 3x^4 - 2x^3 + 6x^2 + x + 2; [1.7, 1.8]$

In Problems 83–86, each equation has a solution r in the interval indicated. Use the method of Example 9 to approximate this solution correct to two decimal places.

83. $8x^4 - 2x^2 + 5x - 1 = 0; 0 \le r \le 1$

84. $x^4 + 8x^3 - x^2 + 2 = 0; -1 \le r \le 0$

85. $2x^3 + 6x^2 - 8x + 2 = 0; -5 \le r \le -4$

86. $3x^3 - 10x + 9 = 0; -3 \le r \le -2$

In Problems 87–90, each polynomial function has exactly one positive zero. Use the method of Example 9 to approximate the zero correct to two decimal places.

87. $f(x) = x^3 + x^2 + x - 4$

88. $f(x) = 2x^4 + x^2 - 1$

89. $f(x) = 2x^4 - 3x^3 - 4x^2 - 8$

90. $f(x) = 3x^3 - 2x^2 - 20$

Mixed Practice

In Problems 91–102, graph each polynomial function.

91. $f(x) = x^3 + 2x^2 - 5x - 6$

92. $f(x) = x^3 + 8x^2 + 11x - 20$

93. $f(x) = 2x^3 - x^2 + 2x - 1$

94. $f(x) = 2x^3 + x^2 + 2x + 1$

95. $f(x) = x^4 + x^2 - 2$

96. $f(x) = x^4 - 3x^2 - 4$

97. $f(x) = 4x^4 + 7x^2 - 2$

98. $f(x) = 4x^4 + 15x^2 - 4$

99. $f(x) = x^4 + x^3 - 3x^2 - x + 2$

100. $f(x) = x^4 - x^3 - 6x^2 + 4x + 8$

101. $f(x) = 4x^5 - 8x^4 - x + 2$

102. $f(x) = 4x^5 + 12x^4 - x - 3$

Applications and Extensions

103. Find k such that $f(x) = x^3 - kx^2 + kx + 2$ has the factor $x - 2$.

104. Find k such that $f(x) = x^4 - kx^3 + kx^2 + 1$ has the factor $x + 2$.

105. What is the remainder when $f(x) = 2x^{20} - 8x^{10} + x - 2$ is divided by $x - 1$?

106. What is the remainder when $f(x) = -3x^{17} + x^9 - x^5 + 2x$ is divided by $x + 1$?

107. Use the Factor Theorem to prove that $x - c$ is a factor of $x^n - c^n$ for any positive integer n.

108. Use the Factor Theorem to prove that $x + c$ is a factor of $x^n + c^n$ if $n \ge 1$ is an odd integer.

109. One solution of the equation $x^3 - 8x^2 + 16x - 3 = 0$ is 3. Find the sum of the remaining solutions.

110. One solution of the equation $x^3 + 5x^2 + 5x - 2 = 0$ is -2. Find the sum of the remaining solutions.

111. Geometry What is the length of the edge of a cube if, after a slice 1 inch thick is cut from one side, the volume remaining is 294 cubic inches?

112. Geometry What is the length of the edge of a cube if its volume could be doubled by an increase of 6 centimeters in one edge, an increase of 12 centimeters in a second edge, and a decrease of 4 centimeters in the third edge?

113. Let $f(x)$ be a polynomial function whose coefficients are integers. Suppose that r is a real zero of f and that the leading coefficient of f is 1. Use the Rational Zeros Theorem to show that r is either an integer or an irrational number.

114. Prove the Rational Zeros Theorem.

[**Hint:** Let $\dfrac{p}{q}$, where p and q have no common factors except 1 and -1, be a zero of the polynomial function

$$f(x) = a_nx^n + a_{n-1}x^{n-1} + \cdots + a_1x + a_0$$

whose coefficients are all integers. Show that

$$a_np^n + a_{n-1}p^{n-1}q + \cdots + a_1pq^{n-1} + a_0q^n = 0$$

Now, because p is a factor of the first n terms of this equation, p must also be a factor of the term a_0q^n. Since p is not a factor of q (why?), p must be a factor of a_0. Similarly, q must be a factor of a_n.]

115. Bisection Method for Approximating Zeros of a Function f We begin with two consecutive integers, a and $a + 1$, such that $f(a)$ and $f(a + 1)$ are of opposite sign. Evaluate f at the midpoint m_1 of a and $a + 1$. If $f(m_1) = 0$, then m_1 is the zero of f, and we are finished. Otherwise, $f(m_1)$ is of opposite sign to either $f(a)$ or $f(a + 1)$. Suppose that it is $f(a)$ and $f(m_1)$ that are of opposite sign. Now evaluate f at the midpoint m_2 of a and m_1. Repeat this process until the desired degree of accuracy is obtained. Note that each iteration places the zero in an interval whose length is half that of the previous interval. Use the bisection method to approximate the zero of $f(x) = 8x^4 - 2x^2 + 5x - 1$ in the interval $[0, 1]$ correct to three decimal places.

[**Hint:** The process ends when both endpoints agree to the desired number of decimal places.]

Explaining Concepts: Discussion and Writing

116. Is $\dfrac{1}{3}$ a zero of $f(x) = 2x^3 + 3x^2 - 6x + 7$? Explain.

117. Is $\dfrac{1}{3}$ a zero of $f(x) = 4x^3 - 5x^2 - 3x + 1$? Explain.

118. Is $\dfrac{3}{5}$ a zero of $f(x) = 2x^6 - 5x^4 + x^3 - x + 1$? Explain.

119. Is $\dfrac{2}{3}$ a zero of $f(x) = x^7 + 6x^5 - x^4 + x + 2$? Explain.

'Are You Prepared?' Answers

1. 3   **2.** $(3x + 2)(2x - 1)$ **3.** Quotient: $3x^3 + 4x^2 + 12x + 43$; Remainder: 125

4. $(0, -3), \left(\dfrac{-1 - \sqrt{13}}{2}, 0\right), \left(\dfrac{-1 + \sqrt{13}}{2}, 0\right)$

4.6 Complex Zeros; Fundamental Theorem of Algebra

PREPARING FOR THIS SECTION *Before getting started, review the following:*

- Complex Numbers (Appendix A, Section A.7, pp. A54–A58)
- Complex Solutions of a Quadratic Equation (Appendix A, Section A.7, pp. A58–A60)

Now Work the 'Are You Prepared?' problems on page 238.

OBJECTIVES **1** Use the Conjugate Pairs Theorem (p. 235)
 2 Find a Polynomial Function with Specified Zeros (p. 236)
 3 Find the Complex Zeros of a Polynomial Function (p. 237)

In Appendix A, Section A.6, we find the real solutions of a quadratic equation, that is, the real zeros of a polynomial function of degree 2. Then, in Section A.7 we find the complex solutions of a quadratic equation, that is, the complex zeros of a polynomial function of degree 2.

In Section 4.5, we found the real zeros of polynomial functions of degree 3 or higher. In this section we will find the *complex zeros* of polynomial functions of degree 3 or higher.

DEFINITION

A variable in the complex number system is referred to as a **complex variable.** A **complex polynomial function** f of degree n is a function of the form

$$f(x) = a_n x^n + a_{n-1} x^{n-1} + \cdots + a_1 x + a_0 \qquad \textbf{(1)}$$

where $a_n, a_{n-1}, \ldots, a_1, a_0$ are complex numbers, $a_n \neq 0$, n is a nonnegative integer, and x is a complex variable. As before, a_n is called the **leading coefficient** of f. A complex number r is called a **complex zero** of f if $f(r) = 0$.

In most of our work the coefficients in (1) will be real numbers.

We have learned that some quadratic equations have no real solutions, but that in the complex number system every quadratic equation has a solution, either real or complex. The next result, proved by Karl Friedrich Gauss (1777–1855) when he was 22 years old,* gives an extension to complex polynomial equations. In fact, this result is so important and useful that it has become known as the **Fundamental Theorem of Algebra.**

FUNDAMENTAL THEOREM OF ALGEBRA

Every complex polynomial function $f(x)$ of degree $n \geq 1$ has at least one complex zero.

We shall not prove this result, as the proof is beyond the scope of this book. However, using the Fundamental Theorem of Algebra and the Factor Theorem, we can prove the following result:

THEOREM

Every complex polynomial function $f(x)$ of degree $n \geq 1$ can be factored into n linear factors (not necessarily distinct) of the form

$$f(x) = a_n(x - r_1)(x - r_2) \cdot \cdots \cdot (x - r_n) \qquad \textbf{(2)}$$

where $a_n, r_1, r_2, \ldots, r_n$ are complex numbers. That is, every complex polynomial function of degree $n \geq 1$ has exactly n complex zeros, some of which may repeat.

Proof Let

$$f(x) = a_n x^n + a_{n-1} x^{n-1} + \cdots + a_1 x + a_0$$

By the Fundamental Theorem of Algebra, f has at least one zero, say r_1. Then, by the Factor Theorem, $x - r_1$ is a factor, and

$$f(x) = (x - r_1)q_1(x)$$

where $q_1(x)$ is a complex polynomial of degree $n - 1$ whose leading coefficient is a_n. Repeating this argument n times, we arrive at

$$f(x) = (x - r_1)(x - r_2) \cdot \cdots \cdot (x - r_n)q_n(x)$$

where $q_n(x)$ is a complex polynomial of degree $n - n = 0$ whose leading coefficient is a_n. That is, $q_n(x) = a_n x^0 = a_n$, and so

$$f(x) = a_n(x - r_1)(x - r_2) \cdot \cdots \cdot (x - r_n)$$

We conclude that every complex polynomial function $f(x)$ of degree $n \geq 1$ has exactly n (not necessarily distinct) zeros. ∎

*In all, Gauss gave four different proofs of this theorem, the first one in 1799 being the subject of his doctoral dissertation.

1 Use the Conjugate Pairs Theorem

We can use the Fundamental Theorem of Algebra to obtain valuable information about the complex zeros of polynomial functions whose coefficients are real numbers.

CONJUGATE PAIRS THEOREM

Let $f(x)$ be a polynomial function whose coefficients are real numbers. If $r = a + bi$ is a zero of f, the complex conjugate $\bar{r} = a - bi$ is also a zero of f.

In other words, for polynomial functions whose coefficients are real numbers, the complex zeros occur in conjugate pairs. This result should not be all that surprising since the complex solutions of a quadratic equation occurred in conjugate pairs.

Proof Let

$$f(x) = a_n x^n + a_{n-1}x^{n-1} + \cdots + a_1 x + a_0$$

where $a_n, a_{n-1}, \ldots, a_1, a_0$ are real numbers and $a_n \neq 0$. If $r = a + bi$ is a zero of f, then $f(r) = f(a + bi) = 0$, so

$$a_n r^n + a_{n-1}r^{n-1} + \cdots + a_1 r + a_0 = 0$$

Take the conjugate of both sides to get

$$\overline{a_n r^n + a_{n-1}r^{n-1} + \cdots + a_1 r + a_0} = \overline{0}$$

$$\overline{a_n r^n} + \overline{a_{n-1}r^{n-1}} + \cdots + \overline{a_1 r} + \overline{a_0} = \overline{0} \qquad \text{The conjugate of a sum equals the sum of the conjugates (see Section A.7).}$$

$$\overline{a_n}(\bar{r})^n + \overline{a_{n-1}}(\bar{r})^{n-1} + \cdots + \overline{a_1}\,\bar{r} + \overline{a_0} = \overline{0} \qquad \text{The conjugate of a product equals the product of the conjugates.}$$

$$a_n(\bar{r})^n + a_{n-1}(\bar{r})^{n-1} + \cdots + a_1\bar{r} + a_0 = 0 \qquad \text{The conjugate of a real number equals the real number.}$$

This last equation states that $f(\bar{r}) = 0$; that is, $\bar{r} = a - bi$ is a zero of f. ∎

The importance of this result should be clear. Once we know that, say, $3 + 4i$ is a zero of a polynomial function with real coefficients, then we know that $3 - 4i$ is also a zero. This result has an important corollary.

COROLLARY

A polynomial function f of odd degree with real coefficients has at least one real zero.

Proof Because complex zeros occur as conjugate pairs in a polynomial function with real coefficients, there will always be an even number of zeros that are not real numbers. Consequently, since f is of odd degree, one of its zeros has to be a real number. ∎

For example, the polynomial function $f(x) = x^5 - 3x^4 + 4x^3 - 5$ has at least one zero that is a real number, since f is of degree 5 (odd) and has real coefficients.

EXAMPLE 1

Using the Conjugate Pairs Theorem

A polynomial function f of degree 5 whose coefficients are real numbers has the zeros $1, 5i$, and $1 + i$. Find the remaining two zeros.

Solution Since f has coefficients that are real numbers, complex zeros appear as conjugate pairs. It follows that $-5i$, the conjugate of $5i$, and $1 - i$, the conjugate of $1 + i$, are the two remaining zeros.

━━━━━**Now Work** PROBLEM 7

2 Find a Polynomial Function with Specified Zeros

EXAMPLE 2   **Finding a Polynomial Function Whose Zeros Are Given**

Find a polynomial function f of degree 4 whose coefficients are real numbers that has the zeros $1, 1,$ and $-4 + i$.

Solution   Since $-4 + i$ is a zero, by the Conjugate Pairs Theorem, $-4 - i$ must also be a zero of f. Because of the Factor Theorem, if $f(c) = 0$, then $x - c$ is a factor of $f(x)$. So we can now write f as

$$f(x) = a(x - 1)(x - 1)[x - (-4 + i)][x - (-4 - i)]$$

where a is any real number. Then

$$
\begin{aligned}
f(x) &= a(x - 1)(x - 1)[x - (-4 + i)][x - (-4 - i)] \\
&= a(x^2 - 2x + 1)[x^2 - (-4 + i)x - (-4 - i)x + (-4 + i)(-4 - i)] \\
&= a(x^2 - 2x + 1)(x^2 + 4x - ix + 4x + ix + 16 + 4i - 4i - i^2) \\
&= a(x^2 - 2x + 1)(x^2 + 8x + 17) \\
&= a(x^4 + 8x^3 + 17x^2 - 2x^3 - 16x^2 - 34x + x^2 + 8x + 17) \\
&= a(x^4 + 6x^3 + 2x^2 - 26x + 17)
\end{aligned}
$$

Exploration

Graph the function f found in Example 2 for $a = 1$. Does the value of a affect the zeros of f? How does the value of a affect the graph of f? What information about f is sufficient to uniquely determine a?

Result   A quick analysis of the polynomial function f tells us what to expect:

At most three turning points.

For large $|x|$, the graph will behave like $y = x^4$.

A repeated real zero at 1 of even multiplicity, so the graph will touch the x-axis at 1.

The only x-intercept is at 1; the y-intercept is 17.

Figure 51 shows the complete graph. (Do you see why? The graph has exactly three turning points.) The value of a causes a stretch or compression; a reflection also occurs if $a < 0$. The zeros are not affected.

If any point other than an x-intercept on the graph of f is known, then a can be determined. For example, if $(2, 3)$ is on the graph, then $f(2) = 3 = a(37)$, so $a = 3/37$. Why won't an x-intercept work?

Figure 51

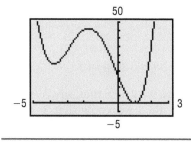

Now we can prove the theorem we conjectured in Section 4.5.

THEOREM   Every polynomial function with real coefficients can be uniquely factored over the real numbers into a product of linear factors and/or irreducible quadratic factors.

Proof   Every complex polynomial function f of degree n has exactly n zeros and can be factored into a product of n linear factors. If its coefficients are real, those zeros that are complex numbers will always occur as conjugate pairs. As a result, if $r = a + bi$ is a complex zero, then so is $\bar{r} = a - bi$. Consequently, when the linear factors $x - r$ and $x - \bar{r}$ of f are multiplied, we have

$$(x - r)(x - \bar{r}) = x^2 - (r + \bar{r})x + r\bar{r} = x^2 - 2ax + a^2 + b^2$$

This second-degree polynomial has real coefficients and is irreducible (over the real numbers). Thus, the factors of f are either linear or irreducible quadratic factors. ∎

Now Work PROBLEM 17

3 Find the Complex Zeros of a Polynomial Function

The steps for finding the complex zeros of a polynomial function are the same as those for finding the real zeros.

EXAMPLE 3	**Finding the Complex Zeros of a Polynomial Function**

Find the complex zeros of the polynomial function

$$f(x) = 3x^4 + 5x^3 + 25x^2 + 45x - 18$$

Write f in factored form.

Solution **STEP 1:** The degree of f is 4. So f will have four complex zeros.

STEP 2: The Rational Zeros Theorem provides information about the potential rational zeros of polynomial functions with integer coefficients. For this polynomial function (which has integer coefficients), the potential rational zeros are

$$\pm\frac{1}{3}, \pm\frac{2}{3}, \pm 1, \pm 2, \pm 3, \pm 6, \pm 9, \pm 18$$

Test 1 first:
$$
\begin{array}{r|rrrr}
1 & 3 & 5 & 25 & 45 & -18 \\
  &   & 3 & 8 & 33 & 78 \\
\hline
  & 3 & 8 & 33 & 78 & 60 \quad \text{1 is not a zero.}
\end{array}
$$

Test -1:
$$
\begin{array}{r|rrrr}
-1 & 3 & 5 & 25 & 45 & -18 \\
  &   & -3 & -2 & -23 & -22 \\
\hline
  & 3 & 2 & 23 & 22 & -40 \quad \text{−1 is not a zero.}
\end{array}
$$

Test 2:
$$
\begin{array}{r|rrrr}
2 & 3 & 5 & 25 & 45 & -18 \\
  &   & 6 & 22 & 94 & 278 \\
\hline
  & 3 & 11 & 47 & 139 & 260 \quad \text{2 is not a zero.}
\end{array}
$$

Test -2:
$$
\begin{array}{r|rrrr}
-2 & 3 & 5 & 25 & 45 & -18 \\
  &   & -6 & 2 & -54 & 18 \\
\hline
  & 3 & -1 & 27 & -9 & 0
\end{array}
$$

Since $f(-2) = 0$, then -2 is a zero and $x + 2$ is a factor of f. The depressed equation is

$$3x^3 - x^2 + 27x - 9 = 0$$

REPEAT STEP 2: Factor the depressed equation by grouping.

$$3x^3 - x^2 + 27x - 9 = 0$$
$$x^2(3x - 1) + 9(3x - 1) = 0 \quad \text{Factor } x^2 \text{ from } 3x^3 - x^2 \text{ and 9 from } 27x - 9.$$
$$(x^2 + 9)(3x - 1) = 0 \quad \text{Factor out the common factor } 3x - 1.$$

$$x^2 + 9 = 0 \quad \text{or} \quad 3x - 1 = 0 \quad \text{Apply the Zero-Product Property.}$$
$$x^2 = -9 \quad \text{or} \quad x = \frac{1}{3}$$
$$x = -3i, \quad x = 3i \quad \text{or} \quad x = \frac{1}{3}$$

The four complex zeros of f are $\left\{-3i,\ 3i,\ -2,\ \dfrac{1}{3}\right\}$.

The factored form of f is

$$f(x) = 3x^4 + 5x^3 + 25x^2 + 45x - 18$$
$$= 3(x + 3i)(x - 3i)(x + 2)\left(x - \frac{1}{3}\right)$$

Now Work PROBLEM **33**

4.6 Assess Your Understanding

'Are You Prepared?' *Answers are given at the end of these exercises. If you get a wrong answer, read the pages listed in red.*

1. Find the sum and the product of the complex numbers $3 - 2i$ and $-3 + 5i$. (pp. A54–A58)

2. In the complex number system, find the complex solutions of the equation $x^2 + 2x + 2 = 0$. (pp. A58–A60)

Concepts and Vocabulary

3. Every polynomial function of odd degree with real coefficients will have at least _____ real zero(s).

4. If $3 + 4i$ is a zero of a polynomial function of degree 5 with real coefficients, then so is _____.

5. **True or False** A polynomial function of degree n with real coefficients has exactly n complex zeros. At most n of them are real zeros.

6. **True or False** A polynomial function of degree 4 with real coefficients could have $-3, 2 + i, 2 - i$, and $-3 + 5i$ as its zeros.

Skill Building

In Problems 7–16, information is given about a polynomial function $f(x)$ whose coefficients are real numbers. Find the remaining zeros of f.

7. Degree 3;   zeros: $3, 4 - i$

8. Degree 3;   zeros: $4, 3 + i$

9. Degree 4;   zeros: $i, 1 + i$

10. Degree 4;   zeros: $1, 2, 2 + i$

11. Degree 5;   zeros: $1, i, 2i$

12. Degree 5;   zeros: $0, 1, 2, i$

13. Degree 4;   zeros: $i, 2, -2$

14. Degree 4;   zeros: $2 - i, -i$

15. Degree 6;   zeros: $2, 2 + i, -3 - i, 0$

16. Degree 6;   zeros: $i, 3 - 2i, -2 + i$

In Problems 17–22, form a polynomial function $f(x)$ with real coefficients having the given degree and zeros. Answers will vary depending on the choice of the leading coefficient.

17. Degree 4;   zeros: $3 + 2i; 4$, multiplicity 2

18. Degree 4;   zeros: $i, 1 + 2i$

19. Degree 5;   zeros: $2; -i; 1 + i$

20. Degree 6;   zeros: $i, 4 - i; 2 + i$

21. Degree 4;   zeros: 3, multiplicity 2; $-i$

22. Degree 5;   zeros: 1, multiplicity 3; $1 + i$

In Problems 23–30, use the given zero to find the remaining zeros of each function.

23. $f(x) = x^3 - 4x^2 + 4x - 16$;   zero: $2i$

24. $g(x) = x^3 + 3x^2 + 25x + 75$;   zero: $-5i$

25. $f(x) = 2x^4 + 5x^3 + 5x^2 + 20x - 12$;   zero: $-2i$

26. $h(x) = 3x^4 + 5x^3 + 25x^2 + 45x - 18$;   zero: $3i$

27. $h(x) = x^4 - 9x^3 + 21x^2 + 21x - 130$;   zero: $3 - 2i$

28. $f(x) = x^4 - 7x^3 + 14x^2 - 38x - 60$;   zero: $1 + 3i$

29. $h(x) = 3x^5 + 2x^4 + 15x^3 + 10x^2 - 528x - 352$;   zero: $-4i$

30. $g(x) = 2x^5 - 3x^4 - 5x^3 - 15x^2 - 207x + 108$;   zero: $3i$

In Problems 31–40, find the complex zeros of each polynomial function. Write f in factored form.

31. $f(x) = x^3 - 1$

32. $f(x) = x^4 - 1$

33. $f(x) = x^3 - 8x^2 + 25x - 26$

34. $f(x) = x^3 + 13x^2 + 57x + 85$

35. $f(x) = x^4 + 5x^2 + 4$

36. $f(x) = x^4 + 13x^2 + 36$

37. $f(x) = x^4 + 2x^3 + 22x^2 + 50x - 75$

38. $f(x) = x^4 + 3x^3 - 19x^2 + 27x - 252$

39. $f(x) = 3x^4 - x^3 - 9x^2 + 159x - 52$

40. $f(x) = 2x^4 + x^3 - 35x^2 - 113x + 65$

Explaining Concepts: Discussion and Writing

In Problems 41 and 42, explain why the facts given are contradictory.

41. $f(x)$ is a polynomial function of degree 3 whose coefficients are real numbers; its zeros are $4 + i, 4 - i,$ and $2 + i$.

42. $f(x)$ is a polynomial function of degree 3 whose coefficients are real numbers; its zeros are $2, i,$ and $3 + i$.

43. $f(x)$ is a polynomial function of degree 4 whose coefficients are real numbers; three of its zeros are $2, 1 + 2i,$ and $1 - 2i$. Explain why the remaining zero must be a real number.

44. $f(x)$ is a polynomial function of degree 4 whose coefficients are real numbers; two of its zeros are -3 and $4 - i$. Explain why one of the remaining zeros must be a real number. Write down one of the missing zeros.

'Are You Prepared?' Answers

1. Sum: $3i$; product: $1 + 21i$ **2.** $-1 - i, \ -1 + i$

CHAPTER REVIEW

Things to Know

Power function (pp. 167–170)

$f(x) = x^n, \ n \geq 2$ even

Domain: all real numbers   Range: nonnegative real numbers

Passes through $(-1, 1), (0, 0), (1, 1)$

Even function

Decreasing on $(-\infty, 0)$, increasing on $(0, \infty)$

$f(x) = x^n, \ n \geq 3$ odd

Domain: all real numbers   Range: all real numbers

Passes through $(-1, -1), (0, 0), (1, 1)$

Odd function

Increasing on $(-\infty, \infty)$

Polynomial function (pp. 166, 175–177)

$f(x) = a_n x^n + a_{n-1} x^{n-1}$
$\qquad + \cdots + a_1 x + a_0, \ a_n \neq 0$

Domain: all real numbers

At most $n - 1$ turning points

End behavior: Behaves like $y = a_n x^n$ for large $|x|$

Real zeros of a polynomial function f (p. 171)

Real numbers for which $f(x) = 0$; the real zeros of f are the x-intercepts of the graph of f.

Rational function (pp. 189–196)

$R(x) = \dfrac{p(x)}{q(x)}$

Domain: $\{x \mid q(x) \neq 0\}$

p, q are polynomial functions and q is not the zero polynomial.

Vertical asymptotes: With $R(x)$ in lowest terms, if $q(r) = 0$ for some real number, then $x = r$ is a vertical asymptote.

Horizontal or oblique asymptote: See the summary on page 196.

Remainder Theorem (p. 222)

If a polynomial function $f(x)$ is divided by $x - c$, then the remainder is $f(c)$.

Factor Theorem (p. 222)

$x - c$ is a factor of a polynomial function $f(x)$ if and only if $f(c) = 0$.

Rational Zeros Theorem (p. 224)

Let f be a polynomial function of degree 1 or higher of the form

$$f(x) = a_n x^n + a_{n-1} x^{n-1} + \cdots + a_1 x + a_0 \qquad a_n \neq 0, a_0 \neq 0$$

where each coefficient is an integer. If $\dfrac{p}{q}$, in lowest terms, is a rational zero of f, then p must be a factor of a_0, and q must be a factor of a_n.

Intermediate Value Theorem (p. 228)

Let f be a polynomial function. If $a < b$ and $f(a)$ and $f(b)$ are of opposite sign, then there is at least one real zero of f between a and b.

Fundamental Theorem of Algebra (p. 234)

Every complex polynomial function $f(x)$ of degree $n \geq 1$ has at least one complex zero.

Conjugate Pairs Theorem (p. 235)

Let $f(x)$ be a polynomial whose coefficients are real numbers. If $r = a + bi$ is a zero of f, then its complex conjugate $\bar{r} = a - bi$ is also a zero of f.

Objectives

Section	You should be able to . . .	Example(s)	Review Exercises
4.1	1 Identify polynomial functions and their degree (p. 166)	1	1–4
	2 Graph polynomial functions using transformations (p. 170)	2, 3	5–10
	3 Identify the real zeros of a polynomial function and their multiplicity (p. 171)	4–6	11–18 (a) and (b)
	4 Analyze the graph of a polynomial function (p. 178)	9–11	11–18
	5 Build cubic models from data (p. 182)	12	88
4.2	1 Find the domain of a rational function (p. 189)	1	19–22
	2 Find the vertical asymptotes of a rational function (p. 192)	4	19–22
	3 Find the horizontal or oblique asymptote of a rational function (p. 193)	5–8	19–22
4.3	1 Analyze the graph of a rational function (p. 199)	1–5	23–34
	2 Solve applied problems involving rational functions (p. 210)	7	87
4.4	1 Solve polynomial inequalities (p. 214)	1, 2	35, 36
	2 Solve rational inequalities (p. 215)	3, 4	37–44
4.5	1 Use the Remainder and Factor Theorems (p. 221)	1, 2	45–50
	2 Use the Rational Zeros Theorem to list the potential rational zeros of a polynomial function (p. 224)	3	51–58
	3 Find the real zeros of a polynomial function (p. 224)	4, 5	53–58
	4 Solve polynomial equations (p. 227)	6	59–62
	5 Use the Theorem for Bounds on Zeros (p. 227)	7	63–66
	6 Use the Intermediate Value Theorem (p. 228)	8	67–74
4.6	1 Use the Conjugate Pairs Theorem (p. 235)	1	75–78
	2 Find a polynomial function with specified zeros (p. 236)	2	75–78
	3 Find the complex zeros of a polynomial (p. 237)	3	79–86

Review Exercises

In Problems 1–4, determine whether the function is a polynomial function, rational function, or neither. For those that are polynomial functions, state the degree. For those that are not polynomial functions, tell why not.

1. $f(x) = 4x^5 - 3x^2 + 5x - 2$

2. $f(x) = \dfrac{3x^5}{2x + 1}$

3. $f(x) = 3x^2 + 5x^{1/2} - 1$

4. $f(x) = 3$

In Problems 5–10, graph each function using transformations (shifting, compressing, stretching, and reflection). Show all the stages.

5. $f(x) = (x + 2)^3$

6. $f(x) = -x^3 + 3$

7. $f(x) = -(x - 1)^4$

8. $f(x) = (x - 1)^4 - 2$

9. $f(x) = (x - 1)^4 + 2$

10. $f(x) = (1 - x)^3$

In Problems 11–18, analyze each polynomial function by following Steps 1 through 6 on page 179.

11. $f(x) = x(x + 2)(x + 4)$

12. $f(x) = x(x - 2)(x - 4)$

13. $f(x) = (x - 2)^2(x + 4)$

14. $f(x) = (x - 2)(x + 4)^2$

15. $f(x) = -2x^3 + 4x^2$

16. $f(x) = -4x^3 + 4x$

17. $f(x) = (x - 1)^2(x + 3)(x + 1)$

18. $f(x) = (x - 4)(x + 2)^2(x - 2)$

In Problems 19–22, find the domain of each rational function. Find any horizontal, vertical, or oblique asymptotes.

19. $R(x) = \dfrac{x + 2}{x^2 - 9}$

20. $R(x) = \dfrac{x^2 + 4}{x - 2}$

21. $R(x) = \dfrac{x^2 + 3x + 2}{(x + 2)^2}$

22. $R(x) = \dfrac{x^3}{x^3 - 1}$

In Problems 23–34, discuss each rational function following the eight steps given on pages 201–202.

23. $R(x) = \dfrac{2x - 6}{x}$

24. $R(x) = \dfrac{4 - x}{x}$

25. $H(x) = \dfrac{x + 2}{x(x - 2)}$

26. $H(x) = \dfrac{x}{x^2 - 1}$

27. $R(x) = \dfrac{x^2 + x - 6}{x^2 - x - 6}$

28. $R(x) = \dfrac{x^2 - 6x + 9}{x^2}$

29. $F(x) = \dfrac{x^3}{x^2 - 4}$

30. $F(x) = \dfrac{3x^3}{(x - 1)^2}$

31. $R(x) = \dfrac{2x^4}{(x - 1)^2}$

32. $R(x) = \dfrac{x^4}{x^2 - 9}$

33. $G(x) = \dfrac{x^2 - 4}{x^2 - x - 2}$

34. $F(x) = \dfrac{(x - 1)^2}{x^2 - 1}$

In Problems 35–44, solve each inequality. Graph the solution set.

35. $x^3 + x^2 < 4x + 4$

36. $x^3 + 4x^2 \geq x + 4$

37. $\dfrac{6}{x + 3} \geq 1$

38. $\dfrac{-2}{1 - 3x} < 1$

39. $\dfrac{2x - 6}{1 - x} < 2$

40. $\dfrac{3 - 2x}{2x + 5} \geq 2$

41. $\dfrac{(x - 2)(x - 1)}{x - 3} \geq 0$

42. $\dfrac{x + 1}{x(x - 5)} \leq 0$

43. $\dfrac{x^2 - 8x + 12}{x^2 - 16} > 0$

44. $\dfrac{x(x^2 + x - 2)}{x^2 + 9x + 20} \leq 0$

In Problems 45–48, find the remainder R when $f(x)$ is divided by $g(x)$. Is g a factor of f?

45. $f(x) = 8x^3 - 3x^2 + x + 4$; $g(x) = x - 1$

46. $f(x) = 2x^3 + 8x^2 - 5x + 5$; $g(x) = x - 2$

47. $f(x) = x^4 - 2x^3 + 15x - 2$; $g(x) = x + 2$

48. $f(x) = x^4 - x^2 + 2x + 2$; $g(x) = x + 1$

49. Find the value of $f(x) = 12x^6 - 8x^4 + 1$ at $x = 4$.

50. Find the value of $f(x) = -16x^3 + 18x^2 - x + 2$ at $x = -2$.

51. List all the potential rational zeros of $f(x) = 12x^8 - x^7 + 6x^4 - x^3 + x - 3$.

52. List all the potential rational zeros of $f(x) = -6x^5 + x^4 + 2x^3 - x + 1$.

In Problems 53–58, use the Rational Zeros Theorem to find all the real zeros of each polynomial function. Use the zeros to factor f over the real numbers.

53. $f(x) = x^3 - 3x^2 - 6x + 8$

54. $f(x) = x^3 - x^2 - 10x - 8$

55. $f(x) = 4x^3 + 4x^2 - 7x + 2$

56. $f(x) = 4x^3 - 4x^2 - 7x - 2$

57. $f(x) = x^4 - 4x^3 + 9x^2 - 20x + 20$

58. $f(x) = x^4 + 6x^3 + 11x^2 + 12x + 18$

In Problems 59–62, solve each equation in the real number system.

59. $2x^4 + 2x^3 - 11x^2 + x - 6 = 0$

60. $3x^4 + 3x^3 - 17x^2 + x - 6 = 0$

61. $2x^4 + 7x^3 + x^2 - 7x - 3 = 0$

62. $2x^4 + 7x^3 - 5x^2 - 28x - 12 = 0$

In Problems 63–66, find bounds to the real zeros of each polynomial function.

63. $f(x) = x^3 - x^2 - 4x + 2$

64. $f(x) = x^3 + x^2 - 10x - 5$

65. $f(x) = 2x^3 - 7x^2 - 10x + 35$

66. $f(x) = 3x^3 - 7x^2 - 6x + 14$

In Problems 67–70, use the Intermediate Value Theorem to show that each polynomial function has a zero in the given interval.

67. $f(x) = 3x^3 - x - 1$; $[0, 1]$

68. $f(x) = 2x^3 - x^2 - 3$; $[1, 2]$

69. $f(x) = 8x^4 - 4x^3 - 2x - 1$; $[0, 1]$

70. $f(x) = 3x^4 + 4x^3 - 8x - 2$; $[1, 2]$

In Problems 71–74, each polynomial function has exactly one positive zero. Approximate the zero correct to two decimal places.

71. $f(x) = x^3 - x - 2$

72. $f(x) = 2x^3 - x^2 - 3$

73. $f(x) = 8x^4 - 4x^3 - 2x - 1$

74. $f(x) = 3x^4 + 4x^3 - 8x - 2$

In Problems 75–78, information is given about a complex polynomial $f(x)$ whose coefficients are real numbers. Find the remaining zeros of f. Then find a polynomial function with real coefficients that has the zeros.

75. Degree 3;   zeros: $4 + i, 6$

76. Degree 3;   zeros: $3 + 4i, 5$

77. Degree 4;   zeros: $i, 1 + i$

78. Degree 4;   zeros: $1, 2, 1 + i$

In Problems 79–86, find the complex zeros of each polynomial function $f(x)$. Write f in factored form.

79. $f(x) = x^3 - 3x^2 - 6x + 8$

80. $f(x) = x^3 - x^2 - 10x - 8$

81. $f(x) = 4x^3 + 4x^2 - 7x + 2$

82. $f(x) = 4x^3 - 4x^2 - 7x - 2$

83. $f(x) = x^4 - 4x^3 + 9x^2 - 20x + 20$

84. $f(x) = x^4 + 6x^3 + 11x^2 + 12x + 18$

85. $f(x) = 2x^4 + 2x^3 - 11x^2 + x - 6$

86. $f(x) = 3x^4 + 3x^3 - 17x^2 + x - 6$

---

87. Making a Can A can in the shape of a right circular cylinder is required to have a volume of 250 cubic centimeters.
   (a) Express the amount A of material to make the can as a function of the radius r of the cylinder.
   (b) How much material is required if the can is of radius 3 centimeters?
   (c) How much material is required if the can is of radius 5 centimeters?
   (d) Graph $A = A(r)$. For what value of r is A smallest?

88. Model It: Poverty Rates The following data represent the percentage of families in the United States whose income is below the poverty level.

Year, t	Percent below Poverty Level, p
1990, 1	10.9
1991, 2	11.5
1992, 3	11.9
1993, 4	12.3
1994, 5	11.6
1995, 6	10.8
1996, 7	11.0
1997, 8	10.3
1998, 9	10.0
1999, 10	9.3
2000, 11	8.7
2001, 12	9.2
2002, 13	9.6
2003, 14	10.0
2004, 15	10.2

Source: U.S. Census Bureau

   (a) With a graphing utility, draw a scatter diagram of the data. Comment on the type of relation that appears to exist between the two variables.

   (b) Decide on a function of best fit to these data (linear, quadratic, or cubic), and use this function to predict the percentage of U.S. families that were below the poverty level in 2005 ($t = 16$).
   (c) Draw the function of best fit on the scatter diagram drawn in part (a).

89. Design a polynomial function with the following characteristics: degree 6; four real zeros, one of multiplicity 3; y-intercept 3; behaves like $y = -5x^6$ for large values of $|x|$. Is this polynomial unique? Compare your polynomial with those of other students. What terms will be the same as everyone else's? Add some more characteristics, such as symmetry or naming the real zeros. How does this modify the polynomial?

90. Design a rational function with the following characteristics: three real zeros, one of multiplicity 2; y-intercept 1; vertical asymptotes $x = -2$ and $x = 3$; oblique asymptote $y = 2x + 1$. Is this rational function unique? Compare yours with those of other students. What will be the same as everyone else's? Add some more characteristics, such as symmetry or naming the real zeros. How does this modify the rational function?

91. The illustration shows the graph of a polynomial function.
   (a) Is the degree of the polynomial even or odd?
   (b) Is the leading coefficient positive or negative?
   (c) Is the function even, odd, or neither?
   (d) Why is x^2 necessarily a factor of the polynomial?
   (e) What is the minimum degree of the polynomial?
   (f) Formulate five different polynomials whose graphs could look like the one shown. Compare yours to those of other students. What similarities do you see? What differences?

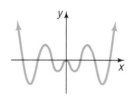

CHAPTER TEST

CHAPTER
Test Prep
VIDEOS

The Chapter Test Prep Videos are step-by-step test solutions available in the Video Resources DVD, in *MyMathLab*, or on this text's You Tube Channel. Flip back to the Student Resources page to see the exact web address for this text's YouTube channel.

1. Graph $f(x) = (x - 3)^4 - 2$ using transformations.

2. For the polynomial function $g(x) = 2x^3 + 5x^2 - 28x - 15$,
   (a) Determine the maximum number of real zeros that the function may have.
   (b) Find bounds to the zeros of the function.
   (c) List the potential rational zeros.
   (d) Determine the real zeros of g. Factor g over the reals.
   (e) Find the x- and y-intercepts of the graph of g.
   (f) Determine whether the graph crosses or touches the x-axis at each x-intercept.
   (g) Find the power function that the graph of g resembles for large values of $|x|$
   (h) Determine the behavior of the graph of g near each x-intercept.
   (i) Put all the information together to obtain the graph of g.

3. Find the complex zeros of $f(x) = x^3 - 4x^2 + 25x - 100$.

4. Solve $3x^3 + 2x - 1 = 8x^2 - 4$ in the complex number system.

In Problems 5 and 6, find the domain of each function. Find any horizontal, vertical, or oblique asymptotes.

5. $g(x) = \dfrac{2x^2 - 14x + 24}{x^2 + 6x - 40}$

6. $r(x) = \dfrac{x^2 + 2x - 3}{x + 1}$

7. Sketch the graph of the function in Problem 6. Label all intercepts, vertical asymptotes, horizontal asymptotes, and oblique asymptotes.

In Problems 8 and 9, write a function that meets the given conditions.

8. Fourth-degree polynomial with real coefficients; zeros: $-2, 0, 3 + i$.

9. Rational function; asymptotes: $y = 2, x = 4$; domain: $\{x | x \neq 4, x \neq 9\}$

10. Use the Intermediate Value Theorem to show that the function $f(x) = -2x^2 - 3x + 8$ has at least one real zero on the interval $[0, 4]$.

11. Solve: $\dfrac{x + 2}{x - 3} < 2$

CUMULATIVE REVIEW

1. Find the distance between the points $P = (1, 3)$ and $Q = (-4, 2)$.

2. Solve the inequality $x^2 \geq x$ and graph the solution set.

3. Solve the inequality $x^2 - 3x < 4$ and graph the solution set.

4. Find a linear function with slope -3 that contains the point $(-1, 4)$. Graph the function.

5. Find the equation of the line parallel to the line $y = 2x + 1$ and containing the point $(3, 5)$. Express your answer in slope–intercept form and graph the line.

6. Graph the equation $y = x^3$.

7. Does the relation $\{(3, 6), (1, 3), (2, 5), (3, 8)\}$ represent a function? Why or why not?

8. Solve the equation $x^3 - 6x^2 + 8x = 0$.

9. Solve the inequality $3x + 2 \leq 5x - 1$ and graph the solution set.

10. Find the center and radius of the circle $x^2 + 4x + y^2 - 2y - 4 = 0$. Graph the circle.

11. For the equation $y = x^3 - 9x$, determine the intercepts and test for symmetry.

12. Find an equation of the line perpendicular to $3x - 2y = 7$ that contains the point $(1, 5)$.

13. Is the following the graph of a function? Why or why not?

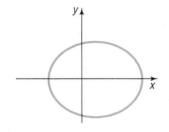

14. For the function $f(x) = x^2 + 5x - 2$, find
    (a) $f(3)$ (b) $f(-x)$
    (c) $-f(x)$ (d) $f(3x)$
    (e) $\dfrac{f(x + h) - f(x)}{h}$ $h \neq 0$

15. Answer the following questions regarding the function
    $$f(x) = \dfrac{x + 5}{x - 1}$$
    (a) What is the domain of f?
    (b) Is the point $(2, 6)$ on the graph of f?
    (c) If $x = 3$, what is $f(x)$? What point is on the graph of f?
    (d) If $f(x) = 9$, what is x? What point is on the graph of f?
    (e) If f a polynomial or rational function?

16. Graph the function $f(x) = -3x + 7$.

17. Graph $f(x) = 2x^2 - 4x + 1$ by determining whether its graph opens up or down and by finding its vertex, axis of symmetry, y-intercept, and x-intercepts, if any.

18. Find the average rate of change of $f(x) = x^2 + 3x + 1$ from 1 to 2. Use this result to find the equation of the secant line containing $(1, f(1))$ and $(2, f(2))$.

19. In parts (a) to (f) on page 244, use the following graph.

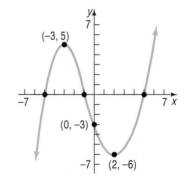

(a) Determine the intercepts.

(b) Based on the graph, tell whether the graph is symmetric with respect to the x-axis, the y-axis, and/or the origin.

(c) Based on the graph, tell whether the function is even, odd, or neither.

(d) List the intervals on which f is increasing. List the intervals on which f is decreasing.

(e) List the numbers, if any, at which f has a local maximum value. What are these local maxima values?

(f) List the numbers, if any, at which f has a local minimum value. What are these local minima values?

20. Determine algebraically whether the function

$$f(x) = \frac{5x}{x^2 - 9}$$

is even, odd, or neither.

21. For the function $f(x) = \begin{cases} 2x + 1 & \text{if } -3 < x < 2 \\ -3x + 4 & \text{if } x \geq 2 \end{cases}$

(a) Find the domain of f.

(b) Locate any intercepts.

(c) Graph the function.

(d) Based on the graph, find the range.

22. Graph the function $f(x) = -3(x + 1)^2 + 5$ using transformations.

23. Suppose that $f(x) = x^2 - 5x + 1$ and $g(x) = -4x - 7$.

(a) Find $f + g$ and state its domain.

(b) Find $\dfrac{f}{g}$ and state its domain.

24. Demand Equation The price p (in dollars) and the quantity x sold of a certain product obey the demand equation

$$p = -\frac{1}{10}x + 150,$$

(a) Express the revenue R as a function of x.

(b) What is the revenue if 100 units are sold?

(c) What quantity x maximizes revenue? What is the maximum revenue?

(d) What price should the company charge to maximize revenue?

CHAPTER PROJECTS

Internet-based Project

I. Length of Day Go to *http://en.wikipedia.org/wiki/Latitude* and read about latitude through the subhead "Effect of Latitude". Now go to *http://www.orchidculture.com/COD/ daylength.html#60N*.

1. For a particular day of the year, record in a table the length of day for the equator (0°N), 5°N, 10°N, ..., 60°N. Enter the data into an Excel spreadsheet, TI-graphing calculator, or some other spreadsheet capable of finding linear, quadratic, and cubic functions of best fit.

2. Draw a scatter diagram of the data with latitude as the independent variable and length of day as the dependent variable using Excel, a TI-graphing calculator, or some other spreadsheet. The Chapter 3 project describes how to draw a scatter diagram in Excel.

3. Determine the linear function of best fit. Graph the linear function of best fit on the scatter diagram. To do this in Excel, click on any data point in the scatter diagram. Now click the Layout menu, select Trendline within the Analysis region, select More Trendline Options. Select the Linear radio button and select Display Equation on Chart. See Figure 52. Move the Trendline Options window off to the side and you will see the linear function of best fit displayed on the scatter diagram. Do you think the function accurately describes the relation between latitude and length of the day?

Figure 52

Format Trendline

Trendline Options

Line Color

Line Style

Shadow

Trendline Options

Trend/Regression Type

- Exponential
- Linear
- Logarithmic
- Polynomial   Order: 2
- Power
- Moving Average   Period: 2

Trendline Name

- Automatic :   Linear (Length)
- Custom:

Forecast

Forward: 0.0   periods

Backward: 0.0   periods

- Set Intercept = 0.0
- Display Equation on chart
- Display R-squared value on chart

Close

4. Determine the quadratic function of best fit. Graph the quadratic function of best fit on the scatter diagram. To do this in Excel, click on any data point in the scatter diagram. Now click the Layout menu, select Trendline within the Analysis region, select More Trendline Options. Select the Polynomial radio button with Order set to 2. Select Display Equation on Chart. Move the Trendline Options window off to the side and you will see the quadratic function of best fit displayed on the scatter diagram. Do you think the function accurately describes the relation between latitude and length of the day?

5. Determine the cubic function of best fit. Graph the cubic function of best fit on the scatter diagram. To do this in Excel, click on any data point in the scatter diagram. Now click the Layout menu, select Trendline within the Analysis region, select More Trendline Options. Select the Polynomial radio button with Order set to 3. Select Display Equation on Chart. Move the Trendline Options window off to the side and you will see the cubic function of best fit displayed on the scatter diagram. Do you think the function accurately describes the relation between latitude and length of the day?

6. Which of the three models seems to fit the data best? Explain your reasoning.

7. Use your model to predict the hours of daylight on the day you selected for Chicago (41.85 degrees north latitude). Go to the Old Farmer's Almanac or other website (such as *http://astro.unl.edu/classaction/animations/coordsmotion/ daylighthoursexplorer.html*) to determine the hours of daylight in Chicago for the day you selected. How do the two compare?

The following project is available at the Instructor's Resource Center (IRC):

II. Theory of Equations The coefficients of a polynomial function can be found if its zeros are known, an advantage of using polynomials in modeling.

Citation: Excel © 2010 Microsoft Corporation. Used with permission from Microsoft.

5

Exponential and Logarithmic Functions

Outline

Depreciation of Cars

You are ready to buy that first new car. You know that cars lose value over time due to depreciation and that different cars have different rates of depreciation. So you will research the depreciation rates for the cars you are thinking of buying. After all, the lower the depreciation rate is, the more the car will be worth each year.

—See the Internet-based Chapter Project I—

◁ **A Look Back** Until now, our study of functions has concentrated on polynomial and rational functions. These functions belong to the class of **algebraic functions,** that is, functions that can be expressed in terms of sums, differences, products, quotients, powers, or roots of polynomials. Functions that are not algebraic are termed **transcendental** (they transcend, or go beyond, algebraic functions).

A Look Ahead ▷ In this chapter, we study two transcendental functions: the exponential function and the logarithmic function. These functions occur frequently in a wide variety of applications, such as biology, chemistry, economics, and psychology.

The chapter begins with a discussion of composite, one-to-one, and inverse functions, concepts needed to see the relationship between exponential and logarithmic functions.

5.1   Composite Functions

PREPARING FOR THIS SECTION *Before getting started, review the following:*

- Find the Value of a Function (Section 2.1, pp. 49–52)
- Domain of a Function (Section 2.1, pp. 52–54)

Now Work the 'Are You Prepared?' problems on page 252.

OBJECTIVES   **1** Form a Composite Function (p. 247)
             2 Find the Domain of a Composite Function (p. 248)

1 Form a Composite Function

Figure 1

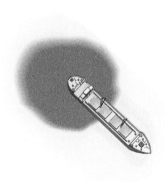

Suppose that an oil tanker is leaking oil and you want to determine the area of the circular oil patch around the ship. See Figure 1. It is determined that the oil is leaking from the tanker in such a way that the radius of the circular patch of oil around the ship is increasing at a rate of 3 feet per minute. Therefore, the radius r of the oil patch at any time t, in minutes, is given by $r(t) = 3t$. So after 20 minutes the radius of the oil patch is $r(20) = 3(20) = 60$ feet.

The area A of a circle as a function of the radius r is given by $A(r) = \pi r^2$. The area of the circular patch of oil after 20 minutes is $A(60) = \pi(60)^2 = 3600\pi$ square feet. Notice that $60 = r(20)$, so $A(60) = A(r(20))$. The argument of the function A is the output of a function!

In general, we can find the area of the oil patch as a function of time t by evaluating $A(r(t))$ and obtaining $A(r(t)) = A(3t) = \pi(3t)^2 = 9\pi t^2$. The function $A(r(t))$ is a special type of function called a *composite function*.

As another example, consider the function $y = (2x + 3)^2$. If we write $y = f(u) = u^2$ and $u = g(x) = 2x + 3$, then, by a substitution process, we can obtain the original function: $y = f(u) = f(g(x)) = (2x + 3)^2$.

In general, suppose that f and g are two functions and that x is a number in the domain of g. By evaluating g at x, we get $g(x)$. If $g(x)$ is in the domain of f, then we may evaluate f at $g(x)$ and obtain the expression $f(g(x))$. The correspondence from x to $f(g(x))$ is called a *composite function* $f \circ g$.

DEFINITION

Given two functions f and g, the **composite function,** denoted by $f \circ g$ (read as "f composed with g"), is defined by

$$(f \circ g)(x) = f(g(x))$$

The domain of $f \circ g$ is the set of all numbers x in the domain of g such that $g(x)$ is in the domain of f.

Look carefully at Figure 2. Only those x's in the domain of g for which $g(x)$ is in the domain of f can be in the domain of $f \circ g$. The reason is that if $g(x)$ is not in the domain of f then $f(g(x))$ is not defined. Because of this, the domain of $f \circ g$ is a subset of the domain of g; the range of $f \circ g$ is a subset of the range of f.

Figure 2

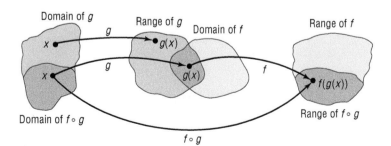

Figure 3 provides a second illustration of the definition. Here x is the input to the function g, yielding $g(x)$. Then $g(x)$ is the input to the function f, yielding $f(g(x))$. Notice that the "inside" function g in $f(g(x))$ is done first.

Figure 3

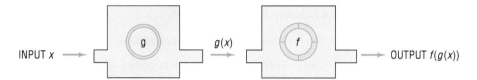

INPUT x → | g | → $g(x)$ → | f | → OUTPUT $f(g(x))$

EXAMPLE 1 | **Evaluating a Composite Function**

Suppose that $f(x) = 2x^2 - 3$ and $g(x) = 4x$. Find:

(a) $(f \circ g)(1)$ (b) $(g \circ f)(1)$ (c) $(f \circ f)(-2)$ (d) $(g \circ g)(-1)$

Solution   (a) $(f \circ g)(1) = f(g(1)) = f(4) = 2 \cdot 4^2 - 3 = 29$

                $g(x) = 4x$ $f(x) = 2x^2 - 3$
                $g(1) = 4$

(b) $(g \circ f)(1) = g(f(1)) = g(-1) = 4 \cdot (-1) = -4$

             $f(x) = 2x^2 - 3$ $g(x) = 4x$
             $f(1) = -1$

(c) $(f \circ f)(-2) = f(f(-2)) = f(5) = 2 \cdot 5^2 - 3 = 47$

               $f(-2) = 2(-2)^2 - 3 = 5$

(d) $(g \circ g)(-1) = g(g(-1)) = g(-4) = 4 \cdot (-4) = -16$

               $g(-1) = -4$

Figure 4

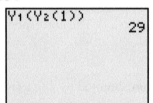

$Y_1(Y_2(1))$
            29

 COMMENT   Graphing calculators can be used to evaluate composite functions.* Let $Y_1 = f(x) = 2x^2 - 3$ and $Y_2 = g(x) = 4x$. Then, using a TI-84 Plus graphing calculator, $(f \circ g)(1)$ is found as shown in Figure 4. Notice that this is the result obtained in Example 1(a). ∎

━━━━**Now Work** PROBLEM 11

2 Find the Domain of a Composite Function

EXAMPLE 2 | **Finding a Composite Function and Its Domain**

Suppose that $f(x) = x^2 + 3x - 1$ and $g(x) = 2x + 3$.

Find: (a) $f \circ g$ (b) $g \circ f$

Then find the domain of each composite function.

Solution   The domain of f and the domain of g are the set of all real numbers.

(a) $(f \circ g)(x) = f(g(x)) = f(2x + 3) = (2x + 3)^2 + 3(2x + 3) - 1$

                      $f(x) = x^2 + 3x - 1$

        $= 4x^2 + 12x + 9 + 6x + 9 - 1 = 4x^2 + 18x + 17$

Since the domains of both f and g are the set of all real numbers, the domain of $f \circ g$ is the set of all real numbers.

*Consult your owner's manual for the appropriate keystrokes.

(b) $(g \circ f)(x) = g(f(x)) = g(x^2 + 3x - 1) = 2(x^2 + 3x - 1) + 3$

$$g(x) = 2x + 3$$

$$= 2x^2 + 6x - 2 + 3 = 2x^2 + 6x + 1$$

Since the domains of both f and g are the set of all real numbers, the domain of $g \circ f$ is the set of all real numbers.

Look back at Figure 2 on page 247. In determining the domain of the composite function $(f \circ g)(x) = f(g(x))$, keep the following two thoughts in mind about the input x.

1. Any x not in the domain of g must be excluded.

2. Any x for which $g(x)$ is not in the domain of f must be excluded.

EXAMPLE 3

Finding the Domain of $f \circ g$

Find the domain of $f \circ g$ if $f(x) = \dfrac{1}{x + 2}$ and $g(x) = \dfrac{4}{x - 1}$.

Solution

For $(f \circ g)(x) = f(g(x))$, first note that the domain of g is $\{x | x \neq 1\}$, so exclude 1 from the domain of $f \circ g$. Next note that the domain of f is $\{x | x \neq -2\}$, which means that $g(x)$ cannot equal -2. Solve the equation $g(x) = -2$ to determine what additional value(s) of x to exclude.

$$\frac{4}{x - 1} = -2 \qquad g(x) = -2$$

$$4 = -2(x - 1)$$

$$4 = -2x + 2$$

$$2x = -2$$

$$x = -1$$

Also exclude -1 from the domain of $f \circ g$.
The domain of $f \circ g$ is $\{x | x \neq -1, x \neq 1\}$.

✓**Check:** For $x = 1, g(x) = \dfrac{4}{x - 1}$ is not defined, so $(f \circ g)(x) = f(g(x))$ is not defined.

For $x = -1, g(-1) = \dfrac{4}{-2} = -2$, and $(f \circ g)(-1) = f(g(-1)) = f(-2)$ is not defined.

━━━━━**Now Work** PROBLEM 21

EXAMPLE 4

Finding a Composite Function and Its Domain

Suppose that $f(x) = \dfrac{1}{x + 2}$ and $g(x) = \dfrac{4}{x - 1}$.

Find: (a) $f \circ g$ (b) $f \circ f$

Then find the domain of each composite function.

Solution

The domain of f is $\{x | x \neq -2\}$ and the domain of g is $\{x | x \neq 1\}$.

(a) $(f \circ g)(x) = f(g(x)) = f\left(\dfrac{4}{x - 1}\right) = \dfrac{1}{\dfrac{4}{x - 1} + 2} = \dfrac{x - 1}{4 + 2(x - 1)} = \dfrac{x - 1}{2x + 2} = \dfrac{x - 1}{2(x + 1)}$

$$f(x) = \frac{1}{x + 2} \qquad \text{Multiply by } \frac{x - 1}{x - 1}.$$

In Example 3, we found the domain of $f \circ g$ to be $\{x | x \neq -1, x \neq 1\}$.

We could also find the domain of $f \circ g$ by first looking at the domain of g: $\{x | x \neq 1\}$. We exclude 1 from the domain of $f \circ g$ as a result. Then we look at $f \circ g$ and notice that x cannot equal -1, since $x = -1$ results in division by 0. So we also exclude -1 from the domain of $f \circ g$. Therefore, the domain of $f \circ g$ is $\{x | x \neq -1, x \neq 1\}$.

(b) $(f \circ f)(x) = f(f(x)) = f\left(\dfrac{1}{x+2}\right) = \dfrac{1}{\underset{\uparrow}{\dfrac{1}{x+2}} + 2} = \dfrac{x+2}{1 + 2(x+2)} = \dfrac{x+2}{2x+5}$

$\underset{f(x) = \frac{1}{x+2}}{\uparrow} \qquad\qquad \underset{\text{Multiply by } \frac{x+2}{x+2}.}{\uparrow}$

The domain of $f \circ f$ consists of those x in the domain of f, $\{x | x \neq -2\}$, for which

$$f(x) = \dfrac{1}{x+2} \neq -2 \qquad \begin{aligned} \tfrac{1}{x+2} &= -2 \\ 1 &= -2(x+2) \\ 1 &= -2x - 4 \\ 2x &= -5 \\ x &= -\tfrac{5}{2} \end{aligned}$$

or, equivalently,

$$x \neq -\dfrac{5}{2}$$

The domain of $f \circ f$ is $\left\{x \mid x \neq -\dfrac{5}{2}, x \neq -2\right\}$.

We could also find the domain of $f \circ f$ by recognizing that -2 is not in the domain of f and so should be excluded from the domain of $f \circ f$. Then, looking at $f \circ f$, we see that x cannot equal $-\dfrac{5}{2}$. Do you see why? Therefore, the domain of $f \circ f$ is $\left\{x \mid x \neq -\dfrac{5}{2}, x \neq -2\right\}$.

──── **Now Work** PROBLEMS 33 AND 35

Look back at Example 2, which illustrates that, in general, $f \circ g \neq g \circ f$. Sometimes $f \circ g$ does equal $g \circ f$, as shown in the next example.

EXAMPLE 5

Showing That Two Composite Functions Are Equal

If $f(x) = 3x - 4$ and $g(x) = \dfrac{1}{3}(x + 4)$, show that

$$(f \circ g)(x) = (g \circ f)(x) = x$$

for every x in the domain of $f \circ g$ and $g \circ f$.

Solution

$(f \circ g)(x) = f(g(x))$

$\qquad = f\left(\dfrac{x+4}{3}\right) \qquad g(x) = \dfrac{1}{3}(x+4) = \dfrac{x+4}{3}$

$\qquad = 3\left(\dfrac{x+4}{3}\right) - 4 \qquad \text{Substitute } g(x) \text{ into the rule for } f, f(x) = 3x - 4.$

$\qquad = x + 4 - 4 = x$

Seeing the Concept

Using a graphing calculator, let

$$Y_1 = f(x) = 3x - 4$$

$$Y_2 = g(x) = \frac{1}{3}(x + 4)$$

$$Y_3 = f \circ g, Y_4 = g \circ f$$

Using the viewing window $-3 \le x \le 3$, $-2 \le y \le 2$, graph only Y_3 and Y_4. What do you see? TRACE to verify that $Y_3 = Y_4$.

$$(g \circ f)(x) = g(f(x))$$
$$= g(3x - 4) \qquad f(x) = 3x - 4$$
$$= \frac{1}{3}[(3x - 4) + 4] \qquad \text{Substitute } f(x) \text{ into the rule for } g, \ g(x) = \frac{1}{3}(x + 4).$$
$$= \frac{1}{3}(3x) = x$$

We conclude that $(f \circ g)(x) = (g \circ f)(x) = x$.

In Section 5.2, we shall see that there is an important relationship between functions f and g for which $(f \circ g)(x) = (g \circ f)(x) = x$.

Now Work PROBLEM 45

Calculus Application

 Some techniques in calculus require that we be able to determine the components of a composite function. For example, the function $H(x) = \sqrt{x + 1}$ is the composition of the functions f and g, where $f(x) = \sqrt{x}$ and $g(x) = x + 1$, because $H(x) = (f \circ g)(x) = f(g(x)) = f(x + 1) = \sqrt{x + 1}$.

EXAMPLE 6 **Finding the Components of a Composite Function**

Find functions f and g such that $f \circ g = H$ if $H(x) = (x^2 + 1)^{50}$.

Solution The function H takes $x^2 + 1$ and raises it to the power 50. A natural way to decompose H is to raise the function $g(x) = x^2 + 1$ to the power 50. If we let $f(x) = x^{50}$ and $g(x) = x^2 + 1$, then

Figure 5

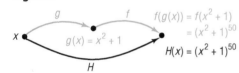

$$(f \circ g)(x) = f(g(x))$$
$$= f(x^2 + 1)$$
$$= (x^2 + 1)^{50} = H(x)$$

See Figure 5.

Other functions f and g may be found for which $f \circ g = H$ in Example 6. For example, if $f(x) = x^2$ and $g(x) = (x^2 + 1)^{25}$, then

$$(f \circ g)(x) = f(g(x)) = f((x^2 + 1)^{25}) = [(x^2 + 1)^{25}]^2 = (x^2 + 1)^{50}$$

Although the functions f and g found as a solution to Example 6 are not unique, there is usually a "natural" selection for f and g that comes to mind first.

EXAMPLE 7 **Finding the Components of a Composite Function**

Find functions f and g such that $f \circ g = H$ if $H(x) = \dfrac{1}{x + 1}$.

Solution Here H is the reciprocal of $g(x) = x + 1$. If we let $f(x) = \dfrac{1}{x}$ and $g(x) = x + 1$, we find that

$$(f \circ g)(x) = f(g(x)) = f(x + 1) = \frac{1}{x + 1} = H(x)$$

 **Now Work** PROBLEM 53

5.1 Assess Your Understanding

'Are You Prepared?' *Answers are given at the end of these exercises. If you get a wrong answer, read the pages listed in* red.

1. Find $f(3)$ if $f(x) = -4x^2 + 5x$. (pp. 49–52)
2. Find $f(3x)$ if $f(x) = 4 - 2x^2$. (pp. 49–52)

3. Find the domain of the function $f(x) = \dfrac{x^2 - 1}{x^2 - 25}$. (pp. 52–54)

Concepts and Vocabulary

4. Given two functions f and g, the _____ _____, denoted $f \circ g$, is defined by $f \circ g(x) = $ _____.

5. *True or False* $f(g(x)) = f(x) \cdot g(x)$.

6. *True or False* The domain of the composite function $(f \circ g)(x)$ is the same as the domain of $g(x)$.

Skill Building

In Problems 7 and 8, evaluate each expression using the values given in the table.

7.

x	-3	-2	-1	0	1	2	3
f(x)	-7	-5	-3	-1	3	5	7
g(x)	8	3	0	-1	0	3	8

(a) $(f \circ g)(1)$
(b) $(f \circ g)(-1)$
(c) $(g \circ f)(-1)$
(d) $(g \circ f)(0)$
(e) $(g \circ g)(-2)$
(f) $(f \circ f)(-1)$

8.

x	-3	-2	-1	0	1	2	3
f(x)	11	9	7	5	3	1	-1
g(x)	-8	-3	0	1	0	-3	-8

(a) $(f \circ g)(1)$
(b) $(f \circ g)(2)$
(c) $(g \circ f)(2)$
(d) $(g \circ f)(3)$
(e) $(g \circ g)(1)$
(f) $(f \circ f)(3)$

In Problems 9 and 10, evaluate each expression using the graphs of $y = f(x)$ and $y = g(x)$ shown in the figure.

9. (a) $(g \circ f)(-1)$ (b) $(g \circ f)(0)$
    (c) $(f \circ g)(-1)$ (d) $(f \circ g)(4)$

10. (a) $(g \circ f)(1)$ (b) $(g \circ f)(5)$
    (c) $(f \circ g)(0)$ (d) $(f \circ g)(2)$

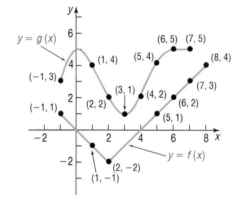

In Problems 11–20, for the given functions f and g, find:

    (a) $(f \circ g)(4)$ (b) $(g \circ f)(2)$ (c) $(f \circ f)(1)$ (d) $(g \circ g)(0)$

11. $f(x) = 2x; \quad g(x) = 3x^2 + 1$

12. $f(x) = 3x + 2; \quad g(x) = 2x^2 - 1$

13. $f(x) = 4x^2 - 3; \quad g(x) = 3 - \dfrac{1}{2}x^2$

14. $f(x) = 2x^2; \quad g(x) = 1 - 3x^2$

15. $f(x) = \sqrt{x}; \quad g(x) = 2x$

16. $f(x) = \sqrt{x + 1}; \quad g(x) = 3x$

17. $f(x) = |x|; \quad g(x) = \dfrac{1}{x^2 + 1}$

18. $f(x) = |x - 2|; \quad g(x) = \dfrac{3}{x^2 + 2}$

19. $f(x) = \dfrac{3}{x + 1}; \quad g(x) = \sqrt[3]{x}$

20. $f(x) = x^{3/2}; \quad g(x) = \dfrac{2}{x + 1}$

In Problems 21–28, find the domain of the composite function $f \circ g$.

21. $f(x) = \dfrac{3}{x - 1}; \quad g(x) = \dfrac{2}{x}$

22. $f(x) = \dfrac{1}{x + 3}; \quad g(x) = -\dfrac{2}{x}$

23. $f(x) = \dfrac{x}{x-1};\quad g(x) = -\dfrac{4}{x}$

24. $f(x) = \dfrac{x}{x+3};\quad g(x) = \dfrac{2}{x}$

25. $f(x) = \sqrt{x};\quad g(x) = 2x + 3$

26. $f(x) = x - 2;\quad g(x) = \sqrt{1-x}$

27. $f(x) = x^2 + 1;\quad g(x) = \sqrt{x-1}$

28. $f(x) = x^2 + 4;\quad g(x) = \sqrt{x-2}$

In Problems 29–44, for the given functions f and g, find:

   (a) $f \circ g$ (b) $g \circ f$ (c) $f \circ f$ (d) $g \circ g$

State the domain of each composite function.

29. $f(x) = 2x + 3;\quad g(x) = 3x$

30. $f(x) = -x;\quad g(x) = 2x - 4$

31. $f(x) = 3x + 1;\quad g(x) = x^2$

32. $f(x) = x + 1;\quad g(x) = x^2 + 4$

33. $f(x) = x^2;\quad g(x) = x^2 + 4$

34. $f(x) = x^2 + 1;\quad g(x) = 2x^2 + 3$

35. $f(x) = \dfrac{3}{x-1};\quad g(x) = \dfrac{2}{x}$

36. $f(x) = \dfrac{1}{x+3};\quad g(x) = -\dfrac{2}{x}$

37. $f(x) = \dfrac{x}{x-1};\quad g(x) = -\dfrac{4}{x}$

38. $f(x) = \dfrac{x}{x+3};\quad g(x) = \dfrac{2}{x}$

39. $f(x) = \sqrt{x};\quad g(x) = 2x + 3$

40. $f(x) = \sqrt{x-2};\quad g(x) = 1 - 2x$

41. $f(x) = x^2 + 1;\quad g(x) = \sqrt{x-1}$

42. $f(x) = x^2 + 4;\quad g(x) = \sqrt{x-2}$

43. $f(x) = \dfrac{x-5}{x+1};\quad g(x) = \dfrac{x+2}{x-3}$

44. $f(x) = \dfrac{2x-1}{x-2};\quad g(x) = \dfrac{x+4}{2x-5}$

In Problems 45–52, show that $(f \circ g)(x) = (g \circ f)(x) = x$.

45. $f(x) = 2x;\quad g(x) = \dfrac{1}{2}x$

46. $f(x) = 4x;\quad g(x) = \dfrac{1}{4}x$

47. $f(x) = x^3;\quad g(x) = \sqrt[3]{x}$

48. $f(x) = x + 5;\quad g(x) = x - 5$

49. $f(x) = 2x - 6;\quad g(x) = \dfrac{1}{2}(x + 6)$

50. $f(x) = 4 - 3x;\quad g(x) = \dfrac{1}{3}(4 - x)$

51. $f(x) = ax + b;\quad g(x) = \dfrac{1}{a}(x - b)\quad a \neq 0$

52. $f(x) = \dfrac{1}{x};\quad g(x) = \dfrac{1}{x}$

In Problems 53–58, find functions f and g so that $f \circ g = H$.

53. $H(x) = (2x + 3)^4$

54. $H(x) = (1 + x^2)^3$

55. $H(x) = \sqrt{x^2 + 1}$

56. $H(x) = \sqrt{1 - x^2}$

57. $H(x) = |2x + 1|$

58. $H(x) = |2x^2 + 3|$

Applications and Extensions

59. If $f(x) = 2x^3 - 3x^2 + 4x - 1$ and $g(x) = 2$, find $(f \circ g)(x)$ and $(g \circ f)(x)$.

60. If $f(x) = \dfrac{x+1}{x-1}$, find $(f \circ f)(x)$.

61. If $f(x) = 2x^2 + 5$ and $g(x) = 3x + a$, find a so that the graph of $f \circ g$ crosses the y-axis at 23.

62. If $f(x) = 3x^2 - 7$ and $g(x) = 2x + a$, find a so that the graph of $f \circ g$ crosses the y-axis at 68.

In Problems 63 and 64, use the functions f and g to find:

   (a) $f \circ g$ (b) $g \circ f$

   (c) the domain of $f \circ g$ and of $g \circ f$

   (d) the conditions for which $f \circ g = g \circ f$

63. $f(x) = ax + b;\quad g(x) = cx + d$

64. $f(x) = \dfrac{ax + b}{cx + d};\quad g(x) = mx$

65. Surface Area of a Balloon The surface area S (in square meters) of a hot-air balloon is given by

$$S(r) = 4\pi r^2$$

where r is the radius of the balloon (in meters). If the radius r is increasing with time t (in seconds) according to the formula $r(t) = \dfrac{2}{3}t^3, t \geq 0$, find the surface area S of the balloon as a function of the time t.

66. Volume of a Balloon The volume V (in cubic meters) of the hot-air balloon described in Problem 65 is given by $V(r) = \dfrac{4}{3}\pi r^3$. If the radius r is the same function of t as in Problem 65, find the volume V as a function of the time t.

67. Automobile Production The number N of cars produced at a certain factory in one day after t hours of operation is given by $N(t) = 100t - 5t^2, 0 \leq t \leq 10$. If the cost C

(in dollars) of producing N cars is $C(N) = 15{,}000 + 8000N$, find the cost C as a function of the time t of operation of the factory.

68. **Environmental Concerns** The spread of oil leaking from a tanker is in the shape of a circle. If the radius r (in feet) of the spread after t hours is $r(t) = 200\sqrt{t}$, find the area A of the oil slick as a function of the time t.

69. **Production Cost** The price p, in dollars, of a certain product and the quantity x sold obey the demand equation

$$p = -\frac{1}{4}x + 100 \quad 0 \le x \le 400$$

Suppose that the cost C, in dollars, of producing x units is

$$C = \frac{\sqrt{x}}{25} + 600$$

Assuming that all items produced are sold, find the cost C as a function of the price p.

[**Hint:** Solve for x in the demand equation and then form the composite.]

70. **Cost of a Commodity** The price p, in dollars, of a certain commodity and the quantity x sold obey the demand equation

$$p = -\frac{1}{5}x + 200 \quad 0 \le x \le 1000$$

Suppose that the cost C, in dollars, of producing x units is

$$C = \frac{\sqrt{x}}{10} + 400$$

Assuming that all items produced are sold, find the cost C as a function of the price p.

71. **Volume of a Cylinder** The volume V of a right circular cylinder of height h and radius r is $V = \pi r^2 h$. If the height is twice the radius, express the volume V as a function of r.

72. **Volume of a Cone** The volume V of a right circular cone is $V = \frac{1}{3}\pi r^2 h$. If the height is twice the radius, express the volume V as a function of r.

73. **Foreign Exchange** Traders often buy foreign currency in hope of making money when the currency's value changes. For example, on June 5, 2009, one U.S. dollar could purchase 0.7143 Euros, and one Euro could purchase 137.402 yen. Let $f(x)$ represent the number of Euros you can buy with x dollars, and let $g(x)$ represent the number of yen you can buy with x Euros.
(a) Find a function that relates dollars to Euros.
(b) Find a function that relates Euros to yen.
(c) Use the results of parts (a) and (b) to find a function that relates dollars to yen. That is, find $(g \circ f)(x) = g(f(x))$.
(d) What is $g(f(1000))$?

74. **Temperature Conversion** The function $C(F) = \frac{5}{9}(F - 32)$ converts a temperature in degrees Fahrenheit, F, to a temperature in degrees Celsius, C. The function $K(C) = C + 273$, converts a temperature in degrees Celsius to a temperature in kelvins, K.
(a) Find a function that converts a temperature in degrees Fahrenheit to a temperature in kelvins.
(b) Determine 80 degrees Fahrenheit in kelvins.

75. **Discounts** The manufacturer of a computer is offering two discounts on last year's model computer. The first discount is a $200 rebate and the second discount is 20% off the regular price, p.
(a) Write a function f that represents the sale price if only the rebate applies.
(b) Write a function g that represents the sale price if only the 20% discount applies.
(c) Find $f \circ g$ and $g \circ f$. What does each of these functions represent? Which combination of discounts represents a better deal for the consumer? Why?

76. If f and g are odd functions, show that the composite function $f \circ g$ is also odd.

77. If f is an odd function and g is an even function, show that the composite functions $f \circ g$ and $g \circ f$ are both even.

'Are You Prepared?' Answers

1. -21 **2.** $4 - 18x^2$ **3.** $\{x \mid x \ne -5, x \ne 5\}$

5.2 One-to-One Functions; Inverse Functions

PREPARING FOR THIS SECTION *Before getting started, review the following:*

- Functions (Section 2.1, pp. 46–54)
- Increasing/Decreasing Functions (Section 2.3, pp. 70–71)
- Rational Expressions (Appendix A, Section A.5, pp. A36–A42)

Now Work the 'Are You Prepared?' problems on page 263.

OBJECTIVES 1 Determine Whether a Function Is One-to-One (p. 255)
2 Determine the Inverse of a Function Defined by a Map or a Set of Ordered Pairs (p. 257)
3 Obtain the Graph of the Inverse Function from the Graph of the Function (p. 259)
4 Find the Inverse of a Function Defined by an Equation (p. 260)

1 Determine Whether a Function Is One-to-One

In Section 2.1, we presented four different ways to represent a function as (1) a map, (2) a set of ordered pairs, (3) a graph, and (4) an equation. For example, Figures 6 and 7 illustrate two different functions represented as mappings. The function in Figure 6 shows the correspondence between states and their population (in millions). The function in Figure 7 shows a correspondence between animals and life expectancy (in years).

Figure 6

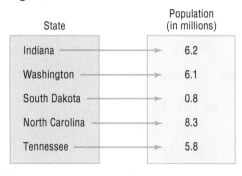

Figure 7

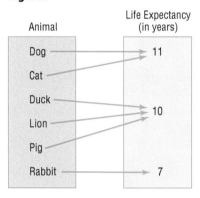

Suppose we asked a group of people to name the state that has a population of 0.8 million based on the function in Figure 6. Everyone in the group would respond South Dakota. Now, if we asked the same group of people to name the animal whose life expectancy is 11 years based on the function in Figure 7, some would respond dog, while others would respond cat. What is the difference between the functions in Figures 6 and 7? In Figure 6, we can see that no two elements in the domain correspond to the same element in the range. In Figure 7, this is not the case: two different elements in the domain correspond to the same element in the range. Functions such as the one in Figure 6 are given a special name.

DEFINITION

A function is **one-to-one** if any two different inputs in the domain correspond to two different outputs in the range. That is, if x_1 and x_2 are two different inputs of a function f, then f is one-to-one if $f(x_1) \neq f(x_2)$.

> **In Words**
> A function is not one-to-one if two different inputs correspond to the same output.

Put another way, a function f is one-to-one if no y in the range is the image of more than one x in the domain. A function is not one-to-one if two different elements in the domain correspond to the same element in the range. So the function in Figure 7 is not one-to-one because two different elements in the domain, *dog* and *cat*, both correspond to 11. Figure 8 illustrates the distinction among one-to-one functions, functions that are not one-to-one, and relations that are not functions.

Figure 8

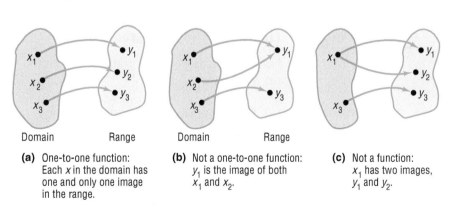

(a) One-to-one function: Each *x* in the domain has one and only one image in the range.

(b) Not a one-to-one function: y_1 is the image of both x_1 and x_2.

(c) Not a function: x_1 has two images, y_1 and y_2.

| EXAMPLE 1 | **Determining Whether a Function Is One-to-One** |

Determine whether the following functions are one-to-one.

(a) For the following function, the domain represents the age of five males and the range represents their HDL (good) cholesterol (mg/dL).

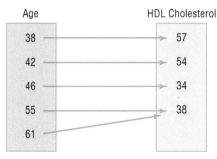

(b) $\{(-2, 6), (-1, 3), (0, 2), (1, 5), (2, 8)\}$

Solution

(a) The function is not one-to-one because there are two different inputs, 55 and 61, that correspond to the same output, 38.

(b) The function is one-to-one because there are no two distinct inputs that correspond to the same output.

━━━ **Now Work** PROBLEMS **11** AND **15**

For functions defined by an equation $y = f(x)$ and for which the graph of f is known, there is a simple test, called the **horizontal-line test,** to determine whether f is one-to-one.

THEOREM

Figure 9
$f(x_1) = f(x_2) = h$ and $x_1 \neq x_2$; f is not a one-to-one function.

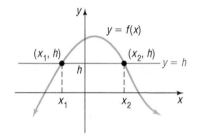

Horizontal-line Test

If every horizontal line intersects the graph of a function f in at most one point, then f is one-to-one.

The reason that this test works can be seen in Figure 9, where the horizontal line $y = h$ intersects the graph at two distinct points, (x_1, h) and (x_2, h). Since h is the image of both x_1 and x_2 and $x_1 \neq x_2$, f is not one-to-one. Based on Figure 9, we can state the horizontal-line test in another way: If the graph of any horizontal line intersects the graph of a function f at more than one point, then f is not one-to-one.

| EXAMPLE 2 | **Using the Horizontal-line Test** |

For each function, use its graph to determine whether the function is one-to-one.
(a) $f(x) = x^2$ (b) $g(x) = x^3$

Solution

(a) Figure 10(a) illustrates the horizontal-line test for $f(x) = x^2$. The horizontal line $y = 1$ intersects the graph of f twice, at $(1, 1)$ and at $(-1, 1)$, so f is not one-to-one.

(b) Figure 10(b) illustrates the horizontal-line test for $g(x) = x^3$. Because every horizontal line intersects the graph of g exactly once, it follows that g is one-to-one.

Figure 10

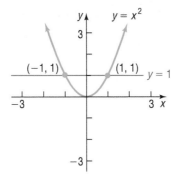

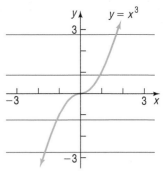

(a) A horizontal line intersects the graph twice; f is not one-to-one

(b) Every horizontal line intersects the graph exactly once; g is one-to-one

-**Now Work**   PROBLEM 19

Look more closely at the one-to-one function $g(x) = x^3$. This function is an increasing function. Because an increasing (or decreasing) function will always have different y-values for unequal x-values, it follows that a function that is increasing (or decreasing) over its domain is also a one-to-one function.

THEOREM

A function that is increasing on an interval I is a one-to-one function on I.
A function that is decreasing on an interval I is a one-to-one function on I.

2 Determine the Inverse of a Function Defined by a Map or a Set of Ordered Pairs

DEFINITION

Suppose that f is a one-to-one function. Then, to each x in the domain of f, there is exactly one y in the range (because f is a function); and to each y in the range of f, there is exactly one x in the domain (because f is one-to-one). The correspondence from the range of f back to the domain of f is called the **inverse function of f.** The symbol f^{-1} is used to denote the inverse of f.

In Words

Suppose that we have a one-to-one function f where the input 5 corresponds to the output 10. In the inverse function f^{-1}, the input 10 would correspond to the output 5.

We will discuss how to find inverses for all four representations of functions: (1) maps, (2) sets of ordered pairs, (3) graphs, and (4) equations. We begin with finding inverses of functions represented by maps or sets of ordered pairs.

EXAMPLE 3

Finding the Inverse of a Function Defined by a Map

Find the inverse of the following function. Let the domain of the function represent certain states, and let the range represent the state's population (in millions). State the domain and the range of the inverse function.

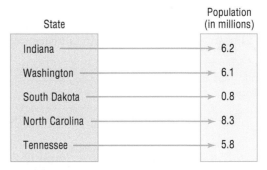

Solution   The function is one-to-one. To find the inverse function, we interchange the elements in the domain with the elements in the range. For example, the function

receives as input Indiana and outputs 6.2 million. So the inverse receives as input 6.2 million and outputs Indiana. The inverse function is shown next.

The domain of the inverse function is {6.2, 6.1, 0.8, 8.3, 5.8}. The range of the inverse function is {Indiana, Washington, South Dakota, North Carolina, Tennessee}.

If the function f is a set of ordered pairs (x, y), then the inverse of f, denoted f^{-1}, is the set of ordered pairs (y, x).

EXAMPLE 4   **Finding the Inverse of a Function Defined by a Set of Ordered Pairs**

Find the inverse of the following one-to-one function:

$$\{(-3, -27), (-2, -8), (-1, -1), (0, 0), (1, 1), (2, 8), (3, 27)\}$$

State the domain and the range of the function and its inverse.

Solution   The inverse of the given function is found by interchanging the entries in each ordered pair and so is given by

$$\{(-27, -3), (-8, -2), (-1, -1), (0, 0), (1, 1), (8, 2), (27, 3)\}$$

The domain of the function is $\{-3, -2, -1, 0, 1, 2, 3\}$. The range of the function is $\{-27, -8, -1, 0, 1, 8, 27\}$. The domain of the inverse function is $\{-27, -8, -1, 0, 1, 8, 27\}$. The range of the inverse function is $\{-3, -2, -1, 0, 1, 2, 3\}$.

—**Now Work**   PROBLEMS 25 AND 29

Figure 11

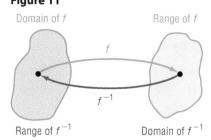

Domain of f Range of f

Range of f^{-1} Domain of f^{-1}

WARNING Be careful! f^{-1} is a symbol for the inverse function of f. The -1 used in f^{-1} is not an exponent. That is, f^{-1} does not mean the reciprocal of f; $f^{-1}(x)$ is not equal to $\dfrac{1}{f(x)}$. ■

Remember, if f is a one-to-one function, it has an inverse function, f^{-1}. See Figure 11.

Based on the results of Example 4 and Figure 11, two facts are now apparent about a one-to-one function f and its inverse f^{-1}.

Domain of f = Range of f^{-1} Range of f = Domain of f^{-1}

Look again at Figure 11 to visualize the relationship. If we start with x, apply f, and then apply f^{-1}, we get x back again. If we start with x, apply f^{-1}, and then apply f, we get the number x back again. To put it simply, what f does, f^{-1} undoes, and vice versa. See the illustration that follows.

Input x from domain of f $\xrightarrow{\text{Apply } f}$ $f(x)$ $\xrightarrow{\text{Apply } f^{-1}}$ $f^{-1}(f(x)) = x$

Input x from domain of f^{-1} $\xrightarrow{\text{Apply } f^{-1}}$ $f^{-1}(x)$ $\xrightarrow{\text{Apply } f}$ $f(f^{-1}(x)) = x$

In other words,

$$f^{-1}(f(x)) = x \quad \text{where } x \text{ is in the domain of } f$$
$$f(f^{-1}(x)) = x \quad \text{where } x \text{ is in the domain of } f^{-1}$$

Consider the function $f(x) = 2x$, which multiplies the argument x by 2. Since f is an increasing function, f is one-to-one. The inverse function f^{-1} undoes whatever f does. So the inverse function of f is $f^{-1}(x) = \dfrac{1}{2}x$, which divides the argument by 2.

For example, $f(3) = 2(3) = 6$ and $f^{-1}(6) = \dfrac{1}{2}(6) = 3$, so f^{-1} undoes what f did. We can verify this by showing that

$$f^{-1}(f(x)) = f^{-1}(2x) = \frac{1}{2}(2x) = x \quad \text{and} \quad f(f^{-1}(x)) = f\left(\frac{1}{2}x\right) = 2\left(\frac{1}{2}x\right) = x$$

See Figure 12.

Figure 12

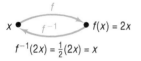

$f^{-1}(2x) = \frac{1}{2}(2x) = x$

EXAMPLE 5   Verifying Inverse Functions

(a) Verify that the inverse of $g(x) = x^3$ is $g^{-1}(x) = \sqrt[3]{x}$ by showing that

$$g^{-1}(g(x)) = g^{-1}(x^3) = \sqrt[3]{x^3} = x \quad \text{for all } x \text{ in the domain of } g$$
$$g(g^{-1}(x)) = g(\sqrt[3]{x}) = (\sqrt[3]{x})^3 = x \quad \text{for all } x \text{ in the domain of } g^{-1}$$

(b) Verify that the inverse of $f(x) = 2x + 3$ is $f^{-1}(x) = \dfrac{1}{2}(x - 3)$ by showing that

$$f^{-1}(f(x)) = f^{-1}(2x + 3) = \frac{1}{2}[(2x + 3) - 3] = \frac{1}{2}(2x) = x \qquad \text{for all } x \text{ in the domain of } f$$
$$f(f^{-1}(x)) = f\left(\frac{1}{2}(x - 3)\right) = 2\left[\frac{1}{2}(x - 3)\right] + 3 = (x - 3) + 3 = x \quad \text{for all } x \text{ in the domain of } f^{-1}$$

EXAMPLE 6   Verifying Inverse Functions

Verify that the inverse of $f(x) = \dfrac{1}{x - 1}$ is $f^{-1}(x) = \dfrac{1}{x} + 1$. For what values of x is $f^{-1}(f(x)) = x$? For what values of x is $f(f^{-1}(x)) = x$?

Solution   The domain of f is $\{x | x \neq 1\}$ and the domain of f^{-1} is $\{x | x \neq 0\}$. Now

$$f^{-1}(f(x)) = f^{-1}\left(\frac{1}{x - 1}\right) = \frac{1}{\frac{1}{x-1}} + 1 = x - 1 + 1 = x \qquad \text{provided } x \neq 1$$

$$f(f^{-1}(x)) = f\left(\frac{1}{x} + 1\right) = \frac{1}{\frac{1}{x} + 1 - 1} = \frac{1}{\frac{1}{x}} = x \qquad \text{provided } x \neq 0$$

Now Work PROBLEM 33

3 Obtain the Graph of the Inverse Function from the Graph of the Function

Figure 13

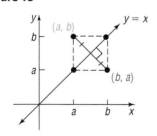

Suppose that (a, b) is a point on the graph of a one-to-one function f defined by $y = f(x)$. Then $b = f(a)$. This means that $a = f^{-1}(b)$, so (b, a) is a point on the graph of the inverse function f^{-1}. The relationship between the point (a, b) on f and the point (b, a) on f^{-1} is shown in Figure 13. The line segment with endpoints (a, b) and (b, a) is perpendicular to the line $y = x$ and is bisected by the line $y = x$. (Do you see why?) It follows that the point (b, a) on f^{-1} is the reflection about the line $y = x$ of the point (a, b) on f.

THEOREM   The graph of a one-to-one function f and the graph of its inverse f^{-1} are symmetric with respect to the line $y = x$.

Figure 14 illustrates this result. Notice that, once the graph of f is known, the graph of f^{-1} may be obtained by reflecting the graph of f about the line $y = x$.

Figure 14

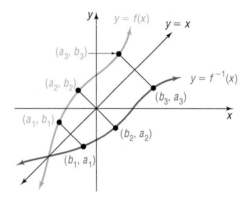

EXAMPLE 7 **Graphing the Inverse Function**

The graph in Figure 15(a) is that of a one-to-one function $y = f(x)$. Draw the graph of its inverse.

Solution Begin by adding the graph of $y = x$ to Figure 15(a). Since the points $(-2, -1)$, $(-1, 0)$, and $(2, 1)$ are on the graph of f, the points $(-1, -2)$, $(0, -1)$, and $(1, 2)$ must be on the graph of f^{-1}. Keeping in mind that the graph of f^{-1} is the reflection about the line $y = x$ of the graph of f, draw f^{-1}. See Figure 15(b).

Figure 15

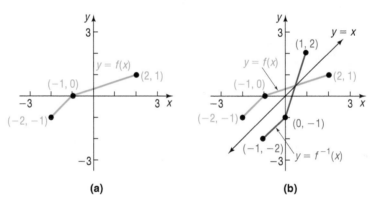

(a)   (b)

Now Work PROBLEM 43

4 Find the Inverse of a Function Defined by an Equation

The fact that the graphs of a one-to-one function f and its inverse function f^{-1} are symmetric with respect to the line $y = x$ tells us more. It says that we can obtain f^{-1} by interchanging the roles of x and y in f. Look again at Figure 14. If f is defined by the equation

$$y = f(x)$$

then f^{-1} is defined by the equation

$$x = f(y)$$

The equation $x = f(y)$ defines f^{-1} *implicitly*. If we can solve this equation for y, we will have the *explicit* form of f^{-1}, that is,

$$y = f^{-1}(x)$$

Let's use this procedure to find the inverse of $f(x) = 2x + 3$. (Since f is a linear function and is increasing, we know that f is one-to-one and so has an inverse function.)

EXAMPLE 8 **How to Find the Inverse Function**

Find the inverse of $f(x) = 2x + 3$. Graph f and f^{-1} on the same coordinate axes.

Step-by-Step Solution

Step 1: Replace $f(x)$ with y. In $y = f(x)$, interchange the variables x and y to obtain $x = f(y)$. This equation defines the inverse function f^{-1} implicitly.

Replace $f(x)$ with y in $f(x) = 2x + 3$ and obtain $y = 2x + 3$. Now interchange the variables x and y to obtain

$$x = 2y + 3$$

This equation defines the inverse f^{-1} implicitly.

Step 2: If possible, solve the implicit equation for y in terms of x to obtain the explicit form of f^{-1}, $y = f^{-1}(x)$.

To find the explicit form of the inverse, solve $x = 2y + 3$ for y.

$$x = 2y + 3$$
$$2y + 3 = x \qquad \text{Reflexive Property; If } a = b, \text{ then } b = a.$$
$$2y = x - 3 \qquad \text{Subtract 3 from both sides.}$$
$$y = \frac{1}{2}(x - 3) \qquad \text{Divide both sides by 2.}$$

The explicit form of the inverse f^{-1} is

$$f^{-1}(x) = \frac{1}{2}(x - 3)$$

Step 3: Check the result by showing that $f^{-1}(f(x)) = x$ and $f(f^{-1}(x)) = x$.

We verified that f and f^{-1} are inverses in Example 5(b).

Figure 16

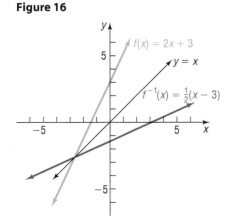

The graphs of $f(x) = 2x + 3$ and its inverse $f^{-1}(x) = \frac{1}{2}(x - 3)$ are shown in Figure 16 . Note the symmetry of the graphs with respect to the line $y = x$.

Procedure for Finding the Inverse of a One-to-One Function

STEP 1: In $y = f(x)$, interchange the variables x and y to obtain

$$x = f(y)$$

This equation defines the inverse function f^{-1} implicitly.

STEP 2: If possible, solve the implicit equation for y in terms of x to obtain the explicit form of f^{-1}:

$$y = f^{-1}(x)$$

STEP 3: Check the result by showing that

$$f^{-1}(f(x)) = x \quad \text{and} \quad f(f^{-1}(x)) = x$$

EXAMPLE 9 **Finding the Inverse Function**

The function

$$f(x) = \frac{2x + 1}{x - 1} \qquad x \neq 1$$

is one-to-one. Find its inverse and check the result.

Solution **STEP 1:** Replace $f(x)$ with y and interchange the variables x and y in

$$y = \frac{2x + 1}{x - 1}$$

to obtain

$$x = \frac{2y + 1}{y - 1}$$

STEP 2: Solve for y.

$$x = \frac{2y + 1}{y - 1}$$

$$x(y - 1) = 2y + 1 \quad \text{Multiply both sides by } y - 1.$$

$$xy - x = 2y + 1 \quad \text{Apply the Distributive Property.}$$

$$xy - 2y = x + 1 \quad \text{Subtract } 2y \text{ from both sides; add } x \text{ to both sides.}$$

$$(x - 2)y = x + 1 \quad \text{Factor.}$$

$$y = \frac{x + 1}{x - 2} \quad \text{Divide by } x - 2.$$

The inverse is

$$f^{-1}(x) = \frac{x + 1}{x - 2} \quad x \neq 2 \quad \text{Replace } y \text{ by } f^{-1}(x).$$

STEP 3: ✓Check:

$$f^{-1}(f(x)) = f^{-1}\left(\frac{2x + 1}{x - 1}\right) = \frac{\dfrac{2x + 1}{x - 1} + 1}{\dfrac{2x + 1}{x - 1} - 2} = \frac{2x + 1 + x - 1}{2x + 1 - 2(x - 1)} = \frac{3x}{3} = x \quad x \neq 1$$

$$f(f^{-1}(x)) = f\left(\frac{x + 1}{x - 2}\right) = \frac{2\left(\dfrac{x + 1}{x - 2}\right) + 1}{\dfrac{x + 1}{x - 2} - 1} = \frac{2(x + 1) + x - 2}{x + 1 - (x - 2)} = \frac{3x}{3} = x \quad x \neq 2$$

↵

Exploration

In Example 9, we found that, if $f(x) = \dfrac{2x + 1}{x - 1}$, then $f^{-1}(x) = \dfrac{x + 1}{x - 2}$. Compare the vertical and horizontal asymptotes of f and f^{-1}.

Result The vertical asymptote of f is $x = 1$, and the horizontal asymptote is $y = 2$. The vertical asymptote of f^{-1} is $x = 2$, and the horizontal asymptote is $y = 1$.

╼**Now Work** PROBLEMS 51 AND 65

If a function is not one-to-one, it has no inverse function. Sometimes, though, an appropriate restriction on the domain of such a function will yield a new function that is one-to-one. Then the function defined on the restricted domain has an inverse function. Let's look at an example of this common practice.

EXAMPLE 10

Finding the Inverse of a Domain-restricted Function

Find the inverse of $y = f(x) = x^2$ if $x \geq 0$. Graph f and f^{-1}.

Solution

The function $y = x^2$ is not one-to-one. [Refer to Example 2(a).] However, if we restrict the domain of this function to $x \geq 0$, as indicated, we have a new function that is increasing and therefore is one-to-one. As a result, the function defined by $y = f(x) = x^2$, $x \geq 0$, has an inverse function, f^{-1}.

Follow the steps given previously to find f^{-1}.

STEP 1: In the equation $y = x^2$, $x \geq 0$, interchange the variables x and y. The result is

$$x = y^2 \quad y \geq 0$$

This equation defines (implicitly) the inverse function.

Figure 17

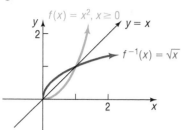

$$f(x) = x^2, x \geq 0$$
$$y = x$$
$$f^{-1}(x) = \sqrt{x}$$

STEP 2: Solve for y to get the explicit form of the inverse. Since $y \geq 0$, only one solution for y is obtained: $y = \sqrt{x}$. So $f^{-1}(x) = \sqrt{x}$.

STEP 3: ✓ **Check:** $f^{-1}(f(x)) = f^{-1}(x^2) = \sqrt{x^2} = |x| = x$ since $x \geq 0$

$$f(f^{-1}(x)) = f(\sqrt{x}) = (\sqrt{x})^2 = x$$

Figure 17 illustrates the graphs of $f(x) = x^2$, $x \geq 0$, and $f^{-1}(x) = \sqrt{x}$.

SUMMARY

1. If a function f is one-to-one, then it has an inverse function f^{-1}.
2. Domain of f = Range of f^{-1}; Range of f = Domain of f^{-1}.
3. To verify that f^{-1} is the inverse of f, show that $f^{-1}(f(x)) = x$ for every x in the domain of f and $f(f^{-1}(x)) = x$ for every x in the domain of f^{-1}.
4. The graphs of f and f^{-1} are symmetric with respect to the line $y = x$.

5.2 Assess Your Understanding

'Are You Prepared?' *Answers are given at the end of these exercises. If you get a wrong answer, read the pages listed in* red.

1. Is the set of ordered pairs $\{(1,3), (2,3), (-1,2)\}$ a function? Why or why not? (pp. 46–54)

2. Where is the function $f(x) = x^2$ increasing? Where is it decreasing? (pp. 70–71)

3. What is the domain of $f(x) = \dfrac{x+5}{x^2 + 3x - 18}$? (pp. 46–54)

4. Simplify: $\dfrac{\frac{1}{x} + 1}{\frac{1}{x^2} - 1}$ (pp. A36–A42)

Concepts and Vocabulary

5. If x_1 and x_2 are two different inputs of a function f, then f is one-to-one if _____.

6. If every horizontal line intersects the graph of a function f at no more than one point, f is a(n) _____ function.

7. If f is a one-to-one function and $f(3) = 8$, then $f^{-1}(8) =$ _____.

8. If f^{-1} denotes the inverse of a function f, then the graphs of f and f^{-1} are symmetric with respect to the line _____.

9. If the domain of a one-to-one function f is $[4, \infty)$, the range of its inverse, f^{-1}, is _____.

10. **True or False** If f and g are inverse functions, the domain of f is the same as the range of g.

Skill Building

In Problems 11–18, determine whether the function is one-to-one.

11.

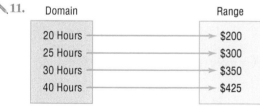

12.

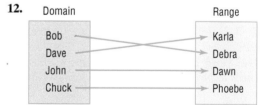

13.

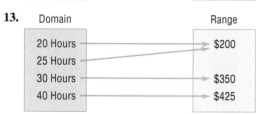

14.

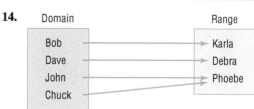

15. $\{(2,6), (-3,6), (4,9), (1,10)\}$

16. $\{(-2,5), (-1,3), (3,7), (4,12)\}$

17. $\{(0,0), (1,1), (2,16), (3,81)\}$

18. $\{(1,2), (2,8), (3,18), (4,32)\}$

In Problems 19–24, the graph of a function f is given. Use the horizontal-line test to determine whether f is one-to-one.

19.

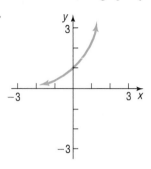

20.

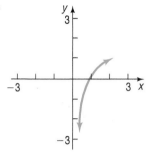

21.

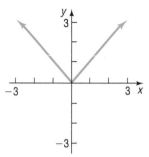

22.

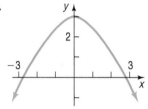

23.

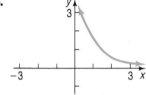

24.

In Problems 25–32, find the inverse of each one-to-one function. State the domain and the range of each inverse function.

25.

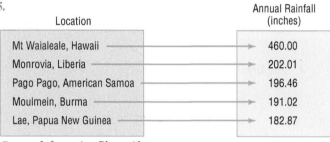

Location	Annual Rainfall (inches)
Mt Waialeale, Hawaii	460.00
Monrovia, Liberia	202.01
Pago Pago, American Samoa	196.46
Moulmein, Burma	191.02
Lae, Papua New Guinea	182.87

Source: Information Please Almanac

26.

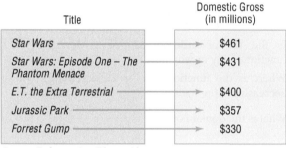

Title	Domestic Gross (in millions)
Star Wars	$461
Star Wars: Episode One – The Phantom Menace	$431
E.T. the Extra Terrestrial	$400
Jurassic Park	$357
Forrest Gump	$330

Source: Information Please Almanac

27.

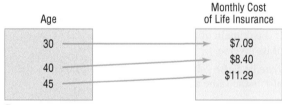

Age	Monthly Cost of Life Insurance
30	$7.09
40	$8.40
45	$11.29

Source: eterm.com

28.

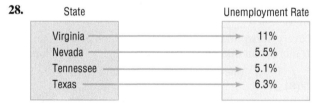

State	Unemployment Rate
Virginia	11%
Nevada	5.5%
Tennessee	5.1%
Texas	6.3%

Source: United States Statistical Abstract

29. $\{(-3, 5), (-2, 9), (-1, 2), (0, 11), (1, -5)\}$

30. $\{(-2, 2), (-1, 6), (0, 8), (1, -3), (2, 9)\}$

31. $\{(-2, 1), (-3, 2), (-10, 0), (1, 9), (2, 4)\}$

32. $\{(-2, -8), (-1, -1), (0, 0), (1, 1), (2, 8)\}$

In Problems 33–42, verify that the functions f and g are inverses of each other by showing that f(g(x)) = x and g(f(x)) = x. Give any values of x that need to be excluded from the domain of f and the domain of g.

33. $f(x) = 3x + 4; \quad g(x) = \frac{1}{3}(x - 4)$

34. $f(x) = 3 - 2x; \quad g(x) = -\frac{1}{2}(x - 3)$

35. $f(x) = 4x - 8; \quad g(x) = \frac{x}{4} + 2$

36. $f(x) = 2x + 6; \quad g(x) = \frac{1}{2}x - 3$

37. $f(x) = x^3 - 8; \quad g(x) = \sqrt[3]{x + 8}$

38. $f(x) = (x - 2)^2, x \geq 2; \quad g(x) = \sqrt{x} + 2$

39. $f(x) = \frac{1}{x}; \quad g(x) = \frac{1}{x}$

40. $f(x) = x; \quad g(x) = x$

41. $f(x) = \frac{2x + 3}{x + 4}; \quad g(x) = \frac{4x - 3}{2 - x}$

42. $f(x) = \frac{x - 5}{2x + 3}; \quad g(x) = \frac{3x + 5}{1 - 2x}$

In Problems 43–48, the graph of a one-to-one function f is given. Draw the graph of the inverse function f^{-1}. For convenience (and as a hint), the graph of y = x is also given.

43.

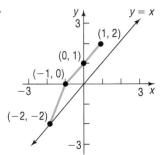

44.

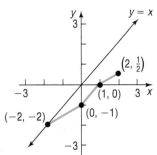

45.

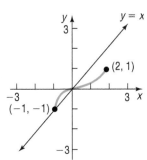

46.

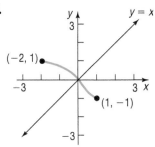

47.

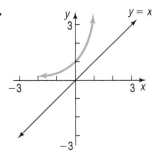

48.

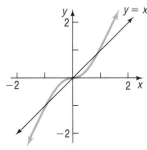

In Problems 49–60, the function f is one-to-one. Find its inverse and check your answer. Graph f, f^{-1}, and y = x on the same coordinate axes.

49. $f(x) = 3x$

50. $f(x) = -4x$

51. $f(x) = 4x + 2$

52. $f(x) = 1 - 3x$

53. $f(x) = x^3 - 1$

54. $f(x) = x^3 + 1$

55. $f(x) = x^2 + 4 \quad x \geq 0$

56. $f(x) = x^2 + 9 \quad x \geq 0$

57. $f(x) = \dfrac{4}{x}$

58. $f(x) = -\dfrac{3}{x}$

59. $f(x) = \dfrac{1}{x - 2}$

60. $f(x) = \dfrac{4}{x + 2}$

In Problems 61–72, the function f is one-to-one. Find its inverse and check your answer.

61. $f(x) = \dfrac{2}{3 + x}$

62. $f(x) = \dfrac{4}{2 - x}$

63. $f(x) = \dfrac{3x}{x + 2}$

64. $f(x) = -\dfrac{2x}{x - 1}$

65. $f(x) = \dfrac{2x}{3x - 1}$

66. $f(x) = -\dfrac{3x + 1}{x}$

67. $f(x) = \dfrac{3x + 4}{2x - 3}$

68. $f(x) = \dfrac{2x - 3}{x + 4}$

69. $f(x) = \dfrac{2x + 3}{x + 2}$

70. $f(x) = \dfrac{-3x - 4}{x - 2}$

71. $f(x) = \dfrac{x^2 - 4}{2x^2} \quad x > 0$

72. $f(x) = \dfrac{x^2 + 3}{3x^2} \quad x > 0$

Applications and Extensions

73. Use the graph of y = f(x) given in Problem 43 to evaluate the following:

(a) $f(-1)$ (b) $f(1)$ (c) $f^{-1}(1)$ (d) $f^{-1}(2)$

74. Use the graph of y = f(x) given in Problem 44 to evaluate the following:

(a) $f(2)$ (b) $f(1)$ (c) $f^{-1}(0)$ (d) $f^{-1}(-1)$

75. If $f(7) = 13$ and f is one-to-one, what is $f^{-1}(13)$?

76. If $g(-5) = 3$ and g is one-to-one, what is $g^{-1}(3)$?

77. The domain of a one-to-one function f is $[5, \infty)$, and its range is $[-2, \infty)$. State the domain and the range of f^{-1}.

78. The domain of a one-to-one function f is $[0, \infty)$, and its range is $[5, \infty)$. State the domain and the range of f^{-1}.

79. The domain of a one-to-one function g is $(-\infty, 0]$, and its range is $[0, \infty)$. State the domain and the range of g^{-1}.

80. The domain of a one-to-one function g is $[0, 15]$, and its range is $(0, 8)$. State the domain and the range of g^{-1}.

81. A function $y = f(x)$ is increasing on the interval $(0, 5)$. What conclusions can you draw about the graph of $y = f^{-1}(x)$?

82. A function $y = f(x)$ is decreasing on the interval $(0, 5)$. What conclusions can you draw about the graph of $y = f^{-1}(x)$?

83. Find the inverse of the linear function

$$f(x) = mx + b \quad m \neq 0$$

84. Find the inverse of the function

$$f(x) = \sqrt{r^2 - x^2} \quad 0 \leq x \leq r$$

85. A function f has an inverse function. If the graph of f lies in quadrant I, in which quadrant does the graph of f^{-1} lie?

86. A function f has an inverse function. If the graph of f lies in quadrant II, in which quadrant does the graph of f^{-1} lie?

87. The function $f(x) = |x|$ is not one-to-one. Find a suitable restriction on the domain of f so that the new function that results is one-to-one. Then find the inverse of f.

88. The function $f(x) = x^4$ is not one-to-one. Find a suitable restriction on the domain of f so that the new function that results is one-to-one. Then find the inverse of f.

In applications, the symbols used for the independent and dependent variables are often based on common usage. So, rather than using $y = f(x)$ to represent a function, an applied problem might use $C = C(q)$ to represent the cost C of manufacturing q units of a good since, in economics, q is used for output. Because of this, the inverse notation f^{-1} used in a pure mathematics problem is not used when finding inverses of applied problems. Rather, the inverse of a function such as $C = C(q)$ will be $q = q(C)$. So $C = C(q)$ is a function that represents the cost C as a function of the output q, while $q = q(C)$ is a function that represents the output q as a function of the cost C. Problems 89–92 illustrate this idea.

89. Vehicle Stopping Distance Taking into account reaction time, the distance d (in feet) that a car requires to come to a complete stop while traveling r miles per hour is given by the function

$$d(r) = 6.97r - 90.39$$

(a) Express the speed r at which the car is traveling as a function of the distance d required to come to a complete stop.

(b) Verify that $r = r(d)$ is the inverse of $d = d(r)$ by showing that $r(d(r)) = r$ and $d(r(d)) = d$.

(c) Predict the speed that a car was traveling if the distance required to stop was 300 feet.

90. Height and Head Circumference The head circumference C of a child is related to the height H of the child (both in inches) through the function

$$H(C) = 2.15C - 10.53$$

(a) Express the head circumference C as a function of height H.

(b) Verify that $C = C(H)$ is the inverse of $H = H(C)$ by showing that $H(C(H)) = H$ and $C(H(C)) = C$.

(c) Predict the head circumference of a child who is 26 inches tall.

91. Ideal Body Weight One model for the ideal body weight W for men (in kilograms) as a function of height h (in inches) is given by the function

$$W(h) = 50 + 2.3(h - 60)$$

(a) What is the ideal weight of a 6-foot male?

(b) Express the height h as a function of weight W.

(c) Verify that $h = h(W)$ is the inverse of $W = W(h)$ by showing that $h(W(h)) = h$ and $W(h(W)) = W$.

(d) What is the height of a male who is at his ideal weight of 80 kilograms?

[**Note:** The ideal body weight W for women (in kilograms) as a function of height h (in inches) is given by $W(h) = 45.5 + 2.3(h - 60)$.]

92. Temperature Conversion The function $F(C) = \dfrac{9}{5}C + 32$ converts a temperature from C degrees Celsius to F degrees Fahrenheit.

(a) Express the temperature in degrees Celsius C as a function of the temperature in degrees Fahrenheit F.

(b) Verify that $C = C(F)$ is the inverse of $F = F(C)$ by showing that $C(F(C)) = C$ and $F(C(F)) = F$.

(c) What is the temperature in degrees Celsius if it is 70 degrees Fahrenheit?

93. Income Taxes The function

$$T(g) = 4675 + 0.25(g - 33,950)$$

represents the 2009 federal income tax T (in dollars) due for a "single" filer whose modified adjusted gross income is g dollars, where $33,950 \leq g \leq 82,250$.

(a) What is the domain of the function T?

(b) Given that the tax due T is an increasing linear function of modified adjusted gross income g, find the range of the function T.

(c) Find adjusted gross income g as a function of federal income tax T. What are the domain and the range of this function?

94. Income Taxes The function

$$T(g) = 1670 + 0.15(g - 16,700)$$

represents the 2009 federal income tax T (in dollars) due for a "married filing jointly" filer whose modified adjusted gross income is g dollars, where $16,700 \leq g \leq 67,900$.

(a) What is the domain of the function T?

(b) Given that the tax due T is an increasing linear function of modified adjusted gross income g, find the range of the function T.

(c) Find adjusted gross income g as a function of federal income tax T. What are the domain and the range of this function?

95. Gravity on Earth If a rock falls from a height of 100 meters on Earth, the height H (in meters) after t seconds is approximately

$$H(t) = 100 - 4.9t^2$$

(a) In general, quadratic functions are not one-to-one. However, the function H is one-to-one. Why?

(b) Find the inverse of H and verify your result.

(c) How long will it take a rock to fall 80 meters?

96. Period of a Pendulum The period T (in seconds) of a simple pendulum as a function of its length l (in feet) is given by

$$T(l) = 2\pi\sqrt{\dfrac{l}{32.2}}$$

(a) Express the length l as a function of the period T.
(b) How long is a pendulum whose period is 3 seconds?

97. Given

$$f(x) = \dfrac{ax + b}{cx + d}$$

find $f^{-1}(x)$. If $c \neq 0$, under what conditions on a, b, c, and d is $f = f^{-1}$?

Explaining Concepts: Discussion and Writing

98. Can a one-to-one function and its inverse be equal? What must be true about the graph of f for this to happen? Give some examples to support your conclusion.

99. Draw the graph of a one-to-one function that contains the points $(-2, -3)$, $(0, 0)$, and $(1, 5)$. Now draw the graph of its inverse. Compare your graph to those of other students. Discuss any similarities. What differences do you see?

100. Give an example of a function whose domain is the set of real numbers and that is neither increasing nor decreasing on its domain, but is one-to-one.

[**Hint:** Use a piecewise-defined function.]

101. Is every odd function one-to-one? Explain.

102. Suppose that $C(g)$ represents the cost C, in dollars, of manufacturing g cars. Explain what $C^{-1}(800{,}000)$ represents.

103. Explain why the horizontal-line test can be used to identify one-to-one functions from a graph.

'Are You Prepared?' Answers

1. Yes; for each input x there is one output y.
2. Increasing on $(0, \infty)$; decreasing on $(-\infty, 0)$
3. $\{x \mid x \neq -6, x \neq 3\}$

4. $\dfrac{x}{1-x}, x \neq 0, x \neq -1$

5.3 Exponential Functions

PREPARING FOR THIS SECTION *Before getting started, review the following:*

- Exponents (Appendix A, Section A.1, pp. A7–A9, and Section A.10, pp. A81–A87)
- Graphing Techniques: Transformations (Section 2.5, pp. 90–99)
- Solving Equations (Appendix A, Section A.6, pp. A44–A51)

- Average Rate of Change (Section 2.3, pp. 74–76)
- Quadratic Functions (Section 3.3, pp. 134–142)
- Linear Functions (Section 3.1, pp. 118–121)
- Horizontal Asymptotes (Section 4.2, pp. 191–192)

Now Work the 'Are You Prepared?' problems on page 278.

OBJECTIVES 1 Evaluate Exponential Functions (p. 267)
2 Graph Exponential Functions (p. 271)
3 Define the Number e (p. 274)
4 Solve Exponential Equations (p. 276)

1 Evaluate Exponential Functions

In Appendix A, Section A.10, we give a definition for raising a real number a to a rational power. Based on that discussion, we gave meaning to expressions of the form

$$a^r$$

where the base a is a positive real number and the exponent r is a rational number.

But what is the meaning of a^x, where the base a is a positive real number and the exponent x is an irrational number? Although a rigorous definition requires methods discussed in calculus, the basis for the definition is easy to follow: Select a rational number r that is formed by truncating (removing) all but a finite number of digits from the irrational number x. Then it is reasonable to expect that

$$a^x \approx a^r$$

For example, take the irrational number $\pi = 3.14159\ldots$. Then an approximation to a^π is

$$a^\pi \approx a^{3.14}$$

where the digits after the hundredths position have been removed from the value for π. A better approximation would be

$$a^\pi \approx a^{3.14159}$$

where the digits after the hundred-thousandths position have been removed. Continuing in this way, we can obtain approximations to a^π to any desired degree of accuracy.

Most calculators have an $\boxed{x^y}$ key or a caret key $\boxed{\wedge}$ for working with exponents. To evaluate expressions of the form a^x, enter the base a, then press the $\boxed{x^y}$ key (or the $\boxed{\wedge}$ key), enter the exponent x, and press $\boxed{=}$ (or $\boxed{\text{ENTER}}$).

EXAMPLE 1   **Using a Calculator to Evaluate Powers of 2**

Using a calculator, evaluate:

(a) $2^{1.4}$ (b) $2^{1.41}$ (c) $2^{1.414}$ (d) $2^{1.4142}$ (e) $2^{\sqrt{2}}$

Solution   (a) $2^{1.4} \approx 2.639015822$ (b) $2^{1.41} \approx 2.657371628$
(c) $2^{1.414} \approx 2.66474965$ (d) $2^{1.4142} \approx 2.665119089$
(e) $2^{\sqrt{2}} \approx 2.665144143$

Now Work PROBLEM 15

It can be shown that the familiar laws for rational exponents hold for real exponents.

THEOREM   **Laws of Exponents**

If s, t, a, and b are real numbers with $a > 0$ and $b > 0$, then

$$a^s \cdot a^t = a^{s+t} \qquad (a^s)^t = a^{st} \qquad (ab)^s = a^s \cdot b^s$$

$$1^s = 1 \qquad a^{-s} = \frac{1}{a^s} = \left(\frac{1}{a}\right)^s \qquad a^0 = 1 \qquad \textbf{(1)}$$

Introduction to Exponential Growth

Suppose a function f has the following two properties:

1. The value of f doubles with every 1-unit increase in the independent variable x.
2. The value of f at $x = 0$ is 5, so $f(0) = 5$.

Table 1 shows values of the function f for $x = 0, 1, 2, 3$, and 4.
We seek an equation $y = f(x)$ that describes this function f. The key fact is that the value of f doubles for every 1-unit increase in x.

$f(0) = 5$
$f(1) = 2f(0) = 2 \cdot 5 = 5 \cdot 2^1$ *Double the value of f at 0 to get the value at 1.*
$f(2) = 2f(1) = 2(5 \cdot 2) = 5 \cdot 2^2$ *Double the value of f at 1 to get the value at 2.*
$f(3) = 2f(2) = 2(5 \cdot 2^2) = 5 \cdot 2^3$
$f(4) = 2f(3) = 2(5 \cdot 2^3) = 5 \cdot 2^4$

The pattern leads us to

$$f(x) = 2f(x-1) = 2(5 \cdot 2^{x-1}) = 5 \cdot 2^x$$

Table 1

x	f(x)
0	5
1	10
2	20
3	40
4	80

DEFINITION

An **exponential function** is a function of the form

$$f(x) = Ca^x$$

where a is a positive real number $(a > 0)$, $a \neq 1$, and $C \neq 0$ is a real number. The domain of f is the set of all real numbers. The base a is the **growth factor,** and because $f(0) = Ca^0 = C$, we call C the **initial value.**

WARNING It is important to distinguish a power function, $g(x) = ax^n$, $n \geq 2$, an integer, from an exponential function, $f(x) = C \cdot a^x$, $a \neq 1$, $a > 0$. In a power function, the base is a variable and the exponent is a constant. In an exponential function, the base is a constant and the exponent is a variable. ∎

In the definition of an exponential function, we exclude the base $a = 1$ because this function is simply the constant function $f(x) = C \cdot 1^x = C$. We also need to exclude bases that are negative; otherwise, we would have to exclude many values of x from the domain, such as $x = \dfrac{1}{2}$ and $x = \dfrac{3}{4}$. [Recall that $(-2)^{1/2} = \sqrt{-2}$, $(-3)^{3/4} = \sqrt[4]{(-3)^3} = \sqrt[4]{-27}$, and so on, are not defined in the set of real numbers.] Finally, transformations (vertical shifts, horizontal shifts, reflections, and so on) of a function of the form $f(x) = Ca^x$ also represent exponential functions.

Some examples of exponential functions are

$$f(x) = 2^x \qquad F(x) = \left(\frac{1}{3}\right)^x + 5 \qquad G(x) = 2 \cdot 3^{x-3}$$

Notice for each function that the base of the exponential expression is a constant and the exponent contains a variable.

In the function $f(x) = 5 \cdot 2^x$, notice that the ratio of consecutive outputs is constant for 1-unit increases in the input. This ratio equals the constant 2, the base of the exponential function. In other words,

$$\frac{f(1)}{f(0)} = \frac{5 \cdot 2^1}{5} = 2 \qquad \frac{f(2)}{f(1)} = \frac{5 \cdot 2^2}{5 \cdot 2^1} = 2 \qquad \frac{f(3)}{f(2)} = \frac{5 \cdot 2^3}{5 \cdot 2^2} = 2 \quad \text{and so on}$$

This leads to the following result.

THEOREM

For an exponential function $f(x) = Ca^x$, where $a > 0$ and $a \neq 1$, if x is any real number, then

$$\frac{f(x + 1)}{f(x)} = a \quad \text{or} \quad f(x + 1) = af(x)$$

In Words

For 1-unit changes in the input x of an exponential function $f(x) = C \cdot a^x$, the ratio of consecutive outputs is the constant a.

Proof

$$\frac{f(x + 1)}{f(x)} = \frac{Ca^{x+1}}{Ca^x} = a^{x+1-x} = a^1 = a \qquad \blacksquare$$

EXAMPLE 2

Identifying Linear or Exponential Functions

Determine whether the given function is linear, exponential, or neither. For those that are linear, find a linear function that models the data. For those that are exponential, find an exponential function that models the data.

(a)

x	y
−1	5
0	2
1	−1
2	−4
3	−7

(b)

x	y
−1	32
0	16
1	8
2	4
3	2

(c)

x	y
−1	2
0	4
1	7
2	11
3	16

Solution For each function, compute the average rate of change of y with respect to x and the ratio of consecutive outputs. If the average rate of change is constant, then the function is linear. If the ratio of consecutive outputs is constant, then the function is exponential.

Table 2

x	y	Average Rate of Change	Ratio of Consecutive Outputs
-1	5		
		$\dfrac{\Delta y}{\Delta x} = \dfrac{2-5}{0-(-1)} = -3$	$\dfrac{2}{5}$
0	2		
		-3	$-\dfrac{1}{2}$
1	-1		
		-3	4
2	-4		
		-3	$\dfrac{7}{4}$
3	-7		

(a)

x	y	Average Rate of Change	Ratio of Consecutive Outputs
-1	32		
		$\dfrac{\Delta y}{\Delta x} = \dfrac{16-32}{0-(-1)} = -16$	$\dfrac{16}{32} = \dfrac{1}{2}$
0	16		
		-8	$\dfrac{8}{16} = \dfrac{1}{2}$
1	8		
		-4	$\dfrac{4}{8} = \dfrac{1}{2}$
2	4		
		-2	$\dfrac{2}{4} = \dfrac{1}{2}$
3	2		

(b)

x	y	Average Rate of Change	Ratio of Consecutive Outputs
-1	2		
		$\dfrac{\Delta y}{\Delta x} = \dfrac{4-2}{0-(-1)} = 2$	2
0	4		
		3	$\dfrac{7}{4}$
1	7		
		4	$\dfrac{11}{7}$
2	11		
		5	$\dfrac{16}{11}$
3	16		

(c)

(a) See Table 2(a). The average rate of change for every 1-unit increase in x is -3. Therefore, the function is a linear function. In a linear function the average rate of change is the slope m, so $m = -3$. The y-intercept b is the value of the function at $x = 0$, so $b = 2$. The linear function that models the data is $f(x) = mx + b = -3x + 2$.

(b) See Table 2(b). For this function, the average rate of change from -1 to 0 is -16, and the average rate of change from 0 to 1 is -8. Because the average rate of change is not constant, the function is not a linear function. The ratio of consecutive outputs for a 1-unit increase in the inputs is a constant, $\dfrac{1}{2}$. Because the ratio of consecutive outputs is constant, the function is an exponential function with growth factor $a = \dfrac{1}{2}$. The initial value of the exponential function is $C = 16$. Therefore, the exponential function that models the data is

$$g(x) = Ca^x = 16 \cdot \left(\frac{1}{2}\right)^x.$$

(c) See Table 2(c). For this function, the average rate of change from -1 to 0 is 2, and the average rate of change from 0 to 1 is 3. Because the average rate of change is not constant, the function is not a linear function. The ratio of consecutive outputs from -1 to 0 is 2, and the ratio of consecutive outputs from 0 to 1 is $\frac{7}{4}$. Because the ratio of consecutive outputs is not a constant, the function is not an exponential function.

Now Work PROBLEM 25

2 Graph Exponential Functions

If we know how to graph an exponential function of the form $f(x) = a^x$, then we could use transformations (shifting, stretching, and so on) to obtain the graph of any exponential function.

First, we graph the exponential function $f(x) = 2^x$.

EXAMPLE 3

Graphing an Exponential Function

Graph the exponential function: $f(x) = 2^x$

Solution

The domain of $f(x) = 2^x$ is the set of all real numbers. We begin by locating some points on the graph of $f(x) = 2^x$, as listed in Table 3.

Since $2^x > 0$ for all x, the range of f is $(0, \infty)$. From this, we conclude that the graph has no x-intercepts, and, in fact, the graph will lie above the x-axis for all x. As Table 3 indicates, the y-intercept is 1. Table 3 also indicates that as $x \rightarrow -\infty$ the values of $f(x) = 2^x$ get closer and closer to 0. We conclude that the x-axis ($y = 0$) is a horizontal asymptote to the graph as $x \rightarrow -\infty$. This gives us the end behavior for x large and negative.

To determine the end behavior for x large and positive, look again at Table 3. As $x \rightarrow \infty$, $f(x) = 2^x$ grows very quickly, causing the graph of $f(x) = 2^x$ to rise very rapidly. It is apparent that f is an increasing function and hence is one-to-one.

Using all this information, we plot some of the points from Table 3 and connect them with a smooth, continuous curve, as shown in Figure 18.

Table 3

x	$f(x) = 2^x$
-10	$2^{-10} \approx 0.00098$
-3	$2^{-3} = \dfrac{1}{8}$
-2	$2^{-2} = \dfrac{1}{4}$
-1	$2^{-1} = \dfrac{1}{2}$
0	$2^0 = 1$
1	$2^1 = 2$
2	$2^2 = 4$
3	$2^3 = 8$
10	$2^{10} = 1024$

Figure 18

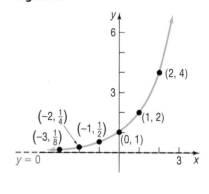

As we shall see, graphs that look like the one in Figure 18 occur very frequently in a variety of situations. For example, the graph in Figure 19 on page 272 illustrates the number of cellular telephone subscribers at the end of each year from 1985 to 2008. We might conclude from this graph that the number of cellular telephone subscribers is growing *exponentially*.

Figure 19

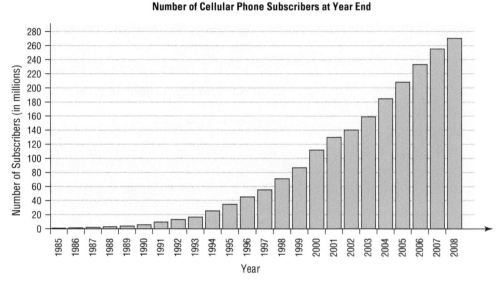

Number of Cellular Phone Subscribers at Year End

We shall have more to say about situations that lead to exponential growth later in this chapter. For now, we continue to seek properties of exponential functions.

The graph of $f(x) = 2^x$ in Figure 18 is typical of all exponential functions of the form $f(x) = a^x$ with $a > 1$. Such functions are increasing functions and hence are one-to-one. Their graphs lie above the x-axis, pass through the point $(0, 1)$, and thereafter rise rapidly as $x \to \infty$. As $x \to -\infty$, the x-axis ($y = 0$) is a horizontal asymptote. There are no vertical asymptotes. Finally, the graphs are smooth and continuous with no corners or gaps.

Figure 20 illustrates the graphs of two more exponential functions whose bases are larger than 1. Notice that the larger the base, the steeper the graph is when $x > 0$, and when $x < 0$, the larger the base, the closer the graph of the equation is to the x-axis.

Figure 20

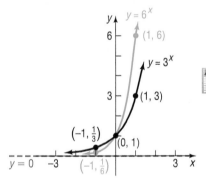

Seeing the Concept

Graph $Y_1 = 2^x$ and compare what you see to Figure 18. Clear the screen and graph $Y_1 = 3^x$ and $Y_2 = 6^x$ and compare what you see to Figure 20. Clear the screen and graph $Y_1 = 10^x$ and $Y_2 = 100^x$.

Properties of the Exponential Function $f(x) = a^x$, $a > 1$

1. The domain is the set of all real numbers or $(-\infty, \infty)$ using interval notation; the range is the set of positive real numbers or $(0, \infty)$ using interval notation.

2. There are no x-intercepts; the y-intercept is 1.

3. The x-axis ($y = 0$) is a horizontal asymptote as $x \to -\infty \left[\lim_{x \to -\infty} a^x = 0 \right]$.

4. $f(x) = a^x$, where $a > 1$, is an increasing function and is one-to-one.

5. The graph of f contains the points $(0, 1)$, $(1, a)$, and $\left(-1, \dfrac{1}{a}\right)$.

6. The graph of f is smooth and continuous, with no corners or gaps. See Figure 21.

Figure 21

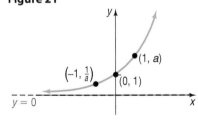

Now consider $f(x) = a^x$ when $0 < a < 1$.

EXAMPLE 4

Graphing an Exponential Function

Graph the exponential function: $f(x) = \left(\dfrac{1}{2}\right)^x$

Solution

The domain of $f(x) = \left(\dfrac{1}{2}\right)^x$ consists of all real numbers. As before, we locate some points on the graph by creating Table 4. Since $\left(\dfrac{1}{2}\right)^x > 0$ for all x, the range of f is the interval $(0, \infty)$. The graph lies above the x-axis and so has no x-intercepts. The y-intercept is 1. As $x \to -\infty$, $f(x) = \left(\dfrac{1}{2}\right)^x$ grows very quickly. As $x \to \infty$, the values of $f(x)$ approach 0. The x-axis $(y = 0)$ is a horizontal asymptote as $x \to \infty$. It is apparent that f is a decreasing function and so is one-to-one. Figure 22 illustrates the graph.

Table 4

x	$f(x) = \left(\dfrac{1}{2}\right)^x$
-10	$\left(\dfrac{1}{2}\right)^{-10} = 1024$
-3	$\left(\dfrac{1}{2}\right)^{-3} = 8$
-2	$\left(\dfrac{1}{2}\right)^{-2} = 4$
-1	$\left(\dfrac{1}{2}\right)^{-1} = 2$
0	$\left(\dfrac{1}{2}\right)^{0} = 1$
1	$\left(\dfrac{1}{2}\right)^{1} = \dfrac{1}{2}$
2	$\left(\dfrac{1}{2}\right)^{2} = \dfrac{1}{4}$
3	$\left(\dfrac{1}{2}\right)^{3} = \dfrac{1}{8}$
10	$\left(\dfrac{1}{2}\right)^{10} \approx 0.00098$

Figure 22

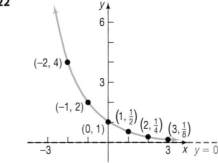

We could have obtained the graph of $y = \left(\dfrac{1}{2}\right)^x$ from the graph of $y = 2^x$ using transformations. The graph of $y = \left(\dfrac{1}{2}\right)^x = 2^{-x}$ is a reflection about the y-axis of the graph of $y = 2^x$ (replace x by $-x$). See Figures 23(a) and (b).

Figure 23

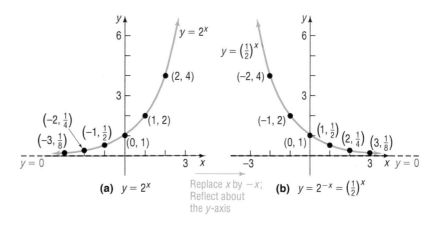

(a) $y = 2^x$

Replace x by $-x$;
Reflect about
the y-axis

(b) $y = 2^{-x} = \left(\dfrac{1}{2}\right)^x$

 Seeing the Concept

Using a graphing utility, simultaneously graph:

(a) $Y_1 = 3^x$, $Y_2 = \left(\dfrac{1}{3}\right)^x$

(b) $Y_1 = 6^x$, $Y_2 = \left(\dfrac{1}{6}\right)^x$

Conclude that the graph of $Y_2 = \left(\dfrac{1}{a}\right)^x$, for $a > 0$, is the reflection about the y-axis of the graph of $Y_1 = a^x$.

The graph of $f(x) = \left(\dfrac{1}{2}\right)^x$ in Figure 22 is typical of all exponential functions of the form $f(x) = a^x$ with $0 < a < 1$. Such functions are decreasing and one-to-one. Their graphs lie above the x-axis and pass through the point $(0, 1)$. The graphs rise rapidly as $x \to -\infty$. As $x \to \infty$, the x-axis $(y = 0)$ is a horizontal asymptote. There are no vertical asymptotes. Finally, the graphs are smooth and continuous, with no corners or gaps.

Figure 24

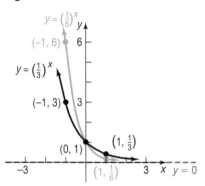

Figure 24 illustrates the graphs of two more exponential functions whose bases are between 0 and 1. Notice that the smaller base results in a graph that is steeper when $x < 0$. When $x > 0$, the graph of the equation with the smaller base is closer to the x-axis.

Properties of the Exponential Function $f(x) = a^x$, $0 < a < 1$

1. The domain is the set of all real numbers or $(-\infty, \infty)$ using interval notation; the range is the set of positive real numbers or $(0, \infty)$ using interval notation.

2. There are no x-intercepts; the y-intercept is 1.

3. The x-axis ($y = 0$) is a horizontal asymptote as $x \to \infty$ $\left[\lim\limits_{x \to \infty} a^x = 0\right]$.

4. $f(x) = a^x$, $0 < a < 1$, is a decreasing function and is one-to-one.

5. The graph of f contains the points $\left(-1, \dfrac{1}{a}\right)$, $(0, 1)$, and $(1, a)$.

6. The graph of f is smooth and continuous, with no corners or gaps. See Figure 25.

Figure 25

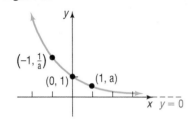

EXAMPLE 5

Graphing Exponential Functions Using Transformations

Graph $f(x) = 2^{-x} - 3$ and determine the domain, range, and horizontal asymptote of f.

Solution Begin with the graph of $y = 2^x$. Figure 26 shows the stages.

Figure 26

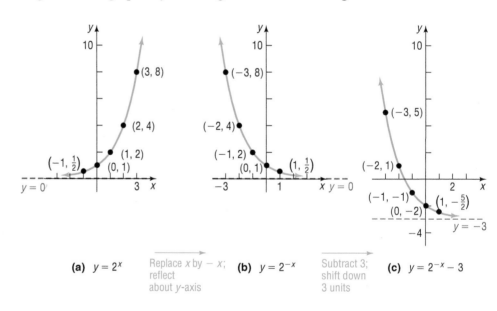

(a) $y = 2^x$ Replace x by $-x$; reflect about y-axis   (b) $y = 2^{-x}$ Subtract 3; shift down 3 units   (c) $y = 2^{-x} - 3$

As Figure 26(c) illustrates, the domain of $f(x) = 2^{-x} - 3$ is the interval $(-\infty, \infty)$ and the range is the interval $(-3, \infty)$. The horizontal asymptote of f is the line $y = -3$.

Now Work PROBLEM 41

3 Define the Number e

As we shall see shortly, many problems that occur in nature require the use of an exponential function whose base is a certain irrational number, symbolized by the letter e.

One way of arriving at this important number e is given next.

DEFINITION   The **number e** is defined as the number that the expression

$$\left(1 + \frac{1}{n}\right)^n \tag{2}$$

approaches as $n \rightarrow \infty$. In calculus, this is expressed using limit notation as

$$e = \lim_{n \to \infty}\left(1 + \frac{1}{n}\right)^n$$

Table 5 illustrates what happens to the defining expression (2) as n takes on increasingly large values. The last number in the right column in the table is correct to nine decimal places and is the same as the entry given for e on your calculator (if expressed correctly to nine decimal places).

The exponential function $f(x) = e^x$, whose base is the number e, occurs with such frequency in applications that it is usually referred to as *the* exponential function. Indeed, most calculators have the key $\boxed{e^x}$ or $\boxed{\exp(x)}$, which may be used to evaluate the exponential function for a given value of x.*

Table 5

n	$\dfrac{1}{n}$	$1 + \dfrac{1}{n}$	$\left(1 + \dfrac{1}{n}\right)^n$
1	1	2	2
2	0.5	1.5	2.25
5	0.2	1.2	2.48832
10	0.1	1.1	2.59374246
100	0.01	1.01	2.704813829
1,000	0.001	1.001	2.716923932
10,000	0.0001	1.0001	2.718145927
100,000	0.00001	1.00001	2.718268237
1,000,000	0.000001	1.000001	2.718280469
1,000,000,000	10^{-9}	$1 + 10^{-9}$	2.718281827

Table 6

x	e^x
-2	$e^{-2} \approx 0.14$
-1	$e^{-1} \approx 0.37$
0	$e^0 \approx 1$
1	$e^1 \approx 2.72$
2	$e^2 \approx 7.39$

Figure 27
$y = e^x$

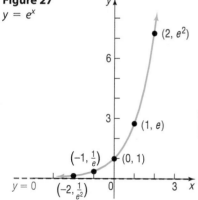

Now use your calculator to approximate e^x for $x = -2$, $x = -1$, $x = 0$, $x = 1$, and $x = 2$, as we have done to create Table 6. The graph of the exponential function $f(x) = e^x$ is given in Figure 27. Since $2 < e < 3$, the graph of $y = e^x$ lies between the graphs of $y = 2^x$ and $y = 3^x$. Do you see why? (Refer to Figures 18 and 20.)

 Seeing the Concept

Graph $Y_1 = e^x$ and compare what you see to Figure 27. Use eVALUEate or TABLE to verify the points on the graph shown in Figure 27. Now graph $Y_2 = 2^x$ and $Y_3 = 3^x$ on the same screen as $Y_1 = e^x$. Notice that the graph of $Y_1 = e^x$ lies between these two graphs.

EXAMPLE 6   **Graphing Exponential Functions Using Transformations**

Graph $f(x) = -e^{x-3}$ and determine the domain, range, and horizontal asymptote of f.

Solution   Begin with the graph of $y = e^x$. Figure 28 shows the stages.

* If your calculator does not have one of these keys, refer to your Owner's Manual.

Figure 28

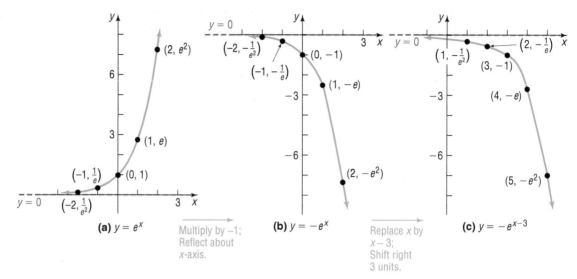

(a) $y = e^x$ → *Multiply by −1; Reflect about x-axis.* → **(b)** $y = -e^x$ → *Replace x by x − 3; Shift right 3 units.* → **(c)** $y = -e^{x-3}$

As Figure 28(c) illustrates, the domain of $f(x) = -e^{x-3}$ is the interval $(-\infty, \infty)$, and the range is the interval $(-\infty, 0)$. The horizontal asymptote is the line $y = 0$.

Now Work PROBLEM 53

4 Solve Exponential Equations

Equations that involve terms of the form a^x, where $a > 0$ and $a \neq 1$, are referred to as **exponential equations.** Such equations can sometimes be solved by appropriately applying the Laws of Exponents and property (3):

$$\text{If}\quad a^u = a^v,\quad \text{then}\quad u = v. \qquad\qquad (3)$$

Property (3) is a consequence of the fact that exponential functions are one-to-one. To use property (3), each side of the equality must be written with the same base.

EXAMPLE 7 | **Solving Exponential Equations**

Solve each exponential equation.

(a) $3^{x+1} = 81$ (b) $4^{2x-1} = 8^{x+3}$

Solution   (a) Since $81 = 3^4$, write the equation as

$$3^{x+1} = 81 = 3^4$$

Now we have the same base, 3, on each side. Set the exponents equal to each other to obtain

$$x + 1 = 4$$
$$x = 3$$

The solution set is $\{3\}$.

(b)
$$4^{2x-1} = 8^{x+3}$$
$$(2^2)^{(2x-1)} = (2^3)^{(x+3)} \qquad 4 = 2^2;\, 8 = 2^3$$
$$2^{2(2x-1)} = 2^{3(x+3)} \qquad (a^r)^s = a^{rs}$$
$$2(2x - 1) = 3(x + 3) \qquad \text{If } a^u = a^v, \text{ then } u = v.$$
$$4x - 2 = 3x + 9$$
$$x = 11$$

The solution set is $\{11\}$.

Now Work PROBLEM 63

EXAMPLE 8   **Solving an Exponential Equation**

Solve: $e^{-x^2} = (e^x)^2 \cdot \dfrac{1}{e^3}$

Solution   Use the Laws of Exponents first to get a single expression with the base e on the right side.

$$(e^x)^2 \cdot \frac{1}{e^3} = e^{2x} \cdot e^{-3} = e^{2x-3}$$

As a result,

$$e^{-x^2} = e^{2x-3}$$
$$-x^2 = 2x - 3 \quad \text{Apply property (3).}$$
$$x^2 + 2x - 3 = 0 \quad \text{Place the quadratic equation in standard form.}$$
$$(x + 3)(x - 1) = 0 \quad \text{Factor.}$$
$$x = -3 \quad \text{or} \quad x = 1 \quad \text{Use the Zero-Product Property.}$$

The solution set is $\{-3, 1\}$.

EXAMPLE 9   **Exponential Probability**

Between 9:00 PM and 10:00 PM cars arrive at Burger King's drive-thru at the rate of 12 cars per hour (0.2 car per minute). The following formula from statistics can be used to determine the probability that a car will arrive within t minutes of 9:00 PM.

$$F(t) = 1 - e^{-0.2t}$$

(a) Determine the probability that a car will arrive within 5 minutes of 9 PM (that is, before 9:05 PM).

(b) Determine the probability that a car will arrive within 30 minutes of 9 PM (before 9:30 PM).

(c) Graph F using your graphing utility.

(d) What value does F approach as t increases without bound in the positive direction?

Solution   (a) The probability that a car will arrive within 5 minutes is found by evaluating $F(t)$ at $t = 5$.

$$F(5) = 1 - e^{-0.2(5)} \approx 0.63212$$
$$\uparrow$$
$$\text{Use a calculator.}$$

We conclude that there is a 63% probability that a car will arrive within 5 minutes.

(b) The probability that a car will arrive within 30 minutes is found by evaluating $F(t)$ at $t = 30$.

$$F(30) = 1 - e^{-0.2(30)} \approx 0.9975$$
$$\uparrow$$
$$\text{Use a calculator.}$$

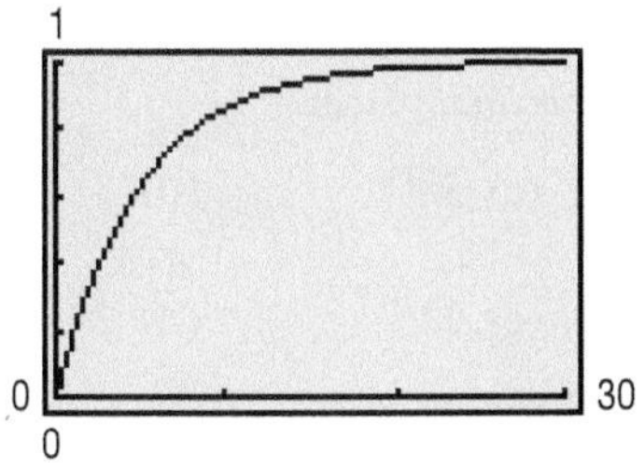

There is a 99.75% probability that a car will arrive within 30 minutes.

(c) See Figure 29 for the graph of F.

(d) As time passes, the probability that a car will arrive increases. The value that F approaches can be found by letting $t \to \infty$. Since $e^{-0.2t} = \dfrac{1}{e^{0.2t}}$, it follows that $e^{-0.2t} \to 0$ as $t \to \infty$. We conclude that F approaches 1 as t gets large. The algebraic analysis is confirmed by Figure 29.

Figure 29

Now Work PROBLEM 107

SUMMARY Properties of the Exponential Function

$f(x) = a^x, \quad a > 1$ Domain: the interval $(-\infty, \infty)$; range: the interval $(0, \infty)$
x-intercepts: none; y-intercept: 1
Horizontal asymptote: x-axis $(y = 0)$ as $x \to -\infty$
Increasing; one-to-one; smooth; continuous
See Figure 21 for a typical graph.

$f(x) = a^x, \quad 0 < a < 1$ Domain: the interval $(-\infty, \infty)$; range: the interval $(0, \infty)$
x-intercepts: none; y-intercept: 1
Horizontal asymptote: x-axis $(y = 0)$ as $x \to \infty$
Decreasing; one-to-one; smooth; continuous
See Figure 25 for a typical graph.

If $a^u = a^v$, then $u = v$.

5.3 Assess Your Understanding

'Are You Prepared?' *Answers are given at the end of these exercises. If you get a wrong answer, read the pages listed in red.*

1. $4^3 = $ _____; $8^{2/3} = $ ____; $3^{-2} = $ _____ . (pp. A7–A9 and pp. A81–A87)

2. Solve: $x^2 + 3x = 4$ (pp. A44–A51)

3. *True or False* To graph $y = (x - 2)^3$, shift the graph of $y = x^3$ to the left 2 units. (pp. 90–99)

4. Find the average rate of change of $f(x) = 3x - 5$ from $x = 0$ to $x = 4$. (pp. 74–76; 118–121)

5. *True or False* The function $f(x) = \dfrac{2x}{x - 3}$ has $y = 2$ as a horizontal asymptote. (pp. 191–192)

Concepts and Vocabulary

6. A(n) _____ is a function of the form $f(x) = Ca^x$, where $a > 0, a \neq 1$, and $C \neq 0$ are real numbers. The base a is the _____ and C is the _____ .

7. For an exponential function $f(x) = Ca^x, \dfrac{f(x + 1)}{f(x)} = $ ___ .

8. *True or False* The domain of the exponential function $f(x) = a^x$, where $a > 0$ and $a \neq 1$, is the set of all real numbers.

9. *True or False* The range of the exponential function $f(x) = a^x$, where $a > 0$ and $a \neq 1$, is the set of all real numbers.

10. *True or False* The graph of the exponential function $f(x) = a^x$, where $a > 0$ and $a \neq 1$, has no x-intercept.

11. The graph of every exponential function $f(x) = a^x$, where $a > 0$ and $a \neq 1$, passes through three points: _____, _____, and _____.

12. If the graph of the exponential function $f(x) = a^x$, where $a > 0$ and $a \neq 1$, is decreasing, then a must be less than _____.

13. If $3^x = 3^4$, then $x = $ _____.

14. *True or False* The graphs of $y = 3^x$ and $y = \left(\dfrac{1}{3}\right)^x$ are identical.

Skill Building

In Problems 15–24, approximate each number using a calculator. Express your answer rounded to three decimal places.

15. (a) $3^{2.2}$ (b) $3^{2.23}$ (c) $3^{2.236}$ (d) $3^{\sqrt{5}}$

16. (a) $5^{1.7}$ (b) $5^{1.73}$ (c) $5^{1.732}$ (d) $5^{\sqrt{3}}$

17. (a) $2^{3.14}$ (b) $2^{3.141}$ (c) $2^{3.1415}$ (d) 2^{π}

18. (a) $2^{2.7}$ (b) $2^{2.71}$ (c) $2^{2.718}$ (d) 2^{e}

19. (a) $3.1^{2.7}$ (b) $3.14^{2.71}$ (c) $3.141^{2.718}$ (d) π^{e}

20. (a) $2.7^{3.1}$ (b) $2.71^{3.14}$ (c) $2.718^{3.141}$ (d) e^{π}

21. $e^{1.2}$ 22. $e^{-1.3}$ 23. $e^{-0.85}$ 24. $e^{2.1}$

In Problems 25–32, determine whether the given function is linear, exponential, or neither. For those that are linear functions, find a linear function that models the data; for those that are exponential, find an exponential function that models the data.

25.

x	f(x)
−1	3
0	6
1	12
2	18
3	30

26.

x	g(x)
−1	2
0	5
1	8
2	11
3	14

27.

x	H(x)
−1	$\frac{1}{4}$
0	1
1	4
2	16
3	64

28.

x	F(x)
−1	$\frac{2}{3}$
0	1
1	$\frac{3}{2}$
2	$\frac{9}{4}$
3	$\frac{27}{8}$

29.

x	f(x)
−1	$\frac{3}{2}$
0	3
1	6
2	12
3	24

30.

x	g(x)
−1	6
0	1
1	0
2	3
3	10

31.

x	H(x)
−1	2
0	4
1	6
2	8
3	10

32.

x	F(x)
−1	$\frac{1}{2}$
0	$\frac{1}{4}$
1	$\frac{1}{8}$
2	$\frac{1}{16}$
3	$\frac{1}{32}$

In Problems 33–40, the graph of an exponential function is given. Match each graph to one of the following functions.

(a) $y = 3^x$ (b) $y = 3^{-x}$ (c) $y = -3^x$ (d) $y = -3^{-x}$

(e) $y = 3^x - 1$ (f) $y = 3^{x-1}$ (g) $y = 3^{1-x}$ (h) $y = 1 - 3^x$

33.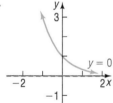

34.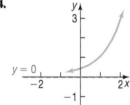

35.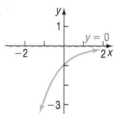

36.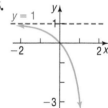

37.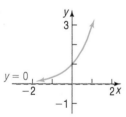

38.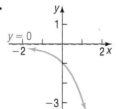

39.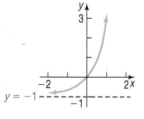

40.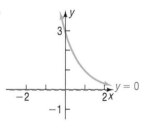

In Problems 41–52, use transformations to graph each function. Determine the domain, range, and horizontal asymptote of each function.

41. $f(x) = 2^x + 1$

42. $f(x) = 3^x - 2$

43. $f(x) = 3^{x-1}$

44. $f(x) = 2^{x+2}$

45. $f(x) = 3 \cdot \left(\frac{1}{2}\right)^x$

46. $f(x) = 4 \cdot \left(\frac{1}{3}\right)^x$

47. $f(x) = 3^{-x} - 2$

48. $f(x) = -3^x + 1$

49. $f(x) = 2 + 4^{x-1}$

50. $f(x) = 1 - 2^{x+3}$

51. $f(x) = 2 + 3^{x/2}$

52. $f(x) = 1 - 2^{-x/3}$

In Problems 53–60, begin with the graph of $y = e^x$ [Figure 27] and use transformations to graph each function. Determine the domain, range, and horizontal asymptote of each function.

53. $f(x) = e^{-x}$

54. $f(x) = -e^x$

55. $f(x) = e^{x+2}$

56. $f(x) = e^x - 1$

57. $f(x) = 5 - e^{-x}$

58. $f(x) = 9 - 3e^{-x}$

59. $f(x) = 2 - e^{-x/2}$

60. $f(x) = 7 - 3e^{2x}$

In Problems 61–80, solve each equation.

61. $7^x = 7^3$

62. $5^x = 5^{-6}$

63. $2^{-x} = 16$

64. $3^{-x} = 81$

65. $\left(\frac{1}{5}\right)^x = \frac{1}{25}$

66. $\left(\frac{1}{4}\right)^x = \frac{1}{64}$

67. $2^{2x-1} = 4$

68. $5^{x+3} = \frac{1}{5}$

69. $3^{x^3} = 9^x$

70. $4^{x^2} = 2^x$

71. $8^{-x+14} = 16^x$

72. $9^{-x+15} = 27^x$

73. $3^{x^2-7} = 27^{2x}$

74. $5^{x^2+8} = 125^{2x}$

75. $4^x \cdot 2^{x^2} = 16^2$

76. $9^{2x} \cdot 27^{x^2} = 3^{-1}$

77. $e^x = e^{3x+8}$

78. $e^{3x} = e^{2-x}$

79. $e^{x^2} = e^{3x} \cdot \frac{1}{e^2}$

80. $(e^4)^x \cdot e^{x^2} = e^{12}$

81. If $4^x = 7$, what does 4^{-2x} equal?

82. If $2^x = 3$, what does 4^{-x} equal?

83. If $3^{-x} = 2$, what does 3^{2x} equal?

84. If $5^{-x} = 3$, what does 5^{3x} equal?

In Problems 85–88, determine the exponential function whose graph is given.

85.

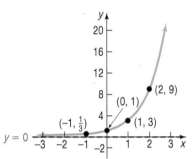

86.

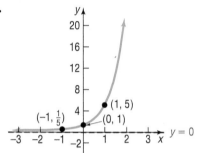

87.

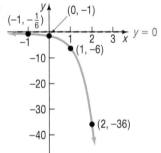

88.

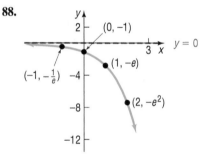

89. Find an exponential function with horizontal asymptote $y = 2$ whose graph contains the points $(0, 3)$ and $(1, 5)$.

90. Find an exponential function with horizontal asymptote $y = -3$ whose graph contains the points $(0, -2)$ and $(-2, 1)$.

Mixed Practice

91. Suppose that $f(x) = 2^x$.
(a) What is $f(4)$? What point is on the graph of f?
(b) If $f(x) = \frac{1}{16}$, what is x? What point is on the graph of f?

92. Suppose that $f(x) = 3^x$.
(a) What is $f(4)$? What point is on the graph of f?
(b) If $f(x) = \frac{1}{9}$, what is x? What point is on the graph of f?

93. Suppose that $g(x) = 4^x + 2$.
(a) What is $g(-1)$? What point is on the graph of g?
(b) If $g(x) = 66$, what is x? What point is on the graph of g?

94. Suppose that $g(x) = 5^x - 3$.
(a) What is $g(-1)$? What point is on the graph of g?
(b) If $g(x) = 122$, what is x? What point is on the graph of g?

95. Suppose that $H(x) = \left(\frac{1}{2}\right)^x - 4$.

(a) What is $H(-6)$? What point is on the graph of H?
(b) If $H(x) = 12$, what is x? What point is on the graph of H?
(c) Find the zero of H.

96. Suppose that $F(x) = \left(\frac{1}{3}\right)^x - 3$.

(a) What is $F(-5)$? What point is on the graph of F?
(b) If $F(x) = 24$, what is x? What point is on the graph of F?
(c) Find the zero of F.

In Problems 97–100, graph each function. Based on the graph, state the domain and the range and find any intercepts.

97. $f(x) = \begin{cases} e^{-x} & \text{if } x < 0 \\ e^x & \text{if } x \geq 0 \end{cases}$

98. $f(x) = \begin{cases} e^x & \text{if } x < 0 \\ e^{-x} & \text{if } x \geq 0 \end{cases}$

99. $f(x) = \begin{cases} -e^x & \text{if } x < 0 \\ -e^{-x} & \text{if } x \geq 0 \end{cases}$

100. $f(x) = \begin{cases} -e^{-x} & \text{if } x < 0 \\ -e^x & \text{if } x \geq 0 \end{cases}$

Applications and Extensions

101. Optics If a single pane of glass obliterates 3% of the light passing through it, the percent p of light that passes through n successive panes is given approximately by the function

$$p(n) = 100(0.97)^n$$

(a) What percent of light will pass through 10 panes?
(b) What percent of light will pass through 25 panes?

102. Atmospheric Pressure The atmospheric pressure p on a balloon or plane decreases with increasing height. This pressure, measured in millimeters of mercury, is related to the height h (in kilometers) above sea level by the function

$$p(h) = 760e^{-0.145h}$$

(a) Find the atmospheric pressure at a height of 2 kilometers (over a mile).
(b) What is it at a height of 10 kilometers (over 30,000 feet)?

103. Depreciation The price p, in dollars, of a Honda Civic DX Sedan that is x years old is modeled by

$$p(x) = 16{,}630(0.90)^x$$

(a) How much should a 3-year-old Civic DX Sedan cost?
(b) How much should a 9-year-old Civic DX Sedan cost?

104. Healing of Wounds The normal healing of wounds can be modeled by an exponential function. If A_0 represents the original area of the wound and if A equals the area of the wound, then the function

$$A(n) = A_0 e^{-0.35n}$$

describes the area of a wound after n days following an injury when no infection is present to retard the healing. Suppose that a wound initially had an area of 100 square millimeters.

(a) If healing is taking place, how large will the area of the wound be after 3 days?
(b) How large will it be after 10 days?

105. Drug Medication The function

$$D(h) = 5e^{-0.4h}$$

can be used to find the number of milligrams D of a certain drug that is in a patient's bloodstream h hours after the drug has been administered. How many milligrams will be present after 1 hour? After 6 hours?

106. Spreading of Rumors A model for the number N of people in a college community who have heard a certain rumor is

$$N = P(1 - e^{-0.15d})$$

where P is the total population of the community and d is the number of days that have elapsed since the rumor began. In a community of 1000 students, how many students will have heard the rumor after 3 days?

107. Exponential Probability Between 12:00 PM and 1:00 PM, cars arrive at Citibank's drive-thru at the rate of 6 cars per hour (0.1 car per minute). The following formula from probability can be used to determine the probability that a car will arrive within t minutes of 12:00 PM:

$$F(t) = 1 - e^{-0.1t}$$

(a) Determine the probability that a car will arrive within 10 minutes of 12:00 PM (that is, before 12:10 PM).
(b) Determine the probability that a car will arrive within 40 minutes of 12:00 PM (before 12:40 PM).
(c) What value does F approach as t becomes unbounded in the positive direction?
(d) Graph F using a graphing utility.
(e) Using INTERSECT, determine how many minutes are needed for the probability to reach 50%.

108. Exponential Probability Between 5:00 PM and 6:00 PM, cars arrive at Jiffy Lube at the rate of 9 cars per hour (0.15 car per minute). The following formula from probability can be used to determine the probability that a car will arrive within t minutes of 5:00 PM:

$$F(t) = 1 - e^{-0.15t}$$

(a) Determine the probability that a car will arrive within 15 minutes of 5:00 PM (that is, before 5:15 PM).
(b) Determine the probability that a car will arrive within 30 minutes of 5:00 PM (before 5:30 PM).
(c) What value does F approach as t becomes unbounded in the positive direction?
(d) Graph F using a graphing utility.
(e) Using INTERSECT, determine how many minutes are needed for the probability to reach 60%.

109. Poisson Probability Between 5:00 PM and 6:00 PM, cars arrive at McDonald's drive-thru at the rate of 20 cars per hour. The following formula from probability can be used to determine the probability that x cars will arrive between 5:00 PM and 6:00 PM.

$$P(x) = \frac{20^x e^{-20}}{x!}$$

where

$$x! = x \cdot (x - 1) \cdot (x - 2) \cdots \cdot 3 \cdot 2 \cdot 1$$

(a) Determine the probability that $x = 15$ cars will arrive between 5:00 PM and 6:00 PM.
(b) Determine the probability that $x = 20$ cars will arrive between 5:00 PM and 6:00 PM.

110. Poisson Probability People enter a line for the *Demon Roller Coaster* at the rate of 4 per minute. The following formula from probability can be used to determine the probability that x people will arrive within the next minute.

$$P(x) = \frac{4^x e^{-4}}{x!}$$

where

$$x! = x \cdot (x - 1) \cdot (x - 2) \cdots 3 \cdot 2 \cdot 1$$

(a) Determine the probability that $x = 5$ people will arrive within the next minute.
(b) Determine the probability that $x = 8$ people will arrive within the next minute.

111. Relative Humidity The relative humidity is the ratio (expressed as a percent) of the amount of water vapor in the air to the maximum amount that it can hold at a specific temperature. The relative humidity, R, is found using the following formula:

$$R = 10^{\left(\frac{4221}{T+459.4} - \frac{4221}{D+459.4} + 2\right)}$$

where T is the air temperature (in °F) and D is the dew point temperature (in °F).
(a) Determine the relative humidity if the air temperature is 50° Fahrenheit and the dew point temperature is 41° Fahrenheit.
(b) Determine the relative humidity if the air temperature is 68° Fahrenheit and the dew point temperature is 59° Fahrenheit.
(c) What is the relative humidity if the air temperature and the dew point temperature are the same?

112. Learning Curve Suppose that a student has 500 vocabulary words to learn. If the student learns 15 words after 5 minutes, the function

$$L(t) = 500(1 - e^{-0.0061t})$$

approximates the number of words L that the student will learn after t minutes.
(a) How many words will the student learn after 30 minutes?
(b) How many words will the student learn after 60 minutes?

113. Current in a *RL* Circuit The equation governing the amount of current I (in amperes) after time t (in seconds) in a single *RL* circuit consisting of a resistance R (in ohms), an inductance L (in henrys), and an electromotive force E (in volts) is

$$I = \frac{E}{R}[1 - e^{-(R/L)t}]$$

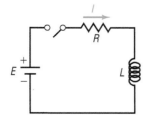

(a) If $E = 120$ volts, $R = 10$ ohms, and $L = 5$ henrys, how much current I_1 is flowing after 0.3 second? After 0.5 second? After 1 second?
(b) What is the maximum current?
(c) Graph this function $I = I_1(t)$, measuring I along the y-axis and t along the x-axis.
(d) If $E = 120$ volts, $R = 5$ ohms, and $L = 10$ henrys, how much current I_2 is flowing after 0.3 second? After 0.5 second? After 1 second?
(e) What is the maximum current?
(f) Graph the function $I = I_2(t)$ on the same coordinate axes as $I_1(t)$.

114. Current in a *RC* Circuit The equation governing the amount of current I (in amperes) after time t (in microseconds) in a single *RC* circuit consisting of a resistance R (in ohms), a capacitance C (in microfarads), and an electromotive force E (in volts) is

$$I = \frac{E}{R}e^{-t/(RC)}$$

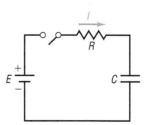

(a) If $E = 120$ volts, $R = 2000$ ohms, and $C = 1.0$ microfarad, how much current I_1 is flowing initially ($t = 0$)? After 1000 microseconds? After 3000 microseconds?
(b) What is the maximum current?
(c) Graph the function $I = I_1(t)$, measuring I along the y-axis and t along the x-axis.
(d) If $E = 120$ volts, $R = 1000$ ohms, and $C = 2.0$ microfarads, how much current I_2 is flowing initially? After 1000 microseconds? After 3000 microseconds?
(e) What is the maximum current?
(f) Graph the function $I = I_2(t)$ on the same coordinate axes as $I_1(t)$.

115. If f is an exponential function of the form $f(x) = C \cdot a^x$ with growth factor 3 and $f(6) = 12$, what is $f(7)$?

116. Another Formula for *e* Use a calculator to compute the values of

$$2 + \frac{1}{2!} + \frac{1}{3!} + \cdots + \frac{1}{n!}$$

for $n = 4, 6, 8,$ and 10. Compare each result with e.
[**Hint:** $1! = 1, 2! = 2 \cdot 1, 3! = 3 \cdot 2 \cdot 1,$
$n! = n(n - 1) \cdots (3)(2)(1).$]

117. Another Formula for *e* Use a calculator to compute the various values of the expression. Compare the values to e.

$$2 + \cfrac{1}{1 + \cfrac{1}{2 + \cfrac{2}{3 + \cfrac{3}{4 + \cfrac{4}{\text{etc.}}}}}}$$

118. Difference Quotient If $f(x) = a^x$, show that

$$\frac{f(x + h) - f(x)}{h} = a^x \cdot \frac{a^h - 1}{h} \qquad h \neq 0$$

119. If $f(x) = a^x$, show that $f(A + B) = f(A) \cdot f(B)$.

120. If $f(x) = a^x$, show that $f(-x) = \frac{1}{f(x)}$.

121. If $f(x) = a^x$, show that $f(\alpha x) = [f(x)]^\alpha$.

Problems 122 and 123 provide definitions for two other transcendental functions.

122. The **hyperbolic sine function,** designated by sinh x, is defined as

$$\sinh x = \frac{1}{2}(e^x - e^{-x})$$

(a) Show that $f(x) = \sinh x$ is an odd function.

(b) Graph $f(x) = \sinh x$ using a graphing utility.

123. The **hyperbolic cosine function,** designated by cosh x, is defined as

$$\cosh x = \frac{1}{2}(e^x + e^{-x})$$

(a) Show that $f(x) = \cosh x$ is an even function.

(b) Graph $f(x) = \cosh x$ using a graphing utility.

(c) Refer to Problem 122. Show that, for every x,

$$(\cosh x)^2 - (\sinh x)^2 = 1$$

124. Historical Problem Pierre de Fermat (1601–1665) conjectured that the function

$$f(x) = 2^{(2^x)} + 1$$

for $x = 1, 2, 3, \ldots$, would always have a value equal to a prime number. But Leonhard Euler (1707–1783) showed that this formula fails for $x = 5$. Use a calculator to determine the prime numbers produced by f for $x = 1, 2, 3, 4$. Then show that $f(5) = 641 \times 6,700,417$, which is not prime.

Explaining Concepts: Discussion and Writing

125. The bacteria in a 4-liter container double every minute. After 60 minutes the container is full. How long did it take to fill half the container?

126. Explain in your own words what the number e is. Provide at least two applications that use this number.

127. Do you think that there is a power function that increases more rapidly than an exponential function whose base is greater than 1? Explain.

128. As the base a of an exponential function $f(x) = a^x$, where $a > 1$ increases, what happens to the behavior of its graph for $x > 0$? What happens to the behavior of its graph for $x < 0$?

129. The graphs of $y = a^{-x}$ and $y = \left(\dfrac{1}{a}\right)^x$ are identical. Why?

'Are You Prepared?' Answers

1. 64; 4; $\dfrac{1}{9}$ **2.** $\{-4, 1\}$ **3.** False   **4.** 3   **5.** True

5.4 Logarithmic Functions

PREPARING FOR THIS SECTION *Before getting started, review the following:*

- Solving Inequalities (Appendix A, Section A.9, pp. A75–A78)
- Quadratic Inequalities (Section 3.5, pp. 155–157)
- Polynomial and Rational Inequalities (Section 4.4, pp. 214–217)
- Solving Equations (Appendix A, Section A.6, pp. A44–A46)

Now Work the 'Are You Prepared?' problems on page 292.

OBJECTIVES   1 Change Exponential Statements to Logarithmic Statements and Logarithmic Statements to Exponential Statements (p. 284)
   2 Evaluate Logarithmic Expressions (p. 284)
   3 Determine the Domain of a Logarithmic Function (p. 285)
   4 Graph Logarithmic Functions (p. 286)
   5 Solve Logarithmic Equations (p. 290)

Recall that a one-to-one function $y = f(x)$ has an inverse function that is defined (implicitly) by the equation $x = f(y)$. In particular, the exponential function $y = f(x) = a^x$, where $a > 0$ and $a \neq 1$, is one-to-one and hence has an inverse function that is defined implicitly by the equation

$$x = a^y, \qquad a > 0, \qquad a \neq 1$$

This inverse function is so important that it is given a name, the *logarithmic function.*

DEFINITION

The **logarithmic function to the base a,** where $a > 0$ and $a \neq 1$, is denoted by $y = \log_a x$ (read as "y is the logarithm to the base a of x") and is defined by

$$y = \log_a x \quad \text{if and only if} \quad x = a^y$$

The domain of the logarithmic function $y = \log_a x$ is $x > 0$.

In Words

When you read $\log_a x$, think to yourself "a raised to what power gives me x."

As this definition illustrates, **a logarithm is a name for a certain exponent.** So, $\log_a x$ represents the exponent to which a must be raised to obtain x.

EXAMPLE 1 **Relating Logarithms to Exponents**

(a) If $y = \log_3 x$, then $x = 3^y$. For example, the logarithmic statement $4 = \log_3 81$ is equivalent to the exponential statement $81 = 3^4$.

(b) If $y = \log_5 x$, then $x = 5^y$. For example, $-1 = \log_5\left(\dfrac{1}{5}\right)$ is equivalent to $\dfrac{1}{5} = 5^{-1}$.

---

1 Change Exponential Statements to Logarithmic Statements and Logarithmic Statements to Exponential Statements

We can use the definition of a logarithm to convert from exponential form to logarithmic form, and vice versa, as the following two examples illustrate.

EXAMPLE 2 **Changing Exponential Statements to Logarithmic Statements**

Change each exponential statement to an equivalent statement involving a logarithm.

(a) $1.2^3 = m$ (b) $e^b = 9$ (c) $a^4 = 24$

Solution Use the fact that $y = \log_a x$ and $x = a^y$, where $a > 0$ and $a \neq 1$, are equivalent.

(a) If $1.2^3 = m$, then $3 = \log_{1.2} m$.

(b) If $e^b = 9$, then $b = \log_e 9$.

(c) If $a^4 = 24$, then $4 = \log_a 24$.

⟶**Now Work** PROBLEM 9

EXAMPLE 3 **Changing Logarithmic Statements to Exponential Statements**

Change each logarithmic statement to an equivalent statement involving an exponent.

(a) $\log_a 4 = 5$ (b) $\log_e b = -3$ (c) $\log_3 5 = c$

Solution (a) If $\log_a 4 = 5$, then $a^5 = 4$.

(b) If $\log_e b = -3$, then $e^{-3} = b$.

(c) If $\log_3 5 = c$, then $3^c = 5$.

⟶**Now Work** PROBLEM 17

---

2 Evaluate Logarithmic Expressions

To find the exact value of a logarithm, we write the logarithm in exponential notation using the fact that $y = \log_a x$ is equivalent to $a^y = x$ and use the fact that if $a^u = a^v$, then $u = v$.

EXAMPLE 4

Finding the Exact Value of a Logarithmic Expression

Find the exact value of:

(a) $\log_2 16$

(b) $\log_3 \dfrac{1}{27}$

Solution

(a) To evaluate $\log_2 16$, think "2 raised to what power yields 16." So,

$$y = \log_2 16$$
$$2^y = 16 \qquad \textit{Change to exponential form.}$$
$$2^y = 2^4 \qquad \textit{16 = 2^4}$$
$$y = 4 \qquad \textit{Equate exponents.}$$

Therefore, $\log_2 16 = 4$.

(b) To evaluate $\log_3 \dfrac{1}{27}$, think "3 raised to what power yields $\dfrac{1}{27}$." So,

$$y = \log_3 \dfrac{1}{27}$$
$$3^y = \dfrac{1}{27} \qquad \textit{Change to exponential form.}$$
$$3^y = 3^{-3} \qquad \textit{$\frac{1}{27} = \frac{1}{3^3} = 3^{-3}$}$$
$$y = -3 \qquad \textit{Equate exponents.}$$

Therefore, $\log_3 \dfrac{1}{27} = -3$.

**Now Work** PROBLEM 25

3 Determine the Domain of a Logarithmic Function

The logarithmic function $y = \log_a x$ has been defined as the inverse of the exponential function $y = a^x$. That is, if $f(x) = a^x$, then $f^{-1}(x) = \log_a x$. Based on the discussion given in Section 5.2 on inverse functions, for a function f and its inverse f^{-1}, we have

$$\text{Domain of } f^{-1} = \text{Range of } f \quad \text{and} \quad \text{Range of } f^{-1} = \text{Domain of } f$$

Consequently, it follows that

> Domain of the logarithmic function = Range of the exponential function = $(0, \infty)$
>
> Range of the logarithmic function = Domain of the exponential function = $(-\infty, \infty)$

In the next box, we summarize some properties of the logarithmic function:

> $y = \log_a x$ (defining equation: $x = a^y$)
> Domain: $0 < x < \infty$ Range: $-\infty < y < \infty$

The domain of a logarithmic function consists of the *positive* real numbers, so the argument of a logarithmic function must be greater than zero.

EXAMPLE 5

Finding the Domain of a Logarithmic Function

Find the domain of each logarithmic function.

(a) $F(x) = \log_2(x + 3)$ (b) $g(x) = \log_5\left(\dfrac{1 + x}{1 - x}\right)$ (c) $h(x) = \log_{1/2}|x|$

Solution

(a) The domain of F consists of all x for which $x + 3 > 0$, that is, $x > -3$. Using interval notation, the domain of f is $(-3, \infty)$.

(b) The domain of g is restricted to

$$\dfrac{1 + x}{1 - x} > 0$$

Solving this inequality, we find that the domain of g consists of all x between -1 and 1, that is, $-1 < x < 1$ or, using interval notation, $(-1, 1)$.

(c) Since $|x| > 0$, provided that $x \neq 0$, the domain of h consists of all real numbers except zero or, using interval notation, $(-\infty, 0) \cup (0, \infty)$.

━━━**Now Work** PROBLEMS 39 AND 45

4 Graph Logarithmic Functions

Since exponential functions and logarithmic functions are inverses of each other, the graph of the logarithmic function $y = \log_a x$ is the reflection about the line $y = x$ of the graph of the exponential function $y = a^x$, as shown in Figure 30.

Figure 30

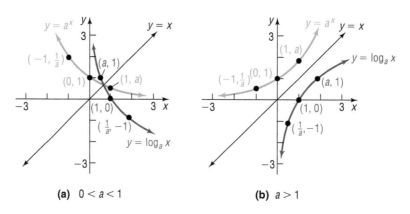

(a) $0 < a < 1$ **(b)** $a > 1$

For example, to graph $y = \log_2 x$, graph $y = 2^x$ and reflect it about the line $y = x$. See Figure 31. To graph $y = \log_{1/3} x$, graph $y = \left(\dfrac{1}{3}\right)^x$ and reflect it about the line $y = x$. See Figure 32.

Figure 31   **Figure 32**

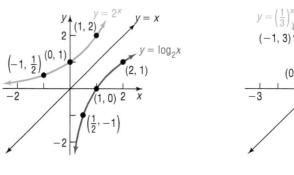

━━━**Now Work** PROBLEM 59

The graphs of $y = \log_a x$ in Figures 30(a) and (b) lead to the following properties.

Properties of the Logarithmic Function $f(x) = \log_a x$

1. The domain is the set of positive real numbers or $(0, \infty)$ using interval notation; the range is the set of all real numbers or $(-\infty, \infty)$ using interval notation.
2. The x-intercept of the graph is 1. There is no y-intercept.
3. The y-axis ($x = 0$) is a vertical asymptote of the graph.
4. A logarithmic function is decreasing if $0 < a < 1$ and increasing if $a > 1$.
5. The graph of f contains the points $(1, 0)$, $(a, 1)$, and $\left(\dfrac{1}{a}, -1\right)$.
6. The graph is smooth and continuous, with no corners or gaps.

If the base of a logarithmic function is the number e, then we have the **natural logarithm function.** This function occurs so frequently in applications that it is given a special symbol, **ln** (from the Latin, *logarithmus naturalis*). That is,

$$y = \ln x \quad \text{if and only if} \quad x = e^y \tag{1}$$

In Words

$y = \log_e x$ is written $y = \ln x$

Since $y = \ln x$ and the exponential function $y = e^x$ are inverse functions, we can obtain the graph of $y = \ln x$ by reflecting the graph of $y = e^x$ about the line $y = x$. See Figure 33.

Using a calculator with an $\boxed{\text{ln}}$ key, we can obtain other points on the graph of $f(x) = \ln x$. See Table 7.

Figure 33

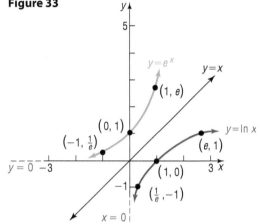

Table 7	x	$\ln x$
	$\dfrac{1}{2}$	-0.69
	2	0.69
	3	1.10

Seeing the Concept

Graph $Y_1 = e^x$ and $Y_2 = \ln x$ on the same square screen. Use eVALUEate to verify the points on the graph given in Figure 33. Do you see the symmetry of the two graphs with respect to the line $y = x$?

EXAMPLE 6 **Graphing a Logarithmic Function and Its Inverse**

(a) Find the domain of the logarithmic function $f(x) = -\ln(x - 2)$.
(b) Graph f.
(c) From the graph, determine the range and vertical asymptote of f.
(d) Find f^{-1}, the inverse of f.
(e) Find the domain and the range of f^{-1}.
(f) Graph f^{-1}.

Solution (a) The domain of f consists of all x for which $x - 2 > 0$ or, equivalently, $x > 2$. The domain of f is $\{x \mid x > 2\}$ or $(2, \infty)$ in interval notation.

(b) To obtain the graph of $y = -\ln(x - 2)$, we begin with the graph of $y = \ln x$ and use transformations. See Figure 34.

Figure 34

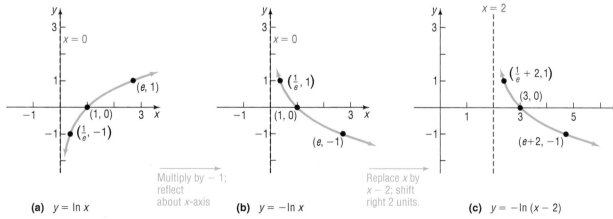

(a) $y = \ln x$ Multiply by -1; reflect about x-axis   (b) $y = -\ln x$ Replace x by $x - 2$; shift right 2 units.   (c) $y = -\ln(x - 2)$

(c) The range of $f(x) = -\ln(x - 2)$ is the set of all real numbers. The vertical asymptote is $x = 2$. [Do you see why? The original asymptote $(x = 0)$ is shifted to the right 2 units.]

(d) To find f^{-1}, begin with $y = -\ln(x - 2)$. The inverse function is defined (implicitly) by the equation

$$x = -\ln(y - 2)$$

Proceed to solve for y.

$$-x = \ln(y - 2) \quad \text{Isolate the logarithm.}$$
$$e^{-x} = y - 2 \quad \text{Change to an exponential statement.}$$
$$y = e^{-x} + 2 \quad \text{Solve for } y.$$

The inverse of f is $f^{-1}(x) = e^{-x} + 2$.

(e) The domain of f^{-1} equals the range of f, which is the set of all real numbers, from part (c). The range of f^{-1} is the domain of f, which is $(2, \infty)$ in interval notation.

(f) To graph f^{-1}, use the graph of f in Figure 34(c) and reflect it about the line $y = x$. See Figure 35. We could also graph $f^{-1}(x) = e^{-x} + 2$ using transformations.

Figure 35

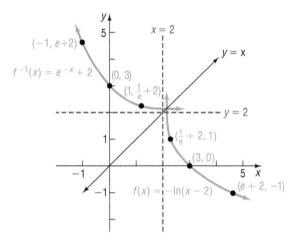

Figure 36

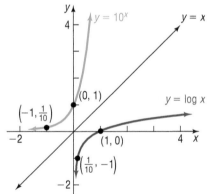

> **Now Work** PROBLEM 71

If the base of a logarithmic function is the number 10, then we have the **common logarithm function.** If the base a of the logarithmic function is not indicated, it is understood to be 10. That is,

$$y = \log x \quad \text{if and only if} \quad x = 10^y$$

Since $y = \log x$ and the exponential function $y = 10^x$ are inverse functions, we can obtain the graph of $y = \log x$ by reflecting the graph of $y = 10^x$ about the line $y = x$. See Figure 36.

EXAMPLE 7

Graphing a Logarithmic Function and Its Inverse

(a) Find the domain of the logarithmic function $f(x) = 3\log(x - 1)$.
(b) Graph f.
(c) From the graph, determine the range and vertical asymptote of f.
(d) Find f^{-1}, the inverse of f.
(e) Find the domain and the range of f^{-1}.
(f) Graph f^{-1}.

Solution

(a) The domain of f consists of all x for which $x - 1 > 0$ or, equivalently, $x > 1$. The domain of f is $\{x | x > 1\}$ or $(1, \infty)$ in interval notation.

(b) To obtain the graph of $y = 3\log(x - 1)$, begin with the graph of $y = \log x$ and use transformations. See Figure 37.

Figure 37

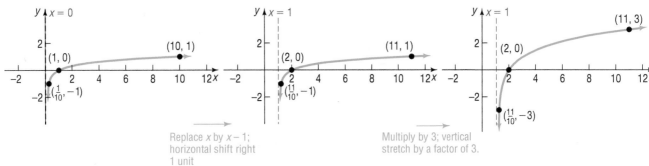

(a) $y = \log x$ **(b)** $y = \log (x - 1)$ **(c)** $y = 3 \log (x - 1)$

(c) The range of $f(x) = 3 \log(x - 1)$ is the set of all real numbers. The vertical asymptote is $x = 1$.

(d) Begin with $y = 3 \log(x - 1)$. The inverse function is defined (implicitly) by the equation

$$x = 3 \log(y - 1)$$

Proceed to solve for y.

$$\frac{x}{3} = \log (y - 1) \quad \text{Isolate the logarithm.}$$

$$10^{x/3} = y - 1 \quad \text{Change to an exponential statement.}$$

$$y = 10^{x/3} + 1 \quad \text{Solve for } y.$$

The inverse of f is $f^{-1}(x) = 10^{x/3} + 1$.

(e) The domain of f^{-1} is the range of f, which is the set of all real numbers, from part (c). The range of f^{-1} is the domain of f, which is $(1, \infty)$ in interval notation.

(f) To graph f^{-1}, we use the graph of f in Figure 37(c) and reflect it about the line $y = x$. See Figure 38. We could also graph $f^{-1}(x) = 10^{x/3} + 1$ using transformations.

Figure 38

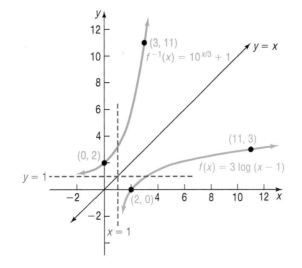

━━━**Now Work** PROBLEM **79**

5 Solve Logarithmic Equations

Equations that contain logarithms are called **logarithmic equations.** Care must be taken when solving logarithmic equations algebraically. In the expression $\log_a M$, remember that a and M are positive and $a \neq 1$. Be sure to check each apparent solution in the original equation and discard any that are extraneous.

Some logarithmic equations can be solved by changing the logarithmic equation to exponential form using the fact that $y = \log_a x$ means $a^y = x$.

EXAMPLE 8

Solving Logarithmic Equations

Solve:

(a) $\log_3(4x - 7) = 2$ (b) $\log_x 64 = 2$

Solution

(a) We can obtain an exact solution by changing the logarithmic equation to exponential form.

$$\log_3(4x - 7) = 2$$
$$4x - 7 = 3^2 \quad \textit{Change to exponential form using } y = \log_a x$$
$$\textit{means } a^y = x.$$
$$4x - 7 = 9$$
$$4x = 16$$
$$x = 4$$

✓Check: $\log_3(4x - 7) = \log_3(4 \cdot 4 - 7) = \log_3 9 = 2 \quad 3^2 = 9$

The solution set is {4}.

(b) We can obtain an exact solution by changing the logarithmic equation to exponential form.

$$\log_x 64 = 2$$
$$x^2 = 64 \qquad \textit{Change to exponential form.}$$
$$x = \pm\sqrt{64} = \pm 8 \quad \textit{Square Root Method}$$

The base of a logarithm is always positive. As a result, we discard -8. We check the solution 8.

✓Check: $\log_8 64 = 2 \quad 8^2 = 64$

The solution set is {8}.

EXAMPLE 9

Using Logarithms to Solve an Exponential Equation

Solve: $e^{2x} = 5$

Solution

We can obtain an exact solution by changing the exponential equation to logarithmic form.

$$e^{2x} = 5$$
$$\ln 5 = 2x \qquad \textit{Change to logarithmic form using the}$$
$$\textit{fact that if } e^y = x \textit{ then } y = \ln x.$$
$$x = \frac{\ln 5}{2} \qquad \textit{Exact solution}$$
$$\approx 0.805 \qquad \textit{Approximate solution}$$

The solution set is $\left\{ \dfrac{\ln 5}{2} \right\}$.

Now Work PROBLEMS 87 AND 99

EXAMPLE 10 | **Alcohol and Driving**

Blood alcohol concentration (BAC) is a measure of the amount of alcohol in a person's bloodstream. A BAC of 0.04% means that a person has 4 parts alcohol per 10,000 parts blood in the body. Relative risk is defined as the likelihood of one event occurring divided by the likelihood of a second event occurring. For example, if an individual with a BAC of 0.02% is 1.4 times as likely to have a car accident as an individual that has not been drinking, the relative risk of an accident with a BAC of 0.02% is 1.4. Recent medical research suggests that the relative risk R of having an accident while driving a car can be modeled by an equation of the form

$$R = e^{kx}$$

where x is the percent of concentration of alcohol in the bloodstream and k is a constant.

(a) Research indicates that the relative risk of a person having an accident with a BAC of 0.02% is 1.4. Find the constant k in the equation.
(b) Using this value of k, what is the relative risk if the concentration is 0.17%?
(c) Using this same value of k, what BAC corresponds to a relative risk of 100?
(d) If the law asserts that anyone with a relative risk of 5 or more should not have driving privileges, at what concentration of alcohol in the bloodstream should a driver be arrested and charged with a DUI (driving under the influence)?

Solution (a) For a concentration of alcohol in the blood of 0.02% and a relative risk of 1.4, we let $x = 0.02$ and $R = 1.4$ in the equation and solve for k.

$$R = e^{kx}$$
$$1.4 = e^{k(0.02)} \qquad R = 1.4; x = 0.02$$
$$0.02k = \ln 1.4 \qquad \text{Change to a logarithmic statement.}$$
$$k = \frac{\ln 1.4}{0.02} \approx 16.82 \quad \text{Solve for } k.$$

(b) For a concentration of 0.17%, we have $x = 0.17$. Using $k = 16.82$ in the equation, we find the relative risk R to be

$$R = e^{kx} = e^{(16.82)(0.17)} \approx 17.5$$

For a concentration of alcohol in the blood of 0.17%, the relative risk of an accident is about 17.5. That is, a person with a BAC of 0.17% is 17.5 times as likely to have a car accident as a person with no alcohol in the bloodstream.

(c) For a relative risk of 100, we have $R = 100$. Using $k = 16.82$ in the equation $R = e^{kx}$, we find the concentration x of alcohol in the blood obeys

$$100 = e^{16.82x} \qquad R = e^{kx}, R = 100; k = 16.82$$
$$16.82x = \ln 100 \qquad \text{Change to a logarithmic statement.}$$
$$x = \frac{\ln 100}{16.82} \approx 0.27 \quad \text{Solve for } x.$$

COMMENT A BAC of 0.30% results in a loss of consciousness in most people. ■

For a concentration of alcohol in the blood of 0.27%, the relative risk of an accident is 100.

(d) For a relative risk of 5, we have $R = 5$. Using $k = 16.82$ in the equation $R = e^{kx}$, we find the concentration x of alcohol in the bloodstream obeys

$$5 = e^{16.82x}$$
$$16.82x = \ln 5$$
$$x = \frac{\ln 5}{16.82} \approx 0.096$$

COMMENT Most states use 0.08% or 0.10% as the blood alcohol content at which a DUI citation is given. ■

A driver with a BAC of 0.096% or more should be arrested and charged with DUI. ↵

SUMMARY Properties of the Logarithmic Function

$f(x) = \log_a x, \quad a > 1$

$(y = \log_a x$ means $x = a^y)$

Domain: the interval $(0, \infty)$; Range: the interval $(-\infty, \infty)$

x-intercept: 1; y-intercept: none; vertical asymptote: $x = 0$ (y-axis); increasing; one-to-one

See Figure 39(a) for a typical graph.

$f(x) = \log_a x, \quad 0 < a < 1$

$(y = \log_a x$ means $x = a^y)$

Domain: the interval $(0, \infty)$; Range: the interval $(-\infty, \infty)$

x-intercept: 1; y-intercept: none; vertical asymptote: $x = 0$ (y-axis); decreasing; one-to-one

See Figure 39(b) for a typical graph.

Figure 39

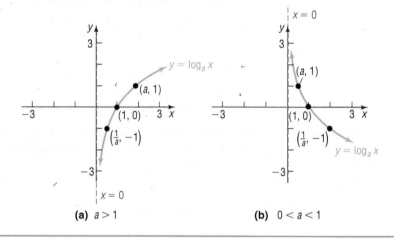

(a) $a > 1$ **(b)** $0 < a < 1$

5.4 Assess Your Understanding

'Are You Prepared?' *Answers are given at the end of these exercises. If you get a wrong answer, read the pages listed in* red.

1. Solve each inequality:
   (a) $3x - 7 \le 8 - 2x$ (pp. A75–A78)
   (b) $x^2 - x - 6 > 0$ (pp. 155–157)

2. Solve the inequality: $\dfrac{x - 1}{x + 4} > 0$ (pp. 214–217)

3. Solve: $2x + 3 = 9$ (pp. A44–A51)

Concepts and Vocabulary

4. The domain of the logarithmic function $f(x) = \log_a x$ is _____.

5. The graph of every logarithmic function $f(x) = \log_a x$, where $a > 0$ and $a \ne 1$, passes through three points: _____, _____, and _____.

6. If the graph of a logarithmic function $f(x) = \log_a x$, where $a > 0$ and $a \ne 1$, is increasing, then its base must be larger than _____.

7. **True or False** If $y = \log_a x$, then $y = a^x$.

8. **True or False** The graph of $f(x) = \log_a x$, where $a > 0$ and $a \ne 1$, has an x-intercept equal to 1 and no y-intercept.

Skill Building

In Problems 9–16, change each exponential statement to an equivalent statement involving a logarithm.

9. $9 = 3^2$

10. $16 = 4^2$

11. $a^2 = 1.6$

12. $a^3 = 2.1$

13. $2^x = 7.2$

14. $3^x = 4.6$

15. $e^x = 8$

16. $e^{2.2} = M$

In Problems 17–24, change each logarithmic statement to an equivalent statement involving an exponent.

17. $\log_2 8 = 3$

18. $\log_3\left(\dfrac{1}{9}\right) = -2$

19. $\log_a 3 = 6$

20. $\log_b 4 = 2$

21. $\log_3 2 = x$

22. $\log_2 6 = x$

23. $\ln 4 = x$

24. $\ln x = 4$

In Problems 25–36, find the exact value of each logarithm without using a calculator.

25. $\log_2 1$

26. $\log_8 8$

27. $\log_5 25$

28. $\log_3\left(\dfrac{1}{9}\right)$

29. $\log_{1/2} 16$

30. $\log_{1/3} 9$

31. $\log_{10} \sqrt{10}$

32. $\log_5 \sqrt[3]{25}$

33. $\log_{\sqrt{2}} 4$

34. $\log_{\sqrt{3}} 9$

35. $\ln \sqrt{e}$

36. $\ln e^3$

In Problems 37–48, find the domain of each function.

37. $f(x) = \ln(x - 3)$

38. $g(x) = \ln(x - 1)$

39. $F(x) = \log_2 x^2$

40. $H(x) = \log_5 x^3$

41. $f(x) = 3 - 2\log_4\left[\dfrac{x}{2} - 5\right]$

42. $g(x) = 8 + 5\ln(2x + 3)$

43. $f(x) = \ln\left(\dfrac{1}{x + 1}\right)$

44. $g(x) = \ln\left(\dfrac{1}{x - 5}\right)$

45. $g(x) = \log_5\left(\dfrac{x + 1}{x}\right)$

46. $h(x) = \log_3\left(\dfrac{x}{x - 1}\right)$

47. $f(x) = \sqrt{\ln x}$

48. $g(x) = \dfrac{1}{\ln x}$

In Problems 49–56, use a calculator to evaluate each expression. Round your answer to three decimal places.

49. $\ln\dfrac{5}{3}$

50. $\dfrac{\ln 5}{3}$

51. $\dfrac{\ln\dfrac{10}{3}}{0.04}$

52. $\dfrac{\ln\dfrac{2}{3}}{-0.1}$

53. $\dfrac{\ln 4 + \ln 2}{\log 4 + \log 2}$

54. $\dfrac{\log 15 + \log 20}{\ln 15 + \ln 20}$

55. $\dfrac{2\ln 5 + \log 50}{\log 4 - \ln 2}$

56. $\dfrac{3\log 80 - \ln 5}{\log 5 + \ln 20}$

57. Find a so that the graph of $f(x) = \log_a x$ contains the point $(2, 2)$.

58. Find a so that the graph of $f(x) = \log_a x$ contains the point $\left(\dfrac{1}{2}, -4\right)$.

In Problems 59–62, graph each function and its inverse on the same Cartesian plane.

59. $f(x) = 3^x; f^{-1}(x) = \log_3 x$

60. $f(x) = 4^x; f^{-1}(x) = \log_4 x$

61. $f(x) = \left(\dfrac{1}{2}\right)^x; f^{-1}(x) = \log_{\frac{1}{2}} x$

62. $f(x) = \left(\dfrac{1}{3}\right)^x; f^{-1}(x) = \log_{\frac{1}{3}} x$

In Problems 63–70, the graph of a logarithmic function is given. Match each graph to one of the following functions:

(a) $y = \log_3 x$

(b) $y = \log_3(-x)$

(c) $y = -\log_3 x$

(d) $y = -\log_3(-x)$

(e) $y = \log_3 x - 1$

(f) $y = \log_3(x - 1)$

(g) $y = \log_3(1 - x)$

(h) $y = 1 - \log_3 x$

63.
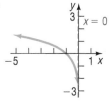

64.
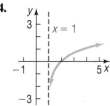

65.
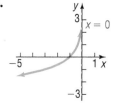

66.
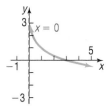

67.
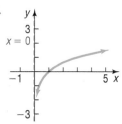

68.
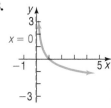

69.
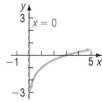

70.
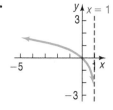

In Problems 71–86, use the given function f to:

    (a) *Find the domain of f.* (b) *Graph f.* (c) *From the graph, determine the range and any asymptotes of f.*
    (d) *Find f^{-1}, the inverse of f.* (e) *Find the domain and the range of f^{-1}.* (f) *Graph f^{-1}.*

71. $f(x) = \ln(x + 4)$

72. $f(x) = \ln(x - 3)$

73. $f(x) = 2 + \ln x$

74. $f(x) = -\ln(-x)$

75. $f(x) = \ln(2x) - 3$ **76.** $f(x) = -2\ln(x + 1)$ **77.** $f(x) = \log(x - 4) + 2$ **78.** $f(x) = \frac{1}{2}\log x - 5$

79. $f(x) = \frac{1}{2}\log(2x)$ **80.** $f(x) = \log(-2x)$ **81.** $f(x) = 3 + \log_3(x + 2)$ **82.** $f(x) = 2 - \log_3(x + 1)$

83. $f(x) = e^{x+2} - 3$ **84.** $f(x) = 3e^x + 2$ **85.** $f(x) = 2^{x/3} + 4$ **86.** $f(x) = -3^{x+1}$

In Problems 87–110, solve each equation.

87. $\log_3 x = 2$ **88.** $\log_5 x = 3$ **89.** $\log_2(2x + 1) = 3$ **90.** $\log_3(3x - 2) = 2$

91. $\log_x 4 = 2$ **92.** $\log_x\left(\frac{1}{8}\right) = 3$ **93.** $\ln e^x = 5$ **94.** $\ln e^{-2x} = 8$

95. $\log_4 64 = x$ **96.** $\log_5 625 = x$ **97.** $\log_3 243 = 2x + 1$ **98.** $\log_6 36 = 5x + 3$

99. $e^{3x} = 10$ **100.** $e^{-2x} = \frac{1}{3}$ **101.** $e^{2x+5} = 8$ **102.** $e^{-2x+1} = 13$

103. $\log_3(x^2 + 1) = 2$ **104.** $\log_5(x^2 + x + 4) = 2$ **105.** $\log_2 8^x = -3$ **106.** $\log_3 3^x = -1$

107. $5e^{0.2x} = 7$ **108.** $8 \cdot 10^{2x-7} = 3$ **109.** $2 \cdot 10^{2-x} = 5$ **110.** $4e^{x+1} = 5$

Mixed Practice

111. Suppose that $G(x) = \log_3(2x + 1) - 2$.
   (a) What is the domain of G?
   (b) What is $G(40)$? What point is on the graph of G?
   (c) If $G(x) = 3$, what is x? What point is on the graph of G?
   (d) What is the zero of G?

112. Suppose that $F(x) = \log_2(x + 1) - 3$.
   (a) What is the domain of F?
   (b) What is $F(7)$? What point is on the graph of F?
   (c) If $F(x) = -1$, what is x? What point is on the graph of F?
   (d) What is the zero of F?

In Problems 113–116, graph each function. Based on the graph, state the domain and the range and find any intercepts.

113. $f(x) = \begin{cases} \ln(-x) & \text{if } x < 0 \\ \ln x & \text{if } x > 0 \end{cases}$

114. $f(x) = \begin{cases} \ln(-x) & \text{if } x \leq -1 \\ -\ln(-x) & \text{if } -1 < x < 0 \end{cases}$

115. $f(x) = \begin{cases} -\ln x & \text{if } 0 < x < 1 \\ \ln x & \text{if } x \geq 1 \end{cases}$

116. $f(x) = \begin{cases} \ln x & \text{if } 0 < x < 1 \\ -\ln x & \text{if } x \geq 1 \end{cases}$

Applications and Extensions

117. Chemistry   The pH of a chemical solution is given by the formula

$$pH = -\log_{10}[H^+]$$

where $[H^+]$ is the concentration of hydrogen ions in moles per liter. Values of pH range from 0 (acidic) to 14 (alkaline).
   (a) What is the pH of a solution for which $[H^+]$ is 0.1?
   (b) What is the pH of a solution for which $[H^+]$ is 0.01?
   (c) What is the pH of a solution for which $[H^+]$ is 0.001?
   (d) What happens to pH as the hydrogen ion concentration decreases?
   (e) Determine the hydrogen ion concentration of an orange (pH = 3.5).
   (f) Determine the hydrogen ion concentration of human blood (pH = 7.4).

118. Diversity Index   **Shannon's diversity index** is a measure of the diversity of a population. The diversity index is given by the formula

$$H = -(p_1 \log p_1 + p_2 \log p_2 + \cdots + p_n \log p_n)$$

where p_1 is the proportion of the population that is species 1, p_2 is the proportion of the population that is species 2, and so on.
   (a) According to the U.S. Census Bureau, the distribution of race in the United States in 2007 was as follows:

Race	Proportion
American Indian or Native Alaskan	0.015
Asian	0.042
Black or African American	0.129
Hispanic	0.125
Native Hawaiian or Pacific Islander	0.003
White	0.686

Source: U.S. Census Bureau

Compute the diversity index of the United States in 2007.

(b) The largest value of the diversity index is given by $H_{\max} = \log(S)$, where S is the number of categories of race. Compute $H_{\max}$.

(c) The **evenness ratio** is given by $E_H = \dfrac{H}{H_{\max}}$, where $0 \le E_H \le 1$. If $E_H = 1$, there is complete evenness. Compute the evenness ratio for the United States.

(d) Obtain the distribution of race for the United States in 2010 from the Census Bureau. Compute Shannon's diversity index. Is the United States becoming more diverse? Why?

119. Atmospheric Pressure The atmospheric pressure p on an object decreases with increasing height. This pressure, measured in millimeters of mercury, is related to the height h (in kilometers) above sea level by the function

$$p(h) = 760e^{-0.145h}$$

(a) Find the height of an aircraft if the atmospheric pressure is 320 millimeters of mercury.

(b) Find the height of a mountain if the atmospheric pressure is 667 millimeters of mercury.

120. Healing of Wounds The normal healing of wounds can be modeled by an exponential function. If A_0 represents the original area of the wound and if A equals the area of the wound, then the function

$$A(n) = A_0 e^{-0.35n}$$

describes the area of a wound after n days following an injury when no infection is present to retard the healing. Suppose that a wound initially had an area of 100 square millimeters.

(a) If healing is taking place, after how many days will the wound be one-half its original size?

(b) How long before the wound is 10% of its original size?

121. Exponential Probability Between 12:00 PM and 1:00 PM, cars arrive at Citibank's drive-thru at the rate of 6 cars per hour (0.1 car per minute). The following formula from statistics can be used to determine the probability that a car will arrive within t minutes of 12:00 PM.

$$F(t) = 1 - e^{-0.1t}$$

(a) Determine how many minutes are needed for the probability to reach 50%.

(b) Determine how many minutes are needed for the probability to reach 80%.

(c) Is it possible for the probability to equal 100%? Explain.

122. Exponential Probability Between 5:00 PM and 6:00 PM, cars arrive at Jiffy Lube at the rate of 9 cars per hour (0.15 car per minute). The following formula from statistics can be used to determine the probability that a car will arrive within t minutes of 5:00 PM.

$$F(t) = 1 - e^{-0.15t}$$

(a) Determine how many minutes are needed for the probability to reach 50%.

(b) Determine how many minutes are needed for the probability to reach 80%.

123. Drug Medication The formula

$$D = 5e^{-0.4h}$$

can be used to find the number of milligrams D of a certain drug that is in a patient's bloodstream h hours after the drug was administered. When the number of milligrams reaches 2, the drug is to be administered again. What is the time between injections?

124. Spreading of Rumors A model for the number N of people in a college community who have heard a certain rumor is

$$N = P(1 - e^{-0.15d})$$

where P is the total population of the community and d is the number of days that have elapsed since the rumor began. In a community of 1000 students, how many days will elapse before 450 students have heard the rumor?

125. Current in a RL Circuit The equation governing the amount of current I (in amperes) after time t (in seconds) in a simple RL circuit consisting of a resistance R (in ohms), an inductance L (in henrys), and an electromotive force E (in volts) is

$$I = \frac{E}{R}[1 - e^{-(R/L)t}]$$

If $E = 12$ volts, $R = 10$ ohms, and $L = 5$ henrys, how long does it take to obtain a current of 0.5 ampere? Of 1.0 ampere? Graph the equation.

126. Learning Curve Psychologists sometimes use the function

$$L(t) = A(1 - e^{-kt})$$

to measure the amount L learned at time t. The number A represents the amount to be learned, and the number k measures the rate of learning. Suppose that a student has an amount A of 200 vocabulary words to learn. A psychologist determines that the student learned 20 vocabulary words after 5 minutes.

(a) Determine the rate of learning k.

(b) Approximately how many words will the student have learned after 10 minutes?

(c) After 15 minutes?

(d) How long does it take for the student to learn 180 words?

Loudness of Sound Problems 127–130 use the following discussion: The **loudness** $L(x)$, measured in decibels (dB), of a sound of intensity x, measured in watts per square meter, is defined as $L(x) = 10 \log \dfrac{x}{I_0}$, where $I_0 = 10^{-12}$ watt per square meter is the least intense sound that a human ear can detect. Determine the loudness, in decibels, of each of the following sounds.

127. Normal conversation: intensity of $x = 10^{-7}$ watt per square meter.

128. Amplified rock music: intensity of 10^{-1} watt per square meter.

129. Heavy city traffic: intensity of $x = 10^{-3}$ watt per square meter.

130. Diesel truck traveling 40 miles per hour 50 feet away: intensity 10 times that of a passenger car traveling 50 miles per hour 50 feet away whose loudness is 70 decibels.

The Richter Scale   *Problems 131 and 132 use the following discussion: The **Richter scale** is one way of converting seismographic readings into numbers that provide an easy reference for measuring the magnitude M of an earthquake. All earthquakes are compared to a **zero-level earthquake** whose seismographic reading measures 0.001 millimeter at a distance of 100 kilometers from the epicenter. An earthquake whose seismographic reading measures x millimeters has **magnitude** M(x), given by*

$$M(x) = \log\left(\frac{x}{x_0}\right)$$

where $x_0 = 10^{-3}$ is the reading of a zero-level earthquake the same distance from its epicenter. In Problems 131 and 132, determine the magnitude of each earthquake.

131. Magnitude of an Earthquake   Mexico City in 1985: seismographic reading of 125,892 millimeters 100 kilometers from the center

132. Magnitude of an Earthquake   San Francisco in 1906: seismographic reading of 50,119 millimeters 100 kilometers from the center

133. Alcohol and Driving   The concentration of alcohol in a person's bloodstream is measurable. Suppose that the relative risk R of having an accident while driving a car can be modeled by an equation of the form

$$R = e^{kx}$$

where x is the percent of concentration of alcohol in the bloodstream and k is a constant.

(a) Suppose that a concentration of alcohol in the bloodstream of 0.03 percent results in a relative risk of an accident of 1.4. Find the constant k in the equation.

(b) Using this value of k, what is the relative risk if the concentration is 0.17 percent?

(c) Using the same value of k, what concentration of alcohol corresponds to a relative risk of 100?

(d) If the law asserts that anyone with a relative risk of having an accident of 5 or more should not have driving privileges, at what concentration of alcohol in the bloodstream should a driver be arrested and charged with a DUI?

(e) Compare this situation with that of Example 10. If you were a lawmaker, which situation would you support? Give your reasons.

Explaining Concepts: Discussion and Writing

134. Is there any function of the form $y = x^{\alpha}, 0 < \alpha < 1$, that increases more slowly than a logarithmic function whose base is greater than 1? Explain.

135. In the definition of the logarithmic function, the base a is not allowed to equal 1. Why?

136. Critical Thinking   In buying a new car, one consideration might be how well the price of the car holds up over time. Different makes of cars have different depreciation rates. One way to compute a depreciation rate for a car is given here. Suppose that the current prices of a certain automobile are as shown in the table.

	Age in Years				
New	**1**	**2**	**3**	**4**	**5**
$38,000	$36,600	$32,400	$28,750	$25,400	$21,200

Use the formula New = Old(e^{Rt}) to find R, the annual depreciation rate, for a specific time t. When might be the best time to trade in the car? Consult the NADA ("blue") book and compare two like models that you are interested in. Which has the better depreciation rate?

'Are You Prepared?' Answers

1. (a) $x \leq 3$ (b) $x < -2$ or $x > 3$ **2.** $x < -4$ or $x > 1$ **3.** $\{3\}$

5.5 Properties of Logarithms

OBJECTIVES   **1** Work with the Properties of Logarithms (p. 296)
 2 Write a Logarithmic Expression as a Sum or Difference of Logarithms (p. 298)
 3 Write a Logarithmic Expression as a Single Logarithm (p. 299)
 4 Evaluate Logarithms Whose Base Is Neither 10 Nor e (p. 301)

1 Work with the Properties of Logarithms

Logarithms have some very useful properties that can be derived directly from the definition and the laws of exponents.

> **EXAMPLE 1**

Establishing Properties of Logarithms

(a) Show that $\log_a 1 = 0$.   (b) Show that $\log_a a = 1$.

Solution

(a) This fact was established when we graphed $y = \log_a x$ (see Figure 30 on page 286). To show the result algebraically, let $y = \log_a 1$. Then

$$
\begin{aligned}
y &= \log_a 1 \\
a^y &= 1 && \text{Change to an exponential statement.} \\
a^y &= a^0 && a^0 = 1 \text{ since } a > 0, a \neq 1 \\
y &= 0 && \text{Solve for } y. \\
\log_a 1 &= 0 && y = \log_a 1
\end{aligned}
$$

(b) Let $y = \log_a a$. Then

$$
\begin{aligned}
y &= \log_a a \\
a^y &= a && \text{Change to an exponential statement.} \\
a^y &= a^1 && a = a^1 \\
y &= 1 && \text{Solve for } y. \\
\log_a a &= 1 && y = \log_a a
\end{aligned}
$$

To summarize:

$$
\log_a 1 = 0 \qquad \log_a a = 1
$$

THEOREM

Properties of Logarithms

In the properties given next, M and a are positive real numbers, $a \neq 1$, and r is any real number.

The number $\log_a M$ is the exponent to which a must be raised to obtain M. That is,

$$
a^{\log_a M} = M \tag{1}
$$

The logarithm to the base a of a raised to a power equals that power. That is,

$$
\log_a a^r = r \tag{2}
$$

The proof uses the fact that $y = a^x$ and $y = \log_a x$ are inverses.

Proof of Property (1)   For inverse functions,

$$
f(f^{-1}(x)) = x \quad \text{for all } x \text{ in the domain of } f^{-1}
$$

Using $f(x) = a^x$ and $f^{-1}(x) = \log_a x$, we find

$$
f(f^{-1}(x)) = a^{\log_a x} = x \quad \text{for } x > 0
$$

Now let $x = M$ to obtain $a^{\log_a M} = M$, where $M > 0$.   ∎

Proof of Property (2)   For inverse functions,

$$
f^{-1}(f(x)) = x \quad \text{for all } x \text{ in the domain of } f
$$

Using $f(x) = a^x$ and $f^{-1}(x) = \log_a x$, we find

$$
f^{-1}(f(x)) = \log_a a^x = x \quad \text{for all real numbers } x
$$

Now let $x = r$ to obtain $\log_a a^r = r$, where r is any real number.   ∎

EXAMPLE 2

Using Properties (1) and (2)

(a) $2^{\log_2 \pi} = \pi$ 　　　　(b) $\log_{0.2} 0.2^{-\sqrt{2}} = -\sqrt{2}$ 　　　　(c) $\ln e^{kt} = kt$

▸ **Now Work** PROBLEM 15

Other useful properties of logarithms are given next.

THEOREM

Properties of Logarithms

In the following properties, M, N, and a are positive real numbers, $a \neq 1$, and r is any real number.

The Log of a Product Equals the Sum of the Logs

$$\log_a(MN) = \log_a M + \log_a N \tag{3}$$

The Log of a Quotient Equals the Difference of the Logs

$$\log_a\!\left(\frac{M}{N}\right) = \log_a M - \log_a N \tag{4}$$

The Log of a Power Equals the Product of the Power and the Log

$$\log_a M^r = r \log_a M \tag{5}$$

$$a^x = e^{x \ln a} \tag{6}$$

We shall derive properties (3), (5), and (6) and leave the derivation of property (4) as an exercise (see Problem 109).

Proof of Property (3) Let $A = \log_a M$ and let $B = \log_a N$. These expressions are equivalent to the exponential expressions

$$a^A = M \quad \text{and} \quad a^B = N$$

Now

$$\begin{aligned}
\log_a(MN) = \log_a(a^A a^B) &= \log_a a^{A+B} &&\text{Law of Exponents} \\
&= A + B &&\text{Property (2) of logarithms} \\
&= \log_a M + \log_a N
\end{aligned}$$
∎

Proof of Property (5) Let $A = \log_a M$. This expression is equivalent to

$$a^A = M$$

Now

$$\begin{aligned}
\log_a M^r = \log_a(a^A)^r &= \log_a a^{rA} &&\text{Law of Exponents} \\
&= rA &&\text{Property (2) of logarithms} \\
&= r \log_a M
\end{aligned}$$
∎

Proof of Property (6) From property (1), with $a = e$, we have

$$e^{\ln M} = M$$

Now let $M = a^x$ and apply property (5).

$$e^{\ln a^x} = e^{x \ln a} = a^x$$
∎

▸ **Now Work** PROBLEM 19

2 Write a Logarithmic Expression as a Sum or Difference of Logarithms

Logarithms can be used to transform products into sums, quotients into differences, and powers into factors. Such transformations prove useful in certain types of calculus problems.

EXAMPLE 3 | **Writing a Logarithmic Expression as a Sum of Logarithms**

Write $\log_a\left(x\sqrt{x^2 + 1}\right)$, $x > 0$, as a sum of logarithms. Express all powers as factors.

Solution

$$\log_a\left(x\sqrt{x^2 + 1}\right) = \log_a x + \log_a \sqrt{x^2 + 1} \quad \log_a(M \cdot N) = \log_a M + \log_a N$$

$$= \log_a x + \log_a(x^2 + 1)^{1/2}$$

$$= \log_a x + \frac{1}{2}\log_a(x^2 + 1) \quad \log_a M^r = r\log_a M$$

EXAMPLE 4 | **Writing a Logarithmic Expression as a Difference of Logarithms**

Write

$$\ln \frac{x^2}{(x - 1)^3} \qquad x > 1$$

as a difference of logarithms. Express all powers as factors.

Solution

$$\ln \frac{x^2}{(x - 1)^3} = \ln x^2 - \ln(x - 1)^3 = 2 \ln x - 3 \ln(x - 1)$$

$$\uparrow \qquad\qquad \uparrow$$

$$\log_a\left(\frac{M}{N}\right) = \log_a M - \log_a N \quad \log_a M^r = r\log_a M$$

EXAMPLE 5 | **Writing a Logarithmic Expression as a Sum and Difference of Logarithms**

Write

$$\log_a \frac{\sqrt{x^2 + 1}}{x^3(x + 1)^4} \quad x > 0$$

as a sum and difference of logarithms. Express all powers as factors.

Solution

$$\log_a \frac{\sqrt{x^2 + 1}}{x^3(x + 1)^4} = \log_a \sqrt{x^2 + 1} - \log_a[x^3(x + 1)^4] \qquad \text{Property (4)}$$

$$= \log_a \sqrt{x^2 + 1} - [\log_a x^3 + \log_a(x + 1)^4] \quad \text{Property (3)}$$

$$= \log_a(x^2 + 1)^{1/2} - \log_a x^3 - \log_a(x + 1)^4$$

$$= \frac{1}{2}\log_a(x^2 + 1) - 3\log_a x - 4\log_a(x + 1) \quad \text{Property (5)}$$

WARNING In using properties (3) through (5), be careful about the values that the variable may assume. For example, the domain of the variable for $\log_a x$ is $x > 0$ and for $\log_a(x - 1)$ it is $x > 1$. If we add these functions, the domain is $x > 1$. That is, the equality

$$\log_a x + \log_a(x - 1) = \log_a[x(x - 1)]$$

is true only for $x > 1$. ∎

━ **Now Work** PROBLEM 51

3 Write a Logarithmic Expression as a Single Logarithm

Another use of properties (3) through (5) is to write sums and/or differences of logarithms with the same base as a single logarithm. This skill will be needed to solve certain logarithmic equations discussed in the next section.

EXAMPLE 6 | **Writing Expressions as a Single Logarithm**

Write each of the following as a single logarithm.

(a) $\log_a 7 + 4 \log_a 3$ (b) $\frac{2}{3}\ln 8 - \ln(5^2 - 1)$

(c) $\log_a x + \log_a 9 + \log_a(x^2 + 1) - \log_a 5$

Solution

(a) $\log_a 7 + 4\log_a 3 = \log_a 7 + \log_a 3^4$ $r\log_a M = \log_a M^r$

$\qquad\qquad\qquad\quad = \log_a 7 + \log_a 81$

$\qquad\qquad\qquad\quad = \log_a(7 \cdot 81)$ $\log_a M + \log_a N = \log_a(M \cdot N)$

$\qquad\qquad\qquad\quad = \log_a 567$

(b) $\dfrac{2}{3}\ln 8 - \ln(5^2 - 1) = \ln 8^{2/3} - \ln(25 - 1)$ $r\log_a M = \log_a M^r$

$\qquad\qquad\qquad\qquad\quad = \ln 4 - \ln 24$ $8^{2/3} = (\sqrt[3]{8})^2 = 2^2 = 4$

$\qquad\qquad\qquad\qquad\quad = \ln\left(\dfrac{4}{24}\right)$ $\log_a M - \log_a N = \log_a\left(\dfrac{M}{N}\right)$

$\qquad\qquad\qquad\qquad\quad = \ln\left(\dfrac{1}{6}\right)$

$\qquad\qquad\qquad\qquad\quad = \ln 1 - \ln 6$

$\qquad\qquad\qquad\qquad\quad = -\ln 6$ $\ln 1 = 0$

(c) $\log_a x + \log_a 9 + \log_a(x^2 + 1) - \log_a 5 = \log_a(9x) + \log_a(x^2 + 1) - \log_a 5$

$\qquad\qquad\qquad\qquad\qquad\qquad\qquad\qquad = \log_a[9x(x^2 + 1)] - \log_a 5$

$\qquad\qquad\qquad\qquad\qquad\qquad\qquad\qquad = \log_a\left[\dfrac{9x(x^2 + 1)}{5}\right]$

WARNING A common error made by some students is to express the logarithm of a sum as the sum of logarithms.

$$\log_a(M + N) \quad \text{is not equal to} \quad \log_a M + \log_a N$$

Correct statement $\log_a(MN) = \log_a M + \log_a N$ Property (3)

Another common error is to express the difference of logarithms as the quotient of logarithms.

$$\log_a M - \log_a N \quad \text{is not equal to} \quad \dfrac{\log_a M}{\log_a N}$$

Correct statement $\log_a M - \log_a N = \log_a\left(\dfrac{M}{N}\right)$ Property (4)

A third common error is to express a logarithm raised to a power as the product of the power times the logarithm.

$$(\log_a M)^r \quad \text{is not equal to} \quad r\log_a M$$

Correct statement $\log_a M^r = r\log_a M$ Property (5)   ■

Now Work PROBLEM 57

Two other properties of logarithms that we need to know are consequences of the fact that the logarithmic function $y = \log_a x$ is a one-to-one function.

THEOREM

Properties of Logarithms

In the following properties, M, N, and a are positive real numbers, $a \neq 1$.

$$\text{If } M = N, \text{ then } \log_a M = \log_a N. \qquad \text{(7)}$$
$$\text{If } \log_a M = \log_a N, \text{ then } M = N. \qquad \text{(8)}$$

When property (7) is used, we start with the equation $M = N$ and say "take the logarithm of both sides" to obtain $\log_a M = \log_a N$.

Properties (7) and (8) are useful for solving *exponential and logarithmic equations*, a topic discussed in the next section.

4 Evaluate Logarithms Whose Base Is Neither 10 Nor e

Logarithms to the base 10, common logarithms, were used to facilitate arithmetic computations before the widespread use of calculators. (See the Historical Feature at the end of this section.) Natural logarithms, that is, logarithms whose base is the number e, remain very important because they arise frequently in the study of natural phenomena.

Common logarithms are usually abbreviated by writing **log,** with the base understood to be 10, just as natural logarithms are abbreviated by **ln,** with the base understood to be e.

Most calculators have both $\boxed{\log}$ and $\boxed{\ln}$ keys to calculate the common logarithm and natural logarithm of a number. Let's look at an example to see how to approximate logarithms having a base other than 10 or e.

EXAMPLE 7   **Approximating a Logarithm Whose Base Is Neither 10 Nor e**

Approximate $\log_2 7$. Round the answer to four decimal places.

Solution   Remember, $\log_2 7$ means "2 raised to what exponent equals 7." If we let $y = \log_2 7$, then $2^y = 7$. Because $2^2 = 4$ and $2^3 = 8$, we expect $\log_2 7$ to be between 2 and 3.

$$2^y = 7$$
$$\ln 2^y = \ln 7 \qquad \text{Property (7)}$$
$$y \ln 2 = \ln 7 \qquad \text{Property (5)}$$
$$y = \frac{\ln 7}{\ln 2} \qquad \text{Exact value}$$
$$y \approx 2.8074 \qquad \text{Approximate value rounded to four decimal places}$$

Example 7 shows how to approximate a logarithm whose base is 2 by changing to logarithms involving the base e. In general, we use the **Change-of-Base Formula.**

THEOREM   **Change-of-Base Formula**

If $a \neq 1$, $b \neq 1$, and M are positive real numbers, then

$$\log_a M = \frac{\log_b M}{\log_b a} \qquad (9)$$

Proof   We derive this formula as follows: Let $y = \log_a M$. Then

$$a^y = M$$
$$\log_b a^y = \log_b M \qquad \text{Property (7)}$$
$$y \log_b a = \log_b M \qquad \text{Property (5)}$$
$$y = \frac{\log_b M}{\log_b a} \qquad \text{Solve for } y.$$
$$\log_a M = \frac{\log_b M}{\log_b a} \qquad y = \log_a M \qquad \blacksquare$$

Since calculators have keys only for $\boxed{\log}$ and $\boxed{\ln}$, in practice, the Change-of-Base Formula uses either $b = 10$ or $b = e$. That is,

$$\log_a M = \frac{\log M}{\log a} \quad \text{and} \quad \log_a M = \frac{\ln M}{\ln a} \qquad (10)$$

EXAMPLE 8	**Using the Change-of-Base Formula**

Approximate:

(a) $\log_5 89$ (b) $\log_{\sqrt{2}} \sqrt{5}$

Round answers to four decimal places.

Solution

(a) $\log_5 89 = \dfrac{\log 89}{\log 5} \approx \dfrac{1.949390007}{0.6989700043}$

≈ 2.7889

or

$\log_5 89 = \dfrac{\ln 89}{\ln 5} \approx \dfrac{4.48863637}{1.609437912}$

≈ 2.7889

(b) $\log_{\sqrt{2}} \sqrt{5} = \dfrac{\log \sqrt{5}}{\log \sqrt{2}} = \dfrac{\frac{1}{2} \log 5}{\frac{1}{2} \log 2}$

$= \dfrac{\log 5}{\log 2} \approx 2.3219$

or

$\log_{\sqrt{2}} \sqrt{5} = \dfrac{\ln \sqrt{5}}{\ln \sqrt{2}} = \dfrac{\frac{1}{2} \ln 5}{\frac{1}{2} \ln 2}$

$= \dfrac{\ln 5}{\ln 2} \approx 2.3219$

➙**Now Work** PROBLEMS 23 AND 71

 COMMENT To graph logarithmic functions when the base is different from e or 10 requires the Change-of-Base Formula. For example, to graph $y = \log_2 x$, we would instead graph $y = \dfrac{\ln x}{\ln 2}$. Try it. ■

➙**Now Work** PROBLEM 79

SUMMARY Properties of Logarithms

In the list that follows, a, b, M, N, and r are real numbers. Also, $a > 0, a \neq 1, b > 0, b \neq 1, M > 0$, and $N > 0$.

Definition

$y = \log_a x$ means $x = a^y$

Properties of logarithms

$\log_a 1 = 0; \quad \log_a a = 1$

$a^{\log_a M} = M; \quad \log_a a^r = r$

$\log_a(MN) = \log_a M + \log_a N$

$\log_a\left(\dfrac{M}{N}\right) = \log_a M - \log_a N$

$\log_a M^r = r \log_a M$

$a^x = e^{x \ln a}$

If $M = N$, then $\log_a M = \log_a N$.

If $\log_a M = \log_a N$, then $M = N$.

Change-of-Base Formula

$\log_a M = \dfrac{\log_b M}{\log_b a}$

Historical Feature

John Napier
(1550–1617)

Logarithms were invented about 1590 by John Napier (1550–1617) and Joost Bürgi (1552–1632), working independently. Napier, whose work had the greater influence, was a Scottish lord, a secretive man whose neighbors were inclined to believe him to be in league with the devil. His approach to logarithms was very different from ours; it was based on the relationship between arithmetic and geometric sequences, discussed in a later chapter, and not on the inverse function relationship of logarithms to exponential functions (described in Section 5.4).

Napier's tables, published in 1614, listed what would now be called *natural logarithms* of sines and were rather difficult to use. A London professor, Henry Briggs, became interested in the tables and visited Napier. In their conversations, they developed the idea of common logarithms, which were published in 1617. Their importance for calculation was immediately recognized, and by 1650 they were being printed as far away as China. They remained an important calculation tool until the advent of the inexpensive handheld calculator about 1972, which has decreased their calculational, but not their theoretical, importance.

A side effect of the invention of logarithms was the popularization of the decimal system of notation for real numbers.

5.5 Assess Your Understanding

Concepts and Vocabulary

1. $\log_a 1 =$ _____

2. $\log_a a =$ _____

3. $a^{\log_a M} =$ _____

4. $\log_a a^r =$ _____

5. $\log_a(MN) =$ _____ + _____

6. $\log_a\left(\dfrac{M}{N}\right) =$ _____ − _____

7. $\log_a M^r =$ _____

8. If $\log_a x = \log_a 6$, then $x =$ _____.

9. If $\log_8 M = \dfrac{\log_5 7}{\log_5 8}$, then $M =$ _____.

10. *True or False* $\ln(x + 3) - \ln(2x) = \dfrac{\ln(x + 3)}{\ln(2x)}$

11. *True or False* $\log_2(3x^4) = 4\log_2(3x)$

12. *True or False* $\dfrac{\ln 8}{\ln 4} = 2$

Skill Building

In Problems 13–28, use properties of logarithms to find the exact value of each expression. Do not use a calculator.

13. $\log_3 3^{71}$

14. $\log_2 2^{-13}$

15. $\ln e^{-4}$

16. $\ln e^{\sqrt{2}}$

17. $2^{\log_2 7}$

18. $e^{\ln 8}$

19. $\log_8 2 + \log_8 4$

20. $\log_6 9 + \log_6 4$

21. $\log_6 18 - \log_6 3$

22. $\log_8 16 - \log_8 2$

23. $\log_2 6 \cdot \log_6 8$

24. $\log_3 8 \cdot \log_8 9$

25. $3^{\log_3 5 - \log_3 4}$

26. $5^{\log_5 6 + \log_5 7}$

27. $e^{\log_{e^2} 16}$

28. $e^{\log_{e^2} 9}$

In Problems 29–36, suppose that $\ln 2 = a$ and $\ln 3 = b$. Use properties of logarithms to write each logarithm in terms of a and b.

29. $\ln 6$

30. $\ln \dfrac{2}{3}$

31. $\ln 1.5$

32. $\ln 0.5$

33. $\ln 8$

34. $\ln 27$

35. $\ln \sqrt[5]{6}$

36. $\ln \sqrt[4]{\dfrac{2}{3}}$

In Problems 37–56, write each expression as a sum and/or difference of logarithms. Express powers as factors.

37. $\log_5(25x)$

38. $\log_3 \dfrac{x}{9}$

39. $\log_2 z^3$

40. $\log_7 x^5$

41. $\ln(ex)$

42. $\ln \dfrac{e}{x}$

43. $\ln \dfrac{x}{e^x}$

44. $\ln(xe^x)$

45. $\log_a(u^2 v^3)$ $u > 0, v > 0$

46. $\log_2\left(\dfrac{a}{b^2}\right)$ $a > 0, b > 0$

47. $\ln\left(x^2\sqrt{1 - x}\right)$ $0 < x < 1$

48. $\ln\left(x\sqrt{1 + x^2}\right)$ $x > 0$

49. $\log_2\left(\dfrac{x^3}{x - 3}\right)$ $x > 3$

50. $\log_5\left(\dfrac{\sqrt[3]{x^2 + 1}}{x^2 - 1}\right)$ $x > 1$

51. $\log\left[\dfrac{x(x + 2)}{(x + 3)^2}\right]$ $x > 0$

52. $\log\left[\dfrac{x^3\sqrt{x + 1}}{(x - 2)^2}\right]$ $x > 2$

53. $\ln\left[\dfrac{x^2 - x - 2}{(x + 4)^2}\right]^{1/3}$ $x > 2$

54. $\ln\left[\dfrac{(x - 4)^2}{x^2 - 1}\right]^{2/3}$ $x > 4$

55. $\ln \dfrac{5x\sqrt{1 + 3x}}{(x - 4)^3}$ $x > 4$

56. $\ln\left[\dfrac{5x^2\sqrt[3]{1 - x}}{4(x + 1)^2}\right]$ $0 < x < 1$

In Problems 57–70, write each expression as a single logarithm.

57. $3\log_5 u + 4\log_5 v$

58. $2\log_3 u - \log_3 v$

59. $\log_3 \sqrt{x} - \log_3 x^3$

60. $\log_2\left(\dfrac{1}{x}\right) + \log_2\left(\dfrac{1}{x^2}\right)$

61. $\log_4(x^2 - 1) - 5\log_4(x + 1)$

62. $\log(x^2 + 3x + 2) - 2\log(x + 1)$

63. $\ln\left(\dfrac{x}{x - 1}\right) + \ln\left(\dfrac{x + 1}{x}\right) - \ln(x^2 - 1)$

64. $\log\left(\dfrac{x^2 + 2x - 3}{x^2 - 4}\right) - \log\left(\dfrac{x^2 + 7x + 6}{x + 2}\right)$

65. $8\log_2\sqrt{3x - 2} - \log_2\left(\dfrac{4}{x}\right) + \log_2 4$

66. $21 \log_3 \sqrt[3]{x} + \log_3(9x^2) - \log_3 9$

67. $2 \log_a(5x^3) - \frac{1}{2} \log_a(2x + 3)$

68. $\frac{1}{3} \log(x^3 + 1) + \frac{1}{2} \log(x^2 + 1)$

69. $2 \log_2(x + 1) - \log_2(x + 3) - \log_2(x - 1)$

70. $3 \log_5(3x + 1) - 2 \log_5(2x - 1) - \log_5 x$

In Problems 71–78, use the Change-of-Base Formula and a calculator to evaluate each logarithm. Round your answer to three decimal places.

71. $\log_3 21$

72. $\log_5 18$

73. $\log_{1/3} 71$

74. $\log_{1/2} 15$

75. $\log_{\sqrt{2}} 7$

76. $\log_{\sqrt{5}} 8$

77. $\log_\pi e$

78. $\log_\pi \sqrt{2}$

In Problems 79–84, graph each function using a graphing utility and the Change-of-Base Formula.

79. $y = \log_4 x$

80. $y = \log_5 x$

81. $y = \log_2(x + 2)$

82. $y = \log_4(x - 3)$

83. $y = \log_{x-1}(x + 1)$

84. $y = \log_{x+2}(x - 2)$

Mixed Practice

85. If $f(x) = \ln x$, $g(x) = e^x$, and $h(x) = x^2$, find:
(a) $(f \circ g)(x)$. What is the domain of $f \circ g$?
(b) $(g \circ f)(x)$. What is the domain of $g \circ f$?
(c) $(f \circ g)(5)$
(d) $(f \circ h)(x)$. What is the domain of $f \circ h$?
(e) $(f \circ h)(e)$

86. If $f(x) = \log_2 x$, $g(x) = 2^x$, and $h(x) = 4x$, find:
(a) $(f \circ g)(x)$. What is the domain of $f \circ g$?
(b) $(g \circ f)(x)$. What is the domain of $g \circ f$?
(c) $(f \circ g)(3)$
(d) $(f \circ h)(x)$. What is the domain of $f \circ h$?
(e) $(f \circ h)(8)$

Applications and Extensions

In Problems 87–96, express y as a function of x. The constant C is a positive number.

87. $\ln y = \ln x + \ln C$

88. $\ln y = \ln(x + C)$

89. $\ln y = \ln x + \ln(x + 1) + \ln C$

90. $\ln y = 2 \ln x - \ln(x + 1) + \ln C$

91. $\ln y = 3x + \ln C$

92. $\ln y = -2x + \ln C$

93. $\ln(y - 3) = -4x + \ln C$

94. $\ln(y + 4) = 5x + \ln C$

95. $3 \ln y = \frac{1}{2} \ln(2x + 1) - \frac{1}{3} \ln(x + 4) + \ln C$

96. $2 \ln y = -\frac{1}{2} \ln x + \frac{1}{3} \ln(x^2 + 1) + \ln C$

97. Find the value of $\log_2 3 \cdot \log_3 4 \cdot \log_4 5 \cdot \log_5 6 \cdot \log_6 7 \cdot \log_7 8$.

98. Find the value of $\log_2 4 \cdot \log_4 6 \cdot \log_6 8$.

99. Find the value of $\log_2 3 \cdot \log_3 4 \cdot \cdots \cdot \log_n(n + 1) \cdot \log_{n+1} 2$.

100. Find the value of $\log_2 2 \cdot \log_2 4 \cdot \cdots \cdot \log_2 2^n$.

101. Show that $\log_a\left(x + \sqrt{x^2 - 1}\right) + \log_a\left(x - \sqrt{x^2 - 1}\right) = 0$.

102. Show that $\log_a\left(\sqrt{x} + \sqrt{x - 1}\right) + \log_a\left(\sqrt{x} - \sqrt{x - 1}\right) = 0$.

103. Show that $\ln(1 + e^{2x}) = 2x + \ln(1 + e^{-2x})$.

104. Difference Quotient If $f(x) = \log_a x$, show that $\dfrac{f(x + h) - f(x)}{h} = \log_a\left(1 + \dfrac{h}{x}\right)^{1/h}$, $h \neq 0$.

105. If $f(x) = \log_a x$, show that $-f(x) = \log_{1/a} x$.

106. If $f(x) = \log_a x$, show that $f(AB) = f(A) + f(B)$.

107. If $f(x) = \log_a x$, show that $f\left(\dfrac{1}{x}\right) = -f(x)$.

108. If $f(x) = \log_a x$, show that $f(x^\alpha) = \alpha f(x)$.

109. Show that $\log_a\left(\dfrac{M}{N}\right) = \log_a M - \log_a N$, where a, M, and N are positive real numbers and $a \neq 1$.

110. Show that $\log_a\left(\dfrac{1}{N}\right) = -\log_a N$, where a and N are positive real numbers and $a \neq 1$.

Explaining Concepts: Discussion and Writing

111. Graph $Y_1 = \log(x^2)$ and $Y_2 = 2 \log(x)$ using a graphing utility. Are they equivalent? What might account for any differences in the two functions?

112. Write an example that illustrates why $(\log_a x)^r \neq r \log_a x$.

113. Write an example that illustrates why $\log_2(x + y) \neq \log_2 x + \log_2 y$.

114. Does $3^{\log_3(-5)} = -5$? Why or why not?

5.6 Logarithmic and Exponential Equations

PREPARING FOR THIS SECTION *Before getting started, review the following:*

- Solving Equations Using a Graphing Utility (Appendix B, Section B.4, pp. B6–B7)
- Solving Quadratic Equations (Appendix A, Section A.6, pp. A47–A51)

Now Work the *'Are You Prepared?'* problems on page 309.

OBJECTIVES   **1** Solve Logarithmic Equations (p. 305)
  2 Solve Exponential Equations (p. 307)
  3 Solve Logarithmic and Exponential Equations Using a Graphing Utility (p. 308)

1 Solve Logarithmic Equations

In Section 5.4 we solved logarithmic equations by changing a logarithmic expression to an exponential expression. That is, we used the definition of a logarithm:

$$y = \log_a x \quad \text{is equivalent to} \quad x = a^y \qquad a > 0, a \neq 1$$

For example, to solve the equation $\log_2(1 - 2x) = 3$, we write the logarithmic equation as an equivalent exponential equation $1 - 2x = 2^3$ and solve for x.

$$\log_2(1 - 2x) = 3$$
$$1 - 2x = 2^3 \qquad \text{\textit{Change to an exponential statement.}}$$
$$-2x = 7 \qquad \text{\textit{Simplify.}}$$
$$x = -\frac{7}{2} \qquad \text{\textit{Solve.}}$$

You should check this solution for yourself.

For most logarithmic equations, some manipulation of the equation (usually using properties of logarithms) is required to obtain a solution. Also, to avoid extraneous solutions with logarithmic equations, we determine the domain of the variable first.

We begin with an example of a logarithmic equation that requires using the fact that a logarithmic function is a one-to-one function:

$$\text{If } \log_a M = \log_a N, \text{ then } M = N \qquad M, N, \text{ and } a \text{ are positive and } a \neq 1.$$

EXAMPLE 1   **Solving a Logarithmic Equation**

Solve: $2 \log_5 x = \log_5 9$

Solution   The domain of the variable in this equation is $x > 0$. Because each logarithm is to the same base, 5, we can obtain an exact solution as follows:

$$2 \log_5 x = \log_5 9$$
$$\log_5 x^2 = \log_5 9 \qquad \text{\textit{r} }\log_a M = \log_a M^r$$
$$x^2 = 9 \qquad \text{\textit{If }} \log_a M = \log_a N, \text{ then } M = N.$$
$$x = 3 \quad \text{or} \quad x = -3$$

Recall that the domain of the variable is $x > 0$. Therefore, -3 is extraneous and we discard it.

✓Check: $2\log_5 3 \overset{?}{=} \log_5 9$

$$\log_5 3^2 \overset{?}{=} \log_5 9 \quad r\log_a M = \log_a M^r$$

$$\log_5 9 = \log_5 9$$

The solution set is $\{3\}$.

──Now Work PROBLEM 13

Often we need to use one or more properties of logarithms to rewrite the equation as a single logarithm. In the next example we employ the log of a product property to solve a logarithmic equation.

EXAMPLE 2 | **Solving a Logarithmic Equation**

Solve: $\log_5(x + 6) + \log_5(x + 2) = 1$

Solution The domain of the variable requires that $x + 6 > 0$ and $x + 2 > 0$, so $x > -6$ and $x > -2$. This means any solution must satisfy $x > -2$. To obtain an exact solution, we need to express the left side as a single logarithm. Then we will change the equation to an equivalent exponential equation.

$$\log_5(x + 6) + \log_5(x + 2) = 1$$

$$\log_5[(x + 6)(x + 2)] = 1 \qquad \log_a M + \log_a N = \log_a(MN)$$

$$(x + 6)(x + 2) = 5^1 = 5 \qquad \text{Change to an exponential statement.}$$

$$x^2 + 8x + 12 = 5 \qquad \text{Simplify.}$$

$$x^2 + 8x + 7 = 0 \qquad \text{Place the quadratic equation in standard form.}$$

$$(x + 7)(x + 1) = 0 \qquad \text{Factor.}$$

$$x = -7 \quad \text{or} \quad x = -1 \qquad \text{Zero-Product Property}$$

WARNING A negative solution is not automatically extraneous. You must determine whether the potential solution causes the argument of any logarithmic expression in the equation to be negative. ■

Only $x = -1$ satisfies the restriction that $x > -2$, so $x = -7$ is extraneous. The solution set is $\{-1\}$, which you should check.

──Now Work PROBLEM 21

EXAMPLE 3 | **Solving a Logarithmic Equation**

Solve: $\ln x = \ln(x + 6) - \ln(x - 4)$

Solution The domain of the variable requires that $x > 0$, $x + 6 > 0$, and $x - 4 > 0$. As a result, the domain of the variable here is $x > 4$. We begin the solution using the log of a difference property.

$$\ln x = \ln(x + 6) - \ln(x - 4)$$

$$\ln x = \ln\left(\frac{x + 6}{x - 4}\right) \qquad \ln M - \ln N = \ln\left(\frac{M}{N}\right)$$

$$x = \frac{x + 6}{x - 4} \qquad \text{If } \ln M = \ln N, \text{ then } M = N.$$

$$x(x - 4) = x + 6 \qquad \text{Multiply both sides by } x - 4.$$

$$x^2 - 4x = x + 6 \qquad \text{Simplify.}$$

$$x^2 - 5x - 6 = 0 \qquad \text{Place the quadratic equation in standard form.}$$

$$(x - 6)(x + 1) = 0 \qquad \text{Factor.}$$

$$x = 6 \quad \text{or} \quad x = -1 \qquad \text{Zero-Product Property}$$

Since the domain of the variable is $x > 4$, we discard -1 as extraneous. The solution set is $\{6\}$, which you should check.

WARNING In using properties of logarithms to solve logarithmic equations, avoid using the property $\log_a x^r = r \log_a x$, when r is even. The reason can be seen in this example:

Solve: $\log_3 x^2 = 4$

Solution: The domain of the variable x is all real numbers except 0.

(a) $\log_3 x^2 = 4$
   $x^2 = 3^4 = 81$ *Change to exponential form.*
   $x = -9 \text{ or } x = 9$

(b) $\log_3 x^2 = 4$ $\log_a x^r = r \log_a x$
   $2 \log_3 x = 4$ *Domain of variable is $x > 0$.*
   $\log_3 x = 2$
   $x = 9$

Both -9 and 9 are solutions of $\log_3 x^2 = 4$ (as you can verify). The solution in part (b) does not find the solution -9 because the domain of the variable was further restricted due to the application of the property $\log_a x^r = r \log_a x$. ∎

─────**Now Work** PROBLEM 31

2 Solve Exponential Equations

In Sections 5.3 and 5.4, we solved exponential equations algebraically by expressing each side of the equation using the same base. That is, we used the one-to-one property of the exponential function:

$$\text{If } a^u = a^v, \quad \text{then } u = v \qquad a > 0, a \neq 1$$

For example, to solve the exponential equation $4^{2x+1} = 16$, notice that $16 = 4^2$ and apply the property above to obtain $2x + 1 = 2$, from which we find $x = \dfrac{1}{2}$.

For most exponential equations, we cannot express each side of the equation using the same base. In such cases, algebraic techniques can sometimes be used to obtain exact solutions.

EXAMPLE 4

Solving Exponential Equations

Solve: (a) $2^x = 5$ (b) $8 \cdot 3^x = 5$

Solution (a) Since 5 cannot be written as an integer power of 2 ($2^2 = 4$ and $2^3 = 8$), write the exponential equation as the equivalent logarithmic equation.

$$2^x = 5$$
$$x = \log_2 5 = \frac{\ln 5}{\ln 2}$$

↑
Change-of-Base Formula (10), Section 5.5

Alternatively, we can solve the equation $2^x = 5$ by taking the natural logarithm (or common logarithm) of each side. Taking the natural logarithm,

$$2^x = 5$$
$$\ln 2^x = \ln 5 \qquad \textit{If } M = N, \textit{ then } \ln M = \ln N.$$
$$x \ln 2 = \ln 5 \qquad \ln M^r = r \ln M$$
$$x = \frac{\ln 5}{\ln 2} \qquad \textit{Exact solution}$$
$$\approx 2.322 \qquad \textit{Approximate solution}$$

The solution set is $\left\{ \dfrac{\ln 5}{\ln 2} \right\}$.

(b) $8 \cdot 3^x = 5$
   $3^x = \dfrac{5}{8}$ *Solve for 3^x.*

$$x = \log_3\left(\frac{5}{8}\right) = \frac{\ln\left(\frac{5}{8}\right)}{\ln 3} \quad \text{Exact solution}$$

$$\approx -0.428 \quad \text{Approximate solution}$$

The solution set is $\left\{ \dfrac{\ln\left(\dfrac{5}{8}\right)}{\ln 3} \right\}$.

━━━━**Now Work**   PROBLEM 35

EXAMPLE 5   **Solving an Exponential Equation**

Solve: $5^{x-2} = 3^{3x+2}$

Solution   Because the bases are different, we first apply property (7), Section 5.5 (take the natural logarithm of each side), and then use a property of logarithms. The result is an equation in x that we can solve.

$$5^{x-2} = 3^{3x+2}$$
$$\ln 5^{x-2} = \ln 3^{3x+2} \qquad \text{If } M = N, \ln M = \ln N.$$
$$(x-2)\ln 5 = (3x+2)\ln 3 \qquad \ln M^r = r \ln M$$
$$(\ln 5)x - 2\ln 5 = (3\ln 3)x + 2\ln 3 \qquad \text{Distribute.}$$
$$(\ln 5)x - (3\ln 3)x = 2\ln 3 + 2\ln 5 \qquad \text{Place terms involving } x \text{ on the left.}$$
$$(\ln 5 - 3\ln 3)x = 2(\ln 3 + \ln 5) \qquad \text{Factor.}$$
$$x = \frac{2(\ln 3 + \ln 5)}{\ln 5 - 3\ln 3} \qquad \text{Exact solution}$$
$$\approx -3.212 \qquad \text{Approximate solution}$$

The solution set is $\left\{ \dfrac{2(\ln 3 + \ln 5)}{\ln 5 - 3\ln 3} \right\}$.

━━━━**Now Work**   PROBLEM 45

EXAMPLE 6   **Solving an Exponential Equation That Is Quadratic in Form**

Solve: $4^x - 2^x - 12 = 0$

Solution   We note that $4^x = (2^2)^x = 2^{(2x)} = (2^x)^2$, so the equation is quadratic in form, and we can rewrite it as

$$(2^x)^2 - 2^x - 12 = 0 \qquad \text{Let } u = 2^x; \text{ then } u^2 - u - 12 = 0.$$

Now we can factor as usual.

$$(2^x - 4)(2^x + 3) = 0 \qquad (u-4)(u+3) = 0$$
$$2^x - 4 = 0 \quad \text{or} \quad 2^x + 3 = 0 \qquad u - 4 = 0 \quad \text{or} \quad u + 3 = 0$$
$$2^x = 4 \qquad\qquad 2^x = -3 \qquad u = 2^x = 4 \qquad u = 2^x = -3$$

The equation on the left has the solution $x = 2$, since $2^x = 4 = 2^2$; the equation on the right has no solution, since $2^x > 0$ for all x. The only solution is 2. The solution set is $\{2\}$.

━━━━**Now Work**   PROBLEM 53

---

3 Solve Logarithmic and Exponential Equations Using a Graphing Utility

The algebraic techniques introduced in this section to obtain exact solutions apply only to certain types of logarithmic and exponential equations. Solutions for other types are usually studied in calculus, using numerical methods. For such types, we can use a graphing utility to approximate the solution.

EXAMPLE 7   **Solving Equations Using a Graphing Utility**

Solve: $x + e^x = 2$

Express the solution(s) rounded to two decimal places.

Solution   The solution is found by graphing $Y_1 = x + e^x$ and $Y_2 = 2$. Since Y_1 is an increasing function (do you know why?), there is only one point of intersection for Y_1 and Y_2. Figure 40 shows the graphs of Y_1 and Y_2. Using the INTERSECT command, the solution is 0.44 rounded to two decimal places.

Figure 40

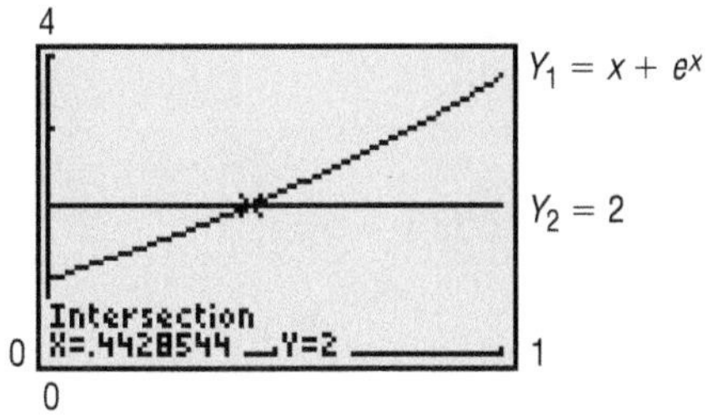

$Y_1 = x + e^x$

$Y_2 = 2$

Intersection
X=.4428544 Y=2

──────Now Work   PROBLEM 63

5.6   Assess Your Understanding

'Are You Prepared?'   *Answers are given at the end of these exercises. If you get a wrong answer, read the pages listed in red.*

1. Solve $x^2 - 7x - 30 = 0$. (pp. A47–A51)

2. Solve $(x + 3)^2 - 4(x + 3) + 3 = 0$. (pp. A47–A51)

3. Approximate the solution(s) to $x^3 = x^2 - 5$ using a graphing utility. (pp. B6–B7)

4. Approximate the solution(s) to $x^3 - 2x + 2 = 0$ using a graphing utility. (pp. B6–B7)

Skill Building

In Problems 5–32, solve each logarithmic equation. Express irrational solutions in exact form and as a decimal rounded to three decimal places.

5. $\log_4 x = 2$

6. $\log(x + 6) = 1$

7. $\log_2(5x) = 4$

8. $\log_3(3x - 1) = 2$

9. $\log_4(x + 2) = \log_4 8$

10. $\log_5(2x + 3) = \log_5 3$

11. $\dfrac{1}{2}\log_3 x = 2\log_3 2$

12. $-2\log_4 x = \log_4 9$

13. $3\log_2 x = -\log_2 27$

14. $2\log_5 x = 3\log_5 4$

15. $3\log_2(x - 1) + \log_2 4 = 5$

16. $2\log_3(x + 4) - \log_3 9 = 2$

17. $\log x + \log(x + 15) = 2$

18. $\log x + \log(x - 21) = 2$

19. $\log(2x + 1) = 1 + \log(x - 2)$

20. $\log(2x) - \log(x - 3) = 1$

21. $\log_2(x + 7) + \log_2(x + 8) = 1$

22. $\log_6(x + 4) + \log_6(x + 3) = 1$

23. $\log_8(x + 6) = 1 - \log_8(x + 4)$

24. $\log_5(x + 3) = 1 - \log_5(x - 1)$

25. $\ln x + \ln(x + 2) = 4$

26. $\ln(x + 1) - \ln x = 2$

27. $\log_3(x + 1) + \log_3(x + 4) = 2$

28. $\log_2(x + 1) + \log_2(x + 7) = 3$

29. $\log_{1/3}(x^2 + x) - \log_{1/3}(x^2 - x) = -1$

30. $\log_4(x^2 - 9) - \log_4(x + 3) = 3$

31. $\log_a(x - 1) - \log_a(x + 6) = \log_a(x - 2) - \log_a(x + 3)$

32. $\log_a x + \log_a(x - 2) = \log_a(x + 4)$

In Problems 33–60, solve each exponential equation. Express irrational solutions in exact form and as a decimal rounded to three decimal places.

33. $2^{x-5} = 8$

34. $5^{-x} = 25$

35. $2^x = 10$

36. $3^x = 14$

37. $8^{-x} = 1.2$

38. $2^{-x} = 1.5$

39. $5(2^{3x}) = 8$

40. $0.3(4^{0.2x}) = 0.2$

41. $3^{1-2x} = 4^x$

42. $2^{x+1} = 5^{1-2x}$

43. $\left(\dfrac{3}{5}\right)^x = 7^{1-x}$

44. $\left(\dfrac{4}{3}\right)^{1-x} = 5^x$

45. $1.2^x = (0.5)^{-x}$

46. $0.3^{1+x} = 1.7^{2x-1}$

47. $\pi^{1-x} = e^x$

48. $e^{x+3} = \pi^x$

49. $2^{2x} + 2^x - 12 = 0$ **50.** $3^{2x} + 3^x - 2 = 0$ **51.** $3^{2x} + 3^{x+1} - 4 = 0$ **52.** $2^{2x} + 2^{x+2} - 12 = 0$

53. $16^x + 4^{x+1} - 3 = 0$ **54.** $9^x - 3^{x+1} + 1 = 0$ **55.** $25^x - 8 \cdot 5^x = -16$ **56.** $36^x - 6 \cdot 6^x = -9$

57. $3 \cdot 4^x + 4 \cdot 2^x + 8 = 0$ **58.** $2 \cdot 49^x + 11 \cdot 7^x + 5 = 0$ **59.** $4^x - 10 \cdot 4^{-x} = 3$ **60.** $3^x - 14 \cdot 3^{-x} = 5$

In Problems 61–74, use a graphing utility to solve each equation. Express your answer rounded to two decimal places.

61. $\log_5(x + 1) - \log_4(x - 2) = 1$ **62.** $\log_2(x - 1) - \log_6(x + 2) = 2$

63. $e^x = -x$ **64.** $e^{2x} = x + 2$ **65.** $e^x = x^2$ **66.** $e^x = x^3$

67. $\ln x = -x$ **68.** $\ln(2x) = -x + 2$ **69.** $\ln x = x^3 - 1$ **70.** $\ln x = -x^2$

71. $e^x + \ln x = 4$ **72.** $e^x - \ln x = 4$ **73.** $e^{-x} = \ln x$ **74.** $e^{-x} = -\ln x$

Mixed Practice

In Problems 75–86, solve each equation. Express irrational solutions in exact form and as a decimal rounded to three decimal places.

75. $\log_2(x + 1) - \log_4 x = 1$ **76.** $\log_2(3x + 2) - \log_4 x = 3$ **77.** $\log_{16} x + \log_4 x + \log_2 x = 7$
[Hint: Change $\log_4 x$ to base 2.]

78. $\log_9 x + 3 \log_3 x = 14$ **79.** $\left(\sqrt[3]{2}\right)^{2-x} = 2^{x^2}$ **80.** $\log_2 x^{\log_2 x} = 4$

81. $\dfrac{e^x + e^{-x}}{2} = 1$ **82.** $\dfrac{e^x + e^{-x}}{2} = 3$ **83.** $\dfrac{e^x - e^{-x}}{2} = 2$
[Hint: Multiply each side by e^x.]

84. $\dfrac{e^x - e^{-x}}{2} = -2$ **85.** $\log_5 x + \log_3 x = 1$ **86.** $\log_2 x + \log_6 x = 3$
                                     [Hint: Use the Change-of-Base Formula.]

87. $f(x) = \log_2(x + 3)$ and $g(x) = \log_2(3x + 1)$.
  (a) Solve $f(x) = 3$. What point is on the graph of f?
  (b) Solve $g(x) = 4$. What point is on the graph of g?
  (c) Solve $f(x) = g(x)$. Do the graphs of f and g intersect?
     If so, where?
  (d) Solve $(f + g)(x) = 7$.
  (e) Solve $(f - g)(x) = 2$.

88. $f(x) = \log_3(x + 5)$ and $g(x) = \log_3(x - 1)$.
  (a) Solve $f(x) = 2$. What point is on the graph of f?
  (b) Solve $g(x) = 3$. What point is on the graph of g?
  (c) Solve $f(x) = g(x)$. Do the graphs of f and g intersect?
     If so, where?
  (d) Solve $(f + g)(x) = 3$.
  (e) Solve $(f - g)(x) = 2$.

89. (a) If $f(x) = 3^{x+1}$ and $g(x) = 2^{x+2}$, graph f and g on the same Cartesian plane.
  (b) Find the point(s) of intersection of the graphs of f and g by solving $f(x) = g(x)$. Round answers to three decimal places. Label any intersection points on the graph drawn in part (a).
  (c) Based on the graph, solve $f(x) > g(x)$.

90. (a) If $f(x) = 5^{x-1}$ and $g(x) = 2^{x+1}$, graph f and g on the same Cartesian plane.
  (b) Find the point(s) of intersection of the graphs of f and g by solving $f(x) = g(x)$. Label any intersection points on the graph drawn in part (a).
  (c) Based on the graph, solve $f(x) > g(x)$.

91. (a) Graph $f(x) = 3^x$ and $g(x) = 10$ on the same Cartesian plane.

  (b) Shade the region bounded by the y-axis, $f(x) = 3^x$, and $g(x) = 10$ on the graph drawn in part (a).
  (c) Solve $f(x) = g(x)$ and label the point of intersection on the graph drawn in part (a).

92. (a) Graph $f(x) = 2^x$ and $g(x) = 12$ on the same Cartesian plane.
  (b) Shade the region bounded by the y-axis, $f(x) = 2^x$, and $g(x) = 12$ on the graph drawn in part (a).
  (c) Solve $f(x) = g(x)$ and label the point of intersection on the graph drawn in part (a).

93. (a) Graph $f(x) = 2^{x+1}$ and $g(x) = 2^{-x+2}$ on the same Cartesian plane.
  (b) Shade the region bounded by the y-axis, $f(x) = 2^{x+1}$, and $g(x) = 2^{-x+2}$ on the graph draw in part (a).
  (c) Solve $f(x) = g(x)$ and label the point of intersection on the graph drawn in part (a).

94. (a) Graph $f(x) = 3^{-x+1}$ and $g(x) = 3^{x-2}$ on the same Cartesian plane.
  (b) Shade the region bounded by the y-axis, $f(x) = 3^{-x+1}$, and $g(x) = 3^{x-2}$ on the graph draw in part (a).
  (c) Solve $f(x) = g(x)$ and label the point of intersection on the graph drawn in part (a).

95. (a) Graph $f(x) = 2^x - 4$.
  (b) Find the zero of f.
  (c) Based on the graph, solve $f(x) < 0$.

96. (a) Graph $g(x) = 3^x - 9$.
  (b) Find the zero of g.
  (c) Based on the graph, solve $g(x) > 0$.

Applications and Extensions

97. A Population Model The resident population of the United States in 2008 was 304 million people and was growing at a rate of 0.9% per year. Assuming that this growth rate continues, the model $P(t) = 304(1.009)^{t-2008}$ represents the population P (in millions of people) in year t.
(a) According to this model, when will the population of the United States be 354 million people?
(b) According to this model, when will the population of the United States be 416 million people?
Source: Statistical Abstract of the United States, 125th ed., 2009

98. A Population Model The population of the world in 2009 was 6.78 billion people and was growing at a rate of 1.14% per year. Assuming that this growth rate continues, the model $P(t) = 6.78(1.0114)^{t-2009}$ represents the population P (in billions of people) in year t.
(a) According to this model, when will the population of the world be 8.7 billion people?

(b) According to this model, when will the population of the world be 14 billion people?
Source: U.S. Census Bureau.

99. Depreciation The value V of a Chevy Cobalt that is t years old can be modeled by $V(t) = 16,500(0.82)^t$.
(a) According to the model, when will the car be worth $9000?
(b) According to the model, when will the car be worth $4000?
(c) According to the model, when will the car be worth $2000?
Source: Kelley Blue Book

100. Depreciation The value V of a Honda Civic DX that is t years old can be modeled by $V(t) = 16,775(0.905)^t$.
(a) According to the model, when will the car be worth $15,000?
(b) According to the model, when will the car be worth $8000?
(c) According to the model, when will the car be worth $4000?
Source: Kelley Blue Book

Explaining Concepts: Discussion and Writing

101. Fill in reasons for each step in the following two solutions.
Solve: $\log_3(x-1)^2 = 2$

Solution A

$\log_3(x-1)^2 = 2$
$(x-1)^2 = 3^2 = 9$ _____
$(x-1) = \pm 3$ _____
$x - 1 = -3 \text{ or } x - 1 = 3$ _____
$x = -2 \text{ or } x = 4$ _____

Solution B

$\log_3(x-1)^2 = 2$
$2 \log_3(x-1) = 2$ _____
$\log_3(x-1) = 1$ _____
$x - 1 = 3^1 = 3$ _____
$x = 4$ _____

Both solutions given in Solution A check. Explain what caused the solution $x = -2$ to be lost in Solution B.

'Are You Prepared?' Answers

1. $\{-3, 10\}$ **2.** $\{-2, 0\}$ **3.** $\{-1.43\}$ **4.** $\{-1.77\}$

5.7 Financial Models

PREPARING FOR THIS SECTION *Before getting started, review the following:*

- Simple Interest (Appendix A, Section A.8, pp. A63–A64)

Now Work the *'Are You Prepared?'* problems on page 318.

OBJECTIVES **1** Determine the Future Value of a Lump Sum of Money (p. 312)
2 Calculate Effective Rates of Return (p. 315)
3 Determine the Present Value of a Lump Sum of Money (p. 316)
4 Determine the Rate of Interest or Time Required to Double a Lump Sum of Money (p. 317)

1 Determine the Future Value of a Lump Sum of Money

Interest is money paid for the use of money. The total amount borrowed (whether by an individual from a bank in the form of a loan or by a bank from an individual in the form of a savings account) is called the **principal.** The **rate of interest,** expressed as a percent, is the amount charged for the use of the principal for a given period of time, usually on a yearly (that is, per annum) basis.

THEOREM **Simple Interest Formula**

If a principal of P dollars is borrowed for a period of t years at a per annum interest rate r, expressed as a decimal, the interest I charged is

$$I = Prt \qquad (1)$$

Interest charged according to formula (1) is called **simple interest.**

In working with problems involving interest, we define the term **payment period** as follows:

Annually: Once per year   **Monthly:** 12 times per year
Semiannually: Twice per year   **Daily:** 365 times per year*
Quarterly: Four times per year

When the interest due at the end of a payment period is added to the principal so that the interest computed at the end of the next payment period is based on this new principal amount (old principal + interest), the interest is said to have been **compounded. Compound interest** is interest paid on the principal and previously earned interest.

EXAMPLE 1 **Computing Compound Interest**

A credit union pays interest of 8% per annum compounded quarterly on a certain savings plan. If $1000 is deposited in such a plan and the interest is left to accumulate, how much is in the account after 1 year?

Solution We use the simple interest formula, $I = Prt$. The principal P is $1000 and the rate of interest is 8% = 0.08. After the first quarter of a year, the time t is $\frac{1}{4}$ year, so the interest earned is

$$I = Prt = (\$1000)(0.08)\left(\frac{1}{4}\right) = \$20$$

* Most banks use a 360-day "year." Why do you think they do?

The new principal is $P + I = \$1000 + \$20 = \$1020$. At the end of the second quarter, the interest on this principal is

$$I = (\$1020)(0.08)\left(\frac{1}{4}\right) = \$20.40$$

At the end of the third quarter, the interest on the new principal of $\$1020 + \$20.40 = \$1040.40$ is

$$I = (\$1040.40)(0.08)\left(\frac{1}{4}\right) = \$20.81$$

Finally, after the fourth quarter, the interest is

$$I = (\$1061.21)(0.08)\left(\frac{1}{4}\right) = \$21.22$$

After 1 year the account contains $\$1061.21 + \$21.22 = \$1082.43$.

The pattern of the calculations performed in Example 1 leads to a general formula for compound interest. To fix our ideas, let P represent the principal to be invested at a per annum interest rate r that is compounded n times per year, so the time of each compounding period is $\frac{1}{n}$ years. (For computing purposes, r is expressed as a decimal.) The interest earned after each compounding period is given by formula (1).

$$\text{Interest} = \text{principal} \times \text{rate} \times \text{time} = P \cdot r \cdot \frac{1}{n} = P \cdot \left(\frac{r}{n}\right)$$

The amount A after one compounding period is

$$A = P + P \cdot \left(\frac{r}{n}\right) = P \cdot \left(1 + \frac{r}{n}\right)$$

After two compounding periods, the amount A, based on the new principal $P \cdot \left(1 + \frac{r}{n}\right)$, is

$$A = \underbrace{P \cdot \left(1 + \frac{r}{n}\right)}_{\substack{\text{New} \\ \text{principal}}} + \underbrace{P \cdot \left(1 + \frac{r}{n}\right)\left(\frac{r}{n}\right)}_{\substack{\text{Interest on} \\ \text{new principal}}} = \underset{\substack{\uparrow \\ \text{Factor out } P \cdot \left(1 + \frac{r}{n}\right).}}{P \cdot \left(1 + \frac{r}{n}\right)\left(1 + \frac{r}{n}\right)} = P \cdot \left(1 + \frac{r}{n}\right)^2$$

After three compounding periods, the amount A is

$$A = P \cdot \left(1 + \frac{r}{n}\right)^2 + P \cdot \left(1 + \frac{r}{n}\right)^2\left(\frac{r}{n}\right) = P \cdot \left(1 + \frac{r}{n}\right)^2 \cdot \left(1 + \frac{r}{n}\right) = P \cdot \left(1 + \frac{r}{n}\right)^3$$

Continuing this way, after n compounding periods (1 year), the amount A is

$$A = P \cdot \left(1 + \frac{r}{n}\right)^n$$

Because t years will contain $n \cdot t$ compounding periods, after t years we have

$$A = P \cdot \left(1 + \frac{r}{n}\right)^{nt}$$

THEOREM **Compound Interest Formula**

The amount A after t years due to a principal P invested at an annual interest rate r compounded n times per year is

$$A = P \cdot \left(1 + \frac{r}{n}\right)^{nt} \tag{2}$$

Exploration

To see the effects of compounding interest monthly on an initial deposit of $1,

graph $Y_1 = \left(1 + \dfrac{r}{12}\right)^{12x}$ with $r = 0.06$

and $r = 0.12$ for $0 \le x \le 30$. What is the future value of $1 in 30 years when the interest rate per annum is $r = 0.06$ (6%)? What is the future value of $1 in 30 years when the interest rate per annum is $r = 0.12$ (12%)? Does doubling the interest rate double the future value?

For example, to rework Example 1, use $P = \$1000$, $r = 0.08$, $n = 4$ (quarterly compounding), and $t = 1$ year to obtain

$$A = P \cdot \left(1 + \frac{r}{n}\right)^{nt} = 1000\left(1 + \frac{0.08}{4}\right)^{4 \cdot 1} = \$1082.43$$

In equation (2), the amount A is typically referred to as the **future value** of the account, while P is called the **present value.**

━━━━━━**Now Work** PROBLEM 7

EXAMPLE 2

Comparing Investments Using Different Compounding Periods

Investing $1000 at an annual rate of 10% compounded annually, semiannually, quarterly, monthly, and daily will yield the following amounts after 1 year:

Annual compounding ($n = 1$): $\quad A = P \cdot (1 + r)$

$$= (\$1000)(1 + 0.10) = \$1100.00$$

Semiannual compounding ($n = 2$): $\quad A = P \cdot \left(1 + \dfrac{r}{2}\right)^2$

$$= (\$1000)(1 + 0.05)^2 = \$1102.50$$

Quarterly compounding ($n = 4$): $\quad A = P \cdot \left(1 + \dfrac{r}{4}\right)^4$

$$= (\$1000)(1 + 0.025)^4 = \$1103.81$$

Monthly compounding ($n = 12$): $\quad A = P \cdot \left(1 + \dfrac{r}{12}\right)^{12}$

$$= (\$1000)\left(1 + \frac{0.10}{12}\right)^{12} = \$1104.71$$

Daily compounding ($n = 365$): $\quad A = P \cdot \left(1 + \dfrac{r}{365}\right)^{365}$

$$= (\$1000)\left(1 + \frac{0.10}{365}\right)^{365} = \$1105.16$$

From Example 2, we can see that the effect of compounding more frequently is that the amount after 1 year is higher: $1000 compounded 4 times a year at 10% results in $1103.81, $1000 compounded 12 times a year at 10% results in $1104.71, and $1000 compounded 365 times a year at 10% results in $1105.16. This leads to the following question: What would happen to the amount after 1 year if the number of times that the interest is compounded were increased without bound?

Let's find the answer. Suppose that P is the principal, r is the per annum interest rate, and n is the number of times that the interest is compounded each year. The amount after 1 year is

$$A = P \cdot \left(1 + \frac{r}{n}\right)^n$$

Rewrite this expression as follows:

$$A = P \cdot \left(1 + \frac{r}{n}\right)^n = P \cdot \left(1 + \frac{1}{\frac{n}{r}}\right)^n = P \cdot \left[\left(1 + \frac{1}{\frac{n}{r}}\right)^{n/r}\right]^r = P \cdot \left[\left(1 + \frac{1}{h}\right)^h\right]^r \quad \textbf{(3)}$$

$$\underset{\uparrow}{} \quad h = \frac{n}{r}$$

Now suppose that the number n of times that the interest is compounded per year gets larger and larger; that is, suppose that $n \to \infty$. Then $h = \dfrac{n}{r} \to \infty$, and the expression in brackets in equation (3) equals e. That is, $A \to Pe^r$.

Table 8 compares $\left(1 + \dfrac{r}{n}\right)^n$, for large values of n, to e^r for $r = 0.05$, $r = 0.10$, $r = 0.15$, and $r = 1$. The larger that n gets, the closer $\left(1 + \dfrac{r}{n}\right)^n$ gets to e^r. No matter how frequent the compounding, the amount after 1 year has the definite ceiling Pe^r.

Table 8

	$\left(1 + \frac{r}{n}\right)^n$			
	$n = 100$	$n = 1000$	$n = 10{,}000$	e^r
$r = 0.05$	1.0512580	1.0512698	1.051271	1.0512711
$r = 0.10$	1.1051157	1.1051654	1.1051704	1.1051709
$r = 0.15$	1.1617037	1.1618212	1.1618329	1.1618342
$r = 1$	2.7048138	2.7169239	2.7181459	2.7182818

When interest is compounded so that the amount after 1 year is Pe^r, we say that the interest is **compounded continuously.**

THEOREM

Continuous Compounding

The amount A after t years due to a principal P invested at an annual interest rate r compounded continuously is

$$A = Pe^{rt} \qquad \qquad (4)$$

EXAMPLE 3

Using Continuous Compounding

The amount A that results from investing a principal P of \$1000 at an annual rate r of 10% compounded continuously for a time t of 1 year is

$$A = \$1000e^{0.10} = (\$1000)(1.10517) = \$1105.17$$

Now Work PROBLEM 13

2 Calculate Effective Rates of Return

Suppose that you have \$1000 and a bank offers to pay you 3% annual interest on a savings account with interest compounded monthly. What annual interest rate do you need to earn to have the same amount at the end of the year if the interest is compounded annually (once per year)? To answer this question, first determine the value of the \$1000 in the account that earns 3% compounded monthly.

$$A = \$1000\left(1 + \frac{0.03}{12}\right)^{12} \qquad \text{Use } A = P\left(1 + \frac{r}{n}\right)^n \text{ with } P = \$1000, r = 0.03, n = 12.$$

$$= \$1030.42$$

So the interest earned is \$30.42. Using $I = Prt$ with $t = 1$, $I = \$30.42$, and $P = \$1000$, we find the annual simple interest rate is $0.03042 = 3.042\%$. This interest rate is known as the *effective rate of interest.*

The **effective rate of interest** is the equivalent annual simple interest rate that would yield the same amount as compounding n times per year, or continuously, after 1 year.

THEOREM

Effective Rate of Interest

The effective rate of interest r_e of an investment earning an annual interest rate r is given by

Compounding n times per year: $r_e = \left(1 + \dfrac{r}{n}\right)^n - 1$

Continuous compounding: $r_e = e^r - 1$

EXAMPLE 4

Computing the Effective Rate of Interest—Which Is the Best Deal?

Suppose you want to open a money market account. You visit three banks to determine their money market rates. Bank A offers you 6% annual interest compounded daily and Bank B offers you 6.02% compounded quarterly. Bank C offers 5.98% compounded continuously. Determine which bank is offering the best deal.

Solution

The bank that offers the best deal is the one with the highest effective interest rate.

Bank A	**Bank B**	**Bank C**
$r_e = \left(1 + \dfrac{0.06}{365}\right)^{365} - 1$	$r_e = \left(1 + \dfrac{0.0602}{4}\right)^4 - 1$	$r_e = e^{0.0598} - 1$
$\approx 1.06183 - 1$	$\approx 1.06157 - 1$	$\approx 1.06162 - 1$
$= 0.06183$	$= 0.06157$	$= 0.06162$
$= 6.183\%$	$= 6.157\%$	$= 6.162\%$

Since the effective rate of interest is highest for Bank A, Bank A is offering the best deal.

─────**Now Work** PROBLEM 23

3 Determine the Present Value of a Lump Sum of Money

When people in finance speak of the "time value of money," they are usually referring to the *present value* of money. The **present value** of A dollars to be received at a future date is the principal that you would need to invest now so that it will grow to A dollars in the specified time period. The present value of money to be received at a future date is always less than the amount to be received, since the amount to be received will equal the present value (money invested now) *plus* the interest accrued over the time period.

We use the compound interest formula (2) to get a formula for present value. If P is the present value of A dollars to be received after t years at a per annum interest rate r compounded n times per year, then, by formula (2),

$$A = P \cdot \left(1 + \frac{r}{n}\right)^{nt}$$

To solve for P, divide both sides by $\left(1 + \dfrac{r}{n}\right)^{nt}$. The result is

$$\frac{A}{\left(1 + \dfrac{r}{n}\right)^{nt}} = P \quad \text{or} \quad P = A \cdot \left(1 + \frac{r}{n}\right)^{-nt}$$

THEOREM

Present Value Formulas

The present value P of A dollars to be received after t years, assuming a per annum interest rate r compounded n times per year, is

$$P = A \cdot \left(1 + \frac{r}{n}\right)^{-nt} \qquad (5)$$

If the interest is compounded continuously,

$$P = Ae^{-rt} \qquad (6)$$

To derive (6), solve formula (4) for P.

EXAMPLE 5

Computing the Value of a Zero-coupon Bond

A zero-coupon (noninterest-bearing) bond can be redeemed in 10 years for $1000. How much should you be willing to pay for it now if you want a return of
(a) 8% compounded monthly?   (b) 7% compounded continuously?

Solution

(a) We are seeking the present value of $1000. Use formula (5) with $A = \$1000$, $n = 12$, $r = 0.08$, and $t = 10$.

$$P = A \cdot \left(1 + \frac{r}{n}\right)^{-nt} = \$1000\left(1 + \frac{0.08}{12}\right)^{-12(10)} = \$450.52$$

For a return of 8% compounded monthly, you should pay $450.52 for the bond.

(b) Here use formula (6) with $A = \$1000$, $r = 0.07$, and $t = 10$.

$$P = Ae^{-rt} = \$1000e^{-(0.07)(10)} = \$496.59$$

For a return of 7% compounded continuously, you should pay $496.59 for the bond.

 **Now Work** PROBLEM 15

---

4 Determine the Rate of Interest or Time Required to Double a Lump Sum of Money

---

EXAMPLE 6

Rate of Interest Required to Double an Investment

What annual rate of interest compounded annually should you seek if you want to double your investment in 5 years?

Solution

If P is the principal and we want P to double, the amount A will be $2P$. We use the compound interest formula with $n = 1$ and $t = 5$ to find r.

$$A = P \cdot \left(1 + \frac{r}{n}\right)^{nt}$$

$$2P = P \cdot (1 + r)^5 \qquad \text{\textit{A = 2P, n = 1, t = 5}}$$

$$2 = (1 + r)^5 \qquad \text{\textit{Divide both sides by P.}}$$

$$1 + r = \sqrt[5]{2} \qquad \text{\textit{Take the fifth root of each side.}}$$

$$r = \sqrt[5]{2} - 1 \approx 1.148698 - 1 = 0.148698$$

The annual rate of interest needed to double the principal in 5 years is 14.87%.

Now Work PROBLEM 31

| EXAMPLE 7 | **Time Required to Double or Triple an Investment** |

(a) How long will it take for an investment to double in value if it earns 5% compounded continuously?

(b) How long will it take to triple at this rate?

Solution (a) If P is the initial investment and we want P to double, the amount A will be $2P$. We use formula (4) for continuously compounded interest with $r = 0.05$. Then

$$A = Pe^{rt}$$
$$2P = Pe^{0.05t} \qquad A = 2P, r = 0.05$$
$$2 = e^{0.05t} \qquad \text{Cancel the P's.}$$
$$0.05t = \ln 2 \qquad \text{Rewrite as a logarithm.}$$
$$t = \frac{\ln 2}{0.05} \approx 13.86 \quad \text{Solve for t.}$$

It will take about 14 years to double the investment.

(b) To triple the investment, we set $A = 3P$ in formula (4).

$$A = Pe^{rt}$$
$$3P = Pe^{0.05t} \qquad A = 3P, r = 0.05$$
$$3 = e^{0.05t} \qquad \text{Cancel the P's.}$$
$$0.05t = \ln 3 \qquad \text{Rewrite as a logarithm.}$$
$$t = \frac{\ln 3}{0.05} \approx 21.97 \quad \text{Solve for t.}$$

It will take about 22 years to triple the investment.

Now Work PROBLEM 35

5.7 Assess Your Understanding

'Are You Prepared?' *Answers are given at the end of these exercises. If you get a wrong answer, read the pages listed in red.*

1. What is the interest due if $500 is borrowed for 6 months at a simple interest rate of 6% per annum? (pp. A63–A64)

2. If you borrow $5000 and, after 9 months, pay off the loan in the amount of $5500, what per annum rate of interest was charged? (pp. A63–A64)

Concepts and Vocabulary

3. The total amount borrowed (whether by an individual from a bank in the form of a loan or by a bank from an individual in the form of a savings account) is called the _____.

4. If a principal of P dollars is borrowed for a period of t years at a per annum interest rate r, expressed as a decimal, the interest I charged is _____ = _____. Interest charged according to this formula is called _____ _____.

5. In working problems involving interest, if the payment period of the interest is quarterly, then interest is paid _____ times per year.

6. The _____ _____ ___ _____ is the equivalent annual simple interest rate that would yield the same amount as compounding n times per year, or continuously, after 1 year.

Skill Building

In Problems 7–14, find the amount that results from each investment.

7. $100 invested at 4% compounded quarterly after a period of 2 years

8. $50 invested at 6% compounded monthly after a period of 3 years

9. $500 invested at 8% compounded quarterly after a period of $2\frac{1}{2}$ years

10. $300 invested at 12% compounded monthly after a period of $1\frac{1}{2}$ years

11. $600 invested at 5% compounded daily after a period of 3 years

12. $700 invested at 6% compounded daily after a period of 2 years

13. $1000 invested at 11% compounded continuously after a period of 2 years

14. $400 invested at 7% compounded continuously after a period of 3 years

In Problems 15–22, find the principal needed now to get each amount; that is, find the present value.

15. To get $100 after 2 years at 6% compounded monthly

16. To get $75 after 3 years at 8% compounded quarterly

17. To get $1000 after $2\frac{1}{2}$ years at 6% compounded daily

18. To get $800 after $3\frac{1}{2}$ years at 7% compounded monthly

19. To get $600 after 2 years at 4% compounded quarterly

20. To get $300 after 4 years at 3% compounded daily

21. To get $80 after $3\frac{1}{4}$ years at 9% compounded continuously

22. To get $800 after $2\frac{1}{2}$ years at 8% compounded continuously

In Problems 23–26, find the effective rate of interest.

23. For 5% compounded quarterly

24. For 6% compounded monthly

25. For 5% compounded continuously

26. For 6% compounded continuously

In Problems 27–30, determine the rate that represents the better deal.

27. 6% compounded quarterly or $6\frac{1}{4}$% compounded annually

28. 9% compounded quarterly or $9\frac{1}{4}$% compounded annually

29. 9% compounded monthly or 8.8% compounded daily

30. 8% compounded semiannually or 7.9% compounded daily

31. What rate of interest compounded annually is required to double an investment in 3 years?

32. What rate of interest compounded annually is required to double an investment in 6 years?

33. What rate of interest compounded annually is required to triple an investment in 5 years?

34. What rate of interest compounded annually is required to triple an investment in 10 years?

35. (a) How long does it take for an investment to double in value if it is invested at 8% compounded monthly?
(b) How long does it take if the interest is compounded continuously?

36. (a) How long does it take for an investment to triple in value if it is invested at 6% compounded monthly?
(b) How long does it take if the interest is compounded continuously?

37. What rate of interest compounded quarterly will yield an effective interest rate of 7%?

38. What rate of interest compounded continuously will yield an effective interest rate of 6%?

Applications and Extensions

39. Time Required to Reach a Goal If Tanisha has $100 to invest at 8% per annum compounded monthly, how long will it be before she has $150? If the compounding is continuous, how long will it be?

40. Time Required to Reach a Goal If Angela has $100 to invest at 10% per annum compounded monthly, how long will it be before she has $175? If the compounding is continuous, how long will it be?

41. Time Required to Reach a Goal How many years will it take for an initial investment of $10,000 to grow to $25,000? Assume a rate of interest of 6% compounded continuously.

42. Time Required to Reach a Goal How many years will it take for an initial investment of $25,000 to grow to $80,000? Assume a rate of interest of 7% compounded continuously.

43. Price Appreciation of Homes What will a $90,000 condominium cost 5 years from now if the price appreciation for condos over that period averages 3% compounded annually?

44. Credit Card Interest A department store charges 1.25% per month on the unpaid balance for customers with charge accounts (interest is compounded monthly). A customer charges $200 and does not pay her bill for 6 months. What is the bill at that time?

45. Saving for a Car Jerome will be buying a used car for $15,000 in 3 years. How much money should he ask his parents for now so that, if he invests it at 5% compounded continuously, he will have enough to buy the car?

46. Paying off a Loan John requires $3000 in 6 months to pay off a loan that has no prepayment privileges. If he has the $3000 now, how much of it should he save in an account paying 3% compounded monthly so that in 6 months he will have exactly $3000?

47. Return on a Stock George contemplates the purchase of 100 shares of a stock selling for $15 per share. The stock pays no dividends. The history of the stock indicates that it should grow at an annual rate of 15% per year.

How much should the 100 shares of stock be worth in 5 years?

48. Return on an Investment A business purchased for $650,000 in 2005 is sold in 2008 for $850,000. What is the annual rate of return for this investment?

49. Comparing Savings Plans Jim places $1000 in a bank account that pays 5.6% compounded continuously. After 1 year, will he have enough money to buy a computer system that costs $1060? If another bank will pay Jim 5.9% compounded monthly, is this a better deal?

50. Savings Plans On January 1, Kim places $1000 in a certificate of deposit that pays 6.8% compounded continuously and matures in 3 months. Then Kim places the $1000 and the interest in a passbook account that pays 5.25% compounded monthly. How much does Kim have in the passbook account on May 1?

51. Comparing IRA Investments Will invests $2000 in his IRA in a bond trust that pays 9% interest compounded semiannually. His friend Henry invests $2000 in his IRA in a certificate of deposit that pays $8\frac{1}{2}\%$ compounded continuously. Who has more money after 20 years, Will or Henry?

52. Comparing Two Alternatives Suppose that April has access to an investment that will pay 10% interest compounded continuously. Which is better: to be given $1000 now so that she can take advantage of this investment opportunity or to be given $1325 after 3 years?

53. College Costs The average annual cost of college at 4-year private colleges was $25,143 in the 2008–2009 academic year. This was a 5.9% increase from the previous year.
Source: The College Board

(a) If the cost of college increases by 5.9% each year, what will be the average cost of college at a 4-year private college for the 2028–2029 academic year?

(b) College savings plans, such as a 529 plan, allow individuals to put money aside now to help pay for college later. If one such plan offers a rate of 4% compounded continuously, how much should be put in a college savings plan in 2010 to pay for 1 year of the cost of college at a 4-year private college for an incoming freshman in 2028?

54. Analyzing Interest Rates on a Mortgage Colleen and Bill have just purchased a house for $650,000, with the seller holding a second mortgage of $100,000. They promise to pay the seller $100,000 plus all accrued interest 5 years from now. The seller offers them three interest options on the second mortgage:

(a) Simple interest at 12% per annum

(b) $11\frac{1}{2}\%$ interest compounded monthly

(c) $11\frac{1}{4}\%$ interest compounded continuously

Which option is best; that is, which results in the least interest on the loan?

55. 2009 Federal Stimulus Package In February 2009, President Obama signed into law a $787 billion federal stimulus package. At that time, 20-year Series EE bonds had a fixed rate of 1.3% compounded semiannually. If the federal government financed the stimulus through EE bonds, how much would it have to pay back in 2029? How much interest was paid to finance the stimulus?
Source: U.S. Treasury Department

56. Per Capita Federal Debt In 2008, the federal debt was about $10 trillion. In 2008, the U.S. population was about 304 million. Assuming that the federal debt is increasing about 7.8% per year and the U.S. population is increasing about 0.9% per year, determine the per capita debt (total debt divided by population) in 2020.

Inflation Problems 57–62 require the following discussion. **Inflation** *is a term used to describe the erosion of the purchasing power of money. For example, if the annual inflation rate is 3%, then $1000 worth of purchasing power now will have only $970 worth of purchasing power in 1 year because 3% of the original $1000 (0.03 × 1000 = 30) has been eroded due to inflation. In general, if the rate of inflation averages r per annum over n years, the amount A that $P will purchase after n years is*

$$A = P \cdot (1 - r)^n$$

where r is expressed as a decimal.

57. Inflation If the inflation rate averages 3%, how much will $1000 purchase in 2 years?

58. Inflation If the inflation rate averages 2%, how much will $1000 purchase in 3 years?

59. Inflation If the amount that $1000 will purchase is only $950 after 2 years, what was the average inflation rate?

60. Inflation If the amount that $1000 will purchase is only $930 after 2 years, what was the average inflation rate?

61. Inflation If the average inflation rate is 2%, how long is it until purchasing power is cut in half?

62. Inflation If the average inflation rate is 4%, how long is it until purchasing power is cut in half?

---

*Problems 63–66 involve zero-coupon bonds. A **zero-coupon bond** is a bond that is sold now at a discount and will pay its face value at the time when it matures; no interest payments are made.*

63. Zero-Coupon Bonds A zero-coupon bond can be redeemed in 20 years for $10,000. How much should you be willing to pay for it now if you want a return of:
(a) 10% compounded monthly?
(b) 10% compounded continuously?

64. Zero-Coupon Bonds A child's grandparents are considering buying a $40,000 face-value, zero-coupon bond at birth so that she will have enough money for her college education 17 years later. If they want a rate of return of 8% compounded annually, what should they pay for the bond?

65. Zero-Coupon Bonds How much should a $10,000 face-value, zero-coupon bond, maturing in 10 years, be sold for now if its rate of return is to be 8% compounded annually?

66. Zero-Coupon Bonds If Pat pays $12,485.52 for a $25,000 face-value, zero-coupon bond that matures in 8 years, what is his annual rate of return?

67. Time to Double or Triple an Investment The formula

$$t = \frac{\ln m}{n \ln\left(1 + \frac{r}{n}\right)}$$

can be used to find the number of years t required to multiply an investment m times when r is the per annum interest rate compounded n times a year.

(a) How many years will it take to double the value of an IRA that compounds annually at the rate of 12%?

(b) How many years will it take to triple the value of a savings account that compounds quarterly at an annual rate of 6%?

(c) Give a derivation of this formula.

68. Time to Reach an Investment Goal The formula

$$t = \frac{\ln A - \ln P}{r}$$

can be used to find the number of years t required for an investment P to grow to a value A when compounded continuously at an annual rate r.

(a) How long will it take to increase an initial investment of $1000 to $8000 at an annual rate of 10%?

(b) What annual rate is required to increase the value of a $2000 IRA to $30,000 in 35 years?

(c) Give a derivation of this formula.

Problems 69–72 require the following discussion. The **Consumer Price Index (CPI)** *indicates the relative change in price over time for a fixed basket of goods and services. It is a cost of living index that helps measure the effect of inflation on the cost of goods and services. The CPI uses the base period 1982–1984 for comparison (the CPI for this period is 100). The CPI for January 2006 was 198.3. This means that $100 in the period 1982–1984 had the same purchasing power as $198.30 in January 2006. In general, if the rate of inflation averages r per annum over n years, then the CPI index after n years is*

$$CPI = CPI_0\left(1 + \frac{r}{100}\right)^n$$

where CPI_0 is the CPI index at the beginning of the n-year period.
Source: U.S. Bureau of Labor Statistics

69. Consumer Price Index

(a) The CPI was 163.0 for 1998 and 215.3 for 2008. Assuming that annual inflation remained constant for this time period, determine the average annual inflation rate.

(b) Using the inflation rate from part (a), in what year will the CPI reach 300?

70. Consumer Price Index If the current CPI is 234.2 and the average annual inflation rate is 2.8%, what will be the CPI in 5 years?

71. Consumer Price Index If the average annual inflation rate is 3.1%, how long will it take for the CPI index to double? (A doubling of the CPI index means purchasing power is cut in half.)

72. Consumer Price Index The base period for the CPI changed in 1998. Under the previous weight and item structure, the CPI for 1995 was 456.5. If the average annual inflation rate was 5.57%, what year was used as the base period for the CPI?

Explaining Concepts: Discussion and Writing

73. Explain in your own words what the term *compound interest* means. What does *continuous compounding* mean?

74. Explain in your own words the meaning of *present value*.

75. Critical Thinking You have just contracted to buy a house and will seek financing in the amount of $100,000. You go to several banks. Bank 1 will lend you $100,000 at the rate of 8.75% amortized over 30 years with a loan origination fee of 1.75%. Bank 2 will lend you $100,000 at the rate of 8.375% amortized over 15 years with a loan origination fee of 1.5%. Bank 3 will lend you $100,000 at the rate of 9.125% amortized over 30 years with no loan origination fee. Bank 4 will lend you $100,000 at the rate of 8.625% amortized over 15 years with no loan origination fee. Which loan would you take? Why? Be sure to have sound reasons for your choice. Use the

information in the table to assist you. If the amount of the monthly payment does not matter to you, which loan would you take? Again, have sound reasons for your choice. Compare your final decision with others in the class. Discuss.

	Monthly Payment	Loan Origination Fee
Bank 1	$786.70	$1,750.00
Bank 2	$977.42	$1,500.00
Bank 3	$813.63	$0.00
Bank 4	$992.08	$0.00

'Are You Prepared?' Answers

1. $15

2. $13\frac{1}{3}\%$

5.8 Exponential Growth and Decay Models; Newton's Law; Logistic Growth and Decay Models

OBJECTIVES **1** Find Equations of Populations That Obey the Law of Uninhibited Growth (p. 322)

2 Find Equations of Populations That Obey the Law of Decay (p. 324)

3 Use Newton's Law of Cooling (p. 325)

4 Use Logistic Models (p. 327)

1 Find Equations of Populations That Obey the Law of Uninhibited Growth

Many natural phenomena have been found to follow the law that an amount A varies with time t according to the function

$$A(t) = A_0 e^{kt} \qquad (1)$$

Here A_0 is the original amount ($t = 0$) and $k \neq 0$ is a constant.

If $k > 0$, then equation (1) states that the amount A is increasing over time; if $k < 0$, the amount A is decreasing over time. In either case, when an amount A varies over time according to equation (1), it is said to follow the **exponential law** or the **law of uninhibited growth** ($k > 0$) **or decay** ($k < 0$). See Figure 41.

For example, we saw in Section 5.7 that continuously compounded interest follows the law of uninhibited growth. In this section we shall look at some additional phenomena that follow the exponential law.

Cell division is the growth process of many living organisms, such as amoebas, plants, and human skin cells. Based on an ideal situation in which no cells die and no by-products are produced, the number of cells present at a given time follows the law of uninhibited growth. Actually, however, after enough time has passed, growth at an exponential rate will cease due to the influence of factors such as lack of living space and dwindling food supply. The law of uninhibited growth accurately models only the early stages of the cell division process.

The cell division process begins with a culture containing N_0 cells. Each cell in the culture grows for a certain period of time and then divides into two identical cells. We assume that the time needed for each cell to divide in two is constant and does not change as the number of cells increases. These new cells then grow, and eventually each divides in two, and so on.

Figure 41

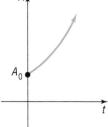

(a) $A(t) = A_0 e^{kt}, k > 0$
Exponential growth

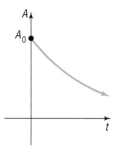

(b) $A(t) = A_0 e^{kt}, k < 0$
Exponential decay

Uninhibited Growth of Cells

A model that gives the number N of cells in a culture after a time t has passed (in the early stages of growth) is

$$N(t) = N_0 e^{kt} \qquad k > 0 \qquad (2)$$

where N_0 is the initial number of cells and k is a positive constant that represents the growth rate of the cells.

In using formula (2) to model the growth of cells, we are using a function that yields positive real numbers, even though we are counting the number of cells, which must be an integer. This is a common practice in many applications.

EXAMPLE 1   **Bacterial Growth**

A colony of bacteria that grows according to the law of uninhibited growth is modeled by the function $N(t) = 100e^{0.045t}$, where N is measured in grams and t is measured in days.

(a) Determine the initial amount of bacteria.
(b) What is the growth rate of the bacteria?
(c) What is the population after 5 days?
(d) How long will it take for the population to reach 140 grams?
(e) What is the doubling time for the population?

Solution

(a) The initial amount of bacteria, N_0, is obtained when $t = 0$, so

$$N_0 = N(0) = 100e^{0.045(0)} = 100 \text{ grams}$$

(b) Compare $N(t) = 100e^{0.045t}$ to $N(t) = N_0e^{kt}$. The value of k, 0.045, indicates a growth rate of 4.5%.

(c) The population after 5 days is $N(5) = 100e^{0.045(5)} \approx 125.2$ grams.

(d) To find how long it takes for the population to reach 140 grams, solve the equation $N(t) = 140$.

$$100e^{0.045t} = 140$$
$$e^{0.045t} = 1.4 \qquad \text{\textit{Divide both sides of the equation by 100.}}$$
$$0.045t = \ln 1.4 \qquad \text{\textit{Rewrite as a logarithm.}}$$
$$t = \frac{\ln 1.4}{0.045} \qquad \text{\textit{Divide both sides of the equation by 0.045.}}$$
$$\approx 7.5 \text{ days}$$

(e) The population doubles when $N(t) = 200$ grams, so we find the doubling time by solving the equation $200 = 100e^{0.045t}$ for t.

$$200 = 100e^{0.045t}$$
$$2 = e^{0.045t} \qquad \text{\textit{Divide both sides of the equation by 100.}}$$
$$\ln 2 = 0.045t \qquad \text{\textit{Rewrite as a logarithm.}}$$
$$t = \frac{\ln 2}{0.045} \qquad \text{\textit{Divide both sides of the equation by 0.045.}}$$
$$\approx 15.4 \text{ days}$$

The population doubles approximately every 15.4 days.

━━━━**Now Work** PROBLEM 1

EXAMPLE 2   **Bacterial Growth**

A colony of bacteria increases according to the law of uninhibited growth.

(a) If N is the number of cells and t is the time in hours, express N as a function of t.
(b) If the number of bacteria doubles in 3 hours, find the function that gives the number of cells in the culture.
(c) How long will it take for the size of the colony to triple?
(d) How long will it take for the population to double a second time (that is, increase four times)?

Solution

(a) Using formula (2), the number N of cells at time t is

$$N(t) = N_0e^{kt}$$

where N_0 is the initial number of bacteria present and k is a positive number.

(b) We seek the number k. The number of cells doubles in 3 hours, so

$$N(3) = 2N_0$$

But $N(3) = N_0 e^{k(3)}$, so

$$N_0 e^{k(3)} = 2N_0$$
$$e^{3k} = 2 \qquad \text{\textit{Divide both sides by } } N_0\text{.}$$
$$3k = \ln 2 \qquad \text{\textit{Write the exponential equation as a logarithm.}}$$
$$k = \frac{1}{3} \ln 2 \approx 0.23105$$

The function that models this growth process is therefore

$$N(t) = N_0 e^{0.23105t}$$

(c) The time t needed for the size of the colony to triple requires that $N = 3N_0$. Substitute $3N_0$ for N to get

$$3N_0 = N_0 e^{0.23105t}$$
$$3 = e^{0.23105t}$$
$$0.23105t = \ln 3$$
$$t = \frac{\ln 3}{0.23105} \approx 4.755 \text{ hours}$$

It will take about 4.755 hours or 4 hours, 45 minutes for the size of the colony to triple.

(d) If a population doubles in 3 hours, it will double a second time in 3 more hours, for a total time of 6 hours.

2 Find Equations of Populations That Obey the Law of Decay

Radioactive materials follow the law of uninhibited decay.

Uninhibited Radioactive Decay

The amount A of a radioactive material present at time t is given by

$$A(t) = A_0 e^{kt} \qquad k < 0 \tag{3}$$

where A_0 is the original amount of radioactive material and k is a negative number that represents the rate of decay.

All radioactive substances have a specific **half-life**, which is the time required for half of the radioactive substance to decay. In **carbon dating,** we use the fact that all living organisms contain two kinds of carbon, carbon 12 (a stable carbon) and carbon 14 (a radioactive carbon with a half-life of 5600 years). While an organism is living, the ratio of carbon 12 to carbon 14 is constant. But when an organism dies, the original amount of carbon 12 present remains unchanged, whereas the amount of carbon 14 begins to decrease. This change in the amount of carbon 14 present relative to the amount of carbon 12 present makes it possible to calculate when the organism died.

EXAMPLE 3 **Estimating the Age of Ancient Tools**

Traces of burned wood along with ancient stone tools in an archeological dig in Chile were found to contain approximately 1.67% of the original amount of carbon 14. If the half-life of carbon 14 is 5600 years, approximately when was the tree cut and burned?

Solution   Using formula (3), the amount A of carbon 14 present at time t is

$$A(t) = A_0 e^{kt}$$

where A_0 is the original amount of carbon 14 present and k is a negative number. We first seek the number k. To find it, we use the fact that after 5600 years half of the original amount of carbon 14 remains, so $A(5600) = \dfrac{1}{2} A_0$. Then

$$\frac{1}{2} A_0 = A_0 e^{k(5600)}$$

$$\frac{1}{2} = e^{5600k} \qquad\qquad \text{Divide both sides of the equation by } A_0.$$

$$5600k = \ln \frac{1}{2} \qquad\qquad \text{Rewrite as a logarithm.}$$

$$k = \frac{1}{5600} \ln \frac{1}{2} \approx -0.000124$$

Formula (3) therefore becomes

$$A(t) = A_0 e^{-0.000124t}$$

If the amount A of carbon 14 now present is 1.67% of the original amount, it follows that

$$0.0167 A_0 = A_0 e^{-0.000124t}$$

$$0.0167 = e^{-0.000124t} \qquad\qquad \text{Divide both sides of the equation by } A_0.$$

$$-0.000124t = \ln 0.0167 \qquad\qquad \text{Rewrite as a logarithm.}$$

$$t = \frac{\ln 0.0167}{-0.000124} \approx 33{,}003 \text{ years}$$

The tree was cut and burned about 33,003 years ago. Some archeologists use this conclusion to argue that humans lived in the Americas 33,000 years ago, much earlier than is generally accepted. ↵

━━━━━**Now Work** PROBLEM 3

3 Use Newton's Law of Cooling

Newton's Law of Cooling* states that the temperature of a heated object decreases exponentially over time toward the temperature of the surrounding medium.

Newton's Law of Cooling

The temperature u of a heated object at a given time t can be modeled by the following function:

$$u(t) = T + (u_0 - T)e^{kt} \qquad k < 0 \tag{4}$$

where T is the constant temperature of the surrounding medium, u_0 is the initial temperature of the heated object, and k is a negative constant.

EXAMPLE 4   **Using Newton's Law of Cooling**

An object is heated to 100°C (degrees Celsius) and is then allowed to cool in a room whose air temperature is 30°C.

(a) If the temperature of the object is 80°C after 5 minutes, when will its temperature be 50°C?

(b) Determine the elapsed time before the temperature of the object is 35°C.

(c) What do you notice about the temperature as time passes?

* Named after Sir Isaac Newton (1643–1727), one of the cofounders of calculus.

Solution

(a) Using formula (4) with $T = 30$ and $u_0 = 100$, the temperature $u(t)$ (in degrees Celsius) of the object at time t (in minutes) is

$$u(t) = 30 + (100 - 30)e^{kt} = 30 + 70e^{kt}$$

where k is a negative constant. To find k, use the fact that $u = 80$ when $t = 5$. Then

$$u(t) = 30 + 70e^{kt}$$
$$80 = 30 + 70e^{k(5)} \qquad u(5) = 80$$
$$50 = 70e^{5k} \qquad \text{Simplify.}$$
$$e^{5k} = \frac{50}{70} \qquad \text{Solve for } e^{5k}.$$
$$5k = \ln\frac{5}{7} \qquad \text{Take ln of both sides.}$$
$$k = \frac{1}{5}\ln\frac{5}{7} \approx -0.0673 \qquad \text{Solve for } k.$$

Formula (4) therefore becomes

$$u(t) = 30 + 70e^{-0.0673t} \tag{5}$$

We want to find t when $u = 50°C$, so

$$50 = 30 + 70e^{-0.0673t}$$
$$20 = 70e^{-0.0673t} \qquad \text{Simplify.}$$
$$e^{-0.0673t} = \frac{20}{70}$$
$$-0.0673t = \ln\frac{2}{7} \qquad \text{Take ln of both sides.}$$
$$t = \frac{\ln\dfrac{2}{7}}{-0.0673} \approx 18.6 \text{ minutes} \qquad \text{Solve for } t.$$

The temperature of the object will be 50°C after about 18.6 minutes or 18 minutes, 36 seconds.

(b) If $u = 35°C$, then, based on equation (5), we have

$$35 = 30 + 70e^{-0.0673t}$$
$$5 = 70e^{-0.0673t} \qquad \text{Simplify.}$$
$$e^{-0.0673t} = \frac{5}{70}$$
$$-0.0673t = \ln\frac{5}{70} \qquad \text{Take ln of both sides.}$$
$$t = \frac{\ln\dfrac{5}{70}}{-0.0673} \approx 39.2 \text{ minutes} \qquad \text{Solve for } t.$$

The object will reach a temperature of 35°C after about 39.2 minutes.

(c) Look at equation (5). As t increases, the exponent $-0.0673t$ becomes unbounded in the negative direction. As a result, the value of $e^{-0.0673t}$ approaches zero so the value of u, the temperature of the object, approaches 30°C, the air temperature of the room.

──────── **Now Work** PROBLEM 13

4 Use Logistic Models

The exponential growth model $A(t) = A_0 e^{kt}$, $k > 0$, assumes uninhibited growth, meaning that the value of the function grows without limit. Recall that we stated that cell division could be modeled using this function, assuming that no cells die and no by-products are produced. However, cell division eventually is limited by factors such as living space and food supply. The **logistic model,** given next, can describe situations where the growth or decay of the dependent variable is limited.

Logistic Model

In a logistic model, the population P after time t is given by the function

$$P(t) = \frac{c}{1 + ae^{-bt}} \qquad \text{(6)}$$

where a, b, and c are constants with $a > 0$ and $c > 0$. The model is a growth model if $b > 0$; the model is a decay model if $b < 0$.

The number c is called the **carrying capacity** (for growth models) because the value $P(t)$ approaches c as t approaches infinity; that is, $\lim\limits_{t \to \infty} P(t) = c$. The number $|b|$ is the growth rate for $b > 0$ and the decay rate for $b < 0$. Figure 42(a) shows the graph of a typical logistic growth function, and Figure 42(b) shows the graph of a typical logistic decay function.

Figure 42

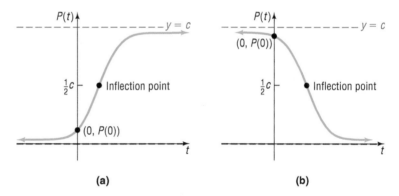

(a)   (b)

Based on the figures, we have the following properties of logistic growth functions.

Properties of the Logistic Model, Equation (6)

1. The domain is the set of all real numbers. The range is the interval $(0, c)$, where c is the carrying capacity.
2. There are no x-intercepts; the y-intercept is $P(0)$.
3. There are two horizontal asymptotes: $y = 0$ and $y = c$.
4. $P(t)$ is an increasing function if $b > 0$ and a decreasing function if $b < 0$.
5. There is an **inflection point** where $P(t)$ equals $\dfrac{1}{2}$ of the carrying capacity.

   The inflection point is the point on the graph where the graph changes from being curved upward to curved downward for growth functions and the point where the graph changes from being curved downward to curved upward for decay functions.
6. The graph is smooth and continuous, with no corners or gaps.

EXAMPLE 5

Fruit Fly Population

Fruit flies are placed in a half-pint milk bottle with a banana (for food) and yeast plants (for food and to provide a stimulus to lay eggs). Suppose that the fruit fly population after t days is given by

$$P(t) = \frac{230}{1 + 56.5e^{-0.37t}}$$

(a) State the carrying capacity and the growth rate.
(b) Determine the initial population.
(c) What is the population after 5 days?
(d) How long does it take for the population to reach 180?
 (e) Use a graphing utility to determine how long it takes for the population to reach one-half of the carrying capacity by graphing $Y_1 = P(t)$ and $Y_2 = 115$ and using INTERSECT.

Solution

(a) As $t \to \infty$, $e^{-0.37t} \to 0$ and $P(t) \to \frac{230}{1}$. The carrying capacity of the half-pint bottle is 230 fruit flies. The growth rate is $|b| = |0.37| = 37\%$ per day.

(b) To find the initial number of fruit flies in the half-pint bottle, evaluate $P(0)$.

$$P(0) = \frac{230}{1 + 56.5e^{-0.37(0)}}$$
$$= \frac{230}{1 + 56.5}$$
$$= 4$$

So, initially, there were 4 fruit flies in the half-pint bottle.

(c) To find the number of fruit flies in the half-pint bottle after 5 days, evaluate $P(5)$.

$$P(5) = \frac{230}{1 + 56.5e^{-0.37(5)}} \approx 23 \text{ fruit flies}$$

After 5 days, there are approximately 23 fruit flies in the bottle.

(d) To determine when the population of fruit flies will be 180, solve the equation $P(t) = 180$.

$$\frac{230}{1 + 56.5e^{-0.37t}} = 180$$
$$230 = 180(1 + 56.5e^{-0.37t})$$
$$1.2778 = 1 + 56.5e^{-0.37t} \qquad \text{Divide both sides by 180.}$$
$$0.2778 = 56.5e^{-0.37t} \qquad \text{Subtract 1 from both sides.}$$
$$0.0049 = e^{-0.37t} \qquad \text{Divide both sides by 56.5.}$$
$$\ln(0.0049) = -0.37t \qquad \text{Rewrite as a logarithmic expression.}$$
$$t \approx 14.4 \text{ days} \qquad \text{Divide both sides by } -0.37.$$

Figure 43

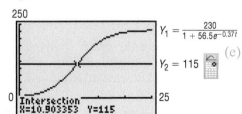

It will take approximately 14.4 days (14 days, 10 hours) for the population to reach 180 fruit flies.

(e) One-half of the carrying capacity is 115 fruit flies. We solve $P(t) = 115$ by graphing $Y_1 = \frac{230}{1 + 56.5e^{-0.37t}}$ and $Y_2 = 115$ and using INTERSECT. See Figure 43. The population will reach one-half of the carrying capacity in about 10.9 days (10 days, 22 hours).

Look back at Figure 43. Notice the point where the graph reaches 115 fruit flies (one-half of the carrying capacity): the graph changes from being curved upward to being curved downward. Using the language of calculus, we say the graph changes from increasing at an increasing rate to increasing at a decreasing rate. For any logistic growth function, when the population reaches one-half the carrying capacity, the population growth starts to slow down.

━━━━▶**Now Work** PROBLEM 23

⌂ Exploration

On the same viewing rectangle, graph

$$Y_1 = \frac{500}{1 + 24e^{-0.03t}} \quad \text{and} \quad Y_2 = \frac{500}{1 + 24e^{-0.08t}}$$

What effect does the growth rate $|b|$ have on the logistic growth function?

EXAMPLE 6

Wood Products

The EFISCEN wood product model classifies wood products according to their life-span. There are four classifications: short (1 year), medium short (4 years), medium long (16 years), and long (50 years). Based on data obtained from the European Forest Institute, the percentage of remaining wood products after t years for wood products with long life-spans (such as those used in the building industry) is given by

$$P(t) = \frac{100.3952}{1 + 0.0316e^{0.0581t}}$$

(a) What is the decay rate?

(b) What is the percentage of remaining wood products after 10 years?

(c) How long does it take for the percentage of remaining wood products to reach 50%?

(d) Explain why the numerator given in the model is reasonable.

Solution

(a) The decay rate is $|b| = |-0.0581| = 5.81\%$.

(b) Evaluate $P(10)$.

$$P(10) = \frac{100.3952}{1 + 0.0316e^{0.0581(10)}} \approx 95.0$$

So 95% of long-life-span wood products remain after 10 years.

(c) Solve the equation $P(t) = 50$.

$$\frac{100.3952}{1 + 0.0316e^{0.0581t}} = 50$$

$$100.3952 = 50(1 + 0.0316e^{0.0581t})$$

$2.0079 = 1 + 0.0316e^{0.0581t}$ Divide both sides by 50.

$1.0079 = 0.0316e^{0.0581t}$ Subtract 1 from both sides.

$31.8956 = e^{0.0581t}$ Divide both sides by 0.0316.

$\ln(31.8956) = 0.0581t$ Rewrite as a logarithmic expression.

$t \approx 59.6$ years   Divide both sides by 0.0581.

It will take approximately 59.6 years for the percentage of long-life-span wood products remaining to reach 50%.

(d) The numerator of 100.3952 is reasonable because the maximum percentage of wood products remaining that is possible is 100%.

5.8 Assess Your Understanding

Applications and Extensions

1. **Growth of an Insect Population** The size P of a certain insect population at time t (in days) obeys the function $P(t) = 500e^{0.02t}$.
   (a) Determine the number of insects at $t = 0$ days.
   (b) What is the growth rate of the insect population?
   (c) What is the population after 10 days?
   (d) When will the insect population reach 800?
   (e) When will the insect population double?

2. **Growth of Bacteria** The number N of bacteria present in a culture at time t (in hours) obeys the law of uninhibited growth $N(t) = 1000e^{0.01t}$.
   (a) Determine the number of bacteria at $t = 0$ hours.
   (b) What is the growth rate of the bacteria?
   (c) What is the population after 4 hours?
   (d) When will the number of bacteria reach 1700?
   (e) When will the number of bacteria double?

3. **Radioactive Decay** Strontium 90 is a radioactive material that decays according to the function $A(t) = A_0e^{-0.0244t}$, where A_0 is the initial amount present and A is the amount present at time t (in years). Assume that a scientist has a sample of 500 grams of strontium 90.
   (a) What is the decay rate of strontium 90?
   (b) How much strontium 90 is left after 10 years?
   (c) When will 400 grams of strontium 90 be left?
   (d) What is the half-life of strontium 90?

4. **Radioactive Decay** Iodine 131 is a radioactive material that decays according to the function $A(t) = A_0e^{-0.087t}$, where A_0 is the initial amount present and A is the amount present at time t (in days). Assume that a scientist has a sample of 100 grams of iodine 131.
   (a) What is the decay rate of iodine 131?
   (b) How much iodine 131 is left after 9 days?
   (c) When will 70 grams of iodine 131 be left?
   (d) What is the half-life of iodine 131?

5. **Growth of a Colony of Mosquitoes** The population of a colony of mosquitoes obeys the law of uninhibited growth.
   (a) If N is the population of the colony and t is the time in days, express N as a function of t.
   (b) If there are 1000 mosquitoes initially and there are 1800 after 1 day, what is the size of the colony after 3 days?
   (c) How long is it until there are 10,000 mosquitoes?

6. **Bacterial Growth** A culture of bacteria obeys the law of uninhibited growth.
   (a) If N is the number of bacteria in the culture and t is the time in hours, express N as a function of t.
   (b) If 500 bacteria are present initially and there are 800 after 1 hour, how many will be present in the culture after 5 hours?
   (c) How long is it until there are 20,000 bacteria?

7. **Population Growth** The population of a southern city follows the exponential law.
   (a) If N is the population of the city and t is the time in years, express N as a function of t.

   (b) If the population doubled in size over an 18-month period and the current population is 10,000, what will the population be 2 years from now?

8. **Population Decline** The population of a midwestern city follows the exponential law.
   (a) If N is the population of the city and t is the time in years, express N as a function of t.
   (b) If the population decreased from 900,000 to 800,000 from 2008 to 2010, what will the population be in 2012?

9. **Radioactive Decay** The half-life of radium is 1690 years. If 10 grams is present now, how much will be present in 50 years?

10. **Radioactive Decay** The half-life of radioactive potassium is 1.3 billion years. If 10 grams is present now, how much will be present in 100 years? In 1000 years?

11. **Estimating the Age of a Tree** A piece of charcoal is found to contain 30% of the carbon 14 that it originally had. When did the tree die from which the charcoal came? Use 5600 years as the half-life of carbon 14.

12. **Estimating the Age of a Fossil** A fossilized leaf contains 70% of its normal amount of carbon 14. How old is the fossil?

13. **Cooling Time of a Pizza Pan** A pizza pan is removed at 5:00 PM from an oven whose temperature is fixed at 450°F into a room that is a constant 70°F. After 5 minutes, the pan is 300°F.
   (a) At what time is the temperature of the pan 135°F?
   (b) Determine the time that needs to elapse before the pan is 160°F.
   (c) What do you notice about the temperature as time passes?

14. **Newton's Law of Cooling** A thermometer reading 72°F is placed in a refrigerator where the temperature is a constant 38°F.
   (a) If the thermometer reads 60°F after 2 minutes, what will it read after 7 minutes?
   (b) How long will it take before the thermometer reads 39°F?
   (c) Determine the time needed to elapse before the thermometer reads 45°F.
   (d) What do you notice about the temperature as time passes?

15. **Newton's Law of Heating** A thermometer reading 8°C is brought into a room with a constant temperature of 35°C. If the thermometer reads 15°C after 3 minutes, what will it read after being in the room for 5 minutes? For 10 minutes?

    [**Hint:** You need to construct a formula similar to equation (4).]

16. **Warming Time of a Beer Stein** A beer stein has a temperature of 28°F. It is placed in a room with a constant temperature of 70°F. After 10 minutes, the temperature of the stein has risen to 35°F. What will the temperature of the stein be after 30 minutes? How long will it take the stein to reach a temperature of 45°F? (See the hint given for Problem 15.)

17. **Decomposition of Chlorine in a Pool** Under certain water conditions, the free chlorine (hypochlorous acid, HOCl) in a swimming pool decomposes according to the law of uninhibited decay. After shocking his pool, Ben tested the water and found the amount of free chlorine to be 2.5 parts per million (ppm). Twenty-four hours later, Ben tested the water again and found the amount of free chlorine to be 2.2 ppm. What will be the reading after 3 days (that is, 72 hours)? When the chlorine level reaches 1.0 ppm, Ben must shock the pool again. How long can Ben go before he must shock the pool again?

18. **Decomposition of Dinitrogen Pentoxide** At 45°C, dinitrogen pentoxide (N_2O_5) decomposes into nitrous dioxide (NO_2) and oxygen (O_2) according to the law of uninhibited decay. An initial amount of 0.25 M of dinitrogen pentoxide decomposes to 0.15 M in 17 minutes. How much dinitrogen pentoxide will remain after 30 minutes? How long will it take until 0.01 M of dinitrogen pentoxide remains?

19. **Decomposition of Sucrose** Reacting with water in an acidic solution at 35°C, sucrose ($C_{12}H_{22}O_{11}$) decomposes into glucose ($C_6H_{12}O_6$) and fructose ($C_6H_{12}O_6$)* according to the law of uninhibited decay. An initial amount of 0.40 M of sucrose decomposes to 0.36 M in 30 minutes. How much sucrose will remain after 2 hours? How long will it take until 0.10 M of sucrose remains?

20. **Decomposition of Salt in Water** Salt (NaCl) decomposes in water into sodium (Na^+) and chloride (Cl^-) ions according to the law of uninhibited decay. If the initial amount of salt is 25 kilograms and, after 10 hours, 15 kilograms of salt is left, how much salt is left after 1 day? How long does it take until $\frac{1}{2}$ kilogram of salt is left?

21. **Radioactivity from Chernobyl** After the release of radioactive material into the atmosphere from a nuclear power plant at Chernobyl (Ukraine) in 1986, the hay in Austria was contaminated by iodine 131 (half-life 8 days). If it is safe to feed the hay to cows when 10% of the iodine 131 remains, how long did the farmers need to wait to use this hay?

22. **Pig Roasts** The hotel Bora-Bora is having a pig roast. At noon, the chef put the pig in a large earthen oven. The pig's original temperature was 75°F. At 2:00 PM the chef checked the pig's temperature and was upset because it had reached only 100°F. If the oven's temperature remains a constant

325°F, at what time may the hotel serve its guests, assuming that pork is done when it reaches 175°F?

23. **Population of a Bacteria Culture** The logistic growth model

$$P(t) = \frac{1000}{1 + 32.33e^{-0.439t}}$$

represents the population (in grams) of a bacterium after t hours.
    (a) Determine the carrying capacity of the environment.
    (b) What is the growth rate of the bacteria?
    (c) Determine the initial population size.
    (d) What is the population after 9 hours?
    (e) When will the population be 700 grams?
    (f) How long does it take for the population to reach one-half the carrying capacity?

24. **Population of an Endangered Species** Often environmentalists capture an endangered species and transport the species to a controlled environment where the species can produce offspring and regenerate its population. Suppose that six American bald eagles are captured, transported to Montana, and set free. Based on experience, the environmentalists expect the population to grow according to the model

$$P(t) = \frac{500}{1 + 83.33e^{-0.162t}}$$

where t is measured in years.

    (a) Determine the carrying capacity of the environment.
    (b) What is the growth rate of the bald eagle?
    (c) What is the population after 3 years?
    (d) When will the population be 300 eagles?
    (e) How long does it take for the population to reach one-half of the carrying capacity?

25. **The *Challenger* Disaster** After the *Challenger* disaster in 1986, a study was made of the 23 launches that preceded the fatal flight. A mathematical model was developed involving the relationship between the Fahrenheit temperature x around the O-rings and the number y of eroded or leaky primary O-rings. The model stated that

$$y = \frac{6}{1 + e^{-(5.085 - 0.1156x)}}$$

where the number 6 indicates the 6 primary O-rings on the spacecraft.

---

* Author's Note: Surprisingly, the chemical formulas for glucose and fructose are the same: This is not a typo.

(a) What is the predicted number of eroded or leaky primary O-rings at a temperature of 100°F?
(b) What is the predicted number of eroded or leaky primary O-rings at a temperature of 60°F?
(c) What is the predicted number of eroded or leaky primary O-rings at a temperature of 30°F?
(d) Graph the equation using a graphing utility. At what temperature is the predicted number of eroded or leaky O-rings 1? 3? 5?

Source: Linda Tappin, "Analyzing Data Relating to the Challenger Disaster," Mathematics Teacher, Vol. 87, No. 6, September 1994, pp. 423–426.

5.9 Building Exponential, Logarithmic, and Logistic Models from Data

PREPARING FOR THIS SECTION *Before getting started, review the following:*

- Building Linear Models from Data (Section 3.2, pp. 128–131)
- Building Cubic Models from Data (Section 4.1, pp. 182–183)
- Building Quadratic Models from Data (Section 3.4, pp. 150–151)

OBJECTIVES   **1** Build an Exponential Model from Data (p. 333)
   2 Build a Logarithmic Model from Data (p. 334)
   3 Build a Logistic Model from Data (p. 335)

In Section 3.2, we discussed how to find the linear function of best fit $(y = ax + b)$, in Section 3.4, we discussed how to find the quadratic function of best fit $(y = ax^2 + bx + c)$, and in Section 4.1, we discussed how to find the cubic function of best fit $(y = ax^3 + bx^2 + cx + d)$.

In this section we discuss how to use a graphing utility to find equations of best fit that describe the relation between two variables when the relation is thought to be exponential $(y = ab^x)$, logarithmic $(y = a + b \ln x)$, or logistic $\left(y = \dfrac{c}{1 + ae^{-bx}}\right)$. As before, we draw a scatter diagram of the data to help to determine the appropriate model to use.

Figure 44 shows scatter diagrams that will typically be observed for the three models. Below each scatter diagram are any restrictions on the values of the parameters.

Figure 44

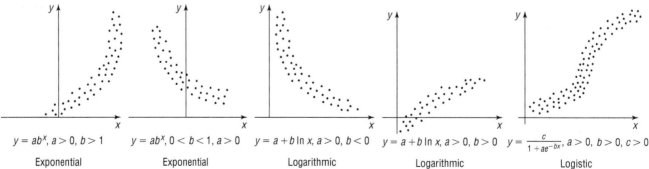

$y = ab^x, a > 0, b > 1$ $y = ab^x, 0 < b < 1, a > 0$ $y = a + b \ln x, a > 0, b < 0$ $y = a + b \ln x, a > 0, b > 0$ $y = \dfrac{c}{1 + ae^{-bx}}, a > 0, b > 0, c > 0$

Exponential   Exponential   Logarithmic   Logarithmic   Logistic

Most graphing utilities have REGression options that fit data to a specific type of curve. Once the data have been entered and a scatter diagram obtained, the type of curve that you want to fit to the data is selected. Then that REGression option is used to obtain the curve of *best fit* of the type selected.

The correlation coefficient r will appear only if the model can be written as a linear expression. As it turns out, r will appear for the linear, power, exponential, and logarithmic models, since these models can be written as a linear expression. Remember, the closer $|r|$ is to 1, the better the fit.

1 Build an Exponential Model from Data

We saw in Section 5.7 that the future value of money behaves exponentially, and we saw in Section 5.8 that growth and decay models also behave exponentially. The next example shows how data can lead to an exponential model.

| EXAMPLE 1 | **Fitting an Exponential Function to Data** |

Kathleen is interested in finding a function that explains the growth of cell phone usage in the United States. She gathers data on the number (in millions) of U.S. cell phone subscribers from 1985 through 2008. The data are shown in Table 9.

(a) Using a graphing utility, draw a scatter diagram with year as the independent variable.

(b) Using a graphing utility, build an exponential model from the data.

(c) Express the function found in part (b) in the form $A = A_0 e^{kt}$.

(d) Graph the exponential function found in part (b) or (c) on the scatter diagram.

(e) Using the solution to part (b) or (c), predict the number of U.S. cell phone subscribers in 2009.

(f) Interpret the value of k found in part (c).

Table 9

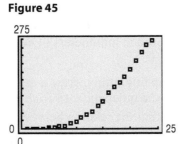

Year, x	Number of Subscribers (in millions), y
1985 ($x = 1$)	0.34
1986 ($x = 2$)	0.68
1987 ($x = 3$)	1.23
1988 ($x = 4$)	2.07
1989 ($x = 5$)	3.51
1990 ($x = 6$)	5.28
1991 ($x = 7$)	7.56
1992 ($x = 8$)	11.03
1993 ($x = 9$)	16.01
1994 ($x = 10$)	24.13
1995 ($x = 11$)	33.76
1996 ($x = 12$)	44.04
1997 ($x = 13$)	55.31
1998 ($x = 14$)	69.21
1999 ($x = 15$)	86.05
2000 ($x = 16$)	109.48
2001 ($x = 17$)	128.37
2002 ($x = 18$)	140.77
2003 ($x = 19$)	158.72
2004 ($x = 20$)	182.14
2005 ($x = 21$)	207.90
2006 ($x = 22$)	233.00
2007 ($x = 23$)	255.40
2008 ($x = 24$)	270.33

Source: ©2010 CTIA–The Wireless Association®. All rights reserved.

Solution

(a) Enter the data into the graphing utility, letting 1 represent 1985, 2 represent 1986, and so on. We obtain the scatter diagram shown in Figure 45.

(b) A graphing utility fits the data in Figure 45 to an exponential function of the form $y = ab^x$ using the EXPonential REGression option. From Figure 46 we find that $y = ab^x = 0.86498(1.31855)^x$. Notice that $|r|$ is close to 1, indicating a good fit.

Figure 45

275

0 ⌞_____⌟ 25
0

Figure 46

```
ExpReg
y=a*b^x
a=.8649775385
b=1.318554023
r²=.9310544659
r=.9649116363
```

(c) To express $y = ab^x$ in the form $A = A_0 e^{kt}$, where $x = t$ and $y = A$, proceed as follows:

$$ab^x = A_0 e^{kt} \quad x = t$$

When $x = t = 0$, we find that $a = A_0$. This leads to

$$a = A_0 \qquad b^x = e^{kt}$$
$$b^x = (e^k)^t$$
$$b = e^k \qquad {\scriptstyle x\,=\,t}$$

Since $y = ab^x = 0.86498(1.31855)^x$, we find that $a = 0.86498$ and $b = 1.31855$.

$$a = A_0 = 0.86498 \quad \text{and} \quad b = e^k = 1.31855$$

We want to find k, so we rewrite $e^k = 1.31855$ as a logarithm and obtain

$$k = \ln(1.31855) \approx 0.2765$$

As a result, $A = A_0 e^{kt} = 0.86498 e^{0.2765t}$.

Figure 47

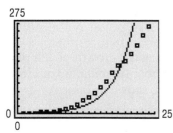

(d) See Figure 47 for the graph of the exponential function of best fit.

(e) Let $t = 25$ (end of 2009) in the function found in part (c). The predicted number (in millions) of cell phone subscribers in the United States in 2009 is

$$A_0 e^{kt} = 0.86498 e^{0.2765(25)} \approx 869$$

This prediction (869 million) far exceeds what the U.S. population was in 2009 (currently the U.S. population is about 304 million). See the answer in part (f).

(f) The value of $k = 0.2765$ represents the growth rate of the number of cell phone subscribers in the United States. Over the period 1985 through 2008, the number of cell phone subscribers grew at an annual rate of 27.65% compounded continuously. This growth rate is not sustainable as we learned in part (e). In Problem 10 you are asked to build a better model from these data.

Now Work PROBLEM 1

2 Build a Logarithmic Model from Data

Many relations between variables do not follow an exponential model; instead, the independent variable is related to the dependent variable using a logarithmic model.

EXAMPLE 2 **Fitting a Logarithmic Function to Data**

Jodi, a meteorologist, is interested in finding a function that explains the relation between the height of a weather balloon (in kilometers) and the atmospheric pressure (measured in millimeters of mercury) on the balloon. She collects the data shown in Table 10.

(a) Using a graphing utility, draw a scatter diagram of the data with atmospheric pressure as the independent variable.

(b) It is known that the relation between atmospheric pressure and height follows a logarithmic model. Using a graphing utility, build a logarithmic model from the data.

(c) Draw the logarithmic function found in part (b) on the scatter diagram.

(d) Use the function found in part (b) to predict the height of the weather balloon if the atmospheric pressure is 560 millimeters of mercury.

Table 10

Atmospheric Pressure, p	Height, h
760	0
740	0.184
725	0.328
700	0.565
650	1.079
630	1.291
600	1.634
580	1.862
550	2.235

Solution

(a) After entering the data into the graphing utility, we obtain the scatter diagram shown in Figure 48.

(b) A graphing utility fits the data in Figure 48 to a logarithmic function of the form $y = a + b \ln x$ by using the LOGarithm REGression option. See Figure 49. The logarithmic model from the data is

$$h(p) = 45.7863 - 6.9025 \ln p$$

where h is the height of the weather balloon and p is the atmospheric pressure. Notice that $|r|$ is close to 1, indicating a good fit.

(c) Figure 50 shows the graph of $h(p) = 45.7863 - 6.9025 \ln p$ on the scatter diagram.

Figure 48

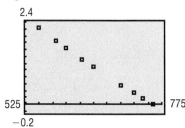

Figure 49

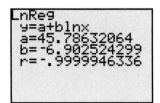

Figure 50

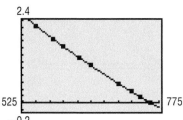

(d) Using the function found in part (b), Jodi predicts the height of the weather balloon when the atmospheric pressure is 560 to be

$$h(560) = 45.7863 - 6.9025 \ln 560$$
$$\approx 2.108 \text{ kilometers}$$

Now Work PROBLEM 5

3 Build a Logistic Model from Data

Logistic growth models can be used to model situations for which the value of the dependent variable is limited. Many real-world situations conform to this scenario. For example, the population of the human race is limited by the availability of natural resources such as food and shelter. When the value of the dependent variable is limited, a logistic growth model is often appropriate.

EXAMPLE 3 **Fitting a Logistic Function to Data**

The data in Table 11 represent the amount of yeast biomass in a culture after t hours.

Table 11

Time (in hours)	Yeast Biomass	Time (in hours)	Yeast Biomass
0	9.6	10	513.3
1	18.3	11	559.7
2	29.0	12	594.8
3	47.2	13	629.4
4	71.1	14	640.8
5	119.1	15	651.1
6	174.6	16	655.9
7	257.3	17	659.6
8	350.7	18	661.8
9	441.0		

Source: Tor Carlson (Über Geschwindigkeit und Grösse der Hefevermehrung in Würze, Biochemische Zeitschrift, Bd. 57, pp. 313–334, 1913)

(a) Using a graphing utility, draw a scatter diagram of the data with time as the independent variable.

(b) Using a graphing utility, build a logistic model from the data.

(c) Using a graphing utility, graph the function found in part (b) on the scatter diagram.

(d) What is the predicted carrying capacity of the culture?

(e) Use the function found in part (b) to predict the population of the culture at $t = 19$ hours.

Solution

(a) See Figure 51 for a scatter diagram of the data.

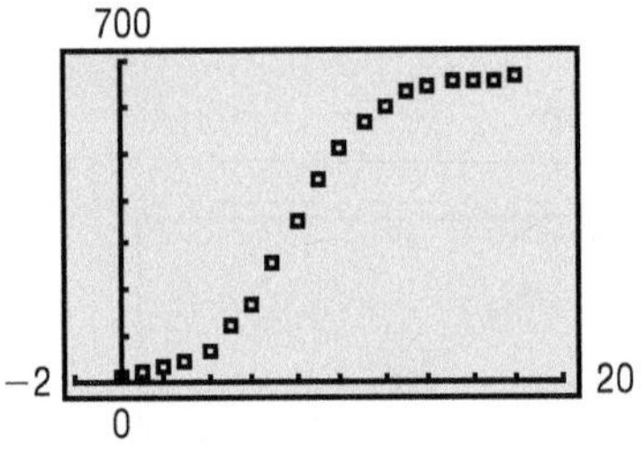

(b) A graphing utility fits a logistic growth model of the form $y = \dfrac{c}{1 + ae^{-bx}}$ by using the LOGISTIC regression option. See Figure 52. The logistic model from the data is

$$y = \frac{663.0}{1 + 71.6e^{-0.5470x}}$$

where y is the amount of yeast biomass in the culture and x is the time.

(c) See Figure 53 for the graph of the logistic model.

Figure 51

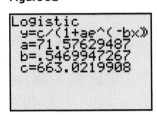

Figure 52

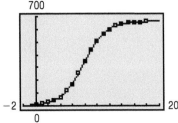

Figure 53

700

-2 ⌊_____⌋ 20
0

(d) Based on the logistic growth model found in part (b), the carrying capacity of the culture is 663.

(e) Using the logistic growth model found in part (b), the predicted amount of yeast biomass at $t = 19$ hours is

$$y = \frac{663.0}{1 + 71.6e^{-0.5470(19)}} \approx 661.5$$

─────── **Now Work** PROBLEM 7

5.9 Assess Your Understanding

Applications and Extensions

1. **Biology** A strain of E-coli Beu 397-recA441 is placed into a nutrient broth at 30° Celsius and allowed to grow. The following data are collected. Theory states that the number of bacteria in the petri dish will initially grow according to the law of uninhibited growth. The population is measured using an optical device in which the amount of light that passes through the petri dish is measured.

Time (hours), x	Population, y
0	0.09
2.5	0.18
3.5	0.26
4.5	0.35
6	0.50

Source: Dr. Polly Lavery, Joliet Junior College

(a) Draw a scatter diagram treating time as the independent variable.

(b) Using a graphing utility, build an exponential model from the data.

(c) Express the function found in part (b) in the form $N(t) = N_0 e^{kt}$.

(d) Graph the exponential function found in part (b) or (c) on the scatter diagram.

(e) Use the exponential function from part (b) or (c) to predict the population at $x = 7$ hours.

(f) Use the exponential function from part (b) or (c) to predict when the population will reach 0.75.

2. **Biology** A strain of E-coli SC18del-recA718 is placed into a nutrient broth at 30° Celsius and allowed to grow. The data on the following page are collected. Theory states that the number of bacteria in the petri dish will initially grow according to the law of uninhibited growth. The population

is measured using an optical device in which the amount of light that passes through the petri dish is measured.

Time (hours), x	Population, y
2.5	0.175
3.5	0.38
4.5	0.63
4.75	0.76
5.25	1.20

Source: Dr. Polly Lavery, Joliet Junior College

(a) Draw a scatter diagram treating time as the independent variable.
(b) Using a graphing utility, build an exponential model from the data.
(c) Express the function found in part (b) in the form $N(t) = N_0 e^{kt}$.
(d) Graph the exponential function found in part (b) or (c) on the scatter diagram.
(e) Use the exponential function from part (b) or (c) to predict the population at $x = 6$ hours.
(f) Use the exponential function from part (b) or (c) to predict when the population will reach 2.1.

3. Chemistry A chemist has a 100-gram sample of a radioactive material. He records the amount of radioactive material every week for 7 weeks and obtains the following data:

Week	Weight (in Grams)
0	100.0
1	88.3
2	75.9
3	69.4
4	59.1
5	51.8
6	45.5

(a) Using a graphing utility, draw a scatter diagram with week as the independent variable.
(b) Using a graphing utility, build an exponential model from the data.
(c) Express the function found in part (b) in the form $A(t) = A_0 e^{kt}$.
(d) Graph the exponential function found in part (b) or (c) on the scatter diagram.
(e) From the result found in part (b), determine the half-life of the radioactive material.
(f) How much radioactive material will be left after 50 weeks?
(g) When will there be 20 grams of radioactive material?

4. Cigarette Exports The following data represent the number of cigarettes (in billions) exported from the United States by year.

Year	Cigarette Exports (in billions of pieces)
1995	231.1
1998	201.3
1999	151.4
2000	147.9
2001	133.9
2002	127.4
2003	121.5
2004	118.7

Source: Statistical Abstract of the United States, 2006

(a) Let $t = $ the number of years since 1995. Using a graphing utility, draw a scatter diagram of the data using t as the independent variable and number of cigarettes as the dependent variable.
(b) Using a graphing utility, build an exponential model from the data.
(c) Express the function found in part (b) in the form $A(t) = A_0 e^{kt}$.
(d) Graph the exponential function found in part (b) or (c) on the scatter diagram.
(e) Use the exponential function from part (b) or (c) to predict the number of cigarettes that will be exported from the United States in 2010.
(f) Use the exponential function from part (b) or (c) to predict when the number of cigarettes exported from the United States will decrease to 50 billion.

5. Economics and Marketing The following data represent the price and quantity demanded in 2009 for Dell personal computers.

Price ($/Computer)	Quantity Demanded
2300	152
2000	159
1700	164
1500	171
1300	176
1200	180
1000	189

(a) Using a graphing utility, draw a scatter diagram of the data with price as the dependent variable.
(b) Using a graphing utility, build a logarithmic model from the data.
(c) Using a graphing utility, draw the logarithmic function found in part (b) on the scatter diagram.
(d) Use the function found in part (b) to predict the number of Dell personal computers that will be demanded if the price is $1650.

6. Economics and Marketing The following data represent the price and quantity supplied in 2009 for Dell personal computers.

Price ($/Computer)	Quantity Supplied
2300	180
2000	173
1700	160
1500	150
1300	137
1200	130
1000	113

(a) Using a graphing utility, draw a scatter diagram of the data with price as the dependent variable.
(b) Using a graphing utility, build a logarithmic model from the data.
(c) Using a graphing utility, draw the logarithmic function found in part (b) on the scatter diagram.
(d) Use the function found in part (b) to predict the number of Dell personal computers that will be supplied if the price is $1650.

7. **Population Model** The following data represent the population of the United States. An ecologist is interested in building a model that describes the population of the United States.

Year	Population
1900	76,212,168
1910	92,228,496
1920	106,021,537
1930	123,202,624
1940	132,164,569
1950	151,325,798
1960	179,323,175
1970	203,302,031
1980	226,542,203
1990	248,709,873
2000	281,421,906

Source: U.S. Census Bureau

(a) Using a graphing utility, draw a scatter diagram of the data using years since 1900 as the independent variable and population as the dependent variable.
(b) Using a graphing utility, build a logistic model from the data.
(c) Using a graphing utility, draw the function found in part (b) on the scatter diagram.
(d) Based on the function found in part (b), what is the carrying capacity of the United States?
(e) Use the function found in part (b) to predict the population of the United States in 2004.
(f) When will the United States population be 300,000,000?
(g) Compare actual U.S. Census figures to the predictions found in parts (e) and (f). Discuss any differences.

8. **Population Model** The following data represent the world population. An ecologist is interested in building a model that describes the world population.

Year	Population (in Billions)
2001	6.17
2002	6.25
2003	6.32
2004	6.40
2005	6.48
2006	6.55
2007	6.63
2008	6.71
2009	6.79

Source: U.S. Census Bureau

(a) Using a graphing utility, draw a scatter diagram of the data using years since 2000 as the independent variable and population as the dependent variable.
(b) Using a graphing utility, build a logistic model from the data.
(c) Using a graphing utility, draw the function found in part (b) on the scatter diagram.
(d) Based on the function found in part (b), what is the carrying capacity of the world?
(e) Use the function found in part (b) to predict the population of the world in 2015.
(f) When will world population be 10 billion?

9. **Cable Subscribers** The following data represent the number of basic cable TV subscribers in the United States. A market researcher believes that external factors, such as satellite TV, have affected the growth of cable subscribers. She is interested in building a model that can be used to describe the number of cable TV subscribers in the United States.

Year	Subscribers (1,000)
1975 ($t = 5$)	9,800
1980 ($t = 10$)	17,500
1985 ($t = 15$)	35,440
1990 ($t = 20$)	50,520
1992 ($t = 22$)	54,300
1994 ($t = 24$)	58,373
1996 ($t = 26$)	62,300
1998 ($t = 28$)	64,650
2000 ($t = 30$)	66,250
2002 ($t = 32$)	66,472
2004 ($t = 34$)	65,727
2006 ($t = 36$)	65,319

Source: Statistical Abstract of the United States, 2009

(a) Using a graphing utility, draw a scatter diagram of the data using the number of years after 1970, t, as the independent variable and number of subscribers as the dependent variable.
(b) Using a graphing utility, build a logistic model from the data.

(c) Using a graphing utility, draw the function found in part (b) on the scatter diagram.
(d) Based on the model found in part (b), what is the maximum number of cable TV subscribers in the United States?
(e) Use the model found in part (b) to predict the number of cable TV subscribers in the United States in 2015.

10. **Cell Phone Users** Refer to the data in Table 9.
    (a) Using a graphing utility, build a logistic model from the data.

(b) Graph the logistic function found in part (b) on a scatter diagram of the data.
(c) What is the predicted carrying capacity of U.S. cell phone subscribers?
(d) Use the model found in part (b) to predict the number of U.S. cell phone subscribers at the end of 2009.
(e) Compare the answer to part (d) above with the answer to Example 1, part (e). How do you explain the different predictions?

Mixed Practice

11. **Age versus Total Cholesterol** The following data represent the age and average total cholesterol for adult males at various ages.

Age	Total Cholesterol
27	189
40	205
50	215
60	210
70	210
80	194

(a) Using a graphing utility, draw a scatter diagram of the data using age, x, as the independent variable and total cholesterol, y, as the dependent variable.
(b) Based on the scatter diagram drawn in part (a), decide on a model (linear, quadratic, cubic, exponential, logarithmic, or logistic) that you think best describes the relation between age and total cholesterol. Be sure to justify your choice of model.
(c) Using a graphing utility, find the model of best fit.
(d) Using a graphing utility, draw the model of best fit on the scatter diagram drawn in part (a).
(e) Use your model to predict the total cholesterol of a 35-year-old male.

12. **Income versus Crime Rate** The following data represent crime rate against individuals (crimes per 1000 households) and their income in the United States in 2006.

Income	Crime Rate
$5000	217.3
11,250	195.7
20,000	183.1
30,000	179.4
42,500	166.2
62,500	166.8
85,000	162.0

Source: Statistical Abstract of the United States, 2009

(a) Using a graphing utility, draw a scatter diagram of the data using income, x, as the independent variable and crime rate, y, as the dependent variable.
(b) Based on the scatter diagram drawn in part (a), decide on a model (linear, quadratic, cubic, exponential, logarithmic, or logistic) that you think best describes the relation between income and crime rate. Be sure to justify your choice of model.
(c) Using a graphing utility, find the model of best fit.
(d) Using a graphing utility, draw the model of best fit on the scatter diagram drawn in part (a).
(e) Use your model to predict the crime rate of a household whose income is $55,000.

13. **Depreciation of a Chevrolet Impala** The following data represent the asking price and age of a Chevrolet Impala SS.

Age	Asking Price
1	$27,417
1	26,750
2	22,995
2	23,195
3	17,999
4	16,995
4	16,490

Source: cars.com

(a) Using a graphing utility, draw a scatter diagram of the data using age, x, as the independent variable and asking price, y, as the dependent variable.
(b) Based on the scatter diagram drawn in part (a), decide on a model (linear, quadratic, cubic, exponential, logarithmic, or logistic) that you think best describes the relation between age and asking price. Be sure to justify your choice of model.
(c) Using a graphing utility, find the model of best fit.
(d) Using a graphing utility, draw the model of best fit on the scatter diagram drawn in part (a).
(e) Use your model to predict the asking price of a Chevrolet Impala SS that is 5 years old.

CHAPTER REVIEW

Things to Know

Composite function (p. 247)

$(f \circ g)(x) = f(g(x))$ The domain of $f \circ g$ is the set of all numbers x in the domain of g for which $g(x)$ is in the domain of f.

One-to-one function f (p. 255)

A function for which any two different inputs in the domain correspond to two different outputs in the range
For any choice of elements x_1, x_2 in the domain of f, if $x_1 \neq x_2$, then $f(x_1) \neq f(x_2)$.

Horizontal-line test (p. 256)

If every horizontal line intersects the graph of a function f in at most one point, f is one-to-one.

Inverse function f^{-1} of f (pp. 257–260)

Domain of f = range of f^{-1}; range of f = domain of f^{-1}
$f^{-1}(f(x)) = x$ for all x in the domain of f
$f(f^{-1}(x)) = x$ for all x in the domain of f^{-1}
The graphs of f and f^{-1} are symmetric with respect to the line $y = x$.

Properties of the exponential function (pp. 269, 272, 274)

$f(x) = Ca^x$, $a > 1, C > 0$

Domain: the interval $(-\infty, \infty)$
Range: the interval $(0, \infty)$
x-intercepts: none; y-intercept: C
Horizontal asymptote: x-axis ($y = 0$) as $x \to -\infty$
Increasing; one-to-one; smooth; continuous
See Figure 21 for a typical graph.

$f(x) = Ca^x$, $0 < a < 1, C > 0$

Domain: the interval $(-\infty, \infty)$
Range: the interval $(0, \infty)$
x-intercepts: none; y-intercept: C
Horizontal asymptote: x-axis ($y = 0$) as $x \to \infty$
Decreasing; one-to-one; smooth; continuous
See Figure 25 for a typical graph.

Number e (p. 275)

Value approached by the expression $\left(1 + \dfrac{1}{n}\right)^n$ as $n \to \infty$; that is, $\displaystyle\lim_{n \to \infty}\left(1 + \dfrac{1}{n}\right)^n = e$.

Property of exponents (p. 276)

If $a^u = a^v$, then $u = v$.

Properties of the logarithmic function (pp. 284–286)

$f(x) = \log_a x$, $a > 1$
($y = \log_a x$ means $x = a^y$)

Domain: the interval $(0, \infty)$
Range: the interval $(-\infty, \infty)$
x-intercept: 1; y-intercept: none
Vertical asymptote: $x = 0$ (y-axis)
Increasing; one-to-one; smooth; continuous
See Figure 39(a) for a typical graph.

$f(x) = \log_a x$, $0 < a < 1$
($y = \log_a x$ means $x = a^y$)

Domain: the interval $(0, \infty)$
Range: the interval $(-\infty, \infty)$
x-intercept: 1; y-intercept: none
Vertical asymptote: $x = 0$ (y-axis)
Decreasing; one-to-one; smooth; continuous
See Figure 39(b) for a typical graph.

Natural logarithm (p. 287)

$y = \ln x$ means $x = e^y$.

Properties of logarithms (pp. 297–298, 300)

$\log_a 1 = 0$ $\log_a a = 1$ $a^{\log_a M} = M$ $\log_a a^r = r$

$\log_a(MN) = \log_a M + \log_a N$ $\log_a\left(\dfrac{M}{N}\right) = \log_a M - \log_a N$

$\log_a M^r = r \log_a M$

If $M = N$, then $\log_a M = \log_a N$. $a^x = e^{x \ln a}$

If $\log_a M = \log_a N$, then $M = N$.

Formulas

Change-of-Base Formula (p. 301)	$\log_a M = \dfrac{\log_b M}{\log_b a}$
Compound Interest Formula (p. 313)	$A = P \cdot \left(1 + \dfrac{r}{n}\right)^{nt}$
Continuous compounding (p. 315)	$A = Pe^{rt}$
Effective rate of interest (p. 316)	Compounding n times per year: $r_e = \left(1 + \dfrac{r}{n}\right)^n - 1$
	Continuous compounding: $r_e = e^r - 1$
Present Value Formulas (p. 317)	$P = A \cdot \left(1 + \dfrac{r}{n}\right)^{-nt}$ or $P = Ae^{-rt}$
Growth and decay (pp. 322, 324)	$A(t) = A_0 e^{kt}$
Newton's Law of Cooling (p. 325)	$u(t) = T + (u_0 - T)e^{kt}$ $k < 0$
Logistic model (p. 327)	$P(t) = \dfrac{c}{1 + ae^{-bt}}$

Objectives

Section		You should be able to ...	Example(s)	Review Exercises
5.1	1	Form a composite function (p. 247)	1, 2, 4, 5	1–12
	2	Find the domain of a composite function (p. 248)	2–4	7–12
5.2	1	Determine whether a function is one-to-one (p. 255)	1, 2	13(a), 14(a), 15, 16
	2	Determine the inverse of a function defined by a map or a set of ordered pairs (p. 257)	3, 4	13(b), 14(b)
	3	Obtain the graph of the inverse function from the graph of the function (p. 259)	7	15, 16
	4	Find the inverse of a function defined by an equation (p. 260)	8, 9, 10	17–22
5.3	1	Evaluate exponential functions (p. 267)	1	23(a), (c), 24(a), (c), 87(a)
	2	Graph exponential functions (p. 271)	3–6	55–60
	3	Define the number e (p. 274)	pg. 429	59, 60
	4	Solve exponential equations (p. 276)	7, 8	63–66, 71, 72, 74–76
5.4	1	Change exponential statements to logarithmic statements and logarithmic statements to exponential statements (p. 284)	2, 3	25–28
	2	Evaluate logarithmic expressions (p. 284)	4	23(b), (d), 24(b), (d), 33, 34, 83(b), 84(b), 85, 86, 88(a), 89
	3	Determine the domain of a logarithmic function (p. 285)	5	29–32, 61(a), 62(a)
	4	Graph logarithmic functions (p. 286)	6, 7	61, 62, 83(a), 84(a)
	5	Solve logarithmic equations (p. 290)	8, 9	67, 68, 73, 83(c), 84(c), 88(b)
5.5	1	Work with the properties of logarithms (p. 296)	1, 2	35–38
	2	Write a logarithmic expression as a sum or difference of logarithms (p. 298)	3–5	39–44
	3	Write a logarithmic expression as a single logarithm (p. 299)	6	45–50
	4	Evaluate logarithms whose base is neither 10 nor e (p. 301)	7, 8	51, 52
5.6	1	Solve logarithmic equations (p. 305)	1–3	67, 68, 77, 78
	2	Solve exponential equations (p. 307)	4–6	63–66, 69–72, 74–76, 79–82
	3	Solve logarithmic and exponential equations using a graphing utility (p. 308)	7	69–82
5.7	1	Determine the future value of a lump sum of money (p. 312)	1–3	90, 92, 97
	2	Calculate effective rates of return (p. 315)	4	90
	3	Determine the present value of a lump sum of money (p. 316)	5	91
	4	Determine the rate of interest or time required to double a lump sum of money (p. 317)	6, 7	90

Section	You should be able to . . .	Example(s)	Review Exercises
5.8	**1** Find equations of populations that obey the law of uninhibited growth (p. 322)	1, 2	95
	2 Find equations of populations that obey the law of decay (p. 324)	3	93, 96
	3 Use Newton's Law of Cooling (p. 325)	4	94
	4 Use logistic models (p. 327)	5, 6	98
5.9	**1** Build an exponential model from data (p. 333)	1	99
	2 Build a logarithmic model from data (p. 334)	2	100
	3 Build a logistic model from data (p. 335)	3	101

Review Exercises

In Problems 1–6, for the given functions f and g find:

(a) $(f \circ g)(2)$ (b) $(g \circ f)(-2)$ (c) $(f \circ f)(4)$ (d) $(g \circ g)(-1)$

1. $f(x) = 3x - 5$; $g(x) = 1 - 2x^2$ **2.** $f(x) = 4 - x$; $g(x) = 1 + x^2$ **3.** $f(x) = \sqrt{x + 2}$; $g(x) = 2x^2 + 1$

4. $f(x) = 1 - 3x^2$; $g(x) = \sqrt{4 - x}$ **5.** $f(x) = e^x$; $g(x) = 3x - 2$ **6.** $f(x) = \dfrac{2}{1 + 2x^2}$; $g(x) = 3x$

In Problems 7–12, find $f \circ g$, $g \circ f$, $f \circ f$, and $g \circ g$ for each pair of functions. State the domain of each composite function.

7. $f(x) = 2 - x$; $g(x) = 3x + 1$ **8.** $f(x) = 2x - 1$; $g(x) = 2x + 1$ **9.** $f(x) = 3x^2 + x + 1$; $g(x) = |3x|$

10. $f(x) = \sqrt{3x}$; $g(x) = 1 + x + x^2$ **11.** $f(x) = \dfrac{x + 1}{x - 1}$; $g(x) = \dfrac{1}{x}$ **12.** $f(x) = \sqrt{x - 3}$; $g(x) = \dfrac{3}{x}$

In Problems 13 and 14, (a) verify that the function is one-to-one, and (b) find the inverse of the given function.

13. $\{(1, 2), (3, 5), (5, 8), (6, 10)\}$ **14.** $\{(-1, 4), (0, 2), (1, 5), (3, 7)\}$

In Problems 15 and 16, state why the graph of the function is one-to-one. Then draw the graph of the inverse function f^{-1}. For convenience (and as a hint), the graph of $y = x$ is also given.

15.

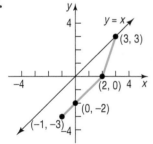

16.

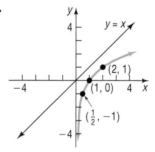

In Problems 17–22, the function f is one-to-one. Find the inverse of each function and check your answer.

17. $f(x) = \dfrac{2x + 3}{5x - 2}$ **18.** $f(x) = \dfrac{2 - x}{3 + x}$ **19.** $f(x) = \dfrac{1}{x - 1}$

20. $f(x) = \sqrt{x - 2}$ **21.** $f(x) = \dfrac{3}{x^{1/3}}$ **22.** $f(x) = x^{1/3} + 1$

In Problems 23 and 24, $f(x) = 3^x$ and $g(x) = \log_3 x$.

23. Evaluate: (a) $f(4)$ (b) $g(9)$ (c) $f(-2)$ (d) $g\left(\dfrac{1}{27}\right)$

24. Evaluate: (a) $f(1)$ (b) $g(81)$ (c) $f(-4)$ (d) $g\left(\dfrac{1}{243}\right)$

In Problems 25 and 26, convert each exponential statement to an equivalent statement involving a logarithm. In Problems 27 and 28, convert each logarithmic statement to an equivalent statement involving an exponent.

25. $5^2 = z$ **26.** $a^5 = m$ **27.** $\log_5 u = 13$ **28.** $\log_a 4 = 3$

In Problems 29–32, find the domain of each logarithmic function.

29. $f(x) = \log(3x - 2)$ **30.** $F(x) = \log_5(2x + 1)$ **31.** $H(x) = \log_2(x^2 - 3x + 2)$ **32.** $F(x) = \ln(x^2 - 9)$

In Problems 33–38, evaluate each expression. Do not use a calculator.

33. $\log_2\left(\dfrac{1}{8}\right)$ **34.** $\log_3 81$ **35.** $\ln e^{\sqrt{2}}$ **36.** $e^{\ln 0.1}$ **37.** $2^{\log_2 0.4}$ **38.** $\log_2 2^{\sqrt{3}}$

In Problems 39–44, write each expression as the sum and/or difference of logarithms. Express powers as factors.

39. $\log_3\left(\dfrac{uv^2}{w}\right)$, $\quad u > 0, v > 0, w > 0$ **40.** $\log_2\left(a^2\sqrt{b}\right)^4$, $\quad a > 0, b > 0$ **41.** $\log\left(x^2\sqrt{x^3 + 1}\right)$, $\quad x > 0$

42. $\log_5\left(\dfrac{x^2 + 2x + 1}{x^2}\right)$, $\quad x > 0$ **43.** $\ln\left(\dfrac{x\sqrt[3]{x^2 + 1}}{x - 3}\right)$, $\quad x > 3$ **44.** $\ln\left(\dfrac{2x + 3}{x^2 - 3x + 2}\right)^2$, $\quad x > 2$

In Problems 45–50, write each expression as a single logarithm.

45. $3\log_4 x^2 + \dfrac{1}{2}\log_4\sqrt{x}$

46. $-2\log_3\left(\dfrac{1}{x}\right) + \dfrac{1}{3}\log_3\sqrt{x}$

47. $\ln\left(\dfrac{x - 1}{x}\right) + \ln\left(\dfrac{x}{x + 1}\right) - \ln(x^2 - 1)$

48. $\log(x^2 - 9) - \log(x^2 + 7x + 12)$

49. $2\log 2 + 3\log x - \dfrac{1}{2}[\log(x + 3) + \log(x - 2)]$

50. $\dfrac{1}{2}\ln(x^2 + 1) - 4\ln\dfrac{1}{2} - \dfrac{1}{2}[\ln(x - 4) + \ln x]$

In Problems 51 and 52, use the Change-of-Base Formula and a calculator to evaluate each logarithm. Round your answer to three decimal places.

51. $\log_4 19$ **52.** $\log_2 21$

In Problems 53 and 54, graph each function using a graphing utility and the Change-of-Base Formula.

53. $y = \log_3 x$ **54.** $y = \log_7 x$

In Problems 55–62, use the given function f to:
(a) Find the domain of f. (b) Graph f. (c) From the graph, determine the range and any asymptotes of f.
(d) Find f^{-1}, the inverse of f. (e) Find the domain and the range of f^{-1}. (f) Graph f^{-1}.

55. $f(x) = 2^{x-3}$ **56.** $f(x) = -2^x + 3$ **57.** $f(x) = \dfrac{1}{2}(3^{-x})$ **58.** $f(x) = 1 + 3^{-x}$

59. $f(x) = 1 - e^{-x}$ **60.** $f(x) = 3e^{x-2}$ **61.** $f(x) = \dfrac{1}{2}\ln(x + 3)$ **62.** $f(x) = 3 + \ln(2x)$

In Problems 63–82, solve each equation. Express irrational solutions in exact form and as a decimal rounded to 3 decimal places.

63. $4^{1-2x} = 2$ **64.** $8^{6+3x} = 4$ **65.** $3^{x^2+x} = \sqrt{3}$ **66.** $4^{x-x^2} = \dfrac{1}{2}$

67. $\log_x 64 = -3$ **68.** $\log_{\sqrt{2}} x = -6$ **69.** $5^x = 3^{x+2}$ **70.** $5^{x+2} = 7^{x-2}$

71. $9^{2x} = 27^{3x-4}$ **72.** $25^{2x} = 5^{x^2-12}$ **73.** $\log_3\sqrt{x - 2} = 2$ **74.** $2^{x+1}\cdot 8^{-x} = 4$

75. $8 = 4^{x^2}\cdot 2^{5x}$ **76.** $2^x\cdot 5 = 10^x$ **77.** $\log_6(x + 3) + \log_6(x + 4) = 1$

78. $\log(7x - 12) = 2\log x$ **79.** $e^{1-x} = 5$ **80.** $e^{1-2x} = 4$

81. $9^x + 4\cdot 3^x - 3 = 0$ **82.** $4^x - 14\cdot 4^{-x} = 5$

83. Suppose that $f(x) = \log_2(x - 2) + 1$.
(a) Graph f.
(b) What is $f(6)$? What point is on the graph of f?
(c) Solve $f(x) = 4$. What point is on the graph of f?
(d) Based on the graph drawn in part (a), solve $f(x) > 0$.
(e) Find $f^{-1}(x)$. Graph f^{-1} on the same Cartesian plane as f.

84. Suppose that $f(x) = \log_3(x + 1) - 4$.
(a) Graph f.
(b) What is $f(8)$? What point is on the graph of f?
(c) Solve $f(x) = -3$. What point is on the graph of f?
(d) Based on the graph drawn in part (a), solve $f(x) < 0$.
(e) Find $f^{-1}(x)$. Graph f^{-1} on the same Cartesian plane as f.

In Problems 85 and 86, use the following result: If x is the atmospheric pressure (measured in millimeters of mercury), then the formula for the altitude h(x) (measured in meters above sea level) is

$$h(x) = (30T + 8000) \log\left(\frac{P_0}{x}\right)$$

where T is the temperature (in degrees Celsius) and P_0 is the atmospheric pressure at sea level, which is approximately 760 millimeters of mercury.

85. Finding the Altitude of an Airplane At what height is a Piper Cub whose instruments record an outside temperature of 0°C and a barometric pressure of 300 millimeters of mercury?

86. Finding the Height of a Mountain How high is a mountain if instruments placed on its peak record a temperature of 5°C and a barometric pressure of 500 millimeters of mercury?

87. Amplifying Sound An amplifier's power output P (in watts) is related to its decibel voltage gain d by the formula

$$P = 25e^{0.1d}$$

(a) Find the power output for a decibel voltage gain of 4 decibels.
(b) For a power output of 50 watts, what is the decibel voltage gain?

88. Limiting Magnitude of a Telescope A telescope is limited in its usefulness by the brightness of the star that it is aimed at and by the diameter of its lens. One measure of a star's brightness is its *magnitude;* the dimmer the star, the larger its magnitude. A formula for the limiting magnitude L of a telescope, that is, the magnitude of the dimmest star that it can be used to view, is given by

$$L = 9 + 5.1 \log d$$

where d is the diameter (in inches) of the lens.
(a) What is the limiting magnitude of a 3.5-inch telescope?
(b) What diameter is required to view a star of magnitude 14?

89. Salvage Value The number of years n for a piece of machinery to depreciate to a known salvage value can be found using the formula

$$n = \frac{\log s - \log i}{\log(1 - d)}$$

where s is the salvage value of the machinery, i is its initial value, and d is the annual rate of depreciation.
(a) How many years will it take for a piece of machinery to decline in value from $90,000 to $10,000 if the annual rate of depreciation is 0.20 (20%)?
(b) How many years will it take for a piece of machinery to lose half of its value if the annual rate of depreciation is 15%?

90. Funding a College Education A child's grandparents purchase a $10,000 bond fund that matures in 18 years to be used for her college education. The bond fund pays 4% interest compounded semiannually. How much will the bond fund be worth at maturity? What is the effective rate of interest? How long will it take the bond to double in value under these terms?

91. Funding a College Education A child's grandparents wish to purchase a bond that matures in 18 years to be used for her college education. The bond pays 4% interest compounded semiannually. How much should they pay so that the bond will be worth $85,000 at maturity?

92. Funding an IRA First Colonial Bankshares Corporation advertised the following IRA investment plans.

Target IRA Plans

For each $5000 Maturity Value Desired	
Deposit:	At a Term of:
$620.17	20 Years
$1045.02	15 Years
$1760.92	10 Years
$2967.26	5 Years

(a) Assuming continuous compounding, what annual rate of interest did they offer?
(b) First Colonial Bankshares claims that $4000 invested today will have a value of over $32,000 in 20 years. Use the answer found in part (a) to find the actual value of $4000 in 20 years. Assume continuous compounding.

93. Estimating the Date That a Prehistoric Man Died The bones of a prehistoric man found in the desert of New Mexico contain approximately 5% of the original amount of carbon 14. If the half-life of carbon 14 is 5600 years, approximately how long ago did the man die?

94. Temperature of a Skillet A skillet is removed from an oven whose temperature is 450°F and placed in a room whose temperature is 70°F. After 5 minutes, the temperature of the skillet is 400°F. How long will it be until its temperature is 150°F?

95. World Population The annual growth rate of the world's population in 2005 was $k = 1.15\% = 0.0115$. The population of the world in 2005 was 6,451,058,790. Letting $t = 0$ represent 2005, use the uninhibited growth model to predict the world's population in the year 2015.
Source: U.S. Census Bureau

96. Radioactive Decay The half-life of radioactive cobalt is 5.27 years. If 100 grams of radioactive cobalt is present now, how much will be present in 20 years? In 40 years?

97. Federal Deficit In fiscal year 2005, the federal deficit was $319 billion. At that time, 10-year treasury notes were paying 4.25% interest per annum. If the federal government financed this deficit through 10-year notes, how much would it have to pay back in 2015?
Source: U.S. Treasury Department

98. Logistic Growth The logistic growth model

$$P(t) = \frac{0.8}{1 + 1.67e^{-0.16t}}$$

represents the proportion of new cars with a global positioning system (GPS). Let $t = 0$ represent 2006, $t = 1$ represent 2007, and so on.

(a) What proportion of new cars in 2006 had a GPS?
(b) Determine the maximum proportion of new cars that have a GPS.
(c) Using a graphing utility, graph $P = P(t)$.
(d) When will 75% of new cars have a GPS?

99. CBL Experiment The following data were collected by placing a temperature probe in a portable heater, removing the probe, and then recording temperature over time.

Time (sec.)	Temperature (°F)
0	165.07
1	164.77
2	163.99
3	163.22
4	162.82
5	161.96
6	161.20
7	160.45
8	159.35
9	158.61
10	157.89
11	156.83
12	156.11
13	155.08
14	154.40
15	153.72

According to Newton's Law of Cooling, these data should follow an exponential model.

(a) Using a graphing utility, draw a scatter diagram for the data.
(b) Using a graphing utility, build an exponential model from the data.
(c) Graph the exponential function found in part (b) on the scatter diagram.
(d) Predict how long it will take for the probe to reach a temperature of 110°F.

100. Wind Chill Factor The following data represent the wind speed (mph) and wind chill factor at an air temperature of 15°F.

(a) Using a graphing utility, draw a scatter diagram with wind speed as the independent variable.
(b) Using a graphing utility, build a logarithmic model from the data.
(c) Using a graphing utility, draw the logarithmic function found in part (b) on the scatter diagram.

(d) Use the function found in part (b) to predict the wind chill factor if the air temperature is 15°F and the wind speed is 23 mph.

Wind Speed (mph)	Wind Chill Factor (°F)
5	7
10	3
15	0
20	−2
25	−4
30	−5
35	−7

Source: U.S. National Weather Service

101. Spreading of a Disease Jack and Diane live in a small town of 50 people. Unfortunately, both Jack and Diane have a cold. Those who come in contact with someone who has this cold will themselves catch the cold. The following data represent the number of people in the small town who have caught the cold after t days.

Days, t	Number of People with Cold, C
0	2
1	4
2	8
3	14
4	22
5	30
6	37
7	42
8	44

(a) Using a graphing utility, draw a scatter diagram of the data. Comment on the type of relation that appears to exist between the days and number of people with a cold.
(b) Using a graphing utility, build a logistic model from the data.
(c) Graph the function found in part (b) on the scatter diagram.
(d) According to the function found in part (b), what is the maximum number of people who will catch the cold? In reality, what is the maximum number of people who could catch the cold?
(e) Sometime between the second and third day, 10 people in the town had a cold. According to the model found in part (b), when did 10 people have a cold?
(f) How long will it take for 46 people to catch the cold?

CHAPTER TEST

The Chapter Test Prep Videos are step-by-step test solutions available in the Video Resources DVD, in MyMathLab, or on this text's You Tube Channel. Flip back to the Student Resources page to see the exact web address for this text's YouTube channel.

1. Given $f(x) = \dfrac{x + 2}{x - 2}$ and $g(x) = 2x + 5$, find:

   (a) $f \circ g$ and state its domain
   (b) $(g \circ f)(-2)$
   (c) $(f \circ g)(-2)$

2. Determine whether the function is one-to-one.
   (a) $y = 4x^2 + 3$
   (b) $y = \sqrt{x + 3} - 5$

3. Find the inverse of $f(x) = \dfrac{2}{3x - 5}$ and check your answer. State the domain and the range of f and f^{-1}.

4. If the point $(3, -5)$ is on the graph of a one-to-one function f, what point must be on the graph of f^{-1}?

In Problems 5–7, solve each equation.

5. $3^x = 243$ 6. $\log_b 16 = 2$

7. $\log_5 x = 4$

In Problems 8–11, use a calculator to evaluate each expression. Round your answer to three decimal places.

8. $e^3 + 2$ 9. $\log 20$

10. $\log_3 21$ 11. $\ln 133$

In Problems 12 and 13, use the given function f to:
   (a) Find the domain of f.
   (b) Graph f.
   (c) From the graph, determine the range and any asymptotes of f.
   (d) Find f^{-1}, the inverse of f.
   (e) Find the domain and the range of f^{-1}.
   (f) Graph f^{-1}.

12. $f(x) = 4^{x+1} - 2$

13. $f(x) = 1 - \log_5(x - 2)$

In Problems 14–19, solve each equation.

14. $5^{x+2} = 125$ 15. $\log(x + 9) = 2$

16. $8 - 2e^{-x} = 4$ 17. $\log(x^2 + 3) = \log(x + 6)$

18. $7^{x+3} = e^x$ 19. $\log_2(x - 4) + \log_2(x + 4) = 3$

20. Write $\log_2\left(\dfrac{4x^3}{x^2 - 3x - 18}\right)$ as the sum and/or difference of logarithms. Express powers as factors.

21. A 50-mg sample of a radioactive substance decays to 34 mg after 30 days. How long will it take for there to be 2 mg remaining?

22. (a) If $1000 is invested at 5% compounded monthly, how much is there after 8 months?
    (b) If you want to have $1000 in 9 months, how much do you need to place in a savings account now that pays 5% compounded quarterly?
    (c) How long does it take to double your money if you can invest it at 6% compounded annually?

23. The decibel level, D, of sound is given by the equation $D = 10 \log\left(\dfrac{I}{I_0}\right)$, where I is the intensity of the sound and $I_0 = 10^{-12}$ watt per square meter.
    (a) If the shout of a single person measures 80 decibels, how loud will the sound be if two people shout at the same time? That is, how loud would the sound be if the intensity doubled?
    (b) The pain threshold for sound is 125 decibels. If the Athens Olympic Stadium 2004 (Olympiako Stadio Athinas 'Spyros Louis') can seat 74,400 people, how many people in the crowd need to shout at the same time for the resulting sound level to meet or exceed the pain threshold? (Ignore any possible sound dampening.)

CUMULATIVE REVIEW

1. Is the following graph the graph of a function? If it is, is the function one-to-one?

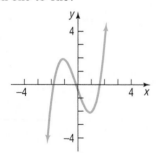

2. For the function $f(x) = 2x^2 - 3x + 1$, find the following:
   (a) $f(3)$ (b) $f(-x)$ (c) $f(x + h)$

3. Determine which of the following points are on the graph of $x^2 + y^2 = 1$.

   (a) $\left(\dfrac{1}{2}, \dfrac{1}{2}\right)$ (b) $\left(\dfrac{1}{2}, \dfrac{\sqrt{3}}{2}\right)$

4. Solve the equation $3(x - 2) = 4(x + 5)$.

5. Graph the line $2x - 4y = 16$.

6. (a) Graph the quadratic function $f(x) = -x^2 + 2x - 3$ by determining whether its graph opens up or down and by finding its vertex, axis of symmetry, y-intercept, and x-intercept(s), if any.
   (b) Solve $f(x) \le 0$.

7. Determine the quadratic function whose graph is given in the figure.

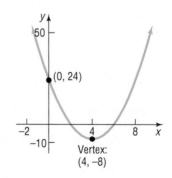

8. Graph $f(x) = 3(x + 1)^3 - 2$ using transformations.

9. Given that $f(x) = x^2 + 2$ and $g(x) = \dfrac{2}{x - 3}$, find $f(g(x))$ and state its domain. What is $f(g(5))$?

10. For the polynomial function $f(x) = 4x^3 + 9x^2 - 30x - 8$:
    (a) Find the real zeros of f.
    (b) Determine the intercepts of the graph of f.
    (c) Use a graphing utility to approximate the local maxima and local minima.
    (d) Draw a complete graph of f. Be sure to label the intercepts and turning points.

11. For the function $g(x) = 3^x + 2$:
    (a) Graph g using transformations. State the domain, range, and horizontal asymptote of g.
    (b) Determine the inverse of g. State the domain, range, and vertical asymptote of g^{-1}.
    (c) On the same graph as g, graph g^{-1}.

12. Solve the equation $4^{x-3} = 8^{2x}$.

13. Solve the equation: $\log_3(x + 1) + \log_3(2x - 3) = \log_9 9$

14. Suppose that $f(x) = \log_3(x + 2)$. Solve:
    (a) $f(x) = 0$ (b) $f(x) > 0$
    (c) $f(x) = 3$

15. **Data Analysis** The following data represent the percent of all drivers by age that have been stopped by the police for any reason within the past year. The median age represents the midpoint of the upper and lower limit for the age range.

Age Range	Median Age, x	Percentage Stopped, y
16–19	17.5	18.2
20–29	24.5	16.8
30–39	34.5	11.3
40–49	44.5	9.4
50–59	54.5	7.7
≥60	69.5	3.8

(a) Using your graphing utility, draw a scatter diagram of the data treating median age, x, as the independent variable.
(b) Determine a model that you feel best describes the relation between median age and percentage stopped. You may choose from among linear, quadratic, cubic, exponential, logarithmic, or logistic models.
(c) Provide a justification for the model that you selected in part (b).

CHAPTER PROJECTS

Internet-based Project

I. **Depreciation of Cars** Kelley Blue Book is an official guide that provides the current retail price of cars. You can access the Kelley Blue Book at your library or online at *www.kbb.com*.

1. Identify three cars that you are considering purchasing and find the Kelley Blue Book value of the cars for 0 (brand new), 1, 2, 3, 4, and 5 years of age. Online, the value of the car can be found by selecting Used Cars, then Used Car Values. Enter the year, make, and model of the car you are selecting. To be consistent, we will

assume the cars will be driven 12,000 miles per year, so a 1-year-old car will have 12,000 miles, a 2-year-old car will have 24,000 miles, and so on. Choose the same options for each year, and finally determine the suggested retail price for cars that are in Excellent, Good, and Fair shape. So, you should have a total of 16 observations (one for a brand new car, 3 for a 1-year-old car, 3 for a 2-year-old car, and so on).

2. Draw a scatter diagram of the data with age as the independent variable and value as the dependent variable using Excel, a TI-graphing calculator, or some other spreadsheet. The Chapter 3 project describes how to draw a scatter diagram in Excel.

3. Determine the exponential function of best fit. Graph the exponential function of best fit on the scatter diagram. To do this in Excel, click on any data point in the scatter diagram. Now click the Layout menu, select Trendline within the Analysis region, select More Trendline Options. Select the Exponential radio button and select Display Equation on Chart. See Figure 54. Move the Trendline Options window off to the side and you will see the exponential function of best fit displayed on the scatter diagram. Do you think the function accurately describes the relation between age of the car and suggested retail price?

Figure 54

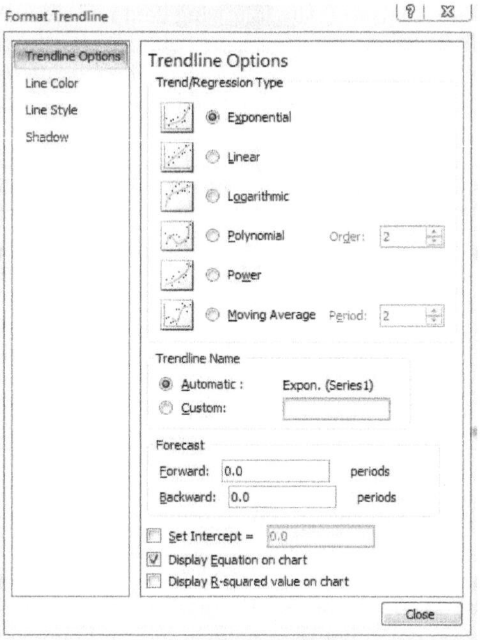

4. The exponential function of best fit is of the form $y = Ce^{rx}$ where y is the suggested retail value of the car and x is the age of the car (in years). What does the value of C represent? What does the value of r represent? What is the depreciation rate for each car that you are considering?

5. Write a report detailing which car you would purchase based on the depreciation rate you found for each car.

The following projects are available on the Instructor's Resource Center (IRC):

II. Hot Coffee A fast-food restaurant wants a special container to hold coffee. The restaurant wishes the container to quickly cool the coffee from 200° to 130°F and keep the liquid between 110° and 130°F as long as possible. The restaurant has three containers to select from. Which one should be purchased?

III. Project at Motorola *Thermal Fatigue of Solder Connections* Product reliability is a major concern of a manufacturer. Here a logarithmic transformation is used to simplify the analysis of a cell phone's ability to withstand temperature change.

Citation: Excel © 2010 Microsoft Corporation. Used with permission from Microsoft.

6

Trigonometric Functions

Outline

Length of Day Revisited

The length of a day depends upon the day of the year as well as the latitude of the location. Latitude gives the location of a point on Earth north or south of the equator. In Chapter 4, we found a model that describes the relation between the length of day and latitude for a specific day of the year. In the Internet Project at the end of this chapter, we will find a model that describes the relation between the length of day and day of the year for a specific latitude.

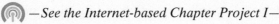 *—See the Internet-based Chapter Project I—*

◁ A Look Back In Chapter 2, we began our discussion of functions. We defined domain and range and independent and dependent variables; we found the value of a function and graphed functions. We continued our study of functions by listing properties that a function might have, like being even or odd, and we created a library of functions, naming key functions and listing their properties, including the graph.

A Look Ahead ▷ In this chapter we define the trigonometric functions, six functions that have wide application. We shall talk about their domain and range, see how to find values, graph them, and develop a list of their properties.

There are two widely accepted approaches to the development of the trigonometric functions: one uses right triangles; the other uses circles, especially the unit circle. In this book, we develop the trigonometric functions using the unit circle. In Chapter 8, we present right triangle trigonometry.

6.1 Angles and Their Measure

PREPARING FOR THIS SECTION *Before getting started, review the following:*

- Circumference and Area of a Circle (Appendix A, Section A.2, p. A16)

- Uniform Motion (Appendix A, Section A.8, pp. A65–A67)

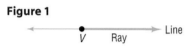 Now Work the 'Are You Prepared?' problems on page 359.

OBJECTIVES
1 Convert between Decimals and Degrees, Minutes, Seconds Measures for Angles (p. 352)
2 Find the Length of an Arc of a Circle (p. 354)
3 Convert from Degrees to Radians and from Radians to Degrees (p. 354)
4 Find the Area of a Sector of a Circle (p. 357)
5 Find the Linear Speed of an Object Traveling in Circular Motion (p. 358)

Figure 1

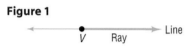
V Ray Line

A **ray,** or **half-line,** is that portion of a line that starts at a point V on the line and extends indefinitely in one direction. The starting point V of a ray is called its **vertex.** See Figure 1.

If two rays are drawn with a common vertex, they form an **angle.** We call one ray of an angle the **initial side** and the other the **terminal side.** The angle formed is identified by showing the direction and amount of rotation from the initial side to the terminal side. If the rotation is in the counterclockwise direction, the angle is **positive;** if the rotation is clockwise, the angle is **negative.** See Figure 2.

Figure 2

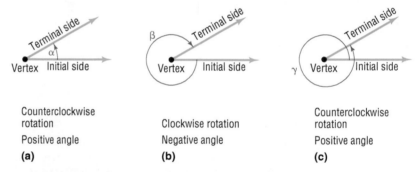

Counterclockwise rotation	Clockwise rotation	Counterclockwise rotation
Positive angle	Negative angle	Positive angle
(a)	**(b)**	**(c)**

Lowercase Greek letters, such as α (alpha), β (beta), γ (gamma), and θ (theta), will often be used to denote angles. Notice in Figure 2(a) that the angle α is positive because the direction of the rotation from the initial side to the terminal side is counterclockwise. The angle β in Figure 2(b) is negative because the rotation is clockwise. The angle γ in Figure 2(c) is positive. Notice that the angle α in Figure 2(a) and the angle γ in Figure 2(c) have the same initial side and the same terminal side. However, α and γ are unequal, because the amount of rotation required to go from the initial side to the terminal side is greater for angle γ than for angle α.

An angle θ is said to be in **standard position** if its vertex is at the origin of a rectangular coordinate system and its initial side coincides with the positive x-axis. See Figure 3.

Figure 3

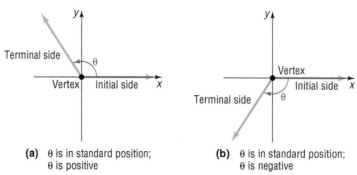

(a) θ is in standard position; θ is positive

(b) θ is in standard position; θ is negative

When an angle θ is in standard position, the terminal side will lie either in a quadrant, in which case we say that θ **lies in that quadrant,** or the terminal side will lie on the x-axis or the y-axis, in which case we say that θ is a **quadrantal angle.** For example, the angle θ in Figure 4(a) lies in quadrant II, the angle θ in Figure 4(b) lies in quadrant IV, and the angle θ in Figure 4(c) is a quadrantal angle.

Figure 4

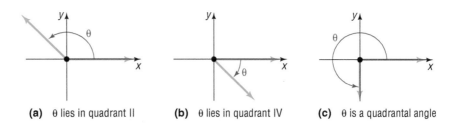

(a) θ lies in quadrant II   **(b)** θ lies in quadrant IV   **(c)** θ is a quadrantal angle

We measure angles by determining the amount of rotation needed for the initial side to become coincident with the terminal side. The two commonly used measures for angles are *degrees* and *radians*.

Degrees

HISTORICAL NOTE One counterclockwise rotation is 360° due to the Babylonian year, which had 360 days. ■

The angle formed by rotating the initial side exactly once in the counterclockwise direction until it coincides with itself (1 revolution) is said to measure 360 degrees, abbreviated 360°. **One degree, 1°,** is $\frac{1}{360}$ revolution. A **right angle** is an angle that measures 90°, or $\frac{1}{4}$ revolution; a **straight angle** is an angle that measures 180°, or $\frac{1}{2}$ revolution. See Figure 5. As Figure 5(b) shows, it is customary to indicate a right angle by using the symbol └.

Figure 5

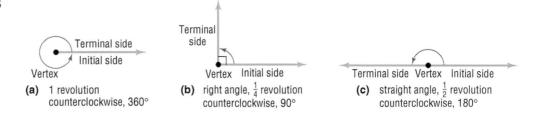

(a) 1 revolution counterclockwise, 360°   **(b)** right angle, $\frac{1}{4}$ revolution counterclockwise, 90°   **(c)** straight angle, $\frac{1}{2}$ revolution counterclockwise, 180°

It is also customary to refer to an angle that measures θ degrees as an angle *of* θ degrees.

EXAMPLE 1

Drawing an Angle

Draw each angle.

(a) 45°   (b) −90°   (c) 225°   (d) 405°

Solution   (a) An angle of 45° is $\frac{1}{2}$ of a right angle.   (b) An angle of −90° is $\frac{1}{4}$ revolution in
                See Figure 6.   the clockwise direction. See Figure 7.

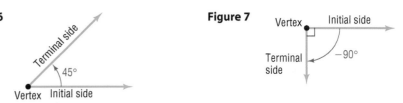

Figure 6

Figure 7

(c) An angle of 225° consists of a rotation through 180° followed by a rotation through 45°. See Figure 8.

(d) An angle of 405° consists of 1 revolution (360°) followed by a rotation through 45°. See Figure 9.

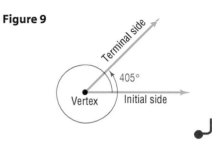

Figure 8

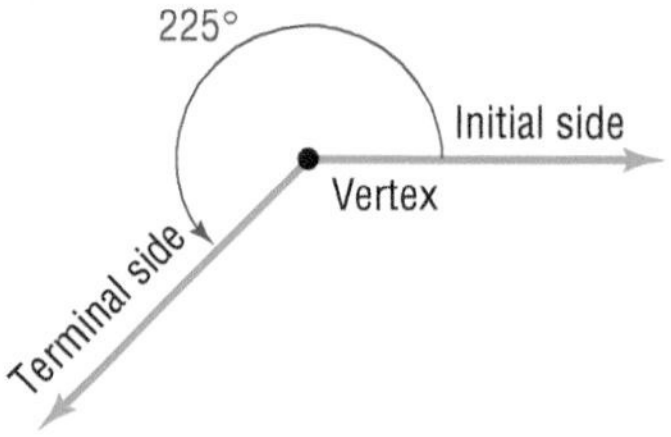

Figure 9

⬤▬▬▶ **Now Work** PROBLEM 11

1 Convert between Decimals and Degrees, Minutes, Seconds Measures for Angles

Although subdivisions of a degree may be obtained by using decimals, we also may use the notion of *minutes* and *seconds*. **One minute,** denoted by **1′**, is defined as $\frac{1}{60}$ degree. **One second,** denoted by **1″**, is defined as $\frac{1}{60}$ minute, or equivalently, $\frac{1}{3600}$ degree. An angle of, say, 30 degrees, 40 minutes, 10 seconds is written compactly as 30°40′10″. To summarize:

$$1 \text{ counterclockwise revolution} = 360°$$
$$1° = 60' \qquad 1' = 60'' \tag{1}$$

It is sometimes necessary to convert from the degree, minute, second notation (D°M′S″) to a decimal form, and vice versa. Check your calculator; it should be capable of doing the conversion for you.

Before using your calculator, though, you must set the mode to degrees because there are two common ways to measure angles: degree mode and radian mode. (We will define radians shortly.) Usually, a menu is used to change from one mode to another. Check your owner's manual to find out how your particular calculator works.

To convert from the degree, minute, second notation (D°M′S″) to a decimal form, and vice versa, follow these examples:

$$15°30' = 15.5° \quad \text{because} \quad 30' = 30 \cdot 1' \underset{\uparrow}{=} 30 \cdot \left(\frac{1}{60}\right)° = 0.5°$$
$$1' = \left(\frac{1}{60}\right)°$$

$$32.25° = 32°15' \quad \text{because} \quad 0.25° = \left(\frac{1}{4}\right)° = \frac{1}{4} \cdot 1° \underset{\uparrow}{=} \frac{1}{4}(60') = 15'$$
$$1° = 60'$$

EXAMPLE 2   **Converting between Degrees, Minutes, Seconds, and Decimal Forms**

(a) Convert 50°6′21″ to a decimal in degrees. Round the answer to four decimal places.

(b) Convert 21.256° to the D°M′S″ form. Round the answer to the nearest second.

Solution   (a) Because $1' = \left(\dfrac{1}{60}\right)^\circ$ and $1'' = \left(\dfrac{1}{60}\right)' = \left(\dfrac{1}{60}\cdot\dfrac{1}{60}\right)^\circ$, we convert as follows:

$$50°6'21'' = 50° + 6' + 21''$$
$$= 50° + 6\cdot\left(\frac{1}{60}\right)^\circ + 21\cdot\left(\frac{1}{60}\cdot\frac{1}{60}\right)^\circ$$
$$\approx 50° + 0.1° + 0.0058°$$
$$= 50.1058°$$

(b) We proceed as follows:

$$21.256° = 21° + 0.256°$$

$\qquad\qquad = 21° + (0.256)(60')$ *Convert fraction of degree to minutes; $1° = 60'$.*

$\qquad\qquad = 21° + 15.36'$

$\qquad\qquad = 21° + 15' + 0.36'$

$\qquad\qquad = 21° + 15' + (0.36)(60'')$ *Convert fraction of minute to seconds; $1' = 60''$.*

$\qquad\qquad = 21° + 15' + 21.6''$

$\qquad\qquad \approx 21°15'22''$ *Round to the nearest second.*

Now Work PROBLEMS 23 AND 29

  In many applications, such as describing the exact location of a star or the precise position of a ship at sea, angles measured in degrees, minutes, and even seconds are used. For calculation purposes, these are transformed to decimal form. In other applications, especially those in calculus, angles are measured using *radians*.

Radians

A **central angle** is a positive angle whose vertex is at the center of a circle. The rays of a central angle subtend (intersect) an arc on the circle. If the radius of the circle is r and the length of the arc subtended by the central angle is also r, then the measure of the angle is **1 radian.** See Figure 10(a).

For a circle of radius 1, the rays of a central angle with measure 1 radian subtend an arc of length 1. For a circle of radius 3, the rays of a central angle with measure 1 radian subtend an arc of length 3. See Figure 10(b).

Figure 10

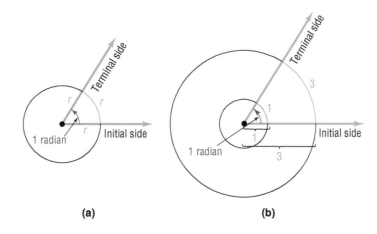

(a)   (b)

Figure 11

$$\frac{\theta}{\theta_1} = \frac{s}{s_1}$$

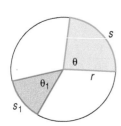

2 Find the Length of an Arc of a Circle

Now consider a circle of radius r and two central angles, θ and θ_1, measured in radians. Suppose that these central angles subtend arcs of lengths s and s_1, respectively, as shown in Figure 11. From geometry, we know that the ratio of the measures of the angles equals the ratio of the corresponding lengths of the arcs subtended by these angles; that is,

$$\frac{\theta}{\theta_1} = \frac{s}{s_1} \qquad (2)$$

Suppose that $\theta_1 = 1$ radian. Refer again to Figure 10(a). The length s_1 of the arc subtended by the central angle $\theta_1 = 1$ radian equals the radius r of the circle. Then $s_1 = r$, so equation (2) reduces to

$$\frac{\theta}{1} = \frac{s}{r} \quad \text{or} \quad s = r\theta \qquad (3)$$

THEOREM

Arc Length

For a circle of radius r, a central angle of θ radians subtends an arc whose length s is

$$s = r\theta \qquad (4)$$

NOTE Formulas must be consistent with regard to the units used. In equation (4), we write

$$s = r\theta$$

To see the units, however, we must go back to equation (3) and write

$$\frac{\theta \text{ radians}}{1 \text{ radian}} = \frac{s \text{ length units}}{r \text{ length units}}$$

$$s \text{ length units} = r \text{ length units} \frac{\theta \text{ radians}}{1 \text{ radian}}$$

Since the radians divide out, we are left with

$$s \text{ length units} = (r \text{ length units})\theta \quad s = r\theta$$

where θ appears to be "dimensionless" but, in fact, is measured in radians. So, in using the formula $s = r\theta$, the dimension for θ is radians, and any convenient unit of length (such as inches or meters) may be used for s and r. ∎

EXAMPLE 3

Finding the Length of an Arc of a Circle

Find the length of the arc of a circle of radius 2 meters subtended by a central angle of 0.25 radian.

Solution Use equation (4) with $r = 2$ meters and $\theta = 0.25$. The length s of the arc is

$$s = r\theta = 2(0.25) = 0.5 \text{ meter}$$

 **Now Work** PROBLEM 71

3 Convert from Degrees to Radians and from Radians to Degrees

Figure 12

1 revolution = 2π radians

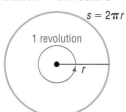

With two ways to measure angles, it is important to be able to convert from one to the other. Consider a circle of radius r. A central angle of 1 revolution will subtend an arc equal to the circumference of the circle (Figure 12). Because the circumference of a circle of radius r equals $2\pi r$, we substitute $2\pi r$ for s in equation (4) to find that, for an angle θ of 1 revolution,

$$s = r\theta$$

$$2\pi r = r\theta \qquad \theta = 1 \text{ revolution; } s = 2\pi r$$

$$\theta = 2\pi \text{ radians} \qquad \text{Solve for } \theta.$$

From this, we have

$$1 \text{ revolution} = 2\pi \text{ radians} \qquad \textbf{(5)}$$

Since 1 revolution = 360°, we have

$$360° = 2\pi \text{ radians}$$

Dividing both sides by 2 yields

$$180° = \pi \text{ radians} \qquad \textbf{(6)}$$

Divide both sides of equation (6) by 180. Then

$$1 \text{ degree} = \frac{\pi}{180} \text{ radian}$$

Divide both sides of (6) by π. Then

$$\frac{180}{\pi} \text{ degrees} = 1 \text{ radian}$$

We have the following two conversion formulas:*

$$1 \text{ degree} = \frac{\pi}{180} \text{ radian} \qquad 1 \text{ radian} = \frac{180}{\pi} \text{ degrees} \qquad \textbf{(7)}$$

EXAMPLE 4   **Converting from Degrees to Radians**

Convert each angle in degrees to radians.

(a) 60° (b) 150° (c) −45° (d) 90° (e) 107°

Solution (a) $60° = 60 \cdot 1 \text{ degree} = 60 \cdot \frac{\pi}{180} \text{ radian} = \frac{\pi}{3} \text{ radians}$

(b) $150° = 150 \cdot 1° = 150 \cdot \frac{\pi}{180} \text{ radian} = \frac{5\pi}{6} \text{ radians}$

(c) $-45° = -45 \cdot \frac{\pi}{180} \text{ radian} = -\frac{\pi}{4} \text{ radian}$

(d) $90° = 90 \cdot \frac{\pi}{180} \text{ radian} = \frac{\pi}{2} \text{ radians}$

(e) $107° = 107 \cdot \frac{\pi}{180} \text{ radian} \approx 1.868 \text{ radians}$

Example 4, parts (a)–(d), illustrates that angles that are "nice" fractions of a revolution are expressed in radian measure as fractional multiples of π, rather than as decimals. For example, a right angle, as in Example 4(d), is left in the form $\frac{\pi}{2}$ radians, which is exact, rather than using the approximation $\frac{\pi}{2} \approx \frac{3.1416}{2} = 1.5708$ radians. When the fractions are not "nice," we use the decimal approximation of the angle, as in Example 4(e).

➤**Now Work** PROBLEMS 35 AND 61

---

* Some students prefer instead to use the proportion $\dfrac{\text{Degree}}{180°} = \dfrac{\text{Radian}}{\pi}$. Then substitute for what is given and solve for the measurement sought.

EXAMPLE 5 | **Converting Radians to Degrees**

Convert each angle in radians to degrees.

(a) $\dfrac{\pi}{6}$ radian

(b) $\dfrac{3\pi}{2}$ radians

(c) $-\dfrac{3\pi}{4}$ radians

(d) $\dfrac{7\pi}{3}$ radians

(e) 3 radians

Solution

(a) $\dfrac{\pi}{6}$ radian $= \dfrac{\pi}{6} \cdot 1$ radian $= \dfrac{\pi}{6} \cdot \dfrac{180}{\pi}$ degrees $= 30°$

(b) $\dfrac{3\pi}{2}$ radians $= \dfrac{3\pi}{2} \cdot \dfrac{180}{\pi}$ degrees $= 270°$

(c) $-\dfrac{3\pi}{4}$ radians $= -\dfrac{3\pi}{4} \cdot \dfrac{180}{\pi}$ degrees $= -135°$

(d) $\dfrac{7\pi}{3}$ radians $= \dfrac{7\pi}{3} \cdot \dfrac{180}{\pi}$ degrees $= 420°$

(e) 3 radians $= 3 \cdot \dfrac{180}{\pi}$ degrees $\approx 171.89°$

-**Now Work** PROBLEM 47

Table 1 lists the degree and radian measures of some commonly encountered angles. You should learn to feel equally comfortable using degree or radian measure for these angles.

Table 1

Degrees	0°	30°	45°	60°	90°	120°	135°	150°	180°
Radians	0	$\dfrac{\pi}{6}$	$\dfrac{\pi}{4}$	$\dfrac{\pi}{3}$	$\dfrac{\pi}{2}$	$\dfrac{2\pi}{3}$	$\dfrac{3\pi}{4}$	$\dfrac{5\pi}{6}$	π
Degrees		210°	225°	240°	270°	300°	315°	330°	360°
Radians		$\dfrac{7\pi}{6}$	$\dfrac{5\pi}{4}$	$\dfrac{4\pi}{3}$	$\dfrac{3\pi}{2}$	$\dfrac{5\pi}{3}$	$\dfrac{7\pi}{4}$	$\dfrac{11\pi}{6}$	2π

EXAMPLE 6 | **Finding the Distance between Two Cities**

The latitude of a location L is the measure of the angle formed by a ray drawn from the center of Earth to the Equator and a ray drawn from the center of Earth to L. See Figure 13(a). Glasgow, Montana, is due north of Albuquerque, New Mexico. Find the distance between Glasgow (48°9′ north latitude) and Albuquerque (35°5′ north latitude). See Figure 13(b). Assume that the radius of Earth is 3960 miles.

Figure 13

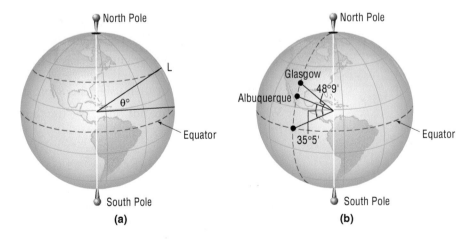

(a)   (b)

Solution The measure of the central angle between the two cities is $48°9' - 35°5' = 13°4'$. Use equation (4), $s = r\theta$. But remember we must first convert the angle of $13°4'$ to radians.

$$\theta = 13°4' \approx 13.0667° = 13.0667 \cdot \frac{\pi}{180} \text{ radian} \approx 0.228 \text{ radian}$$

$$\uparrow$$
$$4' = 4\left(\frac{1}{60}\right)°$$

Use $\theta = 0.228$ radian and $r = 3960$ miles in equation (4). The distance between the two cities is

$$s = r\theta = 3960 \cdot 0.228 \approx 903 \text{ miles}$$

When an angle is measured in degrees, the degree symbol will always be shown. However, when an angle is measured in radians, we will follow the usual practice and omit the word *radians*. So, if the measure of an angle is given as $\frac{\pi}{6}$, it is understood to mean $\frac{\pi}{6}$ radian.

COMMENT If the measure of an angle is given as 5, it is understood to mean 5 radians; if the measure of an angle is given as 5°, it means 5 degrees. ∎

Now Work PROBLEM 101

Figure 14

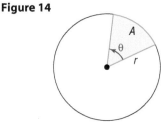

4 Find the Area of a Sector of a Circle

Consider a circle of radius r. Suppose that θ, measured in radians, is a central angle of this circle. See Figure 14. We seek a formula for the area A of the sector (shown in blue) formed by the angle θ.

Now consider a circle of radius r and two central angles θ and θ_1, both measured in radians. See Figure 15. From geometry, we know that the ratio of the measures of the angles equals the ratio of the corresponding areas of the sectors formed by these angles. That is,

$$\frac{\theta}{\theta_1} = \frac{A}{A_1}$$

Figure 15

$$\frac{\theta}{\theta_1} = \frac{A}{A_1}$$

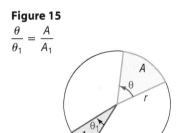

Suppose that $\theta_1 = 2\pi$ radians. Then $A_1 = $ area of the circle $= \pi r^2$. Solving for A, we find

$$A = A_1 \frac{\theta}{\theta_1} = \pi r^2 \frac{\theta}{2\pi} = \frac{1}{2} r^2 \theta$$

$$\uparrow$$
$$A_1 = \pi r^2$$
$$\theta_1 = 2\pi$$

THEOREM

Area of a Sector

The area A of the sector of a circle of radius r formed by a central angle of θ radians is

$$A = \frac{1}{2} r^2 \theta \qquad\qquad (8)$$

EXAMPLE 7

Finding the Area of a Sector of a Circle

Find the area of the sector of a circle of radius 2 feet formed by an angle of $30°$. Round the answer to two decimal places.

Solution Use equation (8) with $r = 2$ feet and $\theta = 30° = \frac{\pi}{6}$ radian. [Remember, in equation (8), θ must be in radians.]

$$A = \frac{1}{2} r^2 \theta = \frac{1}{2}(2)^2 \frac{\pi}{6} = \frac{\pi}{3} \approx 1.05$$

The area A of the sector is 1.05 square feet, rounded to two decimal places.

Now Work PROBLEM 79

5 Find the Linear Speed of an Object Traveling in Circular Motion

Earlier we defined the average speed of an object as the distance traveled divided by the elapsed time. For motion along a circle, we distinguish between **linear speed** and **angular speed.**

DEFINITION

Figure 16
$$v = \frac{s}{t}$$

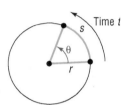

Suppose that an object moves around a circle of radius r at a constant speed. If s is the distance traveled in time t around this circle, then the **linear speed** v of the object is defined as

$$v = \frac{s}{t} \tag{9}$$

As this object travels around the circle, suppose that θ (measured in radians) is the central angle swept out in time t. See Figure 16.

DEFINITION

The **angular speed** ω (the Greek letter omega) of this object is the angle θ (measured in radians) swept out, divided by the elapsed time t; that is,

$$\omega = \frac{\theta}{t} \tag{10}$$

Angular speed is the way the turning rate of an engine is described. For example, an engine idling at 900 rpm (revolutions per minute) is one that rotates at an angular speed of

$$900 \frac{\text{revolutions}}{\text{minute}} = 900 \frac{\text{revolutions}}{\text{minute}} \cdot 2\pi \frac{\text{radians}}{\text{revolution}} = 1800\pi \frac{\text{radians}}{\text{minute}}$$

There is an important relationship between linear speed and angular speed:

$$\text{linear speed} = v = \frac{s}{t} = \frac{r\theta}{t} = r\left(\frac{\theta}{t}\right) = r \cdot \omega$$

$$\underset{(9)}{\uparrow} \quad \underset{s \,=\, r\theta}{\uparrow} \quad \underset{(10)}{\uparrow}$$

$$v = r\omega \tag{11}$$

where ω is measured in radians per unit time.

When using equation (11), remember that $v = \frac{s}{t}$ (the linear speed) has the dimensions of length per unit of time (such as feet per second or miles per hour), r (the radius of the circular motion) has the same length dimension as s, and ω (the angular speed) has the dimensions of radians per unit of time. If the angular speed is given in terms of *revolutions* per unit of time (as is often the case), be sure to convert it to *radians* per unit of time using the fact that 1 revolution $= 2\pi$ radians before attempting to use equation (11).

EXAMPLE 8

Finding Linear Speed

A child is spinning a rock at the end of a 2-foot rope at the rate of 180 revolutions per minute (rpm). Find the linear speed of the rock when it is released.

Solution

Look at Figure 17. The rock is moving around a circle of radius $r = 2$ feet. The angular speed ω of the rock is

$$\omega = 180 \frac{\text{revolutions}}{\text{minute}} = 180 \frac{\text{revolutions}}{\text{minute}} \cdot 2\pi \frac{\text{radians}}{\text{revolution}} = 360\pi \frac{\text{radians}}{\text{minute}}$$

Figure 17

From equation (11), the linear speed v of the rock is

$$v = r\omega = 2 \text{ feet} \cdot 360\pi \frac{\text{radians}}{\text{minute}} = 720\pi \frac{\text{feet}}{\text{minute}} \approx 2262 \frac{\text{feet}}{\text{minute}}$$

The linear speed of the rock when it is released is 2262 ft/min $\approx$ 25.7 mi/hr.

Now Work PROBLEM 97

Historical Feature

Trigonometry was developed by Greek astronomers, who regarded the sky as the inside of a sphere, so it was natural that triangles on a sphere were investigated early (by Menelaus of Alexandria about AD 100) and that triangles in the plane were studied much later. The first book containing a systematic treatment of plane and spherical trigonometry was written by the Persian astronomer Nasir Eddin (about AD 1250).

Regiomontanus (1436–1476) is the person most responsible for moving trigonometry from astronomy into mathematics. His work was improved by Copernicus (1473–1543) and Copernicus's student

Rhaeticus (1514–1576). Rhaeticus's book was the first to define the six trigonometric functions as ratios of sides of triangles, although he did not give the functions their present names. Credit for this is due to Thomas Finck (1583), but Finck's notation was by no means universally accepted at the time. The notation was finally stabilized by the textbooks of Leonhard Euler (1707–1783).

Trigonometry has since evolved from its use by surveyors, navigators, and engineers to present applications involving ocean tides, the rise and fall of food supplies in certain ecologies, brain wave patterns, and many other phenomena.

6.1 Assess Your Understanding

'Are You Prepared?' *Answers are given at the end of these exercises. If you get a wrong answer, read the pages listed in* red.

1. What is the formula for the circumference C of a circle of radius r? What is the formula for the area A of a circle of radius r? (p. A16)

2. If a particle has a speed of r feet per second and travels a distance d (in feet) in time t (in seconds), then $d = $ _____. (pp. A65–A67)

Concepts and Vocabulary

3. An angle θ is in _____ _____ if its vertex is at the origin of a rectangular coordinate system and its initial side coincides with the positive x-axis.

4. A _____ _____ is a positive angle whose vertex is at the center of a circle.

5. If the radius of a circle is r and the length of the arc subtended by a central angle is also r, then the measure of the angle is 1 _____.

6. On a circle of radius r, a central angle of θ radians subtends an arc of length $s = $ ____; the area of the sector formed by this angle θ is $A = $ _____.

7. $180° = $ ____ radians

8. An object travels around a circle of radius r with constant speed. If s is the distance traveled in time t around the circle and θ is the central angle (in radians) swept out in time t, then the linear speed of the object is $v = $ ____ and the angular speed of the object is $\omega = $ ____.

9. *True or False* The angular speed ω of an object traveling around a circle of radius r is the angle θ (measured in radians) swept out, divided by the elapsed time t.

10. *True or False* For circular motion on a circle of radius r, linear speed equals angular speed divided by r.

Skill Building

In Problems 11–22, draw each angle.

11. $30°$

12. $60°$

13. $135°$

14. $-120°$

15. $450°$

16. $540°$

17. $\dfrac{3\pi}{4}$

18. $\dfrac{4\pi}{3}$

19. $-\dfrac{\pi}{6}$

20. $-\dfrac{2\pi}{3}$

21. $\dfrac{16\pi}{3}$

22. $\dfrac{21\pi}{4}$

In Problems 23–28, convert each angle to a decimal in degrees. Round your answer to two decimal places.

23. $40°10'25''$

24. $61°42'21''$

25. $1°2'3''$

26. $73°40'40''$

27. $9°9'9''$

28. $98°22'45''$

In Problems 29–34, convert each angle to D°M'S" form. Round your answer to the nearest second.

29. 40.32° **30.** 61.24° **31.** 18.255° **32.** 29.411° **33.** 19.99° **34.** 44.01°

In Problems 35–46, convert each angle in degrees to radians. Express your answer as a multiple of π.

35. 30° **36.** 120° **37.** 240° **38.** 330° **39.** −60° **40.** −30°

41. 180° **42.** 270° **43.** −135° **44.** −225° **45.** −90° **46.** −180°

In Problems 47–58, convert each angle in radians to degrees.

47. $\dfrac{\pi}{3}$ **48.** $\dfrac{5\pi}{6}$ **49.** $-\dfrac{5\pi}{4}$ **50.** $-\dfrac{2\pi}{3}$ **51.** $\dfrac{\pi}{2}$ **52.** 4π

53. $\dfrac{\pi}{12}$ **54.** $\dfrac{5\pi}{12}$ **55.** $-\dfrac{\pi}{2}$ **56.** $-\pi$ **57.** $-\dfrac{\pi}{6}$ **58.** $-\dfrac{3\pi}{4}$

In Problems 59–64, convert each angle in degrees to radians. Express your answer in decimal form, rounded to two decimal places.

59. 17° **60.** 73° **61.** −40° **62.** −51° **63.** 125° **64.** 350°

In Problems 65–70, convert each angle in radians to degrees. Express your answer in decimal form, rounded to two decimal places.

65. 3.14 **66.** 0.75 **67.** 2 **68.** 3 **69.** 6.32 **70.** $\sqrt{2}$

In Problems 71–78, s denotes the length of the arc of a circle of radius r subtended by the central angle θ. Find the missing quantity. Round answers to three decimal places.

71. $r = 10$ meters, $\theta = \dfrac{1}{2}$ radian, $s = ?$

72. $r = 6$ feet, $\theta = 2$ radians, $s = ?$

73. $\theta = \dfrac{1}{3}$ radian, $s = 2$ feet, $r = ?$

74. $\theta = \dfrac{1}{4}$ radian, $s = 6$ centimeters, $r = ?$

75. $r = 5$ miles, $s = 3$ miles, $\theta = ?$

76. $r = 6$ meters, $s = 8$ meters, $\theta = ?$

77. $r = 2$ inches, $\theta = 30°$, $s = ?$

78. $r = 3$ meters, $\theta = 120°$, $s = ?$

In Problems 79–86, A denotes the area of the sector of a circle of radius r formed by the central angle θ. Find the missing quantity. Round answers to three decimal places.

79. $r = 10$ meters, $\theta = \dfrac{1}{2}$ radian, $A = ?$

80. $r = 6$ feet, $\theta = 2$ radians, $A = ?$

81. $\theta = \dfrac{1}{3}$ radian, $A = 2$ square feet, $r = ?$

82. $\theta = \dfrac{1}{4}$ radian, $A = 6$ square centimeters, $r = ?$

83. $r = 5$ miles, $A = 3$ square miles, $\theta = ?$

84. $r = 6$ meters, $A = 8$ square meters, $\theta = ?$

85. $r = 2$ inches, $\theta = 30°$, $A = ?$

86. $r = 3$ meters, $\theta = 120°$, $A = ?$

In Problems 87–90, find the length s and area A. Round answers to three decimal places.

87.

88.

89.

90.

Applications and Extensions

91. Movement of a Minute Hand The minute hand of a clock is 6 inches long. How far does the tip of the minute hand move in 15 minutes? How far does it move in 25 minutes? Round answers to two decimal places.

92. Movement of a Pendulum A pendulum swings through an angle of 20° each second. If the pendulum is 40 inches long, how far does its tip move each second? Round answers to two decimal places.

93. Area of a Sector Find the area of the sector of a circle of radius 4 meters formed by an angle of 45°. Round the answer to two decimal places.

94. Area of a Sector Find the area of the sector of a circle of radius 3 centimeters formed by an angle of 60°. Round the answer to two decimal places.

95. Watering a Lawn A water sprinkler sprays water over a distance of 30 feet while rotating through an angle of 135°. What area of lawn receives water?

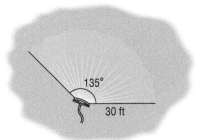

96. Designing a Water Sprinkler An engineer is asked to design a water sprinkler that will cover a field of 100 square yards that is in the shape of a sector of a circle of radius 15 yards. Through what angle should the sprinkler rotate?

97. Motion on a Circle An object is traveling around a circle with a radius of 5 centimeters. If in 20 seconds a central angle of $\frac{1}{3}$ radian is swept out, what is the angular speed of the object? What is its linear speed?

98. Motion on a Circle An object is traveling around a circle with a radius of 2 meters. If in 20 seconds the object travels 5 meters, what is its angular speed? What is its linear speed?

99. Bicycle Wheels The diameter of each wheel of a bicycle is 26 inches. If you are traveling at a speed of 35 miles per hour on this bicycle, through how many revolutions per minute are the wheels turning?

100. Car Wheels The radius of each wheel of a car is 15 inches. If the wheels are turning at the rate of 3 revolutions per second, how fast is the car moving? Express your answer in inches per second and in miles per hour.

In Problems 101–104, the latitude of a location L is the angle formed by a ray drawn from the center of Earth to the Equator and a ray drawn from the center of Earth to L. See the figure.

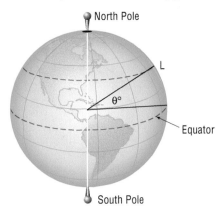

101. Distance between Cities Memphis, Tennessee, is due north of New Orleans, Louisiana. Find the distance between Memphis (35°9′ north latitude) and New Orleans (29°57′ north latitude). Assume that the radius of Earth is 3960 miles.

102. Distance between Cities Charleston, West Virginia, is due north of Jacksonville, Florida. Find the distance between Charleston (38°21′ north latitude) and Jacksonville (30°20′ north latitude). Assume that the radius of Earth is 3960 miles.

103. Linear Speed on Earth Earth rotates on an axis through its poles. The distance from the axis to a location on Earth 30° north latitude is about 3429.5 miles. Therefore, a location on Earth at 30° north latitude is spinning on a circle of radius 3429.5 miles. Compute the linear speed on the surface of Earth at 30° north latitude.

104. Linear Speed on Earth Earth rotates on an axis through its poles. The distance from the axis to a location on Earth 40° north latitude is about 3033.5 miles. Therefore, a location on Earth at 40° north latitude is spinning on a circle of radius 3033.5 miles. Compute the linear speed on the surface of Earth at 40° north latitude.

105. Speed of the Moon The mean distance of the moon from Earth is 2.39×10^5 miles. Assuming that the orbit of the moon around Earth is circular and that 1 revolution takes 27.3 days, find the linear speed of the moon. Express your answer in miles per hour.

106. Speed of Earth The mean distance of Earth from the Sun is 9.29×10^7 miles. Assuming that the orbit of Earth around the Sun is circular and that 1 revolution takes 365 days, find the linear speed of Earth. Express your answer in miles per hour.

107. Pulleys Two pulleys, one with radius 2 inches and the other with radius 8 inches, are connected by a belt. (See the figure.) If the 2-inch pulley is caused to rotate at 3 revolutions per minute, determine the revolutions per minute of the 8-inch pulley.

[**Hint:** The linear speeds of the pulleys are the same; both equal the speed of the belt.]

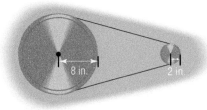

108. Ferris Wheels A neighborhood carnival has a Ferris wheel whose radius is 30 feet. You measure the time it takes for one revolution to be 70 seconds. What is the linear speed (in feet per second) of this Ferris wheel? What is the angular speed in radians per second?

109. Computing the Speed of a River Current To approximate the speed of the current of a river, a circular paddle wheel with radius 4 feet is lowered into the water. If the current causes the wheel to rotate at a speed of 10 revolutions per minute, what is the speed of the current? Express your answer in miles per hour.

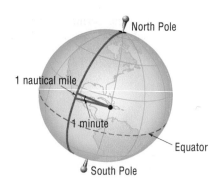

110. Spin Balancing Tires A spin balancer rotates the wheel of a car at 480 revolutions per minute. If the diameter of the wheel is 26 inches, what road speed is being tested? Express your answer in miles per hour. At how many revolutions per minute should the balancer be set to test a road speed of 80 miles per hour?

111. The Cable Cars of San Francisco At the Cable Car Museum you can see the four cable lines that are used to pull cable cars up and down the hills of San Francisco. Each cable travels at a speed of 9.55 miles per hour, caused by a rotating wheel whose diameter is 8.5 feet. How fast is the wheel rotating? Express your answer in revolutions per minute.

112. Difference in Time of Sunrise Naples, Florida, is approximately 90 miles due west of Ft. Lauderdale. How much sooner would a person in Ft. Lauderdale first see the rising Sun than a person in Naples? See the hint.

[**Hint:** Consult the figure. When a person at Q sees the first rays of the Sun, a person at P is still in the dark. The person at P sees the first rays after Earth has rotated so that P is at the location Q. Now use the fact that at the latitude of Ft. Lauderdale in 24 hours an arc of length $2\pi(3559)$ miles is subtended.]

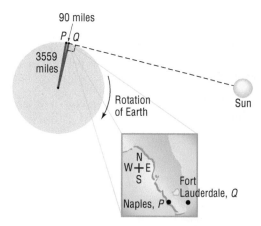

113. Keeping Up with the Sun How fast would you have to travel on the surface of Earth at the equator to keep up with the Sun (that is, so that the Sun would appear to remain in the same position in the sky)?

114. Nautical Miles A **nautical mile** equals the length of arc subtended by a central angle of 1 minute on a great circle[†] on the surface of Earth. See the figure. If the radius of Earth is taken as 3960 miles, express 1 nautical mile in terms of ordinary, or **statute**, miles.

[†] Any circle drawn on the surface of Earth that divides Earth into two equal hemispheres.

115. Approximating the Circumference of Earth Eratosthenes of Cyrene (276–195 BC) was a Greek scholar who lived and worked in Cyrene and Alexandria. One day while visiting in Syene he noticed that the Sun's rays shone directly down a well. On this date 1 year later, in Alexandria, which is 500 miles due north of Syene he measured the angle of the Sun to be about 7.2 degrees. See the figure. Use this information to approximate the radius and circumference of Earth.

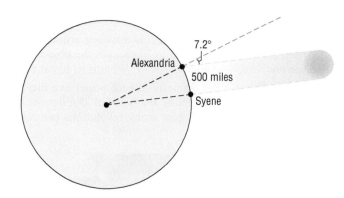

116. Designing a Little League Field For a 60-foot Little League Baseball field, the distance from home base to the nearest fence (or other obstruction) in fair territory should be a minimum of 200 feet. The commissioner of parks and recreation is making plans for a new 60-foot field. Because of limited ground availability, he will use the minimum required distance to the outfield fence. To increase safety, however, he plans to include a 10-foot-wide warning track on the inside of the fence. To further increase safety, the fence and warning track will extend both directions into foul territory. In total, the arc formed by the outfield fence (including the extensions into the foul territories) will be subtended by a central angle at home plate measuring 96°, as illustrated.
(a) Determine the length of the outfield fence.
(b) Determine the area of the warning track.

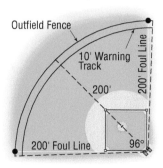

Source: www.littleleague.org

[**Note:** There is a 90° angle between the two foul lines. Then there are two 3° angles between the foul lines and the dotted lines shown. The angle between the two dotted lines outside the 200-foot foul lines is 96°.]

117. Pulleys Two pulleys, one with radius r_1 and the other with radius r_2, are connected by a belt. The pulley with radius r_1 rotates at ω_1 revolutions per minute, whereas the pulley with radius r_2 rotates at ω_2 revolutions per minute. Show that

$$\frac{r_1}{r_2} = \frac{\omega_2}{\omega_1}.$$

Explaining Concepts: Discussion and Writing

118. Do you prefer to measure angles using degrees or radians? Provide justification and a rationale for your choice.

119. What is 1 radian? What is 1 degree?

120. Which angle has the larger measure: 1 degree or 1 radian? Or are they equal?

121. Explain the difference between linear speed and angular speed.

122. For a circle of radius r, a central angle of θ degrees subtends an arc whose length s is $s = \dfrac{\pi}{180}r\theta$. Discuss whether this is a true or false statement. Give reasons to defend your position.

123. Discuss why ships and airplanes use nautical miles to measure distance. Explain the difference between a nautical mile and a statute mile.

124. Investigate the way that speed bicycles work. In particular, explain the differences and similarities between 5-speed and 9-speed derailleurs. Be sure to include a discussion of linear speed and angular speed.

125. In Example 6, we found that the distance between Albuquerque, New Mexico, and Glasgow, Montana, is approximately 903 miles. According to *mapquest.com*, the distance is approximately 1300 miles. What might account for the difference?

'Are You Prepared?' Answers

1. $C = 2\pi r; A = \pi r^2$ **2.** $r \cdot t$

6.2 Trigonometric Functions: Unit Circle Approach

PREPARING FOR THIS SECTION *Before getting started, review the following:*

- Geometry Essentials (Appendix A, Section A.2, pp. A14–A19)
- Unit Circle (Section 1.4, p. 35)
- Symmetry (Section 1.2, pp. 12–14)
- Functions (Section 2.1, pp. 46–56)

Now Work the 'Are You Prepared?' problems on page 375.

OBJECTIVES
1 Find the Exact Values of the Trigonometric Functions Using a Point on the Unit Circle (p. 365)
2 Find the Exact Values of the Trigonometric Functions of Quadrantal Angles (p. 366)
3 Find the Exact Values of the Trigonometric Functions of $\dfrac{\pi}{4} = 45°$ (p. 368)
4 Find the Exact Values of the Trigonometric Functions of $\dfrac{\pi}{6} = 30°$ and $\dfrac{\pi}{3} = 60°$ (p. 369)
5 Find the Exact Values of the Trigonometric Functions for Integer Multiples of $\dfrac{\pi}{6} = 30°, \dfrac{\pi}{4} = 45°,$ and $\dfrac{\pi}{3} = 60°$ (p. 372)
6 Use a Calculator to Approximate the Value of a Trigonometric Function (p. 373)
7 Use a Circle of Radius r to Evaluate the Trigonometric Functions (p. 374)

We now introduce the trigonometric functions using the unit circle.

The Unit Circle

Recall that the unit circle is a circle whose radius is 1 and whose center is at the origin of a rectangular coordinate system. Also recall that any circle of radius r has circumference of length $2\pi r$. Therefore, the unit circle (radius $= 1$) has a circumference of length 2π. In other words, for 1 revolution around the unit circle the length of the arc is 2π units.

The following discussion sets the stage for defining the trigonometric functions using the unit circle.

Let t be any real number. We position the t-axis so that it is vertical with the positive direction up. We place this t-axis in the xy-plane so that $t = 0$ is located at the point $(1, 0)$ in the xy-plane.

If $t \geq 0$, let s be the distance from the origin to t on the t-axis. See the red portion of Figure 18(a).

Now look at the unit circle in Figure 18(a). Beginning at the point $(1, 0)$ on the unit circle, travel $s = t$ units in the counterclockwise direction along the circle, to arrive at the point $P = (x, y)$. In this sense, the length $s = t$ units is being **wrapped** around the unit circle.

If $t < 0$, we begin at the point $(1, 0)$ on the unit circle and travel $s = |t|$ units in the clockwise direction to arrive at the point $P = (x, y)$. See Figure 18(b).

Figure 18

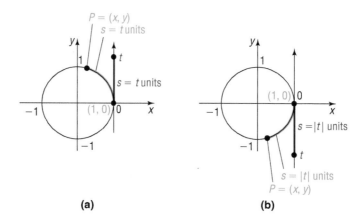

(a)   (b)

If $t > 2\pi$ or if $t < -2\pi$, it will be necessary to travel around the unit circle more than once before arriving at the point P. Do you see why?

Let's describe this process another way. Picture a string of length $s = |t|$ units being wrapped around a circle of radius 1 unit. We start wrapping the string around the circle at the point $(1, 0)$. If $t \geq 0$, we wrap the string in the counterclockwise direction; if $t < 0$, we wrap the string in the clockwise direction. The point $P = (x, y)$ is the point where the string ends.

This discussion tells us that, for any real number t, we can locate a unique point $P = (x, y)$ on the unit circle. We call P **the point on the unit circle that corresponds to t.** This is the important idea here. No matter what real number t is chosen, there is a unique point P on the unit circle corresponding to it. We use the coordinates of the point $P = (x, y)$ on the unit circle corresponding to the real number t to define the **six trigonometric functions of t.**

DEFINITION

Let t be a real number and let $P = (x, y)$ be the point on the unit circle that corresponds to t.

The **sine function** associates with t the y-coordinate of P and is denoted by

$$\sin t = y$$

The **cosine function** associates with t the x-coordinate of P and is denoted by

$$\cos t = x$$

In Words

The sine function takes as input a
real number *t* that corresponds
to a point $P = (x, y)$ on the unit
circle and outputs the *y*-coordinate.
The cosine function takes as input
a real number *t* that corresponds
to a point $P = (x, y)$ on the
unit circle and outputs the
x-coordinate.

If $x \neq 0$, the **tangent function** associates with *t* the ratio of the *y*-coordinate to the *x*-coordinate of *P* and is denoted by

$$\tan t = \frac{y}{x}$$

If $y \neq 0$, the **cosecant function** is defined as

$$\csc t = \frac{1}{y}$$

If $x \neq 0$, the **secant function** is defined as

$$\sec t = \frac{1}{x}$$

If $y \neq 0$, the **cotangent function** is defined as

$$\cot t = \frac{x}{y}$$

Notice in these definitions that if $x = 0$, that is, if the point *P* is on the *y*-axis, then the tangent function and the secant function are undefined. Also, if $y = 0$, that is, if the point *P* is on the *x*-axis, then the cosecant function and the cotangent function are undefined.

Because we use the unit circle in these definitions of the trigonometric functions, they are sometimes referred to as **circular functions.**

1 Find the Exact Values of the Trigonometric Functions Using a Point on the Unit Circle

---

EXAMPLE 1

Finding the Values of the Six Trigonometric Functions Using a Point on the Unit Circle

Let *t* be a real number and let $P = \left(-\frac{1}{2}, \frac{\sqrt{3}}{2} \right)$ be the point on the unit circle that corresponds to *t*. Find the values of $\sin t$, $\cos t$, $\tan t$, $\csc t$, $\sec t$, and $\cot t$.

Figure 19

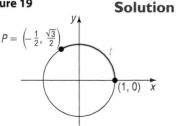

$P = \left(-\frac{1}{2}, \frac{\sqrt{3}}{2} \right)$

Solution

See Figure 19. We follow the definition of the six trigonometric functions, using $P = \left(-\frac{1}{2}, \frac{\sqrt{3}}{2} \right) = (x, y)$. Then, with $x = -\frac{1}{2}$ and $y = \frac{\sqrt{3}}{2}$, we have

$$\sin t = y = \frac{\sqrt{3}}{2} \qquad \cos t = x = -\frac{1}{2} \qquad \tan t = \frac{y}{x} = \frac{\dfrac{\sqrt{3}}{2}}{-\dfrac{1}{2}} = -\sqrt{3}$$

$$\csc t = \frac{1}{y} = \frac{1}{\dfrac{\sqrt{3}}{2}} = \frac{2\sqrt{3}}{3} \qquad \sec t = \frac{1}{x} = \frac{1}{-\dfrac{1}{2}} = -2 \qquad \cot t = \frac{x}{y} = \frac{-\dfrac{1}{2}}{\dfrac{\sqrt{3}}{2}} = -\frac{\sqrt{3}}{3}$$

WARNING When writing the values of the trigonometric functions, do not forget the argument of the function.

$$\sin t = \frac{\sqrt{3}}{2} \quad \text{correct}$$

$$\sin = \frac{\sqrt{3}}{2} \quad \text{incorrect} \quad \blacksquare$$

·····─ **Now Work** PROBLEM 13

Trigonometric Functions of Angles

Let $P = (x, y)$ be the point on the unit circle corresponding to the real number t. See Figure 20(a). Let θ be the angle in standard position, measured in radians, whose terminal side is the ray from the origin through P and whose arc length is $|t|$. See Figure 20(b). Since the unit circle has radius 1 unit, if $s = |t|$ units, then from the arc length formula $s = r\theta$, we have $\theta = t$ radians. See Figures 20(c) and (d).

Figure 20

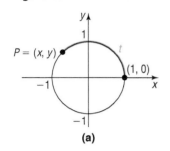
(a)

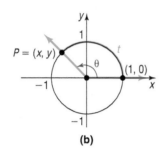
(b)

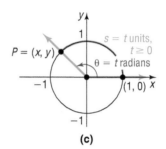
(c)

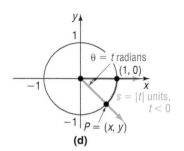
(d)

The point $P = (x, y)$ on the unit circle that corresponds to the real number t is also the point P on the terminal side of the angle $\theta = t$ radians. As a result, we can say that

$$\sin t = \sin \theta$$
$$\uparrow \qquad \uparrow$$
Real number $\qquad \theta = t$ radians

and so on. We can now define the trigonometric functions of the angle θ.

DEFINITION

If $\theta = t$ radians, the **six trigonometric functions of the angle θ** are defined as

$\sin \theta = \sin t$	$\cos \theta = \cos t$	$\tan \theta = \tan t$
$\csc \theta = \csc t$	$\sec \theta = \sec t$	$\cot \theta = \cot t$

Even though the trigonometric functions can be viewed both as functions of real numbers and as functions of angles, it is customary to refer to trigonometric functions of real numbers and trigonometric functions of angles collectively as the *trigonometric functions*. We shall follow this practice from now on.

If an angle θ is measured in degrees, we shall use the degree symbol when writing a trigonometric function of θ, as, for example, in $\sin 30°$ and $\tan 45°$. If an angle θ is measured in radians, then no symbol is used when writing a trigonometric function of θ, as, for example, in $\cos \pi$ and $\sec \dfrac{\pi}{3}$.

Finally, since the values of the trigonometric functions of an angle θ are determined by the coordinates of the point $P = (x, y)$ on the unit circle corresponding to θ, the units used to measure the angle θ are irrelevant. For example, it does not matter whether we write $\theta = \dfrac{\pi}{2}$ radians or $\theta = 90°$. The point on the unit circle corresponding to this angle is $P = (0, 1)$. As a result,

$$\sin \frac{\pi}{2} = \sin 90° = 1 \quad \text{and} \quad \cos \frac{\pi}{2} = \cos 90° = 0$$

2 Find the Exact Values of the Trigonometric Functions of Quadrantal Angles

To find the exact value of a trigonometric function of an angle θ or a real number t requires that we locate the point $P = (x, y)$ on the unit circle that corresponds to t. This is not always easy to do. In the examples that follow, we will evaluate the trigonometric functions of certain angles or real numbers for which this process is relatively easy. A calculator will be used to evaluate the trigonometric functions of most other angles.

EXAMPLE 2

Finding the Exact Values of the Six Trigonometric Functions of Quadrantal Angles

Find the exact values of the six trigonometric functions of:

(a) $\theta = 0 = 0°$

(b) $\theta = \dfrac{\pi}{2} = 90°$

(c) $\theta = \pi = 180°$

(d) $\theta = \dfrac{3\pi}{2} = 270°$

Solution

(a) The point on the unit circle that corresponds to $\theta = 0 = 0°$ is $P = (1, 0)$. See Figure 21(a). Then

$$\sin 0 = \sin 0° = y = 0 \qquad \cos 0 = \cos 0° = x = 1$$

$$\tan 0 = \tan 0° = \frac{y}{x} = 0 \qquad \sec 0 = \sec 0° = \frac{1}{x} = 1$$

Since the y-coordinate of P is 0, csc 0 and cot 0 are not defined.

(b) The point on the unit circle that corresponds to $\theta = \dfrac{\pi}{2} = 90°$ is $P = (0, 1)$. See Figure 21(b). Then

$$\sin \frac{\pi}{2} = \sin 90° = y = 1 \qquad \cos \frac{\pi}{2} = \cos 90° = x = 0$$

$$\csc \frac{\pi}{2} = \csc 90° = \frac{1}{y} = 1 \qquad \cot \frac{\pi}{2} = \cot 90° = \frac{x}{y} = 0$$

Since the x-coordinate of P is 0, $\tan \dfrac{\pi}{2}$ and $\sec \dfrac{\pi}{2}$ are not defined.

(c) The point on the unit circle that corresponds to $\theta = \pi = 180°$ is $P = (-1, 0)$. See Figure 21(c). Then

$$\sin \pi = \sin 180° = y = 0 \qquad \cos \pi = \cos 180° = x = -1$$

$$\tan \pi = \tan 180° = \frac{y}{x} = 0 \qquad \sec \pi = \sec 180° = \frac{1}{x} = -1$$

Since the y-coordinate of P is 0, csc π and cot π are not defined.

(d) The point on the unit circle that corresponds to $\theta = \dfrac{3\pi}{2} = 270°$ is $P = (0, -1)$. See Figure 21(d). Then

$$\sin \frac{3\pi}{2} = \sin 270° = y = -1 \qquad \cos \frac{3\pi}{2} = \cos 270° = x = 0$$

$$\csc \frac{3\pi}{2} = \csc 270° = \frac{1}{y} = -1 \qquad \cot \frac{3\pi}{2} = \cot 270° = \frac{x}{y} = 0$$

Since the x-coordinate of P is 0, $\tan \dfrac{3\pi}{2}$ and $\sec \dfrac{3\pi}{2}$ are not defined.

Figure 21

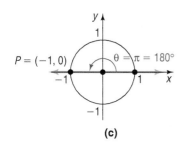

(a)

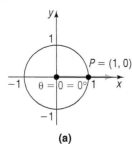

(b)

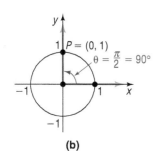

(c)

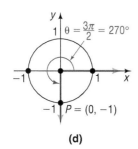

(d)

Table 2 on the next page summarizes the values of the trigonometric functions found in Example 2.

Table 2

Quadrantal Angles							
θ (Radians)	θ (Degrees)	$\sin\theta$	$\cos\theta$	$\tan\theta$	$\csc\theta$	$\sec\theta$	$\cot\theta$
0	0°	0	1	0	Not defined	1	Not defined
$\dfrac{\pi}{2}$	90°	1	0	Not defined	1	Not defined	0
π	180°	0	−1	0	Not defined	−1	Not defined
$\dfrac{3\pi}{2}$	270°	−1	0	Not defined	−1	Not defined	0

There is no need to memorize Table 2. To find the value of a trigonometric function of a quadrantal angle, draw the angle and apply the definition, as we did in Example 2.

EXAMPLE 3

Finding Exact Values of the Trigonometric Functions of Angles That Are Integer Multiples of Quadrantal Angles

Find the exact value of:

(a) $\sin(3\pi)$

(b) $\cos(-270°)$

Solution

(a) See Figure 22(a). The point P on the unit circle that corresponds to $\theta = 3\pi$ is $P = (-1, 0)$, so $\sin(3\pi) = y = 0$.

(b) See Figure 22(b). The point P on the unit circle that corresponds to $\theta = -270°$ is $P = (0, 1)$, so $\cos(-270°) = x = 0$.

Figure 22

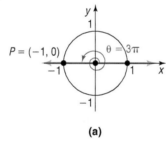

(a)

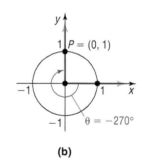

(b)

Now Work PROBLEMS 21 AND 61

---

3 Find the Exact Values of the Trigonometric Functions of $\dfrac{\pi}{4} = 45°$

EXAMPLE 4

Finding the Exact Values of the Trigonometric Functions of $\dfrac{\pi}{4} = 45°$

Find the exact values of the six trigonometric functions of $\dfrac{\pi}{4} = 45°$.

Solution

We seek the coordinates of the point $P = (x, y)$ on the unit circle that corresponds to $\theta = \dfrac{\pi}{4} = 45°$. See Figure 23. First, observe that P lies on the line $y = x$. (Do you

Figure 23

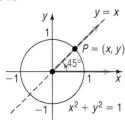

see why? Since $\theta = 45° = \dfrac{1}{2} \cdot 90°$, P must lie on the line that bisects quadrant I.)

Since $P = (x, y)$ also lies on the unit circle, $x^2 + y^2 = 1$, it follows that

$$x^2 + y^2 = 1$$
$$x^2 + x^2 = 1 \quad y = x, x > 0, y > 0$$
$$2x^2 = 1$$
$$x = \frac{1}{\sqrt{2}} = \frac{\sqrt{2}}{2} \qquad y = \frac{\sqrt{2}}{2}$$

Then

$$\sin \frac{\pi}{4} = \sin 45° = \frac{\sqrt{2}}{2} \qquad \cos \frac{\pi}{4} = \cos 45° = \frac{\sqrt{2}}{2} \qquad \tan \frac{\pi}{4} = \tan 45° = \frac{\dfrac{\sqrt{2}}{2}}{\dfrac{\sqrt{2}}{2}} = 1$$

$$\csc \frac{\pi}{4} = \csc 45° = \frac{1}{\dfrac{\sqrt{2}}{2}} = \sqrt{2} \qquad \sec \frac{\pi}{4} = \sec 45° = \frac{1}{\dfrac{\sqrt{2}}{2}} = \sqrt{2} \qquad \cot \frac{\pi}{4} = \cot 45° = \frac{\dfrac{\sqrt{2}}{2}}{\dfrac{\sqrt{2}}{2}} = 1$$

EXAMPLE 5

Finding the Exact Value of a Trigonometric Expression

Find the exact value of each expression.

(a) $\sin 45° \cos 180°$

(b) $\tan \dfrac{\pi}{4} - \sin \dfrac{3\pi}{2}$

(c) $\left(\sec \dfrac{\pi}{4} \right)^2 + \csc \dfrac{\pi}{2}$

Solution

(a) $\sin 45° \cos 180° = \dfrac{\sqrt{2}}{2} \cdot (-1) = -\dfrac{\sqrt{2}}{2}$

                      ↑   ↑

      From Example 4   From Table 2

(b) $\tan \dfrac{\pi}{4} - \sin \dfrac{3\pi}{2} = 1 - (-1) = 2$

           ↑   ↑

    From Example 4   From Table 2

(c) $\left(\sec \dfrac{\pi}{4} \right)^2 + \csc \dfrac{\pi}{2} = \left(\sqrt{2} \right)^2 + 1 = 2 + 1 = 3$

Now Work PROBLEM 35

4 Find the Exact Values of the Trigonometric Functions

of $\dfrac{\pi}{6} = 30°$ and $\dfrac{\pi}{3} = 60°$

Consider a right triangle in which one of the angles is $\dfrac{\pi}{6} = 30°$. It then follows that the third angle is $\dfrac{\pi}{3} = 60°$. Figure 24(a) illustrates such a triangle with hypotenuse of length 1. Our problem is to determine a and b.

We begin by placing next to this triangle another triangle congruent to the first, as shown in Figure 24(b). Notice that we now have a triangle whose three angles each equal 60°. This triangle is therefore equilateral, so each side is of length 1.

Figure 24

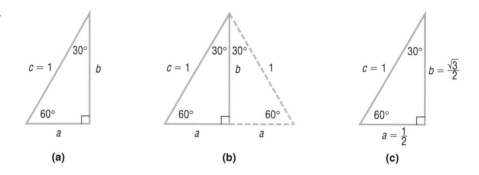

(a)   (b)   (c)

This means the base is $2a = 1$, and so $a = \dfrac{1}{2}$. By the Pythagorean Theorem, b satisfies the equation $a^2 + b^2 = c^2$, so we have

$$a^2 + b^2 = c^2$$

$$\frac{1}{4} + b^2 = 1 \qquad a = \frac{1}{2}, c = 1$$

$$b^2 = 1 - \frac{1}{4} = \frac{3}{4}$$

$$b = \frac{\sqrt{3}}{2} \qquad \begin{array}{l} b > 0 \text{ because } b \\ \text{is the length of the} \\ \text{side of a triangle.} \end{array}$$

This results in Figure 24(c).

EXAMPLE 6   **Finding the Exact Values of the Trigonometric Functions of $\dfrac{\pi}{3} = 60°$**

Find the exact values of the six trigonometric functions of $\dfrac{\pi}{3} = 60°$.

Solution   Position the triangle in Figure 24(c) so that the 60° angle is in standard position. See Figure 25. The point on the unit circle that corresponds to $\theta = \dfrac{\pi}{3} = 60°$ is $P = \left(\dfrac{1}{2}, \dfrac{\sqrt{3}}{2}\right)$. Then

Figure 25

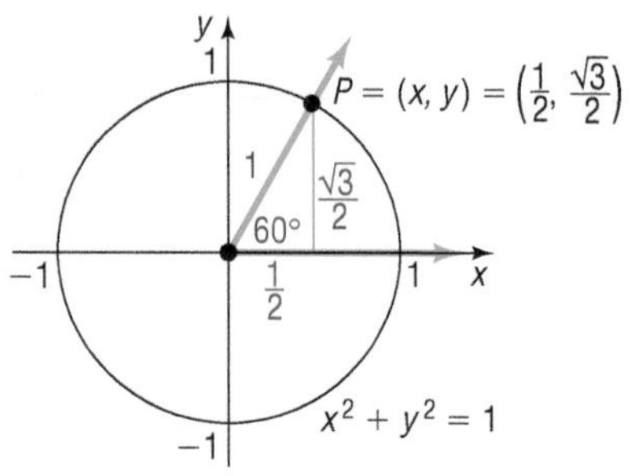

$$\sin\frac{\pi}{3} = \sin 60° = \frac{\sqrt{3}}{2} \qquad\qquad \cos\frac{\pi}{3} = \cos 60° = \frac{1}{2}$$

$$\csc\frac{\pi}{3} = \csc 60° = \frac{1}{\dfrac{\sqrt{3}}{2}} = \frac{2}{\sqrt{3}} = \frac{2\sqrt{3}}{3} \qquad \sec\frac{\pi}{3} = \sec 60° = \frac{1}{\dfrac{1}{2}} = 2$$

$$\tan\frac{\pi}{3} = \tan 60° = \frac{\dfrac{\sqrt{3}}{2}}{\dfrac{1}{2}} = \sqrt{3} \qquad\qquad \cot\frac{\pi}{3} = \cot 60° = \frac{\dfrac{1}{2}}{\dfrac{\sqrt{3}}{2}} = \frac{1}{\sqrt{3}} = \frac{\sqrt{3}}{3}$$

EXAMPLE 7

Finding the Exact Values of the Trigonometric Functions of $\dfrac{\pi}{6} = 30°$

Find the exact values of the trigonometric functions of $\dfrac{\pi}{6} = 30°$.

Solution

Position the triangle in Figure 24(c) so that the 30° angle is in standard position. See Figure 26. The point on the unit circle that corresponds to $\theta = \dfrac{\pi}{6} = 30°$ is $P = \left(\dfrac{\sqrt{3}}{2}, \dfrac{1}{2}\right)$. Then

Figure 26

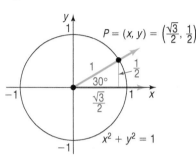

$$\sin\frac{\pi}{6} = \sin 30° = \frac{1}{2} \qquad\qquad \cos\frac{\pi}{6} = \cos 30° = \frac{\sqrt{3}}{2}$$

$$\csc\frac{\pi}{6} = \csc 30° = \frac{1}{\frac{1}{2}} = 2 \qquad \sec\frac{\pi}{6} = \sec 30° = \frac{1}{\frac{\sqrt{3}}{2}} = \frac{2}{\sqrt{3}} = \frac{2\sqrt{3}}{3}$$

$$\tan\frac{\pi}{6} = \tan 30° = \frac{\frac{1}{2}}{\frac{\sqrt{3}}{2}} = \frac{1}{\sqrt{3}} = \frac{\sqrt{3}}{3} \qquad \cot\frac{\pi}{6} = \cot 30° = \frac{\frac{\sqrt{3}}{2}}{\frac{1}{2}} = \sqrt{3}$$

Table 3 summarizes the information just derived for $\dfrac{\pi}{6} = 30°, \dfrac{\pi}{4} = 45°$, and $\dfrac{\pi}{3} = 60°$. Until you memorize the entries in Table 3, you should draw an appropriate diagram to determine the values given in the table.

Table 3

θ (Radians)	θ (Degrees)	$\sin\theta$	$\cos\theta$	$\tan\theta$	$\csc\theta$	$\sec\theta$	$\cot\theta$
$\dfrac{\pi}{6}$	30°	$\dfrac{1}{2}$	$\dfrac{\sqrt{3}}{2}$	$\dfrac{\sqrt{3}}{3}$	2	$\dfrac{2\sqrt{3}}{3}$	$\sqrt{3}$
$\dfrac{\pi}{4}$	45°	$\dfrac{\sqrt{2}}{2}$	$\dfrac{\sqrt{2}}{2}$	1	$\sqrt{2}$	$\sqrt{2}$	1
$\dfrac{\pi}{3}$	60°	$\dfrac{\sqrt{3}}{2}$	$\dfrac{1}{2}$	$\sqrt{3}$	$\dfrac{2\sqrt{3}}{3}$	2	$\dfrac{\sqrt{3}}{3}$

━━━━━ **Now Work** PROBLEM 41

EXAMPLE 8

Constructing a Rain Gutter

Figure 27

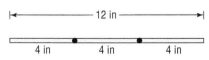

A rain gutter is to be constructed of aluminum sheets 12 inches wide. After marking off a length of 4 inches from each edge, this length is bent up at an angle θ. See Figure 27. The area A of the opening may be expressed as a function of θ as

$$A(\theta) = 16\sin\theta(\cos\theta + 1)$$

Find the area A of the opening for $\theta = 30°$, $\theta = 45°$, and $\theta = 60°$.

Solution For $\theta = 30°$: $A(30°) = 16\sin 30°(\cos 30° + 1)$

$$= 16\left(\frac{1}{2}\right)\left(\frac{\sqrt{3}}{2} + 1\right) = 4\sqrt{3} + 8 \approx 14.9$$

The area of the opening for $\theta = 30°$ is about 14.9 square inches.

For $\theta = 45°$: $A(45°) = 16 \sin 45°(\cos 45° + 1)$

$$= 16\left(\frac{\sqrt{2}}{2}\right)\left(\frac{\sqrt{2}}{2} + 1\right) = 8 + 8\sqrt{2} \approx 19.3$$

The area of the opening for $\theta = 45°$ is about 19.3 square inches.

For $\theta = 60°$: $A(60°) = 16 \sin 60°(\cos 60° + 1)$

$$= 16\left(\frac{\sqrt{3}}{2}\right)\left(\frac{1}{2} + 1\right) = 12\sqrt{3} \approx 20.8$$

The area of the opening for $\theta = 60°$ is about 20.8 square inches.   ♩

5 Find the Exact Values of the Trigonometric Functions for Integer Multiples of $\dfrac{\pi}{6} = 30°$, $\dfrac{\pi}{4} = 45°$, and $\dfrac{\pi}{3} = 60°$

We know the exact values of the trigonometric functions of $\dfrac{\pi}{4} = 45°$. Using symmetry, we can find the exact values of the trigonometric functions of $\dfrac{3\pi}{4} = 135°$, $\dfrac{5\pi}{4} = 225°$, and $\dfrac{7\pi}{4} = 315°$.

Figure 28

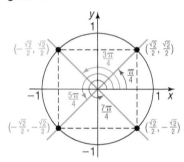

See Figure 28. Using symmetry with respect to the y-axis, the point $\left(-\dfrac{\sqrt{2}}{2}, \dfrac{\sqrt{2}}{2}\right)$ is the point on the unit circle that corresponds to the angle $\dfrac{3\pi}{4} = 135°$.

Similarly, using symmetry with respect to the origin, the point $\left(-\dfrac{\sqrt{2}}{2}, -\dfrac{\sqrt{2}}{2}\right)$ is the point on the unit circle that corresponds to the angle $\dfrac{5\pi}{4} = 225°$. Finally, using symmetry with respect to the x-axis, the point $\left(\dfrac{\sqrt{2}}{2}, -\dfrac{\sqrt{2}}{2}\right)$ is the point on the unit circle that corresponds to the angle $\dfrac{7\pi}{4} = 315°$.

EXAMPLE 9

Finding Exact Values for Multiples of $\dfrac{\pi}{4} = 45°$

Find the exact value of each expression.

(a) $\cos\dfrac{5\pi}{4}$ (b) $\sin 135°$ (c) $\tan 315°$ (d) $\sin\left(-\dfrac{\pi}{4}\right)$ (e) $\cos\dfrac{11\pi}{4}$

Solution   (a) From Figure 28, we see the point $\left(-\dfrac{\sqrt{2}}{2}, -\dfrac{\sqrt{2}}{2}\right)$ corresponds to $\dfrac{5\pi}{4}$, so

$$\cos\dfrac{5\pi}{4} = x = -\dfrac{\sqrt{2}}{2}.$$

(b) Since $135° = \dfrac{3\pi}{4}$, the point $\left(-\dfrac{\sqrt{2}}{2}, \dfrac{\sqrt{2}}{2}\right)$ corresponds to $135°$, so

$$\sin 135° = \dfrac{\sqrt{2}}{2}.$$

(c) Since $315° = \dfrac{7\pi}{4}$, the point $\left(\dfrac{\sqrt{2}}{2}, -\dfrac{\sqrt{2}}{2}\right)$ corresponds to $315°$, so

$$\tan 315° = \dfrac{-\dfrac{\sqrt{2}}{2}}{\dfrac{\sqrt{2}}{2}} = -1.$$

(d) The point $\left(\dfrac{\sqrt{2}}{2}, -\dfrac{\sqrt{2}}{2}\right)$ corresponds to $-\dfrac{\pi}{4}$, so $\sin\left(-\dfrac{\pi}{4}\right) = -\dfrac{\sqrt{2}}{2}$.

(e) The point $\left(-\dfrac{\sqrt{2}}{2}, \dfrac{\sqrt{2}}{2}\right)$ corresponds to $\dfrac{11\pi}{4}$, so $\cos\dfrac{11\pi}{4} = -\dfrac{\sqrt{2}}{2}$.

Now Work PROBLEMS 51 AND 55

The use of symmetry also provides information about certain integer multiples of the angles $\dfrac{\pi}{6} = 30°$ and $\dfrac{\pi}{3} = 60°$. See Figures 29 and 30.

Figure 29

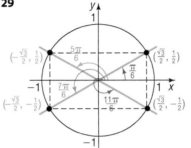

Figure 30

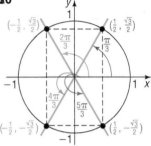

EXAMPLE 10

Finding Exact Values for Multiples of $\dfrac{\pi}{6} = 30°$ or $\dfrac{\pi}{3} = 60°$

Based on Figures 29 and 30, we see that

(a) $\cos 210° = \cos\dfrac{7\pi}{6} = -\dfrac{\sqrt{3}}{2}$

(b) $\sin(-60°) = \sin\left(-\dfrac{\pi}{3}\right) = -\dfrac{\sqrt{3}}{2}$

(c) $\tan\dfrac{5\pi}{3} = \dfrac{-\dfrac{\sqrt{3}}{2}}{\dfrac{1}{2}} = -\sqrt{3}$

(d) $\cos\dfrac{8\pi}{3} \overset{\substack{\frac{8\pi}{3} = 2\pi + \frac{2\pi}{3}\\ \downarrow}}{=} \cos\dfrac{2\pi}{3} = -\dfrac{1}{2}$

Now Work PROBLEM 47

6 Use a Calculator to Approximate the Value of a Trigonometric Function

Before getting started, you must first decide whether to enter the angle in the calculator using radians or degrees and then set the calculator to the correct MODE. Check your instruction manual to find out how your calculator handles degrees and radians. Your calculator has keys marked $\boxed{\sin}$, $\boxed{\cos}$, and $\boxed{\tan}$. To find the values of the remaining three trigonometric functions, secant, cosecant, and cotangent, we use the fact that, if $P = (x, y)$ is a point on the unit circle on the terminal side of θ, then

WARNING On your calculator the second functions $\sin^{-1}$, $\cos^{-1}$, and $\tan^{-1}$ do not represent the reciprocal of sin, cos, and tan. ∎

$$\sec\theta = \dfrac{1}{x} = \dfrac{1}{\cos\theta} \qquad \csc\theta = \dfrac{1}{y} = \dfrac{1}{\sin\theta} \qquad \cot\theta = \dfrac{x}{y} = \dfrac{1}{\dfrac{y}{x}} = \dfrac{1}{\tan\theta}$$

EXAMPLE 11

Using a Calculator to Approximate the Value of a Trigonometric Function

Use a calculator to find the approximate value of:

(a) $\cos 48°$ (b) $\csc 21°$ (c) $\tan\dfrac{\pi}{12}$

Express your answer rounded to two decimal places.

Solution

(a) First, we set the MODE to receive degrees. Rounded to two decimal places,

$$\cos 48° = 0.6691306 \approx 0.67$$

(b) Most calculators do not have a csc key. The manufacturers assume that the user knows some trigonometry. To find the value of csc 21°, use the fact that $\csc 21° = \dfrac{1}{\sin 21°}$. Rounded to two decimal places,

$$\csc 21° \approx 2.79$$

Figure 31

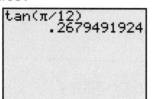

tan(π/12)
.2679491924

(c) Set the MODE to receive radians. Figure 31 shows the solution using a TI-84 Plus graphing calculator. Rounded to two decimal places,

$$\tan \frac{\pi}{12} \approx 0.27$$

Now Work PROBLEM 65

7 Use a Circle of Radius *r* to Evaluate the Trigonometric Functions

Figure 32

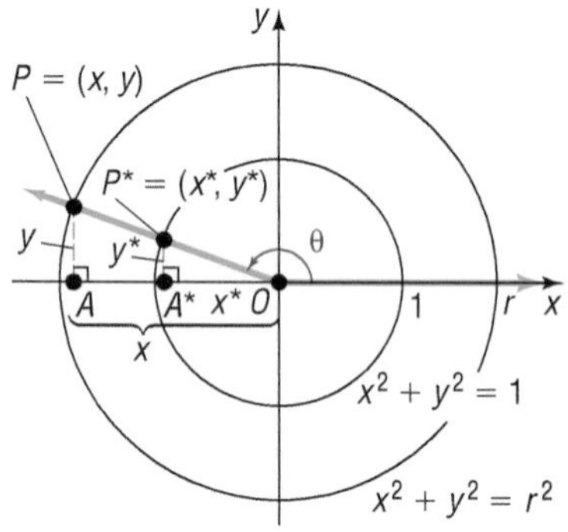

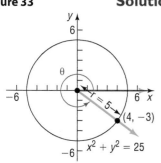

$x^2 + y^2 = 1$

$x^2 + y^2 = r^2$

Until now, finding the exact value of a trigonometric function of an angle θ required that we locate the corresponding point $P = (x, y)$ on the unit circle. In fact, though, any circle whose center is at the origin can be used.

Let θ be any nonquadrantal angle placed in standard position. Let $P = (x, y)$ be the point on the circle $x^2 + y^2 = r^2$ that corresponds to θ, and let $P* = (x*, y*)$ be the point on the unit circle that corresponds to θ. See Figure 32, where θ is shown in quadrant II.

Notice that the triangles $OA*P*$ and OAP are similar; as a result, the ratios of corresponding sides are equal.

$$\frac{y*}{1} = \frac{y}{r} \qquad \frac{x*}{1} = \frac{x}{r} \qquad \frac{y*}{x*} = \frac{y}{x}$$

$$\frac{1}{y*} = \frac{r}{y} \qquad \frac{1}{x*} = \frac{r}{x} \qquad \frac{x*}{y*} = \frac{x}{y}$$

These results lead us to formulate the following theorem:

THEOREM

For an angle θ in standard position, let $P = (x, y)$ be the point on the terminal side of θ that is also on the circle $x^2 + y^2 = r^2$. Then

$$\sin \theta = \frac{y}{r} \qquad\qquad \cos \theta = \frac{x}{r} \qquad\qquad \tan \theta = \frac{y}{x} \quad x \neq 0$$

$$\csc \theta = \frac{r}{y} \quad y \neq 0 \qquad \sec \theta = \frac{r}{x} \quad x \neq 0 \qquad \cot \theta = \frac{x}{y} \quad y \neq 0$$

EXAMPLE 12 | **Finding the Exact Values of the Six Trigonometric Functions**

Find the exact values of each of the six trigonometric functions of an angle θ if $(4, -3)$ is a point on its terminal side in standard position.

Figure 33

Solution

See Figure 33. The point $(4, -3)$ is on a circle of radius $r = \sqrt{4^2 + (-3)^2} = \sqrt{16 + 9} = \sqrt{25} = 5$ with the center at the origin.

For the point $(x, y) = (4, -3)$, we have $x = 4$ and $y = -3$. Since $r = 5$, we find

$$\sin \theta = \frac{y}{r} = -\frac{3}{5} \qquad \cos \theta = \frac{x}{r} = \frac{4}{5} \qquad \tan \theta = \frac{y}{x} = -\frac{3}{4}$$

$$\csc \theta = \frac{r}{y} = -\frac{5}{3} \qquad \sec \theta = \frac{r}{x} = \frac{5}{4} \qquad \cot \theta = \frac{x}{y} = -\frac{4}{3}$$

$x^2 + y^2 = 25$

Now Work PROBLEM 77

Historical Feature

The name *sine* for the sine function is due to a medieval confusion. The name comes from the Sanskrit word *jīva* (meaning chord), first used in India by Araybhata the Elder (AD 510). He really meant half-chord, but abbreviated it. This was brought into Arabic as *jiba*, which was meaningless. Because the proper Arabic word *jaib* would be written the same way (short vowels are not written out in Arabic), *jiba* was pronounced as *jaib*, which meant bosom or hollow, and *jiba* remains as the Arabic word for sine to this day. Scholars translating the Arabic works into Latin found that the word *sinus* also meant bosom or hollow, and from *sinus* we get the word *sine*.

The name *tangent*, due to Thomas Finck (1583), can be understood by looking at Figure 34. The line segment $\overline{DC}$ is tangent to the circle at C. If $d(O, B) = d(O, C) = 1$, then the length of the line segment $\overline{DC}$ is

$$d(D, C) = \frac{d(D, C)}{1} = \frac{d(D, C)}{d(O, C)} = \tan \alpha$$

The old name for the tangent is *umbra versa* (meaning turned shadow), referring to the use of the tangent in solving height problems with shadows.

The names of the remaining functions came about as follows. If α and β are complementary angles, then $\cos \alpha = \sin \beta$. Because β is the complement of α, it was natural to write the cosine of α as *sin co* α. Probably for reasons involving ease of pronunciation, the *co* migrated to the front, and then cosine received a three-letter abbreviation to match sin, sec, and tan. The two other cofunctions were similarly treated, except that the long forms *cotan* and *cosec* survive to this day in some countries.

Figure 34

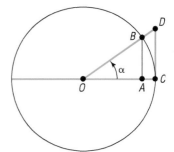

6.2 Assess Your Understanding

'Are You Prepared?' *Answers are given at the end of these exercises. If you get a wrong answer, read the pages listed in* red.

1. In a right triangle, with legs a and b and hypotenuse c, the Pythagorean Theorem states that _____ . (p. A14)

2. The value of the function $f(x) = 3x - 7$ at 5 is _____. (pp. 46–56)

3. **True or False** For a function $y = f(x)$, for each x in the domain, there is exactly one element y in the range. (pp. 46–56)

4. If two triangles are similar, then corresponding angles are _____ and the lengths of corresponding sides are _____ . (pp. A14–A19)

5. What point is symmetric with respect to the y-axis to the point $\left(\frac{1}{2}, \frac{\sqrt{3}}{2}\right)$? (pp. 12–14)

6. If (x, y) is a point on the unit circle in quadrant IV and if $x = \frac{\sqrt{3}}{2}$, what is y? (p. 35)

Concepts and Vocabulary

7. The _____ function takes as input a real number t that corresponds to a point $P = (x, y)$ on the unit circle and outputs the x-coordinate.

8. The point on the unit circle that corresponds to $\theta = \frac{\pi}{2}$ is $P =$ _____.

9. The point on the unit circle that corresponds to $\theta = \frac{\pi}{4}$ is

   $P =$ _____.

10. The point on the unit circle that corresponds to $\theta = \frac{\pi}{3}$ is

    $P =$ _____.

11. For any angle θ in standard position, let $P = (x, y)$ be the point on the terminal side of θ that is also on the circle $x^2 + y^2 = r^2$. Then, $\sin \theta =$ ____ and $\cos \theta =$ ____.

12. **True or False** Exact values can be found for the sine of any angle.

Skill Building

In Problems 13–20, $P = (x, y)$ is the point on the unit circle that corresponds to a real number t. Find the exact values of the six trigonometric functions of t.

13. $\left(\frac{\sqrt{3}}{2}, \frac{1}{2}\right)$

14. $\left(\frac{1}{2}, -\frac{\sqrt{3}}{2}\right)$

15. $\left(-\frac{2}{5}, \frac{\sqrt{21}}{5}\right)$

16. $\left(-\frac{1}{5}, \frac{2\sqrt{6}}{5}\right)$

17. $\left(-\frac{\sqrt{2}}{2}, \frac{\sqrt{2}}{2}\right)$

18. $\left(\frac{\sqrt{2}}{2}, \frac{\sqrt{2}}{2}\right)$

19. $\left(\frac{2\sqrt{2}}{3}, -\frac{1}{3}\right)$

20. $\left(-\frac{\sqrt{5}}{3}, -\frac{2}{3}\right)$

In Problems 21–30, find the exact value. Do not use a calculator.

21. $\sin \dfrac{11\pi}{2}$ **22.** $\cos(7\pi)$ **23.** $\tan(6\pi)$ **24.** $\cot \dfrac{7\pi}{2}$ **25.** $\csc \dfrac{11\pi}{2}$

26. $\sec(8\pi)$ **27.** $\cos\left(-\dfrac{3\pi}{2}\right)$ **28.** $\sin(-3\pi)$ **29.** $\sec(-\pi)$ **30.** $\tan(-3\pi)$

In Problems 31–46, find the exact value of each expression. Do not use a calculator.

31. $\sin 45° + \cos 60°$ **32.** $\sin 30° - \cos 45°$ **33.** $\sin 90° + \tan 45°$ **34.** $\cos 180° - \sin 180°$

35. $\sin 45° \cos 45°$ **36.** $\tan 45° \cos 30°$ **37.** $\csc 45° \tan 60°$ **38.** $\sec 30° \cot 45°$

39. $4 \sin 90° - 3 \tan 180°$ **40.** $5 \cos 90° - 8 \sin 270°$ **41.** $2 \sin \dfrac{\pi}{3} - 3 \tan \dfrac{\pi}{6}$ **42.** $2 \sin \dfrac{\pi}{4} + 3 \tan \dfrac{\pi}{4}$

43. $2 \sec \dfrac{\pi}{4} + 4 \cot \dfrac{\pi}{3}$ **44.** $3 \csc \dfrac{\pi}{3} + \cot \dfrac{\pi}{4}$ **45.** $\csc \dfrac{\pi}{2} + \cot \dfrac{\pi}{2}$ **46.** $\sec \pi - \csc \dfrac{\pi}{2}$

In Problems 47–64, find the exact values of the six trigonometric functions of the given angle. If any are not defined, say "not defined." Do not use a calculator.

47. $\dfrac{2\pi}{3}$ **48.** $\dfrac{5\pi}{6}$ **49.** $210°$ **50.** $240°$ **51.** $\dfrac{3\pi}{4}$ **52.** $\dfrac{11\pi}{4}$

53. $\dfrac{8\pi}{3}$ **54.** $\dfrac{13\pi}{6}$ **55.** $405°$ **56.** $390°$ **57.** $-\dfrac{\pi}{6}$ **58.** $-\dfrac{\pi}{3}$

59. $-135°$ **60.** $-240°$ **61.** $\dfrac{5\pi}{2}$ **62.** 5π **63.** $-\dfrac{14\pi}{3}$ **64.** $-\dfrac{13\pi}{6}$

In Problems 65–76, use a calculator to find the approximate value of each expression rounded to two decimal places.

65. $\sin 28°$ **66.** $\cos 14°$ **67.** $\sec 21°$ **68.** $\cot 70°$

69. $\tan \dfrac{\pi}{10}$ **70.** $\sin \dfrac{\pi}{8}$ **71.** $\cot \dfrac{\pi}{12}$ **72.** $\csc \dfrac{5\pi}{13}$

73. $\sin 1$ **74.** $\tan 1$ **75.** $\sin 1°$ **76.** $\tan 1°$

In Problems 77–84, a point on the terminal side of an angle θ in standard position is given. Find the exact value of each of the six trigonometric functions of θ.

77. $(-3, 4)$ **78.** $(5, -12)$ **79.** $(2, -3)$ **80.** $(-1, -2)$

81. $(-2, -2)$ **82.** $(-1, 1)$ **83.** $\left(\dfrac{1}{3}, \dfrac{1}{4}\right)$ **84.** $(0.3, 0.4)$

---

85. Find the exact value of:
$$\sin 45° + \sin 135° + \sin 225° + \sin 315°$$

86. Find the exact value of:
$$\tan 60° + \tan 150°$$

87. Find the exact value of:
$$\sin 40° + \sin 130° + \sin 220° + \sin 310°$$

88. Find the exact value of:
$$\tan 40° + \tan 140°$$

89. If $f(\theta) = \sin \theta = 0.1$, find $f(\theta + \pi)$.

90. If $f(\theta) = \cos \theta = 0.3$, find $f(\theta + \pi)$.

91. If $f(\theta) = \tan \theta = 3$, find $f(\theta + \pi)$.

92. If $f(\theta) = \cot \theta = -2$, find $f(\theta + \pi)$.

93. If $\sin \theta = \dfrac{1}{5}$, find $\csc \theta$.

94. If $\cos \theta = \dfrac{2}{3}$, find $\sec \theta$.

In Problems 95–106, $f(\theta) = \sin \theta$ and $g(\theta) = \cos \theta$. Find the exact value of each function below if $\theta = 60°$. Do not use a calculator.

95. $f(\theta)$ **96.** $g(\theta)$ **97.** $f\left(\dfrac{\theta}{2}\right)$

98. $g\left(\dfrac{\theta}{2}\right)$ **99.** $[f(\theta)]^2$ **100.** $[g(\theta)]^2$

101. $f(2\theta)$ **102.** $g(2\theta)$ **103.** $2f(\theta)$

104. $2g(\theta)$ **105.** $f(-\theta)$ **106.** $g(-\theta)$

Mixed Practice

In Problems 107–114, $f(x) = \sin x$, $g(x) = \cos x$, $h(x) = 2x$, and $p(x) = \dfrac{x}{2}$. Find the value of each of the following:

107. $(f + g)(30°)$

108. $(f - g)(60°)$

109. $(f \cdot g)\left(\dfrac{3\pi}{4}\right)$

110. $(f \cdot g)\left(\dfrac{4\pi}{3}\right)$

111. $(f \circ h)\left(\dfrac{\pi}{6}\right)$

112. $(g \circ p)(60°)$

113. $(p \circ g)(315°)$

114. $(h \circ f)\left(\dfrac{5\pi}{6}\right)$

115. (a) Find $f\left(\dfrac{\pi}{4}\right)$. What point is on the graph of f?

   (b) Assuming f is one-to-one*, use the result of part (a) to find a point on the graph of f^{-1}.

   (c) What point is on the graph of $y = f\left(x + \dfrac{\pi}{4}\right) - 3$ if $x = \dfrac{\pi}{4}$?

116. (a) Find $g\left(\dfrac{\pi}{6}\right)$. What point is on the graph of g?

   (b) Assuming g is one-to-one*, use the result of part (a) to find a point on the graph of g^{-1}.

   (c) What point is on the graph of $y = 2g\left(x - \dfrac{\pi}{6}\right)$ if $x = \dfrac{\pi}{6}$?

Applications and Extensions

117. Find two negative and three positive angles, expressed in radians, for which the point on the unit circle that corresponds to each angle is $\left(\dfrac{1}{2}, \dfrac{\sqrt{3}}{2}\right)$.

118. Find two negative and three positive angles, expressed in radians, for which the point on the unit circle that corresponds to each angle is $\left(-\dfrac{\sqrt{2}}{2}, \dfrac{\sqrt{2}}{2}\right)$.

119. Use a calculator in radian mode to complete the following table.
What can you conclude about the value of $f(\theta) = \dfrac{\sin \theta}{\theta}$ as θ approaches 0?

θ	0.5	0.4	0.2	0.1	0.01	0.001	0.0001	0.00001
$\sin \theta$								
$f(\theta) = \dfrac{\sin \theta}{\theta}$								

120. Use a calculator in radian mode to complete the following table.
What can you conclude about the value of $g(\theta) = \dfrac{\cos \theta - 1}{\theta}$ as θ approaches 0?

θ	0.5	0.4	0.2	0.1	0.01	0.001	0.0001	0.00001
$\cos \theta - 1$								
$g(\theta) = \dfrac{\cos \theta - 1}{\theta}$								

For Problems 121–124, use the following discussion.

Projectile Motion   The path of a projectile fired at an inclination θ to the horizontal with initial speed v_0 is a parabola (see the figure).

$v_0 =$ Initial speed

Height, H

θ

Range, R

The range R of the projectile, that is, the horizontal distance that the projectile travels, is found by using the function

$$R(\theta) = \frac{v_0^2 \sin(2\theta)}{g}$$

where $g \approx 32.2$ feet per second per second ≈ 9.8 meters per second per second is the acceleration due to gravity. The maximum height H of the projectile is given by the function

$$H(\theta) = \frac{v_0^2 (\sin \theta)^2}{2g}$$

*In Section 7.1, we discuss the necessary domain restriction so that the function is one-to-one.

In Problems 121–124, find the range R and maximum height H.

121. The projectile is fired at an angle of 45° to the horizontal with an initial speed of 100 feet per second.

122. The projectile is fired at an angle of 30° to the horizontal with an initial speed of 150 meters per second.

123. The projectile is fired at an angle of 25° to the horizontal with an initial speed of 500 meters per second.

124. The projectile is fired at an angle of 50° to the horizontal with an initial speed of 200 feet per second.

125. Inclined Plane See the figure.

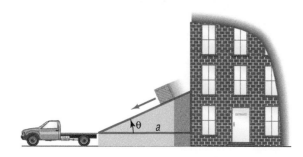

If friction is ignored, the time t (in seconds) required for a block to slide down an inclined plane is given by the function

$$t(\theta) = \sqrt{\frac{2a}{g \sin \theta \cos \theta}}$$

where a is the length (in feet) of the base and $g \approx 32$ feet per second per second is the acceleration due to gravity. How long does it take a block to slide down an inclined plane with base $a = 10$ feet when:
(a) $\theta = 30°$?
(b) $\theta = 45°$?
(c) $\theta = 60°$?

126. Piston Engines In a certain piston engine, the distance x (in centimeters) from the center of the drive shaft to the head of the piston is given by the function

$$x(\theta) = \cos \theta + \sqrt{16 + 0.5 \cos(2\theta)}$$

where θ is the angle between the crank and the path of the piston head. See the figure. Find x when $\theta = 30°$ and when $\theta = 45°$.

127. Calculating the Time of a Trip Two oceanfront homes are located 8 miles apart on a straight stretch of beach, each a

distance of 1 mile from a paved road that parallels the ocean. See the figure.

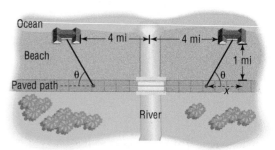

Sally can jog 8 miles per hour along the paved road, but only 3 miles per hour in the sand on the beach. Because of a river directly between the two houses, it is necessary to jog in the sand to the road, continue on the road, and then jog directly back in the sand to get from one house to the other. The time T to get from one house to the other as a function of the angle θ shown in the illustration is

$$T(\theta) = 1 + \frac{2}{3 \sin \theta} - \frac{1}{4 \tan \theta}, \qquad 0° < \theta < 90°$$

(a) Calculate the time T for $\theta = 30°$. How long is Sally on the paved road?
(b) Calculate the time T for $\theta = 45°$. How long is Sally on the paved road?
(c) Calculate the time T for $\theta = 60°$. How long is Sally on the paved road?
(d) Calculate the time T for $\theta = 90°$. Describe the path taken. Why can't the formula for T be used?

128. Designing Fine Decorative Pieces A designer of decorative art plans to market solid gold spheres encased in clear crystal cones. Each sphere is of fixed radius R and will be enclosed in a cone of height h and radius r. See the illustration. Many cones can be used to enclose the sphere, each having a different slant angle θ. The volume V of the cone can be expressed as a function of the slant angle θ of the cone as

$$V(\theta) = \frac{1}{3} \pi R^3 \frac{(1 + \sec \theta)^3}{(\tan \theta)^2}, \qquad 0° < \theta < 90°$$

What volume V is required to enclose a sphere of radius 2 centimeters in a cone whose slant angle θ is 30°? 45°? 60°?

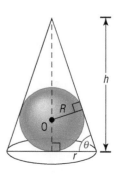

129. Projectile Motion An object is propelled upward at an angle θ, 45° < θ < 90°, to the horizontal with an initial

velocity of v_0 feet per second from the base of an inclined plane that makes an angle of 45° with the horizontal. See the illustration. If air resistance is ignored, the distance R that it travels up the inclined plane as a function of θ is given by

$$R(\theta) = \frac{v_0^2 \sqrt{2}}{32}[\sin(2\theta) - \cos(2\theta) - 1]$$

(a) Find the distance R that the object travels along the inclined plane if the initial velocity is 32 feet per second and $\theta = 60°$.

(b) Graph $R = R(\theta)$ if the initial velocity is 32 feet per second.

(c) What value of θ makes R largest?

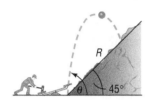

130. If $\theta, 0 < \theta < \pi$, is the angle between the positive x-axis and a nonhorizontal, nonvertical line L, show that the slope m of L equals $\tan \theta$. The angle θ is called the **inclination** of L.

[**Hint:** See the illustration, where we have drawn the line M parallel to L and passing through the origin. Use the fact that M intersects the unit circle at the point $(\cos \theta, \sin \theta)$.]

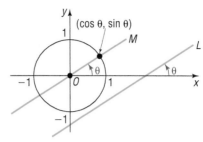

In Problems 131 and 132, use the figure to approximate the value of the six trigonometric functions at t to the nearest tenth. Then use a calculator to approximate each of the six trigonometric functions at t.

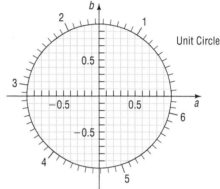

131. (a) $t = 1$ (b) $t = 5.1$
132. (a) $t = 2$ (b) $t = 4$

Explaining Concepts: Discussion and Writing

133. Write a brief paragraph that explains how to quickly compute the trigonometric functions of 30°, 45°, and 60°.

134. Write a brief paragraph that explains how to quickly compute the trigonometric functions of 0°, 90°, 180°, and 270°.

135. How would you explain the meaning of the sine function to a fellow student who has just completed college algebra?

'Are You Prepared?' Answers

1. $c^2 = a^2 + b^2$ **2.** 8   **3.** True   **4.** equal; proportional   **5.** $\left(-\dfrac{1}{2}, \dfrac{\sqrt{3}}{2}\right)$ **6.** $-\dfrac{1}{2}$

6.3 Properties of the Trigonometric Functions

PREPARING FOR THIS SECTION *Before getting started, review the following:*

- Functions (Section 2.1, pp. 46–56)
- Identity (Appendix A, Section A.6, p. A44)
- Even and Odd Functions (Section 2.3, pp. 69–70)

Now Work the 'Are You Prepared?' problems on page 390.

OBJECTIVES **1** Determine the Domain and the Range of the Trigonometric Functions (p. 380)
  2 Determine the Period of the Trigonometric Functions (p. 381)
  3 Determine the Signs of the Trigonometric Functions in a Given Quadrant (p. 383)
  4 Find the Values of the Trigonometric Functions Using Fundamental Identities (p. 384)
  5 Find the Exact Values of the Trigonometric Functions of an Angle Given One of the Functions and the Quadrant of the Angle (p. 386)
  6 Use Even–Odd Properties to Find the Exact Values of the Trigonometric Functions (p. 389)

1 Determine the Domain and the Range of the Trigonometric Functions

Figure 35

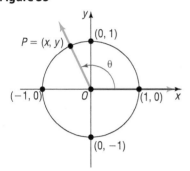

Let θ be an angle in standard position, and let $P = (x, y)$ be the point on the unit circle that corresponds to θ. See Figure 35. Then, by the definition given earlier,

$$\sin \theta = y \qquad \cos \theta = x \qquad \tan \theta = \frac{y}{x} \quad x \neq 0$$

$$\csc \theta = \frac{1}{y} \quad y \neq 0 \qquad \sec \theta = \frac{1}{x} \quad x \neq 0 \qquad \cot \theta = \frac{x}{y} \quad y \neq 0$$

For $\sin \theta$ and $\cos \theta$, there is no concern about dividing by 0, so θ can be any angle. It follows that the domain of the sine function and cosine function is the set of all real numbers.

> The domain of the sine function is the set of all real numbers.
>
> The domain of the cosine function is the set of all real numbers.

For the tangent function and secant function, the x-coordinate of $P = (x, y)$ cannot be 0 since this results in division by 0. See Figure 35. On the unit circle, there are two such points, $(0, 1)$ and $(0, -1)$. These two points correspond to the angles $\frac{\pi}{2}(90°)$ and $\frac{3\pi}{2}(270°)$ or, more generally, to any angle that is an odd integer multiple of $\frac{\pi}{2}(90°)$, such as $\pm\frac{\pi}{2}(\pm90°)$, $\pm\frac{3\pi}{2}(\pm270°)$, $\pm\frac{5\pi}{2}(\pm450°)$, and so on. Such angles must therefore be excluded from the domain of the tangent function and secant function.

> The domain of the tangent function is the set of all real numbers, except odd integer multiples of $\frac{\pi}{2}(90°)$.
>
> The domain of the secant function is the set of all real numbers, except odd integer multiples of $\frac{\pi}{2}(90°)$.

For the cotangent function and cosecant function, the y-coordinate of $P = (x, y)$ cannot be 0 since this results in division by 0. See Figure 35. On the unit circle, there are two such points, $(1, 0)$ and $(-1, 0)$. These two points correspond to the angles $0(0°)$ and $\pi(180°)$ or, more generally, to any angle that is an integer multiple of $\pi(180°)$, such as $0(0°)$, $\pm\pi(\pm180°)$, $\pm2\pi(\pm360°)$, $\pm3\pi(\pm540°)$, and so on. Such angles must therefore be excluded from the domain of the cotangent function and cosecant function.

> The domain of the cotangent function is the set of all real numbers, except integer multiples of $\pi(180°)$.
>
> The domain of the cosecant function is the set of all real numbers, except integer multiples of $\pi(180°)$.

Next we determine the range of each of the six trigonometric functions. Refer again to Figure 35. Let $P = (x, y)$ be the point on the unit circle that corresponds to the angle θ. It follows that $-1 \leq x \leq 1$ and $-1 \leq y \leq 1$. Since $\sin \theta = y$ and $\cos \theta = x$, we have

> $$-1 \leq \sin \theta \leq 1 \qquad -1 \leq \cos \theta \leq 1$$

The range of both the sine function and the cosine function consists of all real numbers between -1 and 1, inclusive. Using absolute value notation, we have $|\sin \theta| \leq 1$ and $|\cos \theta| \leq 1$.

If θ is not an integer multiple of $\pi(180°)$, then $\csc\theta = \dfrac{1}{y}$. Since $y = \sin\theta$ and $|y| = |\sin\theta| \le 1$, it follows that $|\csc\theta| = \dfrac{1}{|\sin\theta|} = \dfrac{1}{|y|} \ge 1 \left(\dfrac{1}{y} \le -1 \text{ or } \dfrac{1}{y} \ge 1\right)$.

Since $\csc\theta = \dfrac{1}{y}$, the range of the cosecant function consists of all real numbers less than or equal to -1 or greater than or equal to 1. That is,

$$\csc\theta \le -1 \quad\text{or}\quad \csc\theta \ge 1$$

If θ is not an odd integer multiple of $\dfrac{\pi}{2}(90°)$, then $\sec\theta = \dfrac{1}{x}$. Since $x = \cos\theta$ and $|x| = |\cos\theta| \le 1$, it follows that $|\sec\theta| = \dfrac{1}{|\cos\theta|} = \dfrac{1}{|x|} \ge 1 \left(\dfrac{1}{x} \le -1 \text{ or } \dfrac{1}{x} \ge 1\right)$.

Since $\sec\theta = \dfrac{1}{x}$, the range of the secant function consists of all real numbers less than or equal to -1 or greater than or equal to 1. That is,

$$\sec\theta \le -1 \quad\text{or}\quad \sec\theta \ge 1$$

The range of both the tangent function and the cotangent function is the set of all real numbers.

$$-\infty < \tan\theta < \infty \qquad -\infty < \cot\theta < \infty$$

You are asked to prove this in Problems 121 and 122.
Table 4 summarizes these results.

Table 4

Function	Symbol	Domain	Range
sine	$f(\theta) = \sin\theta$	All real numbers	All real numbers from -1 to 1, inclusive
cosine	$f(\theta) = \cos\theta$	All real numbers	All real numbers from -1 to 1, inclusive
tangent	$f(\theta) = \tan\theta$	All real numbers, except odd integer multiples of $\dfrac{\pi}{2}(90°)$	All real numbers
cosecant	$f(\theta) = \csc\theta$	All real numbers, except integer multiples of $\pi(180°)$	All real numbers greater than or equal to 1 or less than or equal to -1
secant	$f(\theta) = \sec\theta$	All real numbers, except odd integer multiples of $\dfrac{\pi}{2}(90°)$	All real numbers greater than or equal to 1 or less than or equal to -1
cotangent	$f(\theta) = \cot\theta$	All real numbers, except integer multiples of $\pi(180°)$	All real numbers

━━━━━━➤ **Now Work** PROBLEM 97

2 Determine the Period of the Trigonometric Functions

Figure 36

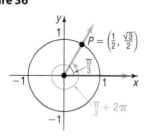

Look at Figure 36. This figure shows that for an angle of $\dfrac{\pi}{3}$ radians the corresponding point P on the unit circle is $\left(\dfrac{1}{2}, \dfrac{\sqrt{3}}{2}\right)$. Notice that, for an angle of $\dfrac{\pi}{3} + 2\pi$ radians, the corresponding point P on the unit circle is also $\left(\dfrac{1}{2}, \dfrac{\sqrt{3}}{2}\right)$. Then

$$\sin\frac{\pi}{3} = \frac{\sqrt{3}}{2} \quad\text{and}\quad \sin\left(\frac{\pi}{3} + 2\pi\right) = \frac{\sqrt{3}}{2}$$

$$\cos\frac{\pi}{3} = \frac{1}{2} \quad\text{and}\quad \cos\left(\frac{\pi}{3} + 2\pi\right) = \frac{1}{2}$$

This example illustrates a more general situation. For a given angle θ, measured in radians, suppose that we know the corresponding point $P = (x, y)$ on the unit circle. Now add 2π to θ. The point on the unit circle corresponding to $\theta + 2\pi$ is

Figure 37

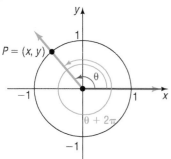

identical to the point P on the unit circle corresponding to θ. See Figure 37. The values of the trigonometric functions of $\theta + 2\pi$ are equal to the values of the corresponding trigonometric functions of θ.

If we add (or subtract) integer multiples of 2π to θ, the values of the sine and cosine function remain unchanged. That is, for all θ

$$\sin(\theta + 2\pi k) = \sin \theta \qquad \cos(\theta + 2\pi k) = \cos \theta$$
$$\text{where } k \text{ is any integer.}$$

(1)

Functions that exhibit this kind of behavior are called *periodic functions*.

DEFINITION

A function f is called **periodic** if there is a positive number p such that, whenever θ is in the domain of f, so is $\theta + p$, and

$$f(\theta + p) = f(\theta)$$

If there is a smallest such number p, this smallest value is called the **(fundamental) period** of f.

Based on equation (1), the sine and cosine functions are periodic. In fact, the sine and cosine functions have period 2π. You are asked to prove this fact in Problems 123 and 124. The secant and cosecant functions are also periodic with period 2π, and the tangent and cotangent functions are periodic with period π. You are asked to prove these statements in Problems 125 through 128.

These facts are summarized as follows:

In Words

Tangent and cotangent have period π; the others have period 2π.

Periodic Properties

$$\sin(\theta + 2\pi) = \sin \theta \quad \cos(\theta + 2\pi) = \cos \theta \quad \tan(\theta + \pi) = \tan \theta$$
$$\csc(\theta + 2\pi) = \csc \theta \quad \sec(\theta + 2\pi) = \sec \theta \quad \cot(\theta + \pi) = \cot \theta$$

Because the sine, cosine, secant, and cosecant functions have period 2π, once we know their values over an interval of length 2π, we know all their values; similarly, since the tangent and cotangent functions have period π, once we know their values over an interval of length π, we know all their values.

EXAMPLE 1

Finding Exact Values Using Periodic Properties

Find the exact value of:

(a) $\sin \dfrac{17\pi}{4}$ (b) $\cos(5\pi)$ (c) $\tan \dfrac{5\pi}{4}$

Solution

(a) It is best to sketch the angle first, as shown in Figure 38(a). Since the period of the sine function is 2π, each full revolution can be ignored. This leaves the angle $\dfrac{\pi}{4}$. Then

$$\sin \frac{17\pi}{4} = \sin\left(\frac{\pi}{4} + 4\pi\right) = \sin \frac{\pi}{4} = \frac{\sqrt{2}}{2}$$

(b) See Figure 38(b). Since the period of the cosine function is 2π, each full revolution can be ignored. This leaves the angle π. Then

$$\cos(5\pi) = \cos(\pi + 4\pi) = \cos \pi = -1$$

(c) See Figure 38(c). Since the period of the tangent function is π, each half-revolution can be ignored. This leaves the angle $\dfrac{\pi}{4}$. Then

$$\tan\frac{5\pi}{4} = \tan\left(\frac{\pi}{4} + \pi\right) = \tan\frac{\pi}{4} = 1$$

Figure 38

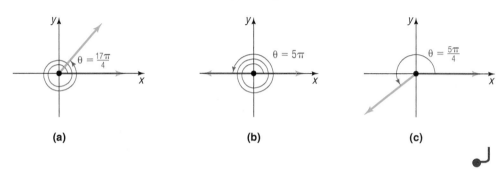

(a)   (b)   (c)

The periodic properties of the trigonometric functions will be very helpful to us when we study their graphs later in the chapter.

━━━━━**Now Work** PROBLEM 11

3 Determine the Signs of the Trigonometric Functions in a Given Quadrant

Figure 39

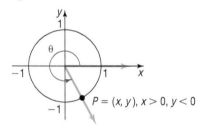

$P = (x, y),\ x > 0,\ y < 0$

Let $P = (x, y)$ be the point on the unit circle that corresponds to the angle θ. If we know in which quadrant the point P lies, then we can determine the signs of the trigonometric functions of θ. For example, if $P = (x, y)$ lies in quadrant IV, as shown in Figure 39, then we know that $x > 0$ and $y < 0$. Consequently,

$$\sin \theta = y < 0 \qquad \cos \theta = x > 0 \qquad \tan \theta = \frac{y}{x} < 0$$

$$\csc \theta = \frac{1}{y} < 0 \qquad \sec \theta = \frac{1}{x} > 0 \qquad \cot \theta = \frac{x}{y} < 0$$

Table 5 lists the signs of the six trigonometric functions for each quadrant. See also Figure 40.

Table 5

Quadrant of P	sin θ, csc θ	cos θ, sec θ	tan θ, cot θ
I	Positive	Positive	Positive
II	Positive	Negative	Negative
III	Negative	Negative	Positive
IV	Negative	Positive	Negative

Figure 40

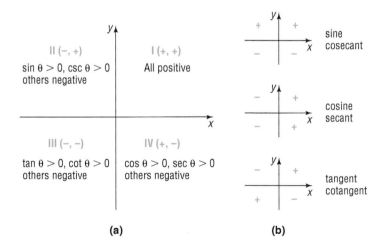

(a)   (b)

EXAMPLE 2

Finding the Quadrant in Which an Angle θ Lies

If $\sin \theta < 0$ and $\cos \theta < 0$, name the quadrant in which the angle θ lies.

Solution Let $P = (x, y)$ be the point on the unit circle corresponding to θ. Then $\sin \theta = y < 0$ and $\cos \theta = x < 0$. Because points in quadrant III have $x < 0$ and $y < 0$, θ lies in quadrant III.

 **Now Work** PROBLEM 27

4 Find the Values of the Trigonometric Functions Using Fundamental Identities

If $P = (x, y)$ is the point on the unit circle corresponding to θ, then

$$\sin \theta = y \qquad \cos \theta = x \qquad \tan \theta = \frac{y}{x} \ \text{ if } x \neq 0$$

$$\csc \theta = \frac{1}{y} \ \text{ if } y \neq 0 \qquad \sec \theta = \frac{1}{x} \ \text{ if } x \neq 0 \qquad \cot \theta = \frac{x}{y} \ \text{ if } y \neq 0$$

Based on these definitions, we have the **reciprocal identities:**

Reciprocal Identities

$$\csc \theta = \frac{1}{\sin \theta} \qquad \sec \theta = \frac{1}{\cos \theta} \qquad \cot \theta = \frac{1}{\tan \theta} \qquad \textbf{(2)}$$

Two other fundamental identities are the **quotient identities.**

Quotient Identities

$$\tan \theta = \frac{\sin \theta}{\cos \theta} \qquad \cot \theta = \frac{\cos \theta}{\sin \theta} \qquad \textbf{(3)}$$

The proofs of identities (2) and (3) follow from the definitions of the trigonometric functions. (See Problems 129 and 130.)

If $\sin \theta$ and $\cos \theta$ are known, identities (2) and (3) make it easy to find the values of the remaining trigonometric functions.

EXAMPLE 3

Finding Exact Values Using Identities When Sine and Cosine Are Given

Given $\sin \theta = \dfrac{\sqrt{5}}{5}$ and $\cos \theta = \dfrac{2\sqrt{5}}{5}$, find the exact values of the four remaining trigonometric functions of θ using identities.

Solution Based on a quotient identity from (3), we have

$$\tan \theta = \frac{\sin \theta}{\cos \theta} = \frac{\dfrac{\sqrt{5}}{5}}{\dfrac{2\sqrt{5}}{5}} = \frac{1}{2}$$

Then we use the reciprocal identities from (2) to get

$$\csc\theta = \frac{1}{\sin\theta} = \frac{1}{\dfrac{\sqrt5}{5}} = \frac{5}{\sqrt5} = \sqrt5 \qquad \sec\theta = \frac{1}{\cos\theta} = \frac{1}{\dfrac{2\sqrt5}{5}} = \frac{5}{2\sqrt5} = \frac{\sqrt5}{2} \qquad \cot\theta = \frac{1}{\tan\theta} = \frac{1}{\dfrac12} = 2$$

↵

━━━━**Now Work** PROBLEM 35

The equation of the unit circle is $x^2 + y^2 = 1$ or, equivalently,

$$y^2 + x^2 = 1$$

If $P = (x, y)$ is the point on the unit circle that corresponds to the angle θ, then $y = \sin\theta$ and $x = \cos\theta$, so we have

$$(\sin\theta)^2 + (\cos\theta)^2 = 1 \qquad\qquad \textbf{(4)}$$

It is customary to write $\sin^2\theta$ instead of $(\sin\theta)^2$, $\cos^2\theta$ instead of $(\cos\theta)^2$, and so on. With this notation, we can rewrite equation (4) as

$$\boxed{\sin^2\theta + \cos^2\theta = 1 \qquad\qquad \textbf{(5)}}$$

If $\cos\theta \neq 0$, we can divide each side of equation (5) by $\cos^2\theta$.

$$\frac{\sin^2\theta}{\cos^2\theta} + \frac{\cos^2\theta}{\cos^2\theta} = \frac{1}{\cos^2\theta}$$

$$\left(\frac{\sin\theta}{\cos\theta}\right)^2 + 1 = \left(\frac{1}{\cos\theta}\right)^2$$

Now use identities (2) and (3) to get

$$\boxed{\tan^2\theta + 1 = \sec^2\theta \qquad\qquad \textbf{(6)}}$$

Similarly, if $\sin\theta \neq 0$, we can divide equation (5) by $\sin^2\theta$ and use identities (2) and (3) to get $1 + \cot^2\theta = \csc^2\theta$, which we write as

$$\boxed{\cot^2\theta + 1 = \csc^2\theta \qquad\qquad \textbf{(7)}}$$

Collectively, the identities in (5), (6), and (7) are referred to as the **Pythagorean identities.**

Let's pause here to summarize the fundamental identities.

Fundamental Identities

$$\tan\theta = \frac{\sin\theta}{\cos\theta} \qquad\qquad\qquad\qquad \cot\theta = \frac{\cos\theta}{\sin\theta}$$

$$\csc\theta = \frac{1}{\sin\theta} \qquad \sec\theta = \frac{1}{\cos\theta} \qquad \cot\theta = \frac{1}{\tan\theta}$$

$$\sin^2\theta + \cos^2\theta = 1 \qquad \tan^2\theta + 1 = \sec^2\theta \qquad \cot^2\theta + 1 = \csc^2\theta$$

EXAMPLE 4

Finding the Exact Value of a Trigonometric Expression Using Identities

Find the exact value of each expression. Do not use a calculator.

(a) $\tan 20° - \dfrac{\sin 20°}{\cos 20°}$
(b) $\sin^2\dfrac{\pi}{12} + \dfrac{1}{\sec^2\dfrac{\pi}{12}}$

Solution (a) $\tan 20° - \dfrac{\sin 20°}{\cos 20°} = \tan 20° - \tan 20° = 0$

$\qquad\qquad\qquad\qquad \underset{\displaystyle \frac{\sin\theta}{\cos\theta} = \tan\theta}{\uparrow}$

(b) $\sin^2 \dfrac{\pi}{12} + \dfrac{1}{\sec^2 \dfrac{\pi}{12}} = \sin^2 \dfrac{\pi}{12} + \cos^2 \dfrac{\pi}{12} = 1$

$\qquad\qquad\qquad \underset{\displaystyle \cos\theta = \frac{1}{\sec\theta}}{\uparrow} \qquad\qquad \underset{\displaystyle \sin^2\theta + \cos^2\theta = 1}{\uparrow}$

Now Work PROBLEM 79

5 Find the Exact Values of the Trigonometric Functions of an Angle Given One of the Functions and the Quadrant of the Angle

Many problems require finding the exact values of the remaining trigonometric functions when the value of one of them is known and the quadrant in which θ lies can be found. There are two approaches to solving such problems. One approach uses a circle of radius r; the other uses identities.

When using identities, sometimes a rearrangement is required. For example, the Pythagorean identity

$$\sin^2 \theta + \cos^2 \theta = 1$$

can be solved for $\sin \theta$ in terms of $\cos \theta$ (or vice versa) as follows:

$$\sin^2 \theta = 1 - \cos^2 \theta$$
$$\sin \theta = \pm\sqrt{1 - \cos^2 \theta}$$

where the $+$ sign is used if $\sin \theta > 0$ and the $-$ sign is used if $\sin \theta < 0$. Similarly, in $\tan^2 \theta + 1 = \sec^2 \theta$, we can solve for $\tan \theta$ (or $\sec \theta$), and in $\cot^2 \theta + 1 = \csc^2 \theta$, we can solve for $\cot \theta$ (or $\csc \theta$).

EXAMPLE 5 **Finding Exact Values Given One Value and the Sign of Another**

Given that $\sin \theta = \dfrac{1}{3}$ and $\cos \theta < 0$, find the exact value of each of the remaining five trigonometric functions.

Solution 1 Using a Circle

Suppose that $P = (x, y)$ is the point on a circle that corresponds to θ. Since $\sin \theta = \dfrac{1}{3} > 0$ and $\cos \theta < 0$, the point $P = (x, y)$ is in quadrant II. Because $\sin \theta = \dfrac{1}{3} = \dfrac{y}{r}$, we let $y = 1$ and $r = 3$. The point $P = (x, y) = (x, 1)$ that corresponds to θ lies on the circle of radius 3 centered at the origin: $x^2 + y^2 = 9$. See Figure 41.

To find x, we use the fact that $x^2 + y^2 = 9$, $y = 1$, and P is in quadrant II (so $x < 0$).

$$x^2 + y^2 = 9$$
$$x^2 + 1^2 = 9 \qquad y = 1$$
$$x^2 = 8$$
$$x = -2\sqrt{2} \quad x < 0$$

Figure 41

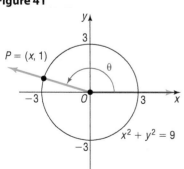

$P = (x, 1)$
$x^2 + y^2 = 9$

Since $x = -2\sqrt{2}$, $y = 1$, and $r = 3$, we find that

$$\cos\theta = \frac{x}{r} = -\frac{2\sqrt{2}}{3} \qquad \tan\theta = \frac{y}{x} = \frac{1}{-2\sqrt{2}} = -\frac{\sqrt{2}}{4}$$

$$\csc\theta = \frac{r}{y} = \frac{3}{1} = 3 \qquad \sec\theta = \frac{r}{x} = \frac{3}{-2\sqrt{2}} = -\frac{3\sqrt{2}}{4} \qquad \cot\theta = \frac{x}{y} = \frac{-2\sqrt{2}}{1} = -2\sqrt{2}$$

Solution 2
Using Identities

First, solve the identity $\sin^2\theta + \cos^2\theta = 1$ for $\cos\theta$.

$$\sin^2\theta + \cos^2\theta = 1$$
$$\cos^2\theta = 1 - \sin^2\theta$$
$$\cos\theta = \pm\sqrt{1 - \sin^2\theta}$$

Because $\cos\theta < 0$, choose the minus sign and use the fact that $\sin\theta = \frac{1}{3}$.

$$\cos\theta = -\sqrt{1 - \sin^2\theta} = -\sqrt{1 - \frac{1}{9}} = -\sqrt{\frac{8}{9}} = -\frac{2\sqrt{2}}{3}$$

$$\uparrow$$
$$\sin\theta = \frac{1}{3}$$

Now we know the values of $\sin\theta$ and $\cos\theta$, so we can use quotient and reciprocal identities to get

$$\tan\theta = \frac{\sin\theta}{\cos\theta} = \frac{\frac{1}{3}}{\frac{-2\sqrt{2}}{3}} = \frac{1}{-2\sqrt{2}} = -\frac{\sqrt{2}}{4} \qquad \cot\theta = \frac{1}{\tan\theta} = -2\sqrt{2}$$

$$\sec\theta = \frac{1}{\cos\theta} = \frac{1}{\frac{-2\sqrt{2}}{3}} = \frac{-3}{2\sqrt{2}} = -\frac{3\sqrt{2}}{4} \qquad \csc\theta = \frac{1}{\sin\theta} = \frac{1}{\frac{1}{3}} = 3$$

Finding the Values of the Trigonometric Functions of θ When the Value of One Function Is Known and the Quadrant of θ Is Known

Given the value of one trigonometric function and the quadrant in which θ lies, the exact value of each of the remaining five trigonometric functions can be found in either of two ways.

Method 1 Using a Circle of Radius r

STEP 1: Draw a circle centered at the origin showing the location of the angle θ and the point $P = (x, y)$ that corresponds to θ. The radius of the circle that contains $P = (x, y)$ is $r = \sqrt{x^2 + y^2}$.

STEP 2: Assign a value to two of the three variables x, y, r based on the value of the given trigonometric function and the location of P.

STEP 3: Use the fact that P lies on the circle $x^2 + y^2 = r^2$ to find the value of the missing variable.

STEP 4: Apply the theorem on page 374 to find the values of the remaining trigonometric functions.

Method 2 Using Identities

Use appropriately selected identities to find the value of each remaining trigonometric function.

EXAMPLE 6

Given the Value of One Trigonometric Function and the Sign of Another, Find the Values of the Remaining Ones

Given that $\tan \theta = \dfrac{1}{2}$ and $\sin \theta < 0$, find the exact value of each of the remaining five trigonometric functions of θ.

Solution 1
Using a Circle

Figure 42

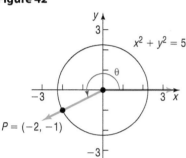

$x^2 + y^2 = 5$

$P = (-2, -1)$

STEP 1: Since $\tan \theta = \dfrac{1}{2} > 0$ and $\sin \theta < 0$, the point $P = (x, y)$ that corresponds to θ lies in quadrant III. See Figure 42.

STEP 2: Since $\tan \theta = \dfrac{1}{2} = \dfrac{y}{x}$ and θ lies in quadrant III, let $x = -2$ and $y = -1$.

STEP 3: With $x = -2$ and $y = -1$, then $r = \sqrt{x^2 + y^2} = \sqrt{(-2)^2 + (-1)^2} = \sqrt{5}$, P lies on the circle $x^2 + y^2 = 5$.

STEP 4: So apply the theorem on page 374 using $x = -2$, $y = -1$, and $r = \sqrt{5}$.

$$\sin \theta = \frac{y}{r} = \frac{-1}{\sqrt{5}} = -\frac{\sqrt{5}}{5} \qquad \cos \theta = \frac{x}{r} = \frac{-2}{\sqrt{5}} = -\frac{2\sqrt{5}}{5}$$

$$\csc \theta = \frac{r}{y} = \frac{\sqrt{5}}{-1} = -\sqrt{5} \qquad \sec \theta = \frac{r}{x} = \frac{\sqrt{5}}{-2} = -\frac{\sqrt{5}}{2} \qquad \cot \theta = \frac{x}{y} = \frac{-2}{-1} = 2$$

Solution 2
Using Identities

Because we know the value of $\tan \theta$, we use the Pythagorean identity that involves $\tan \theta$, that is, $\tan^2 \theta + 1 = \sec^2 \theta$. Since $\tan \theta = \dfrac{1}{2} > 0$ and $\sin \theta < 0$, then θ lies in quadrant III, where $\sec \theta < 0$.

$$\tan^2 \theta + 1 = \sec^2 \theta \qquad \textit{Pythagorean identity}$$

$$\left(\frac{1}{2}\right)^2 + 1 = \sec^2 \theta \qquad \tan \theta = \frac{1}{2}$$

$$\sec^2 \theta = \frac{1}{4} + 1 = \frac{5}{4} \qquad \textit{Proceed to solve for } \sec \theta.$$

$$\sec \theta = -\frac{\sqrt{5}}{2} \qquad \sec \theta < 0$$

Now we know $\tan \theta = \dfrac{1}{2}$ and $\sec \theta = -\dfrac{\sqrt{5}}{2}$. Using reciprocal identities, we find

$$\cos \theta = \frac{1}{\sec \theta} = \frac{1}{-\dfrac{\sqrt{5}}{2}} = -\frac{2}{\sqrt{5}} = -\frac{2\sqrt{5}}{5}$$

$$\cot \theta = \frac{1}{\tan \theta} = \frac{1}{\dfrac{1}{2}} = 2$$

To find $\sin \theta$, use the following reasoning:

$$\tan \theta = \frac{\sin \theta}{\cos \theta} \quad \text{so} \quad \sin \theta = \tan \theta \cdot \cos \theta = \left(\frac{1}{2}\right) \cdot \left(-\frac{2\sqrt{5}}{5}\right) = -\frac{\sqrt{5}}{5}$$

$$\csc \theta = \frac{1}{\sin \theta} = \frac{1}{-\dfrac{\sqrt{5}}{5}} = -\frac{5}{\sqrt{5}} = -\sqrt{5}$$

—**Now Work** PROBLEM 43

6 Use Even–Odd Properties to Find the Exact Values of the Trigonometric Functions

Recall that a function f is even if $f(-\theta) = f(\theta)$ for all θ in the domain of f; a function f is odd if $f(-\theta) = -f(\theta)$ for all θ in the domain of f. We will now show that the trigonometric functions sine, tangent, cotangent, and cosecant are odd functions and the functions cosine and secant are even functions.

Even–Odd Properties

$$\sin(-\theta) = -\sin\theta \qquad \cos(-\theta) = \cos\theta \qquad \tan(-\theta) = -\tan\theta$$
$$\csc(-\theta) = -\csc\theta \qquad \sec(-\theta) = \sec\theta \qquad \cot(-\theta) = -\cot\theta$$

> **In Words**
> Cosine and secant are even functions; the others are odd functions.

Figure 43

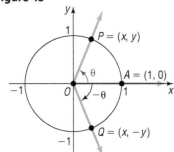

Proof   Let $P = (x, y)$ be the point on the unit circle that corresponds to the angle θ. See Figure 43. Using symmetry, the point Q on the unit circle that corresponds to the angle $-\theta$ will have coordinates $(x, -y)$. Using the definition of the trigonometric functions, we have

$$\sin\theta = y \qquad \sin(-\theta) = -y \qquad \cos\theta = x \qquad \cos(-\theta) = x$$

so

$$\sin(-\theta) = -y = -\sin\theta \qquad \cos(-\theta) = x = \cos\theta$$

Now, using these results and some of the fundamental identities, we have

$$\tan(-\theta) = \frac{\sin(-\theta)}{\cos(-\theta)} = \frac{-\sin\theta}{\cos\theta} = -\tan\theta \qquad \cot(-\theta) = \frac{1}{\tan(-\theta)} = \frac{1}{-\tan\theta} = -\cot\theta$$

$$\sec(-\theta) = \frac{1}{\cos(-\theta)} = \frac{1}{\cos\theta} = \sec\theta \qquad \csc(-\theta) = \frac{1}{\sin(-\theta)} = \frac{1}{-\sin\theta} = -\csc\theta$$

∎

EXAMPLE 7   **Finding Exact Values Using Even–Odd Properties**

Find the exact value of:

(a) $\sin(-45°)$ (b) $\cos(-\pi)$ (c) $\cot\left(-\dfrac{3\pi}{2}\right)$ (d) $\tan\left(-\dfrac{37\pi}{4}\right)$

Solution   (a) $\sin(-45°) = \underset{\uparrow}{-\sin 45°} = -\dfrac{\sqrt{2}}{2}$ (b) $\cos(-\pi) = \underset{\uparrow}{\cos\pi} = -1$

       Odd function   Even function

(c) $\cot\left(-\dfrac{3\pi}{2}\right) = \underset{\uparrow}{-\cot\dfrac{3\pi}{2}} = 0$

            Odd function

(d) $\tan\left(-\dfrac{37\pi}{4}\right) = \underset{\uparrow}{-\tan\dfrac{37\pi}{4}} = -\tan\left(\dfrac{\pi}{4} + 9\pi\right) = \underset{\uparrow}{-\tan\dfrac{\pi}{4}} = -1$

            Odd function   Period is π.

━━━━**Now Work** PROBLEM 59

6.3 Assess Your Understanding

1. The domain of the function $f(x) = \dfrac{x + 1}{2x + 1}$ is _____. (pp. 46–56)

2. A function for which $f(x) = f(-x)$ for all x in the domain of f is called a(n) _____ function. (pp. 69–70)

3. *True or False* The function $f(x) = \sqrt{x}$ is even. (pp. 69–70)

4. *True or False* The equation $x^2 + 2x = (x + 1)^2 - 1$ is an identity. (p. A44)

Concepts and Vocabulary

5. The sine, cosine, cosecant, and secant functions have period ____; the tangent and cotangent functions have period ___.

6. The domain of the tangent function is ____.

7. The range of the sine function is _____.

8. *True or False* The only even trigonometric functions are the cosine and secant functions.

9. $\sin^2 \theta + \cos^2 \theta = $ _____.

10. *True or False* $\sec \theta = \dfrac{1}{\sin \theta}$

Skill Building

In Problems 11–26, use the fact that the trigonometric functions are periodic to find the exact value of each expression. Do not use a calculator.

11. $\sin 405°$ **12.** $\cos 420°$ **13.** $\tan 405°$ **14.** $\sin 390°$ **15.** $\csc 450°$ **16.** $\sec 540°$

17. $\cot 390°$ **18.** $\sec 420°$ **19.** $\cos \dfrac{33\pi}{4}$ **20.** $\sin \dfrac{9\pi}{4}$ **21.** $\tan(21\pi)$ **22.** $\csc \dfrac{9\pi}{2}$

23. $\sec \dfrac{17\pi}{4}$ **24.** $\cot \dfrac{17\pi}{4}$ **25.** $\tan \dfrac{19\pi}{6}$ **26.** $\sec \dfrac{25\pi}{6}$

In Problems 27–34, name the quadrant in which the angle θ lies.

27. $\sin \theta > 0, \quad \cos \theta < 0$ **28.** $\sin \theta < 0, \quad \cos \theta > 0$ **29.** $\sin \theta < 0, \quad \tan \theta < 0$ **30.** $\cos \theta > 0, \quad \tan \theta > 0$

31. $\cos \theta > 0, \quad \tan \theta < 0$ **32.** $\cos \theta < 0, \quad \tan \theta > 0$ **33.** $\sec \theta < 0, \quad \sin \theta > 0$ **34.** $\csc \theta > 0, \quad \cos \theta < 0$

In Problems 35–42, $\sin \theta$ and $\cos \theta$ are given. Find the exact value of each of the four remaining trigonometric functions.

35. $\sin \theta = -\dfrac{3}{5}, \quad \cos \theta = \dfrac{4}{5}$ **36.** $\sin \theta = \dfrac{4}{5}, \quad \cos \theta = -\dfrac{3}{5}$ **37.** $\sin \theta = \dfrac{2\sqrt{5}}{5}, \quad \cos \theta = \dfrac{\sqrt{5}}{5}$

38. $\sin \theta = -\dfrac{\sqrt{5}}{5}, \quad \cos \theta = -\dfrac{2\sqrt{5}}{5}$ **39.** $\sin \theta = \dfrac{1}{2}, \quad \cos \theta = \dfrac{\sqrt{3}}{2}$ **40.** $\sin \theta = \dfrac{\sqrt{3}}{2}, \quad \cos \theta = \dfrac{1}{2}$

41. $\sin \theta = -\dfrac{1}{3}, \quad \cos \theta = \dfrac{2\sqrt{2}}{3}$ **42.** $\sin \theta = \dfrac{2\sqrt{2}}{3}, \quad \cos \theta = -\dfrac{1}{3}$

In Problems 43–58, find the exact value of each of the remaining trigonometric functions of θ.

43. $\sin \theta = \dfrac{12}{13}, \quad \theta$ in quadrant II   **44.** $\cos \theta = \dfrac{3}{5}, \quad \theta$ in quadrant IV   **45.** $\cos \theta = -\dfrac{4}{5}, \quad \theta$ in quadrant III

46. $\sin \theta = -\dfrac{5}{13}, \quad \theta$ in quadrant III   **47.** $\sin \theta = \dfrac{5}{13}, \quad 90° < \theta < 180°$ **48.** $\cos \theta = \dfrac{4}{5}, \quad 270° < \theta < 360°$

49. $\cos \theta = -\dfrac{1}{3}, \quad \dfrac{\pi}{2} < \theta < \pi$ **50.** $\sin \theta = -\dfrac{2}{3}, \quad \pi < \theta < \dfrac{3\pi}{2}$ **51.** $\sin \theta = \dfrac{2}{3}, \quad \tan \theta < 0$

52. $\cos \theta = -\dfrac{1}{4}, \quad \tan \theta > 0$ **53.** $\sec \theta = 2, \quad \sin \theta < 0$ **54.** $\csc \theta = 3, \quad \cot \theta < 0$

55. $\tan \theta = \dfrac{3}{4}, \quad \sin \theta < 0$ **56.** $\cot \theta = \dfrac{4}{3}, \quad \cos \theta < 0$ **57.** $\tan \theta = -\dfrac{1}{3}, \quad \sin \theta > 0$

58. $\sec \theta = -2, \quad \tan \theta > 0$

In Problems 59–76, use the even–odd properties to find the exact value of each expression. Do not use a calculator.

59. $\sin(-60°)$

60. $\cos(-30°)$

61. $\tan(-30°)$

62. $\sin(-135°)$

63. $\sec(-60°)$

64. $\csc(-30°)$

65. $\sin(-90°)$

66. $\cos(-270°)$

67. $\tan\left(-\dfrac{\pi}{4}\right)$

68. $\sin(-\pi)$

69. $\cos\left(-\dfrac{\pi}{4}\right)$

70. $\sin\left(-\dfrac{\pi}{3}\right)$

71. $\tan(-\pi)$

72. $\sin\left(-\dfrac{3\pi}{2}\right)$

73. $\csc\left(-\dfrac{\pi}{4}\right)$

74. $\sec(-\pi)$

75. $\sec\left(-\dfrac{\pi}{6}\right)$

76. $\csc\left(-\dfrac{\pi}{3}\right)$

In Problems 77–88, use properties of the trigonometric functions to find the exact value of each expression. Do not use a calculator.

77. $\sin^2 40° + \cos^2 40°$

78. $\sec^2 18° - \tan^2 18°$

79. $\sin 80° \csc 80°$

80. $\tan 10° \cot 10°$

81. $\tan 40° - \dfrac{\sin 40°}{\cos 40°}$

82. $\cot 20° - \dfrac{\cos 20°}{\sin 20°}$

83. $\cos 400° \cdot \sec 40°$

84. $\tan 200° \cdot \cot 20°$

85. $\sin\left(-\dfrac{\pi}{12}\right) \csc \dfrac{25\pi}{12}$

86. $\sec\left(-\dfrac{\pi}{18}\right) \cdot \cos \dfrac{37\pi}{18}$

87. $\dfrac{\sin(-20°)}{\cos 380°} + \tan 200°$

88. $\dfrac{\sin 70°}{\cos(-430°)} + \tan(-70°)$

89. If $\sin \theta = 0.3$, find the value of:

$$\sin \theta + \sin(\theta + 2\pi) + \sin(\theta + 4\pi)$$

90. If $\cos \theta = 0.2$, find the value of:

$$\cos \theta + \cos(\theta + 2\pi) + \cos(\theta + 4\pi)$$

91. If $\tan \theta = 3$, find the value of:

$$\tan \theta + \tan(\theta + \pi) + \tan(\theta + 2\pi)$$

92. If $\cot \theta = -2$, find the value of:

$$\cot \theta + \cot(\theta - \pi) + \cot(\theta - 2\pi)$$

93. Find the exact value of:

$$\sin 1° + \sin 2° + \sin 3° + \cdots + \sin 358° + \sin 359°$$

94. Find the exact value of:

$$\cos 1° + \cos 2° + \cos 3° + \cdots + \cos 358° + \cos 359°$$

95. What is the domain of the sine function?

96. What is the domain of the cosine function?

97. For what numbers θ is $f(\theta) = \tan \theta$ not defined?

98. For what numbers θ is $f(\theta) = \cot \theta$ not defined?

99. For what numbers θ is $f(\theta) = \sec \theta$ not defined?

100. For what numbers θ is $f(\theta) = \csc \theta$ not defined?

101. What is the range of the sine function?

102. What is the range of the cosine function?

103. What is the range of the tangent function?

104. What is the range of the cotangent function?

105. What is the range of the secant function?

106. What is the range of the cosecant function?

107. Is the sine function even, odd, or neither? Is its graph symmetric? With respect to what?

108. Is the cosine function even, odd, or neither? Is its graph symmetric? With respect to what?

109. Is the tangent function even, odd, or neither? Is its graph symmetric? With respect to what?

110. Is the cotangent function even, odd, or neither? Is its graph symmetric? With respect to what?

111. Is the secant function even, odd, or neither? Is its graph symmetric? With respect to what?

112. Is the cosecant function even, odd, or neither? Is its graph symmetric? With respect to what?

Applications and Extensions

In Problems 113–118, use the periodic and even–odd properties.

113. If $f(\theta) = \sin \theta$ and $f(a) = \dfrac{1}{3}$, find the exact value of:

(a) $f(-a)$ (b) $f(a) + f(a + 2\pi) + f(a + 4\pi)$

114. If $f(\theta) = \cos \theta$ and $f(a) = \dfrac{1}{4}$, find the exact value of:

(a) $f(-a)$ (b) $f(a) + f(a + 2\pi) + f(a - 2\pi)$

115. If $f(\theta) = \tan \theta$ and $f(a) = 2$, find the exact value of:

(a) $f(-a)$ (b) $f(a) + f(a + \pi) + f(a + 2\pi)$

116. If $f(\theta) = \cot \theta$ and $f(a) = -3$, find the exact value of:

(a) $f(-a)$ (b) $f(a) + f(a + \pi) + f(a + 4\pi)$

117. If $f(\theta) = \sec \theta$ and $f(a) = -4$, find the exact value of:

(a) $f(-a)$ (b) $f(a) + f(a + 2\pi) + f(a + 4\pi)$

118. If $f(\theta) = \csc \theta$ and $f(a) = 2$, find the exact value of:

(a) $f(-a)$ (b) $f(a) + f(a + 2\pi) + f(a + 4\pi)$

119. Calculating the Time of a Trip From a parking lot, you want to walk to a house on the beach. The house is located 1500 feet down a paved path that parallels the ocean, which is 500 feet away. See the illustration. Along the path you can walk 300 feet per minute, but in the sand on the beach you can only walk 100 feet per minute.

The time T to get from the parking lot to the beach house can be expressed as a function of the angle θ shown in the illustration and is

$$T(\theta) = 5 - \frac{5}{3 \tan \theta} + \frac{5}{\sin \theta}, \qquad 0 < \theta < \frac{\pi}{2}$$

Calculate the time T if you walk directly from the parking lot to the house.

[Hint: $\tan \theta = \dfrac{500}{1500}$.**]**

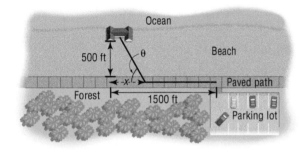

120. Calculating the Time of a Trip Two oceanfront homes are located 8 miles apart on a straight stretch of beach, each a distance of 1 mile from a paved path that parallels the ocean. Sally can jog 8 miles per hour on the paved path, but only 3 miles per hour in the sand on the beach. Because a river flows directly between the two houses, it is necessary to jog in the sand to the road, continue on the path, and then jog directly back in the sand to get from one house to the other. See the illustration. The time T to get from one house to the other as a function of the angle θ shown in the illustration is

$$T(\theta) = 1 + \frac{2}{3 \sin \theta} - \frac{1}{4 \tan \theta} \qquad 0 < \theta < \frac{\pi}{2}$$

(a) Calculate the time T for $\tan \theta = \dfrac{1}{4}$.

(b) Describe the path taken.

(c) Explain why θ must be larger than $14°$.

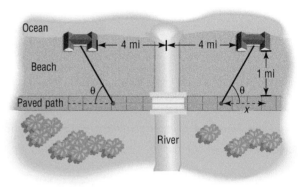

121. Show that the range of the tangent function is the set of all real numbers.

122. Show that the range of the cotangent function is the set of all real numbers.

123. Show that the period of $f(\theta) = \sin \theta$ is 2π.

[Hint: Assume that $0 < p < 2\pi$ exists so that $\sin(\theta + p) = \sin \theta$ for all θ. Let $\theta = 0$ to find p. Then let $\theta = \dfrac{\pi}{2}$ to obtain a contradiction.**]**

124. Show that the period of $f(\theta) = \cos \theta$ is 2π.

125. Show that the period of $f(\theta) = \sec \theta$ is 2π.

126. Show that the period of $f(\theta) = \csc \theta$ is 2π.

127. Show that the period of $f(\theta) = \tan \theta$ is π.

128. Show that the period of $f(\theta) = \cot \theta$ is π.

129. Prove the reciprocal identities given in formula (2).

130. Prove the quotient identities given in formula (3).

131. Establish the identity:

$$(\sin \theta \cos \phi)^2 + (\sin \theta \sin \phi)^2 + \cos^2 \theta = 1$$

Explaining Concepts: Discussion and Writing

132. Write down five properties of the tangent function. Explain the meaning of each.

133. Describe your understanding of the meaning of a periodic function.

134. Explain how to find the value of $\sin 390°$ using periodic properties.

135. Explain how to find the value of $\cos(-45°)$ using even–odd properties.

136. Explain how to find the value of $\sin 390°$ and $\cos(-45°)$ using the unit circle.

'Are You Prepared?' Answers

1. $\left\{ x \mid x \neq -\dfrac{1}{2} \right\}$ **2.** even   **3.** False   **4.** True

6.4 Graphs of the Sine and Cosine Functions*

PREPARING FOR THIS SECTION *Before getting started, review the following:*

- Graphing Techniques: Transformations (Section 2.5, pp. 90–99)

Now Work the 'Are You Prepared?' problems on page 403.

OBJECTIVES 1 Graph Functions of the Form $y = A \sin(\omega x)$ Using Transformations (p. 394)
2 Graph Functions of the Form $y = A \cos(\omega x)$ Using Transformations (p. 396)
3 Determine the Amplitude and Period of Sinusoidal Functions (p. 397)
4 Graph Sinusoidal Functions Using Key Points (p. 398)
5 Find an Equation for a Sinusoidal Graph (p. 402)

Since we want to graph the trigonometric functions in the xy-plane, we shall use the traditional symbols x for the independent variable (or argument) and y for the dependent variable (or value at x) for each function. So we write the six trigonometric functions as

$$y = f(x) = \sin x \qquad y = f(x) = \cos x \qquad y = f(x) = \tan x$$
$$y = f(x) = \csc x \qquad y = f(x) = \sec x \qquad y = f(x) = \cot x$$

 Here the independent variable x represents an angle, measured in radians. In calculus, x will usually be treated as a real number. As we said earlier, these are equivalent ways of viewing x.

The Graph of the Sine Function $y = \sin x$

Since the sine function has period 2π, we only need to graph $y = \sin x$ on the interval $[0, 2\pi]$. The remainder of the graph will consist of repetitions of this portion of the graph.

We begin by constructing Table 6, which lists some points on the graph of $y = \sin x$, $0 \le x \le 2\pi$. As the table shows, the graph of $y = \sin x$, $0 \le x \le 2\pi$, begins at the origin. As x increases from 0 to $\dfrac{\pi}{2}$, the value of $y = \sin x$ increases from 0 to 1; as x increases from $\dfrac{\pi}{2}$ to π to $\dfrac{3\pi}{2}$, the value of y decreases from 1 to 0 to -1; as x increases from $\dfrac{3\pi}{2}$ to 2π, the value of y increases from -1 to 0. If we plot the points listed in Table 6 and connect them with a smooth curve, we obtain the graph shown in Figure 44.

Table 6

x	$y = \sin x$	(x, y)
0	0	$(0, 0)$
$\dfrac{\pi}{6}$	$\dfrac{1}{2}$	$\left(\dfrac{\pi}{6}, \dfrac{1}{2}\right)$
$\dfrac{\pi}{2}$	1	$\left(\dfrac{\pi}{2}, 1\right)$
$\dfrac{5\pi}{6}$	$\dfrac{1}{2}$	$\left(\dfrac{5\pi}{6}, \dfrac{1}{2}\right)$
π	0	$(\pi, 0)$
$\dfrac{7\pi}{6}$	$-\dfrac{1}{2}$	$\left(\dfrac{7\pi}{6}, -\dfrac{1}{2}\right)$
$\dfrac{3\pi}{2}$	-1	$\left(\dfrac{3\pi}{2}, -1\right)$
$\dfrac{11\pi}{6}$	$-\dfrac{1}{2}$	$\left(\dfrac{11\pi}{6}, -\dfrac{1}{2}\right)$
2π	0	$(2\pi, 0)$

Figure 44
$y = \sin x, 0 \le x \le 2\pi$

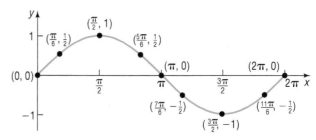

The graph in Figure 44 is one period, or **cycle,** of the graph of $y = \sin x$. To obtain a more complete graph of $y = \sin x$, continue the graph in each direction, as shown in Figure 45.

---

* For those who wish to include phase shifts here, Section 6.6 can be covered immediately after Section 6.4 without loss of continuity.

Figure 45
$y = \sin x, -\infty < x < \infty$

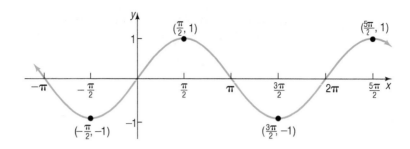

The graph of $y = \sin x$ illustrates some of the facts that we already know about the sine function.

Properties of the Sine Function $y = \sin x$

1. The domain is the set of all real numbers.
2. The range consists of all real numbers from -1 to 1, inclusive.
3. The sine function is an odd function, as the symmetry of the graph with respect to the origin indicates.
4. The sine function is periodic, with period 2π.
5. The x-intercepts are $\ldots, -2\pi, -\pi, 0, \pi, 2\pi, 3\pi, \ldots$; the y-intercept is 0.
6. The absolute maximum is 1 and occurs at $x = \ldots, -\dfrac{3\pi}{2}, \dfrac{\pi}{2}, \dfrac{5\pi}{2}, \dfrac{9\pi}{2}, \ldots$;

   the absolute minimum is -1 and occurs at $x = \ldots, -\dfrac{\pi}{2}, \dfrac{3\pi}{2}, \dfrac{7\pi}{2}, \dfrac{11\pi}{2}, \ldots$.

Now Work PROBLEM 9

1 Graph Functions of the Form $y = A\sin(\omega x)$ Using Transformations

EXAMPLE 1

Graphing Functions of the Form $y = A\sin(\omega x)$ Using Transformations

Graph $y = 3\sin x$ using transformations.

Solution Figure 46 illustrates the steps.

Figure 46

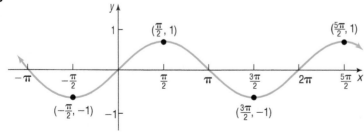

(a) $y = \sin x$

Multiply by 3;
vertical stretch
by a factor of 3

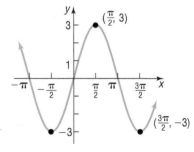

(b) $y = 3\sin x$

| EXAMPLE 2 | **Graphing Functions of the Form $y = A \sin(\omega x)$ Using Transformations** |

Graph $y = -\sin(2x)$ using transformations.

Solution   Figure 47 illustrates the steps.

Figure 47

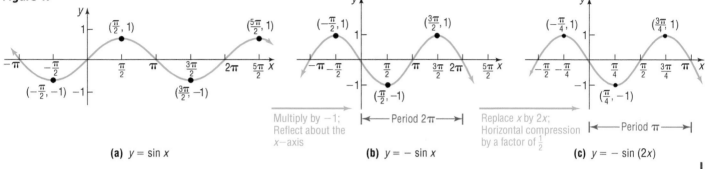

(a) $y = \sin x$

Multiply by -1; Reflect about the x-axis

(b) $y = -\sin x$ — Period 2π —

Replace x by $2x$; Horizontal compression by a factor of $\frac{1}{2}$

(c) $y = -\sin(2x)$ — Period π —

Notice in Figure 47(c) that the period of the function $y = -\sin(2x)$ is π due to the horizontal compression of the original period 2π by a factor of $\frac{1}{2}$.

Now Work   PROBLEM 37 USING TRANSFORMATIONS

The Graph of the Cosine Function

The cosine function also has period 2π. We proceed as we did with the sine function by constructing Table 7, which lists some points on the graph of $y = \cos x$, $0 \le x \le 2\pi$. As the table shows, the graph of $y = \cos x$, $0 \le x \le 2\pi$, begins at the point $(0, 1)$. As x increases from 0 to $\frac{\pi}{2}$ to π, the value of y decreases from 1 to 0 to -1; as x increases from π to $\frac{3\pi}{2}$ to 2π, the value of y increases from -1 to 0 to 1. As before, plot the points in Table 7 to get one period or cycle of the graph. See Figure 48.

Table 7

x	$y = \cos x$	(x, y)
0	1	$(0, 1)$
$\frac{\pi}{3}$	$\frac{1}{2}$	$\left(\frac{\pi}{3}, \frac{1}{2}\right)$
$\frac{\pi}{2}$	0	$\left(\frac{\pi}{2}, 0\right)$
$\frac{2\pi}{3}$	$-\frac{1}{2}$	$\left(\frac{2\pi}{3}, -\frac{1}{2}\right)$
π	-1	$(\pi, -1)$
$\frac{4\pi}{3}$	$-\frac{1}{2}$	$\left(\frac{4\pi}{3}, -\frac{1}{2}\right)$
$\frac{3\pi}{2}$	0	$\left(\frac{3\pi}{2}, 0\right)$
$\frac{5\pi}{3}$	$\frac{1}{2}$	$\left(\frac{5\pi}{3}, \frac{1}{2}\right)$
2π	1	$(2\pi, 1)$

Figure 48
$y = \cos x, 0 \le x \le 2\pi$

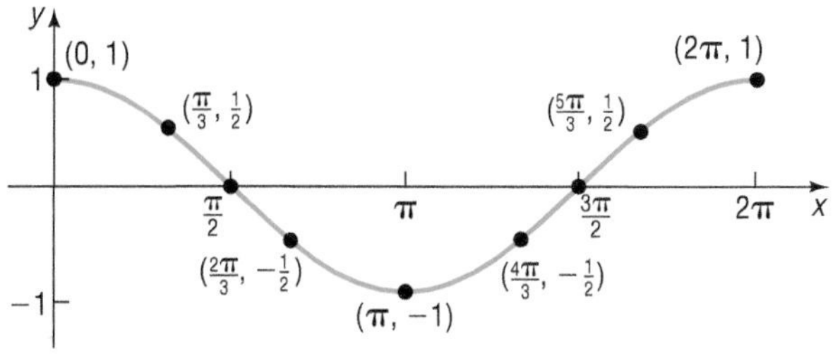

A more complete graph of $y = \cos x$ is obtained by continuing the graph in each direction, as shown in Figure 49.

Figure 49
$y = \cos x, -\infty < x < \infty$

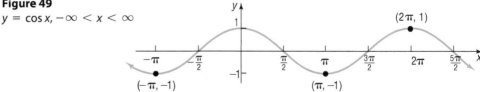

The graph of $y = \cos x$ illustrates some of the facts that we already know about the cosine function.

Properties of the Cosine Function

1. The domain is the set of all real numbers.
2. The range consists of all real numbers from -1 to 1, inclusive.
3. The cosine function is an even function, as the symmetry of the graph with respect to the y-axis indicates.
4. The cosine function is periodic, with period 2π.
5. The x-intercepts are $\ldots, -\dfrac{3\pi}{2}, -\dfrac{\pi}{2}, \dfrac{\pi}{2}, \dfrac{3\pi}{2}, \dfrac{5\pi}{2}, \ldots$; the y-intercept is 1.
6. The absolute maximum is 1 and occurs at $x = \ldots, -2\pi, 0, 2\pi, 4\pi, 6\pi, \ldots$; the absolute minimum is -1 and occurs at $x = \ldots, -\pi, \pi, 3\pi, 5\pi, \ldots$.

2 Graph Functions of the Form $y = A\cos(\omega x)$ Using Transformations

---

EXAMPLE 3 **Graphing Functions of the Form $y = A\cos(\omega x)$ Using Transformations**

Graph $y = 2\cos(3x)$ using transformations.

Solution Figure 50 shows the steps.

Figure 50

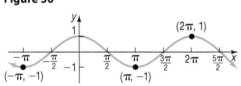

(a) $y = \cos x$

Multiply by 2;
Vertical stretch
by a factor of 2

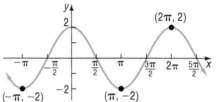

(b) $y = 2\cos x$

Replace x by $3x$;
Horizontal
compression by
a factor of $\frac{1}{3}$

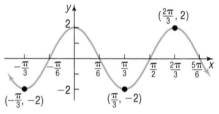

(c) $y = 2\cos(3x)$

Notice in Figure 50(c) that the period of the function $y = 2\cos(3x)$ is $\dfrac{2\pi}{3}$ due to the compression of the original period 2π by a factor of $\dfrac{1}{3}$.

Now Work PROBLEM 45 USING TRANSFORMATIONS

Sinusoidal Graphs

Shift the graph of $y = \cos x$ to the right $\dfrac{\pi}{2}$ units to obtain the graph of $y = \cos\left(x - \dfrac{\pi}{2}\right)$. See Figure 51(a). Now look at the graph of $y = \sin x$ in Figure 51(b). We see that the graph of $y = \sin x$ is the same as the graph of $y = \cos\left(x - \dfrac{\pi}{2}\right)$.

Figure 51

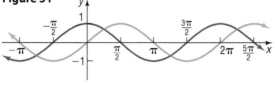

(a) $y = \cos x$ $y = \cos\left(x - \frac{\pi}{2}\right)$

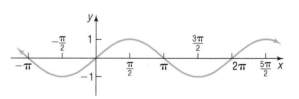

(b) $y = \sin x$

Based on Figure 51, we conjecture that

$$\sin x = \cos\left(x - \frac{\pi}{2}\right)$$

(We shall prove this fact in Chapter 7.) Because of this relationship, the graphs of functions of the form $y = A \sin(\omega x)$ or $y = A \cos(\omega x)$ are referred to as **sinusoidal graphs.**

3 Determine the Amplitude and Period of Sinusoidal Functions

In Figure 52(b) we show the graph of $y = 2 \cos x$. Notice that the values of $y = 2 \cos x$ lie between -2 and 2, inclusive.

Figure 52

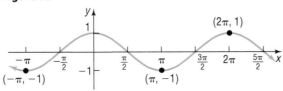

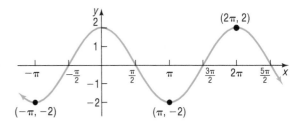

(a) $y = \cos x$ Multiply by 2; Vertical stretch by a factor of 2   **(b)** $y = 2 \cos x$

In general, the values of the functions $y = A \sin x$ and $y = A \cos x$, where $A \neq 0$, will always satisfy the inequalities

$$-|A| \le A \sin x \le |A| \quad \text{and} \quad -|A| \le A \cos x \le |A|$$

respectively. The number $|A|$ is called the **amplitude** of $y = A \sin x$ or $y = A \cos x$. See Figure 53.

Figure 53

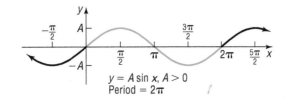

$y = A \sin x, A > 0$
Period $= 2\pi$

In Figure 54(b), we show the graph of $y = \cos(3x)$. Notice that the period of this function is $\dfrac{2\pi}{3}$, due to the horizontal compression of the original period 2π by a factor of $\dfrac{1}{3}$.

Figure 54

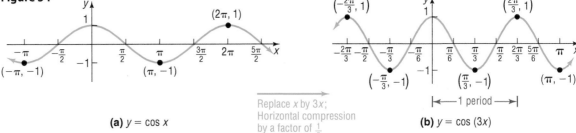

(a) $y = \cos x$ Replace x by $3x$; Horizontal compression by a factor of $\frac{1}{3}$ **(b)** $y = \cos(3x)$

In general, if $\omega > 0$, the functions $y = \sin(\omega x)$ and $y = \cos(\omega x)$ will have period $T = \dfrac{2\pi}{\omega}$. To see why, recall that the graph of $y = \sin(\omega x)$ is obtained from the graph of $y = \sin x$ by performing a horizontal compression or stretch by a factor $\dfrac{1}{\omega}$. This horizontal compression replaces the interval $[0, 2\pi]$, which contains one period of the graph of $y = \sin x$, by the interval $\left[0, \dfrac{2\pi}{\omega}\right]$, which contains one period of the graph of $y = \sin(\omega x)$. So, the function $y = \cos(3x)$, graphed in Figure 54(b), with $\omega = 3$, has period $\dfrac{2\pi}{\omega} = \dfrac{2\pi}{3}$.

One period of the graph of $y = \sin(\omega x)$ or $y = \cos(\omega x)$ is called a **cycle.** Figure 55 illustrates the general situation. The blue portion of the graph is one cycle.

Figure 55

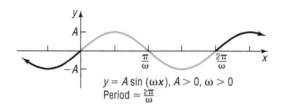

$y = A \sin(\omega x),\ A > 0,\ \omega > 0$
Period $= \frac{2\pi}{\omega}$

NOTE Recall that a function f is even if $f(-x) = f(x)$; a function f is odd if $f(-x) = -f(x)$. Since the sine function is odd, $\sin(-x) = -\sin x$; since the cosine function is even, $\cos(-x) = \cos x$. ■

When graphing $y = \sin(\omega x)$ or $y = \cos(\omega x)$, we want ω to be positive. To graph $y = \sin(-\omega x),\ \omega > 0$ or $y = \cos(-\omega x),\ \omega > 0$, we use the Even–Odd Properties of the sine and cosine functions as follows:

$$\sin(-\omega x) = -\sin(\omega x) \quad \text{and} \quad \cos(-\omega x) = \cos(\omega x)$$

This gives us an equivalent form in which the coefficient of x in the argument is positive. For example,

$$\sin(-2x) = -\sin(2x) \quad \text{and} \quad \cos(-\pi x) = \cos(\pi x)$$

Because of this, we can assume that $\omega > 0$.

THEOREM

If $\omega > 0$, the amplitude and period of $y = A\sin(\omega x)$ and $y = A\cos(\omega x)$ are given by

$$\text{Amplitude} = |A| \qquad \text{Period} = T = \dfrac{2\pi}{\omega} \tag{1}$$

EXAMPLE 4   **Finding the Amplitude and Period of a Sinusoidal Function**

Determine the amplitude and period of $y = 3\sin(4x)$.

Solution   Comparing $y = 3\sin(4x)$ to $y = A\sin(\omega x)$, we find that $A = 3$ and $\omega = 4$. From equation (1),

$$\text{Amplitude} = |A| = 3 \qquad \text{Period} = T = \dfrac{2\pi}{\omega} = \dfrac{2\pi}{4} = \dfrac{\pi}{2}$$

━━━**Now Work** PROBLEM 15

4 Graph Sinusoidal Functions Using Key Points

So far, we have graphed functions of the form $y = A\sin(\omega x)$ or $y = A\cos(\omega x)$ using transformations. We now introduce another method that can be used to graph these functions.

Figure 56 shows one cycle of the graphs of $y = \sin x$ and $y = \cos x$ on the interval $[0, 2\pi]$. Notice that each graph consists of four parts corresponding to the four subintervals:

$$\left[0, \frac{\pi}{2}\right], \quad \left[\frac{\pi}{2}, \pi\right], \quad \left[\pi, \frac{3\pi}{2}\right], \quad \left[\frac{3\pi}{2}, 2\pi\right]$$

Each subinterval is of length $\frac{\pi}{2}$ (the period 2π divided by 4, the number of parts), and the endpoints of these intervals $x = 0$, $x = \frac{\pi}{2}$, $x = \pi$, $x = \frac{3\pi}{2}$, $x = 2\pi$ give rise to five key points on each graph:

For $y = \sin x$: $\quad (0, 0), \left(\frac{\pi}{2}, 1\right), (\pi, 0), \left(\frac{3\pi}{2}, -1\right), (2\pi, 0)$

For $y = \cos x$: $\quad (0, 1), \left(\frac{\pi}{2}, 0\right), (\pi, -1), \left(\frac{3\pi}{2}, 0\right), (2\pi, 1)$

Look again at Figure 56.

Figure 56

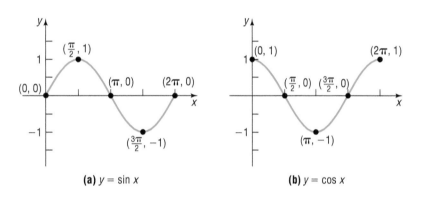

(a) $y = \sin x$ **(b)** $y = \cos x$

EXAMPLE 5	**How to Graph a Sinusoidal Function Using Key Points**

Graph $y = 3\sin(4x)$ using key points.

Step-by-Step Solution

Step 1: Determine the amplitude and period of the sinusoidal function.

Comparing $y = 3\sin(4x)$ to $y = A\sin(\omega x)$, we see that $A = 3$ and $\omega = 4$, so the amplitude is $|A| = 3$ and the period is $\dfrac{2\pi}{\omega} = \dfrac{2\pi}{4} = \dfrac{\pi}{2}$. Because the amplitude is 3, the graph of $y = 3\sin(4x)$ will lie between -3 and 3 on the y-axis. Because the period is $\dfrac{\pi}{2}$, one cycle will begin at $x = 0$ and end at $x = \dfrac{\pi}{2}$.

Step 2: Divide the interval $\left[0, \dfrac{2\pi}{\omega}\right]$ into four subintervals of the same length.

Divide the interval $\left[0, \dfrac{\pi}{2}\right]$ into four subintervals, each of length $\dfrac{\pi}{2} \div 4 = \dfrac{\pi}{8}$, as follows:

$$\left[0, \frac{\pi}{8}\right] \quad \left[\frac{\pi}{8}, \frac{\pi}{8} + \frac{\pi}{8}\right] = \left[\frac{\pi}{8}, \frac{\pi}{4}\right] \quad \left[\frac{\pi}{4}, \frac{\pi}{4} + \frac{\pi}{8}\right] = \left[\frac{\pi}{4}, \frac{3\pi}{8}\right] \quad \left[\frac{3\pi}{8}, \frac{3\pi}{8} + \frac{\pi}{8}\right] = \left[\frac{3\pi}{8}, \frac{\pi}{2}\right]$$

The endpoints of the subintervals are $0, \dfrac{\pi}{8}, \dfrac{\pi}{4}, \dfrac{3\pi}{8}, \dfrac{\pi}{2}$. These values represent the x-coordinates of the five key points on the graph.

Step 3: Use the endpoints of these subintervals to obtain five key points on the graph.

COMMENT We could also obtain the five key points by evaluating $y = 3\sin(4x)$ at each value of x. ∎

To obtain the y-coordinates of the five key points of $y = 3\sin(4x)$, multiply the y-coordinates of the five key points for $y = \sin x$ in Figure 56(a) by $A = 3$. The five key points are

$$(0,0) \quad \left(\frac{\pi}{8}, 3\right) \quad \left(\frac{\pi}{4}, 0\right) \quad \left(\frac{3\pi}{8}, -3\right) \quad \left(\frac{\pi}{2}, 0\right)$$

Step 4: Plot the five key points and draw a sinusoidal graph to obtain the graph of one cycle. Extend the graph in each direction to make it complete.

Plot the five key points obtained in Step 3 and fill in the graph of the sine curve as shown in Figure 57(a). Extend the graph in each direction to obtain the complete graph shown in Figure 57(b). Notice that additional key points appear every $\frac{\pi}{8}$ radian.

Figure 57

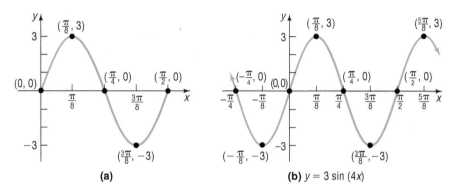

(a)

(b) $y = 3\sin(4x)$

✓ **Check:** Graph $y = 3\sin(4x)$ using transformations. Which graphing method do you prefer?

↵

Now Work PROBLEM 37 USING KEY POINTS

SUMMARY   Steps for Graphing a Sinusoidal Function of the Form $y = A\sin(\omega x)$ or $y = A\cos(\omega x)$ Using Key Points

STEP 1: Determine the amplitude and period of the sinusoidal function.

STEP 2: Divide the interval $\left[0, \frac{2\pi}{\omega}\right]$ into four subintervals of the same length.

STEP 3: Use the endpoints of these subintervals to obtain five key points on the graph.

STEP 4: Plot the five key points and draw a sinusoidal graph to obtain the graph of one cycle. Extend the graph in each direction to make it complete.

EXAMPLE 6   **Graphing a Sinusoidal Function Using Key Points**

Graph $y = 2\sin\left(-\frac{\pi}{2}x\right)$ using key points.

Solution   Since the sine function is odd, we can use the equivalent form:

$$y = -2\sin\left(\frac{\pi}{2}x\right)$$

STEP 1: Comparing $y = -2\sin\left(\frac{\pi}{2}x\right)$ to $y = A\sin(\omega x)$, we find that $A = -2$ and $\omega = \frac{\pi}{2}$. The amplitude is $|A| = |-2| = 2$, and the period is $T = \frac{2\pi}{\omega} = \frac{2\pi}{\frac{\pi}{2}} = 4$.

The graph of $y = -2 \sin\left(\dfrac{\pi}{2}x\right)$ will lie between -2 and 2 on the y-axis. One cycle will begin at $x = 0$ and end at $x = 4$.

STEP 2: Divide the interval $[0, 4]$ into four subintervals, each of length $4 \div 4 = 1$. The x-coordinates of the five key points are

$$0 \qquad 0 + 1 = 1 \qquad 1 + 1 = 2 \qquad 2 + 1 = 3 \qquad 3 + 1 = 4$$

1st x-coordinate   2nd x-coordinate   3rd x-coordinate   4th x-coordinate   5th x-coordinate

STEP 3: Since $y = -2 \sin\left(\dfrac{\pi}{2}x\right)$, multiply the y-coordinates of the five key points in Figure 56(a) by $A = -2$. The five key points on the graph are

$$(0, 0) \quad (1, -2) \quad (2, 0) \quad (3, 2) \quad (4, 0)$$

STEP 4: Plot these five points and fill in the graph of the sine function as shown in Figure 58(a). Extend the graph in each direction to obtain Figure 58(b).

Figure 58

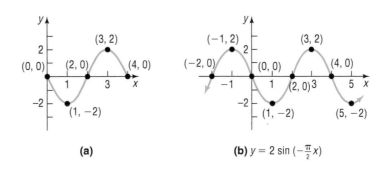

(a)

(b) $y = 2 \sin\left(-\frac{\pi}{2}x\right)$

✓**Check:** Graph $y = 2 \sin\left(-\dfrac{\pi}{2}x\right)$ using transformations. Which graphing method do you prefer?

Now Work PROBLEM **41** USING KEY POINTS

If the function to be graphed is of the form $y = A \sin(\omega x) + B$ [or $y = A \cos(\omega x) + B$], first graph $y = A \sin(\omega x)$ [or $y = A \cos(\omega x)$] and then use a vertical shift.

EXAMPLE 7

Graphing a Sinusoidal Function Using Key Points

Graph $y = -4 \cos(\pi x) - 2$ using key points. Use the graph to determine the domain and the range of $y = -4 \cos(\pi x) - 2$.

Solution

Begin by graphing the function $y = -4 \cos(\pi x)$. Comparing $y = -4 \cos(\pi x)$ with $y = A \cos(\omega x)$, we find that $A = -4$ and $\omega = \pi$. The amplitude is $|A| = |-4| = 4$, and the period is $T = \dfrac{2\pi}{\omega} = \dfrac{2\pi}{\pi} = 2$.

The graph of $y = -4 \cos(\pi x)$ will lie between -4 and 4 on the y-axis. One cycle will begin at $x = 0$ and end at $x = 2$.

Divide the interval $[0, 2]$ into four subintervals, each of length $2 \div 4 = \dfrac{1}{2}$. The x-coordinates of the five key points are

$$0 \qquad 0 + \frac{1}{2} = \frac{1}{2} \qquad \frac{1}{2} + \frac{1}{2} = 1 \qquad 1 + \frac{1}{2} = \frac{3}{2} \qquad \frac{3}{2} + \frac{1}{2} = 2$$

1st x-coordinate   2nd x-coordinate   3rd x-coordinate   4th x-coordinate   5th x-coordinate

Since $y = -4 \cos(\pi x)$, multiply the y-coordinates of the five key points of $y = \cos x$ shown in Figure 56(b) by $A = -4$ to obtain the five key points on the graph of $y = -4\cos(\pi x)$:

$$(0, -4) \quad \left(\frac{1}{2}, 0\right) \quad (1, 4) \quad \left(\frac{3}{2}, 0\right) \quad (2, -4)$$

Plot these five points and fill in the graph of the cosine function as shown in Figure 59(a). Extending the graph in each direction, we obtain Figure 59(b), the graph of $y = -4\cos(\pi x)$.

A vertical shift down 2 units gives the graph of $y = -4\cos(\pi x) - 2$, as shown in Figure 59(c).

Figure 59

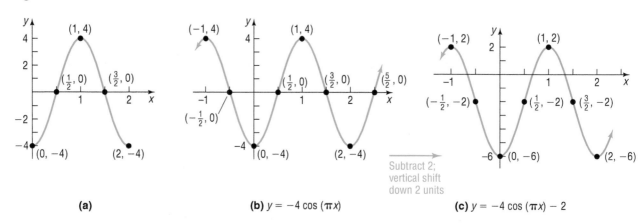

(a)   (b) $y = -4\cos(\pi x)$ (c) $y = -4\cos(\pi x) - 2$

The domain of $y = -4\cos(\pi x) - 2$ is the set of all real numbers or $(-\infty, \infty)$. The range of $y = -4\cos(\pi x) - 2$ is $\{y \mid -6 \le y \le 2\}$ or $[-6, 2]$.

━━━━━**Now Work** PROBLEM **51**

5 Find an Equation for a Sinusoidal Graph

EXAMPLE 8

Finding an Equation for a Sinusoidal Graph

Find an equation for the graph shown in Figure 60.

Figure 60

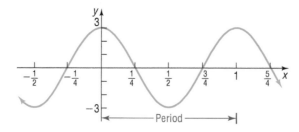

Solution   The graph has the characteristics of a cosine function. Do you see why? The maximum value, 3, occurs at $x = 0$. So we view the equation as a cosine function $y = A\cos(\omega x)$ with $A = 3$ and period $T = 1$. Then $\dfrac{2\pi}{\omega} = 1$, so $\omega = 2\pi$. The cosine function whose graph is given in Figure 60 is

$$y = A\cos(\omega x) = 3\cos(2\pi x)$$

✓**Check:**   Graph $Y_1 = 3\cos(2\pi x)$ and compare the result with Figure 60.

EXAMPLE 9   **Finding an Equation for a Sinusoidal Graph**

Find an equation for the graph shown in Figure 61.

Figure 61

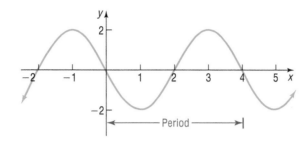

Solution   The graph is sinusoidal, with amplitude $|A| = 2$. The period is 4, so $\dfrac{2\pi}{\omega} = 4$ or
$\omega = \dfrac{\pi}{2}$. Since the graph passes through the origin, it is easier to view the equation
as a sine function,[†] but notice that the graph is actually the reflection of a sine
function about the x-axis (since the graph is decreasing near the origin). This
requires that $A = -2$. The sine function whose graph is given in Figure 61 is

$$y = A \sin(\omega x) = -2 \sin\left(\dfrac{\pi}{2}x\right)$$

 ✓Check: Graph $Y_1 = -2 \sin\left(\dfrac{\pi}{2}x\right)$ and compare the result with Figure 61.

━━━━━**Now Work** PROBLEMS 59 AND 63

6.4 Assess Your Understanding

'Are You Prepared?'   *Answers are given at the end of these exercises. If you get a wrong answer, read the pages listed in red.*

1. Use transformations to graph $y = 3x^2$. (pp. 90–99)

2. Use transformations to graph $y = \sqrt{2x}$. (pp. 90–99)

Concepts and Vocabulary

3. The maximum value of $y = \sin x, 0 \le x \le 2\pi$, is _____ and occurs at $x =$ _____.

4. The function $y = A \sin(\omega x), A > 0$, has amplitude 3 and period 2; then $A =$ _____ and ω _____.

5. The function $y = 3 \cos(6x)$ has amplitude _____ and period _____.

6. *True or False* The graphs of $y = \sin x$ and $y = \cos x$ are identical except for a horizontal shift.

7. *True or False* For $y = 2 \sin(\pi x)$, the amplitude is 2 and the period is $\dfrac{\pi}{2}$.

8. *True or False* The graph of the sine function has infinitely many x-intercepts.

Skill Building

9. $f(x) = \sin x$
   (a) What is the y-intercept of the graph of f?
   (b) For what numbers x, $-\pi \le x \le \pi$, is the graph of f increasing?
   (c) What is the absolute maximum of f?
   (d) For what numbers x, $0 \le x \le 2\pi$, does $f(x) = 0$?

   (e) For what numbers x, $-2\pi \le x \le 2\pi$, does $f(x) = 1$? Where does $f(x) = -1$?
   (f) For what numbers x, $-2\pi \le x \le 2\pi$, does $f(x) = -\dfrac{1}{2}$?
   (g) What are the x-intercepts of f?

[†] The equation could also be viewed as a cosine function with a horizontal shift, but viewing it as a sine function is easier.

10. $g(x) = \cos x$
  (a) What is the y-intercept of the graph of g?
  (b) For what numbers x, $-\pi \le x \le \pi$, is the graph of g decreasing?
  (c) What is the absolute minimum of g?
  (d) For what numbers x, $0 \le x \le 2\pi$, does $g(x) = 0$?

  (e) For what numbers x, $-2\pi \le x \le 2\pi$, does $g(x) = 1$? Where does $g(x) = -1$?
  (f) For what numbers x, $-2\pi \le x \le 2\pi$, does $g(x) = \dfrac{\sqrt{3}}{2}$?
  (g) What are the x-intercepts of g?

In Problems 11–20, determine the amplitude and period of each function without graphing.

11. $y = 2 \sin x$

12. $y = 3 \cos x$

13. $y = -4 \cos(2x)$

14. $y = -\sin\left(\dfrac{1}{2}x\right)$

15. $y = 6 \sin(\pi x)$

16. $y = -3 \cos(3x)$

17. $y = -\dfrac{1}{2}\cos\left(\dfrac{3}{2}x\right)$

18. $y = \dfrac{4}{3}\sin\left(\dfrac{2}{3}x\right)$

19. $y = \dfrac{5}{3}\sin\left(-\dfrac{2\pi}{3}x\right)$

20. $y = \dfrac{9}{5}\cos\left(-\dfrac{3\pi}{2}x\right)$

In Problems 21–30, match the given function to one of the graphs (A)–(J).

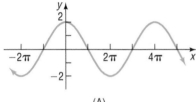

(A)

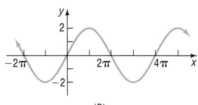

(B)

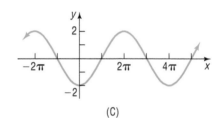

(C)

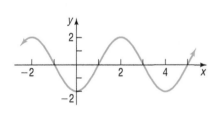

(D)

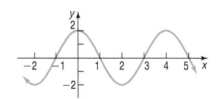

(E)

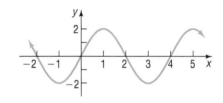

(F)

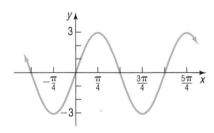

(G)

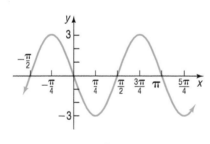

(H)

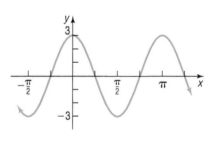

(I)

(J)

21. $y = 2 \sin\left(\dfrac{\pi}{2}x\right)$

22. $y = 2 \cos\left(\dfrac{\pi}{2}x\right)$

23. $y = 2 \cos\left(\dfrac{1}{2}x\right)$

24. $y = 3 \cos(2x)$

25. $y = -3 \sin(2x)$

26. $y = 2 \sin\left(\dfrac{1}{2}x\right)$

27. $y = -2 \cos\left(\dfrac{1}{2}x\right)$

28. $y = -2 \cos\left(\dfrac{\pi}{2}x\right)$

29. $y = 3 \sin(2x)$

30. $y = -2 \sin\left(\dfrac{1}{2}x\right)$

In Problems 31–34, match the given function to one of the graphs (A)–(D).

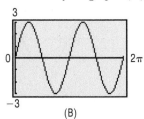

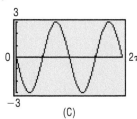

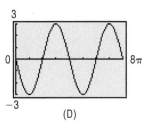

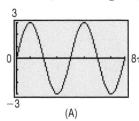

(A)　　　　　　　　(B)　　　　　　　　(C)　　　　　　　　(D)

31. $y = 3 \sin\left(\dfrac{1}{2}x\right)$　　　**32.** $y = -3 \sin(2x)$　　　**33.** $y = 3 \sin(2x)$　　　**34.** $y = -3 \sin\left(\dfrac{1}{2}x\right)$

In Problems 35–58, graph each function. Be sure to label key points and show at least two cycles. Use the graph to determine the domain and the range of each function.

35. $y = 4 \cos x$

36. $y = 3 \sin x$

37. $y = -4 \sin x$

38. $y = -3 \cos x$

39. $y = \cos(4x)$

40. $y = \sin(3x)$

41. $y = \sin(-2x)$

42. $y = \cos(-2x)$

43. $y = 2 \sin\left(\dfrac{1}{2}x\right)$

44. $y = 2 \cos\left(\dfrac{1}{4}x\right)$

45. $y = -\dfrac{1}{2} \cos(2x)$

46. $y = -4 \sin\left(\dfrac{1}{8}x\right)$

47. $y = 2 \sin x + 3$

48. $y = 3 \cos x + 2$

49. $y = 5 \cos(\pi x) - 3$

50. $y = 4 \sin\left(\dfrac{\pi}{2}x\right) - 2$

51. $y = -6 \sin\left(\dfrac{\pi}{3}x\right) + 4$

52. $y = -3 \cos\left(\dfrac{\pi}{4}x\right) + 2$

53. $y = 5 - 3 \sin(2x)$

54. $y = 2 - 4 \cos(3x)$

55. $y = \dfrac{5}{3} \sin\left(-\dfrac{2\pi}{3}x\right)$

56. $y = \dfrac{9}{5} \cos\left(-\dfrac{3\pi}{2}x\right)$

57. $y = -\dfrac{3}{2} \cos\left(\dfrac{\pi}{4}x\right) + \dfrac{1}{2}$

58. $y = -\dfrac{1}{2} \sin\left(\dfrac{\pi}{8}x\right) + \dfrac{3}{2}$

In Problems 59–62, write the equation of a sine function that has the given characteristics.

59. Amplitude: 3
Period: π

60. Amplitude: 2
Period: 4π

61. Amplitude: 3
Period: 2

62. Amplitude: 4
Period: 1

In Problems 63–76, find an equation for each graph.

63.

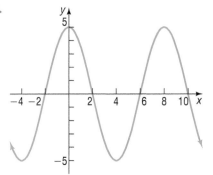

64.

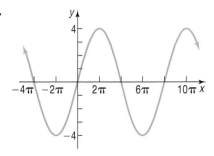

65.

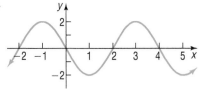

66.

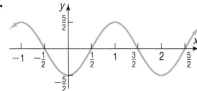

67.

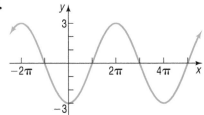

68.

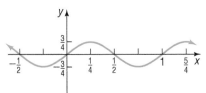

69.

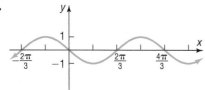

70.

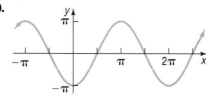

71.

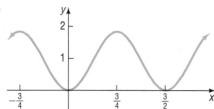

72.

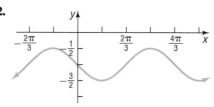

73.

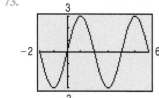

74.

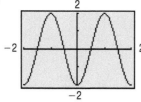

75.

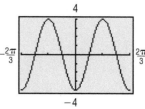

76.

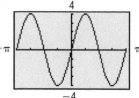

Mixed Practice

In Problems 77–80, find the average rate of change of f from 0 to $\dfrac{\pi}{2}$.

77. $f(x) = \sin x$ **78.** $f(x) = \cos x$ **79.** $f(x) = \sin\left(\dfrac{x}{2}\right)$ **80.** $f(x) = \cos(2x)$

In Problems 81–84, find $(f \circ g)(x)$ and $(g \circ f)(x)$ and graph each of these functions.

81. $f(x) = \sin x$ **82.** $f(x) = \cos x$ **83.** $f(x) = -2x$ **84.** $f(x) = -3x$
  $g(x) = 4x$ $g(x) = \dfrac{1}{2}x$ $g(x) = \cos x$ $g(x) = \sin x$

In Problems 85 and 86, graph each function.

85. $f(x) = \begin{cases} \sin x & 0 \le x < \dfrac{5\pi}{4} \\ \cos x & \dfrac{5\pi}{4} \le x \le 2\pi \end{cases}$

86. $g(x) = \begin{cases} 2\sin x & 0 \le x \le \pi \\ \cos x + 1 & \pi < x \le 2\pi \end{cases}$

Applications and Extensions

87. Alternating Current (ac) Circuits   The current I, in amperes, flowing through an ac (alternating current) circuit at time t in seconds, is

$$I(t) = 220\sin(60\pi t) \qquad t \ge 0$$

What is the period? What is the amplitude? Graph this function over two periods.

88. Alternating Current (ac) Circuits   The current I, in amperes, flowing through an ac (alternating current) circuit at time t in seconds, is

$$I(t) = 120\sin(30\pi t) \qquad t \ge 0$$

What is the period? What is the amplitude? Graph this function over two periods.

89. Alternating Current (ac) Generators   The voltage V, in volts, produced by an ac ggenerator at time t, in seconds, is

$$V(t) = 220\sin(120\pi t)$$

(a) What is the amplitude? What is the period?
(b) Graph V over two periods, beginning at $t = 0$.
(c) If a resistance of $R = 10$ ohms is present, what is the current I?
   [**Hint:** Use Ohm's Law, $V = IR$.]
(d) What is the amplitude and period of the current I?
(e) Graph I over two periods, beginning at $t = 0$.

90. Alternating Current (ac) Generators   The voltage V, in volts, produced by an ac generator at time t, in seconds, is

$$V(t) = 120\sin(120\pi t)$$

(a) What is the amplitude? What is the period?
(b) Graph V over two periods, beginning at $t = 0$.
(c) If a resistance of $R = 20$ ohms is present, what is the current I?
   [**Hint:** Use Ohm's Law, $V = IR$.]
(d) What is the amplitude and period of the current I?
(e) Graph I over two periods, beginning at $t = 0$.

91. Alternating Current (ac) Generators The voltage V produced by an ac generator is sinusoidal. As a function of time, the voltage V is

$$V(t) = V_0 \sin(2\pi f t)$$

where f is the **frequency,** the number of complete oscillations (cycles) per second. [In the United States and Canada, f is 60 hertz (Hz).] The **power** P delivered to a resistance R at any time t is defined as

$$P(t) = \frac{[V(t)]^2}{R}$$

(a) Show that $P(t) = \dfrac{V_0^2}{R} \sin^2(2\pi f t)$.

(b) The graph of P is shown in the figure. Express P as a sinusoidal function.

Power in an ac generator

(c) Deduce that

$$\sin^2(2\pi f t) = \frac{1}{2}[1 - \cos(4\pi f t)]$$

92. Bridge Clearance A one-lane highway runs through a tunnel in the shape of one-half a sine curve cycle. The opening is 28 feet wide at road level and is 15 feet tall at its highest point.

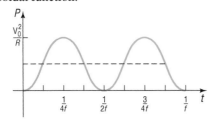

(a) Find an equation for the sine curve that fits the opening. Place the origin at the left end of the sine curve.

(b) If the road is 14 feet wide with 7-foot shoulders on each side, what is the height of the tunnel at the edge of the road?

Source: en.wikipedia.org/wiki/Interstate_Highway_standards and *Ohio Revised Code*

93. Biorhythms In the theory of biorhythms, a sine function of the form

$$P(t) = 50 \sin(\omega t) + 50$$

is used to measure the percent P of a person's potential at time t, where t is measured in days and $t = 0$ is the person's birthday. Three characteristics are commonly measured:

Physical potential: period of 23 days
Emotional potential: period of 28 days
Intellectual potential: period of 33 days

(a) Find ω for each characteristic.

(b) Using a graphing utility, graph all three functions on the same screen.

(c) Is there a time t when all three characteristics have 100% potential? When is it?

(d) Suppose that you are 20 years old today ($t = 7305$ days). Describe your physical, emotional, and intellectual potential for the next 30 days.

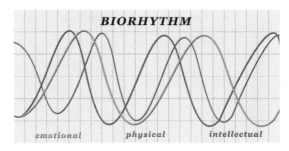

94. Graph $y = |\cos x|$, $-2\pi \le x \le 2\pi$.

95. Graph $y = |\sin x|$, $-2\pi \le x \le 2\pi$.

In Problems 96–99, the graphs of the given pairs of functions intersect infinitely many times. Find four of these points of intersection.

96. $y = \sin x$
$y = \dfrac{1}{2}$

97. $y = \cos x$
$y = \dfrac{1}{2}$

98. $y = 2 \sin x$
$y = -2$

99. $y = \tan x$
$y = 1$

Explaining Concepts: Discussion and Writing

100. Explain how you would scale the x-axis and y-axis before graphing $y = 3 \cos(\pi x)$.

101. Explain the term *amplitude* as it relates to the graph of a sinusoidal function.

102. Explain the term *period* as it relates to the graph of a sinusoidal function.

103. Explain how the amplitude and period of a sinusoidal graph are used to establish the scale on each coordinate axis.

104. Find an application in your major field that leads to a sinusoidal graph. Write a paper about your findings.

Interactive Exercises

Ask your instructor if the applet exercises below are of interest to you.

105. *Open the Trace Sine Curve applet.* On the screen you will see the graph of the unit circle with a point C labeled. Use your mouse and move point C around the unit circle in the counterclockwise direction. What do you notice? In particular, what is the relation between the angle and the y-coordinate of point C?

106. *Open the Trace Cosine Curve applet.* On the screen you will see the graph of the unit circle with a point C labeled. Use your mouse and move point C around the unit circle in the counterclockwise direction. What do you notice? In particular, what is the relation between the angle and the x-coordinate of point C?

107. *Open the Amplitude applet.* On the screen you will see a slider. Move the point along the slider to see the role *a* plays in the graph of $f(x) = a \sin x$.

108. *Open the Period applet.* On the screen you will see a slider. Move the point along the slider to see the role ω plays in the

graph of $f(x) = \sin(\omega x)$. Pay particular attention to the key points matched by color on each graph. For convenience the graph of $g(x) = \sin x$ is shown as a dashed, gray curve.

'Are You Prepared?' Answers

1. Vertical stretch by a factor of 3

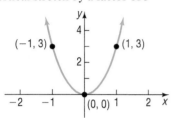

2. Horizontal compression by a factor of $\frac{1}{2}$

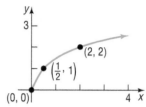

6.5 Graphs of the Tangent, Cotangent, Cosecant, and Secant Functions

PREPARING FOR THIS SECTION *Before getting started, review the following:*

- Vertical Asymptotes (Section 4.2, pp. 191–192)

Now Work the 'Are You Prepared?' problems on page 413.

OBJECTIVES 1 Graph Functions of the Form $y = A \tan(\omega x) + B$ and $y = A \cot(\omega x) + B$ (p. 410)

2 Graph Functions of the Form $y = A \csc(\omega x) + B$ and $y = A \sec(\omega x) + B$ (p. 412)

The Graph of the Tangent Function

Because the tangent function has period π, we only need to determine the graph over some interval of length π. The rest of the graph will consist of repetitions of that graph. Because the tangent function is not defined at $\ldots, -\frac{3\pi}{2}, -\frac{\pi}{2}, \frac{\pi}{2}, \frac{3\pi}{2}, \ldots$, we will concentrate on the interval $\left(-\frac{\pi}{2}, \frac{\pi}{2}\right)$, of length π, and construct Table 8, which lists some points on the graph of $y = \tan x$, $-\frac{\pi}{2} < x < \frac{\pi}{2}$. We plot the points in the table and connect them with a smooth curve. See Figure 62 for a partial graph of $y = \tan x$, where $-\frac{\pi}{3} \leq x \leq \frac{\pi}{3}$.

To complete one period of the graph of $y = \tan x$, we need to investigate the behavior of the function as x approaches $-\frac{\pi}{2}$ and $\frac{\pi}{2}$. We must be careful, though, because $y = \tan x$ is not defined at these numbers. To determine this behavior, we use the identity

$$\tan x = \frac{\sin x}{\cos x}$$

See Table 9. If x is close to $\frac{\pi}{2} \approx 1.5708$, but remains less than $\frac{\pi}{2}$, then $\sin x$ will be close to 1 and $\cos x$ will be positive and close to 0. (To see this, refer back to the graphs of the sine function and the cosine function.) So the ratio $\frac{\sin x}{\cos x}$ will be

Table 8

x	$y = \tan x$	(x, y)
$-\dfrac{\pi}{3}$	$-\sqrt{3} \approx -1.73$	$\left(-\dfrac{\pi}{3}, -\sqrt{3}\right)$
$-\dfrac{\pi}{4}$	-1	$\left(-\dfrac{\pi}{4}, -1\right)$
$-\dfrac{\pi}{6}$	$-\dfrac{\sqrt{3}}{3} \approx -0.58$	$\left(-\dfrac{\pi}{6}, -\dfrac{\sqrt{3}}{3}\right)$
0	0	$(0, 0)$
$\dfrac{\pi}{6}$	$\dfrac{\sqrt{3}}{3} \approx 0.58$	$\left(\dfrac{\pi}{6}, \dfrac{\sqrt{3}}{3}\right)$
$\dfrac{\pi}{4}$	1	$\left(\dfrac{\pi}{4}, 1\right)$
$\dfrac{\pi}{3}$	$\sqrt{3} \approx 1.73$	$\left(\dfrac{\pi}{3}, \sqrt{3}\right)$

Figure 62

$y = \tan x, -\dfrac{\pi}{3} \leq x \leq \dfrac{\pi}{3}$

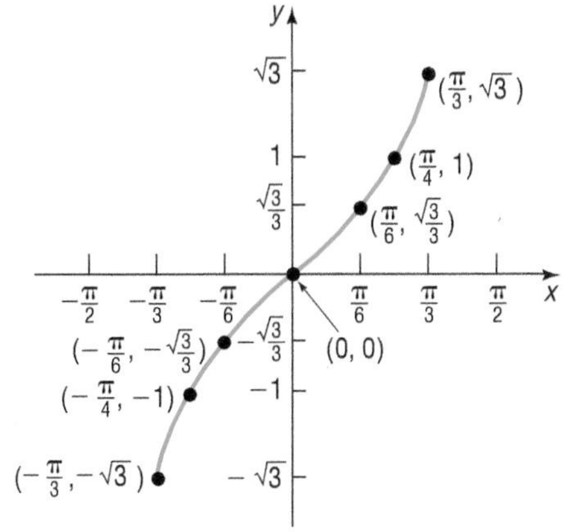

positive and large. In fact, the closer x gets to $\dfrac{\pi}{2}$, the closer $\sin x$ gets to 1 and $\cos x$ gets to 0, so $\tan x$ approaches $\infty \left(\lim\limits_{x \to \frac{\pi}{2}^{-}} \tan x = \infty\right)$. In other words, the vertical line $x = \dfrac{\pi}{2}$ is a vertical asymptote to the graph of $y = \tan x$.

Table 9

x	$\sin x$	$\cos x$	$y = \tan x$
$\dfrac{\pi}{3} \approx 1.05$	$\dfrac{\sqrt{3}}{2}$	$\dfrac{1}{2}$	$\sqrt{3} \approx 1.73$
1.5	0.9975	0.0707	14.1
1.57	0.9999	7.96×10^{-4}	1255.8
1.5707	0.9999	9.6×10^{-5}	$10,381$
$\dfrac{\pi}{2} \approx 1.5708$	1	0	Undefined

If x is close to $-\dfrac{\pi}{2}$, but remains greater than $-\dfrac{\pi}{2}$, then $\sin x$ will be close to -1 and $\cos x$ will be positive and close to 0. The ratio $\dfrac{\sin x}{\cos x}$ approaches $-\infty$ $\left(\lim\limits_{x \to -\frac{\pi}{2}^{+}} \tan x = -\infty\right)$. In other words, the vertical line $x = -\dfrac{\pi}{2}$ is also a vertical asymptote to the graph.

With these observations, we can complete one period of the graph. We obtain the complete graph of $y = \tan x$ by repeating this period, as shown in Figure 63.

Figure 63

$y = \tan x, -\infty < x < \infty, x$ not equal to odd multiples of $\dfrac{\pi}{2}, -\infty < y < \infty$

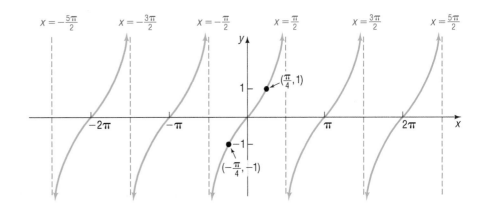

✓ **Check:** Graph $Y_1 = \tan x$ and compare the result with Figure 63. Use TRACE to see what happens as x gets close to $\dfrac{\pi}{2}$, but is less than $\dfrac{\pi}{2}$.

The graph of $y = \tan x$ in Figure 63 on page 409 illustrates the following properties.

Properties of the Tangent Function

1. The domain is the set of all real numbers, except odd multiples of $\dfrac{\pi}{2}$.
2. The range is the set of all real numbers.
3. The tangent function is an odd function, as the symmetry of the graph with respect to the origin indicates.
4. The tangent function is periodic, with period π.
5. The x-intercepts are $\ldots, -2\pi, -\pi, 0, \pi, 2\pi, 3\pi, \ldots$; the y-intercept is 0.
6. Vertical asymptotes occur at $x = \ldots, -\dfrac{3\pi}{2}, -\dfrac{\pi}{2}, \dfrac{\pi}{2}, \dfrac{3\pi}{2}, \ldots$.

Now Work PROBLEMS 7 AND 15

1 Graph Functions of the Form $y = A \tan(\omega x) + B$ and $y = A \cot(\omega x) + B$

For tangent functions, there is no concept of amplitude since the range of the tangent function is $(-\infty, \infty)$. The role of A in $y = A \tan(\omega x) + B$ is to provide the magnitude of the vertical stretch. The period of $y = \tan x$ is π, so the period of $y = A \tan(\omega x) + B$ is $\dfrac{\pi}{\omega}$, caused by the horizontal compression of the graph by a factor of $\dfrac{1}{\omega}$. Finally, the presence of B indicates that a vertical shift is required.

EXAMPLE 1 | **Graphing Functions of the Form $y = A \tan(\omega x) + B$**

Graph: $y = 2 \tan x - 1$. Use the graph to determine the domain and the range of $y = 2 \tan x - 1$.

Solution Figure 64 shows the steps using transformations.

Figure 64

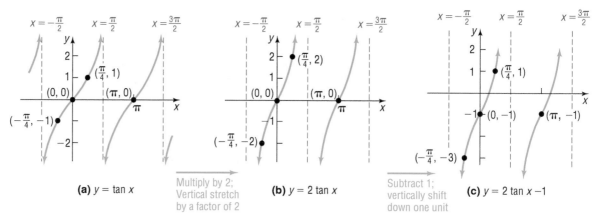

(a) $y = \tan x$

Multiply by 2;
Vertical stretch
by a factor of 2

(b) $y = 2 \tan x$

Subtract 1;
vertically shift
down one unit

(c) $y = 2 \tan x - 1$

✓**Check:** Graph $Y_1 = 2 \tan x - 1$ to verify the graph shown in Figure 64(c).

The domain of $y = 2 \tan x - 1$ is $\left\{ x \,\middle|\, x \neq \dfrac{k\pi}{2}, k \text{ is an odd integer} \right\}$, and the range is the set of all real numbers, or $(-\infty, \infty)$.

EXAMPLE 2 | **Graphing Functions of the Form $y = A \tan(\omega x) + B$**

Graph $y = 3 \tan(2x)$. Use the graph to determine the domain and the range of $y = 3 \tan(2x)$.

Solution Figure 65 shows the steps using transformations.

Figure 65

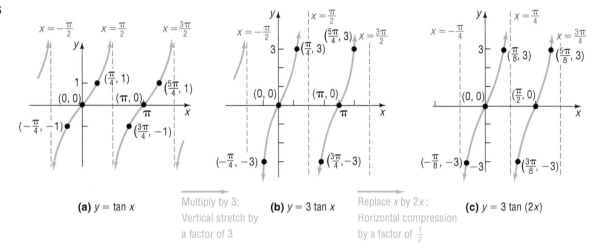

(a) $y = \tan x$

Multiply by 3;
Vertical stretch by
a factor of 3

(b) $y = 3 \tan x$

Replace x by $2x$;
Horizontal compression
by a factor of $\frac{1}{2}$

(c) $y = 3 \tan (2x)$

The domain of $y = 3 \tan (2x)$ is $\left\{ x \mid x \neq \dfrac{k\pi}{4}, k \text{ is an odd integer} \right\}$, and the range is the set of all real numbers or $(-\infty, \infty)$.

 ✓**Check:** Graph $Y_1 = 3 \tan(2x)$ to verify the graph in Figure 65(c).

Notice in Figure 65(c) that the period of $y = 3 \tan(2x)$ is $\dfrac{\pi}{2}$ due to the compression of the original period π by a factor of $\dfrac{1}{2}$. Notice that the asymptotes are $x = -\dfrac{\pi}{4}, x = \dfrac{\pi}{4}, x = \dfrac{3\pi}{4}$, and so on, also due to the compression.

Now Work PROBLEM **21**

Table 10

x	$y = \cot x$	(x, y)
$\dfrac{\pi}{6}$	$\sqrt{3}$	$\left(\dfrac{\pi}{6}, \sqrt{3} \right)$
$\dfrac{\pi}{4}$	1	$\left(\dfrac{\pi}{4}, 1 \right)$
$\dfrac{\pi}{3}$	$\dfrac{\sqrt{3}}{3}$	$\left(\dfrac{\pi}{3}, \dfrac{\sqrt{3}}{3} \right)$
$\dfrac{\pi}{2}$	0	$\left(\dfrac{\pi}{2}, 0 \right)$
$\dfrac{2\pi}{3}$	$-\dfrac{\sqrt{3}}{3}$	$\left(\dfrac{2\pi}{3}, -\dfrac{\sqrt{3}}{3} \right)$
$\dfrac{3\pi}{4}$	-1	$\left(\dfrac{3\pi}{4}, -1 \right)$
$\dfrac{5\pi}{6}$	$-\sqrt{3}$	$\left(\dfrac{5\pi}{6}, -\sqrt{3} \right)$

The Graph of the Cotangent Function

We obtain the graph of $y = \cot x$ as we did the graph of $y = \tan x$. The period of $y = \cot x$ is π. Because the cotangent function is not defined for integer multiples of π, we will concentrate on the interval $(0, \pi)$. Table 10 lists some points on the graph of $y = \cot x, 0 < x < \pi$. As x approaches 0, but remains greater than 0, the value of $\cos x$ will be close to 1 and the value of $\sin x$ will be positive and close to 0. Hence, the ratio $\dfrac{\cos x}{\sin x} = \cot x$ will be positive and large; so as x approaches 0, with $x > 0$, $\cot x$ approaches $\infty (\lim\limits_{x \to 0^+} \cot x = \infty)$. Similarly, as x approaches π, but remains less than π, the value of $\cos x$ will be close to -1, and the value of $\sin x$ will be positive and close to 0. So the ratio $\dfrac{\cos x}{\sin x} = \cot x$ will be negative and will approach $-\infty$ as x approaches $\pi (\lim\limits_{x \to \pi^-} \cot x = -\infty)$. Figure 66 shows the graph.

Figure 66
$y = \cot x, -\infty < x < \infty, x$ not equal to integer multiples of π,
$-\infty < y < \infty$

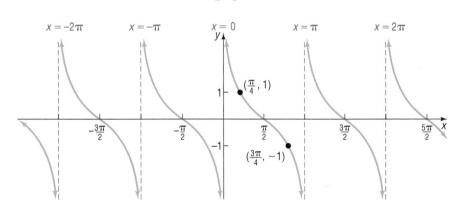

The graph of $y = A \cot(\omega x) + B$ has similar characteristics to those of the tangent function. The cotangent function $y = A \cot(\omega x) + B$ has period $\dfrac{\pi}{\omega}$. The cotangent function has no amplitude. The role of A is to provide the magnitude of the vertical stretch; the presence of B indicates a vertical shift is required.

Now Work PROBLEM 23

The Graphs of the Cosecant Function and the Secant Function

The cosecant and secant functions, sometimes referred to as **reciprocal functions,** are graphed by making use of the reciprocal identities

$$\csc x = \frac{1}{\sin x} \quad \text{and} \quad \sec x = \frac{1}{\cos x}$$

For example, the value of the cosecant function $y = \csc x$ at a given number x equals the reciprocal of the corresponding value of the sine function, provided that the value of the sine function is not 0. If the value of $\sin x$ is 0, then x is an integer multiple of π. At such numbers, the cosecant function is not defined. In fact, the graph of the cosecant function has vertical asymptotes at integer multiples of π. Figure 67 shows the graph.

Figure 67
$y = \csc x, -\infty < x < \infty, x$ not equal to integer multiples of $\pi, |y| \geq 1$

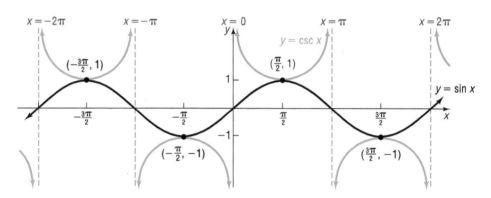

Using the idea of reciprocals, we can similarly obtain the graph of $y = \sec x$. See Figure 68.

Figure 68
$y = \sec x, -\infty < x < \infty, x$ not equal to odd multiples of $\dfrac{\pi}{2}, |y| \geq 1$

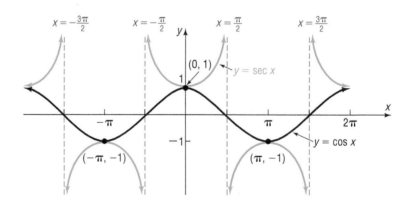

2 Graph Functions of the Form $y = A \csc(\omega x) + B$ and $y = A \sec(\omega x) + B$

The role of A in these functions is to set the range. The range of $y = \csc x$ is $\{y | y \leq -1 \text{ or } y \geq 1\}$ or $\{y | \, |y| \geq 1\}$; the range of $y = A \csc x$ is $\{y | \, |y| \geq |A|\}$, due to the vertical stretch of the graph by a factor of $|A|$. Just as with the sine and cosine functions, the period of $y = \csc(\omega x)$ and $y = \sec(\omega x)$ becomes $\dfrac{2\pi}{\omega}$, due to the horizontal compression of the graph by a factor of $\dfrac{1}{\omega}$. The presence of B indicates that a vertical shift is required.

EXAMPLE 3   **Graphing Functions of the Form y = A csc(ωx) + B**

Graph $y = 2 \csc x - 1$. Use the graph to determine the domain and the range of $y = 2 \csc x - 1$.

Solution   We use transformations. Figure 69 shows the required steps.

Figure 69

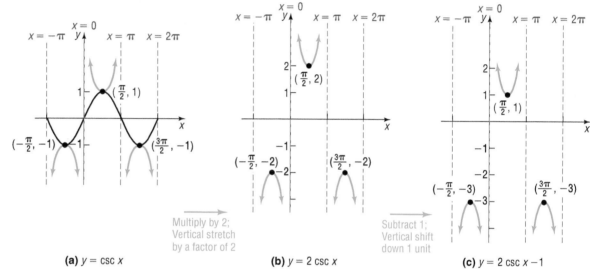

(a) $y = \csc x$ Multiply by 2; Vertical stretch by a factor of 2   **(b)** $y = 2 \csc x$ Subtract 1; Vertical shift down 1 unit   **(c)** $y = 2 \csc x - 1$

The domain of $y = 2 \csc x - 1$ is $\{x \mid x \neq k\pi, k \text{ is an integer}\}$ and the range is $\{y \mid y \leq -3 \text{ or } y \geq 1\}$ or, using interval notation, $(-\infty, -3] \cup [1, \infty)$.

 ✓**Check:** Graph $Y_1 = 2 \csc x - 1$ to verify the graph shown in Figure 69.

Now Work PROBLEM 29

6.5 Assess Your Understanding

'Are You Prepared?' *Answers are given at the end of these exercises. If you get a wrong answer, read the pages listed in red.*

1. The graph of $y = \dfrac{3x - 6}{x - 4}$ has a vertical asymptote. What is it? (pp. 191–192)

2. *True or False* If $x = 3$ is a vertical asymptote of a rational function R, then $\lim\limits_{x \to 3} |R(x)| = \infty$. (pp. 191–192)

Concepts and Vocabulary

3. The graph of $y = \tan x$ is symmetric with respect to the _____ and has vertical asymptotes at _____ .

4. The graph of $y = \sec x$ is symmetric with respect to the _____ and has vertical asymptotes at _____ .

5. It is easiest to graph $y = \sec x$ by first sketching the graph of _____ .

6. *True or False* The graphs of $y = \tan x$, $y = \cot x$, $y = \sec x$, and $y = \csc x$ each have infinitely many vertical asymptotes.

Skill Building

In Problems 7–16, if necessary, refer to the graphs to answer each question.

7. What is the y-intercept of $y = \tan x$?

8. What is the y-intercept of $y = \cot x$?

9. What is the y-intercept of $y = \sec x$?

10. What is the y-intercept of $y = \csc x$?

11. For what numbers x, $-2\pi \le x \le 2\pi$, does $\sec x = 1$? For what numbers x does $\sec x = -1$?

12. For what numbers x, $-2\pi \le x \le 2\pi$, does $\csc x = 1$? For what numbers x does $\csc x = -1$?

13. For what numbers x, $-2\pi \le x \le 2\pi$, does the graph of $y = \sec x$ have vertical asymptotes?

14. For what numbers x, $-2\pi \le x \le 2\pi$, does the graph of $y = \csc x$ have vertical asymptotes?

15. For what numbers x, $-2\pi \le x \le 2\pi$, does the graph of $y = \tan x$ have vertical asymptotes?

16. For what numbers x, $-2\pi \le x \le 2\pi$, does the graph of $y = \cot x$ have vertical asymptotes?

In Problems 17–40, graph each function. Be sure to label key points and show at least two cycles. Use the graph to determine the domain and the range of each function.

17. $y = 3 \tan x$

18. $y = -2 \tan x$

19. $y = 4 \cot x$

20. $y = -3 \cot x$

21. $y = \tan\left(\dfrac{\pi}{2}x\right)$

22. $y = \tan\left(\dfrac{1}{2}x\right)$

23. $y = \cot\left(\dfrac{1}{4}x\right)$

24. $y = \cot\left(\dfrac{\pi}{4}x\right)$

25. $y = 2 \sec x$

26. $y = \dfrac{1}{2}\csc x$

27. $y = -3 \csc x$

28. $y = -4 \sec x$

29. $y = 4 \sec\left(\dfrac{1}{2}x\right)$

30. $y = \dfrac{1}{2}\csc(2x)$

31. $y = -2 \csc(\pi x)$

32. $y = -3 \sec\left(\dfrac{\pi}{2}x\right)$

33. $y = \tan\left(\dfrac{1}{4}x\right) + 1$

34. $y = 2 \cot x - 1$

35. $y = \sec\left(\dfrac{2\pi}{3}x\right) + 2$

36. $y = \csc\left(\dfrac{3\pi}{2}x\right)$

37. $y = \dfrac{1}{2}\tan\left(\dfrac{1}{4}x\right) - 2$

38. $y = 3 \cot\left(\dfrac{1}{2}x\right) - 2$

39. $y = 2 \csc\left(\dfrac{1}{3}x\right) - 1$

40. $y = 3 \sec\left(\dfrac{1}{4}x\right) + 1$

Mixed Practice

In Problems 41–44, find the average rate of change of f from 0 to $\dfrac{\pi}{6}$.

41. $f(x) = \tan x$

42. $f(x) = \sec x$

43. $f(x) = \tan(2x)$

44. $f(x) = \sec(2x)$

In Problems 45–48, find $(f \circ g)(x)$ and $(g \circ f)(x)$ and graph each of these functions.

45. $f(x) = \tan x$
    $g(x) = 4x$

46. $f(x) = 2 \sec x$
    $g(x) = \dfrac{1}{2}x$

47. $f(x) = -2x$
    $g(x) = \cot x$

48. $f(x) = \dfrac{1}{2}x$
    $g(x) = 2 \csc x$

In Problems 49 and 50, graph each function.

49. $f(x) = \begin{cases} \tan x & 0 \le x < \dfrac{\pi}{2} \\ 0 & x = \dfrac{\pi}{2} \\ \sec x & \dfrac{\pi}{2} < x \le \pi \end{cases}$

50. $g(x) = \begin{cases} \csc x & 0 < x < \pi \\ 0 & x = \pi \\ \cot x & \pi < x < 2\pi \end{cases}$

Applications and Extensions

51. Carrying a Ladder around a Corner   Two hallways, one of width 3 feet, the other of width 4 feet, meet at a right angle. See the illustration.

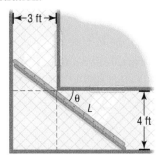

(a) Show that the length L of the line segment shown as a function of the angle θ is

$$L(\theta) = 3 \sec \theta + 4 \csc \theta$$

(b) Graph $L = L(\theta), 0 < \theta < \dfrac{\pi}{2}$.

(c) For what value of θ is L the least?

(d) What is the length of the longest ladder that can be carried around the corner? Why is this also the least value of L?

52. A Rotating Beacon   Suppose that a fire truck is parked in front of a building as shown in the figure.

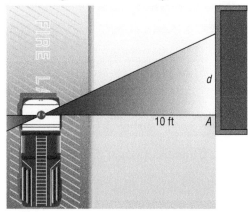

The beacon light on top of the fire truck is located 10 feet from the wall and has a light on each side. If the beacon light rotates 1 revolution every 2 seconds, then a model for determining the distance d, in feet, that the beacon of light is from point A on the wall after t seconds is given by

$$d(t) = |10 \tan(\pi t)|$$

(a) Graph $d(t) = |10 \tan(\pi t)|$ for $0 \le t \le 2$.

(b) For what values of t is the function undefined? Explain what this means in terms of the beam of light on the wall.

(c) Fill in the following table.

t	0	0.1	0.2	0.3	0.4
$d(t) = 10 \tan(\pi t)$					

(d) Compute $\dfrac{d(0.1) - d(0)}{0.1 - 0}, \dfrac{d(0.2) - d(0.1)}{0.2 - 0.1}$, and so on, for each consecutive value of t. These are called **first differences.**

(e) Interpret the first differences found in part (d). What is happening to the speed of the beam of light as d increases?

53. Exploration   Graph

$$y = \tan x \quad \text{and} \quad y = -\cot\left(x + \frac{\pi}{2}\right)$$

Do you think that $\tan x = -\cot\left(x + \dfrac{\pi}{2}\right)$?

'Are You Prepared?' Answers

1. $x = 4$ **2.** True

6.6 Phase Shift; Sinusoidal Curve Fitting

OBJECTIVES **1** Graph Sinusoidal Functions of the Form $y = A \sin(\omega x - \phi) + B$ (p. 415)

  2 Build Sinusoidal Models from Data (p. 419)

Figure 70
One cycle of
$y = A \sin(\omega x), A > 0, \omega > 0$

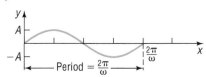

1 Graph Sinusoidal Functions of the Form $y = A \sin(\omega x - \phi) + B$

We have seen that the graph of $y = A \sin(\omega x), \omega > 0$, has amplitude $|A|$ and period $T = \dfrac{2\pi}{\omega}$. One cycle can be drawn as x varies from 0 to $\dfrac{2\pi}{\omega}$ or, equivalently, as ωx varies from 0 to 2π. See Figure 70.

We now want to discuss the graph of

$$y = A \sin(\omega x - \phi)$$

which may also be written as

$$y = A \sin\left[\omega\left(x - \frac{\phi}{\omega}\right)\right]$$

where $\omega > 0$ and ϕ (the Greek letter phi) are real numbers. The graph will be a sine curve with amplitude $|A|$. As $\omega x - \phi$ varies from 0 to 2π, one period will be traced out. This period will begin when

$$\omega x - \phi = 0 \quad \text{or} \quad x = \frac{\phi}{\omega}$$

NOTE We can also find the beginning and end of the period by solving the inequality:

$$0 \le \omega x - \phi \le 2\pi$$
$$\phi \le \omega x \le 2\pi + \phi$$
$$\frac{\phi}{\omega} \le x \le \frac{2\pi}{\omega} + \frac{\phi}{\omega} \quad \blacksquare$$

and will end when

$$\omega x - \phi = 2\pi \quad \text{or} \quad x = \frac{\phi}{\omega} + \frac{2\pi}{\omega}$$

See Figure 71.

We see that the graph of $y = A \sin(\omega x - \phi) = A \sin\left[\omega\left(x - \frac{\phi}{\omega}\right)\right]$ is the same as the graph of $y = A \sin(\omega x)$, except that it has been shifted $\left|\frac{\phi}{\omega}\right|$ units (to the right if $\phi > 0$ and to the left if $\phi < 0$). This number $\frac{\phi}{\omega}$ is called the **phase shift** of the graph of $y = A \sin(\omega x - \phi)$.

Figure 71 One cycle of $y = A \sin(\omega x - \phi), A > 0,$ $\omega > 0, \phi > 0$

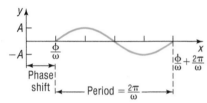

For the graphs of $y = A \sin(\omega x - \phi)$ or $y = A \cos(\omega x - \phi), \omega > 0,$

$$\text{Amplitude} = |A| \qquad \text{Period} = T = \frac{2\pi}{\omega} \qquad \text{Phase shift} = \frac{\phi}{\omega}$$

The phase shift is to the left if $\phi < 0$ and to the right if $\phi > 0$.

EXAMPLE 1

Finding the Amplitude, Period, and Phase Shift of a Sinusoidal Function and Graphing It

Find the amplitude, period, and phase shift of $y = 3 \sin(2x - \pi)$ and graph the function.

Solution We use the same four steps used to graph sinusoidal functions of the form $y = A \sin(\omega x)$ or $y = A \cos(\omega x)$ given on page 400.

STEP 1: Comparing

$$y = 3 \sin(2x - \pi) = 3 \sin\left[2\left(x - \frac{\pi}{2}\right)\right]$$

to

$$y = A \sin(\omega x - \phi) = A \sin\left[\omega\left(x - \frac{\phi}{\omega}\right)\right]$$

we find that $A = 3, \omega = 2,$ and $\phi = \pi$. The graph is a sine curve with amplitude $|A| = 3$, period $T = \frac{2\pi}{\omega} = \frac{2\pi}{2} = \pi$, and phase shift $= \frac{\phi}{\omega} = \frac{\pi}{2}$.

COMMENT We can also find the interval defining one cycle by solving the inequality

$$0 \le 2x - \pi \le 2\pi$$

Then

$$\pi \le 2x \le 3\pi$$

$$\frac{\pi}{2} \le x \le \frac{3\pi}{2} \qquad \blacksquare$$

STEP 2: The graph of $y = 3 \sin(2x - \pi)$ will lie between -3 and 3 on the y-axis. One cycle will begin at $x = \dfrac{\phi}{\omega} = \dfrac{\pi}{2}$ and end at $x = \dfrac{\phi}{\omega} + \dfrac{2\pi}{\omega} = \dfrac{\pi}{2} + \pi = \dfrac{3\pi}{2}$.

To find the five key points, divide the interval $\left[\dfrac{\pi}{2}, \dfrac{3\pi}{2}\right]$ into four subintervals, each of length $\pi \div 4 = \dfrac{\pi}{4}$, by finding the following values of x:

$$\underset{\text{1st x-coordinate}}{\dfrac{\pi}{2}} \quad \underset{\text{2nd x-coordinate}}{\dfrac{\pi}{2} + \dfrac{\pi}{4} = \dfrac{3\pi}{4}} \quad \underset{\text{3rd x-coordinate}}{\dfrac{3\pi}{4} + \dfrac{\pi}{4} = \pi} \quad \underset{\text{4th x-coordinate}}{\pi + \dfrac{\pi}{4} = \dfrac{5\pi}{4}} \quad \underset{\text{5th x-coordinate}}{\dfrac{5\pi}{4} + \dfrac{\pi}{4} = \dfrac{3\pi}{2}}$$

STEP 3: Use these values of x to determine the five key points on the graph:

$$\left(\dfrac{\pi}{2}, 0\right) \quad \left(\dfrac{3\pi}{4}, 3\right) \quad (\pi, 0) \quad \left(\dfrac{5\pi}{4}, -3\right) \quad \left(\dfrac{3\pi}{2}, 0\right)$$

STEP 4: Plot these five points and fill in the graph of the sine function as shown in Figure 72(a). Extending the graph in each direction, we obtain Figure 72(b).

Figure 72

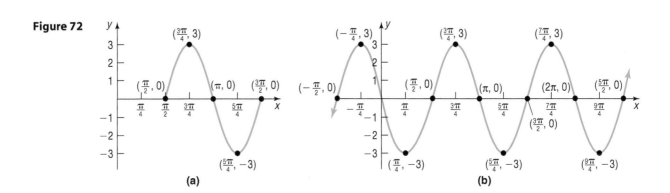

(a) (b)

The graph of $y = 3 \sin(2x - \pi) = 3 \sin\left[2\left(x - \dfrac{\pi}{2}\right)\right]$ may also be obtained using transformations. See Figure 73.

Figure 73

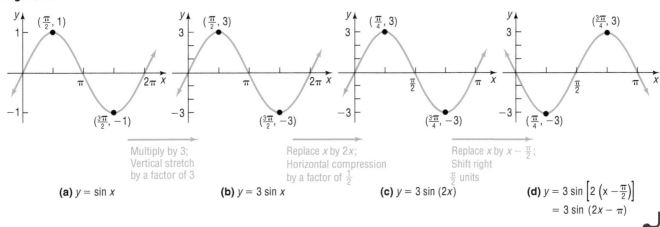

To graph a sinusoidal function of the form $y = A \sin(\omega x - \phi) + B$, first graph the function $y = A \sin(\omega x - \phi)$ and then apply a vertical shift.

EXAMPLE 2

Finding the Amplitude, Period, and Phase Shift of a Sinusoidal Function and Graphing It

Find the amplitude, period, and phase shift of $y = 2\cos(4x + 3\pi) + 1$ and graph the function.

Solution **STEP 1:** Begin by graphing $y = 2\cos(4x + 3\pi)$. Comparing

$$y = 2\cos(4x + 3\pi) = 2\cos\left[4\left(x + \frac{3\pi}{4}\right)\right]$$

to

$$y = A\cos(\omega x - \phi) = A\cos\left[\omega\left(x - \frac{\phi}{\omega}\right)\right]$$

we see that $A = 2$, $\omega = 4$, and $\phi = -3\pi$. The graph is a cosine curve with amplitude $|A| = 2$, period $T = \dfrac{2\pi}{\omega} = \dfrac{2\pi}{4} = \dfrac{\pi}{2}$, and phase shift $= \dfrac{\phi}{\omega} = -\dfrac{3\pi}{4}$.

COMMENT We can also find the interval defining one cycle by solving the inequality

$$0 \le 4x + 3\pi \le 2\pi$$

Then

$$-3\pi \le 4x \le -\pi$$

$$-\frac{3\pi}{4} \le x \le -\frac{\pi}{4} \qquad ■$$

STEP 2: The graph of $y = 2\cos(4x + 3\pi)$ will lie between -2 and 2 on the y-axis. One cycle will begin at $x = \dfrac{\phi}{\omega} = -\dfrac{3\pi}{4}$ and end at $x = \dfrac{\phi}{\omega} + \dfrac{2\pi}{\omega} = -\dfrac{3\pi}{4} + \dfrac{\pi}{2} = -\dfrac{\pi}{4}$. To find the five key points, divide the interval $\left[-\dfrac{3\pi}{4}, -\dfrac{\pi}{4}\right]$ into four subintervals, each of the length $\dfrac{\pi}{2} \div 4 = \dfrac{\pi}{8}$, by finding the following values.

$$-\frac{3\pi}{4} \qquad -\frac{3\pi}{4} + \frac{\pi}{8} = -\frac{5\pi}{8} \qquad -\frac{5\pi}{8} + \frac{\pi}{8} = -\frac{\pi}{2} \qquad -\frac{\pi}{2} + \frac{\pi}{8} = -\frac{3\pi}{8} \qquad -\frac{3\pi}{8} + \frac{\pi}{8} = -\frac{\pi}{4}$$

1st x-coordinate   2nd x-coordinate   3rd x-coordinate   4th x-coordinate   5th x-coordinate

STEP 3: The five key points on the graph of $y = 2\cos(4x + 3\pi)$ are

$$\left(-\frac{3\pi}{4}, 2\right) \quad \left(-\frac{5\pi}{8}, 0\right) \quad \left(-\frac{\pi}{2}, -2\right) \quad \left(-\frac{3\pi}{8}, 0\right) \quad \left(-\frac{\pi}{4}, 2\right)$$

STEP 4: Plot these five points and fill in the graph of the cosine function as shown in Figure 74(a). Extending the graph in each direction, we obtain Figure 74(b), the graph of $y = 2\cos(4x + 3\pi)$.

STEP 5: A vertical shift up 1 unit gives the final graph. See Figure 74(c).

Figure 74

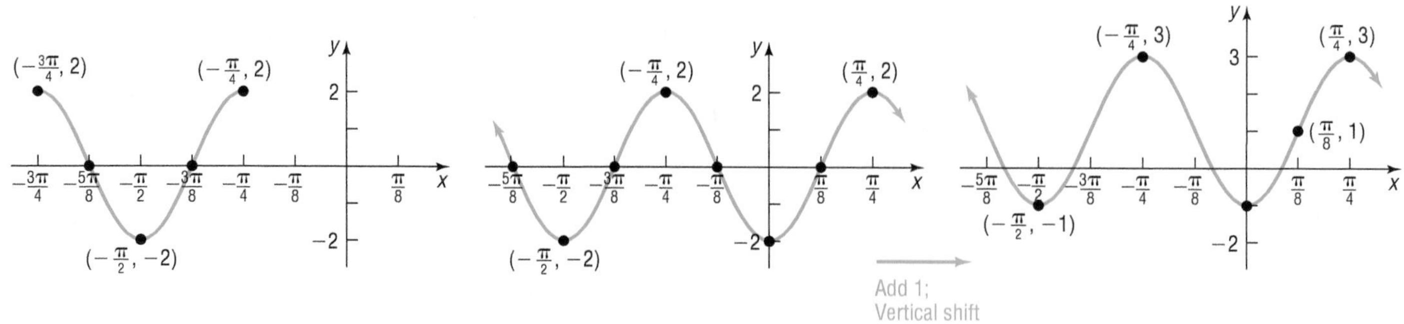

(a)

(b) $y = 2\cos(4x + 3\pi)$

Add 1;
Vertical shift
up 1 unit

(c) $y = 2\cos(4x + 3\pi) + 1$

The graph of $y = 2\cos(4x + 3\pi) + 1 = 2\cos\left[4\left(x + \dfrac{3\pi}{4}\right)\right] + 1$ may also be obtained using transformations. See Figure 75.

Figure 75

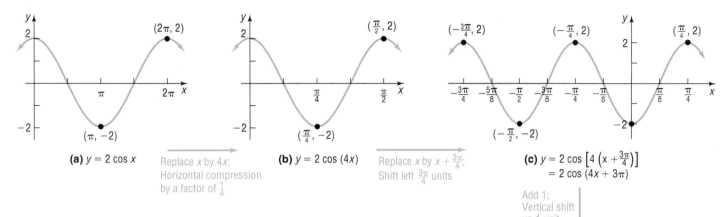

(a) $y = 2 \cos x$

Replace x by $4x$;
Horizontal compression
by a factor of $\frac{1}{4}$

(b) $y = 2 \cos (4x)$

Replace x by $x + \frac{3\pi}{4}$;
Shift left $\frac{3\pi}{4}$ units

(c) $y = 2 \cos \left[4 \left(x + \frac{3\pi}{4} \right) \right]$
$= 2 \cos (4x + 3\pi)$

Add 1;
Vertical shift
up 1 unit

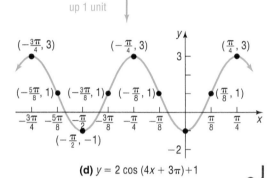

(d) $y = 2 \cos (4x + 3\pi) + 1$

 Now Work PROBLEM 3

SUMMARY   **Steps for Graphing Sinusoidal Functions $y = A \sin(\omega x - \phi) + B$ or**
$y = A \cos(\omega x - \phi) + B$

STEP 1: Determine the amplitude $|A|$, period $T = \dfrac{2\pi}{\omega}$, and phase shift $\dfrac{\phi}{\omega}$.

STEP 2: Determine the starting point of one cycle of the graph, $\dfrac{\phi}{\omega}$. Determine the ending point of one cycle of

the graph, $\dfrac{\phi}{\omega} + \dfrac{2\pi}{\omega}$. Divide the interval $\left[\dfrac{\phi}{\omega}, \dfrac{\phi}{\omega} + \dfrac{2\pi}{\omega} \right]$ into four subintervals, each of length $\dfrac{2\pi}{\omega} \div 4$.

STEP 3: Use the endpoints of the subintervals to find the five key points on the graph.

STEP 4: Plot the five key points and connect them with a sinusoidal graph to obtain one cycle of the graph. Extend the graph in each direction to make it complete.

STEP 5: If $B \neq 0$, apply a vertical shift.

---

2 Build Sinusoidal Models from Data

Scatter diagrams of data sometimes take the form of a sinusoidal function. Let's look at an example.

The data given in Table 11 on page 420 represent the average monthly temperatures in Denver, Colorado. Since the data represent *average* monthly temperatures collected over many years, the data will not vary much from year to year and so will essentially repeat each year. In other words, the data are periodic. Figure 76 shows the scatter diagram of these data repeated over 2 years, where $x = 1$ represents January, $x = 2$ represents February, and so on.

Notice that the scatter diagram looks like the graph of a sinusoidal function. We choose to fit the data to a sine function of the form

$$y = A \sin(\omega x - \phi) + B$$

where A, B, ω, and ϕ are constants.

Table 11

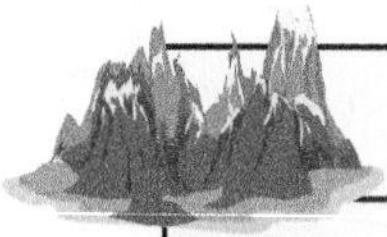

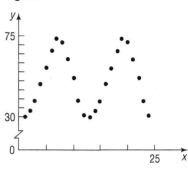

Month, x	Average Monthly Temperature, °F
January, 1	29.7
February, 2	33.4
March, 3	39.0
April, 4	48.2
May, 5	57.2
June, 6	66.9
July, 7	73.5
August, 8	71.4
September, 9	62.3
October, 10	51.4
November, 11	39.0
December, 12	31.0

Source: U.S. National Oceanic and Atmospheric Administration

Figure 76

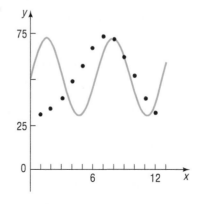

EXAMPLE 3

Finding a Sinusoidal Function from Temperature Data

Fit a sine function to the data in Table 11.

Figure 77

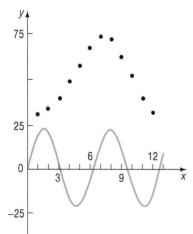

Solution Begin with a scatter diagram of the data for one year. See Figure 77. The data will be fitted to a sine function of the form

$$y = A \sin(\omega x - \phi) + B$$

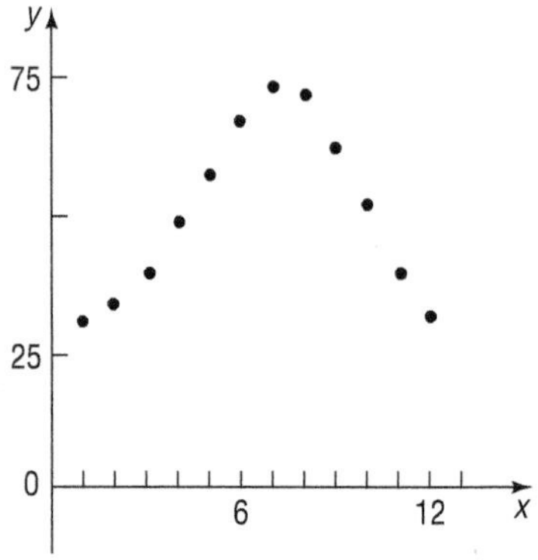

STEP 1: To find the amplitude A, we compute

$$\text{Amplitude} = \frac{\text{largest data value} - \text{smallest data value}}{2}$$

$$= \frac{73.5 - 29.7}{2} = 21.9$$

To see the remaining steps in this process, superimpose the graph of the function $y = 21.9 \sin x$, where x represents months, on the scatter diagram.

Figure 78 shows the two graphs. To fit the data, the graph needs to be shifted vertically, shifted horizontally, and stretched horizontally.

STEP 2: Determine the vertical shift by finding the average of the highest and lowest data values.

$$\text{Vertical shift} = \frac{73.5 + 29.7}{2} = 51.6$$

Now superimpose the graph of $y = 21.9 \sin x + 51.6$ on the scatter diagram. See Figure 79.

Figure 78

Figure 79

Figure 80

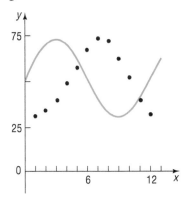

We see that the graph needs to be shifted horizontally and stretched horizontally.

STEP 3: It is easier to find the horizontal stretch factor first. Since the temperatures repeat every 12 months, the period of the function is $T = 12$. Since $T = \dfrac{2\pi}{\omega} = 12$, we find

$$\omega = \frac{2\pi}{12} = \frac{\pi}{6}$$

Now superimpose the graph of $y = 21.9 \sin\left(\dfrac{\pi}{6}x\right) + 51.6$ on the scatter diagram. See Figure 80. We see that the graph still needs to be shifted horizontally.

STEP 4: To determine the horizontal shift, use the period $T = 12$ and divide the interval $[0, 12]$ into four subintervals of length $12 \div 4 = 3$:

$$[0, 3], \quad [3, 6], \quad [6, 9], \quad [9, 12]$$

The sine curve is increasing on the interval $(0, 3)$ and is decreasing on the interval $(3, 9)$, so a local maximum occurs at $x = 3$. The data indicate that a maximum occurs at $x = 7$ (corresponding to July's temperature), so we must shift the graph of the function 4 units to the right by replacing x by $x - 4$. Doing this, we obtain

$$y = 21.9 \sin\left(\frac{\pi}{6}(x - 4)\right) + 51.6$$

Figure 81

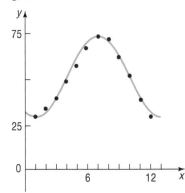

Multiplying out, we find that a sine function of the form $y = A \sin(\omega x - \phi) + B$ that fits the data is

$$y = 21.9 \sin\left(\frac{\pi}{6}x - \frac{2\pi}{3}\right) + 51.6$$

The graph of $y = 21.9 \sin\left(\dfrac{\pi}{6}x - \dfrac{2\pi}{3}\right) + 51.6$ and the scatter diagram of the data are shown in Figure 81.

The steps to fit a sine function

$$y = A \sin(\omega x - \phi) + B$$

to sinusoidal data follow:

Steps for Fitting a Sine Function $y = A \sin(\omega x - \phi) + B$ to Data

STEP 1: Determine A, the amplitude of the function.

$$\text{Amplitude} = \frac{\text{largest data value} - \text{smallest data value}}{2}$$

STEP 2: Determine B, the vertical shift of the function.

$$\text{Vertical shift} = \frac{\text{largest data value} + \text{smallest data value}}{2}$$

STEP 3: Determine ω. Since the period T, the time it takes for the data to repeat, is $T = \dfrac{2\pi}{\omega}$, we have

$$\omega = \frac{2\pi}{T}$$

STEP 4: Determine the horizontal shift of the function by using the period of the data. Divide the period into four subintervals of equal length. Determine the x-coordinate for the maximum of the sine function and the x-coordinate for the maximum value of the data. Use this information to determine the value of the phase shift, $\dfrac{\phi}{\omega}$.

─══════─**Now Work** PROBLEMS 29(a)–(c)

Let's look at another example. Since the number of hours of sunlight in a day cycles annually, the number of hours of sunlight in a day for a given location can be modeled by a sinusoidal function.

The longest day of the year (in terms of hours of sunlight) occurs on the day of the summer solstice. For locations in the northern hemisphere, the summer solstice is the time when the sun is farthest north. In 2010, the summer solstice occurred on June 21 (the 172nd day of the year) at 6:28 AM EDT. The shortest day of the year occurs on the day of the winter solstice. The winter solstice is the time when the Sun is farthest south (again, for locations in the northern hemisphere). In 2010, the winter solstice occurred on December 21 (the 355th day of the year) at 6:38 PM (EST).

EXAMPLE 4

Finding a Sinusoidal Function for Hours of Daylight

According to the *Old Farmer's Almanac,* the number of hours of sunlight in Boston on the summer solstice is 15.30 and the number of hours of sunlight on the winter solstice is 9.08.

(a) Find a sinusoidal function of the form $y = A\sin(\omega x - \phi) + B$ that fits the data.

(b) Use the function found in part (a) to predict the number of hours of sunlight on April 1, the 91st day of the year.

(c) Draw a graph of the function found in part (a).

(d) Look up the number of hours of sunlight for April 1 in the *Old Farmer's Almanac* and compare it to the results found in part (b).

Source: The Old Farmer's Almanac, www.almanac.com/rise

Solution

(a) **STEP 1:** Amplitude $= \dfrac{\text{largest data value} - \text{smallest data value}}{2}$

$$= \frac{15.30 - 9.08}{2} = 3.11$$

STEP 2: Vertical shift $= \dfrac{\text{largest data value} + \text{smallest data value}}{2}$

$$= \frac{15.30 + 9.08}{2} = 12.19$$

STEP 3: The data repeat every 365 days. Since $T = \dfrac{2\pi}{\omega} = 365$, we find

$$\omega = \frac{2\pi}{365}$$

So far, we have $y = 3.11\sin\left(\dfrac{2\pi}{365}x - \phi\right) + 12.19$.

STEP 4: To determine the horizontal shift, we use the period $T = 365$ and divide the interval $[0, 365]$ into four subintervals of length $365 \div 4 = 91.25$:

$$[0, 91.25], \quad [91.25, 182.5], \quad [182.5, 273.75], \quad [273.75, 365]$$

The sine curve is increasing on the interval $(0, 91.25)$ and is decreasing on the interval $(91.25, 273.75)$, so a local maximum occurs at $x = 91.25$.

Since the maximum occurs on the summer solstice at $x = 172$, we must shift the graph of the function $172 - 91.25 = 80.75$ units to the right by replacing x by $x - 80.75$. Doing this, we obtain

$$y = 3.11 \sin\left(\frac{2\pi}{365}(x - 80.75)\right) + 12.19$$

Multiplying out, we find that a sine function of the form $y = A \sin(\omega x - \phi) + B$ that fits the data is

$$y = 3.11 \sin\left(\frac{2\pi}{365}x - \frac{323\pi}{730}\right) + 12.19$$

(b) To predict the number of hours of daylight on April 1, we let $x = 91$ in the function found in part (a) and obtain

$$y = 3.11 \sin\left(\frac{2\pi}{365} \cdot 91 - \frac{323}{730}\pi\right) + 12.19$$

$$\approx 12.74$$

So we predict that there will be about 12.74 hours = 12 hours, 44 minutes of sunlight on April 1 in Boston.

(c) The graph of the function found in part (a) is given in Figure 82.

(d) According to the *Old Farmer's Almanac*, there will be 12 hours 45 minutes of sunlight on April 1 in Boston.

Figure 82

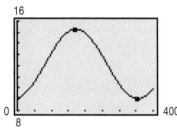

16
0
8
400

━━━**Now Work** PROBLEM 35

Certain graphing utilities (such as a TI-83, TI-84 Plus, and TI-86) have the capability of finding the sine function of best fit for sinusoidal data. At least four data points are required for this process.

EXAMPLE 5

Finding the Sine Function of Best Fit

Use a graphing utility to find the sine function of best fit for the data in Table 11. Graph this function with the scatter diagram of the data.

Solution

Enter the data from Table 11 and execute the SINe REGression program. The result is shown in Figure 83.

The output that the utility provides shows the equation

$$y = a \sin(bx + c) + d$$

The sinusoidal function of best fit is

$$y = 21.15 \sin(0.55x - 2.35) + 51.19$$

where x represents the month and y represents the average temperature.

Figure 84 shows the graph of the sinusoidal function of best fit on the scatter diagram.

Figure 83

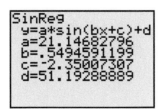

SinReg
y=a*sin(bx+c)+d
a=21.14682796
b=.5494591199
c=-2.35007307
d=51.19288889

Figure 84

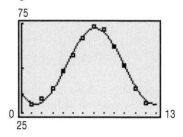

75
0
25
13

━━━**Now Work** PROBLEMS 29(d) AND (e)

6.6 Assess Your Understanding

Concepts and Vocabulary

1. For the graph of $y = A \sin(\omega x - \phi)$, the number $\dfrac{\phi}{\omega}$ is called the _____ _____.

2. *True or False* Only two data points are required by a graphing utility to find the sine function of best fit.

Skill Building

In Problems 3–14, find the amplitude, period, and phase shift of each function. Graph each function. Be sure to label key points. Show at least two periods.

3. $y = 4 \sin(2x - \pi)$

4. $y = 3 \sin(3x - \pi)$

5. $y = 2 \cos\left(3x + \dfrac{\pi}{2}\right)$

6. $y = 3 \cos(2x + \pi)$

7. $y = -3 \sin\left(2x + \dfrac{\pi}{2}\right)$

8. $y = -2 \cos\left(2x - \dfrac{\pi}{2}\right)$

9. $y = 4 \sin(\pi x + 2) - 5$

10. $y = 2 \cos(2\pi x + 4) + 4$

11. $y = 3 \cos(\pi x - 2) + 5$

12. $y = 2 \cos(2\pi x - 4) - 1$

13. $y = -3 \sin\left(-2x + \dfrac{\pi}{2}\right)$

14. $y = -3 \cos\left(-2x + \dfrac{\pi}{2}\right)$

In Problems 15–18, write the equation of a sine function that has the given characteristics.

15. Amplitude: 2
Period: π
Phase shift: $\dfrac{1}{2}$

16. Amplitude: 3
Period: $\dfrac{\pi}{2}$
Phase shift: 2

17. Amplitude: 3
Period: 3π
Phase shift: $-\dfrac{1}{3}$

18. Amplitude: 2
Period: π
Phase shift: -2

Mixed Practice

In Problems 19–26, apply the methods of this and the previous section to graph each function. Be sure to label key points and show at least two periods.

19. $y = 2 \tan(4x - \pi)$

20. $y = \dfrac{1}{2} \cot(2x - \pi)$

21. $y = 3 \csc\left(2x - \dfrac{\pi}{4}\right)$

22. $y = \dfrac{1}{2} \sec(3x - \pi)$

23. $y = -\cot\left(2x + \dfrac{\pi}{2}\right)$

24. $y = -\tan\left(3x + \dfrac{\pi}{2}\right)$

25. $y = -\sec(2\pi x + \pi)$

26. $y = -\csc\left(-\dfrac{1}{2}\pi x + \dfrac{\pi}{4}\right)$

Applications and Extensions

27. Alternating Current (ac) Circuits The current I, in amperes, flowing through an ac (alternating current) circuit at time t, in seconds, is

$$I(t) = 120 \sin\left(30\pi t - \dfrac{\pi}{3}\right) \qquad t \geq 0$$

What is the period? What is the amplitude? What is the phase shift? Graph this function over two periods.

28. Alternating Current (ac) Circuits The current I, in amperes, flowing through an ac (alternating current) circuit at time t, in seconds, is

$$I(t) = 220 \sin\left(60\pi t - \dfrac{\pi}{6}\right) \qquad t \geq 0$$

What is the period? What is the amplitude? What is the phase shift? Graph this function over two periods.

29. Monthly Temperature The following data represent the average monthly temperatures for Juneau, Alaska.

Month, x	Average Monthly Temperature, °F
January, 1	24.2
February, 2	28.4
March, 3	32.7
April, 4	39.7
May, 5	47.0
June, 6	53.0
July, 7	56.0
August, 8	55.0
September, 9	49.4
October, 10	42.2
November, 11	32.0
December, 12	27.1

Source: U.S. National Oceanic and Atmospheric Administration

(a) Draw a scatter diagram of the data for one period.
(b) Find a sinusoidal function of the form
   $y = A \sin(\omega x - \phi) + B$ that models the data.
(c) Draw the sinusoidal function found in part (b) on the scatter diagram.
(d) Use a graphing utility to find the sinusoidal function of best fit.
(e) Draw the sinusoidal function of best fit on a scatter diagram of the data.

30. Monthly Temperature The following data represent the average monthly temperatures for Washington, D.C.
(a) Draw a scatter diagram of the data for one period.
(b) Find a sinusoidal function of the form
   $y = A \sin(\omega x - \phi) + B$ that models the data.
(c) Draw the sinusoidal function found in part (b) on the scatter diagram.
(d) Use a graphing utility to find the sinusoidal function of best fit.
(e) Graph the sinusoidal function of best fit on a scatter diagram of the data.

Month, x	Average Monthly Temperature, °F
January, 1	34.6
February, 2	37.5
March, 3	47.2
April, 4	56.5
May, 5	66.4
June, 6	75.6
July, 7	80.0
August, 8	78.5
September, 9	71.3
October, 10	59.7
November, 11	49.8
December, 12	39.4

Source: U.S. National Oceanic and Atmospheric Administration

31. Monthly Temperature The following data represent the average monthly temperatures for Indianapolis, Indiana.

Month, x	Average Monthly Temperature, °F
January, 1	25.5
February, 2	29.6
March, 3	41.4
April, 4	52.4
May, 5	62.8
June, 6	71.9
July, 7	75.4
August, 8	73.2
September, 9	66.6
October, 10	54.7
November, 11	43.0
December, 12	30.9

Source: U.S. National Oceanic and Atmospheric Administration

(a) Draw a scatter diagram of the data for one period.
(b) Find a sinusoidal function of the form
   $y = A \sin(\omega x - \phi) + B$ that models the data.
(c) Draw the sinusoidal function found in part (b) on the scatter diagram.
(d) Use a graphing utility to find the sinusoidal function of best fit.
(e) Graph the sinusoidal function of best fit on a scatter diagram of the data.

32. Monthly Temperature The following data represent the average monthly temperatures for Baltimore, Maryland.
(a) Draw a scatter diagram of the data for one period.
(b) Find a sinusoidal function of the form
   $y = A \sin(\omega x - \phi) + B$ that models the data.
(c) Draw the sinusoidal function found in part (b) on the scatter diagram.
(d) Use a graphing utility to find the sinusoidal function of best fit.
(e) Graph the sinusoidal function of best fit on a scatter diagram of the data.

Month, x	Average Monthly Temperature, °F
January, 1	31.8
February, 2	34.8
March, 3	44.1
April, 4	53.4
May, 5	63.4
June, 6	72.5
July, 7	77.0
August, 8	75.6
September, 9	68.5
October, 10	56.6
November, 11	46.8
December, 12	36.7

Source: U.S. National Oceanic and Atmospheric Administration

33. Tides The length of time between consecutive high tides is 12 hours and 25 minutes. According to the National Oceanic and Atmospheric Administration, on Saturday, July 25, 2009, in Charleston, South Carolina, high tide occurred at 11:30 AM (11.5 hours) and low tide occurred at 5:31 PM (17.5167 hours). Water heights are measured as the amounts above or below the mean lower low water. The height of the water at high tide was 5.84 feet, and the height of the water at low tide was −0.37 foot.
(a) Approximately when will the next high tide occur?
(b) Find a sinusoidal function of the form
   $y = A \sin(\omega x - \phi) + B$ that models the data.
(c) Use the function found in part (b) to predict the height of the water at 3 PM on July 25, 2009.

34. Tides The length of time between consecutive high tides is 12 hours and 25 minutes. According to the National Oceanic and Atmospheric Administration, on Saturday, July 25, 2009, in Sitka Sound, Alaska, high tide occurred at 2:37 AM (2.6167 hours) and low tide occurred at 9:12 PM (9.2 hours). Water heights are measured as the amounts above or below the mean lower low water. The height of the water at high tide was 11.09 feet, and the height of the water at low tide was −2.49 feet.

(a) Approximately when will the next high tide occur?
(b) Find a sinusoidal function of the form
$y = A \sin(\omega x - \phi) + B$ that models the data.
(c) Use the function found in part (b) to predict the height of the water at 6 PM.

35. **Hours of Daylight** According to the *Old Farmer's Almanac*, in Miami, Florida, the number of hours of sunlight on the summer solstice of 2010 was 13.75, and the number of hours of sunlight on the winter solstice was 10.55.
(a) Find a sinusoidal function of the form
$y = A \sin(\omega x - \phi) + B$ that models the data.
(b) Use the function found in part (a) to predict the number of hours of sunlight on April 1, the 91st day of the year.
(c) Draw a graph of the function found in part (a).
(d) Look up the number of hours of sunlight for April 1 in the *Old Farmer's Almanac*, and compare the actual hours of daylight to the results found in part (c).

36. **Hours of Daylight** According to the *Old Farmer's Almanac*, in Detroit, Michigan, the number of hours of sunlight on the summer solstice of 2010 was 15.30, and the number of hours of sunlight on the winter solstice was 9.10.
(a) Find a sinusoidal function of the form
$y = A \sin(\omega x - \phi) + B$ that models the data.
(b) Use the function found in part (a) to predict the number of hours of sunlight on April 1, the 91st day of the year.
(c) Draw a graph of the function found in part (a).

(d) Look up the number of hours of sunlight for April 1 in the *Old Farmer's Almanac*, and compare the actual hours of daylight to the results found in part (c).

37. **Hours of Daylight** According to the *Old Farmer's Almanac*, in Anchorage, Alaska, the number of hours of sunlight on the summer solstice of 2010 was 19.42 and the number of hours of sunlight on the winter solstice was 5.48.
(a) Find a sinusoidal function of the form
$y = A \sin(\omega x - \phi) + B$ that models the data.
(b) Use the function found in part (a) to predict the number of hours of sunlight on April 1, the 91st day of the year.
(c) Draw a graph of the function found in part (a).
*(d) Look up the number of hours of sunlight for April 1 in the *Old Farmer's Almanac*, and compare the actual hours of daylight to the results found in part (c).

38. **Hours of Daylight** According to the *Old Farmer's Almanac*, in Honolulu, Hawaii, the number of hours of sunlight on the summer solstice of 2010 was 13.43 and the number of hours of sunlight on the winter solstice was 10.85.
(a) Find a sinusoidal function of the form
$y = A \sin(\omega x - \phi) + B$ that models the data.
(b) Use the function found in part (a) to predict the number of hours of sunlight on April 1, the 91st day of the year.
(c) Draw a graph of the function found in part (a).
(d) Look up the number of hours of sunlight for April 1 in the *Old Farmer's Almanac*, and compare the actual hours of daylight to the results found in part (c).

Explaining Concepts: Discussion and Writing

39. Explain how the amplitude and period of a sinusoidal graph are used to establish the scale on each coordinate axis.

40. Find an application in your major field that leads to a sinusoidal graph. Write a paper about your findings.

CHAPTER REVIEW

Things to Know

Definitions

Angle in standard position (p. 350)	Vertex is at the origin; initial side is along the positive x-axis.
1 Degree (1°) (p. 351)	$1° = \dfrac{1}{360}$ revolution
1 Radian (p. 353)	The measure of a central angle of a circle whose rays subtend an arc whose length is the radius of the circle

Trigonometric functions (pp. 364–365, 366) $P = (x, y)$ is the point on the unit circle corresponding to $\theta = t$ radians.

$$\sin t = \sin \theta = y \qquad\qquad \cos t = \cos \theta = x \qquad\qquad \tan t = \tan \theta = \frac{y}{x} \quad x \neq 0$$

$$\csc t = \csc \theta = \frac{1}{y} \quad y \neq 0 \quad \sec t = \sec \theta = \frac{1}{x} \quad x \neq 0 \quad \cot t = \cot \theta = \frac{x}{y} \quad y \neq 0$$

Trigonometric functions using a circle of radius r (p. 374)   For an angle θ in standard position, $P = (x, y)$ is the point on the terminal side of θ that is also on the circle $x^2 + y^2 = r^2$.

$$\sin \theta = \frac{y}{r} \qquad\qquad \cos \theta = \frac{x}{r} \qquad\qquad \tan \theta = \frac{y}{x} \quad x \neq 0$$

$$\csc \theta = \frac{r}{y} \quad y \neq 0 \qquad \sec \theta = \frac{r}{x} \quad x \neq 0 \qquad \cot \theta = \frac{x}{y} \quad y \neq 0$$

Periodic function (p. 382) $f(\theta + p) = f(\theta)$, for all θ, $p > 0$, where the smallest such p is the fundamental period.

Formulas

1 revolution = 360°   (p. 352)

$\qquad\qquad$ = 2π radians (p. 355)

$1° = \dfrac{\pi}{180}$ radian (p. 352)   1 radian = $\dfrac{180}{\pi}$ degrees (p. 352)

$s = r\,\theta$ (p. 354)

θ is measured in radians; s is the length of the arc subtended by the central angle θ of the circle of radius r.

$A = \dfrac{1}{2}r^2\,\theta$ (p. 357)

A is the area of the sector of a circle of radius r formed by a central angle of θ radians.

$v = r\omega$ (p. 358)

v is the linear speed along the circle of radius r; ω is the angular speed (measured in radians per unit time).

Table of Values (pp. 368 and 371)

θ (Radians)	θ (Degrees)	$\sin\theta$	$\cos\theta$	$\tan\theta$	$\csc\theta$	$\sec\theta$	$\cot\theta$
0	0°	0	1	0	Not defined	1	Not defined
$\dfrac{\pi}{6}$	30°	$\dfrac{1}{2}$	$\dfrac{\sqrt{3}}{2}$	$\dfrac{\sqrt{3}}{3}$	2	$\dfrac{2\sqrt{3}}{3}$	$\sqrt{3}$
$\dfrac{\pi}{4}$	45°	$\dfrac{\sqrt{2}}{2}$	$\dfrac{\sqrt{2}}{2}$	1	$\sqrt{2}$	$\sqrt{2}$	1
$\dfrac{\pi}{3}$	60°	$\dfrac{\sqrt{3}}{2}$	$\dfrac{1}{2}$	$\sqrt{3}$	$\dfrac{2\sqrt{3}}{3}$	2	$\dfrac{\sqrt{3}}{3}$
$\dfrac{\pi}{2}$	90°	1	0	Not defined	1	Not defined	0
π	180°	0	−1	0	Not defined	−1	Not defined
$\dfrac{3\pi}{2}$	270°	−1	0	Not defined	−1	Not defined	0

The Unit Circle (pp. 372–373)

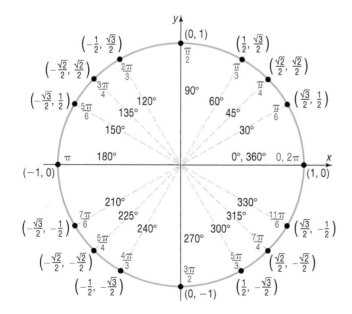

Fundamental identities (p. 385)

$$\tan\theta = \frac{\sin\theta}{\cos\theta} \qquad \cot\theta = \frac{\cos\theta}{\sin\theta}$$

$$\csc\theta = \frac{1}{\sin\theta} \qquad \sec\theta = \frac{1}{\cos\theta} \qquad \cot\theta = \frac{1}{\tan\theta}$$

$$\sin^2\theta + \cos^2\theta = 1 \qquad \tan^2\theta + 1 = \sec^2\theta \qquad \cot^2\theta + 1 = \csc^2\theta$$

Properties of the trigonometric functions

$y = \sin x$ (p. 394)   Domain: $-\infty < x < \infty$
                             Range: $-1 \le y \le 1$
                             Periodic: period $= 2\pi(360°)$
                             Odd function

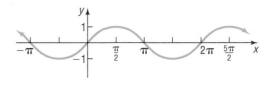

$y = \cos x$ (p. 396)   Domain: $-\infty < x < \infty$
                             Range: $-1 \le y \le 1$
                             Periodic: period $= 2\pi(360°)$
                             Even function

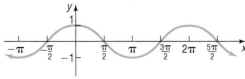

$y = \tan x$ (pp. 408–410)   Domain: $-\infty < x < \infty$, except odd integer multiples of $\frac{\pi}{2}$ $(90°)$
                             Range: $-\infty < y < \infty$
                             Periodic: period $= \pi(180°)$
                             Odd function
                             Vertical asymptotes at odd integer multiples of $\frac{\pi}{2}$

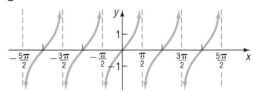

$y = \cot x$ (p. 411)   Domain: $-\infty < x < \infty$, except integer multiples of $\pi(180°)$
                             Range: $-\infty < y < \infty$
                             Periodic: period $= \pi(180°)$
                             Odd function
                             Vertical asymptotes at integer multiples of π

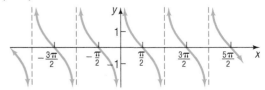

$y = \csc x$ (p. 412)   Domain: $-\infty < x < \infty$, except integer multiples of $\pi(180°)$
                             Range: $|y| \ge 1$ $(y \le -1$ or $y \ge 1)$
                             Periodic: period $= 2\pi(360°)$
                             Odd function
                             Vertical asymptotes at integer multiples of π

$y = \sec x$ (p. 412)   Domain: $-\infty < x < \infty$, except odd integer multiples of $\frac{\pi}{2}$ $(90°)$
                             Range: $|y| \ge 1$ $(y \le -1$ or $y \ge 1)$
                             Periodic: period $= 2\pi(360°)$
                             Even function
                             Vertical asymptotes at odd integer multiples of $\frac{\pi}{2}$

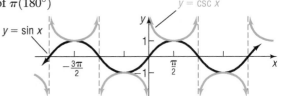

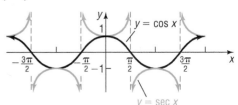

Sinusoidal graphs

$y = A\sin(\omega x) + B, \quad \omega > 0$ Period $= \dfrac{2\pi}{\omega}$ (pp. 398, 416)

$y = A\cos(\omega x) + B, \quad \omega > 0$ Amplitude $= |A|$ (pp. 398, 416)

$y = A\sin(\omega x - \phi) + B = A\sin\left[\omega\left(x - \dfrac{\phi}{\omega}\right)\right] + B$ Phase shift $= \dfrac{\phi}{\omega}$ (p. 416)

$y = A\cos(\omega x - \phi) + B = A\cos\left[\omega\left(x - \dfrac{\phi}{\omega}\right)\right] + B$

Objectives

Section		You should be able to:	Example(s)	Review Exercises
6.1	1	Convert between decimals and degrees, minutes, seconds measures for angles (p. 352)	2	86
	2	Find the length of an arc of a circle (p. 354)	3	87, 88
	3	Convert from degrees to radians and from radians to degrees (p. 354)	4–6	1–8
	4	Find the area of a sector of a circle (p. 357)	7	87
	5	Find the linear speed of an object traveling in circular motion (p. 358)	8	89–92
6.2	1	Find the exact values of the trigonometric functions using a point on the unit circle (p. 365)	1	83, 97
	2	Find the exact values of the trigonometric functions of quadrantal angles (p. 366)	2, 3	10, 17, 18, 20, 97
	3	Find the exact values of the trigonometric functions of $\frac{\pi}{4} = 45°$ (p. 368)	4, 5	9, 11, 13, 15, 16
	4	Find the exact values of the trigonometric functions of $\frac{\pi}{6} = 30°$ and $\frac{\pi}{3} = 60°$ (p. 369)	6–8	9–15
	5	Find the exact values of the trigonometric functions for integer multiples of $\frac{\pi}{6} = 30°$, $\frac{\pi}{4} = 45°$, and $\frac{\pi}{3} = 60°$ (p. 372)	9, 10	13–16, 19, 97
	6	Use a calculator to approximate the value of a trigonometric function (p. 373)	11	79, 80
	7	Use a circle of radius r to evaluate the trigonometric functions (p. 374)	12	84
6.3	1	Determine the domain and the range of the trigonometric functions (p. 380)	pp. 380–381	85
	2	Determine the period of the trigonometric functions (p. 381)	1	85
	3	Determine the signs of the trigonometric functions in a given quadrant (p. 383)	2	81, 82
	4	Find the values of the trigonometric functions using fundamental identities (p. 384)	3, 4	21–30
	5	Find the exact values of the trigonometric functions of an angle given one of the functions and the quadrant of the angle (p. 386)	5, 6	31–46
	6	Use even–odd properties to find the exact values of the trigonometric functions (p. 389)	7	27–30
6.4	1	Graph functions of the form $y = A \sin(\omega x)$ using transformations (p. 394)	1, 2	47
	2	Graph functions of the form $y = A \cos(\omega x)$ using transformations (p. 396)	3	48
	3	Determine the amplitude and period of sinusoidal functions (p. 397)	4	63–68
	4	Graph sinusoidal functions using key points (p. 398)	5–7	47, 48, 67, 68, 93
	5	Find an equation for a sinusoidal graph (p. 402)	8, 9	75–78
6.5	1	Graph functions of the form $y = A \tan(\omega x) + B$ and $y = A \cot(\omega x) + B$ (p. 410)	1, 2	53, 54, 56
	2	Graph functions of the form $y = A \csc(\omega x) + B$ and $y = A \sec(\omega x) + B$ (p. 412)	3	57
6.6	1	Graph sinusoidal functions of the form $y = A \sin(\omega x - \phi) + B$ (p. 415)	1, 2	49, 50, 59, 60, 69–74, 94
	2	Build sinusoidal models from data (p. 419)	3–5	95, 96

Review Exercises

In Problems 1–4, convert each angle in degrees to radians. Express your answer as a multiple of π.

1. $135°$

2. $210°$

3. $18°$

4. $15°$

In Problems 5–8, convert each angle in radians to degrees.

5. $\dfrac{3\pi}{4}$

6. $\dfrac{2\pi}{3}$

7. $-\dfrac{5\pi}{2}$

8. $-\dfrac{3\pi}{2}$

In Problems 9–30, find the exact value of each expression. Do not use a calculator.

9. $\tan \dfrac{\pi}{4} - \sin \dfrac{\pi}{6}$

10. $\cos \dfrac{\pi}{3} + \sin \dfrac{\pi}{2}$

11. $3 \sin 45° - 4 \tan \dfrac{\pi}{6}$

12. $4 \cos 60° + 3 \tan \dfrac{\pi}{3}$

13. $6 \cos \dfrac{3\pi}{4} + 2 \tan\left(-\dfrac{\pi}{3}\right)$

14. $3 \sin \dfrac{2\pi}{3} - 4 \cos \dfrac{5\pi}{2}$

15. $\sec\left(-\dfrac{\pi}{3}\right) - \cot\left(-\dfrac{5\pi}{4}\right)$

16. $4 \csc \dfrac{3\pi}{4} - \cot\left(-\dfrac{\pi}{4}\right)$

17. $\tan \pi + \sin \pi$

18. $\cos \dfrac{\pi}{2} - \csc\left(-\dfrac{\pi}{2}\right)$

19. $\cos 540° - \tan(-405°)$

20. $\sin 270° + \cos(-180°)$

21. $\sin^2 20° + \dfrac{1}{\sec^2 20°}$

22. $\dfrac{1}{\cos^2 40°} - \dfrac{1}{\cot^2 40°}$

23. $\sec 50° \cos 50°$

24. $\tan 10° \cot 10°$

25. $\dfrac{\sin 50°}{\cos 40°}$

26. $\dfrac{\tan 20°}{\cot 70°}$

27. $\dfrac{\sin(-40°)}{\cos 50°}$

28. $\tan(-20°) \cot 20°$

29. $\sin 400° \sec(-50°)$

30. $\cot 200° \cot(-70°)$

In Problems 31–46, find the exact value of each of the remaining trigonometric functions.

31. $\sin \theta = \dfrac{4}{5}, \quad \theta$ is acute

32. $\tan \theta = \dfrac{1}{4}, \quad \theta$ is acute

33. $\tan \theta = \dfrac{12}{5}, \quad \sin \theta < 0$

34. $\cot \theta = \dfrac{12}{5}, \quad \cos \theta < 0$

35. $\sec \theta = -\dfrac{5}{4}, \quad \tan \theta < 0$

36. $\csc \theta = -\dfrac{5}{3}, \quad \cot \theta < 0$

37. $\sin \theta = \dfrac{12}{13}, \quad \theta$ in quadrant II

38. $\cos \theta = -\dfrac{3}{5}, \quad \theta$ in quadrant III

39. $\sin \theta = -\dfrac{5}{13}, \quad \dfrac{3\pi}{2} < \theta < 2\pi$

40. $\cos \theta = \dfrac{12}{13}, \quad \dfrac{3\pi}{2} < \theta < 2\pi$

41. $\tan \theta = \dfrac{1}{3}, \quad 180° < \theta < 270°$

42. $\tan \theta = -\dfrac{2}{3}, \quad 90° < \theta < 180°$

43. $\sec \theta = 3, \quad \dfrac{3\pi}{2} < \theta < 2\pi$

44. $\csc \theta = -4, \quad \pi < \theta < \dfrac{3\pi}{2}$

45. $\cot \theta = -2, \quad \dfrac{\pi}{2} < \theta < \pi$

46. $\tan \theta = -2, \quad \dfrac{3\pi}{2} < \theta < 2\pi$

In Problems 47–62, graph each function. Each graph should contain at least two periods. Use the graph to determine the domain and the range of each function.

47. $y = 2 \sin(4x)$

48. $y = -3 \cos(2x)$

49. $y = -2 \cos\left(x + \dfrac{\pi}{2}\right)$

50. $y = 3 \sin(x - \pi)$

51. $y = \tan(x + \pi)$

52. $y = -\tan\left(x - \dfrac{\pi}{2}\right)$

53. $y = -2 \tan(3x)$

54. $y = 4 \tan(2x)$

55. $y = \cot\left(x + \dfrac{\pi}{4}\right)$

56. $y = -4 \cot(2x)$

57. $y = 4 \sec(2x)$

58. $y = \csc\left(x + \dfrac{\pi}{4}\right)$

59. $y = 4 \sin(2x + 4) - 2$

60. $y = 3 \cos(4x + 2) + 1$

61. $y = 4 \tan\left(\dfrac{x}{2} + \dfrac{\pi}{4}\right)$

62. $y = 5 \cot\left(\dfrac{x}{3} - \dfrac{\pi}{4}\right)$

In Problems 63–66, determine the amplitude and period of each function without graphing.

63. $y = 4 \cos x$

64. $y = \sin(2x)$

65. $y = -8 \sin\left(\dfrac{\pi}{2}x\right)$

66. $y = -2 \cos(3\pi x)$

In Problems 67–74, find the amplitude, period, and phase shift of each function. Graph each function. Show at least two periods.

67. $y = 4 \sin(3x)$

68. $y = 2 \cos\left(\dfrac{1}{3}x\right)$

69. $y = 2 \sin(2x - \pi)$

70. $y = -\cos\left(\dfrac{1}{2}x + \dfrac{\pi}{2}\right)$

71. $y = \dfrac{1}{2} \sin\left(\dfrac{3}{2}x - \pi\right)$

72. $y = \dfrac{3}{2} \cos(6x + 3\pi)$

73. $y = -\dfrac{2}{3} \cos(\pi x - 6)$

74. $y = -7 \sin\left(\dfrac{\pi}{3}x - \dfrac{4}{3}\right)$

In Problems 75–78, find a function whose graph is given.

75.

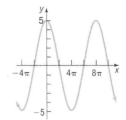

76.

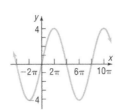

77.

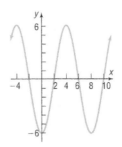

78.

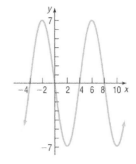

---

79. Use a calculator to approximate $\sin \dfrac{\pi}{8}$. Round the answer to two decimal places.

80. Use a calculator to approximate $\sec 10°$. Round the answer to two decimal places.

81. Determine the signs of the six trigonometric functions of an angle θ whose terminal side is in quadrant III.

82. Name the quadrant θ lies in if $\cos \theta > 0$ and $\tan \theta < 0$.

83. Find the exact values of the six trigonometric functions of t if $P = \left(-\dfrac{1}{3}, \dfrac{2\sqrt{2}}{3}\right)$ is the point on the unit circle that corresponds to t.

84. Find the exact value of $\sin t$, $\cos t$, and $\tan t$ if $P = (-2, 5)$ is the point on the circle that corresponds to t.

85. What is the domain and the range of the secant function? What is the period?

86. (a) Convert the angle $32°20'35''$ to a decimal in degrees. Round the answer to two decimal places.
(b) Convert the angle $63.18°$ to D°M'S'' form. Express the answer to the nearest second.

87. Find the length of the arc subtended by a central angle of $30°$ on a circle of radius 2 feet. What is the area of the sector?

88. The minute hand of a clock is 8 inches long. How far does the tip of the minute hand move in 30 minutes? How far does it move in 20 minutes?

89. Angular Speed of a Race Car A race car is driven around a circular track at a constant speed of 180 miles per hour. If the diameter of the track is $\dfrac{1}{2}$ mile, what is the angular

speed of the car? Express your answer in revolutions per hour (which is equivalent to laps per hour).

90. Merry-Go-Rounds A neighborhood carnival has a merry-go-round whose radius is 25 feet. If the time for one revolution is 30 seconds, how fast is the merry-go-round going?

91. Lighthouse Beacons The Montauk Point Lighthouse on Long Island has dual beams (two light sources opposite each other). Ships at sea observe a blinking light every 5 seconds. What rotation speed is required to do this?

92. Spin Balancing Tires The radius of each wheel of a car is 16 inches. At how many revolutions per minute should a spin balancer be set to balance the tires at a speed of 90 miles per hour? Is the setting different for a wheel of radius 14 inches? If so, what is this setting?

93. Alternating Voltage The electromotive force E, in volts, in a certain ac (alternating circuit) circuit obeys the function

$$E(t) = 120 \sin(120\pi t), \qquad t \geq 0$$

where t is measured in seconds.
(a) What is the maximum value of E?
(b) What is the period?
(c) Graph this function over two periods.

94. Alternating Current The current I, in amperes, flowing through an ac (alternating current) circuit at time t is

$$I(t) = 220 \sin\left(30\pi t + \dfrac{\pi}{6}\right), \qquad t \geq 0$$

(a) What is the period?
(b) What is the amplitude?
(c) What is the phase shift?
(d) Graph this function over two periods.

95. Monthly Temperature The following data represent the average monthly temperatures for Phoenix, Arizona.
(a) Draw a scatter diagram of the data for one period.
(b) Find a sinusoidal function of the form
$y = A \sin(\omega x - \phi) + B$ that fits the data.
(c) Draw the sinusoidal function found in part (b) on the scatter diagram.
(d) Use a graphing utility to find the sinusoidal function of best fit.
(e) Graph the sinusoidal function of best fit on the scatter diagram.

Month, m	Average Monthly Temperature, T
January, 1	51
February, 2	55
March, 3	63
April, 4	67
May, 5	77
June, 6	86
July, 7	90
August, 8	90
September, 9	84
October, 10	71
November, 11	59
December, 12	52

SOURCE: U.S. National Oceanic and Atmospheric Administration

96. Hours of Daylight According to the *Old Farmer's Almanac*, in Las Vegas, Nevada, the number of hours of sunlight on the summer solstice is 14.63 and the number of hours of sunlight on the winter solstice is 9.72.
(a) Find a sinusoidal function of the form
$y = A \sin(\omega x - \phi) + B$ that fits the data.
(b) Use the function found in part (a) to predict the number of hours of sunlight on April 1, the 91st day of the year.
(c) Draw a graph of the function found in part (a).
(d) Look up the number of hours of sunlight for April 1 in the *Old Farmer's Almanac* and compare the actual hours of daylight to the results found in part (c).

97. Unit Circle On the given unit circle, fill in the missing angles (in radians) and the corresponding points P of each angle.

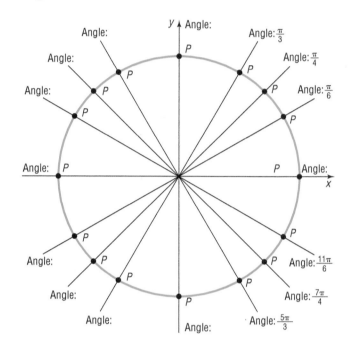

CHAPTER
Test Prep
VIDEOS

The Chapter Test Prep Videos are step-by-step test solutions available in the Video Resources DVD, in *MyMathLab*, or on this text's You**Tube** Channel. Flip back to the Student Resources page to see the exact web address for this text's YouTube channel.

CHAPTER TEST

In Problems 1–3, convert each angle in degrees to radians. Express your answer as a multiple of π.

1. $260°$ **2.** $-400°$ **3.** $13°$

In Problems 4–6 convert each angle in radians to degrees.

4. $-\dfrac{\pi}{8}$ **5.** $\dfrac{9\pi}{2}$ **6.** $\dfrac{3\pi}{4}$

In Problems 7–12, find the exact value of each expression.

7. $\sin\dfrac{\pi}{6}$ **8.** $\cos\left(-\dfrac{5\pi}{4}\right) - \cos\dfrac{3\pi}{4}$

9. $\cos(-120°)$ **10.** $\tan 330°$

11. $\sin\dfrac{\pi}{2} - \tan\dfrac{19\pi}{4}$ **12.** $2\sin^2 60° - 3\cos 45°$

In Problems 13–16, use a calculator to evaluate each expression. Round your answer to three decimal places.

13. $\sin 17°$ **14.** $\cos\dfrac{2\pi}{5}$ **15.** $\sec 229°$ **16.** $\cot\dfrac{28\pi}{9}$

17. Fill in each table entry with the sign of each function.

	sin θ	cos θ	tan θ	sec θ	csc θ	cot θ
θ in QI						
θ in QII						
θ in QIII						
θ in QIV						

18. If $f(x) = \sin x$ and $f(a) = \dfrac{3}{5}$, find $f(-a)$.

In Problems 19–21 find the value of the remaining five trigonometric functions of θ.

19. $\sin\theta = \dfrac{5}{7}$, θ in quadrant II   **20.** $\cos\theta = \dfrac{2}{3}, \dfrac{3\pi}{2} < \theta < 2\pi$

21. $\tan\theta = -\dfrac{12}{5}, \dfrac{\pi}{2} < \theta < \pi$

In Problems 22–24, the point (x, y) is on the terminal side of angle θ in standard position. Find the exact value of the given trigonometric function.

22. $(2, 7)$, $\sin \theta$ **23.** $(-5, 11)$, $\cos \theta$

24. $(6, -3)$, $\tan \theta$

In Problems 25 and 26, graph the function.

25. $y = 2 \sin\left(\dfrac{x}{3} - \dfrac{\pi}{6}\right)$

26. $y = \tan\left(-x + \dfrac{\pi}{4}\right) + 2$

27. Write an equation for a sinusoidal graph with the following properties:

$$A = -3 \quad \text{period} = \frac{2\pi}{3} \quad \text{phase shift} = -\frac{\pi}{4}$$

28. Logan has a garden in the shape of a sector of a circle; the outer rim of the garden is 25 feet long and the central angle of the sector is 50°. She wants to add a 3-foot-wide walk to the outer rim; how many square feet of paving blocks will she need to build the walk?

29. Hungarian Adrian Annus won the gold medal for the hammer throw at the 2004 Olympics in Athens with a winning distance of 83.19 meters.* The event consists of swinging a 16-pound weight attached to a wire 190 centimeters long in a circle and then releasing it. Assuming his release is at a 45° angle to the ground, the hammer will travel a distance of $\dfrac{v_0^2}{g}$ meters, where $g = 9.8$ meters/second² and v_0 is the linear speed of the hammer when released. At what rate (rpm) was he swinging the hammer upon release?

*Annus was stripped of his medal after refusing to cooperate with postmedal drug testing.

CUMULATIVE REVIEW

1. Find the real solutions, if any, of the equation $2x^2 + x - 1 = 0$.

2. Find an equation for the line with slope -3 containing the point $(-2, 5)$.

3. Find an equation for a circle of radius 4 and center at the point $(0, -2)$.

4. Discuss the equation $2x - 3y = 12$. Graph it.

5. Discuss the equation $x^2 + y^2 - 2x + 4y - 4 = 0$. Graph it.

6. Use transformations to graph the function $y = (x - 3)^2 + 2$.

7. Sketch a graph of each of the following functions. Label at least three points on each graph.
   (a) $y = x^2$ (b) $y = x^3$ (c) $y = e^x$
   (d) $y = \ln x$ (e) $y = \sin x$ (f) $y = \tan x$

8. Find the inverse function of $f(x) = 3x - 2$.

9. Find the exact value of $(\sin 14°)^2 + (\cos 14°)^2 - 3$.

10. Graph $y = 3 \sin(2x)$.

11. Find the exact value of $\tan \dfrac{\pi}{4} - 3 \cos \dfrac{\pi}{6} + \csc \dfrac{\pi}{6}$.

12. Find an exponential function for the following graph. Express your answer in the form $y = Ab^x$.

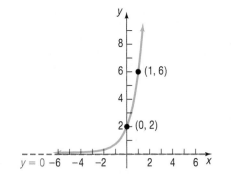

13. Find a sinusoidal function for the following graph.

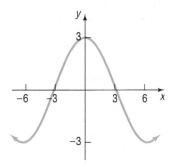

14. (a) Find a linear function that contains the points $(-2, 3)$ and $(1, -6)$. What is the slope? What are the intercepts of the function? Graph the function. Be sure to label the intercepts.
   (b) Find a quadratic function that contains the point $(-2, 3)$ with vertex $(1, -6)$. What are the intercepts of the function? Graph the function.
   (c) Show that there is no exponential function of the form $f(x) = ae^x$ that contains the points $(-2, 3)$ and $(1, -6)$.

15. (a) Find a polynomial function of degree 3 whose y-intercept is 5 and whose x-intercepts are -2, 3, and 5. Graph the function.
   (b) Find a rational function whose y-intercept is 5 and whose x-intercepts are -2, 3, and 5 that has the line $x = 2$ as a vertical asymptote. Graph the function.

CHAPTER PROJECTS

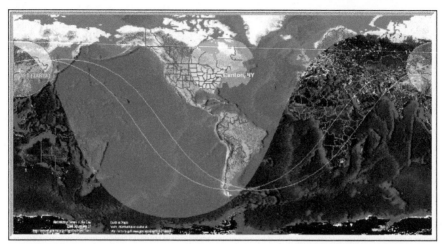

((o)) **Internet-based Project**

I. **Length of Day Revisited** Go to *http://en.wikipedia.org/wiki
/latitude* and read about latitude through the subhead "Effect
of Latitude". Now go to *http://www.orchidculture.com/COD
/daviengtn.nt*.

1. For a particular latitude, record in a table the length of
day for the various days of the year. For January 1, use 1
as the day, for January 16, use 16 as the day, for
February 1, use 32 as the day, and so on. Enter the data
into an Excel spreadsheet using column B for the day of
the year and column C for the length of day.

2. Draw a scatter diagram of the data with day of the year
as the independent variable and length of day as the
dependent variable using Excel. The Chapter 3 project
describes how to draw a scatter diagram in Excel.

3. Determine the sinusoidal function of best fit,
$y = A \sin(Bx + C) + D$ as follows:
   (a) Enter initial guesses as to the values of A, B, C, and
   D into column A with the value of A in cell A1, B in
   cell A2, C in cell A3, and D in cell A4.
   (b) In cell D1 enter "=A$1*sin(A$2*B1 + A$3) + A$4".
   Copy this cell entry into the cells below D1 to as many
   rows as there are data. For example, if column C goes to
   row 23, then column D should also go to row 23.
   (c) Enter "=(D1 − C1)^2" into cell E1. Copy this entry
   below as described in part 3b.
   (d) The idea behind curve fitting is to make the sum of the
   squared differences between what is predicted and
   actual observations as small as possible. Enter
   "=sum(E1..E#)" into cell A6, where # represents the
   row number of the last data point. For example, if you
   have 23 rows of data, enter "=sum(E1..E23)" in cell A6.
   (e) Now, we need to install the Solver feature of Excel.
   To do this, click the Office Button (top-left portion
   of screen), and then select Excel Options. Select
   Add-Ins. In the drop-down menu entitled "Manage,"

choose Excel Add-ins, then click Go . . . Check the
box entitled "Solver Add-in" and click OK. The
Solver add-in is now available in the Data tab. Choose
Solver. Fill in the screen as shown below:

The values for A, B, C, and D are located in cells
A1–A4. What is the sinusoidal function of best fit?

4. Determine the longest day of the year according to your
model. What is the day length on the longest day of the
year? Determine the shortest day of the year according
to your model. What is the day length on the shortest
day of the year?

5. On which days is the day length exactly 12 hours
according to your model?

6. Look up the day on which the Vernal Equinox and
Autumnal Equinox occur. How do they match up with
the results obtained in part 5?

7. Do you think your model accurately describes the
relation between day of the year and length of the day?

8. Use your model to predict the hours of daylight for
the latitude you selected for various days of the year.
Go to the *Old Farmer's Almanac* or other website (such
as *http://astro.unl.edu/classaction/animations/coordsmotion
/daylighthoursexplorer.html*) to determine the hours of
daylight for the latitude you selected. How do the two
compare?

The following projects are available on the Instructor's Resource Center (IRC):

II. **Tides** Data from a tide table are used to build a sine function that models tides.

III. **Project at Motorola** *Digital Transmission over the Air* Learn how Motorola Corporation transmits digital sequences by
modulating the phase of the carrier waves.

IV. **Identifying Mountain Peaks in Hawaii** The visibility of a mountain is affected by its altitude, distance from the viewer, and the
curvature of Earth's surface. Trigonometry can be used to determine whether a distant object can be seen.

V. **CBL Experiment** Technology is used to model and study the effects of damping on sound waves.

Citation: Excel © 2010 Microsoft Corporation. Used with permission from Microsoft.

Analytic Trigonometry

7

Outline

Mapping Your Mind

The ability to organize material in your mind is key to understanding. You have been exposed to a lot of concepts at this point in the course, and it is a worthwhile exercise to organize the material. In the past, we might organize material using index cards or an outline. But in today's digital world, we can use interesting software that allows us to digitally organize the material that is in our mind and share it with anyone on the Web.

 —See the Internet-based Chapter Project I—

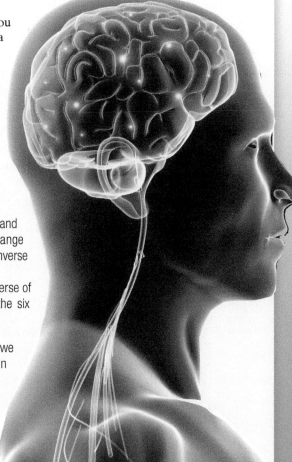

◁ **A Look Back** In Chapter 5, we defined inverse functions and developed their properties, particularly the relationship between the domain and range of a function and its inverse. We learned that the graphs of a function and its inverse are symmetric with respect to the line $y = x$.

We continued in Chapter 5 by defining the exponential function and the inverse of the exponential function, the logarithmic function. In Chapter 6, we defined the six trigonometric functions and looked at their properties.

A Look Ahead ▷ In the first two sections of this chapter, we define the six inverse trigonometric functions and investigate their properties. In Section 7.3, we discuss equations that contain trigonometric functions. In Sections 7.4 through 7.7, we continue the derivation of identities. These identities play an important role in calculus, the physical and life sciences, and economics, where they are used to simplify complicated expressions.

7.1 The Inverse Sine, Cosine, and Tangent Functions

PREPARING FOR THIS SECTION *Before getting started, review the following:*

- Inverse Functions (Section 5.2, pp. 257–263)
- Values of the Trigonometric Functions (Section 6.2, pp. 365–374)

- Properties of the Sine, Cosine, and Tangent Functions (Section 6.3, pp. 379–389)
- Graphs of the Sine, Cosine, and Tangent Functions (Sections 6.4, pp. 393–397 and 6.5, pp. 408–411)

Now Work the 'Are You Prepared?' problems on page 445.

OBJECTIVES **1** Find the Exact Value of an Inverse Sine Function (p. 437)
           2 Find an Approximate Value of an Inverse Sine Function (p. 438)
           3 Use Properties of Inverse Functions to Find Exact Values of Certain Composite Functions (p. 439)
           4 Find the Inverse Function of a Trigonometric Function (p. 444)
           5 Solve Equations Involving Inverse Trigonometric Functions (p. 445)

In Section 5.2 we discussed inverse functions, and we concluded that if a function is one-to-one it will have an inverse function. We also observed that if a function is not one-to-one it may be possible to restrict its domain in some suitable manner so that the restricted function is one-to-one. For example, the function $y = x^2$ is not one-to-one; however, if we restrict the domain to $x \geq 0$, the function is one-to-one.

Other properties of a one-to-one function f and its inverse function f^{-1} that we discussed in Section 5.2 are summarized next.

1. $f^{-1}(f(x)) = x$ for every x in the domain of f and $f(f^{-1}(x)) = x$ for every x in the domain of f^{-1}.
2. Domain of f = range of f^{-1} and range of f = domain of f^{-1}.
3. The graph of f and the graph of f^{-1} are reflections of one another about the line $y = x$.
4. If a function $y = f(x)$ has an inverse function, the implicit equation of the inverse function is $x = f(y)$. If we solve this equation for y, we obtain the explicit equation $y = f^{-1}(x)$.

The Inverse Sine Function

In Figure 1, we show the graph of $y = \sin x$. Because every horizontal line $y = b$, where b is between -1 and 1, inclusive, intersects the graph of $y = \sin x$ infinitely many times, it follows from the horizontal-line test that the function $y = \sin x$ is not one-to-one.

Figure 1
$y = \sin x, -\infty < x < \infty, -1 \leq y \leq 1$

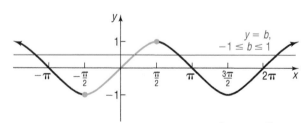

Figure 2
$y = \sin x, -\dfrac{\pi}{2} \leq x \leq \dfrac{\pi}{2}, -1 \leq y \leq 1$

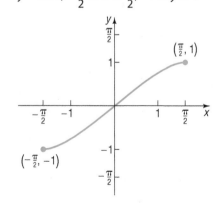

However, if we restrict the domain of $y = \sin x$ to the interval $\left[-\dfrac{\pi}{2}, \dfrac{\pi}{2} \right]$, the restricted function

$$y = \sin x \qquad -\frac{\pi}{2} \leq x \leq \frac{\pi}{2}$$

is one-to-one and so will have an inverse function.* See Figure 2.

* Although there are many other ways to restrict the domain and obtain a one-to-one function, mathematicians have agreed to use the interval $\left[-\dfrac{\pi}{2}, \dfrac{\pi}{2} \right]$ to define the inverse of $y = \sin x$.

REMEMBER The domain of a function *f* equals the range of its inverse, f^{-1}, and the range of a function *f* equals the domain of its inverse, f^{-1}. Because the restricted domain of the sine function is $\left[-\dfrac{\pi}{2}, \dfrac{\pi}{2}\right]$, the range of the inverse sine function is $\left[-\dfrac{\pi}{2}, \dfrac{\pi}{2}\right]$ and because the range of the sine function is $[-1, 1]$, the domain of the inverse sine function is $[-1, 1]$. ∎

An equation for the inverse of $y = f(x) = \sin x$ is obtained by interchanging x and y. The implicit form of the inverse function is $x = \sin y, -\dfrac{\pi}{2} \le y \le \dfrac{\pi}{2}$. The explicit form is called the **inverse sine** of x and is symbolized by $y = f^{-1}(x) = \sin^{-1} x$.

$$y = \sin^{-1} x \quad \text{means} \quad x = \sin y$$
$$\text{where} \quad -1 \le x \le 1 \quad \text{and} \quad -\dfrac{\pi}{2} \le y \le \dfrac{\pi}{2} \tag{1}$$

Because $y = \sin^{-1} x$ means $x = \sin y$, we read $y = \sin^{-1} x$ as "y is the angle or real number whose sine equals x." Alternatively, we can say that "y is the inverse sine of x." Be careful about the notation used. The superscript -1 that appears in $y = \sin^{-1} x$ is not an exponent, but is the symbolism used to denote the inverse function f^{-1} of f. (To avoid this notation, some books use the notation $y = \text{Arcsin } x$ instead of $y = \sin^{-1} x$.)

The inverse of a function f receives as input an element from the range of f and returns as output an element in the domain of f. The restricted sine function, $y = f(x) = \sin x$, receives as input an angle or real number x in the interval $\left[-\dfrac{\pi}{2}, \dfrac{\pi}{2}\right]$ and outputs a real number in the interval $[-1, 1]$. Therefore, the inverse sine function $y = \sin^{-1} x$ receives as input a real number in the interval $[-1, 1]$ or $-1 \le x \le 1$, its domain, and outputs an angle or real number in the interval $\left[-\dfrac{\pi}{2}, \dfrac{\pi}{2}\right]$ or $-\dfrac{\pi}{2} \le y \le \dfrac{\pi}{2}$, its range.

The graph of the inverse sine function can be obtained by reflecting the restricted portion of the graph of $y = f(x) = \sin x$ about the line $y = x$, as shown in Figure 3.

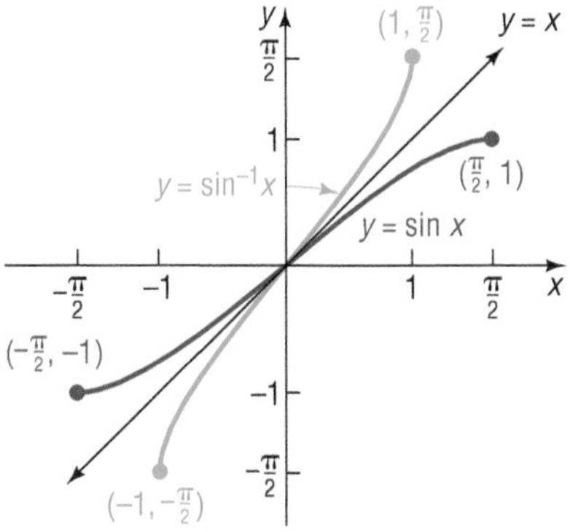

 ✓**Check:** Graph $Y_1 = \sin x$ and $Y_2 = \sin^{-1} x$. Compare the result with Figure 3.

Figure 3

$y = \sin^{-1} x, -1 \le x \le 1, -\dfrac{\pi}{2} \le y \le \dfrac{\pi}{2}$

1 Find the Exact Value of an Inverse Sine Function

For some numbers x, it is possible to find the exact value of $y = \sin^{-1} x$.

EXAMPLE 1

Finding the Exact Value of an Inverse Sine Function

Find the exact value of: $\sin^{-1} 1$

Solution Let $\theta = \sin^{-1} 1$. We seek the angle $\theta, -\dfrac{\pi}{2} \le \theta \le \dfrac{\pi}{2}$, whose sine equals 1.

$$\theta = \sin^{-1} 1 \qquad -\dfrac{\pi}{2} \le \theta \le \dfrac{\pi}{2}$$

$$\sin \theta = 1 \qquad -\dfrac{\pi}{2} \le \theta \le \dfrac{\pi}{2} \quad \text{By definition of } y = \sin^{-1} x$$

Now look at Table 1 below and Figure 4 on page 438.

Table 1

θ	$-\dfrac{\pi}{2}$	$-\dfrac{\pi}{3}$	$-\dfrac{\pi}{4}$	$-\dfrac{\pi}{6}$	0	$\dfrac{\pi}{6}$	$\dfrac{\pi}{4}$	$\dfrac{\pi}{3}$	$\dfrac{\pi}{2}$
$\sin \theta$	-1	$-\dfrac{\sqrt{3}}{2}$	$-\dfrac{\sqrt{2}}{2}$	$-\dfrac{1}{2}$	0	$\dfrac{1}{2}$	$\dfrac{\sqrt{2}}{2}$	$\dfrac{\sqrt{3}}{2}$	1

We see that the only angle θ within the interval $\left[-\dfrac{\pi}{2}, \dfrac{\pi}{2}\right]$ whose sine is 1 is $\dfrac{\pi}{2}$.

(Note that $\sin \dfrac{5\pi}{2}$ also equals 1, but $\dfrac{5\pi}{2}$ lies outside the interval $\left[-\dfrac{\pi}{2}, \dfrac{\pi}{2}\right]$ and hence is not admissible.) So,

$$\sin^{-1} 1 = \frac{\pi}{2}$$

Figure 4

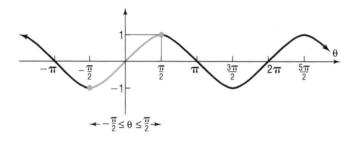

$$-\frac{\pi}{2} \le \theta \le \frac{\pi}{2}$$

━━━━Now Work PROBLEM 13

EXAMPLE 2 | **Finding the Exact Value of an Inverse Sine Function**

Find the exact value of: $\sin^{-1}\left(-\frac{1}{2}\right)$

Solution Let $\theta = \sin^{-1}\left(-\frac{1}{2}\right)$. We seek the angle θ, $-\frac{\pi}{2} \le \theta \le \frac{\pi}{2}$, whose sine equals $-\frac{1}{2}$.

$$\theta = \sin^{-1}\left(-\frac{1}{2}\right) \qquad -\frac{\pi}{2} \le \theta \le \frac{\pi}{2}$$

$$\sin \theta = -\frac{1}{2} \qquad -\frac{\pi}{2} \le \theta \le \frac{\pi}{2}$$

(Refer to Table 1 and Figure 4, if necessary.) The only angle within the interval $\left[-\frac{\pi}{2}, \frac{\pi}{2}\right]$ whose sine is $-\frac{1}{2}$ is $-\frac{\pi}{6}$. So,

$$\sin^{-1}\left(-\frac{1}{2}\right) = -\frac{\pi}{6}$$

━━━━Now Work PROBLEM 19

---

2 Find an Approximate Value of an Inverse Sine Function

For most numbers x, the value $y = \sin^{-1} x$ must be approximated.

EXAMPLE 3 | **Finding an Approximate Value of an Inverse Sine Function**

Find an approximate value of:

(a) $\sin^{-1}\dfrac{1}{3}$ (b) $\sin^{-1}\left(-\dfrac{1}{4}\right)$

Express the answer in radians rounded to two decimal places.

Solution (a) Because we want the angle measured in radians, first set the mode of the calculator to radians.* Rounded to two decimal places, we have

$$\sin^{-1}\frac{1}{3} = 0.34$$

---

* On most calculators, the inverse sine is obtained by pressing ⟨SHIFT⟩ or ⟨2nd⟩, followed by ⟨sin⟩. On some calculators, ⟨sin⁻¹⟩ is pressed first, then 1/3 is entered; on others, this sequence is reversed. Consult your owner's manual for the correct sequence.

Figure 5

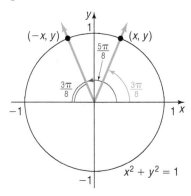

```
sin⁻¹(-1/4)
      -.2526802551
```

(b) Figure 5 shows the solution using a TI-84 Plus graphing calculator in radian mode. $\sin^{-1}\left(-\dfrac{1}{4}\right) = -0.25$, rounded to two decimal places.

━━━**Now Work** PROBLEM 25

3 Use Properties of Inverse Functions to Find Exact Values of Certain Composite Functions

When we discussed functions and their inverses in Section 5.2, we found that $f^{-1}(f(x)) = x$ for all x in the domain of f and $f(f^{-1}(x)) = x$ for all x in the domain of f^{-1}. In terms of the sine function and its inverse, these properties are of the form

$$f^{-1}(f(x)) = \sin^{-1}(\sin x) = x \qquad \text{where } -\frac{\pi}{2} \le x \le \frac{\pi}{2} \qquad \textbf{(2a)}$$

$$f(f^{-1}(x)) = \sin(\sin^{-1} x) = x \qquad \text{where } -1 \le x \le 1 \qquad \textbf{(2b)}$$

EXAMPLE 4

Finding the Exact Value of Certain Composite Functions

Find the exact value of each of the following composite functions:

(a) $\sin^{-1}\left(\sin\dfrac{\pi}{8}\right)$ 　　　　(b) $\sin^{-1}\left(\sin\dfrac{5\pi}{8}\right)$

Solution

(a) The composite function $\sin^{-1}\left(\sin\dfrac{\pi}{8}\right)$ follows the form of equation (2a). Because $\dfrac{\pi}{8}$ is in the interval $\left[-\dfrac{\pi}{2}, \dfrac{\pi}{2}\right]$, we can use (2a). Then

$$\sin^{-1}\left(\sin\frac{\pi}{8}\right) = \frac{\pi}{8}$$

(b) The composite function $\sin^{-1}\left(\sin\dfrac{5\pi}{8}\right)$ follows the form of equation (2a), but $\dfrac{5\pi}{8}$ is not in the interval $\left[-\dfrac{\pi}{2}, \dfrac{\pi}{2}\right]$. To use (2a), we need to find an angle θ in the interval $\left[-\dfrac{\pi}{2}, \dfrac{\pi}{2}\right]$ for which $\sin\theta = \sin\dfrac{5\pi}{8}$. Then, using (2a), $\sin^{-1}\left(\sin\dfrac{5\pi}{8}\right) = \sin^{-1}(\sin\theta) = \theta$, and we are finished.

Figure 6

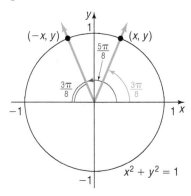

Look at Figure 6. We see that $\sin\dfrac{5\pi}{8} = y = \sin\dfrac{3\pi}{8}$. Since $\dfrac{3\pi}{8}$ is in the interval $\left[-\dfrac{\pi}{2}, \dfrac{\pi}{2}\right]$, we have

$$\sin^{-1}\left(\sin\frac{5\pi}{8}\right) = \sin^{-1}\left(\sin\frac{3\pi}{8}\right) = \frac{3\pi}{8}$$

↑
Apply (2a).

━━━**Now Work** PROBLEM 41

EXAMPLE 5

Finding the Exact Value of Certain Composite Functions

Find the exact value, if any, of each composite function.

(a) $\sin(\sin^{-1} 0.5)$ 　　　　(b) $\sin(\sin^{-1} 1.8)$

Solution   (a) The composite function $\sin(\sin^{-1} 0.5)$ follows the form of equation (2b) and 0.5 is in the interval $[-1, 1]$. So we use (2b):

$$\sin(\sin^{-1} 0.5) = 0.5$$

(b) The composite function $\sin(\sin^{-1} 1.8)$ follows the form of equation (2b), but 1.8 is not in the domain of the inverse sine function. This composite function is not defined.

━━━━━━**Now Work** PROBLEM 45

The Inverse Cosine Function

Figure 7 shows the graph of $y = \cos x$. Because every horizontal line $y = b$, where b is between -1 and 1, inclusive, intersects the graph of $y = \cos x$ infinitely many times, it follows that the cosine function is not one-to-one.

Figure 7
$y = \cos x, -\infty < x < \infty,$
$-1 \le y \le 1$

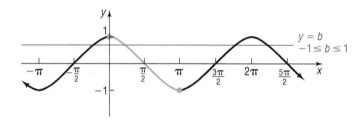

Figure 8
$y = \cos x, 0 \le x \le \pi, -1 \le y \le 1$

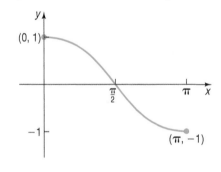

However, if we restrict the domain of $y = \cos x$ to the interval $[0, \pi]$, the restricted function

$$y = \cos x \qquad 0 \le x \le \pi$$

is one-to-one and hence will have an inverse function.* See Figure 8.

An equation for the inverse of $y = f(x) = \cos x$ is obtained by interchanging x and y. The implicit form of the inverse function is $x = \cos y, 0 \le y \le \pi$. The explicit form is called the **inverse cosine** of x and is symbolized by $y = f^{-1}(x) = \cos^{-1} x$ (or by $y = \text{Arccos } x$).

DEFINITION

> $$y = \cos^{-1} x \quad \text{means} \quad x = \cos y$$
>
> where $\quad -1 \le x \le 1 \quad$ and $\quad 0 \le y \le \pi$ **(3)**

Figure 9
$y = \cos^{-1} x, -1 \le x \le 1, 0 \le y \le \pi$

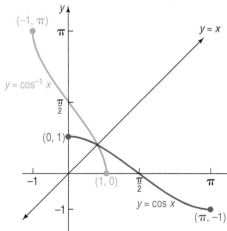

Here y is the angle whose cosine is x. Because the range of the cosine function, $y = \cos x$, is $-1 \le y \le 1$, the domain of the inverse function $y = \cos^{-1} x$ is $-1 \le x \le 1$. Because the restricted domain of the cosine function, $y = \cos x$, is $0 \le x \le \pi$, the range of the inverse function $y = \cos^{-1} x$ is $0 \le y \le \pi$.

The graph of $y = \cos^{-1} x$ can be obtained by reflecting the restricted portion of the graph of $y = \cos x$ about the line $y = x$, as shown in Figure 9.

✓ **Check:** Graph $Y_1 = \cos x$ and $Y_2 = \cos^{-1} x$. Compare the result with Figure 9.

* This is the generally accepted restriction to define the inverse cosine function.

EXAMPLE 6

Finding the Exact Value of an Inverse Cosine Function

Find the exact value of: $\cos^{-1} 0$

Solution

Let $\theta = \cos^{-1} 0$. We seek the angle θ, $0 \le \theta \le \pi$, whose cosine equals 0.

$$\theta = \cos^{-1} 0 \qquad 0 \le \theta \le \pi$$
$$\cos \theta = 0 \qquad 0 \le \theta \le \pi$$

Table 2

θ	$\cos \theta$
0	1
$\dfrac{\pi}{6}$	$\dfrac{\sqrt{3}}{2}$
$\dfrac{\pi}{4}$	$\dfrac{\sqrt{2}}{2}$
$\dfrac{\pi}{3}$	$\dfrac{1}{2}$
$\dfrac{\pi}{2}$	0
$\dfrac{2\pi}{3}$	$-\dfrac{1}{2}$
$\dfrac{3\pi}{4}$	$-\dfrac{\sqrt{2}}{2}$
$\dfrac{5\pi}{6}$	$-\dfrac{\sqrt{3}}{2}$
π	-1

Look at Table 2 and Figure 10.

Figure 10

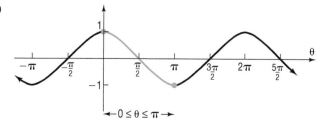

We see that the only angle θ within the interval $[0, \pi]$ whose cosine is 0 is $\dfrac{\pi}{2}$. [Note that $\cos \dfrac{3\pi}{2}$ and $\cos \left(-\dfrac{\pi}{2}\right)$ also equal 0, but they lie outside the interval $[0, \pi]$ and hence are not admissible.] We conclude that

$$\cos^{-1} 0 = \dfrac{\pi}{2}$$

EXAMPLE 7

Finding the Exact Value of an Inverse Cosine Function

Find the exact value of: $\cos^{-1}\left(-\dfrac{\sqrt{2}}{2}\right)$

Solution

Let $\theta = \cos^{-1}\left(-\dfrac{\sqrt{2}}{2}\right)$. We seek the angle θ, $0 \le \theta \le \pi$, whose cosine equals $-\dfrac{\sqrt{2}}{2}$.

$$\theta = \cos^{-1}\left(-\dfrac{\sqrt{2}}{2}\right) \qquad 0 \le \theta \le \pi$$
$$\cos \theta = -\dfrac{\sqrt{2}}{2} \qquad 0 \le \theta \le \pi$$

Look at Table 2 and Figure 11.

Figure 11

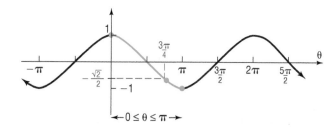

We see that the only angle θ within the interval $[0, \pi]$ whose cosine is $-\dfrac{\sqrt{2}}{2}$ is $\dfrac{3\pi}{4}$. So,

$$\cos^{-1}\left(-\frac{\sqrt{2}}{2}\right) = \frac{3\pi}{4}$$

━━━**Now Work** PROBLEM 23

For the cosine function and its inverse, the following properties hold:

$f^{-1}(f(x)) = \cos^{-1}(\cos x) = x$	where $0 \leq x \leq \pi$	**(4a)**
$f(f^{-1}(x)) = \cos(\cos^{-1} x) = x$	where $-1 \leq x \leq 1$	**(4b)**

EXAMPLE 8

Using Properties of Inverse Functions to Find the Exact Value of Certain Composite Functions

Find the exact value of:

(a) $\cos^{-1}\left(\cos\dfrac{\pi}{12}\right)$ (b) $\cos[\cos^{-1}(-0.4)]$ (c) $\cos^{-1}\left[\cos\left(-\dfrac{2\pi}{3}\right)\right]$ (d) $\cos(\cos^{-1}\pi)$

Solution

(a) $\cos^{-1}\left(\cos\dfrac{\pi}{12}\right) = \dfrac{\pi}{12}$ $\dfrac{\pi}{12}$ is in the interval $[0, \pi]$; use Property (4a).

(b) $\cos[\cos^{-1}(-0.4)] = -0.4$ -0.4 is in the interval $[-1, 1]$; use Property (4b).

(c) The angle $-\dfrac{2\pi}{3}$ is not in the interval $[0, \pi]$ so we cannot use (4a). However, because the cosine function is even, $\cos\left(-\dfrac{2\pi}{3}\right) = \cos\dfrac{2\pi}{3}$. Since $\dfrac{2\pi}{3}$ is in the interval $[0, \pi]$, we have

$$\cos^{-1}\left[\cos\left(-\frac{2\pi}{3}\right)\right] = \cos^{-1}\left(\cos\frac{2\pi}{3}\right) = \frac{2\pi}{3} \qquad \frac{2\pi}{3} \text{ is in the interval } [0, \pi]; \text{ apply (4a).}$$

(d) Because π is not in the interval $[-1, 1]$, the domain of the inverse cosine function, $\cos^{-1}\pi$ is not defined. This means the composite function $\cos(\cos^{-1}\pi)$ is also not defined.

━━━**Now Work** PROBLEMS 37 AND 49

The Inverse Tangent Function

Figure 12 shows the graph of $y = \tan x$. Because every horizontal line intersects the graph infinitely many times, it follows that the tangent function is not one-to-one.

However, if we restrict the domain of $y = \tan x$ to the interval $\left(-\dfrac{\pi}{2}, \dfrac{\pi}{2}\right)$, the restricted function

$$y = \tan x \qquad -\frac{\pi}{2} < x < \frac{\pi}{2}$$

is one-to-one and hence has an inverse function.* See Figure 13.

*This is the generally accepted restriction.

Figure 12
$y = \tan x, -\infty < x < \infty, x$ not equal to odd multiples of $\dfrac{\pi}{2}, -\infty < y < \infty$

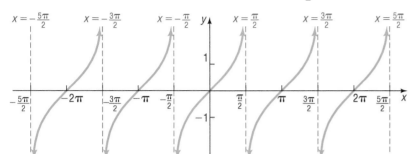

Figure 13
$y = \tan x, -\dfrac{\pi}{2} < x < \dfrac{\pi}{2}, -\infty < y < \infty$

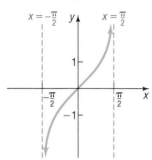

An equation for the inverse of $y = f(x) = \tan x$ is obtained by interchanging x and y. The implicit form of the inverse function is $x = \tan y, -\dfrac{\pi}{2} < y < \dfrac{\pi}{2}$. The explicit form is called the **inverse tangent** of x and is symbolized by $y = f^{-1}(x) = \tan^{-1} x$ (or by $y = \text{Arctan}\, x$).

DEFINITION

> $$y = \tan^{-1} x \quad \text{means} \quad x = \tan y$$
> $$\text{where} \quad -\infty < x < \infty \quad \text{and} \quad -\dfrac{\pi}{2} < y < \dfrac{\pi}{2} \tag{5}$$

Here y is the angle whose tangent is x. The domain of the function $y = \tan^{-1} x$ is $-\infty < x < \infty$, and its range is $-\dfrac{\pi}{2} < y < \dfrac{\pi}{2}$. The graph of $y = \tan^{-1} x$ can be obtained by reflecting the restricted portion of the graph of $y = \tan x$ about the line $y = x$, as shown in Figure 14.

Figure 14
$y = \tan^{-1} x, -\infty < x < \infty, -\dfrac{\pi}{2} < y < \dfrac{\pi}{2}$

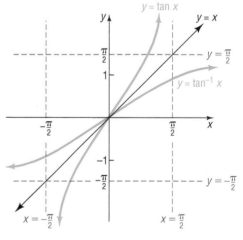

✓**Check:** Graph $Y_1 = \tan x$ and $Y_2 = \tan^{-1} x$. Compare the result with Figure 14.

EXAMPLE 9

Finding the Exact Value of an Inverse Tangent Function

Find the exact value of:

(a) $\tan^{-1} 1$ (b) $\tan^{-1}\left(-\sqrt{3}\right)$

Solution

(a) Let $\theta = \tan^{-1} 1$. We seek the angle $\theta, -\dfrac{\pi}{2} < \theta < \dfrac{\pi}{2}$, whose tangent equals 1.

$$\theta = \tan^{-1} 1 \qquad -\dfrac{\pi}{2} < \theta < \dfrac{\pi}{2}$$
$$\tan \theta = 1 \qquad -\dfrac{\pi}{2} < \theta < \dfrac{\pi}{2}$$

Table 3

θ	$\tan \theta$
$-\dfrac{\pi}{2}$	Undefined
$-\dfrac{\pi}{3}$	$-\sqrt{3}$
$-\dfrac{\pi}{4}$	-1
$-\dfrac{\pi}{6}$	$-\dfrac{\sqrt{3}}{3}$
0	0
$\dfrac{\pi}{6}$	$\dfrac{\sqrt{3}}{3}$
$\dfrac{\pi}{4}$	1
$\dfrac{\pi}{3}$	$\sqrt{3}$
$\dfrac{\pi}{2}$	Undefined

Look at Table 3. The only angle θ within the interval $\left(-\dfrac{\pi}{2}, \dfrac{\pi}{2}\right)$ whose tangent is 1 is $\dfrac{\pi}{4}$. So,

$$\tan^{-1} 1 = \frac{\pi}{4}$$

(b) Let $\theta = \tan^{-1}\left(-\sqrt{3}\right)$. We seek the angle $\theta, -\dfrac{\pi}{2} < \theta < \dfrac{\pi}{2}$, whose tangent equals $-\sqrt{3}$.

$$\theta = \tan^{-1}\left(-\sqrt{3}\right) \qquad -\frac{\pi}{2} < \theta < \frac{\pi}{2}$$
$$\tan \theta = -\sqrt{3} \qquad -\frac{\pi}{2} < \theta < \frac{\pi}{2}$$

Look at Table 3. The only angle θ within the interval $\left(-\dfrac{\pi}{2}, \dfrac{\pi}{2}\right)$ whose tangent is $-\sqrt{3}$ is $-\dfrac{\pi}{3}$. So,

$$\tan^{-1}\left(-\sqrt{3}\right) = -\frac{\pi}{3}$$

 **Now Work** PROBLEM 17

For the tangent function and its inverse, the following properties hold:

$$f^{-1}(f(x)) = \tan^{-1}(\tan x) = x \qquad \text{where } -\frac{\pi}{2} < x < \frac{\pi}{2}$$
$$f(f^{-1}(x)) = \tan(\tan^{-1} x) = x \qquad \text{where } -\infty < x < \infty$$

Now Work PROBLEM 43

4 Find the Inverse Function of a Trigonometric Function

EXAMPLE 10

Finding the Inverse Function of a Trigonometric Function

Find the inverse function f^{-1} of $f(x) = 2 \sin x - 1, -\dfrac{\pi}{2} \le x \le \dfrac{\pi}{2}$. Find the range of f and the domain and range of f^{-1}.

Solution

The function f is one-to-one and so has an inverse function. Follow the steps on page 261 for finding the inverse function.

$$y = 2 \sin x - 1$$
$$x = 2 \sin y - 1 \qquad \text{Interchange } x \text{ and } y.$$
$$x + 1 = 2 \sin y \qquad \text{Proceed to solve for } y.$$
$$\sin y = \frac{x + 1}{2}$$
$$y = \sin^{-1} \frac{x + 1}{2} \qquad \text{Apply the definition (1).}$$

The inverse function is $f^{-1}(x) = \sin^{-1} \dfrac{x + 1}{2}$.

To find the range of f, solve $y = 2 \sin x - 1$ for $\sin x$ and use the fact that $-1 \le \sin x \le 1$.

$$y = 2 \sin x - 1$$
$$\sin x = \frac{y + 1}{2}$$

$$-1 \le \frac{y+1}{2} \le 1$$
$$-2 \le y + 1 \le 2$$
$$-3 \le y \le 1$$

The range of f is $\{y | -3 \le y \le 1\}$ or $[-3, 1]$ using interval notation.
The domain of f^{-1} equals the range of f, $[-3, 1]$.

The range of f^{-1} equals the domain of f, $\left[-\frac{\pi}{2}, \frac{\pi}{2}\right]$.

━━━➤ **Now Work** PROBLEM 55

5 Solve Equations Involving Inverse Trigonometric Functions

Equations that contain inverse trigonometric functions are called **inverse trigonometric equations.**

EXAMPLE 11 | **Solving an Equation Involving an Inverse Trigonometric Function**

Solve the equation: $3 \sin^{-1} x = \pi$

Solution   To solve an equation involving a single inverse trigonometric function, first isolate the inverse trigonometric function.

$$3 \sin^{-1} x = \pi$$
$$\sin^{-1} x = \frac{\pi}{3} \qquad \text{Divide both sides by 3.}$$
$$x = \sin \frac{\pi}{3} \quad y = \sin^{-1} x \text{ means } x = \sin y.$$
$$x = \frac{\sqrt{3}}{2}$$

The solution set is $\left\{\dfrac{\sqrt{3}}{2}\right\}$.

━━━➤ **Now Work** PROBLEM 61

7.1 Assess Your Understanding

'Are You Prepared?' *Answers are given at the end of these exercises. If you get a wrong answer, read the pages listed in red.*

1. What is the domain and the range of $y = \sin x$? (pp. 379–389)

2. A suitable restriction on the domain of the function $f(x) = (x - 1)^2$ to make it one-to-one would be _____. (pp. 257–263)

3. If the domain of a one-to-one function is $[3, \infty)$, the range of its inverse is _____. (pp. 257–263)

4. **True or False** The graph of $y = \cos x$ is decreasing on the interval $[0, \pi]$. (pp. 393–397)

5. $\tan \dfrac{\pi}{4} =$ _____; $\sin \dfrac{\pi}{3} =$ _____ (pp. 365–374)

6. $\sin\left(-\dfrac{\pi}{6}\right) =$ _____; $\cos \pi =$ _____. (pp. 365–374)

Concepts and Vocabulary

7. $y = \sin^{-1} x$ means _____, where $-1 \le x \le 1$ and $-\dfrac{\pi}{2} \le y \le \dfrac{\pi}{2}$.

8. $\cos^{-1}(\cos x) = x$ where _____.

9. $\tan(\tan^{-1} x) = x$ where _____.

10. **True or False** The domain of $y = \sin^{-1} x$ is $-\dfrac{\pi}{2} \le x \le \dfrac{\pi}{2}$.

11. **True or False** $\sin(\sin^{-1} 0) = 0$ and $\cos(\cos^{-1} 0) = 0$.

12. **True or False** $y = \tan^{-1} x$ means $x = \tan y$, where $-\infty < x < \infty$ and $-\dfrac{\pi}{2} < y < \dfrac{\pi}{2}$.

Skill Building

In Problems 13–24, find the exact value of each expression.

13. $\sin^{-1} 0$

14. $\cos^{-1} 1$

15. $\sin^{-1}(-1)$

16. $\cos^{-1}(-1)$

17. $\tan^{-1} 0$

18. $\tan^{-1}(-1)$

19. $\sin^{-1} \dfrac{\sqrt{2}}{2}$

20. $\tan^{-1} \dfrac{\sqrt{3}}{3}$

21. $\tan^{-1} \sqrt{3}$

22. $\sin^{-1}\left(-\dfrac{\sqrt{3}}{2}\right)$

23. $\cos^{-1}\left(-\dfrac{\sqrt{3}}{2}\right)$

24. $\sin^{-1}\left(-\dfrac{\sqrt{2}}{2}\right)$

In Problems 25–36, use a calculator to find the value of each expression rounded to two decimal places.

25. $\sin^{-1} 0.1$

26. $\cos^{-1} 0.6$

27. $\tan^{-1} 5$

28. $\tan^{-1} 0.2$

29. $\cos^{-1} \dfrac{7}{8}$

30. $\sin^{-1} \dfrac{1}{8}$

31. $\tan^{-1}(-0.4)$

32. $\tan^{-1}(-3)$

33. $\sin^{-1}(-0.12)$

34. $\cos^{-1}(-0.44)$

35. $\cos^{-1} \dfrac{\sqrt{2}}{3}$

36. $\sin^{-1} \dfrac{\sqrt{3}}{5}$

In Problems 37–44, find the exact value of each expression. Do not use a calculator.

37. $\cos^{-1}\left(\cos \dfrac{4\pi}{5}\right)$

38. $\sin^{-1}\left[\sin\left(-\dfrac{\pi}{10}\right)\right]$

39. $\tan^{-1}\left[\tan\left(-\dfrac{3\pi}{8}\right)\right]$

40. $\sin^{-1}\left[\sin\left(-\dfrac{3\pi}{7}\right)\right]$

41. $\sin^{-1}\left(\sin \dfrac{9\pi}{8}\right)$

42. $\cos^{-1}\left[\cos\left(-\dfrac{5\pi}{3}\right)\right]$

43. $\tan^{-1}\left(\tan \dfrac{4\pi}{5}\right)$

44. $\tan^{-1}\left[\tan\left(-\dfrac{2\pi}{3}\right)\right]$

In Problems 45–52, find the exact value, if any, of each composite function. If there is no value, say it is "not defined." Do not use a calculator.

45. $\sin\left(\sin^{-1} \dfrac{1}{4}\right)$

46. $\cos\left[\cos^{-1}\left(-\dfrac{2}{3}\right)\right]$

47. $\tan\left(\tan^{-1} 4\right)$

48. $\tan\left[\tan^{-1}(-2)\right]$

49. $\cos\left(\cos^{-1} 1.2\right)$

50. $\sin\left[\sin^{-1}(-2)\right]$

51. $\tan\left(\tan^{-1} \pi\right)$

52. $\sin\left[\sin^{-1}(-1.5)\right]$

In Problems 53–60, find the inverse function f^{-1} of each function f. Find the range of f and the domain and range of f^{-1}.

53. $f(x) = 5 \sin x + 2; -\dfrac{\pi}{2} \le x \le \dfrac{\pi}{2}$

54. $f(x) = 2 \tan x - 3; -\dfrac{\pi}{2} < x < \dfrac{\pi}{2}$

55. $f(x) = -2 \cos(3x); 0 \le x \le \dfrac{\pi}{3}$

56. $f(x) = 3 \sin(2x); -\dfrac{\pi}{4} \le x \le \dfrac{\pi}{4}$

57. $f(x) = -\tan(x + 1) - 3; -1 - \dfrac{\pi}{2} < x < \dfrac{\pi}{2} - 1$

58. $f(x) = \cos(x + 2) + 1; -2 \le x \le \pi - 2$

59. $f(x) = 3 \sin(2x + 1); -\dfrac{1}{2} - \dfrac{\pi}{4} \le x \le -\dfrac{1}{2} + \dfrac{\pi}{4}$

60. $f(x) = 2 \cos(3x + 2); -\dfrac{2}{3} \le x \le -\dfrac{2}{3} + \dfrac{\pi}{3}$

In Problems 61–68, find the exact solution of each equation.

61. $4 \sin^{-1} x = \pi$

62. $2 \cos^{-1} x = \pi$

63. $3 \cos^{-1}(2x) = 2\pi$

64. $-6 \sin^{-1}(3x) = \pi$

65. $3 \tan^{-1} x = \pi$

66. $-4 \tan^{-1} x = \pi$

67. $4 \cos^{-1} x - 2\pi = 2 \cos^{-1} x$

68. $5 \sin^{-1} x - 2\pi = 2 \sin^{-1} x - 3\pi$

Applications and Extensions

In Problems 69–74, use the following discussion. The formula

$$D = 24\left[1 - \dfrac{\cos^{-1}(\tan i \tan \theta)}{\pi}\right]$$

can be used to approximate the number of hours of daylight D when the declination of the Sun is $i°$ at a location $\theta°$ north latitude for any date between the vernal equinox and autumnal equinox. The declination of the Sun is defined as the angle i between the equatorial plane and any ray of light from the Sun. The latitude of a location

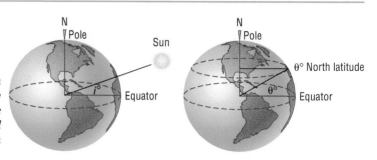

is the angle θ between the Equator and the location on the surface of Earth, with the vertex of the angle located at the center of Earth. See the figure. To use the formula, $\cos^{-1}(\tan i \tan \theta)$ *must be expressed in radians.*

69. Approximate the number of hours of daylight in Houston, Texas (29°45′ north latitude), for the following dates:
  (a) Summer solstice ($i = 23.5°$)
  (b) Vernal equinox ($i = 0°$)
  (c) July 4 ($i = 22°48′$)

70. Approximate the number of hours of daylight in New York, New York (40°45′ north latitude), for the following dates:
  (a) Summer solstice ($i = 23.5°$)
  (b) Vernal equinox ($i = 0°$)
  (c) July 4 ($i = 22°48′$)

71. Approximate the number of hours of daylight in Honolulu, Hawaii (21°18′ north latitude), for the following dates:
  (a) Summer solstice ($i = 23.5°$)
  (b) Vernal equinox ($i = 0°$)
  (c) July 4 ($i = 22°48′$)

72. Approximate the number of hours of daylight in Anchorage, Alaska (61°10′ north latitude), for the following dates:
  (a) Summer solstice ($i = 23.5°$)
  (b) Vernal equinox ($i = 0°$)
  (c) July 4 ($i = 22°48′$)

73. Approximate the number of hours of daylight at the Equator (0° north latitude) for the following dates:
  (a) Summer solstice ($i = 23.5°$)
  (b) Vernal equinox ($i = 0°$)
  (c) July 4 ($i = 22°48′$)
  (d) What do you conclude about the number of hours of daylight throughout the year for a location at the Equator?

74. Approximate the number of hours of daylight for any location that is 66°30′ north latitude for the following dates:
  (a) Summer solstice ($i = 23.5°$)
  (b) Vernal equinox ($i = 0°$)
  (c) July 4 ($i = 22°48′$)
  (d) The number of hours of daylight on the winter solstice may be found by computing the number of hours of daylight on the summer solstice and subtracting this result from 24 hours, due to the symmetry of the orbital path of Earth around the Sun. Compute the number of hours of daylight for this location on the winter solstice. What do you conclude about daylight for a location at 66°30′ north latitude?

75. Being the First to See the Rising Sun Cadillac Mountain, elevation 1530 feet, is located in Acadia National Park, Maine, and is the highest peak on the east coast of the United States. It is said that a person standing on the summit will be the first person in the United States to see the rays of the rising Sun. How much sooner would a person atop

Cadillac Mountain see the first rays than a person standing below, at sea level?

[Hint: Consult the figure. When the person at D sees the first rays of the Sun, the person at P does not. The person at P sees the first rays of the Sun only after Earth has rotated so that P is at location Q. Compute the length of the arc subtended by the central angle θ. Then use the fact that, at the latitude of Cadillac Mountain, in 24 hours a length of $2\pi(2710) \approx 17027.4$ miles is subtended, and find the time that it takes to subtend this length.**]**

76. Movie Theater Screens Suppose that a movie theater has a screen that is 28 feet tall. When you sit down, the bottom of the screen is 6 feet above your eye level. The angle formed by drawing a line from your eye to the bottom of the screen and your eye and the top of the screen is called the **viewing angle.** In the figure, θ is the viewing angle. Suppose that you sit x feet from the screen. The viewing angle θ is given by the function

$$\theta(x) = \tan^{-1}\left(\frac{34}{x}\right) - \tan^{-1}\left(\frac{6}{x}\right)$$

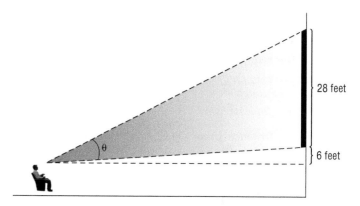

28 feet

6 feet

  (a) What is your viewing angle if you sit 10 feet from the screen? 15 feet? 20 feet?
  (b) If there is 5 feet between the screen and the first row of seats and there is 3 feet between each row, which row results in the largest viewing angle?
  (c) Using a graphing utility, graph

$$\theta(x) = \tan^{-1}\left(\frac{34}{x}\right) - \tan^{-1}\left(\frac{6}{x}\right)$$

  What value of x results in the largest viewing angle?

77. Area under a Curve The area under the graph of $y = \dfrac{1}{1 + x^2}$ and above the x-axis between $x = a$ and $x = b$ is given by

$$\tan^{-1} b - \tan^{-1} a$$

See the figure.

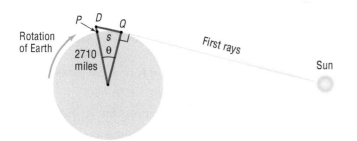

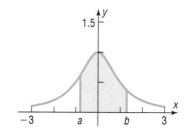

(a) Find the exact area under the graph of $y = \dfrac{1}{1 + x^2}$ and above the x-axis between $x = 0$ and $x = \sqrt{3}$.

(b) Find the exact area under the graph of $y = \dfrac{1}{1 + x^2}$ and above the x-axis between $x = -\dfrac{\sqrt{3}}{3}$ and $x = 1$.

78. **Area under a Curve** The area under the graph of $y = \dfrac{1}{\sqrt{1 - x^2}}$ and above the x-axis between $x = a$ and $x = b$ is given by

$$\sin^{-1} b - \sin^{-1} a$$

See the figure.
(a) Find the exact area under the graph of $y = \dfrac{1}{\sqrt{1 - x^2}}$ and above the x-axis between $x = 0$ and $x = \dfrac{\sqrt{3}}{2}$.

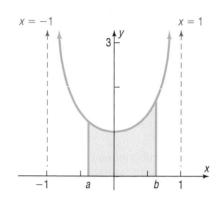

(b) Find the exact area under the graph of $y = \dfrac{1}{\sqrt{1 - x^2}}$ and above the x-axis between $x = -\dfrac{1}{2}$ and $x = \dfrac{1}{2}$.

Problems 79 and 80 require the following discussion:
The shortest distance between two points on Earth's surface can be determined from the latitude and longitude of the two locations. For example, if location 1 has (lat, lon) = (α_1, β_1) and location 2 has (lat, lon) = (α_2, β_2), the shortest distance between the two locations is approximately
$$d = r\cos^{-1}[(\cos \alpha_1 \cos \beta_1 \cos \alpha_2 \cos \beta_2) + (\cos \alpha_1 \sin \beta_1 \cos \alpha_2 \sin \beta_2) + (\sin \alpha_1 \sin \alpha_2)]$$
where r = radius of Earth ≈ 3960 miles and the inverse cosine function is expressed in radians. Also N latitude and E longitude are positive angles while S latitude and W longitude are negative angles.

Source: www.infoplease.com

City	Latitude	Longitude
Chicago, IL	41°50′N	87°37′W
Honolulu, HI	21°18′N	157°50′W
Melbourne, Australia	37°47′S	144°58′E

79. **Shortest Distance from Chicago to Honolulu** Find the shortest distance from Chicago, latitude 41°50′N, longitude 87°37′W to Honolulu, latitude 21°18′N, longitude 157°50′W. Round your answer to the nearest mile.

80. **Shortest Distance from Honolulu to Melbourne, Australia** Find the shortest distance from Honolulu to Melbourne, Australia, latitude 37°47′S, longitude 144°58′E. Round your answer to the nearest mile.

'Are You Prepared?' Answers

1. domain: the set of all real numbers; range: $-1 \le y \le 1$

2. Two answers are possible: $x \le 1$ or $x \ge 1$

3. $[3, \infty)$

4. True

5. $1; \dfrac{\sqrt{3}}{2}$

6. $-\dfrac{1}{2}; -1$

7.2 The Inverse Trigonometric Functions (Continued)

PREPARING FOR THIS SECTION *Before getting started, review the following concepts:*

- Finding Exact Values Given the Value of a Trigonometric Function and the Quadrant of the Angle (Section 6.3, pp. 386–388)
- Graphs of the Secant, Cosecant, and Cotangent Functions (Section 6.5, pp. 412–413)

- Domain and Range of the Secant, Cosecant, and Cotangent Functions (Section 6.3, pp. 380–381)

Now Work the 'Are You Prepared?' problems on page 452.

OBJECTIVES 1 Find the Exact Value of Expressions Involving the Inverse Sine, Cosine, and Tangent Functions (p. 449)

2 Define the Inverse Secant, Cosecant, and Cotangent Functions (p. 450)

3 Use a Calculator to Evaluate $\sec^{-1} x$, $\csc^{-1} x$, and $\cot^{-1} x$ (p. 450)

4 Write a Trigonometric Expression as an Algebraic Expression (p. 451)

1 Find the Exact Value of Expressions Involving the Inverse Sine, Cosine, and Tangent Functions

---

EXAMPLE 1

Finding the Exact Value of Expressions Involving Inverse Trigonometric Functions

Find the exact value of: $\sin\left(\tan^{-1}\dfrac{1}{2}\right)$

Figure 15

$\tan\theta = \dfrac{1}{2}$

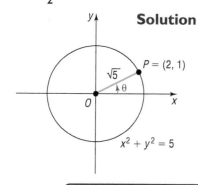

$x^2 + y^2 = 5$

Solution Let $\theta = \tan^{-1}\dfrac{1}{2}$. Then $\tan\theta = \dfrac{1}{2}$, where $-\dfrac{\pi}{2} < \theta < \dfrac{\pi}{2}$. We seek $\sin\theta$. Because

$\tan\theta > 0$, it follows that $0 < \theta < \dfrac{\pi}{2}$, so θ lies in quadrant I. Since $\tan\theta = \dfrac{1}{2} = \dfrac{y}{x}$,

let $x = 2$ and $y = 1$. Since $r = d(O, P) = \sqrt{2^2 + 1^2} = \sqrt{5}$, the point $P = (x, y) = (2, 1)$ is on the circle $x^2 + y^2 = 5$. See Figure 15. Then, with $x = 2, y = 1$, and $r = \sqrt{5}$, we have

$$\sin\left(\tan^{-1}\dfrac{1}{2}\right) = \sin\theta = \underset{\underset{\sin\theta = \frac{y}{r}}{\uparrow}}{\dfrac{1}{\sqrt{5}}} = \dfrac{\sqrt{5}}{5}$$

EXAMPLE 2

Finding the Exact Value of Expressions Involving Inverse Trigonometric Functions

Find the exact value of: $\cos\left[\sin^{-1}\left(-\dfrac{1}{3}\right)\right]$

Solution Let $\theta = \sin^{-1}\left(-\dfrac{1}{3}\right)$. Then $\sin\theta = -\dfrac{1}{3}$ and $-\dfrac{\pi}{2} \leq \theta \leq \dfrac{\pi}{2}$. We seek $\cos\theta$. Because

$\sin\theta < 0$, it follows that $-\dfrac{\pi}{2} \leq \theta < 0$, so θ lies in quadrant IV. Since $\sin\theta = \dfrac{-1}{3} = \dfrac{y}{r}$,

Figure 16

$\sin\theta = -\dfrac{1}{3}$

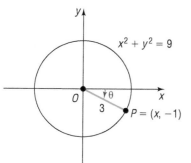

$x^2 + y^2 = 9$

let $y = -1$ and $r = 3$. The point $P = (x, y) = (x, -1), x > 0$, is on a circle of radius 3, $x^2 + y^2 = 9$. See Figure 16. Then

$$x^2 + y^2 = 9$$
$$x^2 + (-1)^2 = 9 \qquad y = -1$$
$$x^2 = 8$$
$$x = 2\sqrt{2} \quad x > 0$$

Then $x = 2\sqrt{2}, y = -1$, and $r = 3$, so

$$\cos\left[\sin^{-1}\left(-\dfrac{1}{3}\right)\right] = \cos\theta = \underset{\underset{\cos\theta = \frac{x}{r}}{\uparrow}}{\dfrac{2\sqrt{2}}{3}}$$

EXAMPLE 3

Finding the Exact Value of Expressions Involving Inverse Trigonometric Functions

Find the exact value of: $\tan\left[\cos^{-1}\left(-\dfrac{1}{3}\right)\right]$

Figure 17

$\cos\theta = -\dfrac{1}{3}$

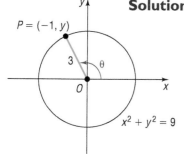

$x^2 + y^2 = 9$

Solution Let $\theta = \cos^{-1}\left(-\dfrac{1}{3}\right)$. Then $\cos\theta = -\dfrac{1}{3}$ and $0 \leq \theta \leq \pi$. We seek $\tan\theta$. Because

$\cos\theta < 0$, it follows that $\dfrac{\pi}{2} < \theta \leq \pi$, so θ lies in quadrant II. Since $\cos\theta = \dfrac{-1}{3} = \dfrac{x}{r}$,

let $x = -1$ and $r = 3$. The point $P = (x, y) = (-1, y), y > 0$, is on a circle of radius $r = 3, x^2 + y^2 = 9$. See Figure 17. Then

$$x^2 + y^2 = 9$$
$$(-1)^2 + y^2 = 9 \qquad x = -1$$
$$y^2 = 8$$
$$y = 2\sqrt{2} \quad y > 0$$

Then, $x = -1$, $y = 2\sqrt{2}$, and $r = 3$, so

$$\tan\left[\cos^{-1}\left(-\frac{1}{3}\right)\right] = \tan\theta \underset{\underset{\tan\theta = \frac{y}{x}}{\uparrow}}{=} \frac{2\sqrt{2}}{-1} = -2\sqrt{2}$$

-**Now Work** PROBLEMS 9 AND 27

2 Define the Inverse Secant, Cosecant, and Cotangent Functions

The inverse secant, inverse cosecant, and inverse cotangent functions are defined as follows:

DEFINITION

$$y = \sec^{-1} x \quad \text{means} \quad x = \sec y \tag{1}$$
$$\text{where} \quad |x| \geq 1 \quad \text{and} \quad 0 \leq y \leq \pi, \quad y \neq \frac{\pi}{2}*$$

$$y = \csc^{-1} x \quad \text{means} \quad x = \csc y \tag{2}$$
$$\text{where} \quad |x| \geq 1 \quad \text{and} \quad -\frac{\pi}{2} \leq y \leq \frac{\pi}{2}, \quad y \neq 0†$$

$$y = \cot^{-1} x \quad \text{means} \quad x = \cot y \tag{3}$$
$$\text{where} \quad -\infty < x < \infty \quad \text{and} \quad 0 < y < \pi$$

You are encouraged to review the graphs of the cotangent, cosecant, and secant functions in Figures 66, 67, and 68 in Section 6.5 to help you to see the basis for these definitions.

EXAMPLE 4 | **Finding the Exact Value of an Inverse Cosecant Function**

Find the exact value of: $\csc^{-1} 2$

Solution Let $\theta = \csc^{-1} 2$. We seek the angle θ, $-\frac{\pi}{2} \leq \theta \leq \frac{\pi}{2}$, $\theta \neq 0$, whose cosecant equals 2 $\left(\text{or, equivalently, whose sine equals } \frac{1}{2}\right)$.

$$\theta = \csc^{-1} 2 \qquad -\frac{\pi}{2} \leq \theta \leq \frac{\pi}{2}, \quad \theta \neq 0$$
$$\csc\theta = 2 \qquad -\frac{\pi}{2} \leq \theta \leq \frac{\pi}{2}, \quad \theta \neq 0 \quad \underset{}{\sin\theta = \frac{1}{2}}$$

The only angle θ in the interval $-\frac{\pi}{2} \leq \theta \leq \frac{\pi}{2}$, $\theta \neq 0$, whose cosecant is 2 $\left[\sin\theta = \frac{1}{2}\right]$ is $\frac{\pi}{6}$, so $\csc^{-1} 2 = \frac{\pi}{6}$.

-**Now Work** PROBLEM 39

3 Use a Calculator to Evaluate $\sec^{-1} x$, $\csc^{-1} x$, and $\cot^{-1} x$

Most calculators do not have keys for evaluating the inverse cotangent, cosecant, and secant functions. The easiest way to evaluate them is to convert to an inverse trigonometric function whose range is the same as the one to be evaluated. In this regard, notice that $y = \cot^{-1} x$ and $y = \sec^{-1} x$, except where undefined, each have the same range as $y = \cos^{-1} x$; $y = \csc^{-1} x$, except where undefined, has the same range as $y = \sin^{-1} x$.

REMEMBER The range of $y = \sin^{-1} x$ is $\left[-\frac{\pi}{2}, \frac{\pi}{2}\right]$; the range of $y = \cos^{-1} x$ is $[0, \pi]$. ∎

*Most books use this definition. A few use the restriction $0 \leq y < \frac{\pi}{2}, \pi \leq y < \frac{3\pi}{2}$.

†Most books use this definition. A few use the restriction $-\pi < y \leq -\frac{\pi}{2}, 0 < y \leq \frac{\pi}{2}$.

EXAMPLE 5	**Approximating the Value of Inverse Trigonometric Functions**

Use a calculator to approximate each expression in radians rounded to two decimal places.

(a) $\sec^{-1} 3$ (b) $\csc^{-1}(-4)$ (c) $\cot^{-1} \dfrac{1}{2}$ (d) $\cot^{-1}(-2)$

Solution   First, set your calculator to radian mode.

(a) Let $\theta = \sec^{-1} 3$. Then $\sec \theta = 3$ and $0 \le \theta \le \pi, \theta \ne \dfrac{\pi}{2}$. We seek $\cos \theta$ because $y = \cos^{-1}x$ has the same range as $y = \sec^{-1}x$, except where undefined. Since $\sec \theta = \dfrac{1}{\cos \theta} = 3$, we have $\cos \theta = \dfrac{1}{3}$. Then $\theta = \cos^{-1} \dfrac{1}{3}$ and

$$\sec^{-1} 3 = \theta = \cos^{-1} \dfrac{1}{3} \approx 1.23$$
$$\uparrow$$
Use a calculator.

(b) Let $\theta = \csc^{-1}(-4)$. Then $\csc \theta = -4, -\dfrac{\pi}{2} \le \theta \le \dfrac{\pi}{2}, \theta \ne 0$. We seek $\sin \theta$ because $y = \sin^{-1}x$ has the same range as $y = \csc^{-1}x$, except where undefined. Since $\csc \theta = \dfrac{1}{\sin \theta} = -4$, we have $\sin \theta = -\dfrac{1}{4}$. Then $\theta = \sin^{-1}\left(-\dfrac{1}{4}\right)$, and

$$\csc^{-1}(-4) = \theta = \sin^{-1}\left(-\dfrac{1}{4}\right) \approx -0.25$$

Figure 18

$\cot \theta = \dfrac{1}{2}, 0 < \theta < \pi$

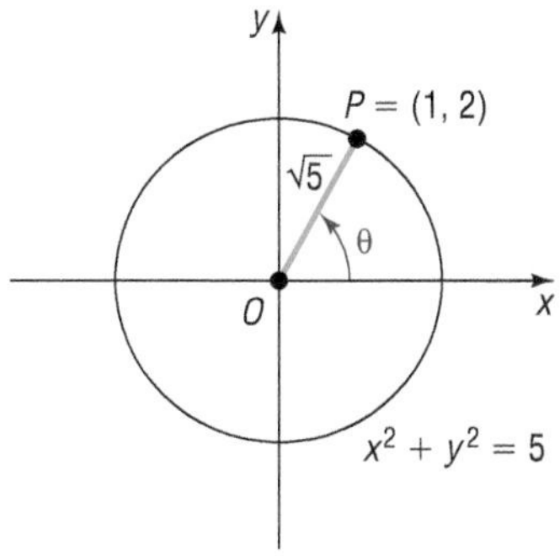

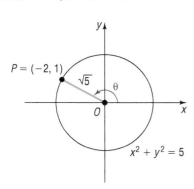

(c) Proceed as before. Let $\theta = \cot^{-1} \dfrac{1}{2}$. Then $\cot \theta = \dfrac{1}{2}, 0 < \theta < \pi$. From these facts we know that θ lies in quadrant I. We seek $\cos \theta$ because $y = \cos^{-1}x$ has the same range as $y = \cot^{-1}x$, except where undefined. To find $\cos \theta$ use Figure 18. Then $\cos \theta = \dfrac{1}{\sqrt{5}}, 0 < \theta < \dfrac{\pi}{2}$, so $\theta = \cos^{-1}\left(\dfrac{1}{\sqrt{5}}\right)$. Then

$$\cot^{-1} \dfrac{1}{2} = \theta = \cos^{-1}\left(\dfrac{1}{\sqrt{5}}\right) \approx 1.11$$

Figure 19

$\cot \theta = -2, 0 < \theta < \pi$

(d) Let $\theta = \cot^{-1}(-2)$. Then $\cot \theta = -2, 0 < \theta < \pi$. From these facts we know that θ lies in quadrant II. We seek $\cos \theta$. To find it we use Figure 19. Then $\cos \theta = -\dfrac{2}{\sqrt{5}}, \dfrac{\pi}{2} < \theta < \pi$, so $\theta = \cos^{-1}\left(-\dfrac{2}{\sqrt{5}}\right)$. Then

$$\cot^{-1}(-2) = \theta = \cos^{-1}\left(-\dfrac{2}{\sqrt{5}}\right) \approx 2.68$$

➤ **Now Work** PROBLEM 45

4 Write a Trigonometric Expression as an Algebraic Expression

EXAMPLE 6	**Writing a Trigonometric Expression as an Algebraic Expression**

Write $\sin(\tan^{-1} u)$ as an algebraic expression containing u.

Solution Let $\theta = \tan^{-1} u$ so that $\tan \theta = u, -\dfrac{\pi}{2} < \theta < \dfrac{\pi}{2}, -\infty < u < \infty$. As a result, we know that $\sec \theta > 0$. Then

$$\sin(\tan^{-1} u) = \sin \theta = \sin \theta \cdot \underset{\uparrow}{\dfrac{\cos \theta}{\cos \theta}} = \underset{\uparrow}{\tan \theta \cos \theta} = \dfrac{\tan \theta}{\sec \theta} = \underset{\uparrow}{\dfrac{\tan \theta}{\sqrt{1 + \tan^2 \theta}}} = \dfrac{u}{\sqrt{1 + u^2}}$$

Multiply by 1: $\dfrac{\cos \theta}{\cos \theta}$. $\dfrac{\sin \theta}{\cos \theta} = \tan \theta$ $\sec^2 \theta = 1 + \tan^2 \theta$

$\sec \theta > 0$

━━━━━**Now Work** PROBLEM 57

7.2 Assess Your Understanding

'Are You Prepared?' *Answers are given at the end of these exercises. If you get a wrong answer, read the pages listed in* red.

1. What is the domain and the range of $y = \sec x$? (pp. 380–381)

2. **True or False** The graph of $y = \sec x$ is one-to-one on the interval $\left[0, \dfrac{\pi}{2}\right)$ and on the interval $\left(\dfrac{\pi}{2}, \pi\right]$. (pp. 412–413)

3. If $\tan \theta = \dfrac{1}{2}, -\dfrac{\pi}{2} < \theta < \dfrac{\pi}{2}$, then $\sin \theta =$ _____. (pp. 386–388)

Concepts and Vocabulary

4. $y = \sec^{-1} x$ means _____, where $|x|$ _____ and _____ $\leq y \leq$ _____, $y \neq \dfrac{\pi}{2}$.

5. To find the inverse secant of a real number x such that $|x| \geq 1$, convert the inverse secant to an inverse _____.

6. **True or False** It is impossible to obtain exact values for the inverse secant function.

7. **True or False** $\csc^{-1} 0.5$ is not defined.

8. **True or False** The domain of the inverse cotangent function is the set of real numbers.

Skill Building

In Problems 9–36, find the exact value of each expression.

9. $\cos\left(\sin^{-1} \dfrac{\sqrt{2}}{2}\right)$

10. $\sin\left(\cos^{-1} \dfrac{1}{2}\right)$

11. $\tan\left[\cos^{-1}\left(-\dfrac{\sqrt{3}}{2}\right)\right]$

12. $\tan\left[\sin^{-1}\left(-\dfrac{1}{2}\right)\right]$

13. $\sec\left(\cos^{-1} \dfrac{1}{2}\right)$

14. $\cot\left[\sin^{-1}\left(-\dfrac{1}{2}\right)\right]$

15. $\csc(\tan^{-1} 1)$

16. $\sec(\tan^{-1} \sqrt{3})$

17. $\sin[\tan^{-1}(-1)]$

18. $\cos\left[\sin^{-1}\left(-\dfrac{\sqrt{3}}{2}\right)\right]$

19. $\sec\left[\sin^{-1}\left(-\dfrac{1}{2}\right)\right]$

20. $\csc\left[\cos^{-1}\left(-\dfrac{\sqrt{3}}{2}\right)\right]$

21. $\cos^{-1}\left(\sin \dfrac{5\pi}{4}\right)$

22. $\tan^{-1}\left(\cot \dfrac{2\pi}{3}\right)$

23. $\sin^{-1}\left[\cos\left(-\dfrac{7\pi}{6}\right)\right]$

24. $\cos^{-1}\left[\tan\left(-\dfrac{\pi}{4}\right)\right]$

25. $\tan\left(\sin^{-1} \dfrac{1}{3}\right)$

26. $\tan\left(\cos^{-1} \dfrac{1}{3}\right)$

27. $\sec\left(\tan^{-1} \dfrac{1}{2}\right)$

28. $\cos\left(\sin^{-1} \dfrac{\sqrt{2}}{3}\right)$

29. $\cot\left[\sin^{-1}\left(-\dfrac{\sqrt{2}}{3}\right)\right]$

30. $\csc[\tan^{-1}(-2)]$

31. $\sin[\tan^{-1}(-3)]$

32. $\cot\left[\cos^{-1}\left(-\dfrac{\sqrt{3}}{3}\right)\right]$

33. $\sec\left(\sin^{-1} \dfrac{2\sqrt{5}}{5}\right)$

34. $\csc\left(\tan^{-1} \dfrac{1}{2}\right)$

35. $\sin^{-1}\left(\cos \dfrac{3\pi}{4}\right)$

36. $\cos^{-1}\left(\sin \dfrac{7\pi}{6}\right)$

In Problems 37–44, find the exact value of each expression.

37. $\cot^{-1} \sqrt{3}$

38. $\cot^{-1} 1$

39. $\csc^{-1}(-1)$

40. $\csc^{-1} \sqrt{2}$

41. $\sec^{-1} \dfrac{2\sqrt{3}}{3}$

42. $\sec^{-1}(-2)$

43. $\cot^{-1}\left(-\dfrac{\sqrt{3}}{3}\right)$

44. $\csc^{-1}\left(-\dfrac{2\sqrt{3}}{3}\right)$

In Problems 45–56, use a calculator to find the value of each expression rounded to two decimal places.

45. $\sec^{-1} 4$

46. $\csc^{-1} 5$

47. $\cot^{-1} 2$

48. $\sec^{-1}(-3)$

49. $\csc^{-1}(-3)$

50. $\cot^{-1}\left(-\dfrac{1}{2}\right)$

51. $\cot^{-1}(-\sqrt{5})$

52. $\cot^{-1}(-8.1)$

53. $\csc^{-1}\left(-\dfrac{3}{2}\right)$

54. $\sec^{-1}\left(-\dfrac{4}{3}\right)$

55. $\cot^{-1}\left(-\dfrac{3}{2}\right)$

56. $\cot^{-1}(-\sqrt{10})$

In Problems 57–66, write each trigonometric expression as an algebraic expression in u.

57. $\cos(\tan^{-1} u)$

58. $\sin(\cos^{-1} u)$

59. $\tan(\sin^{-1} u)$

60. $\tan(\cos^{-1} u)$

61. $\sin(\sec^{-1} u)$

62. $\sin(\cot^{-1} u)$

63. $\cos(\csc^{-1} u)$

64. $\cos(\sec^{-1} u)$

65. $\tan(\cot^{-1} u)$

66. $\tan(\sec^{-1} u)$

Mixed Practice

In Problems 67–78, $f(x) = \sin x, -\dfrac{\pi}{2} \le x \le \dfrac{\pi}{2}, g(x) = \cos x, 0 \le x \le \pi,$ and $h(x) = \tan x, -\dfrac{\pi}{2} < x < \dfrac{\pi}{2}.$ Find the exact value of each composite function.

67. $g\left(f^{-1}\left(\dfrac{12}{13}\right)\right)$

68. $f\left(g^{-1}\left(\dfrac{5}{13}\right)\right)$

69. $g^{-1}\left(f\left(\dfrac{7\pi}{4}\right)\right)$

70. $f^{-1}\left(g\left(\dfrac{5\pi}{6}\right)\right)$

71. $h\left(f^{-1}\left(-\dfrac{3}{5}\right)\right)$

72. $h\left(g^{-1}\left(-\dfrac{4}{5}\right)\right)$

73. $g\left(h^{-1}\left(\dfrac{12}{5}\right)\right)$

74. $f\left(h^{-1}\left(\dfrac{5}{12}\right)\right)$

75. $g^{-1}\left(f\left(-\dfrac{4\pi}{3}\right)\right)$

76. $g^{-1}\left(f\left(-\dfrac{5\pi}{6}\right)\right)$

77. $h\left(g^{-1}\left(-\dfrac{1}{4}\right)\right)$

78. $h\left(f^{-1}\left(-\dfrac{2}{5}\right)\right)$

Applications and Extensions

*Problems 79 and 80 require the following discussion: When granular materials are allowed to fall freely, they form conical (cone-shaped) piles. The naturally occurring angle of slope, measured from the horizontal, at which the loose material comes to rest is called the **angle of repose** and varies for different materials. The angle of repose θ is related to the height h and base radius r of the conical pile by the equation $\theta = \cot^{-1}\dfrac{r}{h}$. See the illustration.*

79. Angle of Repose: Deicing Salt Due to potential transportation issues (for example, frozen waterways) deicing salt used by highway departments in the Midwest must be ordered early and stored for future use. When deicing salt is stored in a pile 14 feet high, the diameter of the base of the pile is 45 feet.
(a) Find the angle of repose for deicing salt.
(b) What is the base diameter of a pile that is 17 feet high?
(c) What is the height of a pile that has a base diameter of approximately 122 feet?
Source: Salt Institute, *The Salt Storage Handbook,* 2006

80. Angle of Repose: Bunker Sand The steepness of sand bunkers on a golf course is affected by the angle of repose of the sand (a larger angle of repose allows for steeper bunkers). A freestanding pile of loose sand from a United States Golf Association (USGA) bunker had a height of 4 feet and a base diameter of approximately 6.68 feet.
(a) Find the angle of repose for USGA bunker sand.
(b) What is the height of such a pile if the diameter of the base is 8 feet?
(c) A 6-foot-high pile of loose Tour Grade 50/50 sand has a base diameter of approximately 8.44 feet. Which type of sand (USGA or Tour Grade 50/50) would be better suited for steep bunkers?
Source: 2004 Annual Report, Purdue University Turfgrass Science Program

81. Artillery A projectile fired into the first quadrant from the origin of a coordinate system will pass through the point (x, y) at time t according to the relationship $\cot \theta = \dfrac{2x}{2y + gt^2},$ where $\theta =$ the angle of elevation of the launcher and $g =$ the acceleration due to gravity $= 32.2$ feet/second^2. An artilleryman is firing at an enemy bunker located 2450 feet up the side of a hill that is 6175 feet away. He fires a round, and exactly 2.27 seconds later he scores a direct hit.

(a) What angle of elevation did he use?
(b) If the angle of elevation is also given by $\sec \theta = \dfrac{v_0 t}{x},$ where v_0 is the muzzle velocity of the weapon, find the muzzle velocity of the artillery piece he used.
Source: www.egwald.com/geometry/projectile3d.php

82. Using a graphing utility, graph $y = \cot^{-1} x.$

83. Using a graphing utility, graph $y = \sec^{-1} x.$

84. Using a graphing utility, graph $y = \csc^{-1} x.$

Explaining Concepts: Discussion and Writing

85. Explain in your own words how you would use your calculator to find the value of $\cot^{-1} 10$.

86. Consult three books on calculus and write down the definition in each of $y = \sec^{-1} x$ and $y = \csc^{-1} x$. Compare these with the definitions given in this book.

'Are You Prepared?' Answers

1. Domain: $\left\{ x \middle| x \neq \text{odd integer multiples of } \dfrac{\pi}{2} \right\}$; range: $\{ y \leq -1 \text{ or } y \geq 1 \}$ **2.** True   **3.** $\dfrac{\sqrt{5}}{5}$

7.3 Trigonometric Equations

PREPARING FOR THIS SECTION *Before getting started, review the following:*

- Solving Equations (Appendix A, Section A.6, pp. A44–A51)
- Values of the Trigonometric Functions (Section 6.2, pp. 365–374)

- Using a Graphing Utility to Solve Equations (Appendix B, Section B.4, pp. B6–B7)

Now Work the 'Are You Prepared?' problems on page 460.

OBJECTIVES **1** Solve Equations Involving a Single Trigonometric Function (p. 454)
  2 Solve Trigonometric Equations Using a Calculator (p. 457)
  3 Solve Trigonometric Equations Quadratic in Form (p. 458)
  4 Solve Trigonometric Equations Using Fundamental Identities (p. 458)
  5 Solve Trigonometric Equations Using a Graphing Utility (p. 459)

1 Solve Equations Involving a Single Trigonometric Function

In this section, we discuss **trigonometric equations,** that is, equations involving trigonometric functions that are satisfied only by some values of the variable (or, possibly, are not satisfied by any values of the variable). The values that satisfy the equation are called **solutions** of the equation.

EXAMPLE 1 **Checking Whether a Given Number Is a Solution of a Trigonometric Equation**

Determine whether $\theta = \dfrac{\pi}{4}$ is a solution of the equation $2 \sin \theta - 1 = 0$. Is $\theta = \dfrac{\pi}{6}$ a solution?

Solution Replace θ by $\dfrac{\pi}{4}$ in the given equation. The result is

$$2 \sin \frac{\pi}{4} - 1 = 2 \cdot \frac{\sqrt{2}}{2} - 1 = \sqrt{2} - 1 \neq 0$$

We conclude that $\dfrac{\pi}{4}$ is not a solution.

Next replace θ by $\dfrac{\pi}{6}$ in the equation. The result is

$$2 \sin \frac{\pi}{6} - 1 = 2 \cdot \frac{1}{2} - 1 = 0$$

We conclude that $\dfrac{\pi}{6}$ is a solution of the given equation.

The equation given in Example 1 has other solutions besides $\theta = \dfrac{\pi}{6}$. For example, $\theta = \dfrac{5\pi}{6}$ is also a solution, as is $\theta = \dfrac{13\pi}{6}$. (You should check this for yourself.) In fact, the equation has an infinite number of solutions due to the periodicity of the sine function, as can be seen in Figure 20 where we graph $y = 2 \sin x - 1$. Each x-intercept of the graph represents a solution to the equation $2 \sin x - 1 = 0$.

Figure 20

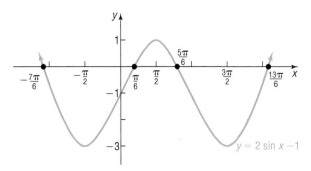

Unless the domain of the variable is restricted, we need to find *all* the solutions of a trigonometric equation. As the next example illustrates, finding all the solutions can be accomplished by first finding solutions over an interval whose length equals the period of the function and then adding multiples of that period to the solutions found.

EXAMPLE 2

Finding All the Solutions of a Trigonometric Equation

Solve the equation: $\cos \theta = \dfrac{1}{2}$

Give a general formula for all the solutions. List eight of the solutions.

Solution The period of the cosine function is 2π. In the interval $[0, 2\pi)$, there are two angles θ for which $\cos \theta = \dfrac{1}{2}$: $\theta = \dfrac{\pi}{3}$ and $\theta = \dfrac{5\pi}{3}$. See Figure 21. Because the cosine function has period 2π, all the solutions of $\cos \theta = \dfrac{1}{2}$ may be given by the general formula

$$\theta = \frac{\pi}{3} + 2k\pi \quad \text{or} \quad \theta = \frac{5\pi}{3} + 2k\pi \quad \text{k any integer}$$

Eight of the solutions are

$$\underbrace{-\frac{5\pi}{3}, \quad -\frac{\pi}{3}}_{k = -1}, \quad \underbrace{\frac{\pi}{3}, \quad \frac{5\pi}{3}}_{k = 0}, \quad \underbrace{\frac{7\pi}{3}, \quad \frac{11\pi}{3}}_{k = 1}, \quad \underbrace{\frac{13\pi}{3}, \quad \frac{17\pi}{3}}_{k = 2}$$

Figure 21

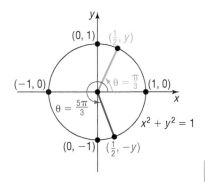

Check: We can verify the solutions by graphing $Y_1 = \cos x$ and $Y_2 = \dfrac{1}{2}$ to determine where the graphs intersect. (Be sure to graph in radian mode.) See Figure 22. The graph of Y_1 intersects the graph of Y_2 at $x = 1.05 \left(\approx \dfrac{\pi}{3} \right)$, $5.24 \left(\approx \dfrac{5\pi}{3} \right)$, $7.33 \left(\approx \dfrac{7\pi}{3} \right)$, and $11.52 \left(\approx \dfrac{11\pi}{3} \right)$, rounded to two decimal places.

Figure 22

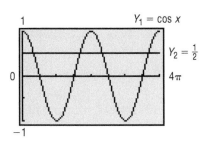

Now Work PROBLEM 35

In most of our work, we shall be interested only in finding solutions of trigonometric equations for $0 \le \theta < 2\pi$.

EXAMPLE 3 **Solving a Linear Trigonometric Equation**

Solve the equation: $2 \sin \theta + \sqrt{3} = 0, \quad 0 \le \theta < 2\pi$

Solution Solve the equation for $\sin \theta$.

$$2 \sin \theta + \sqrt{3} = 0$$
$$2 \sin \theta = -\sqrt{3} \quad \text{Subtract } \sqrt{3} \text{ from both sides.}$$
$$\sin \theta = -\frac{\sqrt{3}}{2} \quad \text{Divide both sides by 2.}$$

In the interval $[0, 2\pi)$, there are two angles θ for which $\sin \theta = -\frac{\sqrt{3}}{2}$: $\theta = \frac{4\pi}{3}$ and $\theta = \frac{5\pi}{3}$. The solution set is $\left\{\frac{4\pi}{3}, \frac{5\pi}{3}\right\}$.

Now Work PROBLEM 11

When the argument of the trigonometric function in an equation is a multiple of θ, the general formula must be used to solve the equation.

EXAMPLE 4 **Solving a Trigonometric Equation**

Solve the equation: $\sin(2\theta) = \frac{1}{2}, \quad 0 \le \theta < 2\pi$

Solution In the interval $[0, 2\pi)$, the sine function equals $\frac{1}{2}$ at $\frac{\pi}{6}$ and $\frac{5\pi}{6}$. See Figure 23(a). So, we

Figure 23

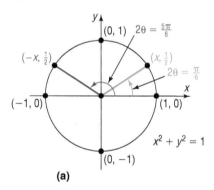

(a)

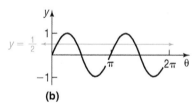

(b)

know that 2θ must equal $\frac{\pi}{6}$ and $\frac{5\pi}{6}$. Here's the problem, however. The period of $y = \sin(2\theta)$ is $\frac{2\pi}{2} = \pi$. So, in the interval $[0, 2\pi)$, the graph of $y = \sin(2\theta)$ will complete two cycles, and the graph of $y = \sin(2\theta)$ will intersect the graph of $y = \frac{1}{2}$ four times. See Figure 23(b). There are four solutions to the equation $\sin(2\theta) = \frac{1}{2}$ in $[0, 2\pi)$. To find these solutions, write the general formula that gives all the solutions.

$$2\theta = \frac{\pi}{6} + 2k\pi \quad \text{or} \quad 2\theta = \frac{5\pi}{6} + 2k\pi \quad \text{k any integer}$$
$$\theta = \frac{\pi}{12} + k\pi \quad \text{or} \quad \theta = \frac{5\pi}{12} + k\pi \quad \text{Divide by 2.}$$

Then

$$\theta = \frac{\pi}{12} + (-1)\pi = \frac{-11\pi}{12} \quad k = -1 \qquad \theta = \frac{5\pi}{12} + (-1)\pi = \frac{-7\pi}{12}$$
$$\theta = \frac{\pi}{12} + (0)\pi = \frac{\pi}{12} \quad k = 0 \qquad \theta = \frac{5\pi}{12} + (0)\pi = \frac{5\pi}{12}$$
$$\theta = \frac{\pi}{12} + (1)\pi = \frac{13\pi}{12} \quad k = 1 \qquad \theta = \frac{5\pi}{12} + (1)\pi = \frac{17\pi}{12}$$
$$\theta = \frac{\pi}{12} + (2)\pi = \frac{25\pi}{12} \quad k = 2 \qquad \theta = \frac{5\pi}{12} + (2)\pi = \frac{29\pi}{12}$$

In the interval $[0, 2\pi)$, the solutions of $\sin(2\theta) = \frac{1}{2}$ are $\theta = \frac{\pi}{12}, \theta = \frac{5\pi}{12}, \theta = \frac{13\pi}{12}$, and $\theta = \frac{17\pi}{12}$. The solution set is $\left\{\frac{\pi}{12}, \frac{5\pi}{12}, \frac{13\pi}{12}, \frac{17\pi}{12}\right\}$. We now know the graph of $y = \sin(2\theta)$ intersects $y = \frac{1}{2}$ at $\left(\frac{\pi}{12}, \frac{1}{2}\right), \left(\frac{5\pi}{12}, \frac{1}{2}\right), \left(\frac{13\pi}{12}, \frac{1}{2}\right)$, and $\left(\frac{17\pi}{12}, \frac{1}{2}\right)$ in the interval $[0, 2\pi)$.

✓**Check:** Verify these solutions by graphing $Y_1 = \sin(2x)$ and $Y_2 = \dfrac{1}{2}$ for $0 \le x \le 2\pi$.

WARNING In solving a trigonometric equation for θ, $0 \le \theta < 2\pi$, in which the argument is not θ (as in Example 4), you must write down all the solutions first and then list those that are in the interval $[0, 2\pi)$. Otherwise, solutions may be lost. For example, in solving $\sin(2\theta) = \dfrac{1}{2}$, if you merely write the solutions $2\theta = \dfrac{\pi}{6}$ and $2\theta = \dfrac{5\pi}{6}$, you will find only $\theta = \dfrac{\pi}{12}$ and $\theta = \dfrac{5\pi}{12}$ and miss the other solutions. ∎

EXAMPLE 5   Solving a Trigonometric Equation

Solve the equation: $\tan\left(\theta - \dfrac{\pi}{2}\right) = 1$, $0 \le \theta < 2\pi$

Solution   The period of the tangent function is π. In the interval $[0, \pi)$, the tangent function has the value 1 when the argument is $\dfrac{\pi}{4}$. Because the argument is $\theta - \dfrac{\pi}{2}$ in the given equation, write the general formula that gives all the solutions.

$$\theta - \frac{\pi}{2} = \frac{\pi}{4} + k\pi \qquad \textit{k any integer}$$

$$\theta = \frac{3\pi}{4} + k\pi$$

In the interval $[0, 2\pi)$, $\theta = \dfrac{3\pi}{4}$ and $\theta = \dfrac{3\pi}{4} + \pi = \dfrac{7\pi}{4}$ are the only solutions. The solution set is $\left\{ \dfrac{3\pi}{4}, \dfrac{7\pi}{4} \right\}$.

━━━ **Now Work** PROBLEM 17

2 Solve Trigonometric Equations Using a Calculator

The next example illustrates how to solve trigonometric equations using a calculator. Remember that the function keys on a calculator will only give values consistent with the definition of the function.

EXAMPLE 6   Solving a Trigonometric Equation with a Calculator

Use a calculator to solve the equation $\tan\theta = -2$, $0 \le \theta < 2\pi$. Express any solutions in radians, rounded to two decimal places.

Solution   To solve $\tan\theta = -2$ on a calculator, first set the mode to radians. Then use the $\boxed{\tan^{-1}}$ key to obtain

$$\theta = \tan^{-1}(-2) \approx -1.1071487$$

Rounded to two decimal places, $\theta = \tan^{-1}(-2) = -1.11$ radian. Because of the definition of $y = \tan^{-1} x$, the angle θ that we obtain is the angle $-\dfrac{\pi}{2} < \theta < \dfrac{\pi}{2}$ for which $\tan\theta = -2$. Since we seek solutions for which $0 \le \theta < 2\pi$, we express the angle as $2\pi - 1.11$.

Another angle for which $\tan\theta = -2$ is $\pi - 1.11$. See Figure 24. The angle $\pi - 1.11$ is the angle in quadrant II, where $\tan\theta = -2$. The solutions for $\tan\theta = -2$, $0 \le \theta < 2\pi$, are

$$\theta = 2\pi - 1.11 \approx 5.17 \text{ radians} \quad \text{and} \quad \theta = \pi - 1.11 \approx 2.03 \text{ radians}$$

The solution set is $\{5.17, 2.03\}$.

Figure 24
$\tan\theta = -2$

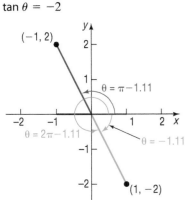

WARNING Example 6 illustrates that caution must be exercised when solving trigonometric equations on a calculator. Remember that the calculator supplies an angle only within the restrictions of the definition of the inverse trigonometric function. To find the remaining solutions, you must identify other quadrants, if any, in which a solution may be located. ∎

━━━━ **Now Work** PROBLEM 45

3 Solve Trigonometric Equations Quadratic in Form

Many trigonometric equations can be solved by applying techniques that we already know, such as applying the quadratic formula (if the equation is a second-degree polynomial) or factoring.

EXAMPLE 7 | **Solving a Trigonometric Equation Quadratic in Form**

Solve the equation: $2 \sin^2 \theta - 3 \sin \theta + 1 = 0, \quad 0 \le \theta < 2\pi$

Solution This equation is a quadratic equation (in $\sin \theta$) that can be factored.

$$2 \sin^2 \theta - 3 \sin \theta + 1 = 0 \qquad \text{\small $2x^2 - 3x + 1 = 0, \quad x = \sin \theta$}$$

$$(2 \sin \theta - 1)(\sin \theta - 1) = 0 \qquad \text{\small $(2x - 1)(x - 1) = 0$}$$

$$2 \sin \theta - 1 = 0 \quad \text{or} \quad \sin \theta - 1 = 0 \qquad \text{\small Use the Zero-Product Property.}$$

$$\sin \theta = \frac{1}{2} \quad \text{or} \qquad \sin \theta = 1$$

Solving each equation in the interval $[0, 2\pi)$, we obtain

$$\theta = \frac{\pi}{6}, \qquad \theta = \frac{5\pi}{6}, \qquad \theta = \frac{\pi}{2}$$

The solution set is $\left\{ \dfrac{\pi}{6}, \dfrac{5\pi}{6}, \dfrac{\pi}{2} \right\}$.

━━━━ **Now Work** PROBLEM 59

4 Solve Trigonometric Equations Using Fundamental Identities

When a trigonometric equation contains more than one trigonometric function, identities sometimes can be used to obtain an equivalent equation that contains only one trigonometric function.

EXAMPLE 8 | **Solving a Trigonometric Equation Using Identities**

Solve the equation: $3 \cos \theta + 3 = 2 \sin^2 \theta, \quad 0 \le \theta < 2\pi$

Solution The equation in its present form contains a sine and a cosine. However, a form of the Pythagorean Identity, $\sin^2 \theta + \cos^2 \theta = 1$, can be used to transform the equation into an equivalent one containing only cosines.

$$3 \cos \theta + 3 = 2 \sin^2 \theta$$

$$3 \cos \theta + 3 = 2(1 - \cos^2 \theta) \qquad \text{\small $\sin^2 \theta = 1 - \cos^2 \theta$}$$

$$3 \cos \theta + 3 = 2 - 2 \cos^2 \theta$$

$$2 \cos^2 \theta + 3 \cos \theta + 1 = 0 \qquad \text{\small Quadratic in $\cos \theta$}$$

$$(2 \cos \theta + 1)(\cos \theta + 1) = 0 \qquad \text{\small Factor.}$$

$$2 \cos \theta + 1 = 0 \quad \text{or} \quad \cos \theta + 1 = 0 \qquad \text{\small Use the Zero-Product Property.}$$

$$\cos \theta = -\frac{1}{2} \quad \text{or} \qquad \cos \theta = -1$$

Solving each equation in the interval $[0, 2\pi)$, we obtain

$$\theta = \frac{2\pi}{3}, \qquad \theta = \frac{4\pi}{3}, \qquad \theta = \pi$$

The solution set is $\left\{ \dfrac{2\pi}{3}, \pi, \dfrac{4\pi}{3} \right\}$.

 ✓**Check:** Graph $Y_1 = 3 \cos x + 3$ and $Y_2 = 2 \sin^2 x, 0 \le x \le 2\pi$, and find the points of intersection. How close are your approximate solutions to the exact ones found in Example 8?

EXAMPLE 9 **Solving a Trigonometric Equation Using Identities**

Solve the equation: $\cos^2 \theta + \sin \theta = 2, \quad 0 \le \theta < 2\pi$

Solution This equation involves two trigonometric functions, sine and cosine. Use a form of the Pythagorean Identity, $\sin^2 \theta + \cos^2 \theta = 1$, to rewrite the equation in terms of $\sin \theta$.

$$\cos^2 \theta + \sin \theta = 2$$
$$(1 - \sin^2 \theta) + \sin \theta = 2 \quad \color{gray}{\cos^2 \theta = 1 - \sin^2 \theta}$$
$$\sin^2 \theta - \sin \theta + 1 = 0$$

This is a quadratic equation in $\sin \theta$. The discriminant is $b^2 - 4ac = 1 - 4 = -3 < 0$. Therefore, the equation has no real solution. The solution set is the empty set, $\varnothing$.

 ✓**Check:** Graph $Y_1 = \cos^2 x + \sin x$ and $Y_2 = 2$ to see that the two graphs never intersect, so the equation $Y_1 = Y_2$ has no real solution.

---

 5 Solve Trigonometric Equations Using a Graphing Utility

The techniques introduced in this section apply only to certain types of trigonometric equations. Solutions for other types are usually studied in calculus, using numerical methods.

EXAMPLE 10 **Solving a Trigonometric Equation Using a Graphing Utility**

Solve: $5 \sin x + x = 3$

Express the solution(s) rounded to two decimal places.

Solution This type of trigonometric equation cannot be solved by previous methods. A graphing utility, though, can be used here. Each solution of this equation is the x-coordinate of a point of intersection of the graphs of $Y_1 = 5 \sin x + x$ and $Y_2 = 3$. See Figure 25.

There are three points of intersection; the x-coordinates are the solutions that we seek. Using INTERSECT, we find

$$x = 0.52, \qquad x = 3.18, \qquad x = 5.71$$

The solution set is $\{0.52, 3.18, 5.71\}$.

Figure 25

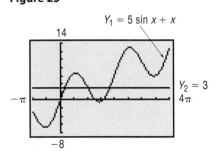

$Y_1 = 5 \sin x + x$

$Y_2 = 3$

Now Work PROBLEM 81

7.3 Assess Your Understanding

'Are You Prepared?' *Answers are given at the end of these exercises. If you get a wrong answer, read the pages listed in* red.

1. Solve: $3x - 5 = -x + 1$ (pp. A44–A51)

2. $\sin\left(\dfrac{\pi}{4}\right) =$ _____; $\cos\left(\dfrac{8\pi}{3}\right) =$ _____
(pp. 365–374)

3. Find the real solutions of $4x^2 - x - 5 = 0$. (pp. A44–A51)

4. Find the real solutions of $x^2 - x - 1 = 0$. (pp. A44–A51)

5. Find the real solutions of $(2x - 1)^2 - 3(2x - 1) - 4 = 0$.
(pp. A44–A51)

6. Use a graphing utility to solve $5x^3 - 2 = x - x^2$. Round answers to two decimal places. (pp. B6–B7)

Concepts and Vocabulary

7. Two solutions of the equation $\sin \theta = \dfrac{1}{2}$ are _____ and

_____.

8. All the solutions of the equation $\sin \theta = \dfrac{1}{2}$ are _____.

9. *True or False* Most trigonometric equations have unique solutions.

10. *True or False* The equation $\sin \theta = 2$ has a real solution that can be found using a calculator.

Skill Building

In Problems 11–34, solve each equation on the interval $0 \le \theta < 2\pi$.

11. $2 \sin \theta + 3 = 2$

12. $1 - \cos \theta = \dfrac{1}{2}$

13. $4 \cos^2 \theta = 1$

14. $\tan^2 \theta = \dfrac{1}{3}$

15. $2 \sin^2 \theta - 1 = 0$

16. $4 \cos^2 \theta - 3 = 0$

17. $\sin(3\theta) = -1$

18. $\tan \dfrac{\theta}{2} = \sqrt{3}$

19. $\cos(2\theta) = -\dfrac{1}{2}$

20. $\tan(2\theta) = -1$

21. $\sec \dfrac{3\theta}{2} = -2$

22. $\cot \dfrac{2\theta}{3} = -\sqrt{3}$

23. $2 \sin \theta + 1 = 0$

24. $\cos \theta + 1 = 0$

25. $\tan \theta + 1 = 0$

26. $\sqrt{3} \cot \theta + 1 = 0$

27. $4 \sec \theta + 6 = -2$

28. $5 \csc \theta - 3 = 2$

29. $3\sqrt{2} \cos \theta + 2 = -1$

30. $4 \sin \theta + 3\sqrt{3} = \sqrt{3}$

31. $\cos\left(2\theta - \dfrac{\pi}{2}\right) = -1$

32. $\sin\left(3\theta + \dfrac{\pi}{18}\right) = 1$

33. $\tan\left(\dfrac{\theta}{2} + \dfrac{\pi}{3}\right) = 1$

34. $\cos\left(\dfrac{\theta}{3} - \dfrac{\pi}{4}\right) = \dfrac{1}{2}$

In Problems 35–44, solve each equation. Give a general formula for all the solutions. List six solutions.

35. $\sin \theta = \dfrac{1}{2}$

36. $\tan \theta = 1$

37. $\tan \theta = -\dfrac{\sqrt{3}}{3}$

38. $\cos \theta = -\dfrac{\sqrt{3}}{2}$

39. $\cos \theta = 0$

40. $\sin \theta = \dfrac{\sqrt{2}}{2}$

41. $\cos(2\theta) = -\dfrac{1}{2}$

42. $\sin(2\theta) = -1$

43. $\sin \dfrac{\theta}{2} = -\dfrac{\sqrt{3}}{2}$

44. $\tan \dfrac{\theta}{2} = -1$

In Problems 45–56, use a calculator to solve each equation on the interval $0 \le \theta < 2\pi$. Round answers to two decimal places.

45. $\sin \theta = 0.4$

46. $\cos \theta = 0.6$

47. $\tan \theta = 5$

48. $\cot \theta = 2$

49. $\cos \theta = -0.9$

50. $\sin \theta = -0.2$

51. $\sec \theta = -4$

52. $\csc \theta = -3$

53. $5 \tan \theta + 9 = 0$

54. $4 \cot \theta = -5$

55. $3 \sin \theta - 2 = 0$

56. $4 \cos \theta + 3 = 0$

In Problems 57–80, solve each equation on the interval $0 \le \theta < 2\pi$.

57. $2\cos^2\theta + \cos\theta = 0$

58. $\sin^2\theta - 1 = 0$

59. $2\sin^2\theta - \sin\theta - 1 = 0$

60. $2\cos^2\theta + \cos\theta - 1 = 0$

61. $(\tan\theta - 1)(\sec\theta - 1) = 0$

62. $(\cot\theta + 1)\left(\csc\theta - \dfrac{1}{2}\right) = 0$

63. $\sin^2\theta - \cos^2\theta = 1 + \cos\theta$

64. $\cos^2\theta - \sin^2\theta + \sin\theta = 0$

65. $\sin^2\theta = 6(\cos(-\theta) + 1)$

66. $2\sin^2\theta = 3(1 - \cos(-\theta))$

67. $\cos\theta = -\sin(-\theta)$

68. $\cos\theta - \sin(-\theta) = 0$

69. $\tan\theta = 2\sin\theta$

70. $\tan\theta = \cot\theta$

71. $1 + \sin\theta = 2\cos^2\theta$

72. $\sin^2\theta = 2\cos\theta + 2$

73. $2\sin^2\theta - 5\sin\theta + 3 = 0$

74. $2\cos^2\theta - 7\cos\theta - 4 = 0$

75. $3(1 - \cos\theta) = \sin^2\theta$

76. $4(1 + \sin\theta) = \cos^2\theta$

77. $\tan^2\theta = \dfrac{3}{2}\sec\theta$

78. $\csc^2\theta = \cot\theta + 1$

79. $\sec^2\theta + \tan\theta = 0$

80. $\sec\theta = \tan\theta + \cot\theta$

In Problems 81–92, use a graphing utility to solve each equation. Express the solution(s) rounded to two decimal places.

81. $x + 5\cos x = 0$

82. $x - 4\sin x = 0$

83. $22x - 17\sin x = 3$

84. $19x + 8\cos x = 2$

85. $\sin x + \cos x = x$

86. $\sin x - \cos x = x$

87. $x^2 - 2\cos x = 0$

88. $x^2 + 3\sin x = 0$

89. $x^2 - 2\sin(2x) = 3x$

90. $x^2 = x + 3\cos(2x)$

91. $6\sin x - e^x = 2, \quad x > 0$

92. $4\cos(3x) - e^x = 1, \quad x > 0$

Mixed Practice

93. What are the zeros of $f(x) = 4\sin^2 x - 3$ on the interval $[0, 2\pi]$?

94. What are the zeros of $f(x) = 2\cos(3x) + 1$ on the interval $[0, \pi]$?

95. $f(x) = 3\sin x$
 (a) Find the zeros of f on the interval $[-2\pi, 4\pi]$.
 (b) Graph $f(x) = 3\sin x$ on the interval $[-2\pi, 4\pi]$.
 (c) Solve $f(x) = \dfrac{3}{2}$ on the interval $[-2\pi, 4\pi]$. What points are on the graph of f? Label these points on the graph drawn in part (b).
 (d) Use the graph drawn in part (b) along with the results of part (c) to determine the values of x such that $f(x) > \dfrac{3}{2}$ on the interval $[-2\pi, 4\pi]$.

96. $f(x) = 2\cos x$
 (a) Find the zeros of f on the interval $[-2\pi, 4\pi]$.
 (b) Graph $f(x) = 2\cos x$ on the interval $[-2\pi, 4\pi]$.
 (c) Solve $f(x) = -\sqrt{3}$ on the interval $[-2\pi, 4\pi]$. What points are on the graph of f? Label these points on the graph drawn in part (b).

 (d) Use the graph drawn in part (b) along with the results of part (c) to determine the values of x such that $f(x) < -\sqrt{3}$ on the interval $[-2\pi, 4\pi]$.

97. $f(x) = 4\tan x$
 (a) Solve $f(x) = -4$.
 (b) For what values of x is $f(x) < -4$ on the interval $\left(-\dfrac{\pi}{2}, \dfrac{\pi}{2}\right)$?

98. $f(x) = \cot x$
 (a) Solve $f(x) = -\sqrt{3}$.
 (b) For what values of x is $f(x) > -\sqrt{3}$ on the interval $(0, \pi)$?

99. (a) Graph $f(x) = 3\sin(2x) + 2$ and $g(x) = \dfrac{7}{2}$ on the same Cartesian plane for the interval $[0, \pi]$.
 (b) Solve $f(x) = g(x)$ on the interval $[0, \pi]$ and label the points of intersection on the graph drawn in part (b).
 (c) Solve $f(x) > g(x)$ on the interval $[0, \pi]$.
 (d) Shade the region bounded by $f(x) = 3\sin(2x) + 2$ and $g(x) = \dfrac{7}{2}$ between the two points found in part (b) on the graph drawn in part (a).

100. (a) Graph $f(x) = 2 \cos \dfrac{x}{2} + 3$ and $g(x) = 4$ on the same Cartesian plane for the interval $[0, 4\pi]$.
   (b) Solve $f(x) = g(x)$ on the interval $[0, 4\pi]$ and label the points of intersection on the graph drawn in part (b).
   (c) Solve $f(x) < g(x)$ on the interval $[0, 4\pi]$.
   (d) Shade the region bounded by $f(x) = 2 \cos \dfrac{x}{2} + 3$ and $g(x) = 4$ between the two points found in part (b) on the graph drawn in part (a).

101. (a) Graph $f(x) = -4 \cos x$ and $g(x) = 2 \cos x + 3$ on the same Cartesian plane for the interval $[0, 2\pi]$.
   (b) Solve $f(x) = g(x)$ on the interval $[0, 2\pi]$ and label the points of intersection on the graph drawn in part (b).

(c) Solve $f(x) > g(x)$ on the interval $[0, 2\pi]$.
(d) Shade the region bounded by $f(x) = -4 \cos x$ and $g(x) = 2 \cos x + 3$ between the two points found in part (b) on the graph drawn in part (a).

102. (a) Graph $f(x) = 2 \sin x$ and $g(x) = -2 \sin x + 2$ on the same Cartesian plane for the interval $[0, 2\pi]$.
   (b) Solve $f(x) = g(x)$ on the interval $[0, 2\pi]$ and label the points of intersection on the graph drawn in part (b).
   (c) Solve $f(x) > g(x)$ on the interval $[0, 2\pi]$.
   (d) Shade the region bounded by $f(x) = 2 \sin x$ and $g(x) = -2 \sin x + 2$ between the two points found in part (b) on the graph drawn in part (a).

Applications and Extensions

103. Blood Pressure Blood pressure is a way of measuring the amount of force exerted on the walls of blood vessels. It is measured using two numbers: systolic (as the heart beats) blood pressure and diastolic (as the heart rests) blood pressure. Blood pressures vary substantially from person to person, but a typical blood pressure is 120/80, which means the systolic blood pressure is 120 mmHg and the diastolic blood pressure is 80 mmHg. Assuming that a person's heart beats 70 times per minute, the blood pressure P of an individual after t seconds can be modeled by the function

$$P(t) = 100 + 20 \sin\left(\frac{7\pi}{3} t\right)$$

(a) In the interval $[0, 1]$, determine the times at which the blood pressure is 100 mmHg.
(b) In the interval $[0, 1]$, determine the times at which the blood pressure is 120 mmHg.
(c) In the interval $[0, 1]$, determine the times at which the blood pressure is between 100 and 105 mmHg.

104. The Ferris Wheel In 1893, George Ferris engineered the Ferris Wheel. It was 250 feet in diameter. If the wheel makes 1 revolution every 40 seconds, then the function

$$h(t) = 125 \sin\left(0.157t - \frac{\pi}{2}\right) + 125$$

represents the height h, in feet, of a seat on the wheel as a function of time t, where t is measured in seconds. The ride begins when $t = 0$.
(a) During the first 40 seconds of the ride, at what time t is an individual on the Ferris Wheel exactly 125 feet above the ground?
(b) During the first 80 seconds of the ride, at what time t is an individual on the Ferris Wheel exactly 250 feet above the ground?
(c) During the first 40 seconds of the ride, over what interval of time t is an individual on the Ferris Wheel more than 125 feet above the ground?

105. Holding Pattern An airplane is asked to stay within a holding pattern near Chicago's O'Hare International

Airport. The function $d(x) = 70 \sin(0.65x) + 150$ represents the distance d, in miles, of the airplane from the airport at time x, in minutes.
(a) When the plane enters the holding pattern, $x = 0$, how far is it from O'Hare?
(b) During the first 20 minutes after the plane enters the holding pattern, at what time x is the plane exactly 100 miles from the airport?
(c) During the first 20 minutes after the plane enters the holding pattern, at what time x is the plane more than 100 miles from the airport?
(d) While the plane is in the holding pattern, will it ever be within 70 miles of the airport? Why?

106. Projectile Motion A golfer hits a golf ball with an initial velocity of 100 miles per hour. The range R of the ball as a function of the angle θ to the horizontal is given by $R(\theta) = 672 \sin(2\theta)$, where R is measured in feet.
(a) At what angle θ should the ball be hit if the golfer wants the ball to travel 450 feet (150 yards)?
(b) At what angle θ should the ball be hit if the golfer wants the ball to travel 540 feet (180 yards)?
(c) At what angle θ should the ball be hit if the golfer wants the ball to travel at least 480 feet (160 yards)?
(d) Can the golfer hit the ball 720 feet (240 yards)?

107. Heat Transfer In the study of heat transfer, the equation $x + \tan x = 0$ occurs. Graph $Y_1 = -x$ and $Y_2 = \tan x$ for $x \geq 0$. Conclude that there are an infinite number of points of intersection of these two graphs. Now find the first two positive solutions of $x + \tan x = 0$ rounded to two decimal places.

108. Carrying a Ladder Around a Corner Two hallways, one of width 3 feet, the other of width 4 feet, meet at a right angle. See the illustration. It can be shown that the length L of the ladder as a function of θ is $L(\theta) = 4 \csc \theta + 3 \sec \theta$.
(a) In calculus, you will be asked to find the length of the longest ladder that can turn the corner by solving the equation

$$3 \sec \theta \tan \theta - 4 \csc \theta \cot \theta = 0, \quad 0° < \theta < 90°$$

Solve this equation for θ.

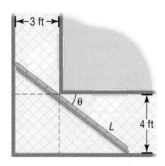

(b) What is the length of the longest ladder that can be carried around the corner?

(c) Graph $L = L(\theta), 0° \le \theta \le 90°$, and find the angle θ that minimizes the length L.

(d) Compare the result with the one found in part (b). Explain why the two answers are the same.

109. Projectile Motion The horizontal distance that a projectile will travel in the air (ignoring air resistance) is given by the equation

$$R(\theta) = \frac{v_0^2 \sin(2\theta)}{g}$$

where v_0 is the initial velocity of the projectile, θ is the angle of elevation, and g is acceleration due to gravity (9.8 meters per second squared).

(a) If you can throw a baseball with an initial speed of 34.8 meters per second, at what angle of elevation θ should you direct the throw so that the ball travels a distance of 107 meters before striking the ground?

(b) Determine the maximum distance that you can throw the ball.

(c) Graph $R = R(\theta)$, with $v_0 = 34.8$ meters per second.

(d) Verify the results obtained in parts (a) and (b) using a graphing utility.

110. Projectile Motion Refer to Problem 109.

(a) If you can throw a baseball with an initial speed of 40 meters per second, at what angle of elevation θ should you direct the throw so that the ball travels a distance of 110 meters before striking the ground?

(b) Determine the maximum distance that you can throw the ball.

(c) Graph $R = R(\theta)$, with $v_0 = 40$ meters per second.

(d) Verify the results obtained in parts (a) and (b) using a graphing utility.

The following discussion of Snell's Law of Refraction* (named after Willebrord Snell, 1580–1626) is needed for Problems 111–118. Light, sound, and other waves travel at different speeds, depending on the media (air, water, wood, and so on) through which they pass. Suppose that light travels from a point A in one medium, where its speed is v_1, to a point B in another medium, where its speed is v_2. Refer to the figure, where the angle θ_1 is called the angle of incidence and the angle θ_2 is the angle of refraction. Snell's Law, which can be proved using calculus, states that

$$\frac{\sin \theta_1}{\sin \theta_2} = \frac{v_1}{v_2}$$

The ratio $\dfrac{v_1}{v_2}$ is called the index of refraction. Some values are given in the table shown to the right.

Some Indexes of Refraction	
Medium	**Index of Refraction†**
Water	1.33
Ethyl alcohol (20°C)	1.36
Carbon disulfide	1.63
Air (1 atm and 0°C)	1.00029
Diamond	2.42
Fused quartz	1.46
Glass, crown	1.52
Glass, dense flint	1.66
Sodium chloride	1.54

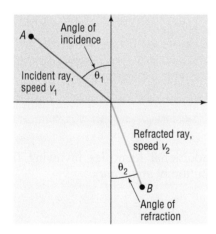

111. The index of refraction of light in passing from a vacuum into water is 1.33. If the angle of incidence is 40°, determine the angle of refraction.

112. The index of refraction of light in passing from a vacuum into dense flint glass is 1.66. If the angle of incidence is 50°, determine the angle of refraction.

113. Ptolemy, who lived in the city of Alexandria in Egypt during the second century AD, gave the measured values in the following table for the angle of incidence θ_1 and the angle of refraction θ_2 for a light beam passing from air into water. Do these values agree with Snell's Law? If so, what index of refraction results? (These data are of interest as the oldest recorded physical measurements.)

θ_1	θ_2	θ_1	θ_2
10°	8°	50°	35°0′
20°	15°30′	60°	40°30′
30°	22°30′	70°	45°30′
40°	29°0′	80°	50°0′

* Because this law was also deduced by René Descartes in France, it is also known as Descartes's Law.

† For light of wavelength 589 nanometers, measured with respect to a vacuum. The index with respect to air is negligibly different in most cases.

114. Bending Light The speed of yellow sodium light (wavelength, 589 nanometers) in a certain liquid is measured to be 1.92×10^8 meters per second. What is the index of refraction of this liquid, with respect to air, for sodium light?*

[**Hint:** The speed of light in air is approximately 2.998×10^8 meters per second.]

115. Bending Light A beam of light with a wavelength of 589 nanometers traveling in air makes an angle of incidence of 40° on a slab of transparent material, and the refracted beam makes an angle of refraction of 26°. Find the index of refraction of the material.*

116. Bending Light A light ray with a wavelength of 589 nanometers (produced by a sodium lamp) traveling through air makes an angle of incidence of 30° on a smooth, flat slab of crown glass. Find the angle of refraction.*

117. A light beam passes through a thick slab of material whose index of refraction is n_2. Show that the emerging beam is parallel to the incident beam.*

118. Brewster's Law If the angle of incidence and the angle of refraction are complementary angles, the angle of incidence is referred to as the Brewster angle θ_B. The Brewster angle is related to the index of refractions of the two media, n_1 and n_2, by the equation $n_1 \sin \theta_B = n_2 \cos \theta_B$, where n_1 is the index of refraction of the incident medium and n_2 is the index of refraction of the refractive medium. Determine the Brewster angle for a light beam traveling through water (at 20°C) that makes an angle of incidence with a smooth, flat slab of crown glass.

* Adapted from Halliday and Resnick, *Fundamentals of Physics*, 7th ed., 2005, John Wiley & Sons.

Explaining Concepts: Discussion and Writing

119. Explain in your own words how you would use your calculator to solve the equation $\cos x = -0.6, 0 \le x < 2\pi$. How would you modify your approach to solve the equation $\cot x = 5, 0 < x < 2\pi$?

120. Provide a justification as to why no further points of intersection (and therefore solutions) exist in Figure 25 on page 459 for $x < -\pi$ or $x > 4\pi$.

'Are You Prepared?' Answers

1. $\left\{ \dfrac{3}{2} \right\}$ **2.** $\dfrac{\sqrt{2}}{2}; -\dfrac{1}{2}$ **3.** $\left\{ -1, \dfrac{5}{4} \right\}$ **4.** $\left\{ \dfrac{1 - \sqrt{5}}{2}, \dfrac{1 + \sqrt{5}}{2} \right\}$ **5.** $\left\{ 0, \dfrac{5}{2} \right\}$ **6.** $\{0.76\}$

7.4 Trigonometric Identities

PREPARING FOR THIS SECTION *Before getting started, review the following:*

- Fundamental Identities (Section 6.3, p. 385)
- Even–Odd Properties (Section 6.3, p. 389)

Now Work the 'Are You Prepared?' problems on page 469.

OBJECTIVES 1 Use Algebra to Simplify Trigonometric Expressions (p. 465)
           2 Establish Identities (p. 466)

In this section we establish some additional identities involving trigonometric functions. But first, we review the definition of an *identity*.

DEFINITION   Two functions f and g are said to be **identically equal** if

$$f(x) = g(x)$$

for every value of x for which both functions are defined. Such an equation is referred to as an **identity.** An equation that is not an identity is called a **conditional equation.**

For example, the following are identities:

$$(x + 1)^2 = x^2 + 2x + 1 \qquad \sin^2 x + \cos^2 x = 1 \qquad \csc x = \frac{1}{\sin x}$$

The following are conditional equations:

$$2x + 5 = 0 \qquad \text{True only if } x = -\frac{5}{2}$$

$$\sin x = 0 \qquad \text{True only if } x = k\pi, \text{ } k \text{ an integer}$$

$$\sin x = \cos x \qquad \text{True only if } x = \frac{\pi}{4} + 2k\pi \text{ or } x = \frac{5\pi}{4} + 2k\pi, \text{ } k \text{ an integer}$$

Below is a list of the trigonometric identities that we have established thus far.

Quotient Identities

$$\tan \theta = \frac{\sin \theta}{\cos \theta} \qquad \cot \theta = \frac{\cos \theta}{\sin \theta}$$

Reciprocal Identities

$$\csc \theta = \frac{1}{\sin \theta} \qquad \sec \theta = \frac{1}{\cos \theta} \qquad \cot \theta = \frac{1}{\tan \theta}$$

Pythagorean Identities

$$\sin^2 \theta + \cos^2 \theta = 1 \qquad \tan^2 \theta + 1 = \sec^2 \theta$$

$$\cot^2 \theta + 1 = \csc^2 \theta$$

Even–Odd Identities

$$\sin(-\theta) = -\sin \theta \qquad \cos(-\theta) = \cos \theta \qquad \tan(-\theta) = -\tan \theta$$

$$\csc(-\theta) = -\csc \theta \qquad \sec(-\theta) = \sec \theta \qquad \cot(-\theta) = -\cot \theta$$

This list of identities comprises what we shall refer to as the **basic trigonometric identities.** These identities should not merely be memorized, but should be *known* (just as you know your name rather than have it memorized). In fact, minor variations of a basic identity are often used. For example, we might want to use

$$\sin^2 \theta = 1 - \cos^2 \theta \quad \text{or} \quad \cos^2 \theta = 1 - \sin^2 \theta$$

instead of $\sin^2 \theta + \cos^2 \theta = 1$. For this reason, among others, you need to know these relationships and be comfortable with variations of them.

1 Use Algebra to Simplify Trigonometric Expressions

The ability to use algebra to manipulate trigonometric expressions is a key skill that one must have to establish identities. Some of the techniques that are used in establishing identities are multiplying by a "well-chosen 1," writing a trigonometric expression over a common denominator, rewriting a trigonometric expression in terms of sine and cosine only, and factoring.

EXAMPLE 1 **Using Algebraic Techniques to Simplify Trigonometric Expressions**

(a) Simplify $\dfrac{\cot\theta}{\csc\theta}$ by rewriting each trigonometric function in terms of sine and cosine functions.

(b) Show that $\dfrac{\cos\theta}{1+\sin\theta} = \dfrac{1-\sin\theta}{\cos\theta}$ by multiplying the numerator and denominator by $1-\sin\theta$.

(c) Simplify $\dfrac{1+\sin u}{\sin u} + \dfrac{\cot u - \cos u}{\cos u}$ by rewriting the expression over a common denominator.

(d) Simplify $\dfrac{\sin^2 v - 1}{\tan v \sin v - \tan v}$ by factoring.

Solution

(a) $\dfrac{\cot\theta}{\csc\theta} = \dfrac{\dfrac{\cos\theta}{\sin\theta}}{\dfrac{1}{\sin\theta}} = \dfrac{\cos\theta}{\sin\theta} \cdot \dfrac{\sin\theta}{1} = \cos\theta$

(b) $\dfrac{\cos\theta}{1+\sin\theta} = \dfrac{\cos\theta}{1+\sin\theta} \cdot \dfrac{1-\sin\theta}{1-\sin\theta} = \dfrac{\cos\theta(1-\sin\theta)}{1-\sin^2\theta}$

  Multiply by a well-chosen 1: $\dfrac{1-\sin\theta}{1-\sin\theta}$.

  $= \dfrac{\cos\theta(1-\sin\theta)}{\cos^2\theta} = \dfrac{1-\sin\theta}{\cos\theta}$

(c) $\dfrac{1+\sin u}{\sin u} + \dfrac{\cot u - \cos u}{\cos u} = \dfrac{1+\sin u}{\sin u} \cdot \dfrac{\cos u}{\cos u} + \dfrac{\cot u - \cos u}{\cos u} \cdot \dfrac{\sin u}{\sin u}$

  $= \dfrac{\cos u + \sin u \cos u + \cot u \sin u - \cos u \sin u}{\sin u \cos u} = \dfrac{\cos u + \dfrac{\cos u}{\sin u} \cdot \sin u}{\sin u \cos u}$

  $\cot u = \dfrac{\cos u}{\sin u}$

  $= \dfrac{\cos u + \cos u}{\sin u \cos u} = \dfrac{2\cos u}{\sin u \cos u} = \dfrac{2}{\sin u}$

(d) $\dfrac{\sin^2 v - 1}{\tan v \sin v - \tan v} = \dfrac{(\sin v + 1)(\sin v - 1)}{\tan v(\sin v - 1)} = \dfrac{\sin v + 1}{\tan v}$

♩

Now Work PROBLEMS 9, 11, AND 13

2 Establish Identities

In the examples that follow, the directions will read "Establish the identity. . . . " As you will see, this is accomplished by starting with one side of the given equation (usually the one containing the more complicated expression) and, using appropriate basic identities and algebraic manipulations, arriving at the other side. The selection of appropriate basic identities to obtain the desired result is learned only through experience and lots of practice.

EXAMPLE 2 **Establishing an Identity**

Establish the identity: $\csc\theta \cdot \tan\theta = \sec\theta$

Solution

NOTE A graphing utility can be used to provide evidence of an identity. For example, if we graph $Y_1 = \csc \theta \cdot \tan \theta$ and $Y_2 = \sec \theta$, the graphs appear to be the same. This provides evidence that $Y_1 = Y_2$. However, it does not prove their equality. A graphing utility cannot be used to establish an identity—identities must be established algebraically. ∎

Start with the left side, because it contains the more complicated expression, and apply a reciprocal identity and a quotient identity.

$$\csc \theta \cdot \tan \theta = \frac{1}{\sin \theta} \cdot \frac{\sin \theta}{\cos \theta} = \frac{1}{\cos \theta} = \sec \theta$$

Having arrived at the right side, the identity is established.

Now Work PROBLEM 19

EXAMPLE 3 | **Establishing an Identity**

Establish the identity: $\sin^2(-\theta) + \cos^2(-\theta) = 1$

Solution Begin with the left side and, because the arguments are $-\theta$, apply Even–Odd Identities.

$$\begin{aligned}
\sin^2(-\theta) + \cos^2(-\theta) &= [\sin(-\theta)]^2 + [\cos(-\theta)]^2 \\
&= (-\sin \theta)^2 + (\cos \theta)^2 && \text{Even–Odd Identities} \\
&= (\sin \theta)^2 + (\cos \theta)^2 \\
&= 1 && \text{Pythagorean Identity}
\end{aligned}$$

EXAMPLE 4 | **Establishing an Identity**

Establish the identity: $\dfrac{\sin^2(-\theta) - \cos^2(-\theta)}{\sin(-\theta) - \cos(-\theta)} = \cos \theta - \sin \theta$

Solution We begin with two observations: The left side contains the more complicated expression. Also, the left side contains expressions with the argument $-\theta$, whereas the right side contains expressions with the argument θ. We decide, therefore, to start with the left side and apply Even–Odd Identities.

$$\begin{aligned}
\frac{\sin^2(-\theta) - \cos^2(-\theta)}{\sin(-\theta) - \cos(-\theta)} &= \frac{[\sin(-\theta)]^2 - [\cos(-\theta)]^2}{\sin(-\theta) - \cos(-\theta)} \\
&= \frac{(-\sin \theta)^2 - (\cos \theta)^2}{-\sin \theta - \cos \theta} && \text{Even–Odd Identities} \\
&= \frac{(\sin \theta)^2 - (\cos \theta)^2}{-\sin \theta - \cos \theta} && \text{Simplify.} \\
&= \frac{(\sin \theta - \cos \theta)(\sin \theta + \cos \theta)}{-(\sin \theta + \cos \theta)} && \text{Factor.} \\
&= \cos \theta - \sin \theta && \text{Cancel and simplify.}
\end{aligned}$$

EXAMPLE 5 | **Establishing an Identity**

Establish the identity: $\dfrac{1 + \tan u}{1 + \cot u} = \tan u$

Solution

$$\begin{aligned}
\frac{1 + \tan u}{1 + \cot u} &= \frac{1 + \tan u}{1 + \dfrac{1}{\tan u}} = \frac{1 + \tan u}{\dfrac{\tan u + 1}{\tan u}} \\
&= \frac{\tan u(1 + \tan u)}{\tan u + 1} = \tan u
\end{aligned}$$

Now Work PROBLEMS 23 AND 27

When sums or differences of quotients appear, it is usually best to rewrite them as a single quotient, especially if the other side of the identity consists of only one term.

EXAMPLE 6

Establishing an Identity

Establish the identity: $\dfrac{\sin \theta}{1 + \cos \theta} + \dfrac{1 + \cos \theta}{\sin \theta} = 2 \csc \theta$

Solution

The left side is more complicated, so we start with it and proceed to add.

$$\frac{\sin \theta}{1 + \cos \theta} + \frac{1 + \cos \theta}{\sin \theta} = \frac{\sin^2 \theta + (1 + \cos \theta)^2}{(1 + \cos \theta)(\sin \theta)} \qquad \text{Add the quotients.}$$

$$= \frac{\sin^2 \theta + 1 + 2 \cos \theta + \cos^2 \theta}{(1 + \cos \theta)(\sin \theta)} \qquad \text{Remove parentheses in the numerator.}$$

$$= \frac{(\sin^2 \theta + \cos^2 \theta) + 1 + 2 \cos \theta}{(1 + \cos \theta)(\sin \theta)} \qquad \text{Regroup.}$$

$$= \frac{2 + 2 \cos \theta}{(1 + \cos \theta)(\sin \theta)} \qquad \text{Pythagorean Identity}$$

$$= \frac{2(1 + \cos \theta)}{(1 + \cos \theta)(\sin \theta)} \qquad \text{Factor and cancel.}$$

$$= \frac{2}{\sin \theta}$$

$$= 2 \csc \theta \qquad \text{Reciprocal Identity}$$

⌐**Now Work** PROBLEM 49

Sometimes it helps to write one side in terms of sine and cosine functions only.

EXAMPLE 7

Establishing an Identity

Establish the identity: $\dfrac{\tan v + \cot v}{\sec v \csc v} = 1$

Solution

$$\frac{\tan v + \cot v}{\sec v \csc v} = \frac{\dfrac{\sin v}{\cos v} + \dfrac{\cos v}{\sin v}}{\dfrac{1}{\cos v} \cdot \dfrac{1}{\sin v}} = \frac{\dfrac{\sin^2 v + \cos^2 v}{\cos v \sin v}}{\dfrac{1}{\cos v \sin v}}$$

$$\underset{\substack{\text{Change to sines} \\ \text{and cosines.}}}{\uparrow} \qquad \underset{\substack{\text{Add the quotients} \\ \text{in the numerator.}}}{\uparrow}$$

$$= \frac{1}{\cos v \sin v} \cdot \frac{\cos v \sin v}{1} = 1$$

$$\underset{\substack{\text{Divide the quotients;} \\ \sin^2 v + \cos^2 v = 1.}}{\uparrow}$$

⌐**Now Work** PROBLEM 69

Sometimes, multiplying the numerator and denominator by an appropriate factor will result in a simplification.

EXAMPLE 8   **Establishing an Identity**

Establish the identity: $\dfrac{1 - \sin \theta}{\cos \theta} = \dfrac{\cos \theta}{1 + \sin \theta}$

Solution   Start with the left side and multiply the numerator and the denominator by $1 + \sin \theta$. (Alternatively, we could multiply the numerator and denominator of the right side by $1 - \sin \theta$.)

$$\frac{1 - \sin \theta}{\cos \theta} = \frac{1 - \sin \theta}{\cos \theta} \cdot \frac{1 + \sin \theta}{1 + \sin \theta} \qquad \text{Multiply the numerator and denominator by } 1 + \sin \theta.$$

$$= \frac{1 - \sin^2 \theta}{\cos \theta (1 + \sin \theta)}$$

$$= \frac{\cos^2 \theta}{\cos \theta (1 + \sin \theta)} \qquad 1 - \sin^2 \theta = \cos^2 \theta$$

$$= \frac{\cos \theta}{1 + \sin \theta} \qquad \text{Cancel.}$$

Now Work   PROBLEM 53

Although a lot of practice is the only real way to learn how to establish identities, the following guidelines should prove helpful.

WARNING Be careful not to handle identities to be established as if they were conditional equations. You cannot establish an identity by such methods as adding the same expression to each side and obtaining a true statement. This practice is not allowed, because the original statement is precisely the one that you are trying to establish. You do not know until it has been established that it is, in fact, true. ∎

Guidelines for Establishing Identities

1. It is almost always preferable to start with the side containing the more complicated expression.
2. Rewrite sums or differences of quotients as a single quotient.
3. Sometimes rewriting one side in terms of sine and cosine functions only will help.
4. Always keep your goal in mind. As you manipulate one side of the expression, you must keep in mind the form of the expression on the other side.

7.4 Assess Your Understanding

'Are You Prepared?' *Answers are given at the end of these exercises. If you get a wrong answer, read the pages listed in* red.

1. **True or False** $\sin^2 \theta = 1 - \cos^2 \theta$. (p. 385)

2. **True or False** $\sin(-\theta) + \cos(-\theta) = \cos \theta - \sin \theta$. (p. 389)

Concepts and Vocabulary

3. Suppose that f and g are two functions with the same domain. If $f(x) = g(x)$ for every x in the domain, the equation is called a(n) _____. Otherwise, it is called a(n) _____ equation.

4. $\tan^2 \theta - \sec^2 \theta =$ _____.

5. $\cos(-\theta) - \cos \theta =$ _____.

6. **True or False** $\sin(-\theta) + \sin \theta = 0$ for any value of θ.

7. **True or False**   In establishing an identity, it is often easiest to just multiply both sides by a well-chosen nonzero expression involving the variable.

8. **True or False** $\tan \theta \cdot \cos \theta = \sin \theta$ for any $\theta \neq (2k + 1)\dfrac{\pi}{2}$.

Skill Building

In Problems 9–18, simplify each trigonometric expression by following the indicated direction.

9. Rewrite in terms of sine and cosine functions:

$\tan \theta \cdot \csc \theta$.

10. Rewrite in terms of sine and cosine functions:

$\cot \theta \cdot \sec \theta$.

11. Multiply $\dfrac{\cos \theta}{1 - \sin \theta}$ by $\dfrac{1 + \sin \theta}{1 + \sin \theta}$.

12. Multiply $\dfrac{\sin \theta}{1 + \cos \theta}$ by $\dfrac{1 - \cos \theta}{1 - \cos \theta}$.

13. Rewrite over a common denominator:

$$\frac{\sin\theta + \cos\theta}{\cos\theta} + \frac{\cos\theta - \sin\theta}{\sin\theta}$$

14. Rewrite over a common denominator:

$$\frac{1}{1 - \cos v} + \frac{1}{1 + \cos v}$$

15. Multiply and simplify: $\dfrac{(\sin\theta + \cos\theta)(\sin\theta + \cos\theta) - 1}{\sin\theta\cos\theta}$

16. Multiply and simplify: $\dfrac{(\tan\theta + 1)(\tan\theta + 1) - \sec^2\theta}{\tan\theta}$

17. Factor and simplify: $\dfrac{3\sin^2\theta + 4\sin\theta + 1}{\sin^2\theta + 2\sin\theta + 1}$

18. Factor and simplify: $\dfrac{\cos^2\theta - 1}{\cos^2\theta - \cos\theta}$

In Problems 19–98, establish each identity.

19. $\csc\theta \cdot \cos\theta = \cot\theta$

20. $\sec\theta \cdot \sin\theta = \tan\theta$

21. $1 + \tan^2(-\theta) = \sec^2\theta$

22. $1 + \cot^2(-\theta) = \csc^2\theta$

23. $\cos\theta(\tan\theta + \cot\theta) = \csc\theta$

24. $\sin\theta(\cot\theta + \tan\theta) = \sec\theta$

25. $\tan u \cot u - \cos^2 u = \sin^2 u$

26. $\sin u \csc u - \cos^2 u = \sin^2 u$

27. $(\sec\theta - 1)(\sec\theta + 1) = \tan^2\theta$

28. $(\csc\theta - 1)(\csc\theta + 1) = \cot^2\theta$

29. $(\sec\theta + \tan\theta)(\sec\theta - \tan\theta) = 1$

30. $(\csc\theta + \cot\theta)(\csc\theta - \cot\theta) = 1$

31. $\cos^2\theta(1 + \tan^2\theta) = 1$

32. $(1 - \cos^2\theta)(1 + \cot^2\theta) = 1$

33. $(\sin\theta + \cos\theta)^2 + (\sin\theta - \cos\theta)^2 = 2$

34. $\tan^2\theta\cos^2\theta + \cot^2\theta\sin^2\theta = 1$

35. $\sec^4\theta - \sec^2\theta = \tan^4\theta + \tan^2\theta$

36. $\csc^4\theta - \csc^2\theta = \cot^4\theta + \cot^2\theta$

37. $\sec u - \tan u = \dfrac{\cos u}{1 + \sin u}$

38. $\csc u - \cot u = \dfrac{\sin u}{1 + \cos u}$

39. $3\sin^2\theta + 4\cos^2\theta = 3 + \cos^2\theta$

40. $9\sec^2\theta - 5\tan^2\theta = 5 + 4\sec^2\theta$

41. $1 - \dfrac{\cos^2\theta}{1 + \sin\theta} = \sin\theta$

42. $1 - \dfrac{\sin^2\theta}{1 - \cos\theta} = -\cos\theta$

43. $\dfrac{1 + \tan v}{1 - \tan v} = \dfrac{\cot v + 1}{\cot v - 1}$

44. $\dfrac{\csc v - 1}{\csc v + 1} = \dfrac{1 - \sin v}{1 + \sin v}$

45. $\dfrac{\sec\theta}{\csc\theta} + \dfrac{\sin\theta}{\cos\theta} = 2\tan\theta$

46. $\dfrac{\csc\theta - 1}{\cot\theta} = \dfrac{\cot\theta}{\csc\theta + 1}$

47. $\dfrac{1 + \sin\theta}{1 - \sin\theta} = \dfrac{\csc\theta + 1}{\csc\theta - 1}$

48. $\dfrac{\cos\theta + 1}{\cos\theta - 1} = \dfrac{1 + \sec\theta}{1 - \sec\theta}$

49. $\dfrac{1 - \sin v}{\cos v} + \dfrac{\cos v}{1 - \sin v} = 2\sec v$

50. $\dfrac{\cos v}{1 + \sin v} + \dfrac{1 + \sin v}{\cos v} = 2\sec v$

51. $\dfrac{\sin\theta}{\sin\theta - \cos\theta} = \dfrac{1}{1 - \cot\theta}$

52. $1 - \dfrac{\sin^2\theta}{1 + \cos\theta} = \cos\theta$

53. $\dfrac{1 - \sin\theta}{1 + \sin\theta} = (\sec\theta - \tan\theta)^2$

54. $\dfrac{1 - \cos\theta}{1 + \cos\theta} = (\csc\theta - \cot\theta)^2$

55. $\dfrac{\cos\theta}{1 - \tan\theta} + \dfrac{\sin\theta}{1 - \cot\theta} = \sin\theta + \cos\theta$

56. $\dfrac{\cot\theta}{1 - \tan\theta} + \dfrac{\tan\theta}{1 - \cot\theta} = 1 + \tan\theta + \cot\theta$

57. $\tan\theta + \dfrac{\cos\theta}{1 + \sin\theta} = \sec\theta$

58. $\dfrac{\sin\theta\cos\theta}{\cos^2\theta - \sin^2\theta} = \dfrac{\tan\theta}{1 - \tan^2\theta}$

59. $\dfrac{\tan\theta + \sec\theta - 1}{\tan\theta - \sec\theta + 1} = \tan\theta + \sec\theta$

60. $\dfrac{\sin\theta - \cos\theta + 1}{\sin\theta + \cos\theta - 1} = \dfrac{\sin\theta + 1}{\cos\theta}$

61. $\dfrac{\tan\theta - \cot\theta}{\tan\theta + \cot\theta} = \sin^2\theta - \cos^2\theta$

62. $\dfrac{\sec\theta - \cos\theta}{\sec\theta + \cos\theta} = \dfrac{\sin^2\theta}{1 + \cos^2\theta}$

63. $\dfrac{\tan u - \cot u}{\tan u + \cot u} + 1 = 2\sin^2 u$

64. $\dfrac{\tan u - \cot u}{\tan u + \cot u} + 2\cos^2 u = 1$

65. $\dfrac{\sec\theta + \tan\theta}{\cot\theta + \cos\theta} = \tan\theta\sec\theta$

66. $\dfrac{\sec\theta}{1 + \sec\theta} = \dfrac{1 - \cos\theta}{\sin^2\theta}$

67. $\dfrac{1 - \tan^2\theta}{1 + \tan^2\theta} + 1 = 2\cos^2\theta$

68. $\dfrac{1 - \cot^2\theta}{1 + \cot^2\theta} + 2\cos^2\theta = 1$

69. $\dfrac{\sec\theta - \csc\theta}{\sec\theta\csc\theta} = \sin\theta - \cos\theta$

70. $\dfrac{\sin^2\theta - \tan\theta}{\cos^2\theta - \cot\theta} = \tan^2\theta$

71. $\sec\theta - \cos\theta = \sin\theta\tan\theta$

72. $\tan\theta + \cot\theta = \sec\theta\csc\theta$

73. $\dfrac{1}{1 - \sin\theta} + \dfrac{1}{1 + \sin\theta} = 2\sec^2\theta$

74. $\dfrac{1 + \sin\theta}{1 - \sin\theta} - \dfrac{1 - \sin\theta}{1 + \sin\theta} = 4\tan\theta\sec\theta$

75. $\dfrac{\sec\theta}{1 - \sin\theta} = \dfrac{1 + \sin\theta}{\cos^3\theta}$

76. $\dfrac{1 + \sin\theta}{1 - \sin\theta} = (\sec\theta + \tan\theta)^2$

77. $\dfrac{(\sec v - \tan v)^2 + 1}{\csc v(\sec v - \tan v)} = 2\tan v$

78. $\dfrac{\sec^2 v - \tan^2 v + \tan v}{\sec v} = \sin v + \cos v$

79. $\dfrac{\sin \theta + \cos \theta}{\cos \theta} - \dfrac{\sin \theta - \cos \theta}{\sin \theta} = \sec \theta \csc \theta$

80. $\dfrac{\sin \theta + \cos \theta}{\sin \theta} - \dfrac{\cos \theta - \sin \theta}{\cos \theta} = \sec \theta \csc \theta$

81. $\dfrac{\sin^3 \theta + \cos^3 \theta}{\sin \theta + \cos \theta} = 1 - \sin \theta \cos \theta$

82. $\dfrac{\sin^3 \theta + \cos^3 \theta}{1 - 2\cos^2 \theta} = \dfrac{\sec \theta - \sin \theta}{\tan \theta - 1}$

83. $\dfrac{\cos^2 \theta - \sin^2 \theta}{1 - \tan^2 \theta} = \cos^2 \theta$

84. $\dfrac{\cos \theta + \sin \theta - \sin^3 \theta}{\sin \theta} = \cot \theta + \cos^2 \theta$

85. $\dfrac{(2\cos^2 \theta - 1)^2}{\cos^4 \theta - \sin^4 \theta} = 1 - 2\sin^2 \theta$

86. $\dfrac{1 - 2\cos^2 \theta}{\sin \theta \cos \theta} = \tan \theta - \cot \theta$

87. $\dfrac{1 + \sin \theta + \cos \theta}{1 + \sin \theta - \cos \theta} = \dfrac{1 + \cos \theta}{\sin \theta}$

88. $\dfrac{1 + \cos \theta + \sin \theta}{1 + \cos \theta - \sin \theta} = \sec \theta + \tan \theta$

89. $(a \sin \theta + b \cos \theta)^2 + (a \cos \theta - b \sin \theta)^2 = a^2 + b^2$

90. $(2a \sin \theta \cos \theta)^2 + a^2(\cos^2 \theta - \sin^2 \theta)^2 = a^2$

91. $\dfrac{\tan \alpha + \tan \beta}{\cot \alpha + \cot \beta} = \tan \alpha \tan \beta$

92. $(\tan \alpha + \tan \beta)(1 - \cot \alpha \cot \beta) + (\cot \alpha + \cot \beta)(1 - \tan \alpha \tan \beta) = 0$

93. $(\sin \alpha + \cos \beta)^2 + (\cos \beta + \sin \alpha)(\cos \beta - \sin \alpha) = 2 \cos \beta(\sin \alpha + \cos \beta)$

94. $(\sin \alpha - \cos \beta)^2 + (\cos \beta + \sin \alpha)(\cos \beta - \sin \alpha) = -2 \cos \beta(\sin \alpha - \cos \beta)$

95. $\ln |\sec \theta| = -\ln |\cos \theta|$

96. $\ln |\tan \theta| = \ln |\sin \theta| - \ln |\cos \theta|$

97. $\ln |1 + \cos \theta| + \ln |1 - \cos \theta| = 2 \ln |\sin \theta|$

98. $\ln |\sec \theta + \tan \theta| + \ln |\sec \theta - \tan \theta| = 0$

In Problems 99–102, show that the functions f and g are identically equal.

99. $f(x) = \sin x \cdot \tan x \qquad g(x) = \sec x - \cos x$

100. $f(x) = \cos x \cdot \cot x \qquad g(x) = \csc x - \sin x$

101. $f(\theta) = \dfrac{1 - \sin \theta}{\cos \theta} - \dfrac{\cos \theta}{1 + \sin \theta} \qquad g(\theta) = 0$

102. $f(\theta) = \tan \theta + \sec \theta \qquad g(\theta) = \dfrac{\cos \theta}{1 - \sin \theta}$

Applications and Extensions

103. Searchlights A searchlight at the grand opening of a new car dealership casts a spot of light on a wall located 75 meters from the searchlight. The acceleration $\ddot{r}$ of the spot of light is found to be $\ddot{r} = 1200 \sec \theta(2 \sec^2 \theta - 1)$. Show that this is equivalent to $\ddot{r} = 1200 \left(\dfrac{1 + \sin^2 \theta}{\cos^3 \theta} \right)$.

Source: Adapted from Hibbeler, *Engineering Mechanics: Dynamics,* 10th ed. © 2004

104. Optical Measurement Optical methods of measurement often rely on the interference of two light waves. If two light waves, identical except for a phase lag, are mixed together, the resulting intensity, or irradiance, is given by $I_t = 4A^2 \dfrac{(\csc \theta - 1)(\sec \theta + \tan \theta)}{\csc \theta \sec \theta}$. Show that this is equivalent to $I_t = (2A \cos \theta)^2$.

Source: Experimental Techniques, July/August 2002

Explaining Concepts: Discussion and Writing

105. Write a few paragraphs outlining your strategy for establishing identities.

106. Write down the three Pythagorean Identities.

107. Why do you think it is usually preferable to start with the side containing the more complicated expression when establishing an identity?

108. Make up an identity that is not a Fundamental Identity.

'Are You Prepared?' Answers

1. True   **2.** True

7.5 Sum and Difference Formulas

PREPARING FOR THIS SECTION *Before getting started, review the following:*

- Distance Formula (Section 1.1, p. 3)
- Values of the Trigonometric Functions (Section 6.2, pp. 365–374)

- Finding Exact Values Given the Value of a Trigonometric Function and the Quadrant of the Angle (Section 6.3, pp. 386–388)

Now Work the 'Are You Prepared?' problems on page 481.

OBJECTIVES   **1** Use Sum and Difference Formulas to Find Exact Values (p. 473)
          2 Use Sum and Difference Formulas to Establish Identities (p. 474)
          3 Use Sum and Difference Formulas Involving Inverse Trigonometric Functions (p. 478)
          4 Solve Trigonometric Equations Linear in Sine and Cosine (p. 479)

In this section, we continue our derivation of trigonometric identities by obtaining formulas that involve the sum or difference of two angles, such as $\cos(\alpha + \beta)$, $\cos(\alpha - \beta)$, or $\sin(\alpha + \beta)$. These formulas are referred to as the **sum and difference formulas.** We begin with the formulas for $\cos(\alpha + \beta)$ and $\cos(\alpha - \beta)$.

THEOREM   **Sum and Difference Formulas for the Cosine Function**

$$\cos(\alpha + \beta) = \cos \alpha \cos \beta - \sin \alpha \sin \beta \qquad \textbf{(1)}$$

$$\cos(\alpha - \beta) = \cos \alpha \cos \beta + \sin \alpha \sin \beta \qquad \textbf{(2)}$$

In Words
Formula (1) states that the cosine of the sum of two angles equals the cosine of the first angle times the cosine of the second angle minus the sine of the first angle times the sine of the second angle.

Proof   We will prove formula (2) first. Although this formula is true for all numbers α and β, we shall assume in our proof that $0 < \beta < \alpha < 2\pi$. We begin with the unit circle and place the angles α and β in standard position, as shown in Figure 26(a). The point P_1 lies on the terminal side of β, so its coordinates are $(\cos \beta, \sin \beta)$; and the point P_2 lies on the terminal side of α, so its coordinates are $(\cos \alpha, \sin \alpha)$.

Figure 26

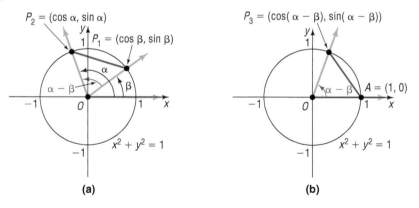

(a)   (b)

Now place the angle $\alpha - \beta$ in standard position, as shown in Figure 26(b). The point A has coordinates $(1, 0)$, and the point P_3 is on the terminal side of the angle $\alpha - \beta$, so its coordinates are $(\cos(\alpha - \beta), \sin(\alpha - \beta))$.

Looking at triangle OP_1P_2 in Figure 26(a) and triangle OAP_3 in Figure 26(b), we see that these triangles are congruent. (Do you see why? We have SAS: two sides and the included angle, $\alpha - \beta$, are equal.) As a result, the unknown side of each triangle must be equal; that is,

$$d(A, P_3) = d(P_1, P_2)$$

Using the distance formula, we find that

$$\sqrt{[\cos(\alpha - \beta) - 1]^2 + [\sin(\alpha - \beta) - 0]^2} = \sqrt{(\cos\alpha - \cos\beta)^2 + (\sin\alpha - \sin\beta)^2} \quad d(A, P_3) = d(P_1, P_2)$$

$$[\cos(\alpha - \beta) - 1]^2 + \sin^2(\alpha - \beta) = (\cos\alpha - \cos\beta)^2 + (\sin\alpha - \sin\beta)^2 \quad \text{Square both sides.}$$

$$\cos^2(\alpha - \beta) - 2\cos(\alpha - \beta) + 1 + \sin^2(\alpha - \beta) = \cos^2\alpha - 2\cos\alpha\cos\beta + \cos^2\beta \quad \text{Multiply out the squared terms.}$$
$$+ \sin^2\alpha - 2\sin\alpha\sin\beta + \sin^2\beta$$

$$2 - 2\cos(\alpha - \beta) = 2 - 2\cos\alpha\cos\beta - 2\sin\alpha\sin\beta \quad \text{Apply a Pythagorean Identity (3 times).}$$

$$-2\cos(\alpha - \beta) = -2\cos\alpha\cos\beta - 2\sin\alpha\sin\beta \quad \text{Subtract 2 from each side.}$$

$$\cos(\alpha - \beta) = \cos\alpha\cos\beta + \sin\alpha\sin\beta \quad \text{Divide each side by } -2.$$

This is formula (2). ∎

The proof of formula (1) follows from formula (2) and the Even–Odd Identities. Use the fact that $\alpha + \beta = \alpha - (-\beta)$. Then

$$\cos(\alpha + \beta) = \cos[\alpha - (-\beta)]$$

$$= \cos\alpha\cos(-\beta) + \sin\alpha\sin(-\beta) \quad \text{Use formula (2).}$$

$$= \cos\alpha\cos\beta - \sin\alpha\sin\beta \quad \text{Even–Odd Identities}$$

1 Use Sum and Difference Formulas to Find Exact Values

One use of formulas (1) and (2) is to obtain the exact value of the cosine of an angle that can be expressed as the sum or difference of angles whose sine and cosine are known exactly.

EXAMPLE 1 **Using the Sum Formula to Find an Exact Value**

Find the exact value of $\cos 75°$.

Solution Since $75° = 45° + 30°$, use formula (1) to obtain

$$\cos 75° = \cos(45° + 30°) = \cos 45° \cos 30° - \sin 45° \sin 30°$$
$$\underset{\text{Formula (1)}}{\uparrow}$$

$$= \frac{\sqrt{2}}{2} \cdot \frac{\sqrt{3}}{2} - \frac{\sqrt{2}}{2} \cdot \frac{1}{2} = \frac{1}{4}\left(\sqrt{6} - \sqrt{2}\right)$$

EXAMPLE 2 **Using the Difference Formula to Find an Exact Value**

Find the exact value of $\cos\dfrac{\pi}{12}$.

Solution
$$\cos\frac{\pi}{12} = \cos\left(\frac{3\pi}{12} - \frac{2\pi}{12}\right) = \cos\left(\frac{\pi}{4} - \frac{\pi}{6}\right)$$

$$= \cos\frac{\pi}{4}\cos\frac{\pi}{6} + \sin\frac{\pi}{4}\sin\frac{\pi}{6} \quad \text{Use formula (2).}$$

$$= \frac{\sqrt{2}}{2} \cdot \frac{\sqrt{3}}{2} + \frac{\sqrt{2}}{2} \cdot \frac{1}{2} = \frac{1}{4}\left(\sqrt{6} + \sqrt{2}\right)$$

Now Work PROBLEM 13

2 Use Sum and Difference Formulas to Establish Identities

Another use of formulas (1) and (2) is to establish other identities. Two important identities we conjectured earlier in Section 6.4 are given next.

$$\cos\left(\frac{\pi}{2} - \theta\right) = \sin\theta \qquad \textbf{(3a)}$$

$$\sin\left(\frac{\pi}{2} - \theta\right) = \cos\theta \qquad \textbf{(3b)}$$

Proof To prove formula (3a), use the formula for $\cos(\alpha - \beta)$ with $\alpha = \dfrac{\pi}{2}$ and $\beta = \theta$.

$$\cos\left(\frac{\pi}{2} - \theta\right) = \cos\frac{\pi}{2}\cos\theta + \sin\frac{\pi}{2}\sin\theta$$

$$= 0 \cdot \cos\theta + 1 \cdot \sin\theta$$

$$= \sin\theta$$

To prove formula (3b), make use of the identity (3a) just established.

$$\sin\left(\frac{\pi}{2} - \theta\right) = \cos\left[\frac{\pi}{2} - \left(\frac{\pi}{2} - \theta\right)\right] = \cos\theta$$

$\uparrow$
Use (3a).

∎

Also, since

$$\cos\left(\frac{\pi}{2} - \theta\right) = \cos\left[-\left(\theta - \frac{\pi}{2}\right)\right] = \cos\left(\theta - \frac{\pi}{2}\right)$$

$\uparrow$
Even Property of Cosine

and since

$$\cos\left(\frac{\pi}{2} - \theta\right) = \sin\theta$$

$\uparrow$
3(a)

it follows that $\cos\left(\theta - \dfrac{\pi}{2}\right) = \sin\theta$. The graphs of $y = \cos\left(\theta - \dfrac{\pi}{2}\right)$ and $y = \sin\theta$ are identical.

Having established the identities in formulas (3a) and (3b), we now can derive the sum and difference formulas for $\sin(\alpha + \beta)$ and $\sin(\alpha - \beta)$.

Proof $\sin(\alpha + \beta) = \cos\left[\dfrac{\pi}{2} - (\alpha + \beta)\right]$ Formula (3a)

$$= \cos\left[\left(\frac{\pi}{2} - \alpha\right) - \beta\right]$$

$$= \cos\left(\frac{\pi}{2} - \alpha\right)\cos\beta + \sin\left(\frac{\pi}{2} - \alpha\right)\sin\beta \quad \text{Formula (2)}$$

$$= \sin\alpha\cos\beta + \cos\alpha\sin\beta \qquad \text{Formulas (3a) and (3b)}$$

$\sin(\alpha - \beta) = \sin[\alpha + (-\beta)]$

$$= \sin\alpha\cos(-\beta) + \cos\alpha\sin(-\beta) \qquad \begin{array}{l}\text{Use the sum formula for}\\ \text{sine just obtained.}\end{array}$$

$$= \sin\alpha\cos\beta + \cos\alpha(-\sin\beta) \qquad \text{Even–Odd Identities}$$

$$= \sin\alpha\cos\beta - \cos\alpha\sin\beta$$

∎

THEOREM

In Words

Formula (4) states that the sine of the sum of two angles equals the sine of the first angle times the cosine of the second angle plus the cosine of the first angle times the sine of the second angle.

Sum and Difference Formulas for the Sine Function

$$\sin(\alpha + \beta) = \sin \alpha \cos \beta + \cos \alpha \sin \beta \qquad \textbf{(4)}$$

$$\sin(\alpha - \beta) = \sin \alpha \cos \beta - \cos \alpha \sin \beta \qquad \textbf{(5)}$$

EXAMPLE 3   **Using the Sum Formula to Find an Exact Value**

Find the exact value of $\sin \dfrac{7\pi}{12}$.

Solution

$$\sin \frac{7\pi}{12} = \sin\left(\frac{3\pi}{12} + \frac{4\pi}{12}\right) = \sin\left(\frac{\pi}{4} + \frac{\pi}{3}\right)$$

$$= \sin \frac{\pi}{4} \cos \frac{\pi}{3} + \cos \frac{\pi}{4} \sin \frac{\pi}{3} \qquad \text{Formula (4)}$$

$$= \frac{\sqrt{2}}{2} \cdot \frac{1}{2} + \frac{\sqrt{2}}{2} \cdot \frac{\sqrt{3}}{2} = \frac{1}{4}\left(\sqrt{2} + \sqrt{6}\right)$$

Now Work PROBLEM 19

EXAMPLE 4   **Using the Difference Formula to Find an Exact Value**

Find the exact value of $\sin 80° \cos 20° - \cos 80° \sin 20°$.

Solution

The form of the expression $\sin 80° \cos 20° - \cos 80° \sin 20°$ is that of the right side of formula (5) for $\sin(\alpha - \beta)$ with $\alpha = 80°$ and $\beta = 20°$. That is,

$$\sin 80° \cos 20° - \cos 80° \sin 20° = \sin(80° - 20°) = \sin 60° = \frac{\sqrt{3}}{2}$$

Now Work PROBLEMS 25 AND 29

EXAMPLE 5   **Finding Exact Values**

If it is known that $\sin \alpha = \dfrac{4}{5}, \dfrac{\pi}{2} < \alpha < \pi$, and that $\sin \beta = -\dfrac{2}{\sqrt{5}} = -\dfrac{2\sqrt{5}}{5}$, $\pi < \beta < \dfrac{3\pi}{2}$, find the exact value of

(a) $\cos \alpha$ (b) $\cos \beta$ (c) $\cos(\alpha + \beta)$ (d) $\sin(\alpha + \beta)$

Figure 27

$\sin \alpha = \dfrac{4}{5}, \dfrac{\pi}{2} < \alpha < \pi$

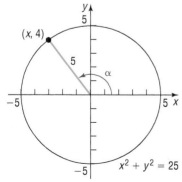

$x^2 + y^2 = 25$

Solution

(a) Since $\sin \alpha = \dfrac{4}{5} = \dfrac{y}{r}$ and $\dfrac{\pi}{2} < \alpha < \pi$, let $y = 4$ and $r = 5$ and place α in quadrant II. The point $P = (x, y) = (x, 4), x < 0$, is on a circle of radius 5, $x^2 + y^2 = 25$. See Figure 27. Then

$$x^2 + y^2 = 25$$
$$x^2 + 16 = 25 \qquad y = 4$$
$$x^2 = 25 - 16 = 9$$
$$x = -3 \qquad x < 0$$

Then

$$\cos \alpha = \frac{x}{r} = -\frac{3}{5}$$

Alternatively, we can find $\cos \alpha$ using identities, as follows:

$$\cos \alpha = -\sqrt{1 - \sin^2 \alpha} = -\sqrt{1 - \frac{16}{25}} = -\sqrt{\frac{9}{25}} = -\frac{3}{5}$$

↑ α in quadrant II,
$\cos \alpha < 0$

Figure 28

$\sin \beta = \dfrac{-2}{\sqrt{5}}, \pi < \beta < \dfrac{3\pi}{2}$

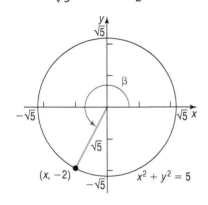

(b) Since $\sin \beta = \dfrac{-2}{\sqrt{5}} = \dfrac{y}{r}$ and $\pi < \beta < \dfrac{3\pi}{2}$, let $y = -2$ and $r = \sqrt{5}$ and place β in quadrant III. The point $P = (x, y) = (x, -2), x < 0$, is on a circle of radius $\sqrt{5}, x^2 + y^2 = 5$. See Figure 28. Then

$$\begin{aligned} x^2 + y^2 &= 5 \\ x^2 + 4 &= 5 \quad y = -2 \\ x^2 &= 1 \\ x &= -1 \quad x < 0 \end{aligned}$$

Then

$$\cos \beta = \frac{x}{r} = \frac{-1}{\sqrt{5}} = -\frac{\sqrt{5}}{5}$$

Alternatively, we can find $\cos \beta$ using identities, as follows:

$$\cos \beta = -\sqrt{1 - \sin^2 \beta} = -\sqrt{1 - \frac{4}{5}} = -\sqrt{\frac{1}{5}} = -\frac{\sqrt{5}}{5}$$

(c) Using the results found in parts (a) and (b) and formula (1), we have

$$\cos(\alpha + \beta) = \cos \alpha \cos \beta - \sin \alpha \sin \beta$$

$$= -\frac{3}{5}\left(-\frac{\sqrt{5}}{5}\right) - \frac{4}{5}\left(-\frac{2\sqrt{5}}{5}\right) = \frac{11\sqrt{5}}{25}$$

(d) $\sin(\alpha + \beta) = \sin \alpha \cos \beta + \cos \alpha \sin \beta$

$$= \frac{4}{5}\left(-\frac{\sqrt{5}}{5}\right) + \left(-\frac{3}{5}\right)\left(-\frac{2\sqrt{5}}{5}\right) = \frac{2\sqrt{5}}{25}$$

⏤**Now Work** PROBLEMS 33(a), (b), AND (c)

EXAMPLE 6 | **Establishing an Identity**

Establish the identity: $\dfrac{\cos(\alpha - \beta)}{\sin \alpha \sin \beta} = \cot \alpha \cot \beta + 1$

Solution

$$\frac{\cos(\alpha - \beta)}{\sin \alpha \sin \beta} = \frac{\cos \alpha \cos \beta + \sin \alpha \sin \beta}{\sin \alpha \sin \beta}$$

$$= \frac{\cos \alpha \cos \beta}{\sin \alpha \sin \beta} + \frac{\sin \alpha \sin \beta}{\sin \alpha \sin \beta}$$

$$= \frac{\cos \alpha}{\sin \alpha} \cdot \frac{\cos \beta}{\sin \beta} + 1$$

$$= \cot \alpha \cot \beta + 1$$

⏤**Now Work** PROBLEMS 47 AND 59

Use the identity $\tan \theta = \dfrac{\sin \theta}{\cos \theta}$ and the sum formulas for $\sin(\alpha + \beta)$ and $\cos(\alpha + \beta)$ to derive a formula for $\tan(\alpha + \beta)$.

Proof $\tan(\alpha + \beta) = \dfrac{\sin(\alpha + \beta)}{\cos(\alpha + \beta)} = \dfrac{\sin \alpha \cos \beta + \cos \alpha \sin \beta}{\cos \alpha \cos \beta - \sin \alpha \sin \beta}$

Now divide the numerator and denominator by $\cos \alpha \cos \beta$.

$$\tan(\alpha + \beta) = \dfrac{\dfrac{\sin \alpha \cos \beta + \cos \alpha \sin \beta}{\cos \alpha \cos \beta}}{\dfrac{\cos \alpha \cos \beta - \sin \alpha \sin \beta}{\cos \alpha \cos \beta}} = \dfrac{\dfrac{\sin \alpha \cos \beta}{\cos \alpha \cos \beta} + \dfrac{\cos \alpha \sin \beta}{\cos \alpha \cos \beta}}{\dfrac{\cos \alpha \cos \beta}{\cos \alpha \cos \beta} - \dfrac{\sin \alpha \sin \beta}{\cos \alpha \cos \beta}}$$

$$= \dfrac{\dfrac{\sin \alpha}{\cos \alpha} + \dfrac{\sin \beta}{\cos \beta}}{1 - \dfrac{\sin \alpha}{\cos \alpha} \cdot \dfrac{\sin \beta}{\cos \beta}} = \dfrac{\tan \alpha + \tan \beta}{1 - \tan \alpha \tan \beta} \qquad\blacksquare$$

Proof   Use the sum formula for $\tan(\alpha + \beta)$ and Even–Odd Properties to get the difference formula.

$$\tan(\alpha - \beta) = \tan[\alpha + (-\beta)] = \dfrac{\tan \alpha + \tan(-\beta)}{1 - \tan \alpha \tan(-\beta)} = \dfrac{\tan \alpha - \tan \beta}{1 + \tan \alpha \tan \beta} \qquad\blacksquare$$

We have proved the following results:

THEOREM

Sum and Difference Formulas for the Tangent Function

> $$\tan(\alpha + \beta) = \dfrac{\tan \alpha + \tan \beta}{1 - \tan \alpha \tan \beta} \qquad (6)$$
>
> $$\tan(\alpha - \beta) = \dfrac{\tan \alpha - \tan \beta}{1 + \tan \alpha \tan \beta} \qquad (7)$$

In Words
Formula (6) states that the tangent of the sum of two angles equals the tangent of the first angle plus the tangent of the second angle, all divided by 1 minus their product.

━━━**Now Work** PROBLEM 33(d)

EXAMPLE 7

Establishing an Identity

Prove the identity: $\tan(\theta + \pi) = \tan \theta$

Solution $\tan(\theta + \pi) = \dfrac{\tan \theta + \tan \pi}{1 - \tan \theta \tan \pi} = \dfrac{\tan \theta + 0}{1 - \tan \theta \cdot 0} = \tan \theta$

The result obtained in Example 7 verifies that the tangent function is periodic with period π, a fact that we discussed earlier.

EXAMPLE 8

Establishing an Identity

Prove the identity: $\tan\left(\theta + \dfrac{\pi}{2}\right) = -\cot \theta$

Solution   We cannot use formula (6), since $\tan \dfrac{\pi}{2}$ is not defined. Instead, we proceed as follows:

WARNING Be careful when using formulas (6) and (7). These formulas can be used only for angles α and β for which $\tan \alpha$ and $\tan \beta$ are defined, that is, all angles except odd integer multiples of $\dfrac{\pi}{2}$.   ∎

$$\tan\left(\theta + \dfrac{\pi}{2}\right) = \dfrac{\sin\left(\theta + \dfrac{\pi}{2}\right)}{\cos\left(\theta + \dfrac{\pi}{2}\right)} = \dfrac{\sin \theta \cos \dfrac{\pi}{2} + \cos \theta \sin \dfrac{\pi}{2}}{\cos \theta \cos \dfrac{\pi}{2} - \sin \theta \sin \dfrac{\pi}{2}}$$

$$= \dfrac{(\sin \theta)(0) + (\cos \theta)(1)}{(\cos \theta)(0) - (\sin \theta)(1)} = \dfrac{\cos \theta}{-\sin \theta} = -\cot \theta$$

3 Use Sum and Difference Formulas Involving Inverse Trigonometric Functions

---

EXAMPLE 9 **Finding the Exact Value of an Expression Involving Inverse Trigonometric Functions**

Find the exact value of: $\sin\left(\cos^{-1}\dfrac{1}{2} + \sin^{-1}\dfrac{3}{5}\right)$

Solution We seek the sine of the sum of two angles, $\alpha = \cos^{-1}\dfrac{1}{2}$ and $\beta = \sin^{-1}\dfrac{3}{5}$. Then

$$\cos\alpha = \frac{1}{2} \quad 0 \le \alpha \le \pi \quad \text{and} \quad \sin\beta = \frac{3}{5} \quad -\frac{\pi}{2} \le \beta \le \frac{\pi}{2}$$

NOTE In Example 9, we could also find $\sin\alpha$ by using $\cos\alpha = \dfrac{1}{2} = \dfrac{x}{r}$, so $x = 1$ and $r = 2$. Then $y = \sqrt{3}$ and $\sin\alpha = \dfrac{y}{r} = \dfrac{\sqrt{3}}{2}$. We could find $\cos\beta$ in a similar fashion. ∎

We use Pythagorean Identities to obtain $\sin\alpha$ and $\cos\beta$. Since $\sin\alpha \ge 0$ and $\cos\beta \ge 0$ (do you know why?), we find

$$\sin\alpha = \sqrt{1 - \cos^2\alpha} = \sqrt{1 - \frac{1}{4}} = \sqrt{\frac{3}{4}} = \frac{\sqrt{3}}{2}$$

$$\cos\beta = \sqrt{1 - \sin^2\beta} = \sqrt{1 - \frac{9}{25}} = \sqrt{\frac{16}{25}} = \frac{4}{5}$$

As a result,

$$\sin\left(\cos^{-1}\frac{1}{2} + \sin^{-1}\frac{3}{5}\right) = \sin(\alpha + \beta) = \sin\alpha\cos\beta + \cos\alpha\sin\beta$$

$$= \frac{\sqrt{3}}{2}\cdot\frac{4}{5} + \frac{1}{2}\cdot\frac{3}{5} = \frac{4\sqrt{3}+3}{10}$$

╼**Now Work** PROBLEM 75

EXAMPLE 10 **Writing a Trigonometric Expression as an Algebraic Expression**

Write $\sin(\sin^{-1}u + \cos^{-1}v)$ as an algebraic expression containing u and v (that is, without any trigonometric functions). Give the restrictions on u and v.

Solution First, for $\sin^{-1}u$, we have $-1 \le u \le 1$, and for $\cos^{-1}v$, we have $-1 \le v \le 1$. Now let $\alpha = \sin^{-1}u$ and $\beta = \cos^{-1}v$. Then

$$\sin\alpha = u \quad -\frac{\pi}{2} \le \alpha \le \frac{\pi}{2} \quad -1 \le u \le 1$$

$$\cos\beta = v \quad 0 \le \beta \le \pi \quad -1 \le v \le 1$$

Since $-\dfrac{\pi}{2} \le \alpha \le \dfrac{\pi}{2}$, we know that $\cos\alpha \ge 0$. As a result,

$$\cos\alpha = \sqrt{1 - \sin^2\alpha} = \sqrt{1 - u^2}$$

Similarly, since $0 \le \beta \le \pi$, we know that $\sin\beta \ge 0$. Then

$$\sin\beta = \sqrt{1 - \cos^2\beta} = \sqrt{1 - v^2}$$

As a result,

$$\sin(\sin^{-1}u + \cos^{-1}v) = \sin(\alpha + \beta) = \sin\alpha\cos\beta + \cos\alpha\sin\beta$$

$$= uv + \sqrt{1 - u^2}\,\sqrt{1 - v^2}$$

╼**Now Work** PROBLEM 85

4 Solve Trigonometric Equations Linear in Sine and Cosine

Sometimes it is necessary to square both sides of an equation to obtain expressions that allow the use of identities. Remember, squaring both sides of an equation may introduce extraneous solutions. As a result, apparent solutions must be checked.

EXAMPLE 11   **Solving a Trigonometric Equation Linear in Sine and Cosine**

Solve the equation: $\sin \theta + \cos \theta = 1, \quad 0 \le \theta < 2\pi$

Solution A   Attempts to use available identities do not lead to equations that are easy to solve. (Try it yourself.) Given the form of this equation, we decide to square each side.

$$\sin \theta + \cos \theta = 1$$

$$(\sin \theta + \cos \theta)^2 = 1 \quad \text{Square each side.}$$

$$\sin^2 \theta + 2 \sin \theta \cos \theta + \cos^2 \theta = 1 \quad \text{Remove parentheses.}$$

$$2 \sin \theta \cos \theta = 0 \quad \sin^2 \theta + \cos^2 \theta = 1$$

$$\sin \theta \cos \theta = 0$$

Setting each factor equal to zero, we obtain

$$\sin \theta = 0 \quad \text{or} \quad \cos \theta = 0$$

The apparent solutions are

$$\theta = 0, \qquad \theta = \pi, \qquad \theta = \frac{\pi}{2}, \qquad \theta = \frac{3\pi}{2}$$

Because we squared both sides of the original equation, we must check these apparent solutions to see if any are extraneous.

$$\theta = 0: \quad \sin 0 + \cos 0 = 0 + 1 = 1 \qquad \text{A solution}$$

$$\theta = \pi: \quad \sin \pi + \cos \pi = 0 + (-1) = -1 \qquad \text{Not a solution}$$

$$\theta = \frac{\pi}{2}: \quad \sin \frac{\pi}{2} + \cos \frac{\pi}{2} = 1 + 0 = 1 \qquad \text{A solution}$$

$$\theta = \frac{3\pi}{2}: \quad \sin \frac{3\pi}{2} + \cos \frac{3\pi}{2} = -1 + 0 = -1 \qquad \text{Not a solution}$$

The values $\theta = \pi$ and $\theta = \dfrac{3\pi}{2}$ are extraneous. The solution set is $\left\{ 0, \dfrac{\pi}{2} \right\}$. ●┘

Solution B   Start with the equation

$$\sin \theta + \cos \theta = 1$$

and divide each side by $\sqrt{2}$. (The reason for this choice will become apparent shortly.) Then

$$\frac{1}{\sqrt{2}} \sin \theta + \frac{1}{\sqrt{2}} \cos \theta = \frac{1}{\sqrt{2}}$$

The left side now resembles the formula for the sine of the sum of two angles, one of which is θ. The other angle is unknown (call it ϕ.) Then

$$\sin(\theta + \phi) = \sin \theta \cos \phi + \cos \theta \sin \phi = \frac{1}{\sqrt{2}} = \frac{\sqrt{2}}{2} \qquad \text{(8)}$$

where

$$\cos \phi = \frac{1}{\sqrt{2}} = \frac{\sqrt{2}}{2} \qquad \sin \phi = \frac{1}{\sqrt{2}} = \frac{\sqrt{2}}{2} \qquad 0 \le \phi < 2\pi$$

Figure 29

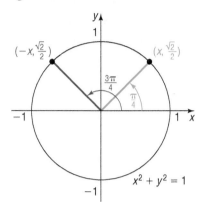

The angle ϕ is therefore $\dfrac{\pi}{4}$. As a result, equation (8) becomes

$$\sin\left(\theta + \frac{\pi}{4}\right) = \frac{\sqrt{2}}{2}$$

In the interval $[0, 2\pi)$, there are two angles whose sine is $\dfrac{\sqrt{2}}{2}$: $\dfrac{\pi}{4}$ and $\dfrac{3\pi}{4}$. See Figure 29. As a result,

$$\theta + \frac{\pi}{4} = \frac{\pi}{4} \quad \text{or} \quad \theta + \frac{\pi}{4} = \frac{3\pi}{4}$$

$$\theta = 0 \quad \text{or} \qquad \theta = \frac{\pi}{2}$$

The solution set is $\left\{0, \dfrac{\pi}{2}\right\}$.

This second method of solution can be used to solve any linear equation in the variables $\sin\theta$ and $\cos\theta$.

EXAMPLE 12

Solving a Trigonometric Equation Linear in $\sin\theta$ and $\cos\theta$

Solve:

$$a \sin\theta + b \cos\theta = c \tag{9}$$

where a, b, and c are constants and either $a \neq 0$ or $b \neq 0$.

Solution   Divide each side of equation (9) by $\sqrt{a^2 + b^2}$. Then

$$\frac{a}{\sqrt{a^2 + b^2}}\sin\theta + \frac{b}{\sqrt{a^2 + b^2}}\cos\theta = \frac{c}{\sqrt{a^2 + b^2}} \tag{10}$$

There is a unique angle $\phi, 0 \leq \phi < 2\pi$, for which

$$\cos\phi = \frac{a}{\sqrt{a^2 + b^2}} \quad \text{and} \quad \sin\phi = \frac{b}{\sqrt{a^2 + b^2}} \tag{11}$$

Figure 30

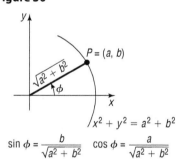

$$\sin\phi = \frac{b}{\sqrt{a^2 + b^2}} \quad \cos\phi = \frac{a}{\sqrt{a^2 + b^2}}$$

Figure 30 shows the situation for $a > 0$ and $b > 0$. Equation (10) may be written as

$$\sin\theta \cos\phi + \cos\theta \sin\phi = \frac{c}{\sqrt{a^2 + b^2}}$$

or, equivalently,

$$\sin(\theta + \phi) = \frac{c}{\sqrt{a^2 + b^2}} \tag{12}$$

where ϕ satisfies equation (11).

If $|c| > \sqrt{a^2 + b^2}$, then $\sin(\theta + \phi) > 1$ or $\sin(\theta + \phi) < -1$, and equation (12) has no solution.

If $|c| \leq \sqrt{a^2 + b^2}$, then the solutions of equation (12) are

$$\theta + \phi = \sin^{-1}\frac{c}{\sqrt{a^2 + b^2}} \quad \text{or} \quad \theta + \phi = \pi - \sin^{-1}\frac{c}{\sqrt{a^2 + b^2}}$$

Because the angle ϕ is determined by equations (11), these give the solutions to equation (9).

─────── **Now Work** PROBLEM 93

SUMMARY   Sum and Difference Formulas

$$\cos(\alpha + \beta) = \cos\alpha\cos\beta - \sin\alpha\sin\beta \qquad \cos(\alpha - \beta) = \cos\alpha\cos\beta + \sin\alpha\sin\beta$$

$$\sin(\alpha + \beta) = \sin\alpha\cos\beta + \cos\alpha\sin\beta \qquad \sin(\alpha - \beta) = \sin\alpha\cos\beta - \cos\alpha\sin\beta$$

$$\tan(\alpha + \beta) = \frac{\tan\alpha + \tan\beta}{1 - \tan\alpha\tan\beta} \qquad \tan(\alpha - \beta) = \frac{\tan\alpha - \tan\beta}{1 + \tan\alpha\tan\beta}$$

7.5 Assess Your Understanding

'Are You Prepared?' *Answers are given at the end of these exercises. If you get a wrong answer, read the pages listed in* red.

1. The distance d from the point $(2, -3)$ to the point $(5, 1)$ is
_____ . (p. 3)

2. If $\sin\theta = \dfrac{4}{5}$ and θ is in quadrant II, then $\cos\theta =$ _____ .
(pp. 386–388)

3. (a) $\sin\dfrac{\pi}{4}\cdot\cos\dfrac{\pi}{3} =$ _____ . (pp. 365–374)

(b) $\tan\dfrac{\pi}{4} - \sin\dfrac{\pi}{6} =$ _____ . (pp. 365–374)

4. If $\sin\alpha = -\dfrac{4}{5}$, $\pi < \alpha < \dfrac{3\pi}{2}$, then $\cos\alpha =$ _____ .
(pp. 386–388)

Concepts and Vocabulary

5. $\cos(\alpha + \beta) = \cos\alpha\cos\beta$ _____ $\sin\alpha\sin\beta$

6. $\sin(\alpha - \beta) = \sin\alpha\cos\beta$ _____ $\cos\alpha\sin\beta$

7. *True or False* $\sin(\alpha + \beta) = \sin\alpha + \sin\beta + 2\sin\alpha\sin\beta$

8. *True or False* $\tan 75° = \tan 30° + \tan 45°$

9. *True or False* $\cos\left(\dfrac{\pi}{2} - \theta\right) = \cos\theta$

10. *True or False*   If $f(x) = \sin x$ and $g(x) = \cos x$, then $g(\alpha + \beta) = g(\alpha)g(\beta) - f(\alpha)f(\beta)$

Skill Building

In Problems 11–22, find the exact value of each expression.

11. $\sin\dfrac{5\pi}{12}$

12. $\sin\dfrac{\pi}{12}$

13. $\cos\dfrac{7\pi}{12}$

14. $\tan\dfrac{7\pi}{12}$

15. $\cos 165°$

16. $\sin 105°$

17. $\tan 15°$

18. $\tan 195°$

19. $\sin\dfrac{17\pi}{12}$

20. $\tan\dfrac{19\pi}{12}$

21. $\sec\left(-\dfrac{\pi}{12}\right)$

22. $\cot\left(-\dfrac{5\pi}{12}\right)$

In Problems 23–32, find the exact value of each expression.

23. $\sin 20°\cos 10° + \cos 20°\sin 10°$

24. $\sin 20°\cos 80° - \cos 20°\sin 80°$

25. $\cos 70°\cos 20° - \sin 70°\sin 20°$

26. $\cos 40°\cos 10° + \sin 40°\sin 10°$

27. $\dfrac{\tan 20° + \tan 25°}{1 - \tan 20°\tan 25°}$

28. $\dfrac{\tan 40° - \tan 10°}{1 + \tan 40°\tan 10°}$

29. $\sin\dfrac{\pi}{12}\cos\dfrac{7\pi}{12} - \cos\dfrac{\pi}{12}\sin\dfrac{7\pi}{12}$

30. $\cos\dfrac{5\pi}{12}\cos\dfrac{7\pi}{12} - \sin\dfrac{5\pi}{12}\sin\dfrac{7\pi}{12}$

31. $\cos\dfrac{\pi}{12}\cos\dfrac{5\pi}{12} + \sin\dfrac{5\pi}{12}\sin\dfrac{\pi}{12}$

32. $\sin\dfrac{\pi}{18}\cos\dfrac{5\pi}{18} + \cos\dfrac{\pi}{18}\sin\dfrac{5\pi}{18}$

In Problems 33–38, find the exact value of each of the following under the given conditions:
   (a) $\sin(\alpha + \beta)$ (b) $\cos(\alpha + \beta)$ (c) $\sin(\alpha - \beta)$ (d) $\tan(\alpha - \beta)$

33. $\sin\alpha = \dfrac{3}{5}, 0 < \alpha < \dfrac{\pi}{2};\quad \cos\beta = \dfrac{2\sqrt{5}}{5}, -\dfrac{\pi}{2} < \beta < 0$

34. $\cos\alpha = \dfrac{\sqrt{5}}{5}, 0 < \alpha < \dfrac{\pi}{2};\quad \sin\beta = -\dfrac{4}{5}, -\dfrac{\pi}{2} < \beta < 0$

35. $\tan\alpha = -\dfrac{4}{3}, \dfrac{\pi}{2} < \alpha < \pi;\quad \cos\beta = \dfrac{1}{2}, 0 < \beta < \dfrac{\pi}{2}$

36. $\tan\alpha = \dfrac{5}{12}, \pi < \alpha < \dfrac{3\pi}{2};\quad \sin\beta = -\dfrac{1}{2}, \pi < \beta < \dfrac{3\pi}{2}$

37. $\sin\alpha = \dfrac{5}{13}, -\dfrac{3\pi}{2} < \alpha < -\pi;\quad \tan\beta = -\sqrt{3}, \dfrac{\pi}{2} < \beta < \pi$

38. $\cos\alpha = \dfrac{1}{2}, -\dfrac{\pi}{2} < \alpha < 0;\quad \sin\beta = \dfrac{1}{3}, 0 < \beta < \dfrac{\pi}{2}$

39. If $\sin \theta = \dfrac{1}{3}$, θ in quadrant II, find the exact value of:

(a) $\cos \theta$

(b) $\sin\left(\theta + \dfrac{\pi}{6}\right)$

(c) $\cos\left(\theta - \dfrac{\pi}{3}\right)$

(d) $\tan\left(\theta + \dfrac{\pi}{4}\right)$

40. If $\cos \theta = \dfrac{1}{4}$, θ in quadrant IV, find the exact value of:

(a) $\sin \theta$

(b) $\sin\left(\theta - \dfrac{\pi}{6}\right)$

(c) $\cos\left(\theta + \dfrac{\pi}{3}\right)$

(d) $\tan\left(\theta - \dfrac{\pi}{4}\right)$

In Problems 41–46, use the figures to evaluate each function if $f(x) = \sin x$, $g(x) = \cos x$, and $h(x) = \tan x$.

41. $f(\alpha + \beta)$

42. $g(\alpha + \beta)$

43. $g(\alpha - \beta)$

44. $f(\alpha - \beta)$

45. $h(\alpha + \beta)$

46. $h(\alpha - \beta)$

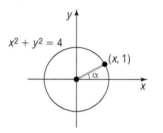

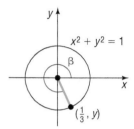

In Problems 47–72, establish each identity.

47. $\sin\left(\dfrac{\pi}{2} + \theta\right) = \cos \theta$

48. $\cos\left(\dfrac{\pi}{2} + \theta\right) = -\sin \theta$

49. $\sin(\pi - \theta) = \sin \theta$

50. $\cos(\pi - \theta) = -\cos \theta$

51. $\sin(\pi + \theta) = -\sin \theta$

52. $\cos(\pi + \theta) = -\cos \theta$

53. $\tan(\pi - \theta) = -\tan \theta$

54. $\tan(2\pi - \theta) = -\tan \theta$

55. $\sin\left(\dfrac{3\pi}{2} + \theta\right) = -\cos \theta$

56. $\cos\left(\dfrac{3\pi}{2} + \theta\right) = \sin \theta$

57. $\sin(\alpha + \beta) + \sin(\alpha - \beta) = 2 \sin \alpha \cos \beta$

58. $\cos(\alpha + \beta) + \cos(\alpha - \beta) = 2 \cos \alpha \cos \beta$

59. $\dfrac{\sin(\alpha + \beta)}{\sin \alpha \cos \beta} = 1 + \cot \alpha \tan \beta$

60. $\dfrac{\sin(\alpha + \beta)}{\cos \alpha \cos \beta} = \tan \alpha + \tan \beta$

61. $\dfrac{\cos(\alpha + \beta)}{\cos \alpha \cos \beta} = 1 - \tan \alpha \tan \beta$

62. $\dfrac{\cos(\alpha - \beta)}{\sin \alpha \cos \beta} = \cot \alpha + \tan \beta$

63. $\dfrac{\sin(\alpha + \beta)}{\sin(\alpha - \beta)} = \dfrac{\tan \alpha + \tan \beta}{\tan \alpha - \tan \beta}$

64. $\dfrac{\cos(\alpha + \beta)}{\cos(\alpha - \beta)} = \dfrac{1 - \tan \alpha \tan \beta}{1 + \tan \alpha \tan \beta}$

65. $\cot(\alpha + \beta) = \dfrac{\cot \alpha \cot \beta - 1}{\cot \beta + \cot \alpha}$

66. $\cot(\alpha - \beta) = \dfrac{\cot \alpha \cot \beta + 1}{\cot \beta - \cot \alpha}$

67. $\sec(\alpha + \beta) = \dfrac{\csc \alpha \csc \beta}{\cot \alpha \cot \beta - 1}$

68. $\sec(\alpha - \beta) = \dfrac{\sec \alpha \sec \beta}{1 + \tan \alpha \tan \beta}$

69. $\sin(\alpha - \beta) \sin(\alpha + \beta) = \sin^2 \alpha - \sin^2 \beta$

70. $\cos(\alpha - \beta) \cos(\alpha + \beta) = \cos^2 \alpha - \sin^2 \beta$

71. $\sin(\theta + k\pi) = (-1)^k \sin \theta$, k any integer

72. $\cos(\theta + k\pi) = (-1)^k \cos \theta$, k any integer

In Problems 73–84, find the exact value of each expression.

73. $\sin\left(\sin^{-1}\dfrac{1}{2} + \cos^{-1} 0\right)$

74. $\sin\left(\sin^{-1}\dfrac{\sqrt{3}}{2} + \cos^{-1} 1\right)$

75. $\sin\left[\sin^{-1}\dfrac{3}{5} - \cos^{-1}\left(-\dfrac{4}{5}\right)\right]$

76. $\sin\left[\sin^{-1}\left(-\dfrac{4}{5}\right) - \tan^{-1}\dfrac{3}{4}\right]$

77. $\cos\left(\tan^{-1}\dfrac{4}{3} + \cos^{-1}\dfrac{5}{13}\right)$

78. $\cos\left[\tan^{-1}\dfrac{5}{12} - \sin^{-1}\left(-\dfrac{3}{5}\right)\right]$

79. $\cos\left(\sin^{-1}\dfrac{5}{13} - \tan^{-1}\dfrac{3}{4}\right)$

80. $\cos\left(\tan^{-1}\dfrac{4}{3} + \cos^{-1}\dfrac{12}{13}\right)$

81. $\tan\left(\sin^{-1}\dfrac{3}{5} + \dfrac{\pi}{6}\right)$

82. $\tan\left(\dfrac{\pi}{4} - \cos^{-1}\dfrac{3}{5}\right)$

83. $\tan\left(\sin^{-1}\dfrac{4}{5} + \cos^{-1} 1\right)$

84. $\tan\left(\cos^{-1}\dfrac{4}{5} + \sin^{-1} 1\right)$

In Problems 85–90, write each trigonometric expression as an algebraic expression containing u and v. Give the restrictions required on u and v.

85. $\cos(\cos^{-1} u + \sin^{-1} v)$

86. $\sin(\sin^{-1} u - \cos^{-1} v)$

87. $\sin(\tan^{-1} u - \sin^{-1} v)$

88. $\cos(\tan^{-1} u + \tan^{-1} v)$

89. $\tan(\sin^{-1} u - \cos^{-1} v)$

90. $\sec(\tan^{-1} u + \cos^{-1} v)$

In Problems 91–96, solve each equation on the interval $0 \le \theta < 2\pi$.

91. $\sin \theta - \sqrt{3} \cos \theta = 1$

92. $\sqrt{3} \sin \theta + \cos \theta = 1$

93. $\sin \theta + \cos \theta = \sqrt{2}$

94. $\sin \theta - \cos \theta = -\sqrt{2}$

95. $\tan \theta + \sqrt{3} = \sec \theta$

96. $\cot \theta + \csc \theta = -\sqrt{3}$

Applications and Extensions

97. Show that $\sin^{-1} v + \cos^{-1} v = \dfrac{\pi}{2}$.

98. Show that $\tan^{-1} v + \cot^{-1} v = \dfrac{\pi}{2}$.

99. Show that $\tan^{-1}\left(\dfrac{1}{v}\right) = \dfrac{\pi}{2} - \tan^{-1} v$, if $v > 0$.

100. Show that $\cot^{-1} e^{v} = \tan^{-1} e^{-v}$.

101. Show that $\sin(\sin^{-1} v + \cos^{-1} v) = 1$.

102. Show that $\cos(\sin^{-1} v + \cos^{-1} v) = 0$.

103. **Calculus** Show that the difference quotient for $f(x) = \sin x$ is given by

$$\frac{f(x + h) - f(x)}{h} = \frac{\sin(x + h) - \sin x}{h}$$

$$= \cos x \cdot \frac{\sin h}{h} - \sin x \cdot \frac{1 - \cos h}{h}$$

104. **Calculus** Show that the difference quotient for $f(x) = \cos x$ is given by

$$\frac{f(x + h) - f(x)}{h} = \frac{\cos(x + h) - \cos x}{h}$$

$$= -\sin x \cdot \frac{\sin h}{h} - \cos x \cdot \frac{1 - \cos h}{h}$$

105. **One, Two, Three**
(a) Show that $\tan(\tan^{-1} 1 + \tan^{-1} 2 + \tan^{-1} 3) = 0$.
(b) Conclude from part (a) that

$$\tan^{-1} 1 + \tan^{-1} 2 + \tan^{-1} 3 = \pi$$

Source: College Mathematics Journal, Vol. 37, No. 3, May 2006

106. **Electric Power** In an alternating current (ac) circuit, the instantaneous power p at time t is given by

$$p(t) = V_m I_m \cos \phi \sin^2(\omega t) - V_m I_m \sin \phi \sin(\omega t) \cos(\omega t)$$

Show that this is equivalent to

$$p(t) = V_m I_m \sin(\omega t) \sin(\omega t - \phi)$$

Source: HyperPhysics, hosted by Georgia State University

107. **Geometry: Angle between Two Lines** Let L_1 and L_2 denote two nonvertical intersecting lines, and let θ denote the acute angle between L_1 and L_2 (see the figure). Show that

$$\tan \theta = \frac{m_2 - m_1}{1 + m_1 m_2}$$

where m_1 and m_2 are the slopes of L_1 and L_2, respectively. **[Hint:** Use the facts that $\tan \theta_1 = m_1$ and $\tan \theta_2 = m_2$.]

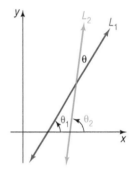

108. If $\alpha + \beta + \gamma = 180°$ and

$$\cot \theta = \cot \alpha + \cot \beta + \cot \gamma, \quad 0 < \theta < 90°$$

show that

$$\sin^3 \theta = \sin(\alpha - \theta) \sin(\beta - \theta) \sin(\gamma - \theta)$$

109. If $\tan \alpha = x + 1$ and $\tan \beta = x - 1$, show that

$$2 \cot(\alpha - \beta) = x^2$$

Explaining Concepts: Discussion and Writing

110. Discuss the following derivation:

$$\tan\left(\theta + \frac{\pi}{2}\right) = \frac{\tan \theta + \tan \dfrac{\pi}{2}}{1 - \tan \theta \tan \dfrac{\pi}{2}} = \frac{\dfrac{\tan \theta}{\tan \dfrac{\pi}{2}} + 1}{\dfrac{1}{\tan \dfrac{\pi}{2}} - \tan \theta} = \frac{0 + 1}{0 - \tan \theta} = \frac{1}{-\tan \theta} = -\cot \theta$$

Can you justify each step?

111. Explain why formula (7) cannot be used to show that

$$\tan\left(\frac{\pi}{2} - \theta\right) = \cot \theta$$

Establish this identity by using formulas (3a) and (3b).

'Are You Prepared?' Answers

1. 5   **2.** $-\dfrac{3}{5}$ **3.** (a) $\dfrac{\sqrt{2}}{4}$ (b) $\dfrac{1}{2}$ **4.** $-\dfrac{3}{5}$

7.6 Double-angle and Half-angle Formulas

OBJECTIVES **1** Use Double-angle Formulas to Find Exact Values (p. 484)
             2 Use Double-angle Formulas to Establish Identities (p. 485)
             3 Use Half-angle Formulas to Find Exact Values (p. 488)

In this section we derive formulas for $\sin(2\theta)$, $\cos(2\theta)$, $\sin\left(\dfrac{1}{2}\theta\right)$, and $\cos\left(\dfrac{1}{2}\theta\right)$ in terms of $\sin \theta$ and $\cos \theta$. They are derived using the sum formulas.

In the sum formulas for $\sin(\alpha + \beta)$ and $\cos(\alpha + \beta)$, let $\alpha = \beta = \theta$. Then

$$\sin(\alpha + \beta) = \sin \alpha \cos \beta + \cos \alpha \sin \beta$$
$$\sin(\theta + \theta) = \sin \theta \cos \theta + \cos \theta \sin \theta$$
$$\sin(2\theta) = 2 \sin \theta \cos \theta$$

and

$$\cos(\alpha + \beta) = \cos \alpha \cos \beta - \sin \alpha \sin \beta$$
$$\cos(\theta + \theta) = \cos \theta \cos \theta - \sin \theta \sin \theta$$
$$\cos(2\theta) = \cos^2 \theta - \sin^2 \theta$$

An application of the Pythagorean Identity $\sin^2 \theta + \cos^2 \theta = 1$ results in two other ways to express $\cos(2\theta)$.

$$\cos(2\theta) = \cos^2 \theta - \sin^2 \theta = (1 - \sin^2 \theta) - \sin^2 \theta = 1 - 2 \sin^2 \theta$$

and

$$\cos(2\theta) = \cos^2 \theta - \sin^2 \theta = \cos^2 \theta - (1 - \cos^2 \theta) = 2 \cos^2 \theta - 1$$

We have established the following **Double-angle Formulas:**

THEOREM   **Double-angle Formulas**

$\sin(2\theta) = 2 \sin \theta \cos \theta$	**(1)**
$\cos(2\theta) = \cos^2 \theta - \sin^2 \theta$	**(2)**
$\cos(2\theta) = 1 - 2 \sin^2 \theta$	**(3)**
$\cos(2\theta) = 2 \cos^2 \theta - 1$	**(4)**

1 Use Double-angle Formulas to Find Exact Values

EXAMPLE 1   **Finding Exact Values Using the Double-angle Formulas**

If $\sin \theta = \dfrac{3}{5}$, $\dfrac{\pi}{2} < \theta < \pi$, find the exact value of:

(a) $\sin(2\theta)$ (b) $\cos(2\theta)$

Solution

(a) Because $\sin(2\theta) = 2\sin\theta\cos\theta$ and we already know that $\sin\theta = \dfrac{3}{5}$, we only need to find $\cos\theta$. Since $\sin\theta = \dfrac{3}{5} = \dfrac{y}{r}$, $\dfrac{\pi}{2} < \theta < \pi$, we let $y = 3$ and $r = 5$ and place θ in quadrant II. The point $P = (x, y) = (x, 3)$ is on a circle of radius 5, $x^2 + y^2 = 25$. See Figure 31. Then

Figure 31

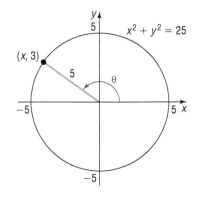

$$x^2 + y^2 = 25$$
$$x^2 = 25 - 9 = 16 \qquad y = 3$$
$$x = -4 \qquad\qquad x < 0$$

We find that $\cos\theta = \dfrac{x}{r} = \dfrac{-4}{5}$. Now use formula (1) to obtain

$$\sin(2\theta) = 2\sin\theta\cos\theta = 2\left(\frac{3}{5}\right)\left(-\frac{4}{5}\right) = -\frac{24}{25}$$

(b) Because we are given $\sin\theta = \dfrac{3}{5}$, it is easiest to use formula (3) to get $\cos(2\theta)$.

$$\cos(2\theta) = 1 - 2\sin^2\theta = 1 - 2\left(\frac{9}{25}\right) = 1 - \frac{18}{25} = \frac{7}{25}$$

WARNING In finding $\cos(2\theta)$ in Example 1(b), we chose to use a version of the Double-angle Formula, formula (3). Note that we are unable to use the Pythagorean Identity $\cos(2\theta) = \pm\sqrt{1 - \sin^2(2\theta)}$, with $\sin(2\theta) = -\dfrac{24}{25}$, because we have no way of knowing which sign to choose. ∎

━━━━**Now Work**   PROBLEMS 7(a) AND (b)

2 Use Double-angle Formulas to Establish Identities

<hr>

EXAMPLE 2   **Establishing Identities**

(a) Develop a formula for $\tan(2\theta)$ in terms of $\tan\theta$.
(b) Develop a formula for $\sin(3\theta)$ in terms of $\sin\theta$ and $\cos\theta$.

Solution

(a) In the sum formula for $\tan(\alpha + \beta)$, let $\alpha = \beta = \theta$. Then

$$\tan(\alpha + \beta) = \frac{\tan\alpha + \tan\beta}{1 - \tan\alpha\tan\beta}$$

$$\tan(\theta + \theta) = \frac{\tan\theta + \tan\theta}{1 - \tan\theta\tan\theta}$$

$$\boxed{\tan(2\theta) = \frac{2\tan\theta}{1 - \tan^2\theta}} \qquad\qquad \textbf{(5)}$$

(b) To get a formula for $\sin(3\theta)$, we write 3θ as $2\theta + \theta$ and use the sum formula.

$$\sin(3\theta) = \sin(2\theta + \theta) = \sin(2\theta)\cos\theta + \cos(2\theta)\sin\theta$$

Now use the Double-angle Formulas to get

$$\sin(3\theta) = (2\sin\theta\cos\theta)(\cos\theta) + (\cos^2\theta - \sin^2\theta)(\sin\theta)$$
$$= 2\sin\theta\cos^2\theta + \sin\theta\cos^2\theta - \sin^3\theta$$
$$= 3\sin\theta\cos^2\theta - \sin^3\theta$$

The formula obtained in Example 2(b) can also be written as

$$\sin(3\theta) = 3\sin\theta\cos^2\theta - \sin^3\theta = 3\sin\theta(1 - \sin^2\theta) - \sin^3\theta$$
$$= 3\sin\theta - 4\sin^3\theta$$

That is, $\sin(3\theta)$ is a third-degree polynomial in the variable $\sin\theta$. In fact, $\sin(n\theta)$, n a positive odd integer, can always be written as a polynomial of degree n in the variable $\sin\theta$.*

$\longrightarrow$ **Now Work** PROBLEM 65

By rearranging the Double-angle Formulas (3) and (4), we obtain other formulas that we will use later in this section.

Begin with formula (3) and proceed to solve for $\sin^2\theta$.

$$\cos(2\theta) = 1 - 2\sin^2\theta$$
$$2\sin^2\theta = 1 - \cos(2\theta)$$

$$\sin^2\theta = \frac{1 - \cos(2\theta)}{2} \tag{6}$$

Similarly, using formula (4), proceed to solve for $\cos^2\theta$.

$$\cos(2\theta) = 2\cos^2\theta - 1$$
$$2\cos^2\theta = 1 + \cos(2\theta)$$

$$\cos^2\theta = \frac{1 + \cos(2\theta)}{2} \tag{7}$$

Formulas (6) and (7) can be used to develop a formula for $\tan^2\theta$.

$$\tan^2\theta = \frac{\sin^2\theta}{\cos^2\theta} = \frac{\dfrac{1 - \cos(2\theta)}{2}}{\dfrac{1 + \cos(2\theta)}{2}}$$

$$\tan^2\theta = \frac{1 - \cos(2\theta)}{1 + \cos(2\theta)} \tag{8}$$

Formulas (6) through (8) do not have to be memorized since their derivations are so straightforward.

Formulas (6) and (7) are important in calculus. The next example illustrates a problem that arises in calculus requiring the use of formula (7).

EXAMPLE 3   **Establishing an Identity**

Write an equivalent expression for $\cos^4\theta$ that does not involve any powers of sine or cosine greater than 1.

*Because of the work done by P. L. Chebyshëv, these polynomials are sometimes called *Chebyshëv polynomials*.

Solution   The idea here is to apply formula (7) twice.

$$\cos^4 \theta = (\cos^2 \theta)^2 = \left(\frac{1 + \cos(2\theta)}{2}\right)^2 \qquad \text{Formula (7)}$$

$$= \frac{1}{4}[1 + 2\cos(2\theta) + \cos^2(2\theta)]$$

$$= \frac{1}{4} + \frac{1}{2}\cos(2\theta) + \frac{1}{4}\cos^2(2\theta)$$

$$= \frac{1}{4} + \frac{1}{2}\cos(2\theta) + \frac{1}{4}\left\{\frac{1 + \cos[2(2\theta)]}{2}\right\} \qquad \text{Formula (7)}$$

$$= \frac{1}{4} + \frac{1}{2}\cos(2\theta) + \frac{1}{8}[1 + \cos(4\theta)]$$

$$= \frac{3}{8} + \frac{1}{2}\cos(2\theta) + \frac{1}{8}\cos(4\theta)$$

Now Work   PROBLEM 41

EXAMPLE 4   **Solving a Trigonometric Equation Using Identities**

Solve the equation: $\sin\theta\cos\theta = -\dfrac{1}{2}$, $0 \le \theta < 2\pi$

Solution   The left side of the given equation is in the form of the Double-angle Formula $2\sin\theta\cos\theta = \sin(2\theta)$, except for a factor of 2. Multiply each side by 2.

$$\sin\theta\cos\theta = -\frac{1}{2}$$

$$2\sin\theta\cos\theta = -1 \qquad \text{Multiply each side by 2.}$$

$$\sin(2\theta) = -1 \qquad \text{Double-angle Formula}$$

The argument here is 2θ. So we need to write all the solutions of this equation and then list those that are in the interval $[0, 2\pi)$. Because $\sin\left(\dfrac{3\pi}{2} + 2\pi k\right) = -1$, for any integer k we have

$$2\theta = \frac{3\pi}{2} + 2k\pi \qquad \text{k any integer}$$

$$\theta = \frac{3\pi}{4} + k\pi$$

$$\theta = \frac{3\pi}{4} + (-1)\pi = -\frac{\pi}{4}, \quad \theta = \frac{3\pi}{4} + (0)\pi = \frac{3\pi}{4}, \quad \theta = \frac{3\pi}{4} + (1)\pi = \frac{7\pi}{4}, \quad \theta = \frac{3\pi}{4} + (2)\pi = \frac{11\pi}{4}$$

$$\underset{k = -1}{\uparrow} \qquad\qquad \underset{k = 0}{\uparrow} \qquad\qquad \underset{k = 1}{\uparrow} \qquad\qquad \underset{k = 2}{\uparrow}$$

The solutions in the interval $[0, 2\pi)$ are

$$\theta = \frac{3\pi}{4}, \qquad \theta = \frac{7\pi}{4}$$

The solution set is $\left\{\dfrac{3\pi}{4}, \dfrac{7\pi}{4}\right\}$.

Now Work   PROBLEM 69

EXAMPLE 5   **Projectile Motion**

Figure 32

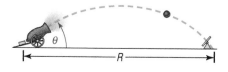

An object is propelled upward at an angle θ to the horizontal with an initial velocity of v_0 feet per second. See Figure 32. If air resistance is ignored, the **range** R, the horizontal distance that the object travels, is given by the function

$$R(\theta) = \frac{1}{16}v_0^2 \sin\theta\cos\theta$$

(a) Show that $R(\theta) = \dfrac{1}{32}v_0^2 \sin(2\theta)$.

(b) Find the angle θ for which R is a maximum.

Solution   (a) Rewrite the given expression for the range using the Double-angle Formula $\sin(2\theta) = 2 \sin \theta \cos \theta$. Then

$$R(\theta) = \frac{1}{16} v_0^2 \sin \theta \cos \theta = \frac{1}{16} v_0^2 \frac{2 \sin \theta \cos \theta}{2} = \frac{1}{32} v_0^2 \sin(2\theta)$$

(b) In this form, the largest value for the range R can be found. For a fixed initial speed v_0, the angle θ of inclination to the horizontal determines the value of R. Since the largest value of a sine function is 1, occurring when the argument 2θ is 90°, it follows that for maximum R we must have

$$2\theta = 90°$$
$$\theta = 45°$$

An inclination to the horizontal of 45° results in the maximum range.

3 Use Half-angle Formulas to Find Exact Values

Another important use of formulas (6) through (8) is to prove the *Half-angle Formulas*. In formulas (6) through (8), let $\theta = \dfrac{\alpha}{2}$. Then

$$\sin^2 \frac{\alpha}{2} = \frac{1 - \cos \alpha}{2} \qquad \cos^2 \frac{\alpha}{2} = \frac{1 + \cos \alpha}{2} \qquad \tan^2 \frac{\alpha}{2} = \frac{1 - \cos \alpha}{1 + \cos \alpha} \qquad (9)$$

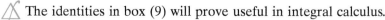 The identities in box (9) will prove useful in integral calculus.

If we solve for the trigonometric functions on the left sides of equations (9), we obtain the Half-angle Formulas.

THEOREM   **Half-angle Formulas**

$$\sin \frac{\alpha}{2} = \pm \sqrt{\frac{1 - \cos \alpha}{2}} \qquad (10a)$$

$$\cos \frac{\alpha}{2} = \pm \sqrt{\frac{1 + \cos \alpha}{2}} \qquad (10b)$$

$$\tan \frac{\alpha}{2} = \pm \sqrt{\frac{1 - \cos \alpha}{1 + \cos \alpha}} \qquad (10c)$$

where the + or − sign is determined by the quadrant of the angle $\dfrac{\alpha}{2}$.

EXAMPLE 6   **Finding Exact Values Using Half-angle Formulas**

Use a Half-angle Formula to find the exact value of:
(a) $\cos 15°$ (b) $\sin(-15°)$

Solution   (a) Because $15° = \dfrac{30°}{2}$, we can use the Half-angle Formula for $\cos \dfrac{\alpha}{2}$ with $\alpha = 30°$. Also, because 15° is in quadrant I, $\cos 15° > 0$, we choose the + sign in using formula (10b):

$$\cos 15° = \cos \frac{30°}{2} = \sqrt{\frac{1 + \cos 30°}{2}}$$

$$= \sqrt{\frac{1 + \sqrt{3}/2}{2}} = \sqrt{\frac{2 + \sqrt{3}}{4}} = \frac{\sqrt{2 + \sqrt{3}}}{2}$$

(b) Use the fact that $\sin(-15°) = -\sin 15°$ and then apply formula (10a).

$$\sin(-15°) = -\sin\frac{30°}{2} = -\sqrt{\frac{1 - \cos 30°}{2}}$$

$$= -\sqrt{\frac{1 - \sqrt{3}/2}{2}} = -\sqrt{\frac{2 - \sqrt{3}}{4}} = -\frac{\sqrt{2 - \sqrt{3}}}{2}$$

It is interesting to compare the answer found in Example 6(a) with the answer to Example 2 of Section 7.5. There we calculated

$$\cos\frac{\pi}{12} = \cos 15° = \frac{1}{4}(\sqrt{6} + \sqrt{2})$$

Based on this and the result of Example 6(a), we conclude that

$$\frac{1}{4}(\sqrt{6} + \sqrt{2}) \quad \text{and} \quad \frac{\sqrt{2 + \sqrt{3}}}{2}$$

are equal. (Since each expression is positive, you can verify this equality by squaring each expression.) Two very different looking, yet correct, answers can be obtained, depending on the approach taken to solve a problem.

➤**Now Work** PROBLEM 19

EXAMPLE 7

Finding Exact Values Using Half-angle Formulas

If $\cos\alpha = -\dfrac{3}{5}$, $\pi < \alpha < \dfrac{3\pi}{2}$, find the exact value of:

(a) $\sin\dfrac{\alpha}{2}$ (b) $\cos\dfrac{\alpha}{2}$ (c) $\tan\dfrac{\alpha}{2}$

Solution

First, observe that if $\pi < \alpha < \dfrac{3\pi}{2}$ then $\dfrac{\pi}{2} < \dfrac{\alpha}{2} < \dfrac{3\pi}{4}$. As a result, $\dfrac{\alpha}{2}$ lies in quadrant II.

(a) Because $\dfrac{\alpha}{2}$ lies in quadrant II, $\sin\dfrac{\alpha}{2} > 0$, so use the $+$ sign in formula (10a) to get

$$\sin\frac{\alpha}{2} = \sqrt{\frac{1 - \cos\alpha}{2}} = \sqrt{\frac{1 - \left(-\dfrac{3}{5}\right)}{2}}$$

$$= \sqrt{\frac{\dfrac{8}{5}}{2}} = \sqrt{\frac{4}{5}} = \frac{2}{\sqrt{5}} = \frac{2\sqrt{5}}{5}$$

(b) Because $\dfrac{\alpha}{2}$ lies in quadrant II, $\cos\dfrac{\alpha}{2} < 0$, so use the $-$ sign in formula (10b) to get

$$\cos\frac{\alpha}{2} = -\sqrt{\frac{1 + \cos\alpha}{2}} = -\sqrt{\frac{1 + \left(-\dfrac{3}{5}\right)}{2}}$$

$$= -\sqrt{\frac{\dfrac{2}{5}}{2}} = -\frac{1}{\sqrt{5}} = -\frac{\sqrt{5}}{5}$$

(c) Because $\dfrac{\alpha}{2}$ lies in quadrant II, $\tan\dfrac{\alpha}{2} < 0$, so use the $-$ sign in formula (10c) to get

$$\tan\frac{\alpha}{2} = -\sqrt{\frac{1-\cos\alpha}{1+\cos\alpha}} = -\sqrt{\frac{1-\left(-\dfrac{3}{5}\right)}{1+\left(-\dfrac{3}{5}\right)}} = -\sqrt{\frac{\dfrac{8}{5}}{\dfrac{2}{5}}} = -2$$

Another way to solve Example 7(c) is to use the results of parts (a) and (b).

$$\tan\frac{\alpha}{2} = \frac{\sin\dfrac{\alpha}{2}}{\cos\dfrac{\alpha}{2}} = \frac{\dfrac{2\sqrt{5}}{5}}{-\dfrac{\sqrt{5}}{5}} = -2$$

Now Work PROBLEMS 7(c) AND (d)

There is a formula for $\tan\dfrac{\alpha}{2}$ that does not contain $+$ and $-$ signs, making it more useful than formula 10(c). To derive it, use the formulas

$$1 - \cos\alpha = 2\sin^2\frac{\alpha}{2} \qquad \text{Formula (9)}$$

and

$$\sin\alpha = \sin\left[2\left(\frac{\alpha}{2}\right)\right] = 2\sin\frac{\alpha}{2}\cos\frac{\alpha}{2} \qquad \text{Double-angle Formula}$$

Then

$$\frac{1-\cos\alpha}{\sin\alpha} = \frac{2\sin^2\dfrac{\alpha}{2}}{2\sin\dfrac{\alpha}{2}\cos\dfrac{\alpha}{2}} = \frac{\sin\dfrac{\alpha}{2}}{\cos\dfrac{\alpha}{2}} = \tan\frac{\alpha}{2}$$

Since it also can be shown that

$$\frac{1-\cos\alpha}{\sin\alpha} = \frac{\sin\alpha}{1+\cos\alpha}$$

we have the following two Half-angle Formulas:

Half-angle Formulas for $\tan\dfrac{\alpha}{2}$

$$\boxed{\tan\frac{\alpha}{2} = \frac{1-\cos\alpha}{\sin\alpha} = \frac{\sin\alpha}{1+\cos\alpha} \qquad \textbf{(11)}}$$

With this formula, the solution to Example 7(c) can be obtained as follows:

$$\cos\alpha = -\frac{3}{5} \qquad \pi < \alpha < \frac{3\pi}{2}$$

$$\sin\alpha = -\sqrt{1-\cos^2\alpha} = -\sqrt{1-\frac{9}{25}} = -\sqrt{\frac{16}{25}} = -\frac{4}{5}$$

Then, by equation (11),

$$\tan\frac{\alpha}{2} = \frac{1-\cos\alpha}{\sin\alpha} = \frac{1-\left(-\dfrac{3}{5}\right)}{-\dfrac{4}{5}} = \frac{\dfrac{8}{5}}{-\dfrac{4}{5}} = -2$$

7.6 Assess Your Understanding

Concepts and Vocabulary

1. $\cos(2\theta) = \cos^2\theta - \underline{\hspace{1cm}} = \underline{\hspace{1cm}} - 1 = 1 - \underline{\hspace{1cm}}$.

2. $\sin^2\dfrac{\theta}{2} = \dfrac{\underline{\hspace{1cm}}}{2}$.

3. $\tan\dfrac{\theta}{2} = \dfrac{1 - \cos\theta}{\underline{\hspace{1cm}}}$.

4. *True or False* $\tan(2\theta) = \dfrac{2\tan\theta}{1 - \tan^2\theta}$

5. *True or False* $\sin(2\theta)$ has two equivalent forms:
$$2\sin\theta\cos\theta \quad \text{and} \quad \sin^2\theta - \cos^2\theta$$

6. *True or False* $\tan(2\theta) + \tan(2\theta) = \tan(4\theta)$

Skill Building

In Problems 7–18, use the information given about the angle θ, $0 \le \theta < 2\pi$, to find the exact value of

(a) $\sin(2\theta)$ (b) $\cos(2\theta)$ (c) $\sin\dfrac{\theta}{2}$ (d) $\cos\dfrac{\theta}{2}$

7. $\sin\theta = \dfrac{3}{5}$, $0 < \theta < \dfrac{\pi}{2}$

8. $\cos\theta = \dfrac{3}{5}$, $0 < \theta < \dfrac{\pi}{2}$

9. $\tan\theta = \dfrac{4}{3}$, $\pi < \theta < \dfrac{3\pi}{2}$

10. $\tan\theta = \dfrac{1}{2}$, $\pi < \theta < \dfrac{3\pi}{2}$

11. $\cos\theta = -\dfrac{\sqrt{6}}{3}$, $\dfrac{\pi}{2} < \theta < \pi$

12. $\sin\theta = -\dfrac{\sqrt{3}}{3}$, $\dfrac{3\pi}{2} < \theta < 2\pi$

13. $\sec\theta = 3$, $\sin\theta > 0$

14. $\csc\theta = -\sqrt{5}$, $\cos\theta < 0$

15. $\cot\theta = -2$, $\sec\theta < 0$

16. $\sec\theta = 2$, $\csc\theta < 0$

17. $\tan\theta = -3$, $\sin\theta < 0$

18. $\cot\theta = 3$, $\cos\theta < 0$

In Problems 19–28, use the Half-angle Formulas to find the exact value of each expression.

19. $\sin 22.5°$

20. $\cos 22.5°$

21. $\tan\dfrac{7\pi}{8}$

22. $\tan\dfrac{9\pi}{8}$

23. $\cos 165°$

24. $\sin 195°$

25. $\sec\dfrac{15\pi}{8}$

26. $\csc\dfrac{7\pi}{8}$

27. $\sin\left(-\dfrac{\pi}{8}\right)$

28. $\cos\left(-\dfrac{3\pi}{8}\right)$

In Problems 29–40, use the figures to evaluate each function given that $f(x) = \sin x$, $g(x) = \cos x$, and $h(x) = \tan x$.

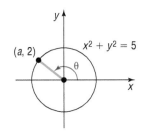

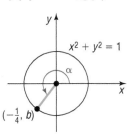

29. $f(2\theta)$

30. $g(2\theta)$

31. $g\left(\dfrac{\theta}{2}\right)$

32. $f\left(\dfrac{\theta}{2}\right)$

33. $h(2\theta)$

34. $h\left(\dfrac{\theta}{2}\right)$

35. $g(2\alpha)$

36. $f(2\alpha)$

37. $f\left(\dfrac{\alpha}{2}\right)$

38. $g\left(\dfrac{\alpha}{2}\right)$

39. $h\left(\dfrac{\alpha}{2}\right)$

40. $h(2\alpha)$

41. Show that $\sin^4\theta = \dfrac{3}{8} - \dfrac{1}{2}\cos(2\theta) + \dfrac{1}{8}\cos(4\theta)$.

42. Show that $\sin(4\theta) = (\cos\theta)(4\sin\theta - 8\sin^3\theta)$.

43. Develop a formula for $\cos(3\theta)$ as a third-degree polynomial in the variable $\cos\theta$.

44. Develop a formula for $\cos(4\theta)$ as a fourth-degree polynomial in the variable $\cos\theta$.

45. Find an expression for $\sin(5\theta)$ as a fifth-degree polynomial in the variable $\sin\theta$.

46. Find an expression for $\cos(5\theta)$ as a fifth-degree polynomial in the variable $\cos\theta$.

In Problems 47–68, establish each identity.

47. $\cos^4\theta - \sin^4\theta = \cos(2\theta)$

48. $\dfrac{\cot\theta - \tan\theta}{\cot\theta + \tan\theta} = \cos(2\theta)$

49. $\cot(2\theta) = \dfrac{\cot^2\theta - 1}{2\cot\theta}$

50. $\cot(2\theta) = \dfrac{1}{2}(\cot\theta - \tan\theta)$

51. $\sec(2\theta) = \dfrac{\sec^2\theta}{2 - \sec^2\theta}$

52. $\csc(2\theta) = \dfrac{1}{2}\sec\theta\csc\theta$

53. $\cos^2(2u) - \sin^2(2u) = \cos(4u)$

54. $(4\sin u\cos u)(1 - 2\sin^2 u) = \sin(4u)$

55. $\dfrac{\cos(2\theta)}{1 + \sin(2\theta)} = \dfrac{\cot\theta - 1}{\cot\theta + 1}$

56. $\sin^2\theta\cos^2\theta = \dfrac{1}{8}[1 - \cos(4\theta)]$

57. $\sec^2\dfrac{\theta}{2} = \dfrac{2}{1 + \cos\theta}$

58. $\csc^2\dfrac{\theta}{2} = \dfrac{2}{1 - \cos\theta}$

59. $\cot^2\dfrac{v}{2} = \dfrac{\sec v + 1}{\sec v - 1}$

60. $\tan\dfrac{v}{2} = \csc v - \cot v$

61. $\cos\theta = \dfrac{1 - \tan^2\dfrac{\theta}{2}}{1 + \tan^2\dfrac{\theta}{2}}$

62. $1 - \dfrac{1}{2}\sin(2\theta) = \dfrac{\sin^3\theta + \cos^3\theta}{\sin\theta + \cos\theta}$

63. $\dfrac{\sin(3\theta)}{\sin\theta} - \dfrac{\cos(3\theta)}{\cos\theta} = 2$

64. $\dfrac{\cos\theta + \sin\theta}{\cos\theta - \sin\theta} - \dfrac{\cos\theta - \sin\theta}{\cos\theta + \sin\theta} = 2\tan(2\theta)$

65. $\tan(3\theta) = \dfrac{3\tan\theta - \tan^3\theta}{1 - 3\tan^2\theta}$

66. $\tan\theta + \tan(\theta + 120°) + \tan(\theta + 240°) = 3\tan(3\theta)$

67. $\ln|\sin\theta| = \dfrac{1}{2}(\ln|1 - \cos(2\theta)| - \ln 2)$

68. $\ln|\cos\theta| = \dfrac{1}{2}(\ln|1 + \cos(2\theta)| - \ln 2)$

In Problems 69–78, solve each equation on the interval $0 \le \theta < 2\pi$.

69. $\cos(2\theta) + 6\sin^2\theta = 4$

70. $\cos(2\theta) = 2 - 2\sin^2\theta$

71. $\cos(2\theta) = \cos\theta$

72. $\sin(2\theta) = \cos\theta$

73. $\sin(2\theta) + \sin(4\theta) = 0$

74. $\cos(2\theta) + \cos(4\theta) = 0$

75. $3 - \sin\theta = \cos(2\theta)$

76. $\cos(2\theta) + 5\cos\theta + 3 = 0$

77. $\tan(2\theta) + 2\sin\theta = 0$

78. $\tan(2\theta) + 2\cos\theta = 0$

Mixed Practice

In Problems 79–90, find the exact value of each expression.

79. $\sin\left(2\sin^{-1}\dfrac{1}{2}\right)$

80. $\sin\left[2\sin^{-1}\dfrac{\sqrt{3}}{2}\right]$

81. $\cos\left(2\sin^{-1}\dfrac{3}{5}\right)$

82. $\cos\left(2\cos^{-1}\dfrac{4}{5}\right)$

83. $\tan\left[2\cos^{-1}\left(-\dfrac{3}{5}\right)\right]$

84. $\tan\left(2\tan^{-1}\dfrac{3}{4}\right)$

85. $\sin\left(2\cos^{-1}\dfrac{4}{5}\right)$

86. $\cos\left[2\tan^{-1}\left(-\dfrac{4}{3}\right)\right]$

87. $\sin^2\left(\dfrac{1}{2}\cos^{-1}\dfrac{3}{5}\right)$

88. $\cos^2\left(\dfrac{1}{2}\sin^{-1}\dfrac{3}{5}\right)$

89. $\sec\left(2\tan^{-1}\dfrac{3}{4}\right)$

90. $\csc\left[2\sin^{-1}\left(-\dfrac{3}{5}\right)\right]$

In Problems 91–93, find the real zeros of each trigonometric function on the interval $0 \le \theta < 2\pi$.

91. $f(x) = \sin(2x) - \sin x$

92. $f(x) = \cos(2x) + \cos x$

93. $f(x) = \cos(2x) + \sin^2 x$

Applications and Extensions

94. Constructing a Rain Gutter A rain gutter is to be constructed of aluminum sheets 12 inches wide. After marking off a length of 4 inches from each edge, this length is bent up at an angle θ. See the illustration. The area A of the opening as a function of θ is given by

$$A(\theta) = 16\sin\theta(\cos\theta + 1) \quad 0° < \theta < 90°$$

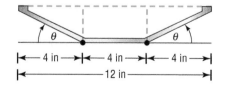

(a) In calculus, you will be asked to find the angle θ that maximizes A by solving the equation

$$\cos(2\theta) + \cos\theta = 0, \quad 0° < \theta < 90°$$

Solve this equation for θ.

(b) What is the maximum area A of the opening?

(c) Graph $A = A(\theta), 0° \le \theta \le 90°$, and find the angle θ that maximizes the area A. Also find the maximum area. Compare the results to the answer found earlier.

95. Laser Projection In a laser projection system, the **optical** or **scanning angle** θ is related to the throw distance D from the scanner to the screen and the projected image width W by the equation

$$D = \frac{\frac{1}{2}W}{\csc\theta - \cot\theta}$$

(a) Show that the projected image width is given by

$$W = 2D\tan\frac{\theta}{2}$$

(b) Find the optical angle if the throw distance is 15 feet and the projected image width is 6.5 feet.

Source: Pangolin Laser Systems, Inc.

96. Product of Inertia The **product of inertia** for an area about inclined axes is given by the formula

$$I_{uv} = I_x\sin\theta\cos\theta - I_y\sin\theta\cos\theta + I_{xy}(\cos^2\theta - \sin^2\theta)$$

Show that this is equivalent to

$$I_{uv} = \frac{I_x - I_y}{2}\sin(2\theta) + I_{xy}\cos(2\theta)$$

Source: Adapted from Hibbeler, *Engineering Mechanics: Statics,* 10th ed., Prentice Hall © 2004.

97. Projectile Motion An object is propelled upward at an angle θ, $45° < \theta < 90°$, to the horizontal with an initial velocity of v_0 feet per second from the base of a plane that makes an angle of $45°$ with the horizontal. See the illustration. If air resistance is ignored, the distance R that it travels up the inclined plane is given by the function

$$R(\theta) = \frac{v_0^2\sqrt{2}}{16}\cos\theta(\sin\theta - \cos\theta)$$

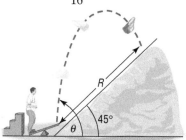

(a) Show that

$$R(\theta) = \frac{v_0^2\sqrt{2}}{32}[\sin(2\theta) - \cos(2\theta) - 1]$$

(b) In calculus, you will be asked to find the angle θ that maximizes R by solving the equation

$$\sin(2\theta) + \cos(2\theta) = 0$$

Solve this equation for θ.

(c) What is the maximum distance R if $v_0 = 32$ feet per second?

(d) Graph $R = R(\theta), 45° \le \theta \le 90°$, and find the angle θ that maximizes the distance R. Also find the maximum distance. Use $v_0 = 32$ feet per second. Compare the results with the answers found earlier.

98. Sawtooth Curve An oscilloscope often displays a sawtooth curve. This curve can be approximated by sinusoidal curves of varying periods and amplitudes. A first approximation to the sawtooth curve is given by

$$y = \frac{1}{2}\sin(2\pi x) + \frac{1}{4}\sin(4\pi x)$$

Show that $y = \sin(2\pi x)\cos^2(\pi x)$.

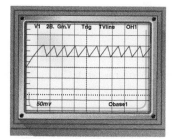

99. Area of an Isosceles Triangle Show that the area A of an isosceles triangle whose equal sides are of length s and θ is the angle between them is

$$A = \frac{1}{2}s^2\sin\theta$$

[**Hint:** See the illustration. The height h bisects the angle θ and is the perpendicular bisector of the base.]

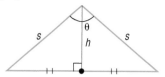

100. Geometry A rectangle is inscribed in a semicircle of radius 1. See the illustration.

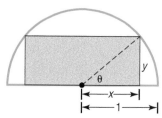

(a) Express the area A of the rectangle as a function of the angle θ shown in the illustration.

(b) Show that $A(\theta) = \sin(2\theta)$.

(c) Find the angle θ that results in the largest area A.

(d) Find the dimensions of this largest rectangle.

101. If $x = 2\tan\theta$, express $\sin(2\theta)$ as a function of x.

102. If $x = 2\tan\theta$, express $\cos(2\theta)$ as a function of x.

103. Find the value of the number C:

$$\frac{1}{2}\sin^2 x + C = -\frac{1}{4}\cos(2x)$$

104. Find the value of the number C:

$$\frac{1}{2}\cos^2 x + C = \frac{1}{4}\cos(2x)$$

105. If $z = \tan\dfrac{\alpha}{2}$, show that $\sin\alpha = \dfrac{2z}{1 + z^2}$.

106. If $z = \tan\dfrac{\alpha}{2}$, show that $\cos\alpha = \dfrac{1 - z^2}{1 + z^2}$.

107. Graph $f(x) = \sin^2 x = \dfrac{1 - \cos(2x)}{2}$ for $0 \le x \le 2\pi$

by using transformations.

108. Repeat Problem 107 for $g(x) = \cos^2 x$.

109. Use the fact that

$$\cos\frac{\pi}{12} = \frac{1}{4}\left(\sqrt{6} + \sqrt{2}\right)$$

to find $\sin\dfrac{\pi}{24}$ and $\cos\dfrac{\pi}{24}$.

110. Show that

$$\cos\frac{\pi}{8} = \frac{\sqrt{2 + \sqrt{2}}}{2}$$

and use it to find $\sin\dfrac{\pi}{16}$ and $\cos\dfrac{\pi}{16}$.

111. Show that

$$\sin^3\theta + \sin^3(\theta + 120°) + \sin^3(\theta + 240°) = -\frac{3}{4}\sin(3\theta)$$

112. If $\tan\theta = a\tan\dfrac{\theta}{3}$, express $\tan\dfrac{\theta}{3}$ in terms of a.

Explaining Concepts: Discussion and Writing

113. Go to the library and research Chebyshëv polynomials. Write a report on your findings.

7.7 Product-to-Sum and Sum-to-Product Formulas

OBJECTIVES **1** Express Products as Sums (p. 494)

2 Express Sums as Products (p. 495)

1 Express Products as Sums

Sum and difference formulas can be used to derive formulas for writing the products of sines and/or cosines as sums or differences. These identities are usually called the **Product-to-Sum Formulas.**

THEOREM   **Product-to-Sum Formulas**

$$\sin\alpha\sin\beta = \frac{1}{2}[\cos(\alpha - \beta) - \cos(\alpha + \beta)] \qquad (1)$$

$$\cos\alpha\cos\beta = \frac{1}{2}[\cos(\alpha - \beta) + \cos(\alpha + \beta)] \qquad (2)$$

$$\sin\alpha\cos\beta = \frac{1}{2}[\sin(\alpha + \beta) + \sin(\alpha - \beta)] \qquad (3)$$

These formulas do not have to be memorized. Instead, you should remember how they are derived. Then, when you want to use them, either look them up or derive them, as needed.

To derive formulas (1) and (2), write down the sum and difference formulas for the cosine:

$$\cos(\alpha - \beta) = \cos\alpha\cos\beta + \sin\alpha\sin\beta \qquad (4)$$

$$\cos(\alpha + \beta) = \cos\alpha\cos\beta - \sin\alpha\sin\beta \qquad (5)$$

Subtract equation (5) from equation (4) to get

$$\cos(\alpha - \beta) - \cos(\alpha + \beta) = 2\sin\alpha\sin\beta$$

from which

$$\sin\alpha\sin\beta = \frac{1}{2}[\cos(\alpha - \beta) - \cos(\alpha + \beta)]$$

Now add equations (4) and (5) to get

$$\cos(\alpha - \beta) + \cos(\alpha + \beta) = 2 \cos \alpha \cos \beta$$

from which

$$\cos \alpha \cos \beta = \frac{1}{2}[\cos(\alpha - \beta) + \cos(\alpha + \beta)]$$

To derive Product-to-Sum Formula (3), use the sum and difference formulas for sine in a similar way. (You are asked to do this in Problem 53.)

EXAMPLE 1   **Expressing Products as Sums**

Express each of the following products as a sum containing only sines or only cosines.

(a) $\sin(6\theta) \sin(4\theta)$ (b) $\cos(3\theta) \cos \theta$ (c) $\sin(3\theta) \cos(5\theta)$

Solution   (a) Use formula (1) to get

$$\sin(6\theta) \sin(4\theta) = \frac{1}{2}[\cos(6\theta - 4\theta) - \cos(6\theta + 4\theta)]$$

$$= \frac{1}{2}[\cos(2\theta) - \cos(10\theta)]$$

(b) Use formula (2) to get

$$\cos(3\theta) \cos \theta = \frac{1}{2}[\cos(3\theta - \theta) + \cos(3\theta + \theta)]$$

$$= \frac{1}{2}[\cos(2\theta) + \cos(4\theta)]$$

(c) Use formula (3) to get

$$\sin(3\theta) \cos(5\theta) = \frac{1}{2}[\sin(3\theta + 5\theta) + \sin(3\theta - 5\theta)]$$

$$= \frac{1}{2}[\sin(8\theta) + \sin(-2\theta)] = \frac{1}{2}[\sin(8\theta) - \sin(2\theta)]$$

⌐**Now Work** PROBLEM 7

2 Express Sums as Products

The **Sum-to-Product Formulas** are given next.

THEOREM   **Sum-to-Product Formulas**

$$\sin \alpha + \sin \beta = 2 \sin \frac{\alpha + \beta}{2} \cos \frac{\alpha - \beta}{2} \tag{6}$$

$$\sin \alpha - \sin \beta = 2 \sin \frac{\alpha - \beta}{2} \cos \frac{\alpha + \beta}{2} \tag{7}$$

$$\cos \alpha + \cos \beta = 2 \cos \frac{\alpha + \beta}{2} \cos \frac{\alpha - \beta}{2} \tag{8}$$

$$\cos \alpha - \cos \beta = -2 \sin \frac{\alpha + \beta}{2} \sin \frac{\alpha - \beta}{2} \tag{9}$$

We will derive formula (6) and leave the derivations of formulas (7) through (9) as exercises (see Problems 54 through 56).

Proof

$$2 \sin \frac{\alpha + \beta}{2} \cos \frac{\alpha - \beta}{2} = 2 \cdot \frac{1}{2} \left[\sin\left(\frac{\alpha + \beta}{2} + \frac{\alpha - \beta}{2} \right) + \sin\left(\frac{\alpha + \beta}{2} - \frac{\alpha - \beta}{2} \right) \right]$$

↑
Product-to-Sum Formula (3)

$$= \sin \frac{2\alpha}{2} + \sin \frac{2\beta}{2} = \sin \alpha + \sin \beta \qquad \blacksquare$$

EXAMPLE 2

Expressing Sums (or Differences) as a Product

Express each sum or difference as a product of sines and/or cosines.

(a) $\sin(5\theta) - \sin(3\theta)$ (b) $\cos(3\theta) + \cos(2\theta)$

Solution (a) Use formula (7) to get

$$\sin(5\theta) - \sin(3\theta) = 2 \sin \frac{5\theta - 3\theta}{2} \cos \frac{5\theta + 3\theta}{2}$$

$$= 2 \sin \theta \cos(4\theta)$$

(b) $\cos(3\theta) + \cos(2\theta) = 2 \cos \dfrac{3\theta + 2\theta}{2} \cos \dfrac{3\theta - 2\theta}{2}$ Formula (8)

$$= 2 \cos \frac{5\theta}{2} \cos \frac{\theta}{2}$$

Now Work PROBLEM 17

7.7 Assess Your Understanding

Skill Building

In Problems 1–6, find the exact value of each expression.

1. $\sin 195° \cdot \cos 75°$ **2.** $\cos 285° \cdot \cos 195°$ **3.** $\sin 285° \cdot \sin 75°$

4. $\sin 75° + \sin 15°$ **5.** $\cos 255° - \cos 195°$ **6.** $\sin 255° - \sin 15°$

In Problems 7–16, express each product as a sum containing only sines or only cosines.

7. $\sin(4\theta) \sin(2\theta)$ **8.** $\cos(4\theta) \cos(2\theta)$ **9.** $\sin(4\theta) \cos(2\theta)$ **10.** $\sin(3\theta) \sin(5\theta)$ **11.** $\cos(3\theta) \cos(5\theta)$

12. $\sin(4\theta) \cos(6\theta)$ **13.** $\sin \theta \sin(2\theta)$ **14.** $\cos(3\theta) \cos(4\theta)$ **15.** $\sin \dfrac{3\theta}{2} \cos \dfrac{\theta}{2}$ **16.** $\sin \dfrac{\theta}{2} \cos \dfrac{5\theta}{2}$

In Problems 17–24, express each sum or difference as a product of sines and/or cosines.

17. $\sin(4\theta) - \sin(2\theta)$ **18.** $\sin(4\theta) + \sin(2\theta)$ **19.** $\cos(2\theta) + \cos(4\theta)$ **20.** $\cos(5\theta) - \cos(3\theta)$

21. $\sin \theta + \sin(3\theta)$ **22.** $\cos \theta + \cos(3\theta)$ **23.** $\cos \dfrac{\theta}{2} - \cos \dfrac{3\theta}{2}$ **24.** $\sin \dfrac{\theta}{2} - \sin \dfrac{3\theta}{2}$

In Problems 25–42, establish each identity.

25. $\dfrac{\sin \theta + \sin(3\theta)}{2 \sin(2\theta)} = \cos \theta$ **26.** $\dfrac{\cos \theta + \cos(3\theta)}{2 \cos(2\theta)} = \cos \theta$ **27.** $\dfrac{\sin(4\theta) + \sin(2\theta)}{\cos(4\theta) + \cos(2\theta)} = \tan(3\theta)$

28. $\dfrac{\cos \theta - \cos(3\theta)}{\sin(3\theta) - \sin \theta} = \tan(2\theta)$ **29.** $\dfrac{\cos \theta - \cos(3\theta)}{\sin \theta + \sin(3\theta)} = \tan \theta$ **30.** $\dfrac{\cos \theta - \cos(5\theta)}{\sin \theta + \sin(5\theta)} = \tan(2\theta)$

31. $\sin \theta [\sin \theta + \sin(3\theta)] = \cos \theta [\cos \theta - \cos(3\theta)]$ **32.** $\sin \theta [\sin(3\theta) + \sin(5\theta)] = \cos \theta [\cos(3\theta) - \cos(5\theta)]$

33. $\dfrac{\sin(4\theta) + \sin(8\theta)}{\cos(4\theta) + \cos(8\theta)} = \tan(6\theta)$ **34.** $\dfrac{\sin(4\theta) - \sin(8\theta)}{\cos(4\theta) - \cos(8\theta)} = -\cot(6\theta)$

35. $\dfrac{\sin(4\theta) + \sin(8\theta)}{\sin(4\theta) - \sin(8\theta)} = -\dfrac{\tan(6\theta)}{\tan(2\theta)}$ **36.** $\dfrac{\cos(4\theta) - \cos(8\theta)}{\cos(4\theta) + \cos(8\theta)} = \tan(2\theta) \tan(6\theta)$

37. $\dfrac{\sin \alpha + \sin \beta}{\sin \alpha - \sin \beta} = \tan \dfrac{\alpha + \beta}{2} \cot \dfrac{\alpha - \beta}{2}$

38. $\dfrac{\cos \alpha + \cos \beta}{\cos \alpha - \cos \beta} = -\cot \dfrac{\alpha + \beta}{2} \cot \dfrac{\alpha - \beta}{2}$

39. $\dfrac{\sin \alpha + \sin \beta}{\cos \alpha + \cos \beta} = \tan \dfrac{\alpha + \beta}{2}$

40. $\dfrac{\sin \alpha - \sin \beta}{\cos \alpha - \cos \beta} = -\cot \dfrac{\alpha + \beta}{2}$

41. $1 + \cos(2\theta) + \cos(4\theta) + \cos(6\theta) = 4 \cos \theta \cos(2\theta) \cos(3\theta)$

42. $1 - \cos(2\theta) + \cos(4\theta) - \cos(6\theta) = 4 \sin \theta \cos(2\theta) \sin(3\theta)$

In Problems 43–46, solve each equation on the interval $0 \le \theta < 2\pi$.

43. $\sin(2\theta) + \sin(4\theta) = 0$

44. $\cos(2\theta) + \cos(4\theta) = 0$

45. $\cos(4\theta) - \cos(6\theta) = 0$

46. $\sin(4\theta) - \sin(6\theta) = 0$

Applications and Extensions

47. Touch-Tone Phones On a Touch-Tone phone, each button produces a unique sound. The sound produced is the sum of two tones, given by

$$y = \sin(2\pi l t) \quad \text{and} \quad y = \sin(2\pi h t)$$

where l and h are the low and high frequencies (cycles per second) shown on the illustration. For example, if you touch 7, the low frequency is $l = 852$ cycles per second and the high frequency is $h = 1209$ cycles per second. The sound emitted by touching 7 is

$$y = \sin[2\pi(852)t] + \sin[2\pi(1209)t]$$

Touch-Tone phone

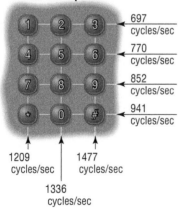

697 cycles/sec
770 cycles/sec
852 cycles/sec
941 cycles/sec

1209 cycles/sec   1477 cycles/sec

1336 cycles/sec

(a) Write this sound as a product of sines and/or cosines.
(b) Determine the maximum value of y.
(c) Graph the sound emitted by touching 7.

48. Touch-Tone Phones

(a) Write the sound emitted by touching the # key as a product of sines and/or cosines.
(b) Determine the maximum value of y.
(c) Graph the sound emitted by touching the # key.

49. Moment of Inertia The moment of inertia I of an object is a measure of how easy it is to rotate the object about some fixed point. In engineering mechanics, it is sometimes necessary to compute moments of inertia with respect to a set of rotated axes. These moments are given by the equations

$$I_u = I_x \cos^2 \theta + I_y \sin^2 \theta - 2I_{xy} \sin \theta \cos \theta$$
$$I_v = I_x \sin^2 \theta + I_y \cos^2 \theta + 2I_{xy} \sin \theta \cos \theta$$

Use Product-to-Sum Formulas to show that

$$I_u = \frac{I_x + I_y}{2} + \frac{I_x - I_y}{2} \cos(2\theta) - I_{xy} \sin(2\theta)$$

and

$$I_v = \frac{I_x + I_y}{2} - \frac{I_x - I_y}{2} \cos(2\theta) + I_{xy} \sin(2\theta)$$

Source: Adapted from Hibbeler, *Engineering Mechanics: Statics*, 10th ed., Prentice Hall © 2004.

50. Projectile Motion The range R of a projectile propelled downward from the top of an inclined plane at an angle θ to the inclined plane is given by

$$R(\theta) = \frac{2v_0^2 \sin \theta \cos(\theta - \phi)}{g \cos^2 \phi}$$

where v_0 is the initial velocity of the projectile, ϕ is the angle the plane makes with respect to the horizontal, and g is acceleration due to gravity.

(a) Show that for fixed v_0 and ϕ the maximum range down the incline is given by $R_{\max} = \dfrac{v_0^2}{g(1 - \sin \phi)}$.

(b) Determine the maximum range if the projectile has an initial velocity of 50 meters/second, the angle of the plane is $\phi = 35°$, and $g = 9.8$ meters/second^2.

51. If $\alpha + \beta + \gamma = \pi$, show that

$$\sin(2\alpha) + \sin(2\beta) + \sin(2\gamma) = 4 \sin \alpha \sin \beta \sin \gamma$$

52. If $\alpha + \beta + \gamma = \pi$, show that

$$\tan \alpha + \tan \beta + \tan \gamma = \tan \alpha \tan \beta \tan \gamma$$

53. Derive formula (3).

54. Derive formula (7).

55. Derive formula (8).

56. Derive formula (9).

CHAPTER REVIEW

Things to Know

Definitions of the six inverse trigonometric functions

$y = \sin^{-1} x$ means $x = \sin y$ where $-1 \le x \le 1$, $\quad -\dfrac{\pi}{2} \le y \le \dfrac{\pi}{2}$ (p. 437)

$y = \cos^{-1} x$ means $x = \cos y$ where $-1 \le x \le 1$, $\quad 0 \le y \le \pi$ (p. 440)

$y = \tan^{-1} x$ means $x = \tan y$ where $-\infty < x < \infty$, $\quad -\dfrac{\pi}{2} < y < \dfrac{\pi}{2}$ (p. 443)

$y = \sec^{-1} x$ means $x = \sec y$ where $|x| \ge 1$, $\quad 0 \le y \le \pi$, $\quad y \ne \dfrac{\pi}{2}$ (p. 450)

$y = \csc^{-1} x$ means $x = \csc y$ where $|x| \ge 1$, $\quad -\dfrac{\pi}{2} \le y \le \dfrac{\pi}{2}$, $\quad y \ne 0$ (p. 450)

$y = \cot^{-1} x$ means $x = \cot y$ where $-\infty < x < \infty$, $\quad 0 < y < \pi$ (p. 450)

Sum and Difference Formulas (pp. 472, 475, and 477)

$$\cos(\alpha + \beta) = \cos\alpha\cos\beta - \sin\alpha\sin\beta \qquad \cos(\alpha - \beta) = \cos\alpha\cos\beta + \sin\alpha\sin\beta$$

$$\sin(\alpha + \beta) = \sin\alpha\cos\beta + \cos\alpha\sin\beta \qquad \sin(\alpha - \beta) = \sin\alpha\cos\beta - \cos\alpha\sin\beta$$

$$\tan(\alpha + \beta) = \frac{\tan\alpha + \tan\beta}{1 - \tan\alpha\tan\beta} \qquad \tan(\alpha - \beta) = \frac{\tan\alpha - \tan\beta}{1 + \tan\alpha\tan\beta}$$

Double-angle Formulas (pp. 484 and 485)

$$\sin(2\theta) = 2\sin\theta\cos\theta \qquad \cos(2\theta) = \cos^2\theta - \sin^2\theta \qquad \tan(2\theta) = \frac{2\tan\theta}{1 - \tan^2\theta}$$

$$\cos(2\theta) = 2\cos^2\theta - 1 \qquad \cos(2\theta) = 1 - 2\sin^2\theta$$

Half-angle Formulas (pp. 488 and 490)

$$\sin^2\frac{\alpha}{2} = \frac{1 - \cos\alpha}{2} \qquad \cos^2\frac{\alpha}{2} = \frac{1 + \cos\alpha}{2} \qquad \tan^2\frac{\alpha}{2} = \frac{1 - \cos\alpha}{1 + \cos\alpha}$$

$$\sin\frac{\alpha}{2} = \pm\sqrt{\frac{1 - \cos\alpha}{2}} \qquad \cos\frac{\alpha}{2} = \pm\sqrt{\frac{1 + \cos\alpha}{2}} \qquad \tan\frac{\alpha}{2} = \pm\sqrt{\frac{1 - \cos\alpha}{1 + \cos\alpha}} = \frac{1 - \cos\alpha}{\sin\alpha} = \frac{\sin\alpha}{1 + \cos\alpha}$$

where the $+$ or $-$ is determined by the quadrant of $\dfrac{\alpha}{2}$.

Product-to-Sum Formulas (p. 494)

$$\sin\alpha\sin\beta = \frac{1}{2}[\cos(\alpha - \beta) - \cos(\alpha + \beta)]$$

$$\cos\alpha\cos\beta = \frac{1}{2}[\cos(\alpha - \beta) + \cos(\alpha + \beta)]$$

$$\sin\alpha\cos\beta = \frac{1}{2}[\sin(\alpha + \beta) + \sin(\alpha - \beta)]$$

Sum-to-Product Formulas (p. 495)

$$\sin\alpha + \sin\beta = 2\sin\frac{\alpha + \beta}{2}\cos\frac{\alpha - \beta}{2} \qquad \sin\alpha - \sin\beta = 2\sin\frac{\alpha - \beta}{2}\cos\frac{\alpha + \beta}{2}$$

$$\cos\alpha + \cos\beta = 2\cos\frac{\alpha + \beta}{2}\cos\frac{\alpha - \beta}{2} \qquad \cos\alpha - \cos\beta = -2\sin\frac{\alpha + \beta}{2}\sin\frac{\alpha - \beta}{2}$$

Objectives

Section		You should be able to ...	Example(s)	Review Exercises
7.1	1	Find the exact value of an inverse sine, cosine, or tangent function (p. 437)	1, 2, 6, 7, 9	1–6
	2	Find an approximate value of an inverse sine function (p. 438)	3	121–124
	3	Use properties of inverse functions to find exact values of certain composite functions (p. 439)	4, 5, 8	9–20
	4	Find the inverse function of a trigonometric function (p. 444)	10	33–36
	5	Solve equations involving inverse trigonometric functions (p. 445)	11	133, 134
7.2	1	Find the exact value of expressions involving the inverse sine, cosine, and tangent functions (p. 449)	1–3	21–32
	2	Define the inverse secant, cosecant, and cotangent functions (p. 450)	4	7, 8, 29, 30
	3	Use a calculator to evaluate $\sec^{-1} x$, $\csc^{-1} x$, and $\cot^{-1} x$ (p. 450)	5	125, 126
	4	Write a trigonometric expression as an algebraic expression (p. 451)	6	37–40
7.3	1	Solve equations involving a single trigonometric function (p. 454)	1–5	97–106
	2	Solve trigonometric equations using a calculator (p. 457)	6	107, 108
	3	Solve trigonometric equations quadratic in form (p. 458)	7	113, 114
	4	Solve trigonometric equations using fundamental identities (p. 458)	8, 9	109–112, 115–118
	5	Solve trigonometric equations using a graphing utility (p. 459)	10	127–132
7.4	1	Use algebra to simplify trigonometric expressions (p. 465)	1	41–72
	2	Establish identities (p. 466)	2–8	41–57
7.5	1	Use sum and difference formulas to find exact values (p. 473)	1, 2	73–78, 81–90(a)–(d), 135
	2	Use sum and difference formulas to establish identities (p. 474)	3–8	59–62
	3	Use sum and difference formulas involving inverse trigonometric functions (p. 478)	9, 10	91–94
	4	Solve trigonometric equations linear in sine and cosine (p. 479)	11, 12	119, 120
7.6	1	Use double-angle formulas to find exact values (p. 484)	1	81–90(e), (f), 95, 96
	2	Use double-angle formulas to establish identities (p. 485)	2–5	58, 65–67
	3	Use half-angle formulas to find exact values (p. 488)	6, 7	79–90(g), (h), 135
7.7	1	Express products as sums (p. 494)	1	68
	2	Express sums as products (p. 495)	2	69–72

Review Exercises

In Problems 1–8, find the exact value of each expression. Do not use a calculator.

1. $\sin^{-1} 1$

2. $\cos^{-1} 0$

3. $\tan^{-1} 1$

4. $\sin^{-1}\left(-\dfrac{1}{2}\right)$

5. $\cos^{-1}\left(-\dfrac{\sqrt{3}}{2}\right)$

6. $\tan^{-1}\left(-\sqrt{3}\right)$

7. $\sec^{-1}\sqrt{2}$

8. $\cot^{-1}(-1)$

In Problems 9–32, find the exact value, if any, of each composite function. If there is no value, say it is "not defined." Do not use a calculator.

9. $\sin^{-1}\left(\sin\dfrac{3\pi}{8}\right)$

10. $\cos^{-1}\left(\cos\dfrac{3\pi}{4}\right)$

11. $\tan^{-1}\left(\tan\dfrac{2\pi}{3}\right)$

12. $\sin^{-1}\left[\sin\left(-\dfrac{\pi}{8}\right)\right]$

13. $\cos^{-1}\left(\cos\dfrac{15\pi}{7}\right)$

14. $\sin^{-1}\left[\sin\left(-\dfrac{8\pi}{9}\right)\right]$

15. $\sin(\sin^{-1} 0.9)$

16. $\cos(\cos^{-1} 0.6)$

17. $\cos[\cos^{-1}(-0.3)]$

18. $\tan\left[\tan^{-1} 5\right]$

19. $\cos[\cos^{-1}(-1.6)]$

20. $\sin(\sin^{-1} 1.6)$

21. $\sin^{-1}\left(\cos\dfrac{2\pi}{3}\right)$

22. $\cos^{-1}\left(\tan\dfrac{3\pi}{4}\right)$

23. $\tan^{-1}\left(\tan\dfrac{7\pi}{4}\right)$

24. $\cos^{-1}\left(\cos\dfrac{7\pi}{6}\right)$

25. $\tan\left[\sin^{-1}\left(-\dfrac{\sqrt{3}}{2}\right)\right]$

26. $\tan\left[\cos^{-1}\left(-\dfrac{1}{2}\right)\right]$

27. $\sec\left(\tan^{-1}\dfrac{\sqrt{3}}{3}\right)$

28. $\csc\left(\sin^{-1}\dfrac{\sqrt{3}}{2}\right)$

29. $\sin\left(\cot^{-1}\dfrac{3}{4}\right)$

30. $\cos\left(\csc^{-1}\dfrac{5}{3}\right)$

31. $\tan\left[\sin^{-1}\left(-\dfrac{4}{5}\right)\right]$

32. $\tan\left[\cos^{-1}\left(-\dfrac{3}{5}\right)\right]$

In Problems 33–36, find the inverse function f^{-1} of each function f. Find the range of f and the domain and range of f^{-1}.

33. $f(x) = 2 \sin(3x)$
$-\dfrac{\pi}{6} \le x \le \dfrac{\pi}{6}$

34. $f(x) = \tan(2x + 3) - 1$
$-\dfrac{3}{2} - \dfrac{\pi}{4} < x < -\dfrac{3}{2} + \dfrac{\pi}{4}$

35. $f(x) = -\cos x + 3$
$0 \le x \le \pi$

36. $f(x) = 2 \sin(-x + 1)$
$1 - \dfrac{\pi}{2} \le x \le 1 + \dfrac{\pi}{2}$

In Problems 37–40, write each trigonometric expression as an algebraic expression in u.

37. $\cos(\sin^{-1} u)$

38. $\cos(\csc^{-1} u)$

39. $\sin(\csc^{-1} u)$

40. $\tan(\csc^{-1} u)$

In Problems 41–72, establish each identity.

41. $\tan \theta \cot \theta - \sin^2 \theta = \cos^2 \theta$

42. $\sin \theta \csc \theta - \sin^2 \theta = \cos^2 \theta$

43. $\sin^2 \theta(1 + \cot^2 \theta) = 1$

44. $(1 - \sin^2 \theta)(1 + \tan^2 \theta) = 1$

45. $5 \cos^2 \theta + 3 \sin^2 \theta = 3 + 2 \cos^2 \theta$

46. $4 \sin^2 \theta + 2 \cos^2 \theta = 4 - 2 \cos^2 \theta$

47. $\dfrac{1 - \cos \theta}{\sin \theta} + \dfrac{\sin \theta}{1 - \cos \theta} = 2 \csc \theta$

48. $\dfrac{\sin \theta}{1 + \cos \theta} + \dfrac{1 + \cos \theta}{\sin \theta} = 2 \csc \theta$

49. $\dfrac{\cos \theta}{\cos \theta - \sin \theta} = \dfrac{1}{1 - \tan \theta}$

50. $1 - \dfrac{\sin^2 \theta}{1 + \cos \theta} = \cos \theta$

51. $\dfrac{\csc \theta}{1 + \csc \theta} = \dfrac{1 - \sin \theta}{\cos^2 \theta}$

52. $\dfrac{1 + \sec \theta}{\sec \theta} = \dfrac{\sin^2 \theta}{1 - \cos \theta}$

53. $\csc \theta - \sin \theta = \cos \theta \cot \theta$

54. $\dfrac{\csc \theta}{1 - \cos \theta} = \dfrac{1 + \cos \theta}{\sin^3 \theta}$

55. $\dfrac{1 - \sin \theta}{\sec \theta} = \dfrac{\cos^3 \theta}{1 + \sin \theta}$

56. $\dfrac{1 - \cos \theta}{1 + \cos \theta} = (\csc \theta - \cot \theta)^2$

57. $\dfrac{1 - 2 \sin^2 \theta}{\sin \theta \cos \theta} = \cot \theta - \tan \theta$

58. $\dfrac{(2 \sin^2 \theta - 1)^2}{\sin^4 \theta - \cos^4 \theta} = 1 - 2 \cos^2 \theta$

59. $\dfrac{\cos(\alpha + \beta)}{\cos \alpha \sin \beta} = \cot \beta - \tan \alpha$

60. $\dfrac{\sin(\alpha - \beta)}{\sin \alpha \cos \beta} = 1 - \cot \alpha \tan \beta$

61. $\dfrac{\cos(\alpha - \beta)}{\cos \alpha \cos \beta} = 1 + \tan \alpha \tan \beta$

62. $\dfrac{\cos(\alpha + \beta)}{\sin \alpha \cos \beta} = \cot \alpha - \tan \beta$

63. $(1 + \cos \theta) \tan \dfrac{\theta}{2} = \sin \theta$

64. $\sin \theta \tan \dfrac{\theta}{2} = 1 - \cos \theta$

65. $2 \cot \theta \cot(2\theta) = \cot^2 \theta - 1$

66. $2 \sin(2\theta)(1 - 2 \sin^2 \theta) = \sin(4\theta)$

67. $1 - 8 \sin^2 \theta \cos^2 \theta = \cos(4\theta)$

68. $\dfrac{\sin(3\theta) \cos \theta - \sin \theta \cos(3\theta)}{\sin(2\theta)} = 1$

69. $\dfrac{\sin(2\theta) + \sin(4\theta)}{\cos(2\theta) + \cos(4\theta)} = \tan(3\theta)$

70. $\dfrac{\sin(2\theta) + \sin(4\theta)}{\sin(2\theta) - \sin(4\theta)} + \dfrac{\tan(3\theta)}{\tan \theta} = 0$

71. $\dfrac{\cos(2\theta) - \cos(4\theta)}{\cos(2\theta) + \cos(4\theta)} - \tan \theta \tan(3\theta) = 0$

72. $\cos(2\theta) - \cos(10\theta) = \tan(4\theta)[\sin(2\theta) + \sin(10\theta)]$

In Problems 73–80, find the exact value of each expression.

73. $\sin 165°$

74. $\tan 105°$

75. $\cos \dfrac{5\pi}{12}$

76. $\sin\left(-\dfrac{\pi}{12}\right)$

77. $\cos 80° \cos 20° + \sin 80° \sin 20°$

78. $\sin 70° \cos 40° - \cos 70° \sin 40°$

79. $\tan \dfrac{\pi}{8}$

80. $\sin \dfrac{5\pi}{8}$

In Problems 81–90, use the information given about the angles α and β to find the exact value of:

(a) $\sin(\alpha + \beta)$

(b) $\cos(\alpha + \beta)$

(c) $\sin(\alpha - \beta)$

(d) $\tan(\alpha + \beta)$

(e) $\sin(2\alpha)$

(f) $\cos(2\beta)$

(g) $\sin \dfrac{\beta}{2}$

(h) $\cos \dfrac{\alpha}{2}$

81. $\sin \alpha = \dfrac{4}{5}, 0 < \alpha < \dfrac{\pi}{2}; \sin \beta = \dfrac{5}{13}, \dfrac{\pi}{2} < \beta < \pi$

82. $\cos \alpha = \dfrac{4}{5}, 0 < \alpha < \dfrac{\pi}{2}; \cos \beta = \dfrac{5}{13}, -\dfrac{\pi}{2} < \beta < 0$

83. $\sin \alpha = -\dfrac{3}{5}, \pi < \alpha < \dfrac{3\pi}{2}; \cos \beta = \dfrac{12}{13}, \dfrac{3\pi}{2} < \beta < 2\pi$

84. $\sin \alpha = -\dfrac{4}{5}, -\dfrac{\pi}{2} < \alpha < 0; \cos \beta = -\dfrac{5}{13}, \dfrac{\pi}{2} < \beta < \pi$

85. $\tan\alpha = \dfrac{3}{4}, \pi < \alpha < \dfrac{3\pi}{2}; \tan\beta = \dfrac{12}{5}, 0 < \beta < \dfrac{\pi}{2}$

86. $\tan\alpha = -\dfrac{4}{3}, \dfrac{\pi}{2} < \alpha < \pi; \cot\beta = \dfrac{12}{5}, \pi < \beta < \dfrac{3\pi}{2}$

87. $\sec\alpha = 2, -\dfrac{\pi}{2} < \alpha < 0; \sec\beta = 3, \dfrac{3\pi}{2} < \beta < 2\pi$

88. $\csc\alpha = 2, \dfrac{\pi}{2} < \alpha < \pi; \sec\beta = -3, \dfrac{\pi}{2} < \beta < \pi$

89. $\sin\alpha = -\dfrac{2}{3}, \pi < \alpha < \dfrac{3\pi}{2}; \cos\beta = -\dfrac{2}{3}, \pi < \beta < \dfrac{3\pi}{2}$

90. $\tan\alpha = -2, \dfrac{\pi}{2} < \alpha < \pi; \cot\beta = -2, \dfrac{\pi}{2} < \beta < \pi$

In Problems 91–96, find the exact value of each expression.

91. $\cos\left(\sin^{-1}\dfrac{3}{5} - \cos^{-1}\dfrac{1}{2}\right)$

92. $\sin\left(\cos^{-1}\dfrac{5}{13} - \cos^{-1}\dfrac{4}{5}\right)$

93. $\tan\left[\sin^{-1}\left(-\dfrac{1}{2}\right) - \tan^{-1}\dfrac{3}{4}\right]$

94. $\cos\left[\tan^{-1}(-1) + \cos^{-1}\left(-\dfrac{4}{5}\right)\right]$

95. $\sin\left[2\cos^{-1}\left(-\dfrac{3}{5}\right)\right]$

96. $\cos\left(2\tan^{-1}\dfrac{4}{3}\right)$

In Problems 97–120, solve each equation on the interval $0 \le \theta < 2\pi$.

97. $\cos\theta = \dfrac{1}{2}$

98. $\sin\theta = -\dfrac{\sqrt{3}}{2}$

99. $2\cos\theta + \sqrt{2} = 0$

100. $\tan\theta + \sqrt{3} = 0$

101. $\sin(2\theta) + 1 = 0$

102. $\cos(2\theta) = 0$

103. $\tan(2\theta) = 0$

104. $\sin(3\theta) = 1$

105. $\sec^2\theta = 4$

106. $\csc^2\theta = 1$

107. $0.2\sin\theta = 0.05$

108. $0.9\cos(2\theta) = 0.7$

109. $\sin\theta + \sin(2\theta) = 0$

110. $\cos(2\theta) = \sin\theta$

111. $\sin(2\theta) - \cos\theta - 2\sin\theta + 1 = 0$

112. $\sin(2\theta) - \sin\theta - 2\cos\theta + 1 = 0$

113. $2\sin^2\theta - 3\sin\theta + 1 = 0$

114. $2\cos^2\theta + \cos\theta - 1 = 0$

115. $4\sin^2\theta = 1 + 4\cos\theta$

116. $8 - 12\sin^2\theta = 4\cos^2\theta$

117. $\sin(2\theta) = \sqrt{2}\cos\theta$

118. $1 + \sqrt{3}\cos\theta + \cos(2\theta) = 0$

119. $\sin\theta - \cos\theta = 1$

120. $\sin\theta - \sqrt{3}\cos\theta = 2$

In Problems 121–126, use a calculator to find an approximate value for each expression, rounded to two decimal places.

121. $\sin^{-1}0.7$

122. $\cos^{-1}\dfrac{4}{5}$

123. $\tan^{-1}(-2)$

124. $\cos^{-1}(-0.2)$

125. $\sec^{-1}3$

126. $\cot^{-1}(-4)$

In Problems 127–132, use a graphing utility to solve each equation on the interval $0 \le x \le 2\pi$. Approximate any solutions rounded to two decimal places.

127. $2x = 5\cos x$

128. $2x = 5\sin x$

129. $2\sin x + 3\cos x = 4x$

130. $3\cos x + x = \sin x$

131. $\sin x = \ln x$

132. $\sin x = e^{-x}$

In Problems 133 and 134, find the exact solution of each equation.

133. $-3\sin^{-1}x = \pi$

134. $2\cos^{-1}x + \pi = 4\cos^{-1}x$

135. Use a half-angle formula to find the exact value of $\sin 15°$. Then use a difference formula to find the exact value of $\sin 15°$. Show that the answers found are the same.

136. If you are given the value of $\cos\theta$ and want the exact value of $\cos(2\theta)$, what form of the double-angle formula for $\cos(2\theta)$ is most efficient to use?

CHAPTER TEST

CHAPTER
Test Prep
VIDEOS

The Chapter Test Prep Videos are step-by-step test solutions available in the Video Resources DVD, in MyMathLab, or on this text's You Tube Channel. Flip back to the Student Resources page to see the exact web address for this text's YouTube channel.

In Problems 1–6, find the exact value of each expression. Express angles in radians.

1. $\sec^{-1}\left(\dfrac{2}{\sqrt{3}}\right)$

2. $\sin^{-1}\left(-\dfrac{\sqrt{2}}{2}\right)$

3. $\sin^{-1}\left(\sin\dfrac{11\pi}{5}\right)$

4. $\tan\left(\tan^{-1}\dfrac{7}{3}\right)$

5. $\cot\left(\csc^{-1}\sqrt{10}\right)$

6. $\sec\left(\cos^{-1}\left(-\dfrac{3}{4}\right)\right)$

In Problems 7–10, use a calculator to evaluate each expression. Express angles in radians rounded to two decimal places.

7. $\sin^{-1}0.382$

8. $\sec^{-1}1.4$

9. $\tan^{-1}3$

10. $\cot^{-1}5$

In Problems 11–16 establish each identity.

11. $\dfrac{\csc\theta + \cot\theta}{\sec\theta + \tan\theta} = \dfrac{\sec\theta - \tan\theta}{\csc\theta - \cot\theta}$

12. $\sin\theta\tan\theta + \cos\theta = \sec\theta$

13. $\tan\theta + \cot\theta = 2\csc(2\theta)$

14. $\dfrac{\sin(\alpha + \beta)}{\tan\alpha + \tan\beta} = \cos\alpha\cos\beta$

15. $\sin(3\theta) = 3\sin\theta - 4\sin^3\theta$

16. $\dfrac{\tan\theta - \cot\theta}{\tan\theta + \cot\theta} = 1 - 2\cos^2\theta$

In Problems 17–24 use sum, difference, product, or half-angle formulas to find the exact value of each expression.

17. $\cos 15°$

18. $\tan 75°$

19. $\sin\left(\dfrac{1}{2}\cos^{-1}\dfrac{3}{5}\right)$

20. $\tan\left(2\sin^{-1}\dfrac{6}{11}\right)$

21. $\cos\left(\sin^{-1}\dfrac{2}{3} + \tan^{-1}\dfrac{3}{2}\right)$

22. $\sin 75° \cos 15°$

23. $\sin 75° + \sin 15°$

24. $\cos 65° \cos 20° + \sin 65° \sin 20°$

In Problems 25–29, solve each equation on $0 \leq \theta < 2\pi$.

25. $4\sin^2\theta - 3 = 0$

26. $-3\cos\left(\dfrac{\pi}{2} - \theta\right) = \tan\theta$

27. $\cos^2\theta + 2\sin\theta\cos\theta - \sin^2\theta = 0$

28. $\sin(\theta + 1) = \cos\theta$

29. $4\sin^2\theta + 7\sin\theta = 2$

CUMULATIVE REVIEW

1. Find the real solutions, if any, of the equation $3x^2 + x - 1 = 0$.

2. Find an equation for the line containing the points $(-2, 5)$ and $(4, -1)$. What is the distance between these points? What is their midpoint?

3. Test the equation $3x + y^2 = 9$ for symmetry with respect to the x-axis, y-axis, and origin. List the intercepts.

4. Use transformations to graph the equation $y = |x - 3| + 2$.

5. Use transformations to graph the equation $y = 3e^x - 2$.

6. Use transformations to graph the equation
$y = \cos\left(x - \dfrac{\pi}{2}\right) - 1$.

7. Sketch a graph of each of the following functions. Label at least three points on each graph. Name the inverse function of each and show its graph.
   (a) $y = x^3$
   (b) $y = e^x$

(c) $y = \sin x, \quad -\dfrac{\pi}{2} \leq x \leq \dfrac{\pi}{2}$

(d) $y = \cos x, \quad 0 \leq x \leq \pi$

8. If $\sin\theta = -\dfrac{1}{3}$ and $\pi < \theta < \dfrac{3\pi}{2}$, find the exact value of:
   (a) $\cos\theta$
   (b) $\tan\theta$
   (c) $\sin(2\theta)$
   (d) $\cos(2\theta)$
   (e) $\sin\left(\dfrac{1}{2}\theta\right)$
   (f) $\cos\left(\dfrac{1}{2}\theta\right)$

9. Find the exact value of $\cos(\tan^{-1}2)$.

10. If $\sin\alpha = \dfrac{1}{3}, \dfrac{\pi}{2} < \alpha < \pi$, and $\cos\beta = -\dfrac{1}{3}, \pi < \beta < \dfrac{3\pi}{2}$, find the exact value of:
   (a) $\cos\alpha$
   (b) $\sin\beta$
   (c) $\cos(2\alpha)$
   (d) $\cos(\alpha + \beta)$
   (e) $\sin\dfrac{\beta}{2}$

11. For the function

$$f(x) = 2x^5 - x^4 - 4x^3 + 2x^2 + 2x - 1:$$

(a) Find the real zeros and their multiplicity.
(b) Find the intercepts.
(c) Find the power function that the graph of f resembles for large $|x|$.
(d) Graph f using a graphing utility.
(e) Approximate the turning points, if any exist.
(f) Use the information obtained in parts (a)–(e) to sketch a graph of f by hand.
(g) Identify the intervals on which f is increasing, decreasing, or constant.

12. If $f(x) = 2x^2 + 3x + 1$ and $g(x) = x^2 + 3x + 2$, solve:

(a) $f(x) = 0$ (b) $f(x) = g(x)$

(c) $f(x) > 0$ (d) $f(x) \geq g(x)$

CHAPTER PROJECTS

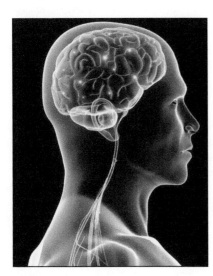

thoughts digitally and share these thoughts with anyone on the Web. By organizing your thoughts, you are able to see the big picture and then communicate this big picture to others. You are also able to see how various concepts relate to each other.

1. Go to *http://www.mindomo.com* and register. Learn how to use Mindomo. A great video on using Mindomo can be found at *http://www.screencast.com/users /Rose_Jenkins/folders/Default/media/edd9bd1b-62a7-45b3 -9dd2-fa467d2e8eb3*.

2. Use an Internet search engine to research Mind Mapping. Write a few paragraphs that explain the history and benefit of mind mapping.

3. Create a MindMap that explains the following:
(a) The six trigonometric functions and their properties (including the inverses of these functions)
(b) The fundamental trigonometric identities.
When creating your map, be creative. Perhaps you can share ideas about when a particular identity might be used, or when a particular identity cannot be used.

4. Share the MindMap so that students in your class can view it.

Internet-based Project

I. Mapping Your Mind The goal of this project is to organize the material learned in Chapters 6 and 7 in our minds. To do this, we will use mind mapping software called Mindomo. Mindomo is free software that allows you to organize your

The following projects are available on the Instructor's Resource Center (IRC):

II. Waves Wave motion is described by a sinusoidal equation. The Principle of Superposition of two waves is discussed.

III. Project at Motorola *Sending Pictures Wirelessly* The electronic transmission of pictures is made practical by image compression, mathematical methods that greatly reduce the number of bits of data used to compose the picture.

IV. Calculus of Differences Finding consecutive difference quotients is called finding finite differences and is used to analyze the graph of an unknown function.

Applications of Trigonometric Functions

Outline

From Lewis and Clark to Landsat

For $140, you can buy a handheld Global Positioning System receiver that will gauge your latitude and longitude to within a couple of meters. But in 1804, when Meriwether Lewis and William Clark ventured across the Louisiana Territory, a state of the art positioning system consisted of an octant, a pocket chronometer, and a surveyor's compass.

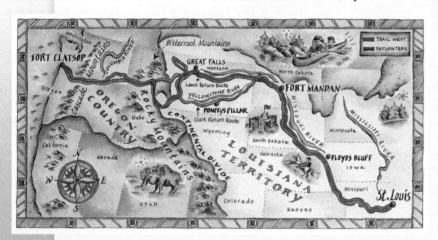

But somehow, Clark—the cartographer in the group—made do. When San Francisco map collector David Rumsey took his copy of Lewis and Clark's published map of their journey, scanned it into a computer, and matched landmarks such as river junctions against corresponding features on today's maps, he found that it took only a slight amount of digital stretching and twisting to make Clark's map conform to modern coordinates. In fact, Rumsey was able to combine Clark's depiction of his party's route to the Pacific with pages from government atlases from the 1870s and 1970s and photos from NASA Landsat satellites, creating a digital composite that documents not only a historic adventure, but also the history of mapmaking itself.

Source: Used with permission of *Technology Review*, from W. Roush, "From Lewis and Clark to Landsat: David Rumsey's Digital maps Marry Past and Present," 108, no. 7, © 2005; permission conveyed through Copyright Clearance Center, Inc.

—See the Chapter Project II—

◁ **A Look Back** In Chapter 6, we defined the six trigonometric functions using the unit circle. In particular, we learned to evaluate the trigonometric functions. We also learned how to graph sinusoidal functions. In Chapter 7, we defined the inverse trigonometric functions and solved equations involving the trigonometric functions.

A Look Ahead ▷ In this chapter, we define the trigonometric functions using right triangles and then use the trigonometric functions to solve applied problems. The first four sections deal with applications involving right triangles and *oblique triangles*, triangles that do not have a right angle. To solve problems involving oblique triangles, we will develop the Law of Sines and the Law of Cosines. We will also develop formulas for finding the area of a triangle.

The final section deals with applications of sinusoidal functions involving simple harmonic motion and damped motion.

8.1 Right Triangle Trigonometry; Applications

PREPARING FOR THIS SECTION *Before getting started, review the following:*

- Pythagorean Theorem (Appendix A, Section A.2, pp. A14–A15)
- Trigonometric Equations (Section 7.3, pp. 454–459)

 Now Work the 'Are You Prepared?' problems on page 512.

OBJECTIVES 1 Find the Value of Trigonometric Functions of Acute Angles Using Right Triangles (p. 505)
2 Use the Complementary Angle Theorem (p. 507)
3 Solve Right Triangles (p. 507)
4 Solve Applied Problems (p. 508)

1 Find the Value of Trigonometric Functions of Acute Angles Using Right Triangles

A triangle in which one angle is a right angle (90°) is called a **right triangle.** Recall that the side opposite the right angle is called the **hypotenuse,** and the remaining two sides are called the **legs** of the triangle. In Figure 1(a), we have labeled the hypotenuse as *c* to indicate that its length is *c* units, and, in a like manner, we have labeled the legs as *a* and *b*. Because the triangle is a right triangle, the Pythagorean Theorem tells us that

$$a^2 + b^2 = c^2$$

In Figure 1(a), we also show the angle θ. The angle θ is an **acute angle:** that is, $0° < \theta < 90°$ for θ measured in degrees and $0 < \theta < \dfrac{\pi}{2}$ for θ measured in radians.

Place θ in standard position, as shown in Figure 1(b). Then the coordinates of the point P are (a, b). Also, P is a point on the terminal side of θ that is on the circle $x^2 + y^2 = c^2$. (Do you see why?)

Figure 1

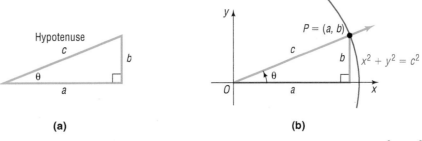

(a)   (b)

Now use the theorem on page 374 with a circle of radius c, $x^2 + y^2 = c^2$. By referring to the lengths of the sides of the triangle by the names hypotenuse (c), opposite (b), and adjacent (a), as indicated in Figure 2, we can express the trigonometric functions of θ as ratios of the sides of a right triangle.

Figure 2

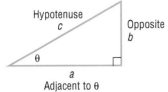

$$\sin \theta = \frac{\text{Opposite}}{\text{Hypotenuse}} = \frac{b}{c} \qquad \csc \theta = \frac{\text{Hypotenuse}}{\text{Opposite}} = \frac{c}{b}$$

$$\cos \theta = \frac{\text{Adjacent}}{\text{Hypotenuse}} = \frac{a}{c} \qquad \sec \theta = \frac{\text{Hypotenuse}}{\text{Adjacent}} = \frac{c}{a} \qquad \textbf{(1)}$$

$$\tan \theta = \frac{\text{Opposite}}{\text{Adjacent}} = \frac{b}{a} \qquad \cot \theta = \frac{\text{Adjacent}}{\text{Opposite}} = \frac{a}{b}$$

Notice that each trigonometric function of the acute angle θ is positive.

| EXAMPLE 1 | **Finding the Value of Trigonometric Functions from a Right Triangle** |

Find the exact value of the six trigonometric functions of the angle θ in Figure 3.

Solution We see in Figure 3 that the two given sides of the triangle are

$$c = \text{Hypotenuse} = 5, \quad a = \text{Adjacent} = 3$$

Figure 3

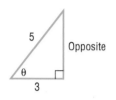

To find the length of the opposite side, we use the Pythagorean Theorem.

$$(\text{Adjacent})^2 + (\text{Opposite})^2 = (\text{Hypotenuse})^2$$
$$3^2 + (\text{Opposite})^2 = 5^2$$
$$(\text{Opposite})^2 = 25 - 9 = 16$$
$$\text{Opposite} = 4$$

Now that we know the lengths of the three sides, we use the ratios in equations (1) to find the value of each of the six trigonometric functions.

$$\sin\theta = \frac{\text{Opposite}}{\text{Hypotenuse}} = \frac{4}{5} \quad \cos\theta = \frac{\text{Adjacent}}{\text{Hypotenuse}} = \frac{3}{5} \quad \tan\theta = \frac{\text{Opposite}}{\text{Adjacent}} = \frac{4}{3}$$

$$\csc\theta = \frac{\text{Hypotenuse}}{\text{Opposite}} = \frac{5}{4} \quad \sec\theta = \frac{\text{Hypotenuse}}{\text{Adjacent}} = \frac{5}{3} \quad \cot\theta = \frac{\text{Adjacent}}{\text{Opposite}} = \frac{3}{4}$$

━━━━**Now Work** PROBLEM 9

The values of the trigonometric functions of an acute angle are ratios of the lengths of the sides of a right triangle. This way of viewing the trigonometric functions leads to many applications and, in fact, was the point of view used by early mathematicians (before calculus) in studying the subject of trigonometry.

| EXAMPLE 2 | **Constructing a Rain Gutter** |

A rain gutter is to be constructed of aluminum sheets 12 inches wide. See Figure 4(a). After marking off a length of 4 inches from each edge, the sides are bent up at an angle θ. See Figure 4(b).

(a) Express the area A of the opening as a function of θ.
    [**Hint:** Let b denote the vertical height of the bend.]

 (b) Graph $A = A(\theta)$. Find the angle θ that makes A largest. (This bend will allow the most water to flow through the gutter.)

Figure 4

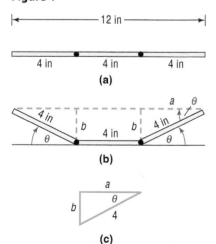

Solution

(a) Look again at Figure 4(b). The area A of the opening is the sum of the areas of two congruent right triangles and one rectangle. Look at Figure 4(c), which shows the triangle on the right in Figure 4(b) redrawn. We see that

$$\cos\theta = \frac{a}{4} \quad \text{so} \quad a = 4\cos\theta \qquad \sin\theta = \frac{b}{4} \quad \text{so} \quad b = 4\sin\theta$$

The area of the triangle is

$$\text{area} = \frac{1}{2}(\text{base})(\text{height}) = \frac{1}{2}ab = \frac{1}{2}(4\cos\theta)(4\sin\theta) = 8\sin\theta\cos\theta$$

So the area of the two congruent triangles is $16\sin\theta\cos\theta$.
    The rectangle has length 4 and height b, so its area is

$$4b = 4(4\sin\theta) = 16\sin\theta$$

Figure 5

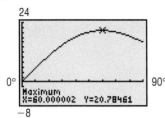

The area A of the opening is

$$A = \text{area of the two triangles} + \text{area of the rectangle}$$

$$A(\theta) = 16 \sin \theta \cos \theta + 16 \sin \theta = 16 \sin \theta(\cos \theta + 1)$$

(b) Figure 5 shows the graph of $A = A(\theta)$. Using MAXIMUM, the angle θ that makes A largest is $60°$.

2 Use the Complementary Angle Theorem

Two acute angles are called **complementary** if their sum is a right angle. Because the sum of the angles of any triangle is $180°$, it follows that, for a right triangle, the two acute angles are complementary.

Refer now to Figure 6. We have labeled the angle opposite side b as B and the angle opposite side a as A. Notice that side b is adjacent to angle A and side a is adjacent to angle B. As a result,

Figure 6

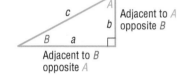

$$\sin B = \frac{b}{c} = \cos A \qquad \cos B = \frac{a}{c} = \sin A \qquad \tan B = \frac{b}{a} = \cot A$$

$$\csc B = \frac{c}{b} = \sec A \qquad \sec B = \frac{c}{a} = \csc A \qquad \cot B = \frac{a}{b} = \tan A \tag{2}$$

Because of these relationships, the functions sine and cosine, tangent and cotangent, and secant and cosecant are called **cofunctions** of each other. The identities (2) may be expressed in words as follows:

THEOREM

Complementary Angle Theorem

Cofunctions of complementary angles are equal.

Examples of this theorem are given next:

Complementary angles

$$\sin 30° = \cos 60°$$

Cofunctions

Complementary angles

$$\tan 40° = \cot 50°$$

Cofunctions

Complementary angles

$$\sec 80° = \csc 10°$$

Cofunctions

EXAMPLE 3   **Using the Complementary Angle Theorem**

(a) $\sin 62° = \cos(90° - 62°) = \cos 28°$

(b) $\tan \dfrac{\pi}{12} = \cot\left(\dfrac{\pi}{2} - \dfrac{\pi}{12}\right) = \cot \dfrac{5\pi}{12}$

(c) $\sin^2 40° + \sin^2 50° = \sin^2 40° + \cos^2 40° = 1$

$$\uparrow$$
$$\sin 50° = \cos 40°$$

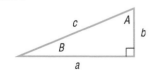
Now Work   PROBLEM **19**

3 Solve Right Triangles

Figure 7

In the discussion that follows, we will always label a right triangle so that side a is opposite angle A, side b is opposite angle B, and side c is the hypotenuse, as shown in Figure 7. **To solve a right triangle** means to find the missing lengths of its sides and the measurements of its angles. We shall follow the practice of expressing the lengths of the sides rounded to two decimal places and expressing angles in degrees rounded to one decimal place. (Be sure that your calculator is in degree mode.)

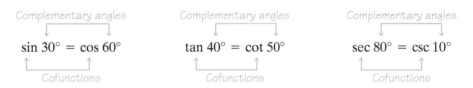

To solve a right triangle, we need to know one of the acute angles A or B and a side, or else two sides. Then we make use of the Pythagorean Theorem and the fact that the sum of the angles of a triangle is $180°$. The sum of the angles A and B in a right triangle is therefore $90°$.

THEOREM

For the right triangle shown in Figure 7, we have

$$c^2 = a^2 + b^2 \qquad A + B = 90°$$

EXAMPLE 4

Solving a Right Triangle

Use Figure 8. If $b = 2$ and $A = 40°$, find $a, c,$ and B.

Solution

Since $A = 40°$ and $A + B = 90°$, it follows that $B = 50°$. To find the sides a and c, use the facts that

$$\tan 40° = \frac{a}{2} \quad \text{and} \quad \cos 40° = \frac{2}{c}$$

Now solve for a and c.

$$a = 2 \tan 40° \approx 1.68 \quad \text{and} \quad c = \frac{2}{\cos 40°} \approx 2.61$$

Figure 8

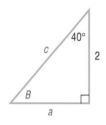

⟶ **Now Work** PROBLEM 29

EXAMPLE 5

Solving a Right Triangle

Use Figure 9. If $a = 3$ and $b = 2$, find $c, A,$ and B.

Solution

Since $a = 3$ and $b = 2$, then, by the Pythagorean Theorem, we have

$$c^2 = a^2 + b^2 = 3^2 + 2^2 = 9 + 4 = 13$$
$$c = \sqrt{13} \approx 3.61$$

Figure 9

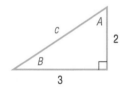

To find angle A, use the fact that

$$\tan A = \frac{3}{2} \quad \text{so} \quad A = \tan^{-1} \frac{3}{2}$$

Set the mode on your calculator to degrees. Then, rounded to one decimal place, we find that $A = 56.3°$. Since $A + B = 90°$, we find that $B = 33.7°$.

NOTE To avoid round-off errors when using a calculator, we will store unrounded values in memory for use in subsequent calculations. ■

⟶ **Now Work** PROBLEM 39

4 Solve Applied Problems*

In addition to developing models using right triangles, we can use right triangle trigonometry to measure heights and distances that are either awkward or impossible to measure by ordinary means. When using right triangles to solve these problems, pay attention to the known measures. This will indicate what trigonometric function to use. For example, if we know the measure of an angle and the length of the side adjacent to the angle, and wish to find the length of the opposite side, we would use the tangent function. Do you know why?

---

* In applied problems, it is important that answers be reported with both justifiable accuracy and appropriate significant figures. In this chapter we shall assume that the problem data are accurate to the number of significant digits resulting in sides being rounded to two decimal places and angles being rounded to one decimal place.

| EXAMPLE 6 | **Finding the Width of a River** |

A surveyor can measure the width of a river by setting up a transit* at a point C on one side of the river and taking a sighting of a point A on the other side. Refer to Figure 10. After turning through an angle of 90° at C, the surveyor walks a distance of 200 meters to point B. Using the transit at B, the angle θ is measured and found to be 20°. What is the width of the river rounded to the nearest meter?

Figure 10

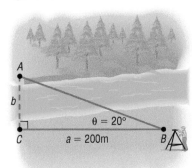

Solution

We seek the length of side b. We know a and θ. So we use the fact that b is opposite θ and a is adjacent to θ and write

$$\tan \theta = \frac{b}{a}$$

which leads to

$$\tan 20° = \frac{b}{200}$$

$$b = 200 \tan 20° \approx 72.79 \text{ meters}$$

The width of the river is 73 meters, rounded to the nearest meter.

—**Now Work** PROBLEM 49

| EXAMPLE 7 | **Finding the Inclination of a Mountain Trail** |

A straight trail leads from the Alpine Hotel, elevation 8000 feet, to a scenic overlook, elevation 11,100 feet. The length of the trail is 14,100 feet. What is the inclination (grade) of the trail? That is, what is the angle B in Figure 11?

Solution

As we can see in Figure 11, we know the length of the side opposite angle B is $11,100 - 8000 = 3100$ feet and the length of the hypotenuse is 14,100 feet. The angle B obeys the equation

$$\sin B = \frac{3100}{14,100}$$

Using a calculator,

$$B = \sin^{-1}\frac{3100}{14,100} \approx 12.7°$$

The inclination (grade) of the trail is approximately 12.7°.

Figure 11

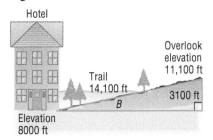

—**Now Work** PROBLEM 55

Vertical heights can sometimes be measured using either the *angle of elevation* or the *angle of depression*. If a person is looking up at an object, the acute angle measured from the horizontal to a line of sight to the object is called the **angle of elevation.** See Figure 12(a).

* An instrument used in surveying to measure angles.

Figure 12

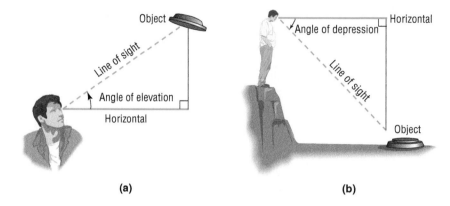

(a)   (b)

If a person is standing on a cliff looking down at an object, the acute angle made by the line of sight to the object and the horizontal is called the **angle of depression.** See Figure 12(b).

| EXAMPLE 8 | **Finding the Height of a Cloud** |

Meteorologists find the height of a cloud using an instrument called a **ceilometer.** A ceilometer consists of a **light projector** that directs a vertical light beam up to the cloud base and a **light detector** that scans the cloud to detect the light beam. See Figure 13(a). On December 8, 2010, at Midway Airport in Chicago, a ceilometer was employed to find the height of the cloud cover. It was set up with its light detector 300 feet from its light projector. If the angle of elevation from the light detector to the base of the cloud was 75°, what was the height of the cloud cover?

Figure 13

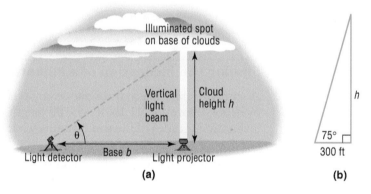

(a)   (b)

Solution   Figure 13(b) illustrates the situation. To find the height h, use the fact that $\tan 75° = \dfrac{h}{300}$, so

$$h = 300 \tan 75° \approx 1120 \text{ feet}$$

The ceiling (height to the base of the cloud cover) was approximately 1120 feet.

Now Work PROBLEM 51

The idea behind Example 8 can also be used to find the height of an object with a base that is not accessible to the horizontal.

| EXAMPLE 9 | **Finding the Height of a Statue on a Building** |

Adorning the top of the Board of Trade building in Chicago is a statue of Ceres, the Roman goddess of wheat. From street level, two observations are taken 400 feet from the center of the building. The angle of elevation to the base of the statue is found to be 55.1° and the angle of elevation to the top of the statue is 56.5°. See Figure 14(a). What is the height of the statue?

Figure 14

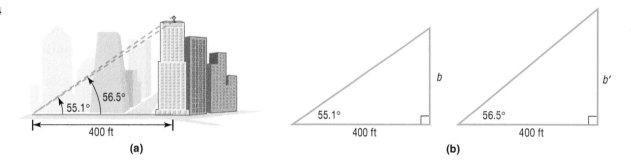

(a)   (b)

Solution   Figure 14(b) shows two triangles that replicate Figure 14(a). The height of the statue of Ceres will be $b' - b$. To find b and b', refer to Figure 14(b).

$$\tan 55.1° = \frac{b}{400} \qquad\qquad \tan 56.5° = \frac{b'}{400}$$

$$b = 400 \tan 55.1° \approx 573.39 \qquad\qquad b' = 400 \tan 56.5° \approx 604.33$$

The height of the statue is approximately $604.33 - 573.39 = 30.94$ feet ≈ 31 feet.

 **Now Work** PROBLEM 71

EXAMPLE 10   The Gibb's Hill Lighthouse, Southampton, Bermuda

In operation since 1846, the Gibb's Hill Lighthouse stands 117 feet high on a hill 245 feet high, so its beam of light is 362 feet above sea level. A brochure states that the light can be seen on the horizon about 26 miles from the lighthouse. Verify the accuracy of this statement.

Solution   Figure 15 illustrates the situation. The central angle θ, positioned at the center of Earth, radius 3960 miles, obeys the equation

Figure 15

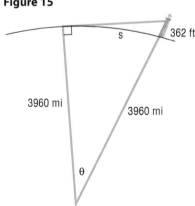

$$\cos\theta = \frac{3960}{3960 + \dfrac{362}{5280}} \approx 0.999982687 \quad \text{1 mile = 5280 feet}$$

Solving for θ, we find

$$\theta \approx 0.33715° \approx 20.23'$$

The brochure does not indicate whether the distance is measured in nautical miles or statute miles. Let's calculate both distances.

The distance s in nautical miles (refer to Problem 114, p. 362) is the measure of the angle θ in minutes, so $s \approx 20.23$ nautical miles.

The distance s in statute miles is given by the formula $s = r\theta$, where θ is measured in radians. Then, since

$$\theta \approx 20.23' \approx 0.33715° \approx 0.00588 \text{ radian}$$

$$1' = \frac{1°}{60} \qquad 1° = \frac{\pi}{180} \text{ radian}$$

Figure 16

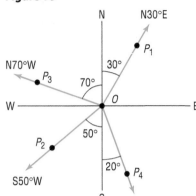

we find that

$$s = r\theta \approx (3960)(0.00588) \approx 23.3 \text{ miles}$$

In either case, it would seem that the brochure overstated the distance somewhat.

In navigation and surveying, the **direction** or **bearing** from a point O to a point P equals the acute angle θ between the ray OP and the vertical line through O, the north–south line.

Figure 16 illustrates some bearings. Notice that the bearing from O to P_1 is denoted by the symbolism N30°E, indicating that the bearing is 30° east of north. In writing the bearing from O to P, the direction north or south always appears first, followed by an acute angle, followed by east or west. In Figure 16, the bearing from O to P_2 is S50°W, and from O to P_3 it is N70°W.

EXAMPLE 11 Finding the Bearing of an Object

In Figure 16, what is the bearing from O to an object at P_4?

Solution The acute angle between the ray OP_4 and the north–south line through O is given as 20°. The bearing from O to P_4 is S20°E.

EXAMPLE 12 Finding the Bearing of an Airplane

A Boeing 777 aircraft takes off from O'Hare Airport on runway 2 LEFT, which has a bearing of N20°E.* After flying for 1 mile, the pilot of the aircraft requests permission to turn 90° and head toward the northwest. The request is granted. After the plane goes 2 miles in this direction, what bearing should the control tower use to locate the aircraft?

Figure 17

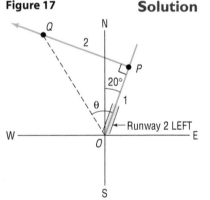

Solution Figure 17 illustrates the situation. After flying 1 mile from the airport O (the control tower), the aircraft is at P. After turning 90° toward the northwest and flying 2 miles, the aircraft is at the point Q. In triangle OPQ, the angle θ obeys the equation

$$\tan\theta = \frac{2}{1} = 2 \quad \text{so} \quad \theta = \tan^{-1} 2 \approx 63.4°$$

The acute angle between north and the ray OQ is $63.4° - 20° = 43.4°$. The bearing of the aircraft from O to Q is N43.4°W.

Now Work PROBLEM 63

8.1 Assess Your Understanding

'Are You Prepared?' *Answers are given at the end of these exercises. If you get a wrong answer, read the pages listed in red.*

1. In a right triangle, if the length of the hypotenuse is 5 and the length of one of the other sides is 3, what is the length of the third side? (pp. A14–A15)

2. If θ is an acute angle, solve the equation $\tan\theta = \frac{1}{2}$. Express your answer in degrees, rounded to one decimal place. (pp. 454–459)

3. If θ is an acute angle, solve the equation $\sin\theta = \frac{1}{2}$. (pp. 454–459)

---

* In air navigation, the term **azimuth** denotes the positive angle measured clockwise from the north (N) to a ray OP. In Figure 16, the azimuth from O to P_1 is 30°; the azimuth from O to P_2 is 230°; the azimuth from O to P_3 is 290°. In naming runways, the units digit is left off the azimuth. Runway 2 LEFT means the left runway with a direction of azimuth 20° (bearing N20°E). Runway 23 is the runway with azimuth 230° and bearing S50°W.

Concepts and Vocabulary

4. *True or False* $\sin 52° = \cos 48°$.

5. *True or False* In a right triangle, one of the angles is 90° and the sum of the other two angles is 90°.

6. When you look up at an object, the acute angle measured from the horizontal to a line-of-sight observation of the object is called the _____ ___ _____ .

7. *True or False* In a right triangle, if two sides are known, we can solve the triangle.

8. *True or False* In a right triangle, if we know the two acute angles, we can solve the triangle.

Skill Building

In Problems 9–18, find the exact value of the six trigonometric functions of the angle θ in each figure.

9.

10.

11.

12.

13.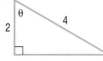

14.

15.

16.

17.

18.

In Problems 19–28, find the exact value of each expression. Do not use a calculator.

19. $\sin 38° - \cos 52°$

20. $\tan 12° - \cot 78°$

21. $\dfrac{\cos 10°}{\sin 80°}$

22. $\dfrac{\cos 40°}{\sin 50°}$

23. $1 - \cos^2 20° - \cos^2 70°$

24. $1 + \tan^2 5° - \csc^2 85°$

25. $\tan 20° - \dfrac{\cos 70°}{\cos 20°}$

26. $\cot 40° - \dfrac{\sin 50°}{\sin 40°}$

27. $\cos 35° \sin 55° + \sin 35° \cos 55°$

28. $\sec 35° \csc 55° - \tan 35° \cot 55°$

In Problems 29–42, use the right triangle shown below. Then, using the given information, solve the triangle.

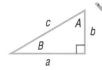

29. $b = 5$, $B = 20°$; find a, c, and A

30. $b = 4$, $B = 10°$; find a, c, and A

31. $a = 6$, $B = 40°$; find b, c, and A

32. $a = 7$, $B = 50°$; find b, c, and A

33. $b = 4$, $A = 10°$; find a, c, and B

34. $b = 6$, $A = 20°$; find a, c, and B

35. $a = 5$, $A = 25°$; find b, c, and B

36. $a = 6$, $A = 40°$; find b, c, and B

37. $c = 9$, $B = 20°$; find b, a, and A

38. $c = 10$, $A = 40°$; find b, a, and B

39. $a = 5$, $b = 3$; find c, A, and B

40. $a = 2$, $b = 8$; find c, A, and B

41. $a = 2$, $c = 5$; find b, A, and B

42. $b = 4$, $c = 6$; find a, A, and B

Applications and Extensions

43. Geometry The hypotenuse of a right triangle is 5 inches. If one leg is 2 inches, find the degree measure of each angle.

44. Geometry The hypotenuse of a right triangle is 3 feet. If one leg is 1 foot, find the degree measure of each angle.

45. Geometry A right triangle has a hypotenuse of length 8 inches. If one angle is 35°, find the length of each leg.

46. Geometry A right triangle has a hypotenuse of length 10 centimeters. If one angle is 40°, find the length of each leg.

47. Geometry A right triangle contains a 25° angle.
(a) If one leg is of length 5 inches, what is the length of the hypotenuse?
(b) There are two answers. How is this possible?

48. Geometry A right triangle contains an angle of $\dfrac{\pi}{8}$ radian.
(a) If one leg is of length 3 meters, what is the length of the hypotenuse?
(b) There are two answers. How is this possible?

49. Finding the Width of a Gorge Find the distance from A to C across the gorge illustrated in the figure.

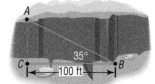

50. Finding the Distance across a Pond Find the distance from A to C across the pond illustrated in the figure.

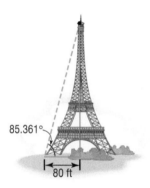

51. The Eiffel Tower The tallest tower built before the era of television masts, the Eiffel Tower was completed on March 31, 1889. Find the height of the Eiffel Tower (before a television mast was added to the top) using the information given in the illustration.

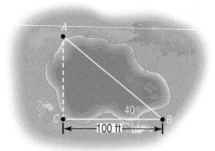

52. Finding the Distance of a Ship from Shore A person in a small boat, offshore from a vertical cliff known to be 100 feet in height, takes a sighting of the top of the cliff. If the angle of elevation is found to be 25°, how far offshore is the boat?

53. Finding the Distance to a Plateau Suppose that you are headed toward a plateau 50 meters high. If the angle of elevation to the top of the plateau is 20°, how far are you from the base of the plateau?

54. Finding the Reach of a Ladder A 22-foot extension ladder leaning against a building makes a 70° angle with the ground. How far up the building does the ladder touch?

55. Finding the Angle of Elevation of the Sun At 10 AM on April 26, 2009, a building 300 feet high casts a shadow 50 feet long. What was the angle of elevation of the Sun?

56. Directing a Laser Beam A laser beam is to be directed through a small hole in the center of a circle of radius 10 feet. The origin of the beam is 35 feet from the circle (see the figure). At what angle of elevation should the beam be aimed to ensure that it goes through the hole?

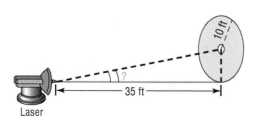

57. Finding the Speed of a Truck A state trooper is hidden 30 feet from a highway. One second after a truck passes, the angle θ between the highway and the line of observation from the patrol car to the truck is measured. See the illustration.

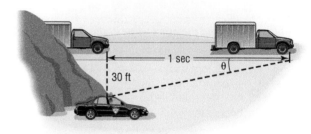

(a) If the angle measures 15°, how fast is the truck traveling? Express the answer in feet per second and in miles per hour.
(b) If the angle measures 20°, how fast is the truck traveling? Express the answer in feet per second and in miles per hour.
(c) If the speed limit is 55 miles per hour and a speeding ticket is issued for speeds of 5 miles per hour or more over the limit, for what angles should the trooper issue a ticket?

58. Security A security camera in a neighborhood bank is mounted on a wall 9 feet above the floor. What angle of depression should be used if the camera is to be directed to a spot 6 feet above the floor and 12 feet from the wall?

59. Parallax One method of measuring the distance from Earth to a star is the parallax method. The idea behind computing this distance is to measure the angle formed between the Earth and the star at two different points in time. Typically, the measurements are taken so that the side opposite the angle is as large as possible. Therefore, the optimal approach is to measure the angle when Earth is on opposite sides of the Sun, as shown in the figure.

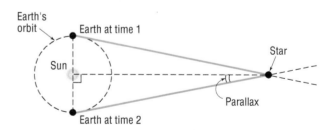

(a) Proxima Centauri is 4.22 light-years from Earth. If 1 light-year is about 5.9 trillion miles, how many miles is Proxima Centauri from Earth?
(b) The mean distance from Earth to the Sun is 93,000,000 miles. What is the parallax of Proxima Centauri?

60. Parallax See Problem 59. 61 Cygni, sometimes called Bessel's Star (after Friedrich Bessel, who measured the distance from Earth to the star in 1838), is a star in the constellation Cygnus.
(a) 61 Cygni is 11.14 light-years from Earth. If 1 light-year is about 5.9 trillion miles, how many miles is 61 Cygni from Earth?
(b) The mean distance from Earth to the Sun is 93,000,000 miles. What is the parallax of 61 Cygni?

61. Washington Monument The angle of elevation of the Sun is 35.1° at the instant the shadow cast by the Washington Monument is 789 feet long. Use this information to calculate the height of the monument.

62. Finding the Length of a Mountain Trail A straight trail with an inclination of 17° leads from a hotel at an elevation of 9000 feet to a mountain lake at an elevation of 11,200 feet. What is the length of the trail?

63. Finding the Bearing of an Aircraft A DC-9 aircraft leaves Midway Airport from runway 4 RIGHT, whose bearing is N40°E. After flying for $\frac{1}{2}$ mile, the pilot requests permission to turn 90° and head toward the southeast. The permission is granted. After the airplane goes 1 mile in this direction, what bearing should the control tower use to locate the aircraft?

64. Finding the Bearing of a Ship A ship leaves the port of Miami with a bearing of S80°E and a speed of 15 knots. After 1 hour, the ship turns 90° toward the south. After 2 hours, maintaining the same speed, what is the bearing to the ship from port?

65. Niagara Falls Incline Railway Situated between Portage Road and the Niagara Parkway directly across from the Canadian Horseshoe Falls, the Falls Incline Railway is a funicular that carries passengers up an embankment to Table Rock Observation Point. If the length of the track is 51.8 meters and the angle of inclination is 36°2′, determine the height of the embankment.
Source: www.niagaraparks.com

66. Willis Tower Willis Tower in Chicago is the third tallest building in the world and is topped by a high antenna. A surveyor on the ground makes the following measurement:
1. The angle of elevation from his position to the top of the building is 34°.
2. The distance from his position to the top of the building is 2593 feet.
3. The distance from his position to the top of the antenna is 2743 feet.
(a) How far away from the (base of the) building is the surveyor located?
(b) How tall is the building?
(c) What is the angle of elevation from the surveyor to the top of the antenna?
(d) How tall is the antenna?
Source: www.infoplease.com/ce6/us/A0844218.html

67. Constructing a Highway A highway whose primary directions are north–south is being constructed along the west coast of Florida. Near Naples, a bay obstructs the straight path of the road. Since the cost of a bridge is prohibitive, engineers decide to go around the bay. The illustration shows the path that they decide on and the measurements taken. What is the length of highway needed to go around the bay?

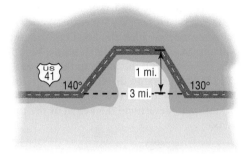

68. Photography A camera is mounted on a tripod 4 feet high at a distance of 10 feet from George, who is 6 feet tall. See the illustration. If the camera lens has angles of depression and elevation of 20°, will George's feet and head be seen by the lens? If not, how far back will the camera need to be moved to include George's feet and head?

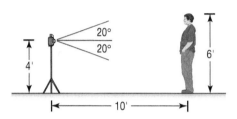

69. Finding the Distance between Two Objects A blimp, suspended in the air at a height of 500 feet, lies directly over a line from Soldier Field to the Adler Planetarium on Lake Michigan (see the figure). If the angle of depression from the blimp to the stadium is 32° and from the blimp to the planetarium is 23°, find the distance between Soldier Field and the Adler Planetarium.

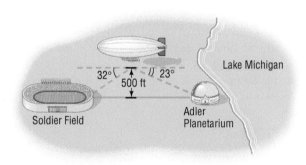

70. Hot-Air Balloon While taking a ride in a hot-air balloon in Napa Valley, Francisco wonders how high he is. To find out, he chooses a landmark that is to the east of the balloon and measures the angle of depression to be 54°. A few minutes later, after traveling 100 feet east, the angle of depression to the same landmark is determined to be 61°. Use this information to determine the height of the balloon.

71. Mt. Rushmore To measure the height of Lincoln's caricature on Mt. Rushmore, two sightings 800 feet from the base of the mountain are taken. If the angle of elevation to the bottom of Lincoln's face is 32° and the angle of elevation to the top is 35°, what is the height of Lincoln's face?

72. The CN Tower The CN Tower, located in Toronto, Canada, is the tallest structure in the Americas. While visiting Toronto, a tourist wondered what the height of the tower above the top of the Sky Pod is. While standing 4000 feet from the tower, she measured the angle to the top of the Sky Pod to be 20.1°. At this same distance, the angle of elevation to the top of the tower was found to be 24.4°. Use this information to determine the height of the tower above the Sky Pod.

73. Chicago Skyscrapers The angle of inclination from the base of the John Hancock Center to the top of the main structure of the Willis Tower is approximately 10.3°. If the main structure of the Willis Tower is 1451 feet tall, how far apart are the two skyscrapers? Assume the bases of the two buildings are at the same elevation.

Source: www.emporis.com

74. Estimating the Width of the Mississippi River A tourist at the top of the Gateway Arch (height, 630 feet) in St. Louis, Missouri, observes a boat moored on the Illinois side of the Mississippi River 2070 feet directly across from the Arch. She also observes a boat moored on the Missouri side directly across from the first boat (see diagram). Given that $B = \cot^{-1}\dfrac{67}{55}$, estimate the width of the Mississippi River at the St. Louis riverfront.

Source: U.S. Army Corps of Engineers

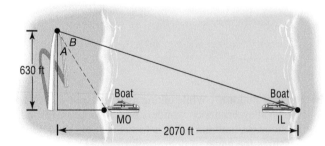

75. Finding the Pitch of a Roof A carpenter is preparing to put a roof on a garage that is 20 feet by 40 feet by 20 feet. A steel support beam 46 feet in length is positioned in the center of the garage. To support the roof, another beam will be attached to the top of the center beam (see the figure). At what angle of elevation is the new beam? In other words, what is the pitch of the roof?

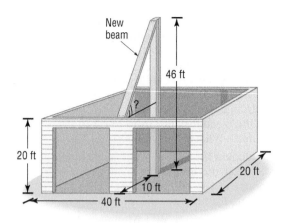

76. Shooting Free Throws in Basketball The eyes of a basketball player are 6 feet above the floor. The player is at the free-throw line, which is 15 feet from the center of the basket rim (see the figure). What is the angle of elevation from the player's eyes to the center of the rim?

[**Hint:** The rim is 10 feet above the floor.]

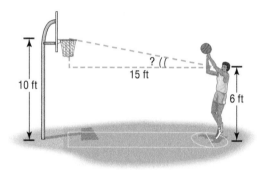

77. Geometry Find the value of the angle θ in degrees rounded to the nearest tenth of a degree.

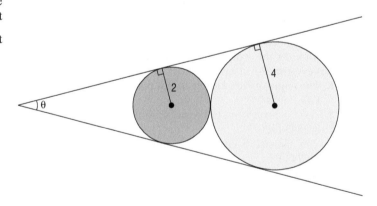

78. Surveillance Satellites A surveillance satellite circles Earth at a height of h miles above the surface. Suppose that d is the distance, in miles, on the surface of Earth that can be observed from the satellite. See the illustration on the following page.
(a) Find an equation that relates the central angle θ to the height h.
(b) Find an equation that relates the observable distance d and θ.
(c) Find an equation that relates d and h.
(d) If d is to be 2500 miles, how high must the satellite orbit above Earth?

(e) If the satellite orbits at a height of 300 miles, what distance d on the surface can be observed?

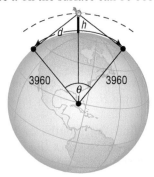

79. Calculating Pool Shots A pool player located at **X** wants to shoot the white ball off the top cushion and hit the red

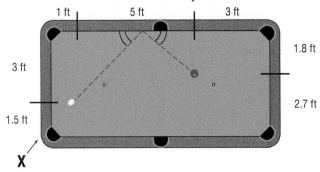

ball dead center. He knows from physics that the white ball will come off a cushion at the same angle as it hits a cushion. Where on the top cushion should he hit the white ball?

80. The Freedom Tower The Freedom Tower is to be the centerpiece of the rebuilding of the World Trade Center in New York City. The tower will be 1776 feet tall (not including a broadcast antenna). The angle of elevation from the base of an office building to the top of the tower is 34°. The angle of elevation from the helipad on the roof of the office building to the top of the tower is 20°.

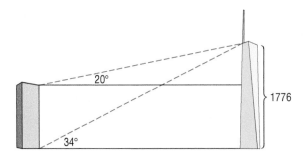

(a) How far away is the office building from the Freedom Tower? Assume the side of the tower is vertical. Round to the nearest foot.
(b) How tall is the office building? Round to the nearest foot.

Explaining Concepts: Discussion and Writing

81. Explain how you would measure the width of the Grand Canyon from a point on its ridge.

82. Explain how you would measure the height of a TV tower that is on the roof of a tall building.

83. The Gibb's Hill Lighthouse. Southampton, Bermuda In operation since 1846, the Gibb's Hill Lighthouse stands

117 feet high on a hill 245 feet high, so its beam of light is 362 feet above sea level. A brochure states that ships 40 miles away can see the light and planes flying at 10,000 feet can see it 120 miles away. Verify the accuracy of these statements. What assumption did the brochure make about the height of the ship?

'Are You Prepared?' Answers

1. 4   **2.** 26.6°   **3.** 30°

8.2 The Law of Sines

PREPARING FOR THIS SECTION *Before getting started, review the following:*

- Trigonometric Equations (Section 7.3, pp. 454–459)
- Difference Formula for the Sine Function (Section 7.5, p. 475)
- Geometry Essentials (Appendix A, Section A.2, pp. A14–A19)

Now Work the 'Are You Prepared?' problems on page 524.

OBJECTIVES **1** Solve SAA or ASA Triangles (p. 518)
              2 Solve SSA Triangles (p. 519)
              3 Solve Applied Problems (p. 522)

If none of the angles of a triangle is a right angle, the triangle is called **oblique.** An oblique triangle will have either three acute angles or two acute angles and one obtuse angle (an angle between 90° and 180°). See Figure 18.

Figure 18

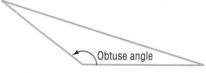

(a) All angles are acute   **(b)** Two acute angles and one obtuse angle

Figure 19

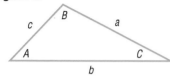

In the discussion that follows, we will always label an oblique triangle so that side a is opposite angle A, side b is opposite angle B, and side c is opposite angle C, as shown in Figure 19.

To **solve an oblique triangle** means to find the lengths of its sides and the measurements of its angles. To do this, we shall need to know the length of one side* along with (i) two angles; (ii) one angle and one other side; or (iii) the other two sides. There are four possibilities to consider:

CASE 1: One side and two angles are known (ASA or SAA).
CASE 2: Two sides and the angle opposite one of them are known (SSA).
CASE 3: Two sides and the included angle are known (SAS).
CASE 4: Three sides are known (SSS).

Figure 20 illustrates the four cases.

Figure 20

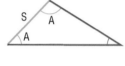
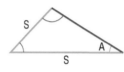
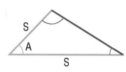
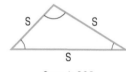

Case 1: ASA   Case 1: SAA   Case 2: SSA   Case 3: SAS   Case 4: SSS

WARNING *Oblique triangles cannot be solved using the methods of Section 8.1. Do you know why?* ∎

The **Law of Sines** is used to solve triangles for which Case 1 or 2 holds. Cases 3 and 4 are considered when we study the Law of Cosines in the next section.

THEOREM   **Law of Sines**

For a triangle with sides a, b, c and opposite angles A, B, C, respectively,

$$\frac{\sin A}{a} = \frac{\sin B}{b} = \frac{\sin C}{c} \tag{1}$$

A proof of the Law of Sines is given at the end of this section. The Law of Sines actually consists of three equalities:

$$\frac{\sin A}{a} = \frac{\sin B}{b} \qquad \frac{\sin A}{a} = \frac{\sin C}{c} \qquad \frac{\sin B}{b} = \frac{\sin C}{c}$$

Formula (1) is a compact way to write these three equations.

In applying the Law of Sines to solve triangles, we use the fact that the sum of the angles of any triangle equals 180°; that is,

$$A + B + C = 180° \tag{2}$$

1 Solve SAA or ASA Triangles

Our first two examples show how to solve a triangle when one side and two angles are known (Case 1: SAA or ASA).

* The reason we need to know the length of one side is that, if we only know the angles, this will result in a family of *similar triangles*.

EXAMPLE 1

Using the Law of Sines to Solve an SAA Triangle

Solve the triangle: $A = 40°, B = 60°, a = 4$

Solution

Figure 21 shows the triangle that we want to solve. The third angle C is found using equation (2).

Figure 21

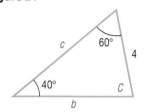

$$A + B + C = 180°$$
$$40° + 60° + C = 180°$$
$$C = 80°$$

Now use the Law of Sines (twice) to find the unknown sides b and c.

$$\frac{\sin A}{a} = \frac{\sin B}{b} \qquad \frac{\sin A}{a} = \frac{\sin C}{c}$$

Because $a = 4, A = 40°, B = 60°$, and $C = 80°$, we have

$$\frac{\sin 40°}{4} = \frac{\sin 60°}{b} \qquad \frac{\sin 40°}{4} = \frac{\sin 80°}{c}$$

Solving for b and c, we find that

$$b = \frac{4 \sin 60°}{\sin 40°} \approx 5.39 \qquad c = \frac{4 \sin 80°}{\sin 40°} \approx 6.13$$

COMMENT Although not a check, we can verify the reasonableness of our answer by determining if the longest side is opposite the largest angle and the shortest side is opposite the smallest angle. ∎

Notice in Example 1 that we found b and c by working with the given side a. This is better than finding b first and working with a rounded value of b to find c.

Now Work PROBLEM 9

EXAMPLE 2

Using the Law of Sines to Solve an ASA Triangle

Solve the triangle: $A = 35°, B = 15°, c = 5$

Solution

Figure 22 illustrates the triangle that we want to solve. Because we know two angles ($A = 35°$ and $B = 15°$), we find the third angle using equation (2).

Figure 22

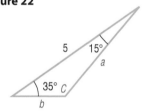

$$A + B + C = 180°$$
$$35° + 15° + C = 180°$$
$$C = 130°$$

Now we know the three angles and one side ($c = 5$) of the triangle. To find the remaining two sides a and b, use the Law of Sines (twice).

$$\frac{\sin A}{a} = \frac{\sin C}{c} \qquad\qquad \frac{\sin B}{b} = \frac{\sin C}{c}$$

$$\frac{\sin 35°}{a} = \frac{\sin 130°}{5} \qquad\qquad \frac{\sin 15°}{b} = \frac{\sin 130°}{5}$$

$$a = \frac{5 \sin 35°}{\sin 130°} \approx 3.74 \qquad\qquad b = \frac{5 \sin 15°}{\sin 130°} \approx 1.69$$

Now Work PROBLEM 23

Figure 23

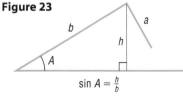

$\sin A = \frac{h}{b}$

2 Solve SSA Triangles

Case 2 (SSA), which applies to triangles for which two sides and the angle opposite one of them are known, is referred to as the **ambiguous case,** because the known information may result in one triangle, two triangles, or no triangle at all. Suppose that we are given sides a and b and angle A, as illustrated in Figure 23. The key to determining the possible triangles, if any, that may be formed from the given information lies primarily with the relative size of side a, the height h, and the fact that $h = b \sin A$.

No Triangle If $a < h = b \sin A$, then side a is not sufficiently long to form a triangle. See Figure 24.

One Right Triangle If $a = h = b \sin A$, then side a is just long enough to form a right triangle. See Figure 25.

Figure 24
$a < h = b \sin A$

Figure 25
$a = h = b \sin A$

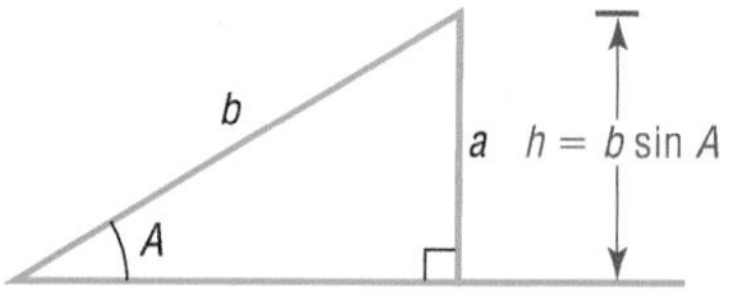

Two Triangles If $h = b \sin A < a$, and $a < b$, two distinct triangles can be formed from the given information. See Figure 26.

One Triangle If $a \geq b$, only one triangle can be formed. See Figure 27.

Figure 26
$b \sin A < a$ and $a < b$

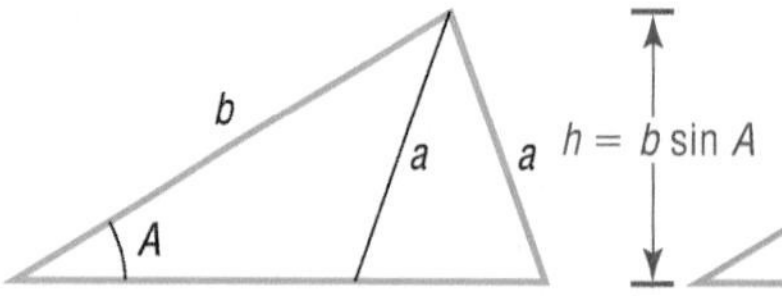

Figure 27
$a \geq b$

Fortunately, we do not have to rely on an illustration or complicated relationships to draw the correct conclusion in the ambiguous case. The Law of Sines will lead us to the correct determination. Let's see how.

EXAMPLE 3

Using the Law of Sines to Solve an SSA Triangle (One Solution)

Solve the triangle: $a = 3, b = 2, A = 40°$

Solution

See Figure 28(a). Because we know an angle ($A = 40°$), the side opposite the known angle ($a = 3$), and the side opposite angle B ($b = 2$), we use the Law of Sines to find the angle B.

Figure 28(a)

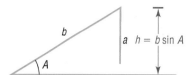

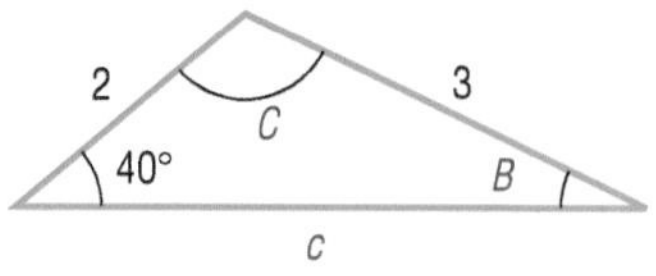

$$\frac{\sin A}{a} = \frac{\sin B}{b}$$

Then

$$\frac{\sin 40°}{3} = \frac{\sin B}{2}$$

$$\sin B = \frac{2 \sin 40°}{3} \approx 0.43$$

There are two angles $B, 0° < B < 180°$, for which $\sin B \approx 0.43$.

$$B_1 \approx 25.4° \quad \text{and} \quad B_2 \approx 180° - 25.4° = 154.6°$$

The second possibility, $B_2 \approx 154.6°$, is ruled out, because $A = 40°$ makes $A + B_2 \approx 194.6° > 180°$. Now, using $B_1 \approx 25.4°$, we find that

$$C = 180° - A - B_1 \approx 180° - 40° - 25.4° = 114.6°$$

COMMENT Here we computed B_1 by determining the value of $\sin^{-1}\left(\frac{2 \sin 40°}{3}\right)$. If you use the rounded value and evaluate $\sin^{-1}(0.43)$, you will obtain a slightly different result. ∎

The third side c may now be determined using the Law of Sines.

$$\frac{\sin A}{a} = \frac{\sin C}{c}$$

$$\frac{\sin 40°}{3} = \frac{\sin 114.6°}{c}$$

$$c = \frac{3 \sin 114.6°}{\sin 40°} \approx 4.24$$

Figure 28(b)

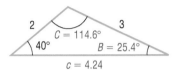

Figure 28(b) illustrates the solved triangle.

EXAMPLE 4   **Using the Law of Sines to Solve an SSA Triangle (Two Solutions)**

Solve the triangle: $a = 6, b = 8, A = 35°$

Solution   See Figure 29(a). Because $a = 6, b = 8$, and $A = 35°$ are known, use the Law of Sines to find the angle B.

Figure 29(a)

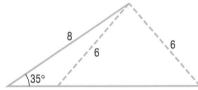

Then

$$\frac{\sin A}{a} = \frac{\sin B}{b}$$

$$\frac{\sin 35°}{6} = \frac{\sin B}{8}$$

$$\sin B = \frac{8 \sin 35°}{6} \approx 0.76$$

$$B_1 \approx 49.9° \quad \text{or} \quad B_2 \approx 180° - 49.9° = 130.1°$$

For both choices of B, we have $A + B < 180°$. There are two triangles, one containing the angle $B_1 \approx 49.9°$ and the other containing the angle $B_2 \approx 130.1°$. The third angle C is either

$$C_1 = 180° - A - B_1 \approx 95.1° \quad \text{or} \quad C_2 = 180° - A - B_2 \approx 14.9°$$

$$\uparrow \qquad\qquad\qquad\qquad\qquad\qquad \uparrow$$

$$A = 35° \qquad\qquad\qquad\qquad\qquad A = 35°$$
$$B_1 = 49.9° \qquad\qquad\qquad\qquad B_2 = 130.1°$$

The third side c obeys the Law of Sines, so we have

Figure 29(b)

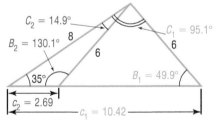

$$\frac{\sin A}{a} = \frac{\sin C_1}{c_1} \qquad\qquad \frac{\sin A}{a} = \frac{\sin C_2}{c_2}$$

$$\frac{\sin 35°}{6} = \frac{\sin 95.1°}{c_1} \qquad\qquad \frac{\sin 35°}{6} = \frac{\sin 14.9°}{c_2}$$

$$c_1 = \frac{6 \sin 95.1°}{\sin 35°} \approx 10.42 \qquad c_2 = \frac{6 \sin 14.9°}{\sin 35°} \approx 2.69$$

The two solved triangles are illustrated in Figure 29(b).

EXAMPLE 5   **Using the Law of Sines to Solve an SSA Triangle (No Solution)**

Solve the triangle: $a = 2, c = 1, C = 50°$

Solution   Because $a = 2, c = 1$, and $C = 50°$ are known, use the Law of Sines to find the angle A.

$$\frac{\sin A}{a} = \frac{\sin C}{c}$$

$$\frac{\sin A}{2} = \frac{\sin 50°}{1}$$

$$\sin A = 2 \sin 50° \approx 1.53$$

Figure 30

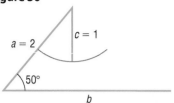

Since there is no angle A for which $\sin A > 1$, there can be no triangle with the given measurements. Figure 30 illustrates the measurements given. Notice that, no matter how we attempt to position side c, it will never touch side b to form a triangle.

Now Work PROBLEMS 25 AND 31

3 Solve Applied Problems

EXAMPLE 6

Finding the Height of a Mountain

To measure the height of a mountain, a surveyor takes two sightings of the peak at a distance 900 meters apart on a direct line to the mountain.* See Figure 31(a). The first observation results in an angle of elevation of 47°, and the second results in an angle of elevation of 35°. If the transit is 2 meters high, what is the height h of the mountain?

Figure 31

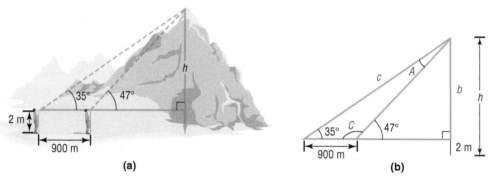

(a)   (b)

Solution   Figure 31(b) shows the triangles that replicate the illustration in Figure 31(a). Since $C + 47° = 180°$, we find that $C = 133°$. Also, since $A + C + 35° = 180°$, we find that $A = 180° - 35° - C = 145° - 133° = 12°$. Use the Law of Sines to find c.

$$\frac{\sin A}{a} = \frac{\sin C}{c} \qquad A = 12°, C = 133°, a = 900$$

$$c = \frac{900 \sin 133°}{\sin 12°} \approx 3165.86$$

Using the larger right triangle, we have

$$\sin 35° = \frac{b}{c} \qquad c = 3165.86$$
$$b = 3165.86 \sin 35° \approx 1815.86 \approx 1816 \text{ meters}$$

The height of the peak from ground level is approximately $1816 + 2 = 1818$ meters.

Now Work PROBLEM 39

EXAMPLE 7

Rescue at Sea

Coast Guard Station Zulu is located 120 miles due west of Station X-ray. A ship at sea sends an SOS call that is received by each station. The call to Station Zulu indicates that the bearing of the ship from Zulu is N40°E (40° east of north). The call to Station X-ray indicates that the bearing of the ship from X-ray is N30°W (30° west of north).

(a) How far is each station from the ship?

(b) If a helicopter capable of flying 200 miles per hour is dispatched from the nearest station to the ship, how long will it take to reach the ship?

* For simplicity, we assume that these sightings are at the same level.

Solution   (a) Figure 32 illustrates the situation. The angle C is found to be

$$C = 180° - 50° - 60° = 70°$$

The Law of Sines can now be used to find the two distances a and b that we seek.

Figure 32

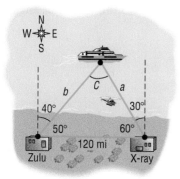

$$\frac{\sin 50°}{a} = \frac{\sin 70°}{120}$$

$$a = \frac{120 \sin 50°}{\sin 70°} \approx 97.82 \text{ miles}$$

$$\frac{\sin 60°}{b} = \frac{\sin 70°}{120}$$

$$b = \frac{120 \sin 60°}{\sin 70°} \approx 110.59 \text{ miles}$$

Station Zulu is about 111 miles from the ship, and Station X-ray is about 98 miles from the ship.

(b) The time t needed for the helicopter to reach the ship from Station X-ray is found by using the formula

$$(\text{Rate}, r)(\text{Time}, t) = \text{Distance}, a$$

Then

$$t = \frac{a}{r} = \frac{97.82}{200} \approx 0.49 \text{ hour} \approx 29 \text{ minutes}$$

It will take about 29 minutes for the helicopter to reach the ship.

━━━━━**Now Work** PROBLEM 37

Proof of the Law of Sines   To prove the Law of Sines, construct an altitude of length h from one of the vertices of a triangle. Figure 33(a) shows h for a triangle with three acute angles, and Figure 33(b) shows h for a triangle with an obtuse angle. In each case, the altitude is drawn from the vertex at B. Using either illustration, we have

Figure 33

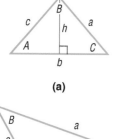

(a)

(b)

$$\sin C = \frac{h}{a}$$

from which

$$h = a \sin C \tag{3}$$

From Figure 33(a), it also follows that

$$\sin A = \frac{h}{c}$$

from which

$$h = c \sin A \tag{4}$$

From Figure 33(b), it follows that

$$\sin(180° - A) = \sin A = \frac{h}{c}$$

$$\uparrow$$

$$\sin(180° - A) = \sin 180° \cos A - \cos 180° \sin A = \sin A$$

which again gives

$$h = c \sin A$$

So, whether the triangle has three acute angles or has two acute angles and one obtuse angle, equations (3) and (4) hold. As a result, we may equate the expressions for h in equations (3) and (4) to get

$$a \sin C = c \sin A$$

Figure 34

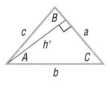

(a)

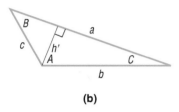

(b)

from which

$$\frac{\sin A}{a} = \frac{\sin C}{c} \qquad \textbf{(5)}$$

In a similar manner, by constructing the altitude h' from the vertex of angle A as shown in Figure 34, we can show that

$$\sin B = \frac{h'}{c} \quad \text{and} \quad \sin C = \frac{h'}{b} \quad .$$

Equating the expressions for h', we find that

$$h' = c \sin B = b \sin C$$

from which

$$\frac{\sin B}{b} = \frac{\sin C}{c} \qquad \textbf{(6)}$$

When equations (5) and (6) are combined, we have equation (1), the Law of Sines. ■

8.2 Assess Your Understanding

'Are You Prepared?' *Answers are given at the end of these exercises. If you get a wrong answer, read the pages listed in red.*

1. The difference formula for the sine function is $\sin(A - B) = $ ____. (p. 475)

2. If θ is an acute angle, solve the equation $\cos \theta = \dfrac{\sqrt{3}}{2}$. (pp. 454–459)

3. The two triangles shown are similar. Find the missing length. (pp. A14–A19)

Concepts and Vocabulary

4. If none of the angles of a triangle is a right angle, the triangle is called _____.

5. For a triangle with sides a, b, c and opposite angles A, B, C, the Law of Sines states that _____.

6. **True or False** An oblique triangle in which two sides and an angle are given always results in at least one triangle.

7. **True or False** The Law of Sines can be used to solve triangles where three sides are known.

8. Triangles for which two sides and the angle opposite one of them are known (SSA) are referred to as the _____ _____.

Skill Building

In Problems 9–16, solve each triangle.

9.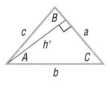

10.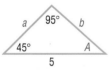

11.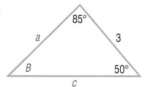

12.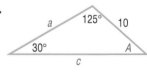

13.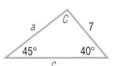

14.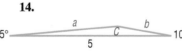

15.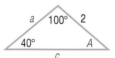

16.

In Problems 17–24, solve each triangle.

17. $A = 40°$, $B = 20°$, $a = 2$

18. $A = 50°$, $C = 20°$, $a = 3$

19. $B = 70°$, $C = 10°$, $b = 5$

20. $A = 70°$, $B = 60°$, $c = 4$

21. $A = 110°$, $C = 30°$, $c = 3$

22. $B = 10°$, $C = 100°$, $b = 2$

23. $A = 40°$, $B = 40°$, $c = 2$

24. $B = 20°$, $C = 70°$, $a = 1$

In Problems 25–36, two sides and an angle are given. Determine whether the given information results in one triangle, two triangles, or no triangle at all. Solve any triangle(s) that results.

25. $a = 3$, $b = 2$, $A = 50°$

26. $b = 4$, $c = 3$, $B = 40°$

27. $b = 5$, $c = 3$, $B = 100°$

28. $a = 2$, $c = 1$, $A = 120°$

29. $a = 4$, $b = 5$, $A = 60°$

30. $b = 2$, $c = 3$, $B = 40°$

31. $b = 4$, $c = 6$, $B = 20°$

32. $a = 3$, $b = 7$, $A = 70°$

33. $a = 2$, $c = 1$, $C = 100°$

34. $b = 4$, $c = 5$, $B = 95°$

35. $a = 2$, $c = 1$, $C = 25°$

36. $b = 4$, $c = 5$, $B = 40°$

Applications and Extensions

37. **Rescue at Sea** Coast Guard Station Able is located 150 miles due south of Station Baker. A ship at sea sends an SOS call that is received by each station. The call to Station Able indicates that the ship is located N55°E; the call to Station Baker indicates that the ship is located S60°E.
    (a) How far is each station from the ship?
    (b) If a helicopter capable of flying 200 miles per hour is dispatched from the station nearest the ship, how long will it take to reach the ship?

38. **Distance to the Moon** At exactly the same time, Tom and Alice measured the angle of elevation to the moon while standing exactly 300 km apart. The angle of elevation to the moon for Tom was 49.8974° and the angle of elevation to the moon for Alice was 49.9312°. See the figure. To the nearest 1000 km, how far was the moon from Earth when the measurement was obtained?

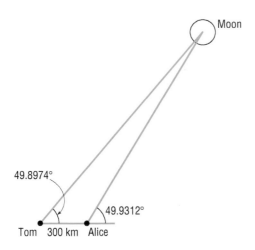

39. **Finding the Length of a Ski Lift** Consult the figure. To find the length of the span of a proposed ski lift from P to Q, a surveyor measures $\angle DPQ$ to be 25° and then walks off a distance of 1000 feet to R and measures $\angle PRQ$ to be 15°. What is the distance from P to Q?

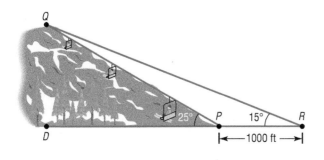

40. **Finding the Height of a Mountain** Use the illustration in Problem 39 to find the height QD of the mountain.

41. **Finding the Height of an Airplane** An aircraft is spotted by two observers who are 1000 feet apart. As the airplane passes over the line joining them, each observer takes a sighting of the angle of elevation to the plane, as indicated in the figure. How high is the airplane?

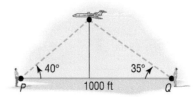

42. **Finding the Height of the Bridge over the Royal Gorge** The highest bridge in the world is the bridge over the Royal Gorge of the Arkansas River in Colorado. Sightings to the same point at water level directly under the bridge are taken from each side of the 880-foot-long bridge, as indicated in the figure. How high is the bridge?

Source: Guinness Book of World Records

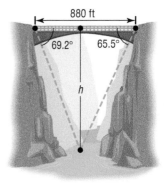

43. **Landscaping** Pat needs to determine the height of a tree before cutting it down to be sure that it will not fall on a nearby fence. The angle of elevation of the tree from one position on a flat path from the tree is 30°, and from a second position 40 feet farther along this path it is 20°. What is the height of the tree?

44. **Construction** A loading ramp 10 feet long that makes an angle of 18° with the horizontal is to be replaced by one that makes an angle of 12° with the horizontal. How long is the new ramp?

45. **Commercial Navigation** Adam must fly home to St. Louis from a business meeting in Oklahoma City. One flight option

flies directly to St. Louis, a distance of about 461.1 miles. A second flight option flies first to Kansas City and then connects to St. Louis. The bearing from Oklahoma City to Kansas City is N29.6°E, and the bearing from Oklahoma City to St. Louis is N57.7°E. The bearing from St. Louis to Oklahoma City is S57.7°W, and the bearing from St. Louis to Kansas City is N79.4°W. How many more frequent flyer miles will Adam receive if he takes the connecting flight rather than the direct flight?

Source: www.landings.com

46. Time Lost due to a Navigation Error In attempting to fly from city P to city Q, an aircraft followed a course that was 10° in error, as indicated in the figure. After flying a distance of 50 miles, the pilot corrected the course by turning at point R and flying 70 miles farther. If the constant speed of the aircraft was 250 miles per hour, how much time was lost due to the error?

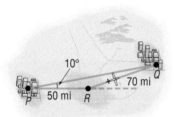

47. Finding the Lean of the Leaning Tower of Pisa The famous Leaning Tower of Pisa was originally 184.5 feet high.* At a distance of 123 feet from the base of the tower, the angle of elevation to the top of the tower is found to be 60°. Find $\angle RPQ$ indicated in the figure. Also, find the perpendicular distance from R to PQ.

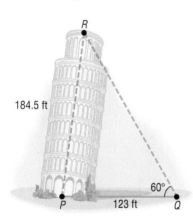

48. Crankshafts on Cars On a certain automobile, the crankshaft is 3 inches long and the connecting rod is 9 inches long (see the figure). At the time when $\angle OPQ$ is 15°, how far is the piston (P) from the center (O) of the crankshaft?

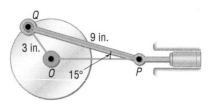

49. Constructing a Highway U.S. 41, a highway whose primary directions are north–south, is being constructed along the west coast of Florida. Near Naples, a bay obstructs the straight path of the road. Since the cost of a bridge is prohibitive, engineers decide to go around the bay. The illustration shows the path that they decide on and the measurements taken. What is the length of highway needed to go around the bay?

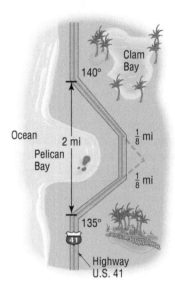

50. Calculating Distances at Sea The navigator of a ship at sea spots two lighthouses that she knows to be 3 miles apart along a straight seashore. She determines that the angles formed between two line-of-sight observations of the lighthouses and the line from the ship directly to shore are 15° and 35°. See the illustration.
(a) How far is the ship from lighthouse P?
(b) How far is the ship from lighthouse Q?
(c) How far is the ship from shore?

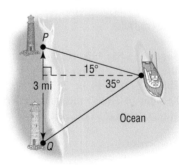

---

* On February 27, 1964, the government of Italy requested aid in preventing the tower from toppling. A multinational task force of engineers, mathematicians, and historians was assigned and met on the Azores islands to discuss stabilization methods. After over two decades of work on the subject, the tower was closed to the public in January 1990. During the time that the tower was closed, the bells were removed to relieve some weight, and cables were cinched around the third level and anchored several hundred meters away. Apartments and houses in the path of the tower were vacated for safety concerns. After a decade of corrective reconstruction and stabilization efforts, the tower was reopened to the public on December 15, 2001. Many methods were proposed to stabilize the tower, including the addition of 800 metric tons of lead counterweights to the raised end of the base. The final solution to correcting the lean was to remove 38 cubic meters of soil from underneath the raised end. The tower has been declared stable for at least another 300 years.

Source: http://en.wikipedia.org/wiki/Leaning_Tower_of_Pisa

51. Designing an Awning   An awning that covers a sliding glass door that is 88 inches tall forms an angle of 50° with the wall. The purpose of the awning is to prevent sunlight from entering the house when the angle of elevation of the Sun is more than 65°. See the figure. Find the length L of the awning.

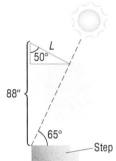

52. Finding Distances   A forest ranger is walking on a path inclined at 5° to the horizontal directly toward a 100-foot-tall fire observation tower. The angle of elevation from the path to the top of the tower is 40°. How far is the ranger from the tower at this time?

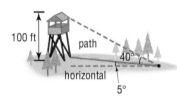

53. Great Pyramid of Cheops   One of the original Seven Wonders of the World, the Great Pyramid of Cheops was built about 2580 BC. Its original height was 480 feet 11 inches, but owing to the loss of its topmost stones, it is now shorter. Find the current height of the Great Pyramid using the information given in the illustration.

Source: Guinness Book of World Records

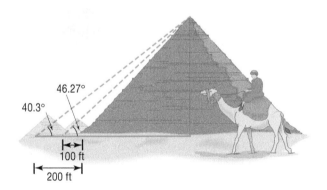

54. Determining the Height of an Aircraft   Two sensors are spaced 700 feet apart along the approach to a small airport. When an aircraft is nearing the airport, the angle of elevation from the first sensor to the aircraft is 20°, and from the second sensor to the aircraft it is 15°. Determine how high the aircraft is at this time.

55. Mercury   The distance from the Sun to Earth is approximately 149,600,000 kilometers (km). The distance from the Sun to Mercury is approximately 57,910,000 km. The **elongation angle** α is the angle formed between the line of sight from Earth to the Sun and the line of sight from Earth to Mercury. See the figure. Suppose that the elongation angle for Mercury is 15°. Use this information to find the possible distances between Earth and Mercury.

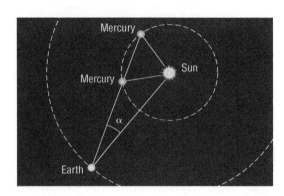

56. Venus   The distance from the Sun to Earth is approximately 149,600,000 km. The distance from the Sun to Venus is approximately 108,200,000 km. The elongation angle α is the angle formed between the line of sight from Earth to the Sun and the line of sight from Earth to Venus. Suppose that the elongation angle for Venus is 10°. Use this information to find the possible distances between Earth and Venus.

57. The Original Ferris Wheel   George Washington Gale Ferris, Jr., designed the original Ferris wheel for the 1893 World's Columbian Exposition in Chicago, Illinois. The wheel had 36 equally spaced cars each the size of a school bus. The distance between adjacent cars was approximately 22 feet. Determine the diameter of the wheel to the nearest foot.

Source: Carnegie Library of Pittsburgh, www.clpgh.org

58. Mollweide's Formula   For any triangle, Mollweide's Formula (named after Karl Mollweide, 1774–1825) states that

$$\frac{a + b}{c} = \frac{\cos\left[\frac{1}{2}(A - B)\right]}{\sin\left(\frac{1}{2}C\right)}$$

Derive it.

[**Hint:** Use the Law of Sines and then a Sum-to-Product Formula. Notice that this formula involves all six parts of a triangle. As a result, it is sometimes used to check the solution of a triangle.]

59. Mollweide's Formula   Another form of Mollweide's Formula is

$$\frac{a - b}{c} = \frac{\sin\left[\frac{1}{2}(A - B)\right]}{\cos\left(\frac{1}{2}C\right)}$$

Derive it.

60. For any triangle, derive the formula

$$a = b \cos C + c \cos B$$

[**Hint:** Use the fact that $\sin A = \sin(180° - B - C)$.]

61. Law of Tangents For any triangle, derive the Law of Tangents.

$$\frac{a - b}{a + b} = \frac{\tan\left[\frac{1}{2}(A - B)\right]}{\tan\left[\frac{1}{2}(A + B)\right]}$$

[**Hint:** Use Mollweide's Formula.]

62. Circumscribing a Triangle Show that

$$\frac{\sin A}{a} = \frac{\sin B}{b} = \frac{\sin C}{c} = \frac{1}{2r}$$

where r is the radius of the circle circumscribing the triangle PQR whose sides are a, b, and c, as shown in the figure.

[**Hint:** Draw the diameter PP'. Then $B = \angle PQR = \angle PP'R$, and angle $\angle PRP' = 90°$.]

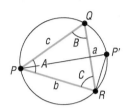

Explaining Concepts: Discussion and Writing

63. Make up three problems involving oblique triangles. One should result in one triangle, the second in two triangles, and the third in no triangle.

64. What do you do first if you are asked to solve a triangle and are given one side and two angles?

65. What do you do first if you are asked to solve a triangle and are given two sides and the angle opposite one of them?

'Are You Prepared?' Answers

1. $\sin A \cos B - \cos A \sin B$ **2.** $30°$ or $\dfrac{\pi}{6}$ **3.** $\dfrac{15}{2}$

8.3 The Law of Cosines

PREPARING FOR THIS SECTION *Before getting started, review the following:*

- Trigonometric Equations (Section 7.3, pp. 454–459)
- Distance Formula (Section 1.1, p. 3)

Now Work the 'Are You Prepared?' problems on page 531.

OBJECTIVES **1** Solve SAS Triangles (p. 529)
2 Solve SSS Triangles (p. 530)
3 Solve Applied Problems (p. 530)

In the previous section, we used the Law of Sines to solve Case 1 (SAA or ASA) and Case 2 (SSA) of an oblique triangle. In this section, we derive the Law of Cosines and use it to solve the remaining cases, 3 and 4.

CASE 3: Two sides and the included angle are known (SAS).
CASE 4: Three sides are known (SSS).

THEOREM **Law of Cosines**

For a triangle with sides a, b, c and opposite angles A, B, C, respectively,

$$c^2 = a^2 + b^2 - 2ab \cos C \qquad (1)$$
$$b^2 = a^2 + c^2 - 2ac \cos B \qquad (2)$$
$$a^2 = b^2 + c^2 - 2bc \cos A \qquad (3)$$

Figure 35

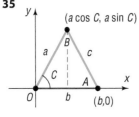

(a) Angle C is acute

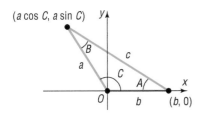

(b) Angle C is obtuse

Proof   We will prove only formula (1) here. Formulas (2) and (3) may be proved using the same argument.

We begin by strategically placing a triangle on a rectangular coordinate system so that the vertex of angle C is at the origin and side b lies along the positive x-axis. Regardless of whether C is acute, as in Figure 35(a), or obtuse, as in Figure 35(b), the vertex of angle B has coordinates $(a \cos C, a \sin C)$. The vertex of angle A has coordinates $(b, 0)$.

We use the distance formula to compute c^2.

$$\begin{aligned} c^2 &= (b - a \cos C)^2 + (0 - a \sin C)^2 \\ &= b^2 - 2ab \cos C + a^2 \cos^2 C + a^2 \sin^2 C \\ &= b^2 - 2ab \cos C + a^2(\cos^2 C + \sin^2 C) \\ &= a^2 + b^2 - 2ab \cos C \end{aligned}$$ ∎

Each of formulas (1), (2), and (3) may be stated in words as follows:

THEOREM

Law of Cosines

The square of one side of a triangle equals the sum of the squares of the other two sides minus twice their product times the cosine of their included angle.

Observe that if the triangle is a right triangle (so that, say, $C = 90°$), formula (1) becomes the familiar Pythagorean Theorem: $c^2 = a^2 + b^2$. The Pythagorean Theorem is a special case of the Law of Cosines!

1 Solve SAS Triangles

The Law of Cosines is used to solve Case 3 (SAS), which applies to triangles for which two sides and the included angle are known.

EXAMPLE 1

Using the Law of Cosines to Solve an SAS Triangle

Solve the triangle: $a = 2$, $b = 3$, $C = 60°$

Solution   See Figure 36. Because we know two sides, a and b, and the included angle, $C = 60°$, the Law of Cosines makes it easy to find the third side, c.

Figure 36

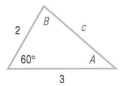

$$\begin{aligned} c^2 &= a^2 + b^2 - 2ab \cos C \\ &= 2^2 + 3^2 - 2 \cdot 2 \cdot 3 \cdot \cos 60° \qquad \text{\small $a = 2, b = 3, C = 60°$} \\ &= 13 - \left(12 \cdot \frac{1}{2}\right) = 7 \\ c &= \sqrt{7} \end{aligned}$$

Side c is of length $\sqrt{7}$. To find the angles A and B, we may use either the Law of Sines or the Law of Cosines. It is preferable to use the Law of Cosines, since it will lead to an equation with one solution. Using the Law of Sines would lead to an equation with two solutions that would need to be checked to determine which solution fits the given data.* We choose to use formulas (2) and (3) of the Law of Cosines to find A and B.

For A:

$$\begin{aligned} a^2 &= b^2 + c^2 - 2bc \cos A \\ 2bc \cos A &= b^2 + c^2 - a^2 \\ \cos A &= \frac{b^2 + c^2 - a^2}{2bc} = \frac{9 + 7 - 4}{2 \cdot 3\sqrt{7}} = \frac{12}{6\sqrt{7}} = \frac{2\sqrt{7}}{7} \\ A &= \cos^{-1} \frac{2\sqrt{7}}{7} \approx 40.9° \end{aligned}$$

---

* The Law of Sines can be used if the angle sought is opposite the smaller side, thus ensuring it must be acute. (In Figure 36, use the Law of Sines to find A, the angle opposite the smaller side.)

For *B*:

$$b^2 = a^2 + c^2 - 2ac \cos B$$

COMMENT We could also have found
B using the fact that the sum
$$A + B + C = 180°$$
so B = 180° − 40.9° − 60° = 79.1°.
However, using the Law of Cosines twice
allows for a check. ■

$$\cos B = \frac{a^2 + c^2 - b^2}{2ac} = \frac{4 + 7 - 9}{4\sqrt{7}} = \frac{2}{4\sqrt{7}} = \frac{\sqrt{7}}{14}$$

$$B = \cos^{-1}\frac{\sqrt{7}}{14} \approx 79.1°$$

Notice that $A + B + C = 40.9° + 79.1° + 60° = 180°$, as required.

Now Work PROBLEM 9

2 Solve SSS Triangles

The next example illustrates how the Law of Cosines is used when three sides of a triangle are known, Case 4 (SSS).

EXAMPLE 2

Using the Law of Cosines to Solve an SSS Triangle

Solve the triangle: $a = 4, b = 3, c = 6$

Solution

See Figure 37. To find the angles A, B, and C, we proceed as we did to find the angles in the solution to Example 1.

Figure 37

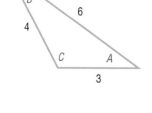

For *A*:

$$\cos A = \frac{b^2 + c^2 - a^2}{2bc} = \frac{9 + 36 - 16}{2 \cdot 3 \cdot 6} = \frac{29}{36}$$

$$A = \cos^{-1}\frac{29}{36} \approx 36.3°$$

For *B*:

$$\cos B = \frac{a^2 + c^2 - b^2}{2ac} = \frac{16 + 36 - 9}{2 \cdot 4 \cdot 6} = \frac{43}{48}$$

$$B = \cos^{-1}\frac{43}{48} \approx 26.4°$$

Since we know A and B,

$$C = 180° - A - B \approx 180° - 36.3° - 26.4° = 117.3°$$

Now Work PROBLEM 15

3 Solve Applied Problems

EXAMPLE 3

Correcting a Navigational Error

A motorized sailboat leaves Naples, Florida, bound for Key West, 150 miles away. Maintaining a constant speed of 15 miles per hour, but encountering heavy crosswinds and strong currents, the crew finds, after 4 hours, that the sailboat is off course by 20°.

(a) How far is the sailboat from Key West at this time?

(b) Through what angle should the sailboat turn to correct its course?

(c) How much time has been added to the trip because of this? (Assume that the speed remains at 15 miles per hour.)

Solution   See Figure 38. With a speed of 15 miles per hour, the sailboat has gone 60 miles after 4 hours. We seek the distance x of the sailboat from Key West. We also seek the angle θ that the sailboat should turn through to correct its course.

(a) To find x, we use the Law of Cosines, since we know two sides and the included angle.

$$x^2 = 150^2 + 60^2 - 2(150)(60) \cos 20° \approx 9185.53$$
$$x \approx 95.8$$

The sailboat is about 96 miles from Key West.

(b) We now know three sides of the triangle, so we can use the Law of Cosines again to find the angle A opposite the side of length 150 miles.

$$150^2 = 96^2 + 60^2 - 2(96)(60) \cos A$$
$$9684 = -11{,}520 \cos A$$
$$\cos A \approx -0.8406$$
$$A \approx 147.2°$$

The sailboat should turn through an angle of

$$\theta = 180° - A \approx 180° - 147.2° = 32.8°$$

The sailboat should turn through an angle of about 33° to correct its course.

(c) The total length of the trip is now $60 + 96 = 156$ miles. The extra 6 miles will only require about 0.4 hour or 24 minutes more if the speed of 15 miles per hour is maintained.

Figure 38

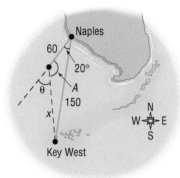

Naples
60
20°
θ
A
150
x
Key West
N
W—E
S

━━━**Now Work**   PROBLEM 45

Historical Feature

The Law of Sines was known vaguely long before it was explicitly stated by Nasir Eddin (about AD 1250). Ptolemy (about AD 150) was aware of it in a form using a chord function instead of the sine function. But it was first clearly stated in Europe by Regiomontanus, writing in 1464.

The Law of Cosines appears first in Euclid's *Elements* (Book II), but in a well-disguised form in which squares built on the sides of triangles are added and a rectangle representing the cosine term is subtracted. It was thus known to all mathematicians because of their familiarity with Euclid's work. An early modern form of the Law of Cosines, that for finding the angle when the sides are known, was stated by François Viète (in 1593).

The Law of Tangents (see Problem 61 of Exercise 8.2) has become obsolete. In the past it was used in place of the Law of Cosines, because the Law of Cosines was very inconvenient for calculation with logarithms or slide rules. Mixing of addition and multiplication is now very easy on a calculator, however, and the Law of Tangents has been shelved along with the slide rule.

8.3 Assess Your Understanding

'Are You Prepared?'   *Answers are given at the end of these exercises. If you get a wrong answer, read the pages listed in* red.

1. Write the formula for the distance d from $P_1 = (x_1, y_1)$ to $P_2 = (x_2, y_2)$. (p. 3)

2. If θ is an acute angle, solve the equation $\cos \theta = \dfrac{\sqrt{2}}{2}$. (pp. 454–459)

Concepts and Vocabulary

3. If three sides of a triangle are given, the Law of _____ is used to solve the triangle.

4. If one side and two angles of a triangle are given, the Law of _____ is used to solve the triangle.

5. If two sides and the included angle of a triangle are given, the Law of _____ is used to solve the triangle.

6. *True or False*   Given only the three sides of a triangle, there is insufficient information to solve the triangle.

7. *True or False*   Given two sides and the included angle, the first thing to do to solve the triangle is to use the Law of Sines.

8. *True or False*   A special case of the Law of Cosines is the Pythagorean Theorem.

Skill Building

In Problems 9–16, solve each triangle.

9.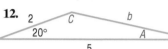

10.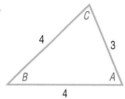

11.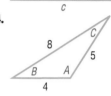

12.

13.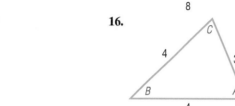

14.

15.

16.

In Problems 17–32, solve each triangle.

17. $a = 3, \quad b = 4, \quad C = 40°$

18. $a = 2, \quad c = 1, \quad B = 10°$

19. $b = 1, \quad c = 3, \quad A = 80°$

20. $a = 6, \quad b = 4, \quad C = 60°$

21. $a = 3, \quad c = 2, \quad B = 110°$

22. $b = 4, \quad c = 1, \quad A = 120°$

23. $a = 2, \quad b = 2, \quad C = 50°$

24. $a = 3, \quad c = 2, \quad B = 90°$

25. $a = 12, \quad b = 13, \quad c = 5$

26. $a = 4, \quad b = 5, \quad c = 3$

27. $a = 2, \quad b = 2, \quad c = 2$

28. $a = 3, \quad b = 3, \quad c = 2$

29. $a = 5, \quad b = 8, \quad c = 9$

30. $a = 4, \quad b = 3, \quad c = 6$

31. $a = 10, \quad b = 8, \quad c = 5$

32. $a = 9, \quad b = 7, \quad c = 10$

Mixed Practice

In Problems 33–42, solve each triangle using either the Law of Sines or the Law of Cosines.

33. $B = 20°, C = 75°, b = 5$

34. $A = 50°, B = 55°, c = 9$

35. $a = 6, b = 8, c = 9$

36. $a = 14, b = 7, A = 85°$

37. $B = 35°, C = 65°, a = 15$

38. $a = 4, c = 5, B = 55°$

39. $A = 10°, a = 3, b = 10$

40. $A = 65°, B = 72°, b = 7$

41. $b = 5, c = 12, A = 60°$

42. $a = 10, b = 10, c = 15$

Applications and Extensions

43. Distance to the Green A golfer hits an errant tee shot that lands in the rough. A marker in the center of the fairway is 150 yards from the center of the green. While standing on the marker and facing the green, the golfer turns 110° toward his ball. He then paces off 35 yards to his ball. See the figure. How far is the ball from the center of the green?

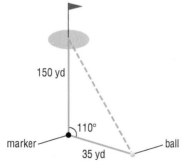

44. Navigation An airplane flies due north from Ft. Myers to Sarasota, a distance of 150 miles, and then turns through an angle of 50° and flies to Orlando, a distance of 100 miles. See the figure.

(a) How far is it directly from Ft. Myers to Orlando?
(b) What bearing should the pilot use to fly directly from Ft. Myers to Orlando?

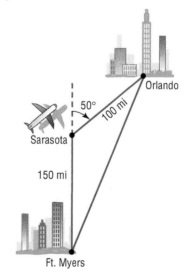

45. Avoiding a Tropical Storm A cruise ship maintains an average speed of 15 knots in going from San Juan, Puerto Rico, to Barbados, West Indies, a distance of 600 nautical miles. To avoid a tropical storm, the captain heads out of San Juan in a direction of 20° off a direct heading to Barbados. The captain maintains the 15-knot speed for 10 hours, after which time the path to Barbados becomes clear of storms.
(a) Through what angle should the captain turn to head directly to Barbados?
(b) Once the turn is made, how long will it be before the ship reaches Barbados if the same 15-knot speed is maintained?

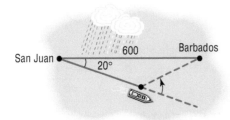

46. Revising a Flight Plan In attempting to fly from Chicago to Louisville, a distance of 330 miles, a pilot inadvertently took a course that was 10° in error, as indicated in the figure.
(a) If the aircraft maintains an average speed of 220 miles per hour and if the error in direction is discovered after 15 minutes, through what angle should the pilot turn to head toward Louisville?
(b) What new average speed should the pilot maintain so that the total time of the trip is 90 minutes?

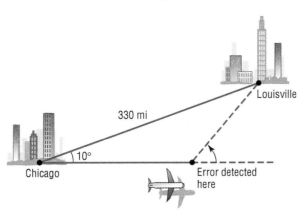

47. Major League Baseball Field A Major League baseball diamond is actually a square 90 feet on a side. The pitching rubber is located 60.5 feet from home plate on a line joining home plate and second base.
(a) How far is it from the pitching rubber to first base?
(b) How far is it from the pitching rubber to second base?
(c) If a pitcher faces home plate, through what angle does he need to turn to face first base?

48. Little League Baseball Field According to Little League baseball official regulations, the diamond is a square 60 feet on a side. The pitching rubber is located 46 feet from home plate on a line joining home plate and second base.
(a) How far is it from the pitching rubber to first base?
(b) How far is it from the pitching rubber to second base?
(c) If a pitcher faces home plate, through what angle does he need to turn to face first base?

49. Finding the Length of a Guy Wire The height of a radio tower is 500 feet, and the ground on one side of the tower slopes upward at an angle of 10° (see the figure).
(a) How long should a guy wire be if it is to connect to the top of the tower and be secured at a point on the sloped side 100 feet from the base of the tower?
(b) How long should a second guy wire be if it is to connect to the middle of the tower and be secured at a point 100 feet from the base on the flat side?

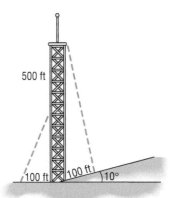

50. Finding the Length of a Guy Wire A radio tower 500 feet high is located on the side of a hill with an inclination to the horizontal of 5°. See the figure. How long should two guy wires be if they are to connect to the top of the tower and be secured at two points 100 feet directly above and directly below the base of the tower?

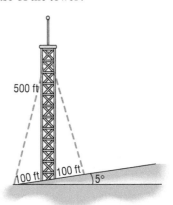

51. Wrigley Field, Home of the Chicago Cubs The distance from home plate to the fence in dead center in Wrigley Field is 400 feet (see the figure). How far is it from the fence in dead center to third base?

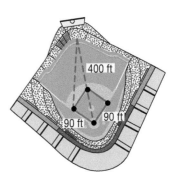

52. Little League Baseball   The distance from home plate to the fence in dead center at the Oak Lawn Little League field is 280 feet. How far is it from the fence in dead center to third base?

[**Hint:** The distance between the bases in Little League is 60 feet.]

53. Building a Swing Set   Clint is building a wooden swing set for his children. Each supporting end of the swing set is to be an A-frame constructed with two 10-foot-long 4 by 4s joined at a 45° angle. To prevent the swing set from tipping over, Clint wants to secure the base of each A-frame to concrete footings. How far apart should the footings for each A-frame be?

54. Rods and Pistons   Rod OA rotates about the fixed point O so that point A travels on a circle of radius r. Connected to point A is another rod AB of length $L > 2r$, and point B is connected to a piston. See the figure. Show that the distance x between point O and point B is given by

$$x = r \cos \theta + \sqrt{r^2 \cos^2 \theta + L^2 - r^2}$$

where θ is the angle of rotation of rod OA.

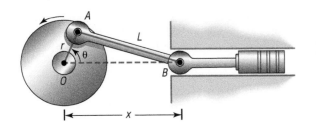

55. Geometry   Show that the length d of a chord of a circle of radius r is given by the formula

$$d = 2r \sin \frac{\theta}{2}$$

where θ is the central angle formed by the radii to the ends of the chord. See the figure. Use this result to derive the fact that $\sin \theta < \theta$, where $\theta > 0$ is measured in radians.

56. For any triangle, show that

$$\cos \frac{C}{2} = \sqrt{\frac{s(s - c)}{ab}}$$

where $s = \frac{1}{2}(a + b + c)$.

[**Hint:** Use a Half-angle Formula and the Law of Cosines.]

57. For any triangle show that

$$\sin \frac{C}{2} = \sqrt{\frac{(s - a)(s - b)}{ab}}$$

where $s = \frac{1}{2}(a + b + c)$.

58. Use the Law of Cosines to prove the identity

$$\frac{\cos A}{a} + \frac{\cos B}{b} + \frac{\cos C}{c} = \frac{a^2 + b^2 + c^2}{2abc}$$

Explaining Concepts: Discussion and Writing

59. What do you do first if you are asked to solve a triangle and are given two sides and the included angle?

60. What do you do first if you are asked to solve a triangle and are given three sides?

61. Make up an applied problem that requires using the Law of Cosines.

62. Write down your strategy for solving an oblique triangle.

63. State the Law of Cosines in words.

'Are You Prepared?' Answers

1. $d = \sqrt{(x_2 - x_1)^2 + (y_2 - y_1)^2}$ **2.** $\theta = 45°$ or $\dfrac{\pi}{4}$

8.4 Area of a Triangle

PREPARING FOR THIS SECTION *Before getting started, review the following:*

• Geometry Essentials (Appendix A, Section A.2, pp. A14–A19)

Now Work the *'Are You Prepared?'* problem on page 537.

OBJECTIVES **1** Find the Area of SAS Triangles (p. 535)
2 Find the Area of SSS Triangles (p. 536)

In this section, we derive several formulas for calculating the area of a triangle. The most familiar of these is the following:

THEOREM

The area K of a triangle is

$$K = \frac{1}{2}bh \tag{1}$$

where b is the base and h is an altitude drawn to that base.

COMMENT Typically A is used for area, but we use A as the measure of an angle, so we use K for area to avoid confusion. ∎

Proof The derivation of this formula is rather easy once a rectangle of base b and height h is constructed around the triangle. See Figures 39 and 40.

Triangles 1 and 2 in Figure 40 are equal in area, as are triangles 3 and 4. Consequently, the area of the triangle with base b and altitude h is exactly half the area of the rectangle, which is bh.

Figure 39

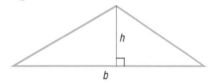

Figure 40

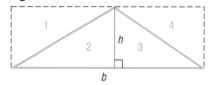 ∎

1 Find the Area of SAS Triangles

If the base b and altitude h to that base are known, then we can find the area of such a triangle using formula (1). Usually, though, the information required to use formula (1) is not given. Suppose, for example, that we know two sides a and b and the included angle C. See Figure 41. Then the altitude h can be found by noting that

Figure 41

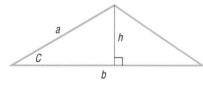

$$\frac{h}{a} = \sin C$$

so that

$$h = a \sin C$$

Using this fact in formula (1) produces

$$K = \frac{1}{2}bh = \frac{1}{2}b(a \sin C) = \frac{1}{2}ab \sin C$$

We now have the formula

$$K = \frac{1}{2}ab \sin C \tag{2}$$

By dropping altitudes from the other two vertices of the triangle, we obtain the following corresponding formulas:

$$K = \frac{1}{2}bc \sin A \qquad (3)$$

$$K = \frac{1}{2}ac \sin B \qquad (4)$$

It is easiest to remember these formulas using the following wording:

THEOREM

The area K of a triangle equals one-half the product of two of its sides times the sine of their included angle.

EXAMPLE 1 **Finding the Area of an SAS Triangle**

Find the area K of the triangle for which $a = 8$, $b = 6$, and $C = 30°$.

Figure 42

Solution See Figure 42. Use formula (2) to get

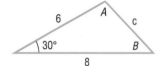

$$K = \frac{1}{2}ab \sin C = \frac{1}{2} \cdot 8 \cdot 6 \cdot \sin 30° = 12 \text{ square units}$$

═══ **Now Work** PROBLEM 5

2 Find the Area of SSS Triangles

If the three sides of a triangle are known, another formula, called **Heron's Formula** (named after Heron of Alexandria), can be used to find the area of a triangle.

THEOREM **Heron's Formula**

The area K of a triangle with sides $a, b,$ and c is

$$K = \sqrt{s(s - a)(s - b)(s - c)} \qquad (5)$$

where $s = \frac{1}{2}(a + b + c)$.

EXAMPLE 2 **Finding the Area of an SSS Triangle**

Find the area of a triangle whose sides are 4, 5, and 7.

Solution Let $a = 4, b = 5,$ and $c = 7$. Then

$$s = \frac{1}{2}(a + b + c) = \frac{1}{2}(4 + 5 + 7) = 8$$

Heron's Formula gives the area K as

$$K = \sqrt{s(s - a)(s - b)(s - c)} = \sqrt{8 \cdot 4 \cdot 3 \cdot 1} = \sqrt{96} = 4\sqrt{6} \text{ square units}$$

═══ **Now Work** PROBLEM 11

Proof of Heron's Formula The proof that we give uses the Law of Cosines and is quite different from the proof given by Heron.

From the Law of Cosines,

$$c^2 = a^2 + b^2 - 2ab \cos C$$

and the Half-angle Formula

$$\cos^2\frac{C}{2} = \frac{1 + \cos C}{2}$$

we find that

$$\cos^2\frac{C}{2} = \frac{1 + \cos C}{2} = \frac{1 + \dfrac{a^2 + b^2 - c^2}{2ab}}{2}$$

$$= \frac{a^2 + 2ab + b^2 - c^2}{4ab} = \frac{(a + b)^2 - c^2}{4ab}$$

$$= \frac{(a + b - c)(a + b + c)}{4ab} = \frac{2(s - c) \cdot 2s}{4ab} = \frac{s(s - c)}{ab} \qquad (6)$$

$\uparrow$ \qquad\qquad\qquad\qquad $\uparrow$

Factor. \qquad\qquad\qquad $a + b - c = a + b + c - 2c$

$\qquad\qquad\qquad\qquad\qquad\qquad = 2s - 2c = 2(s - c)$

Similarly, using $\sin^2\dfrac{C}{2} = \dfrac{1 - \cos C}{2}$, we find that

$$\sin^2\frac{C}{2} = \frac{(s - a)(s - b)}{ab} \qquad (7)$$

Now we use formula (2) for the area.

$$K = \frac{1}{2}ab \sin C$$

$$= \frac{1}{2}ab \cdot 2 \sin\frac{C}{2}\cos\frac{C}{2} \qquad \sin C = \sin\left[2\left(\frac{C}{2}\right)\right] = 2\sin\frac{C}{2}\cos\frac{C}{2}$$

$$= ab\sqrt{\frac{(s - a)(s - b)}{ab}}\sqrt{\frac{s(s - c)}{ab}} \qquad \text{Use equations (6) and (7).}$$

$$= \sqrt{s(s - a)(s - b)(s - c)} \qquad\qquad\qquad \blacksquare$$

Historical Feature

Heron's Formula (also known as *Hero's Formula*) is due to Heron of Alexandria (first century AD), who had, besides his mathematical talents, a good deal of engineering skills. In various temples his mechanical devices produced effects that seemed supernatural, and visitors presumably were thus influenced to generosity. Heron's book *Metrica*, on making such devices, has survived and was discovered in 1896 in the city of Constantinople.

Heron's Formulas for the area of a triangle caused some mild discomfort in Greek mathematics, because a product with two factors was an area, while one with three factors was a volume, but four factors seemed contradictory in Heron's time.

8.4 Assess Your Understanding

'Are You Prepared?' *The answer is given at the end of these exercises. If you get the wrong answer, read the page listed in red.*

1. The area K of a triangle, whose base is b and whose height is h is _____. (pp. A14–A19)

Concepts and Vocabulary

2. If two sides a and b and the included angle C are known in a triangle, then the area K is found using the formula

$$K = \underline{\hspace{2cm}}.$$

3. The area K of a triangle with sides a, b, and c is

$$K = \underline{\hspace{4cm}} \qquad \text{where } s = \underline{\hspace{3cm}}.$$

4. ***True or False*** Heron's formula is used to find the area of SSS triangles.

Skill Building

In Problems 5–12, find the area of each triangle. Round answers to two decimal places.

5.
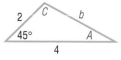

6.
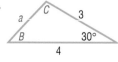

7.
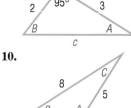

8.
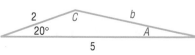

9.
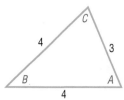

10.
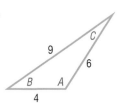

11.

12.

In Problems 13–24, find the area of each triangle. Round answers to two decimal places.

13. $a = 3$, $b = 4$, $C = 40°$

14. $a = 2$, $c = 1$, $B = 10°$

15. $b = 1$, $c = 3$, $A = 80°$

16. $a = 6$, $b = 4$, $C = 60°$

17. $a = 3$, $c = 2$, $B = 110°$

18. $b = 4$, $c = 1$, $A = 120°$

19. $a = 12$, $b = 13$, $c = 5$

20. $a = 4$, $b = 5$, $c = 3$

21. $a = 2$, $b = 2$, $c = 2$

22. $a = 3$, $b = 3$, $c = 2$

23. $a = 5$, $b = 8$, $c = 9$

24. $a = 4$, $b = 3$, $c = 6$

Applications and Extensions

25. Area of an ASA Triangle   If two angles and the included side are given, the third angle is easy to find. Use the Law of Sines to show that the area K of a triangle with side a and angles A, B, and C is

$$K = \frac{a^2 \sin B \sin C}{2 \sin A}$$

26. Area of a Triangle   Prove the two other forms of the formula given in Problem 25.

$$K = \frac{b^2 \sin A \sin C}{2 \sin B} \quad \text{and} \quad K = \frac{c^2 \sin A \sin B}{2 \sin C}$$

In Problems 27–32, use the results of Problem 25 or 26 to find the area of each triangle. Round answers to two decimal places.

27. $A = 40°$, $B = 20°$, $a = 2$

28. $A = 50°$, $C = 20°$, $a = 3$

29. $B = 70°$, $C = 10°$, $b = 5$

30. $A = 70°$, $B = 60°$, $c = 4$

31. $A = 110°$, $C = 30°$, $c = 3$

32. $B = 10°$, $C = 100°$, $b = 2$

33. Area of a Segment   Find the area of the segment (shaded in blue in the figure) of a circle whose radius is 8 feet, formed by a central angle of 70°.

[**Hint:** Subtract the area of the triangle from the area of the sector to obtain the area of the segment.]

34. Area of a Segment   Find the area of the segment of a circle whose radius is 5 inches, formed by a central angle of 40°.

35. Cost of a Triangular Lot   The dimensions of a triangular lot are 100 feet by 50 feet by 75 feet. If the price of such land is $3 per square foot, how much does the lot cost?

36. Amount of Material to Make a Tent   A cone-shaped tent is made from a circular piece of canvas 24 feet in diameter by removing a sector with central angle 100° and connecting the ends. What is the surface area of the tent?

37. Dimensions of Home Plate   The dimensions of home plate at any major league baseball stadium are shown. Find the area of home plate.

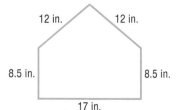

38. Computing Areas   See the figure on page 539. Find the area of the shaded region enclosed in a semicircle of diameter 10 inches. The length of the chord PQ is 8 inches.

[**Hint:** Triangle PQR is a right triangle.]

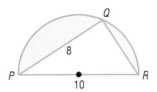

39. Geometry Consult the figure, which shows a circle of radius r with center at O. Find the area K of the shaded region as a function of the central angle θ.

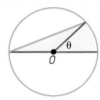

40. Approximating the Area of a Lake To approximate the area of a lake, a surveyor walks around the perimeter of the lake, taking the measurements shown in the illustration. Using this technique, what is the approximate area of the lake?

[**Hint:** Use the Law of Cosines on the three triangles shown and then find the sum of their areas.]

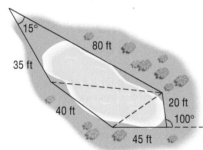

41. The Flatiron Building Completed in 1902 in New York City, the Flatiron Building is triangular shaped and bounded by 22nd Street, Broadway, and 5th Avenue. The building measures approximately 87 feet on the 22nd Street side, 190 feet on the Broadway side, and 173 feet on the 5th Avenue side. Approximate the ground area covered by the building.

Source: Sarah Bradford Landau and Carl W. Condit, *Rise of the New York Skyscraper: 1865–1913.* New Haven, CT: Yale University Press, 1996

42. Bermuda Triangle The Bermuda Triangle is roughly defined by Hamilton, Bermuda; San Juan, Puerto Rico; and Fort Lauderdale, Florida. The distances from Hamilton to Fort Lauderdale, Fort Lauderdale to San Juan, and San Juan to Hamilton are approximately 1028, 1046, and 965 miles, respectively. Ignoring the curvature of Earth, approximate the area of the Bermuda Triangle.

Source: www.worldatlas.com

43. Geometry Refer to the figure. If $|OA| = 1$, show that:

(a) Area $\triangle OAC = \dfrac{1}{2}\sin \alpha \cos \alpha$

(b) Area $\triangle OCB = \dfrac{1}{2}|OB|^2 \sin \beta \cos \beta$

(c) Area $\triangle OAB = \dfrac{1}{2}|OB| \sin(\alpha + \beta)$

(d) $|OB| = \dfrac{\cos \alpha}{\cos \beta}$

(e) $\sin(\alpha + \beta) = \sin \alpha \cos \beta + \cos \alpha \sin \beta$

[**Hint:** Area $\triangle OAB$ = Area $\triangle OAC$ + Area $\triangle OCB$.]

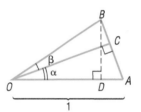

44. Geometry Refer to the figure, in which a unit circle is drawn. The line segment DB is tangent to the circle and θ is acute.

(a) Express the area of $\triangle OBC$ in terms of $\sin \theta$ and $\cos \theta$.

(b) Express the area of $\triangle OBD$ in terms of $\sin \theta$ and $\cos \theta$.

(c) The area of the sector $\overparen{OBC}$ of the circle is $\dfrac{1}{2}\theta$, where θ is measured in radians. Use the results of parts (a) and (b) and the fact that

$$\text{Area } \triangle OBC < \text{Area } \overparen{OBC} < \text{Area } \triangle OBD$$

to show that

$$1 < \frac{\theta}{\sin \theta} < \frac{1}{\cos \theta}$$

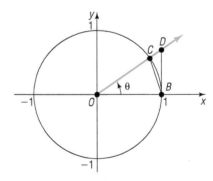

45. The Cow Problem* A cow is tethered to one corner of a square barn, 10 feet by 10 feet, with a rope 100 feet long. What is the maximum grazing area for the cow?

[See the illustration on page 540.]

---

* Suggested by Professor Teddy Koukounas of Suffolk Community College, who learned of it from an old farmer in Virginia. Solution provided by Professor Kathleen Miranda of SUNY at Old Westbury.

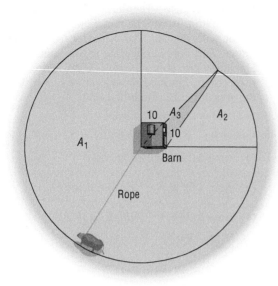

46. Another Cow Problem If the barn in Problem 45 is rectangular, 10 feet by 20 feet, what is the maximum grazing area for the cow?

47. Perfect Triangles A *perfect triangle* is one having natural number sides for which the area is numerically equal to the perimeter. Show that the triangles with the given side lengths are perfect.

(a) 9, 10, 17   (b) 6, 25, 29

Source: M.V. Bonsangue, G. E. Gannon, E. Buchman, and N. Gross, "In Search of Perfect Triangles," *Mathematics Teacher,* Vol. 92, No. 1, 1999: 56–61

48. If h_1, h_2, and h_3 are the altitudes dropped from P, Q, and R, respectively, in a triangle (see the figure), show that

$$\frac{1}{h_1} + \frac{1}{h_2} + \frac{1}{h_3} = \frac{s}{K}$$

where K is the area of the triangle and $s = \frac{1}{2}(a + b + c)$.

[**Hint:** $h_1 = \frac{2K}{a}$.]

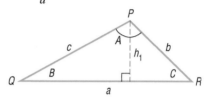

49. Show that a formula for the altitude h from a vertex to the opposite side a of a triangle is

$$h = \frac{a \sin B \sin C}{\sin A}$$

Inscribed Circle *For Problems 50–53, the lines that bisect each angle of a triangle meet in a single point O, and the perpendicular distance r from O to each side of the triangle is the same. The circle with center at O and radius r is called the **inscribed circle** of the triangle (see the figure).*

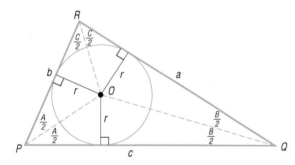

50. Apply the formula from Problem 49 to triangle OPQ to show that

$$r = \frac{c \sin \dfrac{A}{2} \sin \dfrac{B}{2}}{\cos \dfrac{C}{2}}$$

51. Use the result of Problem 50 and the results of Problems 56 and 57 in Section 8.3 to show that

$$\cot \frac{C}{2} = \frac{s - c}{r}$$

where $s = \frac{1}{2}(a + b + c)$.

52. Show that

$$\cot \frac{A}{2} + \cot \frac{B}{2} + \cot \frac{C}{2} = \frac{s}{r}$$

53. Show that the area K of triangle PQR is $K = rs$, where $s = \frac{1}{2}(a + b + c)$. Then show that

$$r = \sqrt{\frac{(s - a)(s - b)(s - c)}{s}}$$

Explaining Concepts: Discussion and Writing

54. What do you do first if you are asked to find the area of a triangle and are given two sides and the included angle?

55. What do you do first if you are asked to find the area of a triangle and are given three sides?

56. State the area of an SAS triangle in words.

'Are You Prepared?' Answer

1. $K = \frac{1}{2}bh$

8.5 Simple Harmonic Motion; Damped Motion; Combining Waves

PREPARING FOR THIS SECTION *Before getting started, review the following:*

• Sinusoidal Graphs (Section 6.4, pp. 397–403)

Now Work the *'Are You Prepared?'* problem on page 547.

OBJECTIVES 1 Build a Model for an Object in Simple Harmonic Motion (p. 541)
           2 Analyze Simple Harmonic Motion (p. 543)
           3 Analyze an Object in Damped Motion (p. 544)
           4 Graph the Sum of Two Functions (p. 545)

1 Build a Model for an Object in Simple Harmonic Motion

Many physical phenomena can be described as simple harmonic motion. Radio and television waves, light waves, sound waves, and water waves exhibit motion that is simple harmonic.

The swinging of a pendulum, the vibrations of a tuning fork, and the bobbing of a weight attached to a coiled spring are examples of vibrational motion. In this type of motion, an object swings back and forth over the same path. In Figure 43, the point B is the **equilibrium (rest) position** of the vibrating object. The **amplitude** is the distance from the object's rest position to its point of greatest displacement (either point A or point C in Figure 43). The **period** is the time required to complete one vibration, that is, the time it takes to go from, say, point A through B to C and back to A.

Simple harmonic motion is a special kind of vibrational motion in which the acceleration a of the object is directly proportional to the negative of its displacement d from its rest position. That is, $a = -kd, k > 0$.

For example, when the mass hanging from the spring in Figure 43 is pulled down from its rest position B to the point C, the force of the spring tries to restore the mass to its rest position. Assuming that there is no frictional force* to retard the motion, the amplitude will remain constant. The force increases in direct proportion to the distance that the mass is pulled from its rest position. Since the force increases directly, the acceleration of the mass of the object must do likewise, because (by Newton's Second Law of Motion) force is directly proportional to acceleration. As a result, the acceleration of the object varies directly with its displacement, and the motion is an example of simple harmonic motion.

Simple harmonic motion is related to circular motion. To see this relationship, consider a circle of radius a, with center at $(0, 0)$. See Figure 44. Suppose that an

Vibrating tuning fork

Figure 43

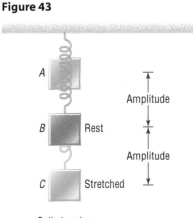

Coiled spring

Figure 44

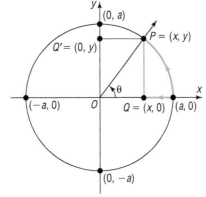

* If friction is present, the amplitude will decrease with time to 0. This type of motion is an example of **damped motion**, which is discussed later in this section.

object initially placed at $(a, 0)$ moves counterclockwise around the circle at a constant angular speed ω. Suppose further that after time t has elapsed the object is at the point $P = (x, y)$ on the circle. The angle θ, in radians, swept out by the ray $\overrightarrow{OP}$ in this time t is

$$\theta = \omega t$$

The coordinates of the point P at time t are

$$x = a \cos \theta = a \cos(\omega t)$$

$$y = a \sin \theta = a \sin(\omega t)$$

Corresponding to each position $P = (x, y)$ of the object moving about the circle, there is the point $Q = (x, 0)$, called the **projection of P on the x-axis**. As P moves around the circle at a constant rate, the point Q moves back and forth between the points $(a, 0)$ and $(-a, 0)$ along the x-axis with a motion that is simple harmonic. Similarly, for each point P there is a point $Q' = (0, y)$, called the **projection of P on the y-axis**. As P moves around the circle, the point Q' moves back and forth between the points $(0, a)$ and $(0, -a)$ on the y-axis with a motion that is simple harmonic. Simple harmonic motion can be described as the projection of constant circular motion on a coordinate axis.

To put it another way, again consider a mass hanging from a spring where the mass is pulled down from its rest position to the point C and then released. See Figure 45(a). The graph shown in Figure 45(b) describes the displacement d of the object from its rest position as a function of time t, assuming that no frictional force is present.

Figure 45

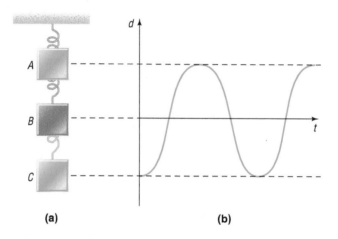

(a)   (b)

THEOREM

Simple Harmonic Motion

An object that moves on a coordinate axis so that the distance d from its rest position at time t is given by either

$$d = a \cos(\omega t) \quad \text{or} \quad d = a \sin(\omega t)$$

where a and $\omega > 0$ are constants, moves with simple harmonic motion. The motion has amplitude $|a|$ and period $\dfrac{2\pi}{\omega}$.

The **frequency** f of an object in simple harmonic motion is the number of oscillations per unit time. Since the period is the time required for one oscillation, it follows that the frequency is the reciprocal of the period; that is,

$$f = \frac{\omega}{2\pi} \quad \omega > 0$$

EXAMPLE 1	**Build a Model for an Object in Harmonic Motion**

Figure 46

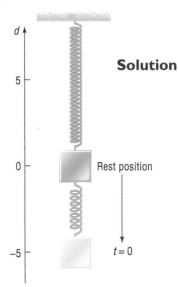

COMMENT In the solution to Example 1, we let a = −5, since the object is pulled down. If the initial direction were up, we would let a = 5. ∎

Suppose that an object attached to a coiled spring is pulled down a distance of 5 inches from its rest position and then released. If the time for one oscillation is 3 seconds, develop a model that relates the displacement d of the object from its rest position after time t (in seconds). Assume no friction.

Solution

The motion of the object is simple harmonic. See Figure 46. When the object is released ($t = 0$), the displacement of the object from the rest position is −5 units (since the object was pulled down). Because $d = -5$ when $t = 0$, it is easier to use the cosine function*

$$d = a \cos(\omega t)$$

to describe the motion. Now the amplitude is $|-5| = 5$ and the period is 3, so

$$a = -5 \quad \text{and} \quad \frac{2\pi}{\omega} = \text{period} = 3, \quad \text{so} \quad \omega = \frac{2\pi}{3}$$

An equation that models the motion of the object is

$$d = -5 \cos\left[\frac{2\pi}{3}t\right]$$

━━━━▶ **Now Work** PROBLEM 5

2 Analyze Simple Harmonic Motion

EXAMPLE 2	**Analyzing the Motion of an Object**

Suppose that the displacement d (in meters) of an object at time t (in seconds) satisfies the equation

$$d = 10 \sin(5t)$$

(a) Describe the motion of the object.
(b) What is the maximum displacement from its resting position?
(c) What is the time required for one oscillation?
(d) What is the frequency?

Solution

Observe that the given equation is of the form

$$d = a \sin(\omega t) \quad d = 10 \sin(5t)$$

where $a = 10$ and $\omega = 5$.

(a) The motion is simple harmonic.

(b) The maximum displacement of the object from its resting position is the amplitude: $|a| = 10$ meters.

(c) The time required for one oscillation is the period:

$$\text{Period} = \frac{2\pi}{\omega} = \frac{2\pi}{5} \text{ seconds}$$

(d) The frequency is the reciprocal of the period. Thus,

$$\text{Frequency} = f = \frac{5}{2\pi} \text{ oscillation per second}$$

━━━━▶ **Now Work** PROBLEM 13

* No phase shift is required if a cosine function is used.

3 Analyze an Object in Damped Motion

Most physical phenomena are affected by friction or other resistive forces. These forces remove energy from a moving system and thereby damp its motion. For example, when a mass hanging from a spring is pulled down a distance a and released, the friction in the spring causes the distance that the mass moves from its at-rest position to decrease over time. As a result, the amplitude of any real oscillating spring or swinging pendulum decreases with time due to air resistance, friction, and so forth. See Figure 47.

Figure 47

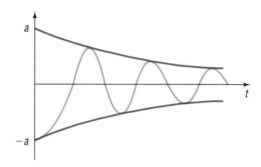

A model that describes this phenomenon maintains a sinusoidal component, but the amplitude of this component will decrease with time to account for the damping effect. In addition, the period of the oscillating component will be affected by the damping. The next result, from physics, describes damped motion.

THEOREM

Damped Motion

The displacement d of an oscillating object from its at-rest position at time t is given by

$$d(t) = ae^{-bt/(2m)} \cos\left(\sqrt{\omega^2 - \frac{b^2}{4m^2}}\, t\right)$$

where b is the **damping factor** or **damping coefficient** and m is the mass of the oscillating object. Here $|a|$ is the displacement at $t = 0$, and $\dfrac{2\pi}{\omega}$ is the period under simple harmonic motion (no damping).

Notice for $b = 0$ (zero damping) that we have the formula for simple harmonic motion with amplitude $|a|$ and period $\dfrac{2\pi}{\omega}$.

EXAMPLE 3

Analyzing a Damped Vibration Curve

Analyze the damped vibration curve

$$d(t) = e^{-t/\pi} \cos t, \quad t \geq 0$$

Solution

The displacement d is the product of $y = e^{-t/\pi}$ and $y = \cos t$. Using properties of absolute value and the fact that $|\cos t| \leq 1$, we find that

$$|d(t)| = |e^{-t/\pi} \cos t| = |e^{-t/\pi}||\cos t| \leq |e^{-t/\pi}| \underset{\underset{e^{-t/\pi} > 0}{\uparrow}}{=} e^{-t/\pi}$$

As a result,

$$-e^{-t/\pi} \leq d(t) \leq e^{-t/\pi}$$

This means that the graph of d will lie between the graphs of $y = e^{-t/\pi}$ and $y = -e^{-t/\pi}$, the **bounding curves** of d.

Also, the graph of d will touch these graphs when $|\cos t| = 1$, that is, when $t = 0, \pi, 2\pi$, and so on. The x-intercepts of the graph of d occur when $\cos t = 0$, that is, at $\dfrac{\pi}{2}, \dfrac{3\pi}{2}, \dfrac{5\pi}{2}$, and so on. See Table 1.

Table 1

t	0	$\dfrac{\pi}{2}$	π	$\dfrac{3\pi}{2}$	2π
$e^{-t/\pi}$	1	$e^{-1/2}$	e^{-1}	$e^{-3/2}$	e^{-2}
$\cos t$	1	0	-1	0	1
$d(t) = e^{-t/\pi}\cos t$	1	0	$-e^{-1}$	0	e^{-2}
Point on graph of d	$(0, 1)$	$\left(\dfrac{\pi}{2}, 0\right)$	$(\pi, -e^{-1})$	$\left(\dfrac{3\pi}{2}, 0\right)$	$(2\pi, e^{-2})$

We graph $y = \cos t$, $y = e^{-t/\pi}$, $y = -e^{-t/\pi}$, and $d(t) = e^{-t/\pi}\cos t$ in Figure 48.

Figure 48

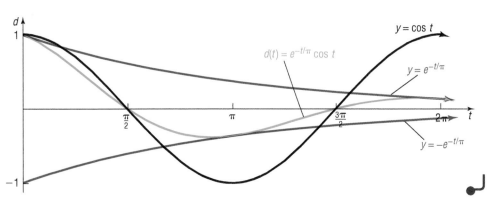

Figure 49

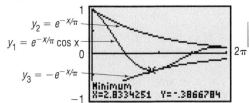

Exploration

Graph $Y_1 = e^{-x/\pi}\cos x$, along with $Y_2 = e^{-x/\pi}$, and $Y_3 = -e^{-x/\pi}$, for $0 \le x \le 2\pi$. Determine where Y_1 has its first turning point (local minimum). Compare this to where Y_1 intersects Y_3.

Result Figure 49 shows the graphs of $Y_1 = e^{-x/\pi}\cos x$, $Y_2 = e^{-x/\pi}$, and $Y_3 = -e^{-x/\pi}$. Using MINIMUM, the first turning point occurs at $x \approx 2.83$; Y_1 INTERSECTS Y_3 at $x = \pi \approx 3.14$.

━━━━━➤ **Now Work** PROBLEM 21

4 Graph the Sum of Two Functions

Many physical and biological applications require the graph of the sum of two functions, such as

$$f(x) = x + \sin x \quad \text{or} \quad g(x) = \sin x + \cos(2x)$$

For example, if two tones are emitted, the sound produced is the sum of the waves produced by the two tones. See Problem 57 for an explanation of Touch-Tone phones.

To graph the sum of two (or more) functions, we can use the method of adding y-coordinates described next.

EXAMPLE 4 | **Graphing the Sum of Two Functions**

Use the method of adding y-coordinates to graph $f(x) = x + \sin x$.

Solution First, graph the component functions,

$$y = f_1(x) = x \qquad y = f_2(x) = \sin x$$

on the same coordinate system. See Figure 50(a). Now, select several values of x, say, $x = 0$, $x = \dfrac{\pi}{2}$, $x = \pi$, $x = \dfrac{3\pi}{2}$, and $x = 2\pi$, at which we compute $f(x) = f_1(x) + f_2(x)$. Table 2 shows the computation. We plot these points and connect them to get the graph, as shown in Figure 50(b).

Table 2

x	0	$\dfrac{\pi}{2}$	π	$\dfrac{3\pi}{2}$	2π
$y = f_1(x) = x$	0	$\dfrac{\pi}{2}$	π	$\dfrac{3\pi}{2}$	2π
$y = f_2(x) = \sin x$	0	1	0	-1	0
$f(x) = x + \sin x$	0	$\dfrac{\pi}{2} + 1 \approx 2.57$	π	$\dfrac{3\pi}{2} - 1 \approx 3.71$	2π
Point on graph of f	$(0, 0)$	$\left(\dfrac{\pi}{2}, 2.57\right)$	(π, π)	$\left(\dfrac{3\pi}{2}, 3.71\right)$	$(2\pi, 2\pi)$

Figure 50

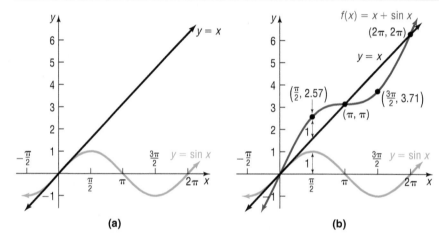

(a)   (b)

In Figure 50(b), notice that the graph of $f(x) = x + \sin x$ intersects the line $y = x$ whenever $\sin x = 0$. Also, notice that the graph of f is not periodic.

 ✓Check: Graph $Y_1 = x$, $Y_2 = \sin x$, and $Y_3 = x + \sin x$ and compare the result with Figure 50(b). Use INTERSECT to verify that the graphs of Y_1 and Y_3 intersect when $\sin x = 0$.

The next example shows a periodic graph.

EXAMPLE 5   **Graphing the Sum of Two Sinusoidal Functions**

Use the method of adding y-coordinates to graph
$$f(x) = \sin x + \cos(2x)$$

Solution   Table 3 shows the steps for computing several points on the graph of f. Figure 51 on page 547 ilustrates the graphs of the component functions, $y = f_1(x) = \sin x$ and $y = f_2(x) = \cos(2x)$, and the graph of $f(x) = \sin x + \cos(2x)$, which is shown in red.

Table 3

x	$-\dfrac{\pi}{2}$	0	$\dfrac{\pi}{2}$	π	$\dfrac{3\pi}{2}$	2π
$y = f_1(x) = \sin x$	-1	0	1	0	-1	0
$y = f_2(x) = \cos(2x)$	-1	1	-1	1	-1	1
$f(x) = \sin x + \cos(2x)$	-2	1	0	1	-2	1
Point on graph of f	$\left(-\dfrac{\pi}{2}, -2\right)$	$(0, 1)$	$\left(\dfrac{\pi}{2}, 0\right)$	$(\pi, 1)$	$\left(\dfrac{3\pi}{2}, -2\right)$	$(2\pi, 1)$

Figure 51

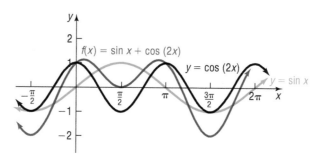

Notice that f is periodic, with period 2π.

 ✓**Check:** Graph $Y_1 = \sin x$, $Y_2 = \cos(2x)$, and $Y_3 = \sin x + \cos(2x)$ and compare the result with Figure 51.

Now Work PROBLEM 25

8.5 Assess Your Understanding

'Are You Prepared?' *The answer is given at the end of these exercises. If you get a wrong answer, read the pages listed in red.*

1. The amplitude A and period T of $f(x) = 5\sin(4x)$ are _____ and _____. (pp. 397–403)

Concepts and Vocabulary

2. The motion of an object obeys the equation $d = 4\cos(6t)$. Such motion is described as _____ _____. The number 4 is called the _____.

3. When a mass hanging from a spring is pulled down and then released, the motion is called _____ _____ if there

is no frictional force to retard the motion, and the motion is called _____ if there is friction.

4. *True or False* If the distance d of an object from its rest position at time t is given by a sinusoidal graph, the motion of the object is simple harmonic motion.

Skill Building

In Problems 5–8, an object attached to a coiled spring is pulled down a distance a from its rest position and then released. Assuming that the motion is simple harmonic with period T, write an equation that relates the displacement d of the object from its rest position after t seconds. Also assume that the positive direction of the motion is up.

5. $a = 5$; $T = 2$ seconds

6. $a = 10$; $T = 3$ seconds

7. $a = 6$; $T = \pi$ seconds

8. $a = 4$; $T = \dfrac{\pi}{2}$ seconds

9. Rework Problem 5 under the same conditions except that, at time $t = 0$, the object is at its resting position and moving down.

10. Rework Problem 6 under the same conditions except that, at time $t = 0$, the object is at its resting position and moving down.

11. Rework Problem 7 under the same conditions except that, at time $t = 0$, the object is at its resting position and moving down.

12. Rework Problem 8 under the same conditions except that, at time $t = 0$, the object is at its resting position and moving down.

In Problems 13–20, the displacement d (in meters) of an object at time t (in seconds) is given.
  (a) *Describe the motion of the object.*
  (b) *What is the maximum displacement from its resting position?*
  (c) *What is the time required for one oscillation?*
  (d) *What is the frequency?*

13. $d = 5\sin(3t)$

14. $d = 4\sin(2t)$

15. $d = 6\cos(\pi t)$

16. $d = 5\cos\left(\dfrac{\pi}{2}t\right)$

17. $d = -3\sin\left(\dfrac{1}{2}t\right)$

18. $d = -2\cos(2t)$

19. $d = 6 + 2\cos(2\pi t)$

20. $d = 4 + 3\sin(\pi t)$

In Problems 21–24, graph each damped vibration curve for $0 \le t \le 2\pi$.

21. $d(t) = e^{-t/\pi} \cos(2t)$ **22.** $d(t) = e^{-t/2\pi} \cos(2t)$ **23.** $d(t) = e^{-t/2\pi} \cos t$ **24.** $d(t) = e^{-t/4\pi} \cos t$

In Problems 25–32, use the method of adding y-coordinates to graph each function.

25. $f(x) = x + \cos x$ **26.** $f(x) = x + \cos(2x)$ **27.** $f(x) = x - \sin x$

28. $f(x) = x - \cos x$ **29.** $f(x) = \sin x + \cos x$ **30.** $f(x) = \sin(2x) + \cos x$

31. $g(x) = \sin x + \sin(2x)$ **32.** $g(x) = \cos(2x) + \cos x$

Mixed Practice

In Problems 33–38, (a) use the Product-to-Sum Formulas to express each product as a sum, and (b) use the method of adding y-coordinates to graph each function on the interval $[0, 2\pi]$.

33. $f(x) = \sin(2x) \sin x$ **34.** $F(x) = \sin(3x) \sin x$ **35.** $G(x) = \cos(4x) \cos(2x)$

36. $h(x) = \cos(2x) \cos(x)$ **37.** $H(x) = 2\sin(3x) \cos(x)$ **38.** $g(x) = 2\sin x \cos(3x)$

Applications and Extensions

In Problems 39–44, an object of mass m (in grams) attached to a coiled spring with damping factor b (in grams per second) is pulled down a distance a (in centimeters) from its rest position and then released. Assume that the positive direction of the motion is up and the period is T (in seconds) under simple harmonic motion.

   (a) *Write an equation that relates the distance d of the object from its rest position after t seconds.*

   (b) *Graph the equation found in part (a) for 5 oscillations using a graphing utility.*

39. $m = 25$, $a = 10$, $b = 0.7$, $T = 5$ **40.** $m = 20$, $a = 15$, $b = 0.75$, $T = 6$

41. $m = 30$, $a = 18$, $b = 0.6$, $T = 4$ **42.** $m = 15$, $a = 16$, $b = 0.65$, $T = 5$

43. $m = 10$, $a = 5$, $b = 0.8$, $T = 3$ **44.** $m = 10$, $a = 5$, $b = 0.7$, $T = 3$

In Problems 45–50, the distance d (in meters) of the bob of a pendulum of mass m (in kilograms) from its rest position at time t (in seconds) is given. The bob is released from the left of its rest position and represents a negative direction.

   (a) *Describe the motion of the object. Be sure to give the mass and damping factor.*

   (b) *What is the initial displacement of the bob? That is, what is the displacement at $t = 0$?*

   (c) *Graph the motion using a graphing utility.*

   (d) *What is the displacement of the bob at the start of the second oscillation?*

   (e) *What happens to the displacement of the bob as time increases without bound?*

45. $d = -20e^{-0.7t/40} \cos\left(\sqrt{\left(\dfrac{2\pi}{5}\right)^2 - \dfrac{0.49}{1600}}\, t\right)$ **46.** $d = -20e^{-0.8t/40} \cos\left(\sqrt{\left(\dfrac{2\pi}{5}\right)^2 - \dfrac{0.64}{1600}}\, t\right)$

47. $d = -30e^{-0.6t/80} \cos\left(\sqrt{\left(\dfrac{2\pi}{7}\right)^2 - \dfrac{0.36}{6400}}\, t\right)$ **48.** $d = -30e^{-0.5t/70} \cos\left(\sqrt{\left(\dfrac{\pi}{2}\right)^2 - \dfrac{0.25}{4900}}\, t\right)$

49. $d = -15e^{-0.9t/30} \cos\left(\sqrt{\left(\dfrac{\pi}{3}\right)^2 - \dfrac{0.81}{900}}\, t\right)$ **50.** $d = -10e^{-0.8t/50} \cos\left(\sqrt{\left(\dfrac{2\pi}{3}\right)^2 - \dfrac{0.64}{2500}}\, t\right)$

51. Loudspeaker A loudspeaker diaphragm is oscillating in simple harmonic motion described by the equation $d = a \cos(\omega t)$ with a frequency of 520 hertz (cycles per second) and a maximum displacement of 0.80 millimeter. Find ω and then determine the equation that describes the movement of the diaphragm.

52. Colossus Added to Six Flags St. Louis in 1986, the Colossus is a giant Ferris wheel. Its diameter is 165 feet, it rotates at a rate of about 1.6 revolutions per minute, and the bottom of the wheel is 15 feet above the ground. Determine an equation that

relates a rider's height above the ground at time t. Assume the passenger begins the ride at the bottom of the wheel.

Source: Six Flags Theme Parks, Inc.

53. Tuning Fork The end of a tuning fork moves in simple harmonic motion described by the equation $d = a \sin(\omega t)$. If a tuning fork for the note A above middle C on an even-tempered scale (A_4, the tone by which an orchestra tunes itself) has a frequency of 440 hertz (cycles per second), find ω. If the maximum displacement of the end of the tuning fork is 0.01 millimeter, determine the equation that describes the movement of the tuning fork.

Source: David Lapp. *Physics of Music and Musical Instruments.* Medford, MA: Tufts University, 2003

54. Tuning Fork The end of a tuning fork moves in simple harmonic motion described by the equation $d = a \sin(\omega t)$. If a tuning fork for the note E above middle C on an even-tempered scale (E_4) has a frequency of approximately 329.63 hertz (cycles per second), find ω. If the maximum displacement of the end of the tuning fork is 0.025 millimeter, determine the equation that describes the movement of the tuning fork.

Source: David Lapp. *Physics of Music and Musical Instruments.* Medford, MA: Tufts University, 2003

55. Charging a Capacitor See the illustration. If a charged capacitor is connected to a coil by closing a switch, energy is transferred to the coil and then back to the capacitor in an oscillatory motion. The voltage V (in volts) across the capacitor will gradually diminish to 0 with time t (in seconds).

(a) Graph the function relating V and t:

$$V(t) = e^{-t/3} \cos(\pi t), \qquad 0 \le t \le 3$$

(b) At what times t will the graph of V touch the graph of $y = e^{-t/3}$? When does the graph of V touch the graph of $y = -e^{-t/3}$?

(c) When will the voltage V be between -0.4 and 0.4 volt?

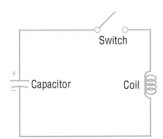

56. The Sawtooth Curve An oscilloscope often displays a *sawtooth curve.* This curve can be approximated by sinusoidal curves of varying periods and amplitudes.

(a) Use a graphing utility to graph the following function, which can be used to approximate the sawtooth curve.

$$f(x) = \frac{1}{2}\sin(2\pi x) + \frac{1}{4}\sin(4\pi x), \qquad 0 \le x \le 4$$

(b) A better approximation to the sawtooth curve is given by

$$f(x) = \frac{1}{2}\sin(2\pi x) + \frac{1}{4}\sin(4\pi x) + \frac{1}{8}\sin(8\pi x)$$

Use a graphing utility to graph this function for $0 \le x \le 4$ and compare the result to the graph obtained in part (a).

(c) A third and even better approximation to the sawtooth curve is given by

$$f(x) = \frac{1}{2}\sin(2\pi x) + \frac{1}{4}\sin(4\pi x) + \frac{1}{8}\sin(8\pi x) + \frac{1}{16}\sin(16\pi x)$$

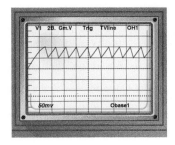

Use a graphing utility to graph this function for $0 \le x \le 4$ and compare the result to the graphs obtained in parts (a) and (b).

(d) What do you think the next approximation to the sawtooth curve is?

57. Touch-Tone Phones On a Touch-Tone phone, each button produces a unique sound. The sound produced is the sum of two tones, given by

$$y = \sin(2\pi l t) \quad \text{and} \quad y = \sin(2\pi h t)$$

where l and h are the low and high frequencies (cycles per second) shown in the illustration. For example, if you touch 7, the low frequency is $l = 852$ cycles per second and the high frequency is $h = 1209$ cycles per second. The sound emitted by touching 7 is

$$y = \sin[2\pi(852)t] + \sin[2\pi(1209)t]$$

Use a graphing utility to graph the sound emitted by touching 7.

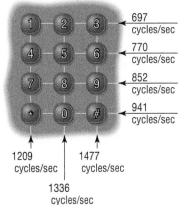

Touch-Tone phone

58. Use a graphing utility to graph the sound emitted by the * key on a Touch-Tone phone. See Problem 57.

59. CBL Experiment Pendulum motion is analyzed to estimate simple harmonic motion. A plot is generated with the position of the pendulum over time. The graph is used to find a sinusoidal curve of the form $y = A\cos[B(x - C)] + D$. Determine the amplitude, period, and frequency. (Activity 16, Real-World Math with the CBL System.)

60. CBL Experiment The sound from a tuning fork is collected over time. Determine the amplitude, frequency, and period of the graph. A model of the form $y = A\cos[B(x - C)]$ is fitted to the data. (Activity 23, Real-World Math with the CBL System.)

Explaining Concepts: Discussion and Writing

61. Use a graphing utility to graph the function $f(x) = \dfrac{\sin x}{x}$, $x > 0$. Based on the graph, what do you conjecture about the value of $\dfrac{\sin x}{x}$ for x close to 0?

62. Use a graphing utility to graph $y = x \sin x$, $y = x^2 \sin x$, and $y = x^3 \sin x$ for $x > 0$. What patterns do you observe?

63. Use a graphing utility to graph $y = \dfrac{1}{x} \sin x$, $y = \dfrac{1}{x^2} \sin x$, and $y = \dfrac{1}{x^3} \sin x$ for $x > 0$. What patterns do you observe?

64. How would you explain to a friend what simple harmonic motion is? How would you explain damped motion?

'Are You Prepared?' Answer

1. $A = 5; T = \dfrac{\pi}{2}$

CHAPTER REVIEW

Things to Know

Formulas

Law of Sines (p. 518)	$\dfrac{\sin A}{a} = \dfrac{\sin B}{b} = \dfrac{\sin C}{c}$
Law of Cosines (p. 528)	$c^2 = a^2 + b^2 - 2ab \cos C$ $b^2 = a^2 + c^2 - 2ac \cos B$ $a^2 = b^2 + c^2 - 2bc \cos A$
Area of a triangle (pp. 535–536)	$K = \dfrac{1}{2}bh \quad K = \dfrac{1}{2}ab \sin C \quad K = \dfrac{1}{2}bc \sin A \quad K = \dfrac{1}{2}ac \sin B$ $K = \sqrt{s(s-a)(s-b)(s-c)} \quad \text{where} \quad s = \dfrac{1}{2}(a + b + c)$

Objectives

Section		You should be able to . . .	Example(s)	Review Exercises
8.1	1	Find the value of trigonometric functions of acute angles using right triangles (p. 505)	1, 2	1–4, 46
	2	Use the complementary angle theorem (p. 507)	3	5–10
	3	Solve right triangles (p. 507)	4, 5	11–14, 46
	4	Solve applied problems (p. 508)	6–12	47–52, 60–62
8.2	1	Solve SAA or ASA triangles (p. 518)	1, 2	15, 16, 32
	2	Solve SSA triangles (p. 519)	3–5	17–20, 22, 27, 28, 31
	3	Solve applied problems (p. 522)	6, 7	53–55
8.3	1	Solve SAS triangles (p. 529)	1	21, 25, 26, 33, 34
	2	Solve SSS triangles (p. 530)	2	23, 24, 29, 30
	3	Solve applied problems (p. 530)	3	56, 57
8.4	1	Find the area of SAS triangles (p. 535)	1	35–38, 45, 58, 59
	2	Find the area of SSS triangles (p. 536)	2	39–42
8.5	1	Build a model for an object in simple harmonic motion (p. 541)	1	63, 64
	2	Analyze simple harmonic motion (p. 543)	2	65–68
	3	Analyze an object in damped motion (p. 544)	3	69–72
	4	Graph the sum of two functions (p. 545)	4, 5	73, 74

Review Exercises

In Problems 1–4, find the exact value of the six trigonometric functions of the angle θ in each figure.

1.

2.

3.

4.

In Problems 5–10, find the exact value of each expression. Do not use a calculator.

5. $\cos 62° - \sin 28°$

6. $\tan 15° - \cot 75°$

7. $\dfrac{\sec 55°}{\csc 35°}$

8. $\dfrac{\tan 40°}{\cot 50°}$

9. $\cos^2 40° + \cos^2 50°$

10. $\tan^2 40° - \csc^2 50°$

In Problems 11–14, solve each triangle.

11.

12.

13.

14.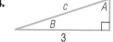

In Problems 15–34, find the remaining angle(s) and side(s) of each triangle, if it (they) exists. If no triangle exists, say "No triangle."

15. $A = 50°$, $B = 30°$, $a = 1$

16. $A = 10°$, $C = 40°$, $c = 2$

17. $A = 100°$, $a = 5$, $c = 2$

18. $a = 2$, $c = 5$, $A = 60°$

19. $a = 3$, $c = 1$, $C = 110°$

20. $a = 3$, $c = 1$, $C = 20°$

21. $a = 3$, $c = 1$, $B = 100°$

22. $a = 3$, $b = 5$, $B = 80°$

23. $a = 2$, $b = 3$, $c = 1$

24. $a = 10$, $b = 7$, $c = 8$

25. $a = 1$, $b = 3$, $C = 40°$

26. $a = 4$, $b = 1$, $C = 100°$

27. $a = 5$, $b = 3$, $A = 80°$

28. $a = 2$, $b = 3$, $A = 20°$

29. $a = 1$, $b = \dfrac{1}{2}$, $c = \dfrac{4}{3}$

30. $a = 3$, $b = 2$, $c = 2$

31. $a = 3$, $A = 10°$, $b = 4$

32. $a = 4$, $A = 20°$, $B = 100°$

33. $c = 5$, $b = 4$, $A = 70°$

34. $a = 1$, $b = 2$, $C = 60°$

In Problems 35–44, find the area of each triangle.

35. $a = 2$, $b = 3$, $C = 40°$

36. $b = 5$, $c = 5$, $A = 20°$

37. $b = 4$, $c = 10$, $A = 70°$

38. $a = 2$, $b = 1$, $C = 100°$

39. $a = 4$, $b = 3$, $c = 5$

40. $a = 10$, $b = 7$, $c = 8$

41. $a = 4$, $b = 2$, $c = 5$

42. $a = 3$, $b = 2$, $c = 2$

43. $A = 50°$, $B = 30°$, $a = 1$

44. $A = 10°$, $C = 40°$, $c = 3$

---

45. Area of a Segment Find the area of the segment of a circle whose radius is 6 inches formed by a central angle of 50°.

46. Geometry The hypotenuse of a right triangle is 12 feet. If one leg is 8 feet, find the degree measure of each angle.

47. Finding the Width of a River Find the distance from *A* to *C* across the river illustrated in the figure.

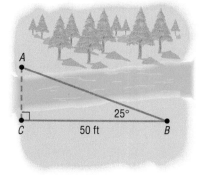

48. Finding the Height of a Building Find the height of the building shown in the figure.

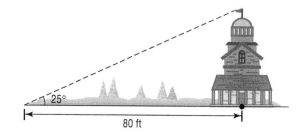

49. Finding the Distance to Shore The Willis Tower in Chicago is 1454 feet tall and is situated about 1 mile inland from the shore of Lake Michigan, as indicated in the figure on the following page. An observer in a pleasure boat on the lake directly in front of the Willis Tower looks at the top of the tower and measures the angle of elevation as 5°. How far offshore is the boat?

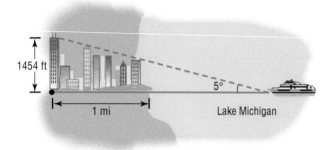

1454 ft

5°

1 mi

Lake Michigan

50. **Measuring the Length of a Lake** From a stationary hot-air balloon 500 feet above the ground, two sightings of a lake are made (see the figure). How long is the lake?

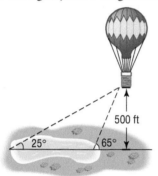

500 ft

25°   65°

51. **Finding the Speed of a Glider** From a glider 200 feet above the ground, two sightings of a stationary object directly in front are taken 1 minute apart (see the figure). What is the speed of the glider?

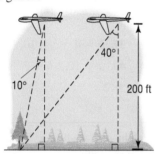

40°

10°   200 ft

52. **Finding the Grade of a Mountain Trail** A straight trail with a uniform inclination leads from a hotel, elevation 5000 feet, to a lake in a valley, elevation 4100 feet. The length of the trail is 4100 feet. What is the inclination (grade) of the trail?

53. **Finding the Height of a Helicopter** Two observers simultaneously measure the angle of elevation of a helicopter. One angle is measured as 25°, the other as 40° (see the figure). If the observers are 100 feet apart and the helicopter lies over the line joining them, how high is the helicopter?

54. **Determining Distances at Sea** Rebecca, the navigator of a ship at sea, spots two lighthouses that she knows to be 2 miles apart along a straight shoreline. She determines that the angles formed between two line-of-sight observations of the lighthouses and the line from the ship directly to shore are 12° and 30°. See the illustration.
   (a) How far is the ship from lighthouse L_1?
   (b) How far is the ship from lighthouse L_2?
   (c) How far is the ship from shore?

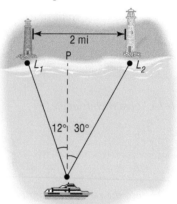

2 mi

P

L_1 L_2

12° 30°

55. **Constructing a Highway** A highway whose primary directions are north–south is being constructed along the west coast of Florida. Near Naples, a bay obstructs the straight path of the road. Since the cost of a bridge is prohibitive, engineers decide to go around the bay. The illustration shows the path that they decide on and the measurements taken. What is the length of highway needed to go around the bay?

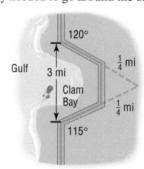

120°

Gulf   3 mi $\frac{1}{4}$ mi

Clam
Bay

$\frac{1}{4}$ mi

115°

56. **Correcting a Navigational Error** A sailboat leaves St. Thomas bound for an island in the British West Indies, 200 miles away. Maintaining a constant speed of 18 miles per hour, but encountering heavy crosswinds and strong currents, the crew finds after 4 hours that the sailboat is off course by 15°.
   (a) How far is the sailboat from the island at this time?
   (b) Through what angle should the sailboat turn to correct its course?
   (c) How much time has been added to the trip because of this? (Assume that the speed remains at 18 miles per hour.)

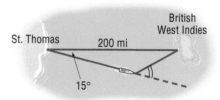

British
West Indies

St. Thomas   200 mi

15°

57. Surveying Two homes are located on opposite sides of a small hill. See the illustration. To measure the distance between them, a surveyor walks a distance of 50 feet from house P to point R, uses a transit to measure $\angle PRQ$, which is found to be 80°, and then walks to house Q, a distance of 60 feet. How far apart are the houses?

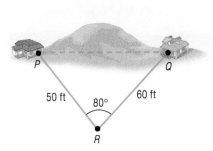

58. Approximating the Area of a Lake To approximate the area of a lake, Cindy walks around the perimeter of the lake, taking the measurements shown in the illustration. Using this technique, what is the approximate area of the lake?

[**Hint:** Use the Law of Cosines on the three triangles shown and then find the sum of their areas.]

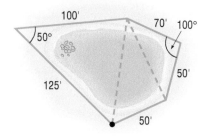

59. Calculating the Cost of Land The irregular parcel of land shown in the figure is being sold for $100 per square foot. What is the cost of this parcel?

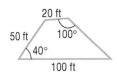

60. Finding the Bearing of a Ship The *Majesty* leaves the Port at Boston for Bermuda with a bearing of S80°E at an average speed of 10 knots. After 1 hour, the ship turns 90° toward the southwest. After 2 hours at an average speed of 20 knots, what is the bearing of the ship from Boston?

61. Drive Wheels of an Engine The drive wheel of an engine is 13 inches in diameter, and the pulley on the rotary pump is 5 inches in diameter. If the shafts of the drive wheel and the pulley are 2 feet apart, what length of belt is required to join them as shown in the figure?

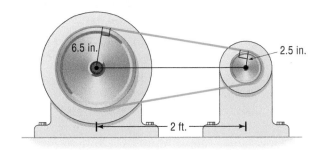

62. Rework Problem 61 if the belt is crossed, as shown in the figure.

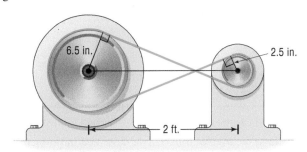

In Problems 63 and 64, an object attached to a coiled spring is pulled down a distance a from its rest position and then released. Assuming that the motion is simple harmonic with period T, develop a model that relates the displacement d of the object from its rest position after t seconds. Also assume that the positive direction of the motion is up.

63. $a = 3$; $T = 4$ seconds

64. $a = 5$; $T = 6$ seconds

In Problems 65–68, the distance d (in feet) that an object travels in time t (in seconds) is given.
(a) Describe the motion of the object.
(b) What is the maximum displacement from its rest position?
(c) What is the time required for one oscillation?
(d) What is the frequency?

65. $d = 6\sin(2t)$

66. $d = 2\cos(4t)$

67. $d = -2\cos(\pi t)$

68. $d = -3\sin\left[\dfrac{\pi}{2}t\right]$

In Problems 69 and 70, an object of mass m attached to a coiled spring with damping factor b is pulled down a distance a from its rest position and then released. Assume that the positive direction of the motion is up and the period is T under simple harmonic motion.
(a) Develop a model that relates the distance d of the object from its rest position after t seconds.
(b) Graph the equation found in part (a) for 5 oscillations.

69. $m = 40$ grams; $a = 15$ centimeters; $b = 0.75$ gram/second; $T = 5$ seconds

70. $m = 25$ grams; $a = 13$ centimeters; $b = 0.65$ gram/second; $T = 4$ seconds

In Problems 71 and 72, the distance d (in meters) of the bob of a pendulum of mass m (in kilograms) from its rest position at time t (in seconds) is given.
(a) Describe the motion of the object.
(b) What is the initial displacement of the bob? That is, what is the displacement at t = 0?
(c) Graph the motion using a graphing utility.
(d) What is the displacement of the bob at the start of the second oscillation?
(e) What happens to the displacement of the bob as time increases without bound?

71. $d = -15e^{-0.6t/40} \cos\left(\sqrt{\left(\dfrac{2\pi}{5}\right)^2 - \dfrac{0.36}{1600}}\, t \right)$

72. $d = -20e^{-0.5t/60} \cos\left(\sqrt{\left(\dfrac{2\pi}{3}\right)^2 - \dfrac{0.25}{3600}}\, t \right)$

In Problems 73 and 74, graph each function.

73. $y = 2\sin x + \cos(2x), \quad 0 \le x \le 2\pi$

74. $y = 2\cos(2x) + \sin\dfrac{x}{2}, \quad 0 \le x \le 2\pi$

CHAPTER TEST

CHAPTER
Test Prep
VIDEOS

The Chapter Test Prep Videos are step-by-step test solutions available in the Video Resources DVD, in *MyMathLab*, or on this text's You**Tube** Channel. Flip back to the Student Resources page to see the exact web address for this text's YouTube channel.

---

1. Find the exact value of the six trigonometric functions of the angle θ in the figure.

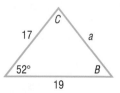

2. Find the exact value of $\sin 40° - \cos 50°$.

In Problems 3–5, use the given information to determine the three remaining parts of each triangle.

3.

4.

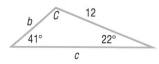

5.

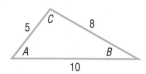

In Problems 6–8, solve each triangle.

6. $A = 55°, \quad C = 20°, \quad a = 4$

7. $a = 3, \quad b = 7, \quad A = 40°$

8. $a = 8, \quad b = 4, \quad C = 70°$

---

9. Find the area of the triangle described in Problem 8.

10. Find the area of the triangle described in Problem 5.

11. A 12-foot ladder leans against a building. The top of the ladder leans against the wall 10.5 feet from the ground. What is the angle formed by the ground and the ladder?

12. A hot-air balloon is flying at a height of 600 feet and is directly above the Marshall Space Flight Center in Huntsville, Alabama. The pilot of the balloon looks down at the airport that is known to be 5 miles from the Marshall Space Flight Center. What is the angle of depression from the balloon to the airport?

13. Find the area of the shaded region enclosed in a semicircle of diameter 8 centimeters. The length of the chord AB is 6 centimeters.

[**Hint:** Triangle ABC is a right triangle.]

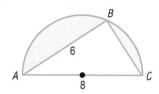

14. Find the area of the quadrilateral shown.

15. Madison wants to swim across Lake William from the fishing lodge (A) to the boat ramp (B), but she wants to know the distance first. Highway 20 goes right past the boat ramp and County Road 3 goes to the lodge. The two roads intersect at point (C), 4.2 miles from the ramp and 3.5 miles from the lodge. Madison uses a transit to measure the angle of intersection of the two roads to be 32°. How far will she need to swim?

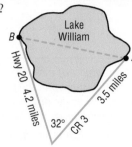

16. Given that $\triangle OAB$ is an isosceles triangle and the shaded sector is a semicircle, find the area of the entire region. Express your answer as a decimal rounded to two places.

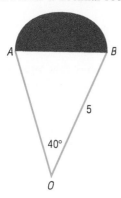

17. The area of the triangle shown below is $54\sqrt{6}$ square units; find the lengths of the sides.

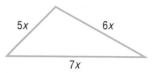

18. Logan is playing on her swing. One full swing (front to back to front) takes 6 seconds and at the peak of her swing she is at an angle of $42°$ with the vertical. If her swing is 5 feet long, and we ignore all resistive forces, build a model that relates her horizontal displacement (from the rest position) after time t.

CUMULATIVE REVIEW

1. Find the real solutions, if any, of the equation $3x^2 + 1 = 4x$.

2. Find an equation for the circle with center at the point $(-5, 1)$ and radius 3. Graph this circle.

3. Determine the domain of the function
$$f(x) = \sqrt{x^2 - 3x - 4}$$

4. Graph the function $y = 3\sin(\pi x)$.

5. Graph the function $y = -2\cos(2x - \pi)$.

6. If $\tan\theta = -2$ and $\dfrac{3\pi}{2} < \theta < 2\pi$, find the exact value of:

  (a) $\sin\theta$ (b) $\cos\theta$ (c) $\sin(2\theta)$

  (d) $\cos(2\theta)$ (e) $\sin\left(\dfrac{1}{2}\theta\right)$ (f) $\cos\left(\dfrac{1}{2}\theta\right)$

7. Graph each of the following functions on the interval $[0, 4]$:

  (a) $y = e^x$ (b) $y = \sin x$

  (c) $y = e^x \sin x$ (d) $y = 2x + \sin x$

8. Sketch the graph of each of the following functions:

  (a) $y = x$ (b) $y = x^2$

  (c) $y = \sqrt{x}$ (d) $y = x^3$

  (e) $y = e^x$ (f) $y = \ln x$

  (g) $y = \sin x$ (h) $y = \cos x$

  (i) $y = \tan x$

9. Solve the triangle: $a = 20$, $c = 15$, $C = 40°$

10. In the complex number system, solve the equation
$$3x^5 - 10x^4 + 21x^3 - 42x^2 + 36x - 8 = 0$$

11. Analyze the graph of the rational function
$$R(x) = \frac{2x^2 - 7x - 4}{x^2 + 2x - 15}$$

12. Solve $3^x = 12$. Round your answer to two decimal places.

13. Solve $\log_3(x + 8) + \log_3 x = 2$.

14. Suppose that $f(x) = 4x + 5$ and $g(x) = x^2 + 5x - 24$.

  (a) Solve $f(x) = 0$.   (b) Solve $f(x) = 13$.

  (c) Solve $f(x) = g(x)$.   (d) Solve $f(x) > 0$.

  (e) Solve $g(x) \le 0$.   (f) Graph $y = f(x)$.

  (g) Graph $y = g(x)$.

CHAPTER PROJECTS

I. **Spherical Trigonometry** When the distance between two locations on the surface of Earth is small, we can compute the distance in statutory miles. Using this assumption, we can use the Law of Sines and the Law of Cosines to approximate distances and angles. However, if you look at a globe, you notice that Earth is a sphere, so, as the distance between two points on its surface increases, the linear distance is less accurate because of curvature. Under this circumstance, we need to take into account the curvature of Earth when using the Law of Sines and the Law of Cosines.

1. Draw a spherical triangle and label each vertex by A, B, and C. Then connect each vertex by a radius to the center O of the sphere. Now draw tangent lines to the sides a and b of the triangle that go through C. Extend the lines OA and OB to intersect the tangent lines at P and Q, respectively. See the figure. List the plane right triangles. Determine the measures of the central angles.

2. Apply the Law of Cosines to triangles OPQ and CPQ to find two expressions for the length of PQ.

3. Subtract the expressions in part (2) from each other. Solve for the term containing $\cos c$.

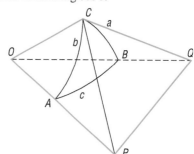

4. Use the Pythagorean Theorem to find another value for $OQ^2 - CQ^2$ and $OP^2 - CP^2$. Now solve for $\cos c$.

5. Replacing the ratios in part (4) by the cosines of the sides of the spherical triangle, you should now have the Law of Cosines for spherical triangles:

$$\cos c = \cos a \cos b + \sin a \sin b \cos C$$

Source: For the spherical Law of Cosines; see *Mathematics from the Birth of Numbers* by Jan Gullberg. W. W. Norton & Co., Publishers, 1996, pp. 491–494.

II. The Lewis and Clark Expedition Lewis and Clark followed several rivers in their trek from what is now Great Falls, Montana, to the Pacific coast. First, they went down the Missouri and Jefferson rivers from Great Falls to Lemhi, Idaho. Because the two cities are on different longitudes and different latitudes, we must account for the curvature of Earth when computing the distance that they traveled. Assume that the radius of Earth is 3960 miles.

1. Great Falls is at approximately 47.5°N and 111.3°W. Lemhi is at approximately 45.5°N and 113.5°W. (We will

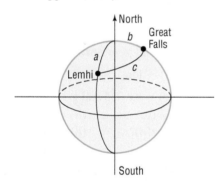

assume that the rivers flow straight from Great Falls to Lemhi on the surface of Earth.) This line is called a geodesic line. Apply the Law of Cosines for a spherical triangle to find the angle between Great Falls and Lemhi. (The central angles are found by using the differences in the latitudes and longitudes of the towns. See the diagram.) Then find the length of the arc joining the two towns. (Recall $s = r\theta$.)

2. From Lemhi, they went up the Bitteroot River and the Snake River to what is now Lewiston and Clarkston on the border of Idaho and Washington. Although this is not really a side to a triangle, we will make a side that goes from Lemhi to Lewiston and Clarkston. If Lewiston and Clarkston are at about 46.5°N 117.0°W, find the distance from Lemhi using the Law of Cosines for a spherical triangle and the arc length.

3. How far did the explorers travel just to get that far?

4. Draw a plane triangle connecting the three towns. If the distance from Lewiston to Great Falls is 282 miles and the angle at Great Falls is 42° and the angle at Lewiston is 48.5°, find the distance from Great Falls to Lemhi and from Lemhi to Lewiston. How do these distances compare with the ones computed in parts (1) and (2)?

Source: For Lewis and Clark Expedition: *American Journey: The Quest for Liberty to 1877, Texas Edition.* Prentice Hall, 1992, p. 345.

Source: For map coordinates: *National Geographic Atlas of the World,* published by National Geographic Society, 1981, pp. 74–75.

Citation: Used with permission of *Technology Review*, from W. Roush, "From Lewis and Clark to Landsat: David Rumsey's Digital maps Marry Past and Present," 108, no. 7, © 2005; permission conveyed through Copyright Clearance Center, Inc.

The following projects are available at the Instructor's Resource Center (IRC):

III. Project at Motorola: *How Can You Build or Analyze a Vibration Profile?* Fourier functions are not only important to analyze vibrations, but they are also what a mathematician would call interesting. Complete the project to see why.

IV. Leaning Tower of Pisa Trigonometry is used to analyze the apparent height and tilt of the Leaning Tower of Pisa.

V. Locating Lost Treasure Clever treasure seekers who know the Law of Sines are able to efficiently find a buried treasure.

VI. Jacob's Field Angles of elevation and the Law of Sines are used to determine the height of the stadium wall and the distance from home plate to the top of the wall.

Polar Coordinates; Vectors

9

Outline

How Do Airplanes Fly?

Have you ever watched a big jetliner lumber into position on the runway for takeoff and wonder, "How does that thing ever get off the ground?" You know it's because of the wing that it stays up in the air, but how does it really work?

When air flows around a wing, it creates lift. The way it creates lift is based on the wing's movement through the air and the air pressure created around the wing. An airplane's wing, in varying degrees depending on the type and design of the airplane, is curved over the top of the wing and straighter underneath the wing. As air hits the wing, it is "split in two," with air moving both over and under the wing. Since the top of the wing has more curve than the bottom of the wing, the air moving over the top of the wing has farther to travel, and thus must move faster than the air moving underneath the wing. The air moving over the top of the wing now exerts less air pressure on the wing than the slower-moving air under the wing. Lift is created.

The difference in air pressure is the primary force creating lift on a wing, but one other force exerted on the wing also helps to produce lift. This is the force of deflection. Air moving along the underside of the wing is deflected downward. Remember the Newtonian principle: For every action, there is an equal and opposite reaction. The air that is deflected downward (action) helps to push the wing upward (reaction), producing more lift.

These two natural forces on the wing, pressure and deflection, produce lift. The faster the wing moves through the air, the greater the forces become, and the greater the lift.

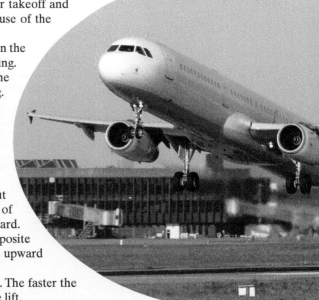

Source: Thomas Schueneman. How do airplanes fly? http://meme.essortment.com/howdoairplane_rlmi.htm, accessed August 2006. © 2002 by Thomas Schueneman. Reprinted with permission.

—See Chapter Project I—

◁ A Look Back, A Look Ahead ▷
This chapter is in two parts: Polar Coordinates, Sections 9.1–9.3, and Vectors, Sections 9.4–9.7. They are independent of each other and may be covered in any order.

Sections 9.1–9.3: In Chapter 1 we introduced rectangular coordinates x and y and discussed the graph of an equation in two variables involving x and y. In Sections 9.1 and 9.2, we introduce polar coordinates, an alternative to rectangular coordinates, and discuss graphing equations that involve polar coordinates. In Section 5.3, we discussed raising a real number to a real power. In Section 9.3 we extend this idea by raising a complex number to a real power. As it turns out, polar coordinates are useful for the discussion.

Sections 9.4–9.7: We have seen in many chapters that we are often required to solve an equation to obtain a solution to applied problems. In the last four sections of this chapter, we develop the notion of a vector and show how it can be used to model applied problems in physics and engineering.

9.1 Polar Coordinates

PREPARING FOR THIS SECTION *Before getting started, review the following:*

- Rectangular Coordinates (Section 1.1, pp. 2–6)
- Definition of the Trigonometric Functions (Section 6.2, pp. 363–366)
- Inverse Tangent Function (Section 7.1, pp. 442–444)
- Completing the Square (Appendix A, Section A.3, pp. A29–A30)

Now Work the 'Are You Prepared?' problems on page 565.

OBJECTIVES **1** Plot Points Using Polar Coordinates (p. 558)
2 Convert from Polar Coordinates to Rectangular Coordinates (p. 560)
3 Convert from Rectangular Coordinates to Polar Coordinates (p. 562)
4 Transform Equations between Polar and Rectangular Forms (p. 564)

So far, we have always used a system of rectangular coordinates to plot points in the plane. Now we are ready to describe another system, called *polar coordinates*. As we shall soon see, in many instances polar coordinates offer certain advantages over rectangular coordinates.

In a rectangular coordinate system, you will recall, a point in the plane is represented by an ordered pair of numbers (x, y), where x and y equal the signed distance of the point from the y-axis and x-axis, respectively. In a polar coordinate system, we select a point, called the **pole,** and then a ray with vertex at the pole, called the **polar axis.** See Figure 1. Comparing the rectangular and polar coordinate systems, we see that the origin in rectangular coordinates coincides with the pole in polar coordinates, and the positive x-axis in rectangular coordinates coincides with the polar axis in polar coordinates.

Figure 1

1 Plot Points Using Polar Coordinates

A point P in a polar coordinate system is represented by an ordered pair of numbers (r, θ). If $r > 0$, then r is the distance of the point from the pole; θ is an angle (in degrees or radians) formed by the polar axis and a ray from the pole through the point. We call the ordered pair (r, θ) the **polar coordinates** of the point. See Figure 2.

As an example, suppose that a point P has polar coordinates $\left(2, \dfrac{\pi}{4}\right)$. We locate P by first drawing an angle of $\dfrac{\pi}{4}$ radian, placing its vertex at the pole and its initial side along the polar axis. Then go out a distance of 2 units along the terminal side of the angle to reach the point P. See Figure 3.

Figure 2   **Figure 3**

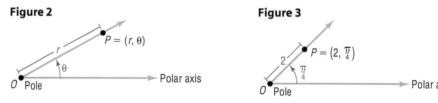

In using polar coordinates (r, θ), it is possible for r to be negative. When this happens, instead of the point being on the terminal side of θ, it is on the ray from the pole extending in the direction *opposite* the terminal side of θ at a distance $|r|$ units from the pole. See Figure 4 for an illustration.

For example, to plot the point $\left(-3, \dfrac{2\pi}{3}\right)$, use the ray in the opposite direction of $\dfrac{2\pi}{3}$ and go out $|-3| = 3$ units along that ray. See Figure 5.

Figure 4

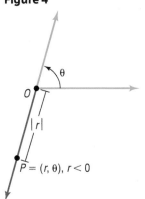

Figure 5

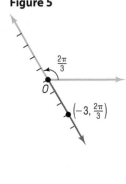

EXAMPLE 1 | **Plotting Points Using Polar Coordinates**

Plot the points with the following polar coordinates:

(a) $\left(3, \dfrac{5\pi}{3}\right)$ (b) $\left(2, -\dfrac{\pi}{4}\right)$ (c) $(3, 0)$ (d) $\left(-2, \dfrac{\pi}{4}\right)$

Solution   Figure 6 shows the points.

Figure 6

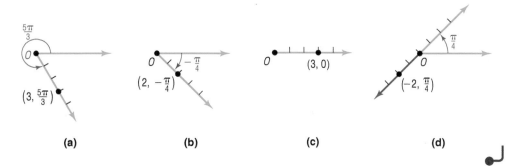

(a)   (b)   (c)   (d)

Now Work PROBLEMS **9, 17,** AND **27**

Recall that an angle measured counterclockwise is positive and an angle measured clockwise is negative. This convention has some interesting consequences relating to polar coordinates.

EXAMPLE 2 | **Finding Several Polar Coordinates of a Single Point**

Consider again the point P with polar coordinates $\left(2, \dfrac{\pi}{4}\right)$, as shown in Figure 7(a). Because $\dfrac{\pi}{4}$, $\dfrac{9\pi}{4}$, and $-\dfrac{7\pi}{4}$ all have the same terminal side, we also could have located this point P by using the polar coordinates $\left(2, \dfrac{9\pi}{4}\right)$ or $\left(2, -\dfrac{7\pi}{4}\right)$, as shown in Figures 7(b) and (c). The point $\left(2, \dfrac{\pi}{4}\right)$ can also be represented by the polar coordinates $\left(-2, \dfrac{5\pi}{4}\right)$. See Figure 7(d).

Figure 7

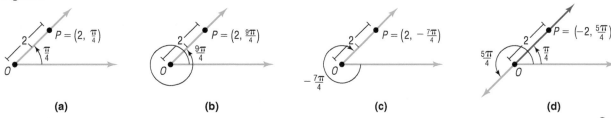

(a)   (b)   (c)   (d)

EXAMPLE 3	**Finding Other Polar Coordinates of a Given Point**

Plot the point P with polar coordinates $\left(3, \dfrac{\pi}{6}\right)$, and find other polar coordinates (r, θ) of this same point for which:

(a) $r > 0$, $2\pi \le \theta < 4\pi$ (b) $r < 0$, $0 \le \theta < 2\pi$

(c) $r > 0$, $-2\pi \le \theta < 0$

Solution The point $\left(3, \dfrac{\pi}{6}\right)$ is plotted in Figure 8.

Figure 8

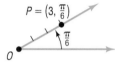

(a) Add 1 revolution (2π radians) to the angle $\dfrac{\pi}{6}$ to get $P = \left(3, \dfrac{\pi}{6} + 2\pi\right) = \left(3, \dfrac{13\pi}{6}\right)$. See Figure 9.

(b) Add $\dfrac{1}{2}$ revolution (π radians) to the angle $\dfrac{\pi}{6}$ and replace 3 by -3 to get $P = \left(-3, \dfrac{\pi}{6} + \pi\right) = \left(-3, \dfrac{7\pi}{6}\right)$. See Figure 10.

(c) Subtract 2π from the angle $\dfrac{\pi}{6}$ to get $P = \left(3, \dfrac{\pi}{6} - 2\pi\right) = \left(3, -\dfrac{11\pi}{6}\right)$. See Figure 11.

Figure 9	**Figure 10**	**Figure 11**
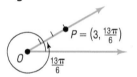	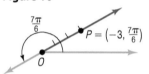	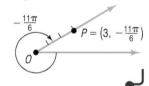

These examples show a major difference between rectangular coordinates and polar coordinates. A point has exactly one pair of rectangular coordinates; however, a point has infinitely many pairs of polar coordinates.

SUMMARY

A point with polar coordinates (r, θ), θ in radians, can also be represented by either of the following:

$$(r, \theta + 2\pi k) \quad \text{or} \quad (-r, \theta + \pi + 2\pi k) \qquad k \text{ any integer}$$

The polar coordinates of the pole are $(0, \theta)$, where θ can be any angle.

Now Work PROBLEM 31

2 Convert from Polar Coordinates to Rectangular Coordinates

Sometimes we need to convert coordinates or equations in rectangular form to polar form, and vice versa. To do this, recall that the origin in rectangular coordinates is the pole in polar coordinates and that the positive x-axis in rectangular coordinates is the polar axis in polar coordinates.

THEOREM **Conversion from Polar Coordinates to Rectangular Coordinates**

If P is a point with polar coordinates (r, θ), the rectangular coordinates (x, y) of P are given by

$x = r \cos \theta \qquad y = r \sin \theta$	**(1)**

Figure 12

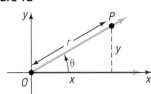

Proof Suppose that P has the polar coordinates (r, θ). We seek the rectangular coordinates (x, y) of P. Refer to Figure 12.

If $r = 0$, then, regardless of θ, the point P is the pole, for which the rectangular coordinates are $(0, 0)$. Formula (1) is valid for $r = 0$.

If $r > 0$, the point P is on the terminal side of θ, and $r = d(O, P) = \sqrt{x^2 + y^2}$. Since

$$\cos \theta = \frac{x}{r} \qquad \sin \theta = \frac{y}{r}$$

we have

$$x = r \cos \theta \qquad y = r \sin \theta$$

If $r < 0$ and θ is in radians, the point $P = (r, \theta)$ can be represented as $(-r, \pi + \theta)$, where $-r > 0$. Since

$$\cos(\pi + \theta) = -\cos \theta = \frac{x}{-r} \qquad \sin(\pi + \theta) = -\sin \theta = \frac{y}{-r}$$

we have

$$x = r \cos \theta \qquad y = r \sin \theta \qquad \blacksquare$$

EXAMPLE 4   **Converting from Polar Coordinates to Rectangular Coordinates**

Find the rectangular coordinates of the points with the following polar coordinates:

(a) $\left(6, \dfrac{\pi}{6}\right)$ (b) $\left(-4, -\dfrac{\pi}{4}\right)$

Solution   Use formula (1): $x = r \cos \theta$ and $y = r \sin \theta$.

Figure 13

(a) Figure 13(a) shows $\left(6, \dfrac{\pi}{6}\right)$ plotted. Notice that $\left(6, \dfrac{\pi}{6}\right)$ lies in quadrant I of the rectangular coordinate system. So we expect both the x-coordinate and the y-coordinate to be positive. With $r = 6$ and $\theta = \dfrac{\pi}{6}$, we have

$$x = r \cos \theta = 6 \cos \frac{\pi}{6} = 6 \cdot \frac{\sqrt{3}}{2} = 3\sqrt{3}$$

$$y = r \sin \theta = 6 \sin \frac{\pi}{6} = 6 \cdot \frac{1}{2} = 3$$

The rectangular coordinates of the point $\left(6, \dfrac{\pi}{6}\right)$ are $\left(3\sqrt{3}, 3\right)$, which lies in quadrant I, as expected.

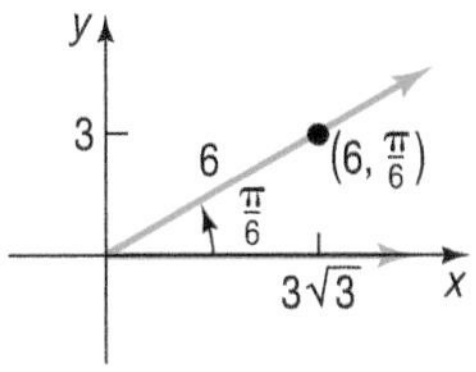

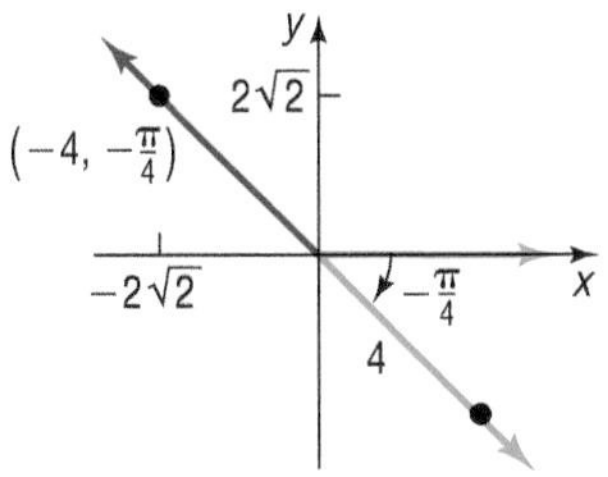

(b) Figure 13(b) shows $\left(-4, -\dfrac{\pi}{4}\right)$ plotted. Notice that $\left(-4, -\dfrac{\pi}{4}\right)$ lies in quadrant II of the rectangular coordinate system. With $r = -4$ and $\theta = -\dfrac{\pi}{4}$, we have

$$x = r \cos \theta = -4 \cos\left(-\frac{\pi}{4}\right) = -4 \cdot \frac{\sqrt{2}}{2} = -2\sqrt{2}$$

$$y = r \sin \theta = -4 \sin\left(-\frac{\pi}{4}\right) = -4\left(-\frac{\sqrt{2}}{2}\right) = 2\sqrt{2}$$

The rectangular coordinates of the point $\left(-4, -\dfrac{\pi}{4}\right)$ are $\left(-2\sqrt{2}, 2\sqrt{2}\right)$, which lies in quadrant II, as expected.

COMMENT Many calculators have the capability of converting from polar coordinates to rectangular coordinates. Consult your owner's manual for the proper keystrokes. Since in most cases this procedure is tedious, you will find that using formula (1) is faster. ∎

Now Work PROBLEMS **39** AND **51**

3 Convert from Rectangular Coordinates to Polar Coordinates

Converting from rectangular coordinates (x, y) to polar coordinates (r, θ) is a little more complicated. Notice that we begin each example by plotting the given rectangular coordinates.

EXAMPLE 5

How to Convert from Rectangular Coordinates to Polar Coordinates with the Point on a Coordinate Axis

Find polar coordinates of a point whose rectangular coordinates are $(0, 3)$.

Step-by-Step Solution

Step 1: Plot the point (x, y) and note the quadrant the point lies in or the coordinate axis the point lies on.

Figure 14

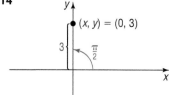

Plot the point $(0, 3)$ in a rectangular coordinate system. See Figure 14. The point lies on the positive y-axis.

Step 2: Determine the distance r from the origin to the point.

The point $(0, 3)$ lies on the y-axis a distance of 3 units from the origin (pole), so $r = 3$.

Step 3: Determine θ.

A ray with vertex at the pole through $(0, 3)$ forms an angle $\theta = \dfrac{\pi}{2}$ with the polar axis.

Polar coordinates for this point can be given by $\left(3, \dfrac{\pi}{2}\right)$. Other possible representations include $\left(-3, -\dfrac{\pi}{2}\right)$ and $\left(3, \dfrac{5\pi}{2}\right)$.

 COMMENT Most graphing calculators have the capability of converting from rectangular coordinates to polar coordinates. Consult your owner's manual for the proper keystrokes. ◼

Figure 15 shows polar coordinates of points that lie on either the x-axis or the y-axis. In each illustration, $a > 0$.

Figure 15

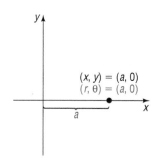

(a) $(x, y) = (a, 0),\ a > 0$

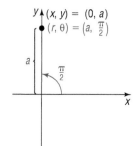

(b) $(x, y) = (0, a),\ a > 0$

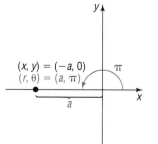

(c) $(x, y) = (-a, 0),\ a > 0$

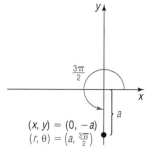

(d) $(x, y) = (0, -a),\ a > 0$

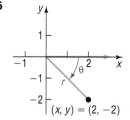

━━━ **Now Work** PROBLEM 55

EXAMPLE 6

How to Convert from Rectangular Coordinates to Polar Coordinates with the Point in a Quadrant

Find the polar coordinates of a point whose rectangular coordinates are $(2, -2)$.

Step-by-Step Solution

Step 1: Plot the point (x, y) and note the quadrant the point lies in or the coordinate axis the point lies on.

Figure 16

Plot the point $(2, -2)$ in a rectangular coordinate system. See Figure 16. The point lies in quadrant IV.

Step 2: Determine the distance r from the origin to the point using $r = \sqrt{x^2 + y^2}$.

$$r = \sqrt{x^2 + y^2} = \sqrt{(2)^2 + (-2)^2} = \sqrt{8} = 2\sqrt{2}$$

Step 3: Determine θ.

Find θ by recalling that $\tan \theta = \dfrac{y}{x}$, so $\theta = \tan^{-1} \dfrac{y}{x}$, $-\dfrac{\pi}{2} < \theta < \dfrac{\pi}{2}$. Since $(2, -2)$ lies in quadrant IV, we know that $-\dfrac{\pi}{2} < \theta < 0$. As a result,

$$\theta = \tan^{-1} \frac{y}{x} = \tan^{-1}\left(\frac{-2}{2}\right) = \tan^{-1}(-1) = -\frac{\pi}{4}$$

A set of polar coordinates for the point $(2, -2)$ is $\left(2\sqrt{2}, -\dfrac{\pi}{4}\right)$. Other possible representations include $\left(2\sqrt{2}, \dfrac{7\pi}{4}\right)$ and $\left(-2\sqrt{2}, \dfrac{3\pi}{4}\right)$.

EXAMPLE 7

Converting from Rectangular Coordinates to Polar Coordinates

Find polar coordinates of a point whose rectangular coordinates are $\left(-1, -\sqrt{3}\right)$.

Solution

Figure 17

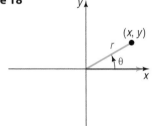

$(x, y) = (-1, -\sqrt{3})$

STEP 1: See Figure 17. The point lies in quadrant III.
STEP 2: The distance r from the origin to the point $\left(-1, -\sqrt{3}\right)$ is

$$r = \sqrt{(-1)^2 + \left(-\sqrt{3}\right)^2} = \sqrt{4} = 2$$

STEP 3: To find θ, use $\alpha = \tan^{-1} \dfrac{y}{x} = \tan^{-1} \dfrac{-\sqrt{3}}{-1} = \tan^{-1}\sqrt{3}$, $-\dfrac{\pi}{2} < \alpha < \dfrac{\pi}{2}$. Since the point $\left(-1, -\sqrt{3}\right)$ lies in quadrant III and the inverse tangent function gives an angle in quadrant I, add π to the result to obtain an angle in quadrant III.

$$\theta = \pi + \tan^{-1}\sqrt{3} = \pi + \frac{\pi}{3} = \frac{4\pi}{3}$$

A set of polar coordinates for this point is $\left(2, \dfrac{4\pi}{3}\right)$. Other possible representations include $\left(-2, \dfrac{\pi}{3}\right)$ and $\left(2, -\dfrac{2\pi}{3}\right)$.

Figure 18 shows how to find polar coordinates of a point that lies in a quadrant when its rectangular coordinates (x, y) are given.

Figure 18

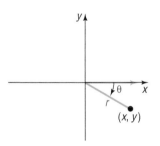

(a) $r = \sqrt{x^2 + y^2}$
$\theta = \tan^{-1} \dfrac{y}{x}$

(b) $r = \sqrt{x^2 + y^2}$
$\theta = \pi + \tan^{-1} \dfrac{y}{x}$

(c) $r = \sqrt{x^2 + y^2}$
$\theta = \pi + \tan^{-1} \dfrac{y}{x}$

(d) $r = \sqrt{x^2 + y^2}$
$\theta = \tan^{-1} \dfrac{y}{x}$

Based on the preceding discussion, we have the formulas

$$r^2 = x^2 + y^2 \qquad \tan \theta = \frac{y}{x} \qquad \text{if } x \neq 0 \qquad \textbf{(2)}$$

To use formula (2) effectively, follow these steps:

STEP 1: Always plot the point (x, y) first, as we did in Examples 5, 6, and 7. Note the quadrant the point lies in or the coordinate axis the point lies on.

STEP 2: If $x = 0$ or $y = 0$, use your illustration to find r. If $x \neq 0$ and $y \neq 0$, then $r = \sqrt{x^2 + y^2}$.

STEP 3: Find θ. If $x = 0$ or $y = 0$, use your illustration to find θ. If $x \neq 0$ and $y \neq 0$, note the quadrant in which the point lies.

$$\text{Quadrant I or IV:} \quad \theta = \tan^{-1}\frac{y}{x}$$

$$\text{Quadrant II or III:} \quad \theta = \pi + \tan^{-1}\frac{y}{x}$$

══════ **Now Work** PROBLEM 59

4 Transform Equations between Polar and Rectangular Forms

Formulas (1) and (2) may also be used to transform equations from polar form to rectangular form, and vice versa. Two common techniques for transforming an equation from polar form to rectangular form are the following:

1. Multiplying both sides of the equation by r
2. Squaring both sides of the equation

EXAMPLE 8 **Transforming an Equation from Polar to Rectangular Form**

Transform the equation $r = 6\cos\theta$ from polar coordinates to rectangular coordinates, and identify the graph.

Solution If we multiply each side by r, it will be easier to apply formulas (1) and (2).

$$r = 6\cos\theta$$
$$r^2 = 6r\cos\theta \quad \text{Multiply each side by } r.$$
$$x^2 + y^2 = 6x \quad \quad r^2 = x^2 + y^2;\ x = r\cos\theta$$

This is the equation of a circle. Proceed to complete the square to obtain the standard form of the equation.

$$x^2 + y^2 = 6x$$
$$(x^2 - 6x) + y^2 = 0 \quad \text{General form}$$
$$(x^2 - 6x + 9) + y^2 = 9 \quad \text{Complete the square in x.}$$
$$(x - 3)^2 + y^2 = 9 \quad \text{Factor.}$$

This is the standard form of the equation of a circle with center $(3, 0)$ and radius 3.

══════ **Now Work** PROBLEM 75

EXAMPLE 9 **Transforming an Equation from Rectangular to Polar Form**

Transform the equation $4xy = 9$ from rectangular coordinates to polar coordinates.

Solution   Use formula (1): $x = r \cos \theta$ and $y = r \sin \theta$.

$$4xy = 9$$
$$4(r \cos \theta)(r \sin \theta) = 9 \quad \text{x = r cos } \theta, \text{ y = r sin } \theta$$
$$4r^2 \cos \theta \sin \theta = 9$$

This is the polar form of the equation. It can be simplified as shown next:

$$2r^2(2 \sin \theta \cos \theta) = 9 \quad \text{Factor out } 2r^2.$$
$$2r^2 \sin(2\theta) = 9 \quad \text{Double-angle Formula}$$

 Now Work PROBLEM 69

9.1 Assess Your Understanding

'Are You Prepared?' *Answers are given at the end of these exercises. If you get a wrong answer, read the pages listed in* red.

1. Plot the point whose rectangular coordinates are $(3, -1)$. What quadrant does the point lie in? (pp. 2–6)

2. To complete the square of $x^2 + 6x$, add _____. (pp. A29–A30)

3. If $P = (a, b)$ is a point on the terminal side of the angle θ at a distance r from the origin, then $\tan \theta =$ ____. (pp. 363–366)

4. $\tan^{-1}(-1) =$ _____ . (pp. 442–444)

Concepts and Vocabulary

5. The origin in rectangular coordinates coincides with the _____ in polar coordinates; the positive x-axis in rectangular coordinates coincides with the _____ _____ in polar coordinates.

6. *True or False* In the polar coordinates (r, θ), r can be negative.

7. *True or False* The polar coordinates of a point are unique.

8. If P is a point with polar coordinates (r, θ), the rectangular coordinates (x, y) of P are given by $x =$ _____ and $y =$ _____.

Skill Building

In Problems 9–16, match each point in polar coordinates with either A, B, C, or D on the graph.

9. $\left(2, -\dfrac{11\pi}{6}\right)$

10. $\left(-2, -\dfrac{\pi}{6}\right)$

11. $\left(-2, \dfrac{\pi}{6}\right)$

12. $\left(2, \dfrac{7\pi}{6}\right)$

13. $\left(2, \dfrac{5\pi}{6}\right)$

14. $\left(-2, \dfrac{5\pi}{6}\right)$

15. $\left(-2, \dfrac{7\pi}{6}\right)$

16. $\left(2, \dfrac{11\pi}{6}\right)$

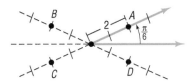

In Problems 17–30, plot each point given in polar coordinates.

17. $(3, 90°)$

18. $(4, 270°)$

19. $(-2, 0)$

20. $(-3, \pi)$

21. $\left(6, \dfrac{\pi}{6}\right)$

22. $\left(5, \dfrac{5\pi}{3}\right)$

23. $(-2, 135°)$

24. $(-3, 120°)$

25. $\left(4, -\dfrac{2\pi}{3}\right)$

26. $\left(2, -\dfrac{5\pi}{4}\right)$

27. $\left(-1, -\dfrac{\pi}{3}\right)$

28. $\left(-3, -\dfrac{3\pi}{4}\right)$

29. $(-2, -\pi)$

30. $\left(-3, -\dfrac{\pi}{2}\right)$

In Problems 31–38, plot each point given in polar coordinates, and find other polar coordinates (r, θ) of the point for which:

  (a) $r > 0, \quad -2\pi \le \theta < 0$
  (b) $r < 0, \quad 0 \le \theta < 2\pi$
  (c) $r > 0, \quad 2\pi \le \theta < 4\pi$

31. $\left(5, \dfrac{2\pi}{3}\right)$

32. $\left(4, \dfrac{3\pi}{4}\right)$

33. $(-2, 3\pi)$

34. $(-3, 4\pi)$

35. $\left(1, \dfrac{\pi}{2}\right)$

36. $(2, \pi)$

37. $\left(-3, -\dfrac{\pi}{4}\right)$

38. $\left(-2, -\dfrac{2\pi}{3}\right)$

In Problems 39–54, the polar coordinates of a point are given. Find the rectangular coordinates of each point.

39. $\left(3, \dfrac{\pi}{2}\right)$ **40.** $\left(4, \dfrac{3\pi}{2}\right)$ **41.** $(-2, 0)$ **42.** $(-3, \pi)$

43. $(6, 150°)$ **44.** $(5, 300°)$ **45.** $\left(-2, \dfrac{3\pi}{4}\right)$ **46.** $\left(-2, \dfrac{2\pi}{3}\right)$

47. $\left(-1, -\dfrac{\pi}{3}\right)$ **48.** $\left(-3, -\dfrac{3\pi}{4}\right)$ **49.** $(-2, -180°)$ **50.** $(-3, -90°)$

51. $(7.5, 110°)$ **52.** $(-3.1, 182°)$ **53.** $(6.3, 3.8)$ **54.** $(8.1, 5.2)$

In Problems 55–66, the rectangular coordinates of a point are given. Find polar coordinates for each point.

55. $(3, 0)$ **56.** $(0, 2)$ **57.** $(-1, 0)$ **58.** $(0, -2)$

59. $(1, -1)$ **60.** $(-3, 3)$ **61.** $\left(\sqrt{3}, 1\right)$ **62.** $\left(-2, -2\sqrt{3}\right)$

63. $(1.3, -2.1)$ **64.** $(-0.8, -2.1)$ **65.** $(8.3, 4.2)$ **66.** $(-2.3, 0.2)$

In Problems 67–74, the letters x and y represent rectangular coordinates. Write each equation using polar coordinates (r, θ).

67. $2x^2 + 2y^2 = 3$ **68.** $x^2 + y^2 = x$ **69.** $x^2 = 4y$ **70.** $y^2 = 2x$

71. $2xy = 1$ **72.** $4x^2y = 1$ **73.** $x = 4$ **74.** $y = -3$

In Problems 75–82, the letters r and θ represent polar coordinates. Write each equation using rectangular coordinates (x, y).

75. $r = \cos\theta$ **76.** $r = \sin\theta + 1$ **77.** $r^2 = \cos\theta$ **78.** $r = \sin\theta - \cos\theta$

79. $r = 2$ **80.** $r = 4$ **81.** $r = \dfrac{4}{1 - \cos\theta}$ **82.** $r = \dfrac{3}{3 - \cos\theta}$

Applications and Extensions

83. Chicago In Chicago, the road system is set up like a Cartesian plane, where streets are indicated by the number of blocks they are from Madison Street and State Street. For example, Wrigley Field in Chicago is located at 1060 West Addison, which is 10 blocks west of State Street and 36 blocks north of Madison Street. Treat the intersection of Madison Street and State Street as the origin of a coordinate system, with east being the positive x-axis.

(a) Write the location of Wrigley Field using rectangular coordinates.

(b) Write the location of Wrigley Field using polar coordinates. Use the east direction for the polar axis. Express θ in degrees.

(c) U.S. Cellular Field, home of the White Sox, is located at 35th and Princeton, which is 3 blocks west of State Street and 35 blocks south of Madison. Write the location of U.S. Cellular Field using rectangular coordinates.

(d) Write the location of U.S. Cellular Field using polar coordinates. Use the east direction for the polar axis. Express θ in degrees.

84. Show that the formula for the distance d between two points $P_1 = (r_1, \theta_1)$ and $P_2 = (r_2, \theta_2)$ is

$$d = \sqrt{r_1^2 + r_2^2 - 2r_1r_2\cos(\theta_2 - \theta_1)}$$

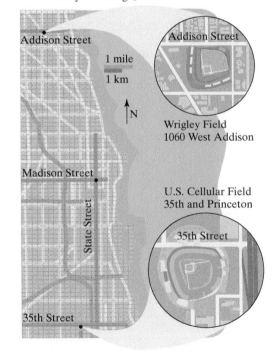

City of Chicago, Illinois

Addison Street

1 mile
1 km

N

Addison Street

Wrigley Field
1060 West Addison

Madison Street

State Street

U.S. Cellular Field
35th and Princeton

35th Street

35th Street

Explaining Concepts: Discussion and Writing

85. In converting from polar coordinates to rectangular coordinates, what formulas will you use?

86. Explain how you proceed to convert from rectangular coordinates to polar coordinates.

87. Is the street system in your town based on a rectangular coordinate system, a polar coordinate system, or some other system? Explain.

'Are You Prepared?' Answers

1. 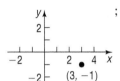 ; quadrant IV   **2.** 9   **3.** $\dfrac{b}{a}$ **4.** $-\dfrac{\pi}{4}$

9.2 Polar Equations and Graphs

PREPARING FOR THIS SECTION *Before getting started, review the following:*

- Symmetry (Section 1.2, pp. 12–14)
- Circles (Section 1.4, pp. 34–37)
- Even–Odd Properties of Trigonometric Functions (Section 6.3, p. 389)

- Difference Formulas for Sine and Cosine (Section 7.4, pp. 472 and 475)
- Values of the Sine and Cosine Functions at Certain Angles (Section 6.2, pp. 366–375)

Now Work the *'Are You Prepared?'* problems on page 579.

OBJECTIVES **1** Identify and Graph Polar Equations by Converting to Rectangular Equations (p. 568)

2 Test Polar Equations for Symmetry (p. 571)

3 Graph Polar Equations by Plotting Points (p. 572)

Just as a rectangular grid may be used to plot points given by rectangular coordinates, as in Figure 19(a), we can use a grid consisting of concentric circles (with centers at the pole) and rays (with vertices at the pole) to plot points given by polar coordinates, as shown in Figure 19(b). We use such **polar grids** to graph *polar equations*.

Figure 19

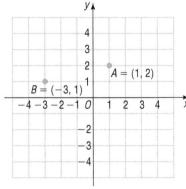

(a) Rectangular grid

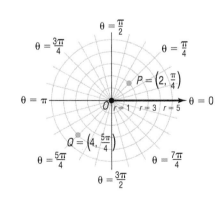

(b) Polar grid

DEFINITION

An equation whose variables are polar coordinates is called a **polar equation.** The **graph of a polar equation** consists of all points whose polar coordinates satisfy the equation.

1 Identify and Graph Polar Equations by Converting to Rectangular Equations

One method used to graph a polar equation is to convert the equation to rectangular coordinates. In the discussion that follows, (x, y) represent the rectangular coordinates of a point P, and (r, θ) represent polar coordinates of the point P.

EXAMPLE 1   **Identifying and Graphing a Polar Equation (Circle)**

Identify and graph the equation: $r = 3$

Solution   Convert the polar equation to a rectangular equation.

$$r = 3$$
$$r^2 = 9 \quad \text{Square both sides.}$$
$$x^2 + y^2 = 9 \quad r^2 = x^2 + y^2$$

The graph of $r = 3$ is a circle, with center at the pole and radius 3. See Figure 20.

Figure 20
$r = 3 \text{ or } x^2 + y^2 = 9$

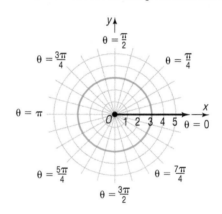

━━━━━━━ **Now Work** PROBLEM 13

EXAMPLE 2   **Identifying and Graphing a Polar Equation (Line)**

Identify and graph the equation: $\theta = \dfrac{\pi}{4}$

Solution   Convert the polar equation to a rectangular equation.

Figure 21
$\theta = \dfrac{\pi}{4} \text{ or } y = x$

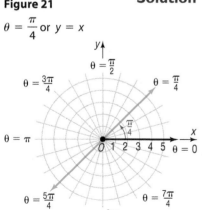

$$\theta = \frac{\pi}{4}$$
$$\tan \theta = \tan \frac{\pi}{4} \quad \text{Take the tangent of both sides.}$$
$$\frac{y}{x} = 1 \quad \tan \theta = \frac{y}{x}; \tan \frac{\pi}{4} = 1$$
$$y = x$$

The graph of $\theta = \dfrac{\pi}{4}$ is a line passing through the pole making an angle of $\dfrac{\pi}{4}$ with the polar axis. See Figure 21.

━━━━━━━ **Now Work** PROBLEM 15

EXAMPLE 3

Identifying and Graphing a Polar Equation (Horizontal Line)

Identify and graph the equation: $r \sin \theta = 2$

Solution

Since $y = r \sin \theta$, we can write the equation as

$$y = 2$$

We conclude that the graph of $r \sin \theta = 2$ is a horizontal line 2 units above the pole. See Figure 22.

Figure 22
$r \sin \theta = 2$ or $y = 2$

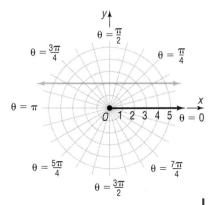

COMMENT A graphing utility can be used to graph polar equations. Read Using a Graphing Utility to Graph a Polar Equation, Appendix B, Section B.8. ■

EXAMPLE 4

Identifying and Graphing a Polar Equation (Vertical Line)

Identify and graph the equation: $r \cos \theta = -3$

Solution

Since $x = r \cos \theta$, we can write the equation as

$$x = -3$$

We conclude that the graph of $r \cos \theta = -3$ is a vertical line 3 units to the left of the pole. See Figure 23.

Figure 23
$r \cos \theta = -3$ or $x = -3$

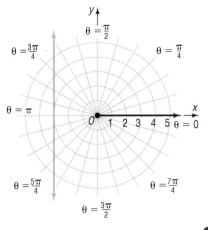

Based on Examples 3 and 4, we are led to the following results. (The proofs are left as exercises. See Problems 81 and 82.)

THEOREM

Let a be a real number. Then the graph of the equation

$$r \sin \theta = a$$

is a horizontal line. It lies a units above the pole if $a \geq 0$ and $|a|$ units below the pole if $a < 0$.

The graph of the equation

$$r \cos \theta = a$$

is a vertical line. It lies a units to the right of the pole if $a \geq 0$ and $|a|$ units to the left of the pole if $a < 0$.

━━Now Work PROBLEM 19

EXAMPLE 5 **Identifying and Graphing a Polar Equation (Circle)**

Identify and graph the equation: $r = 4 \sin \theta$

Solution To transform the equation to rectangular coordinates, multiply each side by r.

$$r^2 = 4r \sin \theta$$

Now use the facts that $r^2 = x^2 + y^2$ and $y = r \sin \theta$. Then

$$x^2 + y^2 = 4y$$

$$x^2 + (y^2 - 4y) = 0$$

$$x^2 + (y^2 - 4y + 4) = 4 \qquad \text{Complete the square in } y.$$

$$x^2 + (y - 2)^2 = 4 \qquad \text{Factor.}$$

This is the standard equation of a circle with center at $(0, 2)$ in rectangular coordinates and radius 2. See Figure 24.

Figure 24
$r = 4 \sin \theta$ or $x^2 + (y - 2)^2 = 4$

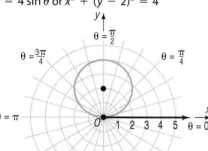

EXAMPLE 6 **Identifying and Graphing a Polar Equation (Circle)**

Identify and graph the equation: $r = -2 \cos \theta$

Solution Proceed as in Example 5.

$$r^2 = -2r \cos \theta \qquad \text{Multiply both sides by } r.$$

$$x^2 + y^2 = -2x \qquad r^2 = x^2 + y^2; \quad x = r \cos \theta$$

$$x^2 + 2x + y^2 = 0$$

$$(x^2 + 2x + 1) + y^2 = 1 \qquad \text{Complete the square in } x.$$

$$(x + 1)^2 + y^2 = 1 \qquad \text{Factor.}$$

This is the standard equation of a circle with center at $(-1, 0)$ in rectangular coordinates and radius 1. See Figure 25.

Figure 25
$r = -2 \cos \theta$ or $(x + 1)^2 + y^2 = 1$

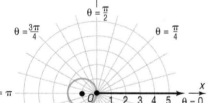

Exploration

Using a square screen, graph $r_1 = \sin \theta$, $r_2 = 2 \sin \theta$, and $r_3 = 3 \sin \theta$. Do you see the pattern? Clear the screen and graph $r_1 = -\sin \theta$, $r_2 = -2 \sin \theta$, and $r_3 = -3 \sin \theta$. Do you see the pattern? Clear the screen and graph $r_1 = \cos \theta$, $r_2 = 2 \cos \theta$, and $r_3 = 3 \cos \theta$. Do you see the pattern? Clear the screen and graph $r_1 = -\cos \theta$, $r_2 = -2 \cos \theta$, and $r_3 = -3 \cos \theta$. Do you see the pattern?

Based on Examples 5 and 6 and the preceding Exploration, we are led to the following results. (The proofs are left as exercises. See Problems 83–86.)

THEOREM Let a be a positive real number. Then

Equation	Description
(a) $r = 2a \sin \theta$	Circle: radius a; center at $(0, a)$ in rectangular coordinates
(b) $r = -2a \sin \theta$	Circle: radius a; center at $(0, -a)$ in rectangular coordinates
(c) $r = 2a \cos \theta$	Circle: radius a; center at $(a, 0)$ in rectangular coordinates
(d) $r = -2a \cos \theta$	Circle: radius a; center at $(-a, 0)$ in rectangular coordinates

Each circle passes through the pole.

Now Work PROBLEM 21

The method of converting a polar equation to an identifiable rectangular equation to obtain the graph is not always helpful, nor is it always necessary. Usually, we set up a table that lists several points on the graph. By checking for symmetry, it may be possible to reduce the number of points needed to draw the graph.

2 Test Polar Equations for Symmetry

In polar coordinates, the points (r, θ) and $(r, -\theta)$ are symmetric with respect to the polar axis (and to the x-axis). See Figure 26(a). The points (r, θ) and $(r, \pi - \theta)$ are symmetric with respect to the line $\theta = \dfrac{\pi}{2}$ (the y-axis). See Figure 26(b). The points (r, θ) and $(-r, \theta)$ are symmetric with respect to the pole (the origin). See Figure 26(c).

Figure 26

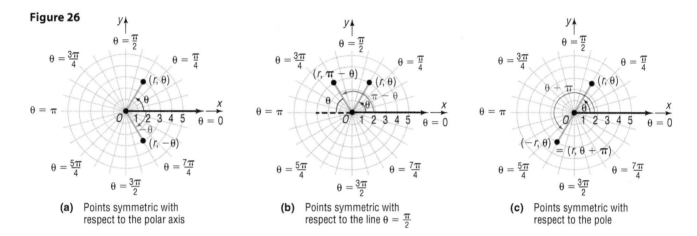

(a) Points symmetric with respect to the polar axis

(b) Points symmetric with respect to the line $\theta = \dfrac{\pi}{2}$

(c) Points symmetric with respect to the pole

The following tests are a consequence of these observations.

THEOREM

Tests for Symmetry

Symmetry with Respect to the Polar Axis (x-Axis)

In a polar equation, replace θ by $-\theta$. If an equivalent equation results, the graph is symmetric with respect to the polar axis.

Symmetry with Respect to the Line $\theta = \dfrac{\pi}{2}$ (y-Axis)

In a polar equation, replace θ by $\pi - \theta$. If an equivalent equation results, the graph is symmetric with respect to the line $\theta = \dfrac{\pi}{2}$.

Symmetry with Respect to the Pole (Origin)

In a polar equation, replace r by $-r$ or θ by $\theta + \pi$. If an equivalent equation results, the graph is symmetric with respect to the pole.

The three tests for symmetry given here are *sufficient* conditions for symmetry, but they are not *necessary* conditions. That is, an equation may fail these tests and still have a graph that is symmetric with respect to the polar axis, the line $\theta = \dfrac{\pi}{2}$, or the pole. For example, the graph of $r = \sin(2\theta)$ turns out to be symmetric with respect to the polar axis, the line $\theta = \dfrac{\pi}{2}$, and the pole, but only the test for symmetry with respect to the pole (replace θ by $\theta + \pi$) works. See also Problems 87–89.

3 Graph Polar Equations by Plotting Points

EXAMPLE 7

Graphing a Polar Equation (Cardioid)

Graph the equation: $r = 1 - \sin \theta$

Solution

Check for symmetry first.

Polar Axis: Replace θ by $-\theta$. The result is

$$r = 1 - \sin(-\theta) = 1 + \sin \theta \quad \text{sin}\,(-\theta) = -\sin \theta$$

The test fails, so the graph may or may not be symmetric with respect to the polar axis.

The Line $\theta = \dfrac{\pi}{2}$: Replace θ by $\pi - \theta$. The result is

$$r = 1 - \sin(\pi - \theta) = 1 - (\sin \pi \cos \theta - \cos \pi \sin \theta)$$
$$= 1 - [0 \cdot \cos \theta - (-1) \sin \theta] = 1 - \sin \theta$$

The test is satisfied, so the graph is symmetric with respect to the line $\theta = \dfrac{\pi}{2}$.

The Pole: Replace r by $-r$. Then the result is $-r = 1 - \sin \theta$, so $r = -1 + \sin \theta$. The test fails. Replace θ by $\theta + \pi$. The result is

$$r = 1 - \sin(\theta + \pi)$$
$$= 1 - [\sin \theta \cos \pi + \cos \theta \sin \pi]$$
$$= 1 - [\sin \theta \cdot (-1) + \cos \theta \cdot 0]$$
$$= 1 + \sin \theta$$

This test also fails. So the graph may or may not be symmetric with respect to the pole.

Next, identify points on the graph by assigning values to the angle θ and calculating the corresponding values of r. Due to the periodicity of the sine function and the symmetry with respect to the line $\theta = \dfrac{\pi}{2}$, we only need to assign values to θ from $-\dfrac{\pi}{2}$ to $\dfrac{\pi}{2}$, as given in Table 1.

Now plot the points (r, θ) from Table 1 and trace out the graph, beginning at the point $\left(2, -\dfrac{\pi}{2}\right)$ and ending at the point $\left(0, \dfrac{\pi}{2}\right)$. Then reflect this portion of the graph about the line $\theta = \dfrac{\pi}{2}$ (the y-axis) to obtain the complete graph. See Figure 27.

Table 1

θ	$r = 1 - \sin \theta$
$-\dfrac{\pi}{2}$	$1 - (-1) = 2$
$-\dfrac{\pi}{3}$	$1 - \left(-\dfrac{\sqrt{3}}{2}\right) \approx 1.87$
$-\dfrac{\pi}{6}$	$1 - \left(-\dfrac{1}{2}\right) = \dfrac{3}{2}$
0	$1 - 0 = 1$
$\dfrac{\pi}{6}$	$1 - \dfrac{1}{2} = \dfrac{1}{2}$
$\dfrac{\pi}{3}$	$1 - \dfrac{\sqrt{3}}{2} \approx 0.13$
$\dfrac{\pi}{2}$	$1 - 1 = 0$

Figure 27
$r = 1 - \sin \theta$

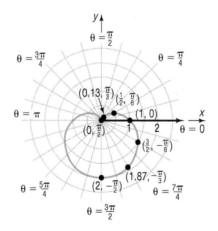

Exploration

Graph $r_1 = 1 + \sin \theta$. Clear the screen and graph $r_1 = 1 - \cos \theta$. Clear the screen and graph $r_1 = 1 + \cos \theta$. Do you see a pattern?

The curve in Figure 27 is an example of a *cardioid* (a heart-shaped curve).

DEFINITION

Cardioids are characterized by equations of the form

$$r = a(1 + \cos \theta) \qquad r = a(1 + \sin \theta)$$
$$r = a(1 - \cos \theta) \qquad r = a(1 - \sin \theta)$$

where $a > 0$. The graph of a cardioid passes through the pole.

────── **Now Work** PROBLEM 37

EXAMPLE 8

Graphing a Polar Equation (Limaçon without an Inner Loop)

Graph the equation: $r = 3 + 2 \cos \theta$

Solution

Check for symmetry first.

Polar Axis: Replace θ by $-\theta$. The result is

$$r = 3 + 2 \cos(-\theta) = 3 + 2 \cos \theta \quad \cos(-\theta) = \cos \theta$$

The test is satisfied, so the graph is symmetric with respect to the polar axis.

The Line $\theta = \dfrac{\pi}{2}$: Replace θ by $\pi - \theta$. The result is

$$r = 3 + 2 \cos(\pi - \theta) = 3 + 2(\cos \pi \cos \theta + \sin \pi \sin \theta)$$
$$= 3 - 2 \cos \theta$$

The test fails, so the graph may or may not be symmetric with respect to the line $\theta = \dfrac{\pi}{2}$.

The Pole: Replace r by $-r$. The test fails, so the graph may or may not be symmetric with respect to the pole. Replace θ by $\theta + \pi$. The test fails, so the graph may or may not be symmetric with respect to the pole.

Next, identify points on the graph by assigning values to the angle θ and calculating the corresponding values of r. Due to the periodicity of the cosine function and the symmetry with respect to the polar axis, we only need to assign values to θ from 0 to π, as given in Table 2.

Now plot the points (r, θ) from Table 2 and trace out the graph, beginning at the point $(5, 0)$ and ending at the point $(1, \pi)$. Then reflect this portion of the graph about the polar axis (the x-axis) to obtain the complete graph. See Figure 28.

Table 2

θ	$r = 3 + 2 \cos \theta$
0	$3 + 2(1) = 5$
$\dfrac{\pi}{6}$	$3 + 2\left(\dfrac{\sqrt{3}}{2}\right) \approx 4.73$
$\dfrac{\pi}{3}$	$3 + 2\left(\dfrac{1}{2}\right) = 4$
$\dfrac{\pi}{2}$	$3 + 2(0) = 3$
$\dfrac{2\pi}{3}$	$3 + 2\left(-\dfrac{1}{2}\right) = 2$
$\dfrac{5\pi}{6}$	$3 + 2\left(-\dfrac{\sqrt{3}}{2}\right) \approx 1.27$
π	$3 + 2(-1) = 1$

Figure 28
$r = 3 + 2 \cos \theta$

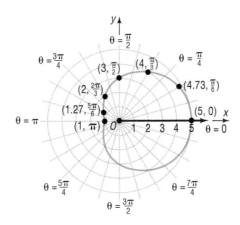

 Exploration

Graph $r_1 = 3 - 2 \cos \theta$. Clear the screen and graph $r_1 = 3 + 2 \sin \theta$. Clear the screen and graph $r_1 = 3 - 2 \sin \theta$. Do you see a pattern?

The curve in Figure 28 is an example of a *limaçon* (a French word for *snail*) *without an inner loop*.

DEFINITION

Limaçons without an inner loop are characterized by equations of the form

$$r = a + b \cos \theta \qquad r = a + b \sin \theta$$
$$r = a - b \cos \theta \qquad r = a - b \sin \theta$$

where $a > 0$, $b > 0$, and $a > b$. The graph of a limaçon without an inner loop does not pass through the pole.

────▶ **Now Work** PROBLEM 43

EXAMPLE 9

Graphing a Polar Equation (Limaçon with an Inner Loop)

Graph the equation: $r = 1 + 2 \cos \theta$

Solution

First, check for symmetry.

Polar Axis: Replace θ by $-\theta$. The result is

$$r = 1 + 2 \cos(-\theta) = 1 + 2 \cos \theta$$

The test is satisfied, so the graph is symmetric with respect to the polar axis.

Table 3

θ	$r = 1 + 2 \cos \theta$
0	$1 + 2(1) = 3$
$\dfrac{\pi}{6}$	$1 + 2\left(\dfrac{\sqrt{3}}{2}\right) \approx 2.73$
$\dfrac{\pi}{3}$	$1 + 2\left(\dfrac{1}{2}\right) = 2$
$\dfrac{\pi}{2}$	$1 + 2(0) = 1$
$\dfrac{2\pi}{3}$	$1 + 2\left(-\dfrac{1}{2}\right) = 0$
$\dfrac{5\pi}{6}$	$1 + 2\left(-\dfrac{\sqrt{3}}{2}\right) \approx -0.73$
π	$1 + 2(-1) = -1$

The Line $\theta = \dfrac{\pi}{2}$: Replace θ by $\pi - \theta$. The result is

$$r = 1 + 2 \cos(\pi - \theta) = 1 + 2(\cos \pi \cos \theta + \sin \pi \sin \theta)$$
$$= 1 - 2 \cos \theta$$

The test fails, so the graph may or may not be symmetric with respect to the line $\theta = \dfrac{\pi}{2}$.

The Pole: Replace r by $-r$. The test fails, so the graph may or may not be symmetric with respect to the pole. Replace θ by $\theta + \pi$. The test fails, so the graph may or may not be symmetric with respect to the pole.

Next, identify points on the graph of $r = 1 + 2 \cos \theta$ by assigning values to the angle θ and calculating the corresponding values of r. Due to the periodicity of the cosine function and the symmetry with respect to the polar axis, we only need to assign values to θ from 0 to π, as given in Table 3.

Now plot the points (r, θ) from Table 3, beginning at $(3, 0)$ and ending at $(-1, \pi)$. See Figure 29(a). Finally, reflect this portion of the graph about the polar axis (the x-axis) to obtain the complete graph. See Figure 29(b).

Figure 29

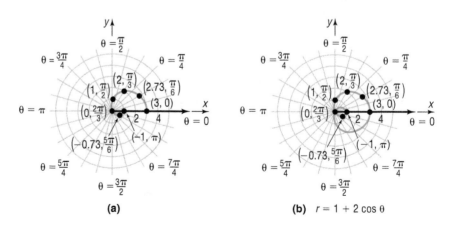

(a)

(b) $r = 1 + 2 \cos \theta$

Exploration

Graph $r_1 = 1 - 2 \cos \theta$. Clear the screen and graph $r_1 = 1 + 2 \sin \theta$. Clear the screen and graph $r_1 = 1 - 2 \sin \theta$. Do you see a pattern?

The curve in Figure 29(b) is an example of a *limaçon with an inner loop*.

DEFINITION

Limaçons with an inner loop are characterized by equations of the form

$$r = a + b\cos\theta \qquad r = a + b\sin\theta$$
$$r = a - b\cos\theta \qquad r = a - b\sin\theta$$

where $a > 0, b > 0$, and $a < b$. The graph of a limaçon with an inner loop will pass through the pole twice.

━━━━**Now Work** PROBLEM 45

EXAMPLE 10

Graphing a Polar Equation (Rose)

Graph the equation: $r = 2\cos(2\theta)$

Solution

Check for symmetry.

Polar Axis: If we replace θ by $-\theta$, the result is

$$r = 2\cos[2(-\theta)] = 2\cos(2\theta)$$

The test is satisfied, so the graph is symmetric with respect to the polar axis.

The Line $\theta = \dfrac{\pi}{2}$: If we replace θ by $\pi - \theta$, we obtain

$$r = 2\cos[2(\pi - \theta)] = 2\cos(2\pi - 2\theta) = 2\cos(2\theta)$$

The test is satisfied, so the graph is symmetric with respect to the line $\theta = \dfrac{\pi}{2}$.

The Pole: Since the graph is symmetric with respect to both the polar axis and the line $\theta = \dfrac{\pi}{2}$, it must be symmetric with respect to the pole.

Next, construct Table 4. Due to the periodicity of the cosine function and the symmetry with respect to the polar axis, the line $\theta = \dfrac{\pi}{2}$, and the pole, we consider only values of θ from 0 to $\dfrac{\pi}{2}$.

Plot and connect these points in Figure 30(a). Finally, because of symmetry, reflect this portion of the graph first about the polar axis (the x-axis) and then about the line $\theta = \dfrac{\pi}{2}$ (the y-axis) to obtain the complete graph. See Figure 30(b).

Table 4

θ	$r = 2\cos(2\theta)$
0	$2(1) = 2$
$\dfrac{\pi}{6}$	$2\left(\dfrac{1}{2}\right) = 1$
$\dfrac{\pi}{4}$	$2(0) = 0$
$\dfrac{\pi}{3}$	$2\left(-\dfrac{1}{2}\right) = -1$
$\dfrac{\pi}{2}$	$2(-1) = -2$

Figure 30

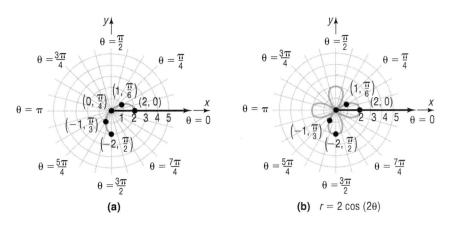

(a)

(b) $r = 2\cos(2\theta)$

Exploration

Graph $r_1 = 2\cos(4\theta)$; clear the screen and graph $r_1 = 2\cos(6\theta)$. How many petals did each of these graphs have?

Clear the screen and graph, in order, each on a clear screen, $r_1 = 2\cos(3\theta)$, $r_1 = 2\cos(5\theta)$, and $r_1 = 2\cos(7\theta)$. What do you notice about the number of petals?

The curve in Figure 30(b) is called a *rose* with four petals.

DEFINITION **Rose** curves are characterized by equations of the form

$$r = a \cos(n\theta), \qquad r = a \sin(n\theta), \qquad a \neq 0$$

and have graphs that are rose shaped. If $n \neq 0$ is even, the rose has $2n$ petals; if $n \neq \pm 1$ is odd, the rose has n petals.

Now Work PROBLEM 49

EXAMPLE 11 **Graphing a Polar Equation (Lemniscate)**

Graph the equation: $r^2 = 4 \sin(2\theta)$

Solution We leave it to you to verify that the graph is symmetric with respect to the pole. Because of the symmetry with respect to the pole, we only need to consider values of θ between $\theta = 0$ and $\theta = \pi$. Note that there are no points on the graph for $\frac{\pi}{2} < \theta < \pi$ (quadrant II), since $r^2 < 0$ for such values. Table 5 lists points on the graph for values of $\theta = 0$ through $\theta = \frac{\pi}{2}$. The points from Table 5 where $r \geq 0$ are plotted in Figure 31(a). The remaining points on the graph may be obtained by using symmetry. Figure 31(b) shows the final graph drawn.

Table 5

θ	$r^2 = 4\sin(2\theta)$	r
0	$4(0) = 0$	0
$\dfrac{\pi}{6}$	$4\left(\dfrac{\sqrt{3}}{2}\right) = 2\sqrt{3}$	± 1.9
$\dfrac{\pi}{4}$	$4(1) = 4$	± 2
$\dfrac{\pi}{3}$	$4\left(\dfrac{\sqrt{3}}{2}\right) = 2\sqrt{3}$	± 1.9
$\dfrac{\pi}{2}$	$4(0) = 0$	0

Figure 31

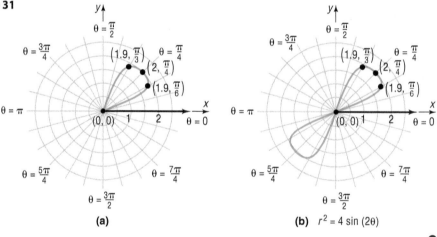

(a)

(b) $r^2 = 4 \sin(2\theta)$

The curve in Figure 31(b) is an example of a *lemniscate* (from the Greek word *ribbon*).

DEFINITION **Lemniscates** are characterized by equations of the form

$$r^2 = a^2 \sin(2\theta) \qquad r^2 = a^2 \cos(2\theta)$$

where $a \neq 0$, and have graphs that are propeller shaped.

Now Work PROBLEM 53

EXAMPLE 12 **Graphing a Polar Equation (Spiral)**

Graph the equation: $r = e^{\theta/5}$

Solution The tests for symmetry with respect to the pole, the polar axis, and the line $\theta = \frac{\pi}{2}$ fail. Furthermore, there is no number θ for which $r = 0$, so the graph does not pass through the pole. Observe that r is positive for all θ, r increases as θ increases, $r \to 0$

Table 6

θ	$r = e^{\theta/5}$
$-\dfrac{3\pi}{2}$	0.39
$-\pi$	0.53
$-\dfrac{\pi}{2}$	0.73
$-\dfrac{\pi}{4}$	0.85
0	1
$\dfrac{\pi}{4}$	1.17
$\dfrac{\pi}{2}$	1.37
π	1.87
$\dfrac{3\pi}{2}$	2.57
2π	3.51

as $\theta \to -\infty$, and $r \to \infty$ as $\theta \to \infty$. With the help of a calculator, we obtain the values in Table 6. See Figure 32.

Figure 32
$r = e^{\theta/5}$

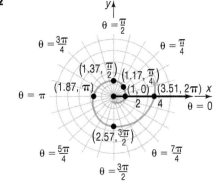

The curve in Figure 32 is called a **logarithmic spiral,** since its equation may be written as $\theta = 5 \ln r$ and it spirals infinitely both toward the pole and away from it.

Classification of Polar Equations

The equations of some lines and circles in polar coordinates and their corresponding equations in rectangular coordinates are given in Table 7. Also included are the names and graphs of a few of the more frequently encountered polar equations.

Table 7

Lines			
Description	Line passing through the pole making an angle α with the polar axis	Vertical line	Horizontal line
Rectangular equation	$y = (\tan \alpha)x$	$x = a$	$y = b$
Polar equation	$\theta = \alpha$	$r \cos \theta = a$	$r \sin \theta = b$
Typical graph			

Circles			
Description	Center at the pole, radius a	Passing through the pole, tangent to the line $\theta = \dfrac{\pi}{2}$, center on the polar axis, radius a	Passing through the pole, tangent to the polar axis, center on the line $\theta = \dfrac{\pi}{2}$, radius a
Rectangular equation	$x^2 + y^2 = a^2, \quad a > 0$	$x^2 + y^2 = \pm 2ax, \quad a > 0$	$x^2 + y^2 = \pm 2ay, \quad a > 0$
Polar equation	$r = a, \quad a > 0$	$r = \pm 2a \cos \theta, \quad a > 0$	$r = \pm 2a \sin \theta, \quad a > 0$
Typical graph			

(continued)

Table 7 (Continued)

Other Equations		
Name	Cardioid	Limaçon without inner loop	Limaçon with inner loop
Polar equations	$r = a \pm a\cos\theta, \quad a > 0$	$r = a \pm b\cos\theta, \quad 0 < b < a$	$r = a \pm b\cos\theta, \quad 0 < a < b$
	$r = a \pm a\sin\theta, \quad a > 0$	$r = a \pm b\sin\theta, \quad 0 < b < a$	$r = a \pm b\sin\theta, \quad 0 < a < b$

Typical graph

(cardioid graph)	(limaçon without inner loop graph)	(limaçon with inner loop graph)

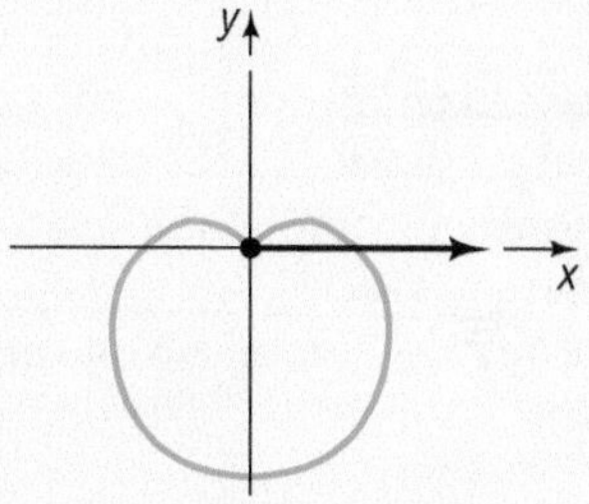

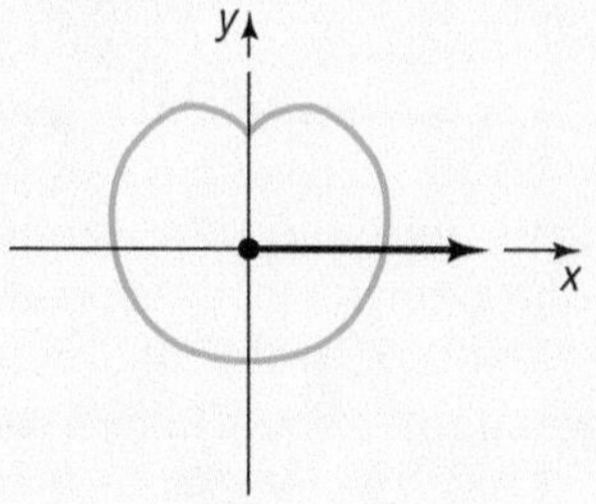

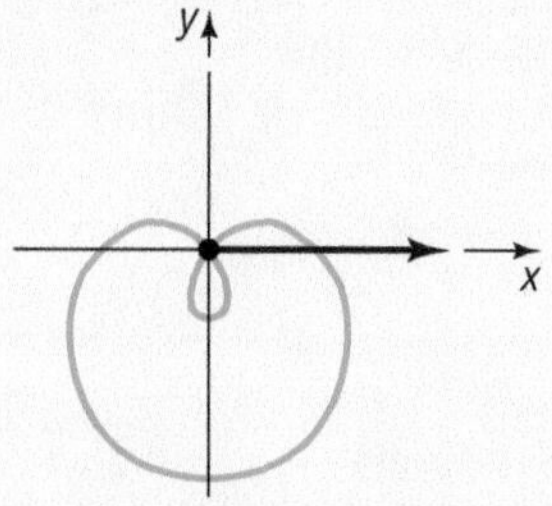

Name	Lemniscate	Rose with three petals	Rose with four petals
Polar equations	$r^2 = a^2\cos(2\theta), \quad a > 0$	$r = a\sin(3\theta), \quad a > 0$	$r = a\sin(2\theta), \quad a > 0$
	$r^2 = a^2\sin(2\theta), \quad a > 0$	$r = a\cos(3\theta), \quad a > 0$	$r = a\cos(2\theta), \quad a > 0$

Typical graph

(lemniscate graph)	(rose with three petals graph)	(rose with four petals graph)

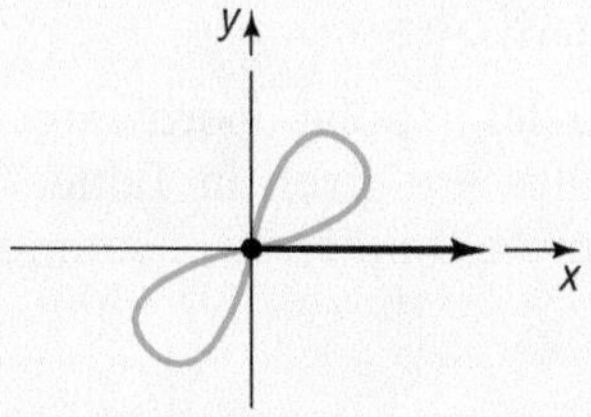

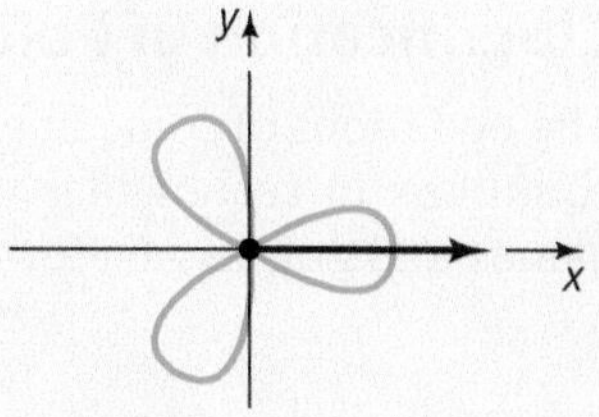

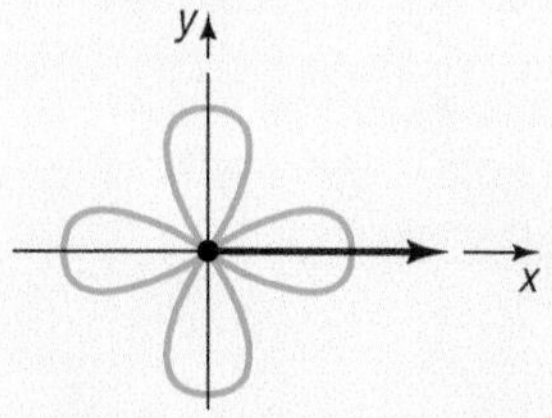

Sketching Quickly

If a polar equation involves only a sine (or cosine) function, you can quickly obtain a sketch of its graph by making use of Table 7, periodicity, and a short table.

EXAMPLE 13 **Sketching the Graph of a Polar Equation Quickly**

Graph the equation: $r = 2 + 2\sin\theta$

Solution You should recognize the polar equation: Its graph is a cardioid. The period of $\sin\theta$ is 2π, so form a table using $0 \le \theta \le 2\pi$, compute r, plot the points (r, θ), and sketch the graph of a cardioid as θ varies from 0 to 2π. See Table 8 and Figure 33.

Table 8

θ	$r = 2 + 2\sin\theta$
0	$2 + 2(0) = 2$
$\dfrac{\pi}{2}$	$2 + 2(1) = 4$
π	$2 + 2(0) = 2$
$\dfrac{3\pi}{2}$	$2 + 2(-1) = 0$
2π	$2 + 2(0) = 2$

Figure 33
$r = 2 + 2\sin\theta$

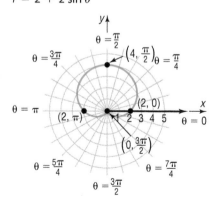

△ **Calculus Comment**   For those of you who are planning to study calculus, a comment about one important role of polar equations is in order.

In rectangular coordinates, the equation $x^2 + y^2 = 1$, whose graph is the unit circle, is not the graph of a function. In fact, it requires two functions to obtain the graph of the unit circle:

$$y_1 = \sqrt{1 - x^2} \quad \text{Upper semicircle} \qquad y_2 = -\sqrt{1 - x^2} \quad \text{Lower semicircle}$$

In polar coordinates, the equation $r = 1$, whose graph is also the unit circle, does define a function. For each choice of θ, there is only one corresponding value of r, that is, $r = 1$. Since many problems in calculus require the use of functions, the opportunity to express nonfunctions in rectangular coordinates as functions in polar coordinates becomes extremely useful.

Note also that the vertical-line test for functions is valid only for equations in rectangular coordinates.

Historical Feature

Jakob Bernoulli (1654–1705)

Polar coordinates seem to have been invented by Jakob Bernoulli (1654–1705) in about 1691, although, as with most such ideas, earlier traces of the notion exist. Early users of calculus remained committed to rectangular coordinates, and polar coordinates did not become widely used until the early 1800s. Even then, it was mostly geometers who used them for describing odd curves. Finally, about the mid-1800s, applied mathematicians realized the tremendous simplification that polar coordinates make possible in the description of objects with circular or cylindrical symmetry. From then on their use became widespread.

9.2 Assess Your Understanding

'Are You Prepared?'   *Answers are given at the end of these exercises. If you get a wrong answer, read the pages listed in* red.

1. If the rectangular coordinates of a point are $(4, -6)$, the point symmetric to it with respect to the origin is _____. (pp. 12–14)

2. The difference formula for cosine is $\cos(A - B) = $ _____. (p. 472)

3. The standard equation of a circle with center at $(-2, 5)$ and radius 3 is _____. (pp. 34–37)

4. Is the sine function even, odd, or neither? (p. 389)

5. $\sin \dfrac{5\pi}{4} = $ _____ . (pp. 366–375)

6. $\cos \dfrac{2\pi}{3} = $ _____ . (pp. 366–375)

Concepts and Vocabulary

7. An equation whose variables are polar coordinates is called a(n) _____ _____.

8. *True or False*   The tests for symmetry in polar coordinates are necessary, but not sufficient.

9. To test if the graph of a polar equation may be symmetric with respect to the polar axis, replace θ by _____.

10. To test if the graph of a polar equation may be symmetric with respect to the line $\theta = \dfrac{\pi}{2}$, replace θ by _____.

11. *True or False*   A cardiod passes through the pole.

12. Rose curves are characterized by equations of the form $r = a \cos(n\,\theta)$ or $r = a \sin(n\,\theta), a \neq 0$. If $n \neq 0$ is even, the rose has _____ petals; if $n \neq \pm 1$ is odd, the rose has _____ petals.

Skill Building

In Problems 13–28, transform each polar equation to an equation in rectangular coordinates. Then identify and graph the equation.

13. $r = 4$

14. $r = 2$

15. $\theta = \dfrac{\pi}{3}$

16. $\theta = -\dfrac{\pi}{4}$

17. $r \sin \theta = 4$

18. $r \cos \theta = 4$

19. $r \cos \theta = -2$

20. $r \sin \theta = -2$

21. $r = 2 \cos \theta$ **22.** $r = 2 \sin \theta$ **23.** $r = -4 \sin \theta$ **24.** $r = -4 \cos \theta$

25. $r \sec \theta = 4$ **26.** $r \csc \theta = 8$ **27.** $r \csc \theta = -2$ **28.** $r \sec \theta = -4$

In Problems 29–36, match each of the graphs (A) through (H) to one of the following polar equations.

29. $r = 2$ **30.** $\theta = \dfrac{\pi}{4}$ **31.** $r = 2 \cos \theta$ **32.** $r \cos \theta = 2$

33. $r = 1 + \cos \theta$ **34.** $r = 2 \sin \theta$ **35.** $\theta = \dfrac{3\pi}{4}$ **36.** $r \sin \theta = 2$

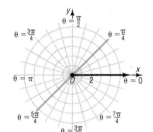
(A)

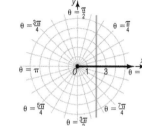
(B)

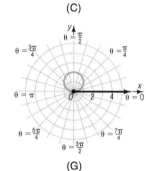
(C)

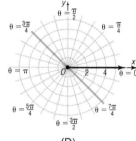
(D)

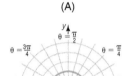
(E)

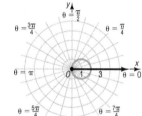
(F)

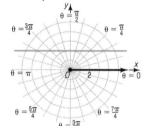
(G)

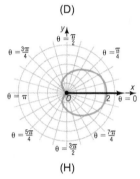
(H)

In Problems 37–60, identify and graph each polar equation.

37. $r = 2 + 2 \cos \theta$ **38.** $r = 1 + \sin \theta$ **39.** $r = 3 - 3 \sin \theta$ **40.** $r = 2 - 2 \cos \theta$

41. $r = 2 + \sin \theta$ **42.** $r = 2 - \cos \theta$ **43.** $r = 4 - 2 \cos \theta$ **44.** $r = 4 + 2 \sin \theta$

45. $r = 1 + 2 \sin \theta$ **46.** $r = 1 - 2 \sin \theta$ **47.** $r = 2 - 3 \cos \theta$ **48.** $r = 2 + 4 \cos \theta$

49. $r = 3 \cos(2\theta)$ **50.** $r = 2 \sin(3\theta)$ **51.** $r = 4 \sin(5\theta)$ **52.** $r = 3 \cos(4\theta)$

53. $r^2 = 9 \cos(2\theta)$ **54.** $r^2 = \sin(2\theta)$ **55.** $r = 2^\theta$ **56.** $r = 3^\theta$

57. $r = 1 - \cos \theta$ **58.** $r = 3 + \cos \theta$ **59.** $r = 1 - 3 \cos \theta$ **60.** $r = 4 \cos(3\theta)$

Mixed Practice

In Problems 61–66, graph each pair of polar equations on the same polar grid. Find the polar coordinates of the point(s) of intersection and label the point(s) on the graph.

61. $r = 8 \cos \theta; r = 2 \sec \theta$ **62.** $r = 8 \sin \theta; r = 4 \csc \theta$ **63.** $r = \sin \theta; r = 1 + \cos \theta$

64. $r = 3; r = 2 + 2 \cos \theta$ **65.** $r = 1 + \sin \theta; r = 1 + \cos \theta$ **66.** $r = 1 + \cos \theta; r = 3 \cos \theta$

Applications and Extensions

In Problems 67–70, the polar equation for each graph is either $r = a + b \cos \theta$ or $r = a + b \sin \theta$, $a > 0$. Select the correct equation and find the values of a and b.

67.

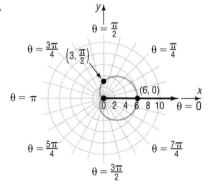

68.

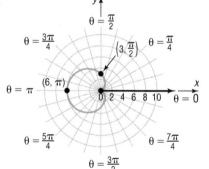

69.

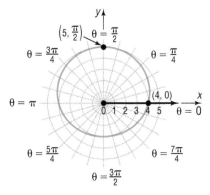

70.

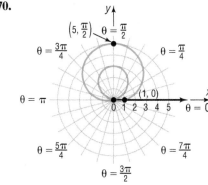

In Problems 71–80, graph each polar equation.

71. $r = \dfrac{2}{1 - \cos \theta}$ *(parabola)*

72. $r = \dfrac{2}{1 - 2 \cos \theta}$ *(hyperbola)*

73. $r = \dfrac{1}{3 - 2 \cos \theta}$ *(ellipse)*

74. $r = \dfrac{1}{1 - \cos \theta}$ *(parabola)*

75. $r = \theta, \quad \theta \geq 0$ *(spiral of Archimedes)*

76. $r = \dfrac{3}{\theta}$ *(reciprocal spiral)*

77. $r = \csc \theta - 2, \quad 0 < \theta < \pi$ *(conchoid)*

78. $r = \sin \theta \tan \theta$ *(cissoid)*

79. $r = \tan \theta, \quad -\dfrac{\pi}{2} < \theta < \dfrac{\pi}{2}$ *(kappa curve)*

80. $r = \cos \dfrac{\theta}{2}$

81. Show that the graph of the equation $r \sin \theta = a$ is a horizontal line a units above the pole if $a \geq 0$ and $|a|$ units below the pole if $a < 0$.

82. Show that the graph of the equation $r \cos \theta = a$ is a vertical line a units to the right of the pole if $a \geq 0$ and $|a|$ units to the left of the pole if $a < 0$.

83. Show that the graph of the equation $r = 2a \sin \theta, a > 0$, is a circle of radius a with center at $(0, a)$ in rectangular coordinates.

84. Show that the graph of the equation $r = -2a \sin \theta, a > 0$, is a circle of radius a with center at $(0, -a)$ in rectangular coordinates.

85. Show that the graph of the equation $r = 2a \cos \theta, a > 0$, is a circle of radius a with center at $(a, 0)$ in rectangular coordinates.

86. Show that the graph of the equation $r = -2a \cos \theta, a > 0$, is a circle of radius a with center at $(-a, 0)$ in rectangular coordinates.

Explaining Concepts: Discussion and Writing

87. Explain why the following test for symmetry is valid: Replace r by $-r$ and θ by $-\theta$ in a polar equation. If an equivalent equation results, the graph is symmetric with respect to the line $\theta = \dfrac{\pi}{2}$ (*y*-axis).

    (a) Show that the test on page 571 fails for $r^2 = \cos \theta$, yet this new test works.

    (b) Show that the test on page 571 works for $r^2 = \sin \theta$, yet this new test fails.

88. Write down two different tests for symmetry with respect to the polar axis. Find examples in which one test works and the other fails. Which test do you prefer to use? Justify your answer.

89. The tests for symmetry given on page 571 are sufficient, but not necessary. Explain what this means.

90. Explain why the vertical-line test used to identify functions in rectangular coordinates does not work for equations expressed in polar coordinates.

9.3 The Complex Plane; De Moivre's Theorem

PREPARING FOR THIS SECTION *Before getting started, review the following:*

- Complex Numbers (Appendix A, Section A.7, pp. A54–A58)
- Value of the Sine and Cosine Functions at Certain Angles (Section 6.2, pp. 366–375)

- Sum and Difference Formulas for Sine and Cosine (Section 7.4, pp. 472 and 475)

Now Work the *'Are You Prepared?'* problems on page 588.

OBJECTIVES 1 Plot Points in the Complex Plane (p. 582)
2 Convert a Complex Number between Rectangular Form and Polar Form (p. 583)
3 Find Products and Quotients of Complex Numbers in Polar Form (p. 584)
4 Use De Moivre's Theorem (p. 585)
5 Find Complex Roots (p. 586)

Figure 34
Complex plane

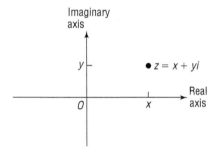

1 Plot Points in the Complex Plane

Complex numbers are discussed in Appendix A, Section A.7. In that discussion, we were not prepared to give a geometric interpretation of a complex number. Now we are ready.

A complex number $z = x + yi$ can be interpreted geometrically as the point (x, y) in the xy-plane. Each point in the plane corresponds to a complex number and, conversely, each complex number corresponds to a point in the plane. We refer to the collection of such points as the **complex plane.** The x-axis will be referred to as the **real axis,** because any point that lies on the real axis is of the form $z = x + 0i = x$, a real number. The y-axis is called the **imaginary axis,** because any point that lies on it is of the form $z = 0 + yi = yi$, a pure imaginary number. See Figure 34.

EXAMPLE 1

Figure 35

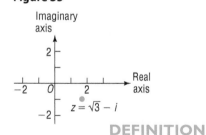

Plotting a Point in the Complex Plane

Plot the point corresponding to $z = \sqrt{3} - i$ in the complex plane.

Solution The point corresponding to $z = \sqrt{3} - i$ has the rectangular coordinates $(\sqrt{3}, -1)$. The point, located in quadrant IV, is plotted in Figure 35.

DEFINITION

Let $z = x + yi$ be a complex number. The **magnitude** or **modulus** of z, denoted by $|z|$, is defined as the distance from the origin to the point (x, y). That is,

$$|z| = \sqrt{x^2 + y^2} \tag{1}$$

Figure 36

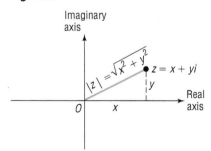

See Figure 36 for an illustration.

This definition for $|z|$ is consistent with the definition for the absolute value of a real number: If $z = x + yi$ is real, then $z = x + 0i$ and

$$|z| = \sqrt{x^2 + 0^2} = \sqrt{x^2} = |x|$$

For this reason, the magnitude of z is sometimes called the **absolute value of z.**

Recall that if $z = x + yi$ then its **conjugate,** denoted by $\bar{z}$, is $\bar{z} = x - yi$. Because $z\bar{z} = x^2 + y^2$, which is a nonnegative real number, it follows from equation (1) that the magnitude of z can be written as

$$|z| = \sqrt{z\bar{z}} \qquad (2)$$

2 Convert a Complex Number between Rectangular Form and Polar Form

When a complex number is written in the standard form $z = x + yi$, we say that it is in **rectangular,** or **Cartesian, form,** because (x, y) are the rectangular coordinates of the corresponding point in the complex plane. Suppose that (r, θ) are the polar coordinates of this point. Then

$$x = r\cos\theta, \qquad y = r\sin\theta \qquad (3)$$

DEFINITION

If $r \geq 0$ and $0 \leq \theta < 2\pi$, the complex number $z = x + yi$ may be written in **polar form** as

$$z = x + yi = (r\cos\theta) + (r\sin\theta)i = r(\cos\theta + i\sin\theta) \qquad (4)$$

Figure 37

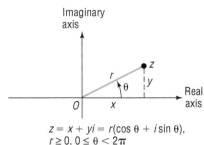

$z = x + yi = r(\cos\theta + i\sin\theta)$,
$r \geq 0, 0 \leq \theta < 2\pi$

See Figure 37.

If $z = r(\cos\theta + i\sin\theta)$ is the polar form of a complex number,* the angle θ, $0 \leq \theta < 2\pi$, is called the **argument of z.**

Also, because $r \geq 0$, we have $r = \sqrt{x^2 + y^2}$. From equation (1), it follows that the magnitude of $z = r(\cos\theta + i\sin\theta)$ is

$$|z| = r$$

EXAMPLE 2

Writing a Complex Number in Polar Form

Write an expression for $z = \sqrt{3} - i$ in polar form.

Solution

The point, located in quadrant IV, is plotted in Figure 35. Because $x = \sqrt{3}$ and $y = -1$, it follows that

$$r = \sqrt{x^2 + y^2} = \sqrt{(\sqrt{3})^2 + (-1)^2} = \sqrt{4} = 2$$

So

$$\sin\theta = \frac{y}{r} = \frac{-1}{2}, \qquad \cos\theta = \frac{x}{r} = \frac{\sqrt{3}}{2}, \qquad 0 \leq \theta < 2\pi$$

The angle $\theta, 0 \leq \theta < 2\pi$, that satisfies both equations is $\theta = \dfrac{11\pi}{6}$. With $\theta = \dfrac{11\pi}{6}$ and $r = 2$, the polar form of $z = \sqrt{3} - i$ is

$$z = r(\cos\theta + i\sin\theta) = 2\left(\cos\frac{11\pi}{6} + i\sin\frac{11\pi}{6}\right)$$

Now Work PROBLEM 11

EXAMPLE 3

Plotting a Point in the Complex Plane and Converting from Polar to Rectangular Form

Plot the point corresponding to $z = 2(\cos 30° + i\sin 30°)$ in the complex plane, and write an expression for z in rectangular form.

* Some books abbreviate the polar form using $z = r(\cos\theta + i\sin\theta) = r \operatorname{cis} \theta$.

Figure 38

Imaginary axis

$z = 2(\cos 30° + i \sin 30°)$

$30°$

Real axis

Solution   To plot the complex number $z = 2(\cos 30° + i \sin 30°)$, plot the point whose polar coordinates are $(r, \theta) = (2, 30°)$, as shown in Figure 38. In rectangular form,

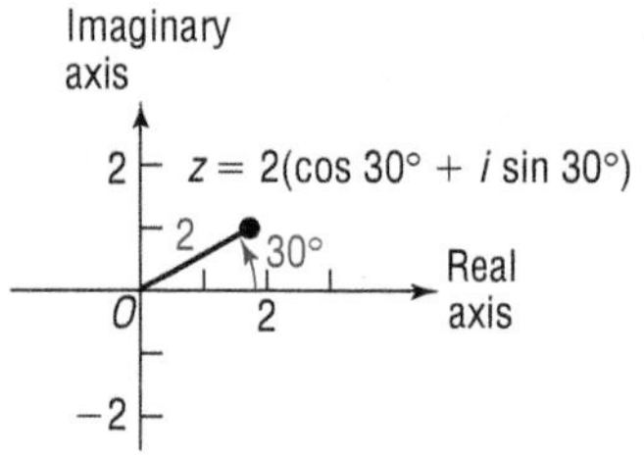

$$z = 2(\cos 30° + i \sin 30°) = 2\left(\frac{\sqrt{3}}{2} + \frac{1}{2}i\right) = \sqrt{3} + i$$

Now Work PROBLEM 23

3 Find Products and Quotients of Complex Numbers in Polar Form

The polar form of a complex number provides an alternative method for finding products and quotients of complex numbers.

THEOREM   Let $z_1 = r_1(\cos \theta_1 + i \sin \theta_1)$ and $z_2 = r_2(\cos \theta_2 + i \sin \theta_2)$ be two complex numbers. Then

$$z_1 z_2 = r_1 r_2 [\cos(\theta_1 + \theta_2) + i \sin(\theta_1 + \theta_2)] \tag{5}$$

If $z_2 \neq 0$, then

$$\frac{z_1}{z_2} = \frac{r_1}{r_2}[\cos(\theta_1 - \theta_2) + i \sin(\theta_1 - \theta_2)] \tag{6}$$

In Words

The magnitude of a complex number z is r and its argument is θ, so when
$$z = r(\cos \theta + i \sin \theta)$$
the magnitude of the product (quotient) of two complex numbers equals the product (quotient) of their magnitudes; the argument of the product (quotient) of two complex numbers is determined by the sum (difference) of their arguments.

Proof   We will prove equation (5). The proof of equation (6) is left as an exercise (see Problem 66).

$$\begin{aligned} z_1 z_2 &= [r_1(\cos \theta_1 + i \sin \theta_1)][r_2(\cos \theta_2 + i \sin \theta_2)] \\ &= r_1 r_2[(\cos \theta_1 + i \sin \theta_1)(\cos \theta_2 + i \sin \theta_2)] \\ &= r_1 r_2[(\cos \theta_1 \cos \theta_2 - \sin \theta_1 \sin \theta_2) + i(\sin \theta_1 \cos \theta_2 + \cos \theta_1 \sin \theta_2)] \\ &= r_1 r_2[\cos(\theta_1 + \theta_2) + i \sin(\theta_1 + \theta_2)] \end{aligned}$$

EXAMPLE 4   **Finding Products and Quotients of Complex Numbers in Polar Form**

If $z = 3(\cos 20° + i \sin 20°)$ and $w = 5(\cos 100° + i \sin 100°)$, find the following (leave your answers in polar form):

(a) zw (b) $\dfrac{z}{w}$

Solution   (a) $zw = [3(\cos 20° + i \sin 20°)][5(\cos 100° + i \sin 100°)]$
$= (3 \cdot 5)[\cos(20° + 100°) + i \sin(20° + 100°)]$
$= 15(\cos 120° + i \sin 120°)$ Apply equation (5).

(b) $\dfrac{z}{w} = \dfrac{3(\cos 20° + i \sin 20°)}{5(\cos 100° + i \sin 100°)}$

$= \dfrac{3}{5}[\cos(20° - 100°) + i \sin(20° - 100°)]$ Apply equation (6).

$= \dfrac{3}{5}[\cos(-80°) + i \sin(-80°)]$

$= \dfrac{3}{5}(\cos 280° + i \sin 280°)$ The argument must lie between 0° and 360°.

Now Work PROBLEM 33

4 Use De Moivre's Theorem

De Moivre's Theorem, stated by Abraham De Moivre (1667–1754) in 1730, but already known to many people by 1710, is important for the following reason: The fundamental processes of algebra are the four operations of addition, subtraction, multiplication, and division, together with powers and the extraction of roots. De Moivre's Theorem allows these latter fundamental algebraic operations to be applied to complex numbers.

De Moivre's Theorem, in its most basic form, is a formula for raising a complex number z to the power n, where $n \geq 1$ is a positive integer. Let's see if we can conjecture the form of the result.

Let $z = r(\cos \theta + i \sin \theta)$ be a complex number. Then, based on equation (5), we have

$$n = 2: \quad z^2 = r^2[\cos(2\theta) + i \sin(2\theta)] \qquad \text{Equation (5)}$$

$$\begin{aligned} n = 3: \quad z^3 &= z^2 \cdot z \\ &= \{r^2[\cos(2\theta) + i\sin(2\theta)]\}[r(\cos\theta + i\sin\theta)] \\ &= r^3[\cos(3\theta) + i\sin(3\theta)] \qquad \text{Equation (5)} \end{aligned}$$

$$\begin{aligned} n = 4: \quad z^4 &= z^3 \cdot z \\ &= \{r^3[\cos(3\theta) + i\sin(3\theta)]\}[r(\cos\theta + i\sin\theta)] \\ &= r^4[\cos(4\theta) + i\sin(4\theta)] \qquad \text{Equation (5)} \end{aligned}$$

Do you see the pattern?

THEOREM

De Moivre's Theorem

If $z = r(\cos \theta + i \sin \theta)$ is a complex number, then

$$z^n = r^n[\cos(n\theta) + i \sin(n\theta)] \qquad \textbf{(7)}$$

where $n \geq 1$ is a positive integer.

The proof of De Moivre's Theorem requires mathematical induction (which is not discussed until Section 12.4), so it is omitted here.

EXAMPLE 5

Using De Moivre's Theorem

Write $[2(\cos 20° + i \sin 20°)]^3$ in the standard form $a + bi$.

Solution

$$[2(\cos 20° + i \sin 20°)]^3 = 2^3[\cos(3 \cdot 20°) + i \sin(3 \cdot 20°)] \quad \text{Apply De Moivre's Theorem.}$$

$$= 8(\cos 60° + i \sin 60°)$$

$$= 8\left(\frac{1}{2} + \frac{\sqrt{3}}{2}i\right) = 4 + 4\sqrt{3}i$$

Now Work   PROBLEM 41

EXAMPLE 6

Using De Moivre's Theorem

Write $(1 + i)^5$ in the standard form $a + bi$.

Solution

To apply De Moivre's Theorem, we must first write the complex number in polar form. Since the magnitude of $1 + i$ is $\sqrt{1^2 + 1^2} = \sqrt{2}$, we begin by writing

NOTE We could also write $1 + i$ in polar form by following the approach used in Example 2. ∎

$$1 + i = \sqrt{2}\left(\frac{1}{\sqrt{2}} + \frac{1}{\sqrt{2}}i\right) = \sqrt{2}\left(\cos\frac{\pi}{4} + i \sin\frac{\pi}{4}\right)$$

Now

$$(1 + i)^5 = \left[\sqrt{2}\left(\cos\frac{\pi}{4} + i\sin\frac{\pi}{4}\right)\right]^5$$

$$= \left(\sqrt{2}\right)^5\left[\cos\left(5\cdot\frac{\pi}{4}\right) + i\sin\left(5\cdot\frac{\pi}{4}\right)\right]$$

$$= 4\sqrt{2}\left(\cos\frac{5\pi}{4} + i\sin\frac{5\pi}{4}\right)$$

$$= 4\sqrt{2}\left[-\frac{1}{\sqrt{2}} + \left(-\frac{1}{\sqrt{2}}\right)i\right] = -4 - 4i$$

5 Find Complex Roots

Let w be a given complex number, and let $n \geq 2$ denote a positive integer. Any complex number z that satisfies the equation

$$z^n = w$$

is called a **complex nth root** of w. In keeping with previous usage, if $n = 2$, the solutions of the equation $z^2 = w$ are called **complex square roots** of w, and if $n = 3$, the solutions of the equation $z^3 = w$ are called **complex cube roots** of w.

THEOREM

Finding Complex Roots

Let $w = r(\cos\theta_0 + i\sin\theta_0)$ be a complex number, and let $n \geq 2$ be an integer. If $w \neq 0$, there are n distinct complex nth roots of w, given by the formula

$$z_k = \sqrt[n]{r}\left[\cos\left(\frac{\theta_0}{n} + \frac{2k\pi}{n}\right) + i\sin\left(\frac{\theta_0}{n} + \frac{2k\pi}{n}\right)\right] \qquad \textbf{(8)}$$

where $k = 0, 1, 2, \ldots, n - 1$.

Proof (Outline)   We will not prove this result in its entirety. Instead, we shall show only that each z_k in equation (8) satisfies the equation $z_k^n = w$, proving that each z_k is a complex nth root of w.

$$z_k^n = \left\{\sqrt[n]{r}\left[\cos\left(\frac{\theta_0}{n} + \frac{2k\pi}{n}\right) + i\sin\left(\frac{\theta_0}{n} + \frac{2k\pi}{n}\right)\right]\right\}^n$$

$$= (\sqrt[n]{r})^n\left\{\cos\left[n\left(\frac{\theta_0}{n} + \frac{2k\pi}{n}\right)\right] + i\sin\left[n\left(\frac{\theta_0}{n} + \frac{2k\pi}{n}\right)\right]\right\} \qquad \text{Apply De Moivre's Theorem.}$$

$$= r[\cos(\theta_0 + 2k\pi) + i\sin(\theta_0 + 2k\pi)] \qquad \text{Simplify.}$$

$$= r(\cos\theta_0 + i\sin\theta_0) = w \qquad \text{The Periodic Property}$$

So each z_k, $k = 0, 1, \ldots, n - 1$, is a complex nth root of w. To complete the proof, we would need to show that each z_k, $k = 0, 1, \ldots, n - 1$, is, in fact, distinct and that there are no complex nth roots of w other than those given by equation (8). ∎

EXAMPLE 7   **Finding Complex Cube Roots**

Find the complex cube roots of $-1 + \sqrt{3}i$. Leave your answers in polar form, with the argument in degrees.

Solution   First, express $-1 + \sqrt{3}i$ in polar form using degrees.

$$-1 + \sqrt{3}i = 2\left(-\frac{1}{2} + \frac{\sqrt{3}}{2}i\right) = 2(\cos 120° + i\sin 120°)$$

The three complex cube roots of $-1 + \sqrt{3}i = 2(\cos 120° + i \sin 120°)$ are

$$z_k = \sqrt[3]{2}\left[\cos\left(\frac{120°}{3} + \frac{360°k}{3}\right) + i \sin\left(\frac{120°}{3} + \frac{360°k}{3}\right)\right]$$

$$= \sqrt[3]{2}[\cos(40° + 120°k) + i \sin(40° + 120°k)] \qquad k = 0, 1, 2$$

So

WARNING Most graphing utilities will only provide the answer z_0 to the calculation $(-1 + \sqrt{3}i) \wedge \left(\frac{1}{3}\right)$. The paragraph following Example 7 explains how to obtain z_1 and z_2 from z_0. ∎

$$z_0 = \sqrt[3]{2}[\cos(40° + 120° \cdot 0) + i \sin(40° + 120° \cdot 0)] = \sqrt[3]{2}(\cos 40° + i \sin 40°)$$

$$z_1 = \sqrt[3]{2}[\cos(40° + 120° \cdot 1) + i \sin(40° + 120° \cdot 1)] = \sqrt[3]{2}(\cos 160° + i \sin 160°)$$

$$z_2 = \sqrt[3]{2}[\cos(40° + 120° \cdot 2) + i \sin(40° + 120° \cdot 2)] = \sqrt[3]{2}(\cos 280° + i \sin 280°)$$

Notice that each of the three complex roots of $-1 + \sqrt{3}i$ has the same magnitude, $\sqrt[3]{2}$. This means that the points corresponding to each cube root lie the same distance from the origin; that is, the three points lie on a circle with center at the origin and radius $\sqrt[3]{2}$. Furthermore, the arguments of these cube roots are 40°, 160°, and 280°, the difference of consecutive pairs being $120° = \frac{360°}{3}$. This means that the three points are equally spaced on the circle, as shown in Figure 39. These results are not coincidental. In fact, you are asked to show that these results hold for complex nth roots in Problems 63 through 65.

Figure 39

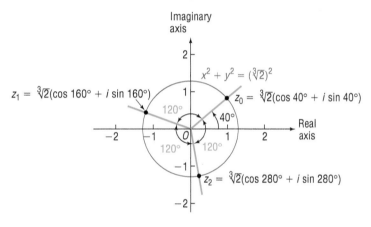

$z_1 = \sqrt[3]{2}(\cos 160° + i \sin 160°)$

$x^2 + y^2 = (\sqrt[3]{2})^2$

$z_0 = \sqrt[3]{2}(\cos 40° + i \sin 40°)$

$z_2 = \sqrt[3]{2}(\cos 280° + i \sin 280°)$

━━━▶ **Now Work** PROBLEM **5 3**

Historical Feature

John Wallis

The Babylonians, Greeks, and Arabs considered square roots of negative quantities to be impossible and equations with complex solutions to be unsolvable. The first hint that there was some connection between real solutions of equations and complex numbers came when Girolamo Cardano (1501–1576) and Tartaglia (1499–1557) found *real* roots of cubic equations by taking cube roots of *complex* quantities. For centuries thereafter,

mathematicians worked with complex numbers without much belief in their actual existence. In 1673, John Wallis appears to have been the first to suggest the graphical representation of complex numbers, a truly significant idea that was not pursued further until about 1800. Several people, including Karl Friedrich Gauss (1777–1855), then rediscovered the idea, and graphical representation helped to establish complex numbers as equal members of the number family. In practical applications, complex numbers have found their greatest uses in the study of alternating current, where they are a commonplace tool, and in the field of subatomic physics.

Historical Problems

1. The quadratic formula will work perfectly well if the coefficients are complex numbers. Solve the following. [**Hint:** The answers are "nice."]

(a) $z^2 - (2 + 5i)z - 3 + 5i = 0$

(b) $z^2 - (1 + i)z - 2 - i = 0$

9.3 Assess Your Understanding

1. The conjugate of $-4 - 3i$ is _____ . (pp. A54–A58)

2. The sum formula for the sine function is $\sin(A + B) =$ _____ . (p. 475)

3. The sum formula for the cosine function is $\cos(A + B) =$ _____ . (p. 472)

4. $\sin 120° =$ _____ ; $\cos 240° =$ _____ . (pp. 366–375)

Concepts and Vocabulary

5. In the complex plane, the x-axis is referred to as the _____ axis and the y-axis is called the _____ axis.

6. When a complex number z is written in the polar form $z = r(\cos \theta + i \sin \theta)$, the nonnegative number r is the _____ or _____ of z, and the angle θ, $0 \le \theta < 2\pi$, is the _____ of z.

7. Let $z_1 = r_1(\cos \theta_1 + i \sin \theta_1)$ and $z_2 = r_2(\cos \theta_2 + i \sin \theta_2)$ be two complex numbers. Then
$z_1 z_2 =$ _____ $[\cos ($ _____ $) + i \sin ($ _____ $)]$.

8. If $z = r(\cos \theta + i \sin \theta)$ is a complex number, then $z^n =$ ____ $[\cos($ ____ $) + i \sin($ ____ $)]$.

9. Every nonzero complex number will have exactly _____ distinct cube roots.

10. *True or False* The polar form of a nonzero complex number is unique.

Skill Building

In Problems 11–22, plot each complex number in the complex plane and write it in polar form. Express the argument in degrees.

11. $1 + i$

12. $-1 + i$

13. $\sqrt{3} - i$

14. $1 - \sqrt{3}i$

15. $-3i$

16. -2

17. $4 - 4i$

18. $9\sqrt{3} + 9i$

19. $3 - 4i$

20. $2 + \sqrt{3}i$

21. $-2 + 3i$

22. $\sqrt{5} - i$

In Problems 23–32, write each complex number in rectangular form.

23. $2(\cos 120° + i \sin 120°)$

24. $3(\cos 210° + i \sin 210°)$

25. $4\left(\cos \dfrac{7\pi}{4} + i \sin \dfrac{7\pi}{4} \right)$

26. $2\left(\cos \dfrac{5\pi}{6} + i \sin \dfrac{5\pi}{6} \right)$

27. $3\left(\cos \dfrac{3\pi}{2} + i \sin \dfrac{3\pi}{2} \right)$

28. $4\left(\cos \dfrac{\pi}{2} + i \sin \dfrac{\pi}{2} \right)$

29. $0.2(\cos 100° + i \sin 100°)$

30. $0.4(\cos 200° + i \sin 200°)$

31. $2\left(\cos \dfrac{\pi}{18} + i \sin \dfrac{\pi}{18} \right)$

32. $3\left(\cos \dfrac{\pi}{10} + i \sin \dfrac{\pi}{10} \right)$

In Problems 33–40, find zw and $\dfrac{z}{w}$. Leave your answers in polar form.

33. $z = 2(\cos 40° + i \sin 40°)$
$w = 4(\cos 20° + i \sin 20°)$

34. $z = \cos 120° + i \sin 120°$
$w = \cos 100° + i \sin 100°$

35. $z = 3(\cos 130° + i \sin 130°)$
$w = 4(\cos 270° + i \sin 270°)$

36. $z = 2(\cos 80° + i \sin 80°)$
$w = 6(\cos 200° + i \sin 200°)$

37. $z = 2\left(\cos \dfrac{\pi}{8} + i \sin \dfrac{\pi}{8} \right)$
$w = 2\left(\cos \dfrac{\pi}{10} + i \sin \dfrac{\pi}{10} \right)$

38. $z = 4\left(\cos \dfrac{3\pi}{8} + i \sin \dfrac{3\pi}{8} \right)$
$w = 2\left(\cos \dfrac{9\pi}{16} + i \sin \dfrac{9\pi}{16} \right)$

39. $z = 2 + 2i$
$w = \sqrt{3} - i$

40. $z = 1 - i$
$w = 1 - \sqrt{3}i$

In Problems 41–52, write each expression in the standard form $a + bi$.

41. $[4(\cos 40° + i \sin 40°)]^3$

42. $[3(\cos 80° + i \sin 80°)]^3$

43. $\left[2\left(\cos \dfrac{\pi}{10} + i \sin \dfrac{\pi}{10} \right) \right]^5$

44. $\left[\sqrt{2}\left(\cos \dfrac{5\pi}{16} + i \sin \dfrac{5\pi}{16} \right) \right]^4$

45. $\left[\sqrt{3}(\cos 10° + i \sin 10°) \right]^6$

46. $\left[\dfrac{1}{2}(\cos 72° + i \sin 72°) \right]^5$

47. $\left[\sqrt{5}\left(\cos \dfrac{3\pi}{16} + i \sin \dfrac{3\pi}{16} \right) \right]^4$

48. $\left[\sqrt{3}\left(\cos \dfrac{5\pi}{18} + i \sin \dfrac{5\pi}{18} \right) \right]^6$

49. $(1 - i)^5$

50. $\left(\sqrt{3} - i \right)^6$

51. $\left(\sqrt{2} - i \right)^6$

52. $\left(1 - \sqrt{5}i \right)^8$

In Problems 53–60, find all the complex roots. Leave your answers in polar form with the argument in degrees.

53. The complex cube roots of $1 + i$

54. The complex fourth roots of $\sqrt{3} - i$

55. The complex fourth roots of $4 - 4\sqrt{3}i$

56. The complex cube roots of $-8 - 8i$

57. The complex fourth roots of $-16i$

58. The complex cube roots of -8

59. The complex fifth roots of i

60. The complex fifth roots of $-i$

Applications and Extensions

61. Find the four complex fourth roots of unity (1) and plot them.

62. Find the six complex sixth roots of unity (1) and plot them.

63. Show that each complex nth root of a nonzero complex number w has the same magnitude.

64. Use the result of Problem 63 to draw the conclusion that each complex nth root lies on a circle with center at the origin. What is the radius of this circle?

65. Refer to Problem 64. Show that the complex nth roots of a nonzero complex number w are equally spaced on the circle.

66. Prove equation (6).

67. Mandelbrot Sets

(a) Consider the expression $a_n = (a_{n-1})^2 + z$, where z is some complex number (called the **seed**) and $a_0 = z$. Compute $a_1\,(=a_0^2 + z)$, $a_2\,(=a_1^2 + z)$, $a_3\,(=a_2^2 + z)$, a_4, a_5, and a_6 for the following seeds: $z_1 = 0.1 - 0.4i$, $z_2 = 0.5 + 0.8i$, $z_3 = -0.9 + 0.7i$, $z_4 = -1.1 + 0.1i$, $z_5 = 0 - 1.3i$, and $z_6 = 1 + 1i$.

(b) The dark portion of the graph represents the set of all values $z = x + yi$ that are in the Mandelbrot set. Determine which complex numbers in part (a) are in this

set by plotting them on the graph. Do the complex numbers that are not in the Mandelbrot set have any common characteristics regarding the values of a_6 found in part (a)?

(c) Compute $|z| = \sqrt{x^2 + y^2}$ for each of the complex numbers in part (a). Now compute $|a_6|$ for each of the complex numbers in part (a). For which complex numbers is $|a_6| \le |z|$ and $|z| \le 2$? Conclude that the criterion for a complex number to be in the Mandelbrot set is that $|a_n| \le |z|$ and $|z| \le 2$.

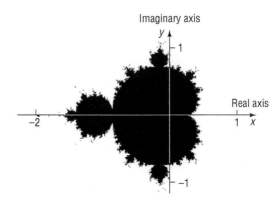

'Are You Prepared?' Answers

1. $-4 + 3i$ **2.** $\sin A \cos B + \cos A \sin B$ **3.** $\cos A \cos B - \sin A \sin B$ **4.** $\dfrac{\sqrt{3}}{2}; -\dfrac{1}{2}$

9.4 Vectors

OBJECTIVES **1** Graph Vectors (p. 592)

2 Find a Position Vector (p. 592)

3 Add and Subtract Vectors Algebraically (p. 594)

4 Find a Scalar Multiple and the Magnitude of a Vector (p. 595)

5 Find a Unit Vector (p. 595)

6 Find a Vector from Its Direction and Magnitude (p. 596)

7 Model with Vectors (p. 597)

In simple terms, a **vector** (derived from the Latin *vehere*, meaning "to carry") is a quantity that has both magnitude and direction. It is customary to represent a vector by using an arrow. The length of the arrow represents the **magnitude** of the vector, and the arrowhead indicates the **direction** of the vector.

Many quantities in physics can be represented by vectors. For example, the velocity of an aircraft can be represented by an arrow that points in the direction of

Figure 40

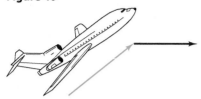

movement; the length of the arrow represents speed. If the aircraft speeds up, we lengthen the arrow; if the aircraft changes direction, we introduce an arrow in the new direction. See Figure 40. Based on this representation, it is not surprising that vectors and *directed line segments* are somehow related.

Geometric Vectors

If P and Q are two distinct points in the xy-plane, there is exactly one line containing both P and Q [Figure 41(a)]. The points on that part of the line that joins P to Q, including P and Q, form what is called the **line segment** $\overline{PQ}$ [Figure 41(b)]. If we order the points so that they proceed from P to Q, we have a **directed line segment** from P to Q, or a **geometric vector,** which we denote by $\overrightarrow{PQ}$. In a directed line segment $\overrightarrow{PQ}$, we call P the **initial point** and Q the **terminal point,** as indicated in Figure 41(c).

Figure 41

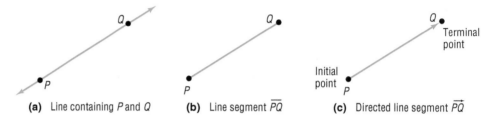

(a) Line containing P and Q **(b)** Line segment $\overline{PQ}$ **(c)** Directed line segment $\overrightarrow{PQ}$

The magnitude of the directed line segment $\overrightarrow{PQ}$ is the distance from the point P to the point Q; that is, it is the length of the line segment. The direction of $\overrightarrow{PQ}$ is from P to Q. If a vector $\mathbf{v}^*$ has the same magnitude and the same direction as the directed line segment $\overrightarrow{PQ}$, we write

$$\mathbf{v} = \overrightarrow{PQ}$$

The vector $\mathbf{v}$ whose magnitude is 0 is called the **zero vector, 0.** The zero vector is assigned no direction.

Two vectors $\mathbf{v}$ and $\mathbf{w}$ are **equal,** written

$$\mathbf{v} = \mathbf{w}$$

if they have the same magnitude and the same direction.

For example, the three vectors shown in Figure 42 have the same magnitude and the same direction, so they are equal, even though they have different initial points and different terminal points. As a result, we find it useful to think of a vector simply as an arrow, keeping in mind that two arrows (vectors) are equal if they have the same direction and the same magnitude (length).

Figure 42

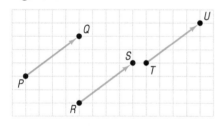

Figure 43

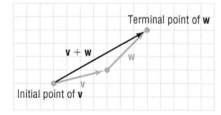

Adding Vectors Geometrically

The **sum** $\mathbf{v} + \mathbf{w}$ of two vectors is defined as follows: We position the vectors $\mathbf{v}$ and $\mathbf{w}$ so that the terminal point of $\mathbf{v}$ coincides with the initial point of $\mathbf{w}$, as shown in Figure 43. The vector $\mathbf{v} + \mathbf{w}$ is then the unique vector whose initial point coincides with the initial point of $\mathbf{v}$ and whose terminal point coincides with the terminal point of $\mathbf{w}$.

Vector addition is **commutative.** That is, if $\mathbf{v}$ and $\mathbf{w}$ are any two vectors, then

$$\mathbf{v} + \mathbf{w} = \mathbf{w} + \mathbf{v}$$

---

* Boldface letters will be used to denote vectors, to distinguish them from numbers. For handwritten work, an arrow is placed over the letter to signify a vector. For example, we write a vector by hand as $\overrightarrow{v}$.

Figure 44

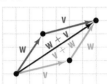

Figure 44 illustrates this fact. (Observe that the commutative property is another way of saying that opposite sides of a parallelogram are equal and parallel.)

Vector addition is also **associative.** That is, if **u**, **v**, and **w** are vectors, then

$$\mathbf{u} + (\mathbf{v} + \mathbf{w}) = (\mathbf{u} + \mathbf{v}) + \mathbf{w}$$

Figure 45
$(\mathbf{u} + \mathbf{v}) + \mathbf{w} = \mathbf{u} + (\mathbf{v} + \mathbf{w})$

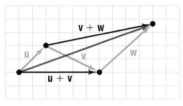

Figure 45 illustrates the associative property for vectors.

The zero vector **0** has the property that

$$\mathbf{v} + \mathbf{0} = \mathbf{0} + \mathbf{v} = \mathbf{v}$$

for any vector **v**.

Figure 46

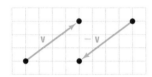

If **v** is a vector, then $-\mathbf{v}$ is the vector having the same magnitude as **v**, but whose direction is opposite to **v**, as shown in Figure 46.
Furthermore,

$$\mathbf{v} + (-\mathbf{v}) = \mathbf{0}$$

Figure 47

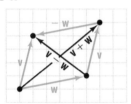

If **v** and **w** are two vectors, we define the **difference v − w** as

$$\mathbf{v} - \mathbf{w} = \mathbf{v} + (-\mathbf{w})$$

Figure 47 illustrates the relationships among **v**, **w**, **v** + **w**, and **v** − **w**.

Multiplying Vectors by Numbers Geometrically

When dealing with vectors, we refer to real numbers as **scalars.** Scalars are quantities that have only magnitude. Examples of scalar quantities from physics are temperature, speed, and time. We now define how to multiply a vector by a scalar.

DEFINITION

If α is a scalar and **v** is a vector, the **scalar multiple** $\alpha\mathbf{v}$ is defined as follows:

1. If $\alpha > 0$, $\alpha\mathbf{v}$ is the vector whose magnitude is α times the magnitude of **v** and whose direction is the same as **v**.
2. If $\alpha < 0$, $\alpha\mathbf{v}$ is the vector whose magnitude is $|\alpha|$ times the magnitude of **v** and whose direction is opposite that of **v**.
3. If $\alpha = 0$ or if $\mathbf{v} = \mathbf{0}$, then $\alpha\mathbf{v} = \mathbf{0}$.

Figure 48

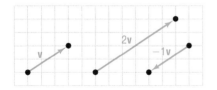

See Figure 48 for some illustrations.
For example, if **a** is the acceleration of an object of mass m due to a force **F** being exerted on it, then, by Newton's second law of motion, $\mathbf{F} = m\mathbf{a}$. Here, $m\mathbf{a}$ is the product of the scalar m and the vector **a**.
Scalar multiples have the following properties:

$$0\mathbf{v} = \mathbf{0} \quad 1\mathbf{v} = \mathbf{v} \quad -1\mathbf{v} = -\mathbf{v}$$
$$(\alpha + \beta)\mathbf{v} = \alpha\mathbf{v} + \beta\mathbf{v} \quad \alpha(\mathbf{v} + \mathbf{w}) = \alpha\mathbf{v} + \alpha\mathbf{w}$$
$$\alpha(\beta\mathbf{v}) = (\alpha\beta)\mathbf{v}$$

1 Graph Vectors

EXAMPLE 1 | **Graphing Vectors**

Use the vectors illustrated in Figure 49 to graph each of the following vectors:

(a) $\mathbf{v} - \mathbf{w}$ (b) $2\mathbf{v} + 3\mathbf{w}$ (c) $2\mathbf{v} - \mathbf{w} + \mathbf{u}$

Solution | Figure 50 illustrates each graph.

Figure 49

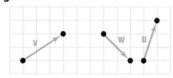

Figure 50

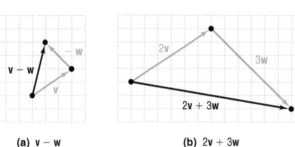

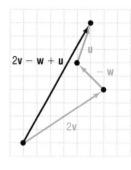

(a) $\mathbf{v} - \mathbf{w}$ (b) $2\mathbf{v} + 3\mathbf{w}$ (c) $2\mathbf{v} - \mathbf{w} + \mathbf{u}$

Now Work PROBLEMS 9 AND 11

Magnitude of a Vector

We use the symbol $\|\mathbf{v}\|$ to represent the **magnitude** of a vector $\mathbf{v}$. Since $\|\mathbf{v}\|$ equals the length of a directed line segment, it follows that $\|\mathbf{v}\|$ has the following properties:

THEOREM | **Properties of $\|\mathbf{v}\|$**

If $\mathbf{v}$ is a vector and if α is a scalar, then

(a) $\|\mathbf{v}\| \geq 0$ (b) $\|\mathbf{v}\| = 0$ if and only if $\mathbf{v} = \mathbf{0}$

(c) $\|-\mathbf{v}\| = \|\mathbf{v}\|$ (d) $\|\alpha\mathbf{v}\| = |\alpha|\|\mathbf{v}\|$

Property (a) is a consequence of the fact that distance is a nonnegative number. Property (b) follows because the length of the directed line segment $\overrightarrow{PQ}$ is positive unless P and Q are the same point, in which case the length is 0. Property (c) follows because the length of the line segment $\overline{PQ}$ equals the length of the line segment $\overline{QP}$. Property (d) is a direct consequence of the definition of a scalar multiple.

DEFINITION | A vector $\mathbf{u}$ for which $\|\mathbf{u}\| = 1$ is called a **unit vector.**

2 Find a Position Vector

To compute the magnitude and direction of a vector, we need an algebraic way of representing vectors.

DEFINITION | An **algebraic vector** $\mathbf{v}$ is represented as

$$\mathbf{v} = \langle a, b \rangle$$

where a and b are real numbers (scalars) called the **components** of the vector $\mathbf{v}$.

Figure 51

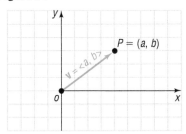

We use a rectangular coordinate system to represent algebraic vectors in the plane. If $\mathbf{v} = \langle a, b \rangle$ is an algebraic vector whose initial point is at the origin, then $\mathbf{v}$ is called a **position vector.** See Figure 51. Notice that the terminal point of the position vector $\mathbf{v} = \langle a, b \rangle$ is $P = (a, b)$.

The next result states that any vector whose initial point is not at the origin is equal to a unique position vector.

THEOREM

Suppose that $\mathbf{v}$ is a vector with initial point $P_1 = (x_1, y_1)$, not necessarily the origin, and terminal point $P_2 = (x_2, y_2)$. If $\mathbf{v} = \overrightarrow{P_1 P_2}$, then $\mathbf{v}$ is equal to the position vector

$$\mathbf{v} = \langle x_2 - x_1, y_2 - y_1 \rangle \tag{1}$$

> **In Words**
>
> An algebraic vector represents "driving directions" to get from the initial point to the terminal point of a vector. So, if $\mathbf{v} = \langle 5, 4 \rangle$, travel 5 units right and 4 units up from the initial point to arrive at the terminal point.

To see why this is true, look at Figure 52.

Figure 52
$\mathbf{v} = \langle a, b \rangle = \langle x_2 - x_1, y_2 - y_1 \rangle$

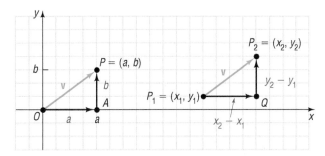

Triangle OPA and triangle $P_1 P_2 Q$ are congruent. [Do you see why? The line segments have the same magnitude, so $d(O, P) = d(P_1, P_2)$; and they have the same direction, so $\angle POA = \angle P_2 P_1 Q$. Since the triangles are right triangles, we have angle–side–angle.] It follows that corresponding sides are equal. As a result, $x_2 - x_1 = a$ and $y_2 - y_1 = b$, so $\mathbf{v}$ may be written as

$$\mathbf{v} = \langle a, b \rangle = \langle x_2 - x_1, y_2 - y_1 \rangle$$

Because of this result, we can replace any algebraic vector by a unique position vector, and vice versa. This flexibility is one of the main reasons for the wide use of vectors.

EXAMPLE 2

Finding a Position Vector

Figure 53

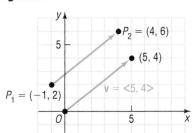

Find the position vector of the vector $\mathbf{v} = \overrightarrow{P_1 P_2}$ if $P_1 = (-1, 2)$ and $P_2 = (4, 6)$.

Solution By equation (1), the position vector equal to $\mathbf{v}$ is

$$\mathbf{v} = \langle 4 - (-1), 6 - 2 \rangle = \langle 5, 4 \rangle$$

See Figure 53.

Two position vectors **v** and **w** are equal if and only if the terminal point of **v** is the same as the terminal point of **w**. This leads to the following result:

THEOREM   **Equality of Vectors**

Two vectors **v** and **w** are equal if and only if their corresponding components are equal. That is,

> If $\mathbf{v} = \langle a_1, b_1 \rangle$ and $\mathbf{w} = \langle a_2, b_2 \rangle$
> then $\mathbf{v} = \mathbf{w}$ if and only if $a_1 = a_2$ and $b_1 = b_2$.

Figure 54

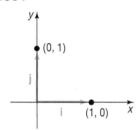

We now present an alternative representation of a vector in the plane that is common in the physical sciences. Let **i** denote the unit vector whose direction is along the positive x-axis; let **j** denote the unit vector whose direction is along the positive y-axis. Then $\mathbf{i} = \langle 1, 0 \rangle$ and $\mathbf{j} = \langle 0, 1 \rangle$, as shown in Figure 54. Any vector $\mathbf{v} = \langle a, b \rangle$ can be written using the unit vectors **i** and **j** as follows:

$$\mathbf{v} = \langle a, b \rangle = a\langle 1, 0 \rangle + b\langle 0, 1 \rangle = a\mathbf{i} + b\mathbf{j}$$

We call a and b the **horizontal** and **vertical components** of **v**, respectively. For example, if $\mathbf{v} = \langle 5, 4 \rangle = 5\mathbf{i} + 4\mathbf{j}$, then 5 is the horizontal component and 4 is the vertical component.

Now Work PROBLEM 29

3 Add and Subtract Vectors Algebraically

We define the sum, difference, scalar multiple, and magnitude of algebraic vectors in terms of their components.

DEFINITION

Let $\mathbf{v} = a_1\mathbf{i} + b_1\mathbf{j} = \langle a_1, b_1 \rangle$ and $\mathbf{w} = a_2\mathbf{i} + b_2\mathbf{j} = \langle a_2, b_2 \rangle$ be two vectors, and let α be a scalar. Then

> $$\mathbf{v} + \mathbf{w} = (a_1 + a_2)\mathbf{i} + (b_1 + b_2)\mathbf{j} = \langle a_1 + a_2, b_1 + b_2 \rangle \qquad (2)$$
> $$\mathbf{v} - \mathbf{w} = (a_1 - a_2)\mathbf{i} + (b_1 - b_2)\mathbf{j} = \langle a_1 - a_2, b_1 - b_2 \rangle \qquad (3)$$
> $$\alpha\mathbf{v} = (\alpha a_1)\mathbf{i} + (\alpha b_1)\mathbf{j} = \langle \alpha a_1, \alpha b_1 \rangle \qquad (4)$$
> $$\|\mathbf{v}\| = \sqrt{a_1^2 + b_1^2} \qquad (5)$$

In Words

To add two vectors, add corresponding components. To subtract two vectors, subtract corresponding components.

These definitions are compatible with the geometric definitions given earlier in this section. See Figure 55.

Figure 55

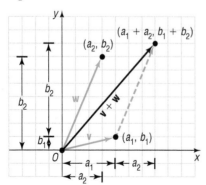

(a) Illustration of property (2)

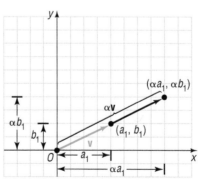

(b) Illustration of property (4), $\alpha > 0$

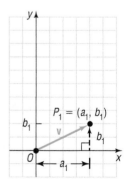

(c) Illustration of property (5):
$\|\mathbf{v}\|$ = Distance from O to P_1
$\|\mathbf{v}\| = \sqrt{a_1^2 + b_1^2}$

EXAMPLE 3

Adding and Subtracting Vectors

If $\mathbf{v} = 2\mathbf{i} + 3\mathbf{j} = \langle 2, 3 \rangle$ and $\mathbf{w} = 3\mathbf{i} - 4\mathbf{j} = \langle 3, -4 \rangle$, find:

(a) $\mathbf{v} + \mathbf{w}$ (b) $\mathbf{v} - \mathbf{w}$

Solution

(a) $\mathbf{v} + \mathbf{w} = (2\mathbf{i} + 3\mathbf{j}) + (3\mathbf{i} - 4\mathbf{j}) = (2 + 3)\mathbf{i} + (3 - 4)\mathbf{j} = 5\mathbf{i} - \mathbf{j}$

or

$\mathbf{v} + \mathbf{w} = \langle 2, 3 \rangle + \langle 3, -4 \rangle = \langle 2 + 3, 3 + (-4) \rangle = \langle 5, -1 \rangle$

(b) $\mathbf{v} - \mathbf{w} = (2\mathbf{i} + 3\mathbf{j}) - (3\mathbf{i} - 4\mathbf{j}) = (2 - 3)\mathbf{i} + [3 - (-4)]\mathbf{j} = -\mathbf{i} + 7\mathbf{j}$

or

$\mathbf{v} - \mathbf{w} = \langle 2, 3 \rangle - \langle 3, -4 \rangle = \langle 2 - 3, 3 - (-4) \rangle = \langle -1, 7 \rangle$

4 Find a Scalar Multiple and the Magnitude of a Vector

EXAMPLE 4

Finding Scalar Multiples and Magnitudes of Vectors

If $\mathbf{v} = 2\mathbf{i} + 3\mathbf{j} = \langle 2, 3 \rangle$ and $\mathbf{w} = 3\mathbf{i} - 4\mathbf{j} = \langle 3, -4 \rangle$, find:

(a) $3\mathbf{v}$ (b) $2\mathbf{v} - 3\mathbf{w}$ (c) $\|\mathbf{v}\|$

Solution

(a) $3\mathbf{v} = 3(2\mathbf{i} + 3\mathbf{j}) = 6\mathbf{i} + 9\mathbf{j}$

or

$3\mathbf{v} = 3\langle 2, 3 \rangle = \langle 6, 9 \rangle$

(b) $2\mathbf{v} - 3\mathbf{w} = 2(2\mathbf{i} + 3\mathbf{j}) - 3(3\mathbf{i} - 4\mathbf{j}) = 4\mathbf{i} + 6\mathbf{j} - 9\mathbf{i} + 12\mathbf{j}$

$= -5\mathbf{i} + 18\mathbf{j}$

or

$2\mathbf{v} - 3\mathbf{w} = 2\langle 2, 3 \rangle - 3\langle 3, -4 \rangle = \langle 4, 6 \rangle - \langle 9, -12 \rangle$

$= \langle 4 - 9, 6 - (-12) \rangle = \langle -5, 18 \rangle$

(c) $\|\mathbf{v}\| = \|2\mathbf{i} + 3\mathbf{j}\| = \sqrt{2^2 + 3^2} = \sqrt{13}$

━━━━━**Now Work** PROBLEMS 35 AND 41

For the remainder of the section, we will express a vector $\mathbf{v}$ in the form $a\mathbf{i} + b\mathbf{j}$.

5 Find a Unit Vector

Recall that a unit vector $\mathbf{u}$ is a vector for which $\|\mathbf{u}\| = 1$. In many applications, it is useful to be able to find a unit vector $\mathbf{u}$ that has the same direction as a given vector $\mathbf{v}$.

THEOREM

Unit Vector in the Direction of v

For any nonzero vector $\mathbf{v}$, the vector

$$\mathbf{u} = \frac{\mathbf{v}}{\|\mathbf{v}\|}$$

is a unit vector that has the same direction as $\mathbf{v}$.

Proof Let $\mathbf{v} = a\mathbf{i} + b\mathbf{j}$. Then $\|\mathbf{v}\| = \sqrt{a^2 + b^2}$ and

$$\mathbf{u} = \frac{\mathbf{v}}{\|\mathbf{v}\|} = \frac{a\mathbf{i} + b\mathbf{j}}{\sqrt{a^2 + b^2}} = \frac{a}{\sqrt{a^2 + b^2}}\mathbf{i} + \frac{b}{\sqrt{a^2 + b^2}}\mathbf{j}$$

The vector **u** is in the same direction as **v**, since $\|\mathbf{v}\| > 0$. Furthermore,

$$\|\mathbf{u}\| = \sqrt{\frac{a^2}{a^2 + b^2} + \frac{b^2}{a^2 + b^2}} = \sqrt{\frac{a^2 + b^2}{a^2 + b^2}} = 1$$

That is, **u** is a unit vector in the direction of **v**. ∎

As a consequence of this theorem, if **u** is a unit vector in the same direction as a vector **v**, then **v** may be expressed as

$$\mathbf{v} = \|\mathbf{v}\|\mathbf{u} \qquad (6)$$

This way of expressing a vector is useful in many applications.

EXAMPLE 5

Finding a Unit Vector

Find a unit vector in the same direction as $\mathbf{v} = 4\mathbf{i} - 3\mathbf{j}$.

Solution   We find $\|\mathbf{v}\|$ first.

$$\|\mathbf{v}\| = \|4\mathbf{i} - 3\mathbf{j}\| = \sqrt{16 + 9} = 5$$

Now we multiply **v** by the scalar $\dfrac{1}{\|\mathbf{v}\|} = \dfrac{1}{5}$. A unit vector in the same direction as **v** is

$$\frac{\mathbf{v}}{\|\mathbf{v}\|} = \frac{4\mathbf{i} - 3\mathbf{j}}{5} = \frac{4}{5}\mathbf{i} - \frac{3}{5}\mathbf{j}$$

✓**Check:** This vector is, in fact, a unit vector because

$$\left(\frac{4}{5}\right)^2 + \left(-\frac{3}{5}\right)^2 = \frac{16}{25} + \frac{9}{25} = \frac{25}{25} = 1$$

⏎

══**Now Work** PROBLEM 51

---

6 Find a Vector from Its Direction and Magnitude

If a vector represents the speed and direction of an object, it is called a **velocity vector**. If a vector represents the direction and amount of a force acting on an object, it is called a **force vector**. In many applications, a vector is described in terms of its magnitude and direction, rather than in terms of its components. For example, a ball thrown with an initial speed of 25 miles per hour at an angle of 30° to the horizontal is a velocity vector.

Suppose that we are given the magnitude $\|\mathbf{v}\|$ of a nonzero vector **v** and the **direction angle** α, $0° \le \alpha < 360°$, between **v** and **i**. To express **v** in terms of $\|\mathbf{v}\|$ and α, first find the unit vector **u** having the same direction as **v**.

$$\mathbf{u} = \frac{\mathbf{v}}{\|\mathbf{v}\|} \quad \text{or} \quad \mathbf{v} = \|\mathbf{v}\|\mathbf{u} \qquad (7)$$

Figure 56

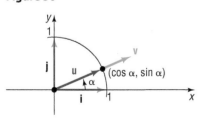

Look at Figure 56. The coordinates of the terminal point of **u** are $(\cos\alpha, \sin\alpha)$. Then $\mathbf{u} = \cos\alpha\,\mathbf{i} + \sin\alpha\,\mathbf{j}$ and, from (7),

$$\mathbf{v} = \|\mathbf{v}\|(\cos\alpha\,\mathbf{i} + \sin\alpha\,\mathbf{j}) \qquad (8)$$

where α is the direction angle between **v** and **i**.

EXAMPLE 6 | **Writing a Vector When Its Magnitude and Direction Are Given**

A ball is thrown with an initial speed of 25 miles per hour in a direction that makes an angle of 30° with the positive x-axis. Express the velocity vector **v** in terms of **i** and **j**. What is the initial speed in the horizontal direction? What is the initial speed in the vertical direction?

Solution

The magnitude of **v** is $\|\mathbf{v}\| = 25$ miles per hour, and the angle between the direction of **v** and **i**, the positive x-axis, is $\alpha = 30°$. By equation (8),

Figure 57

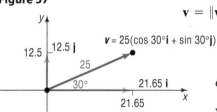

$$\mathbf{v} = \|\mathbf{v}\|(\cos \alpha \mathbf{i} + \sin \alpha \mathbf{j}) = 25(\cos 30°\mathbf{i} + \sin 30°\mathbf{j}) = 25\left(\frac{\sqrt{3}}{2}\mathbf{i} + \frac{1}{2}\mathbf{j}\right) = \frac{25\sqrt{3}}{2}\mathbf{i} + \frac{25}{2}\mathbf{j}$$

The initial speed of the ball in the horizontal direction is the horizontal component of **v**, $\frac{25\sqrt{3}}{2} \approx 21.65$ miles per hour. The initial speed in the vertical direction is the vertical component of **v**, $\frac{25}{2} = 12.5$ miles per hour. See Figure 57.

➤ **Now Work** PROBLEM 57

EXAMPLE 7 | **Finding the Direction Angle of a Vector**

Find the direction angle α of $\mathbf{v} = 4\mathbf{i} - 4\mathbf{j}$.

Figure 58

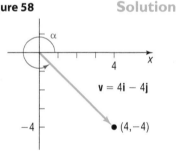

Solution

See Figure 58. The direction angle α of $\mathbf{v} = 4\mathbf{i} - 4\mathbf{j}$ can be found by solving

$$\tan \alpha = \frac{-4}{4} = -1$$

Because $0° \le \alpha < 360°$, the direction angle is $\alpha = 315°$.

➤ **Now Work** PROBLEM 63

Figure 59

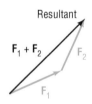

7 Model with Vectors

Because forces can be represented by vectors, two forces "combine" the way that vectors "add." If $\mathbf{F}_1$ and $\mathbf{F}_2$ are two forces simultaneously acting on an object, the vector sum $\mathbf{F}_1 + \mathbf{F}_2$ is the **resultant force.** The resultant force produces the same effect on the object as that obtained when the two forces $\mathbf{F}_1$ and $\mathbf{F}_2$ act on the object. See Figure 59.

EXAMPLE 8 | **Finding the Actual Speed and Direction of an Aircraft**

A Boeing 737 aircraft maintains a constant airspeed of 500 miles per hour headed due south. The jet stream is 80 miles per hour in the northeasterly direction.

(a) Express the velocity $\mathbf{v}_a$ of the 737 relative to the air and the velocity $\mathbf{v}_w$ of the jet stream in terms of **i** and **j**.

(b) Find the velocity of the 737 relative to the ground.

(c) Find the actual speed and direction of the 737 relative to the ground.

Solution

Figure 60

(a) Set up a coordinate system in which north (N) is along the positive y-axis. See Figure 60. The velocity of the 737 relative to the air is $\mathbf{v}_a = -500\mathbf{j}$. The velocity of the jet stream $\mathbf{v}_w$ has magnitude 80 and direction NE (northeast), so the angle between $\mathbf{v}_w$ and $\mathbf{i}$ is 45°. We express $\mathbf{v}_w$ in terms of $\mathbf{i}$ and $\mathbf{j}$ as

$$\mathbf{v}_w = 80(\cos 45° \mathbf{i} + \sin 45° \mathbf{j}) = 80\left(\frac{\sqrt{2}}{2}\mathbf{i} + \frac{\sqrt{2}}{2}\mathbf{j}\right) = 40\sqrt{2}(\mathbf{i} + \mathbf{j})$$

(b) The velocity of the 737 relative to the ground $\mathbf{v}_g$ is

$$\mathbf{v}_g = \mathbf{v}_a + \mathbf{v}_w = -500\mathbf{j} + 40\sqrt{2}(\mathbf{i} + \mathbf{j}) = 40\sqrt{2}\mathbf{i} + \left(40\sqrt{2} - 500\right)\mathbf{j}$$

(c) The actual speed of the 737 is

$$\|\mathbf{v}_g\| = \sqrt{\left(40\sqrt{2}\right)^2 + \left(40\sqrt{2} - 500\right)^2} \approx 447 \text{ miles per hour}$$

To find the actual direction of the 737 relative to the ground, determine the direction angle of $\mathbf{v}_g$. The direction angle is found by solving

$$\tan \alpha = \frac{40\sqrt{2} - 500}{40\sqrt{2}}$$

Then $\alpha \approx -82.7°$. The 737 is traveling S7.3°E.

─────**Now Work** PROBLEM 77

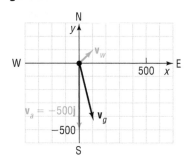

EXAMPLE 9 | **Finding the Weight of a Piano**

Two movers require a magnitude of force of 300 pounds to push a piano up a ramp inclined at an angle 20° from the horizontal. How much does the piano weigh?

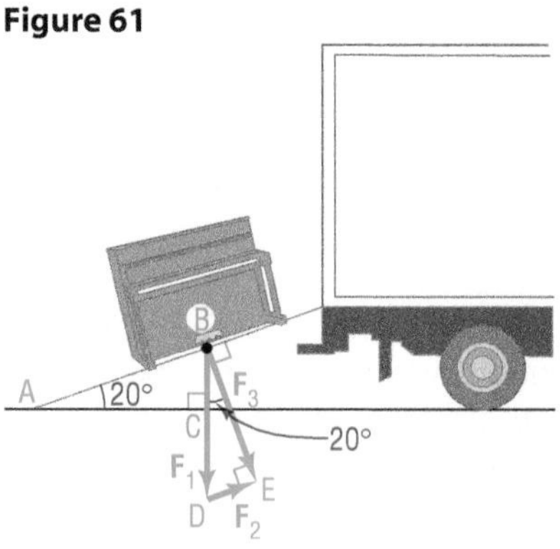

Solution

Let $\mathbf{F}_1$ represent the force of gravity, $\mathbf{F}_2$ represent the force required to move the piano up the ramp, and $\mathbf{F}_3$ represent the force of the piano against the ramp. See Figure 61. The angle between the ground and the ramp is the same as the angle between $\mathbf{F}_1$ and $\mathbf{F}_3$ because triangles ABC and BDE are similar, so $\angle BAC = \angle DBE = 20°$. We wish to find the magnitude of $\mathbf{F}_1$. So,

Figure 61

$$\sin 20° = \frac{\|\mathbf{F}_2\|}{\|\mathbf{F}_1\|} = \frac{300}{\|\mathbf{F}_1\|}$$

$$\|\mathbf{F}_1\| = \frac{300 \text{ lb}}{\sin 20°} \approx 877 \text{ lb}$$

The piano weighs approximately 877 pounds.

An object is said to be in **static equilibrium** if (1) the object is at rest and (2) the sum of all forces acting on the object is zero, that is, if the resultant force is 0.

EXAMPLE 10 | **An Object in Static Equilibrium**

A box of supplies that weighs 1200 pounds is suspended by two cables attached to the ceiling, as shown in Figure 62. What are the tensions in the two cables?

Solution

Draw a force diagram using the vectors shown in Figure 63. The tensions in the cables are the magnitudes $\|\mathbf{F}_1\|$ and $\|\mathbf{F}_2\|$ of the force vectors $\mathbf{F}_1$ and $\mathbf{F}_2$. The magnitude of the force vector $\mathbf{F}_3$ equals 1200 pounds, the weight of the box. Now write each force vector in terms of the unit vectors $\mathbf{i}$ and $\mathbf{j}$. For $\mathbf{F}_1$ and $\mathbf{F}_2$, we use equation (8). Remember that α is the angle between the vector and the positive x-axis.

Figure 62

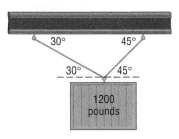

Figure 63

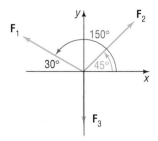

$$F_1 = \|F_1\|(\cos 150°i + \sin 150°j) = \|F_1\|\left(-\frac{\sqrt{3}}{2}i + \frac{1}{2}j\right) = -\frac{\sqrt{3}}{2}\|F_1\|i + \frac{1}{2}\|F_1\|j$$

$$F_2 = \|F_2\|(\cos 45°i + \sin 45°j) = \|F_2\|\left(\frac{\sqrt{2}}{2}i + \frac{\sqrt{2}}{2}j\right) = \frac{\sqrt{2}}{2}\|F_2\|i + \frac{\sqrt{2}}{2}\|F_2\|j$$

$$F_3 = -1200j$$

For static equilibrium, the sum of the force vectors must equal zero.

$$F_1 + F_2 + F_3 = -\frac{\sqrt{3}}{2}\|F_1\|i + \frac{1}{2}\|F_1\|j + \frac{\sqrt{2}}{2}\|F_2\|i + \frac{\sqrt{2}}{2}\|F_2\|j - 1200j = 0$$

The **i** component and **j** component will each equal zero. This results in the two equations

$$-\frac{\sqrt{3}}{2}\|F_1\| + \frac{\sqrt{2}}{2}\|F_2\| = 0 \qquad \textbf{(9)}$$

$$\frac{1}{2}\|F_1\| + \frac{\sqrt{2}}{2}\|F_2\| - 1200 = 0 \qquad \textbf{(10)}$$

We solve equation (9) for $\|F_2\|$ and obtain

$$\|F_2\| = \frac{\sqrt{3}}{\sqrt{2}}\|F_1\| \qquad \textbf{(11)}$$

Substituting into equation (10) and solving for $\|F_1\|$, we obtain

$$\frac{1}{2}\|F_1\| + \frac{\sqrt{2}}{2}\left(\frac{\sqrt{3}}{\sqrt{2}}\|F_1\|\right) - 1200 = 0$$

$$\frac{1}{2}\|F_1\| + \frac{\sqrt{3}}{2}\|F_1\| - 1200 = 0$$

$$\frac{1 + \sqrt{3}}{2}\|F_1\| = 1200$$

$$\|F_1\| = \frac{2400}{1 + \sqrt{3}} \approx 878.5 \text{ pounds}$$

Substituting this value into equation (11) yields $\|F_2\|$.

$$\|F_2\| = \frac{\sqrt{3}}{\sqrt{2}}\|F_1\| = \frac{\sqrt{3}}{\sqrt{2}} \cdot \frac{2400}{1 + \sqrt{3}} \approx 1075.9 \text{ pounds}$$

The left cable has tension of approximately 878.5 pounds and the right cable has tension of approximately 1075.9 pounds.

Now Work PROBLEM **85**

Historical Feature

*Josiah Gibbs
(1839–1903)*

The history of vectors is surprisingly complicated for such a natural concept. In the *xy*-plane, complex numbers do a good job of imitating vectors. About 1840, mathematicians became interested in finding a system that would do for three dimensions what the complex numbers do for two dimensions. Hermann Grassmann (1809–1877), in Germany, and William Rowan Hamilton (1805–1865), in Ireland, both attempted to find solutions.

Hamilton's system was the *quaternions*, which are best thought of as a real number plus a vector, and do for four dimensions what complex numbers do for two dimensions. In this system the order of multiplication matters; that is, **ab** ≠ **ba**. Also, two products of

vectors emerged, the scalar (or dot) product and the vector (or cross) product.

Grassmann's abstract style, although easily read today, was almost impenetrable during the previous century, and only a few of his ideas were appreciated. Among those few were the same scalar and vector products that Hamilton had found.

About 1880, the American physicist Josiah Willard Gibbs (1839–1903) worked out an algebra involving only the simplest concepts: the vectors and the two products. He then added some calculus, and the resulting system was simple, flexible, and well adapted to expressing a large number of physical laws. This system remains in use essentially unchanged. Hamilton's and Grassmann's more extensive systems each gave birth to much interesting mathematics, but little of this mathematics is seen at elementary levels.

9.4 Assess Your Understanding

Concepts and Vocabulary

1. A _____ is a quantity that has both magnitude and direction.

2. If **v** is a vector, then **v** + (−**v**) = _____.

3. A vector **u** for which ∥**u**∥ = 1 is called a(n) _____ vector.

4. If **v** = <*a*, *b*> is an algebraic vector whose initial point is the origin, then **v** is called a(n) _____ vector.

5. If **v** = *a***i** + *b***j**, then *a* is called the _____ component of **v** and *b* is called the _____ component of **v**.

6. If **F**₁ and **F**₂ are two forces simultaneously acting on an object, the vector sum **F**₁ + **F**₂ is called the _____ force.

7. *True or False* Force is an example of a vector.

8. *True or False* Mass is an example of a vector.

Skill Building

In Problems 9–16, use the vectors in the figure at the right to graph each of the following vectors.

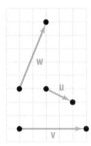

9. **v** + **w**

10. **u** + **v**

11. 3**v**

12. 4**w**

13. **v** − **w**

14. **u** − **v**

15. 3**v** + **u** − 2**w**

16. 2**u** − 3**v** + **w**

In Problems 17–24, use the figure at the right. Determine whether the given statement is true or false.

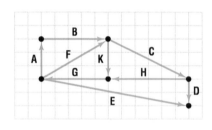

17. **A** + **B** = **F**

18. **K** + **G** = **F**

19. **C** = **D** − **E** + **F**

20. **G** + **H** + **E** = **D**

21. **E** + **D** = **G** + **H**

22. **H** − **C** = **G** − **F**

23. **A** + **B** + **K** + **G** = 0

24. **A** + **B** + **C** + **H** + **G** = 0

25. If ∥**v**∥ = 4, what is ∥3**v**∥?

26. If ∥**v**∥ = 2, what is ∥−4**v**∥?

*In Problems 27–34, the vector **v** has initial point P and terminal point Q. Write **v** in the form a**i** + b**j**; that is, find its position vector.*

27. *P* = (0, 0); *Q* = (3, 4)

28. *P* = (0, 0); *Q* = (−3, −5)

29. *P* = (3, 2); *Q* = (5, 6)

30. *P* = (−3, 2); *Q* = (6, 5)

31. *P* = (−2, −1); *Q* = (6, −2)

32. *P* = (−1, 4); *Q* = (6, 2)

33. *P* = (1, 0); *Q* = (0, 1)

34. *P* = (1, 1); *Q* = (2, 2)

*In Problems 35–40, find ∥**v**∥.*

35. **v** = 3**i** − 4**j**

36. **v** = −5**i** + 12**j**

37. **v** = **i** − **j**

38. **v** = −**i** − **j**

39. **v** = −2**i** + 3**j**

40. **v** = 6**i** + 2**j**

*In Problems 41–46, find each quantity if **v** = 3**i** − 5**j** and **w** = −2**i** + 3**j**.*

41. 2**v** + 3**w**

42. 3**v** − 2**w**

43. ∥**v** − **w**∥

44. ∥**v** + **w**∥

45. ∥**v**∥ − ∥**w**∥

46. ∥**v**∥ + ∥**w**∥

*In Problems 47–52, find the unit vector in the same direction as **v**.*

47. **v** = 5**i**

48. **v** = −3**j**

49. **v** = 3**i** − 4**j**

50. **v** = −5**i** + 12**j**

51. **v** = **i** − **j**

52. **v** = 2**i** − **j**

53. Find a vector **v** whose magnitude is 4 and whose component in the **i** direction is twice the component in the **j** direction.

54. Find a vector **v** whose magnitude is 3 and whose component in the **i** direction is equal to the component in the **j** direction.

55. If **v** = 2**i** − **j** and **w** = x**i** + 3**j**, find all numbers x for which ‖**v** + **w**‖ = 5.

56. If P = (−3, 1) and Q = (x, 4), find all numbers x such that the vector represented by $\overrightarrow{PQ}$ has length 5.

In Problems 57–62, write the vector **v** *in the form a***i** + *b***j**, *given its magnitude* ‖**v**‖ *and the angle* α *it makes with the positive x-axis.*

57. ‖**v**‖ = 5, α = 60°

58. ‖**v**‖ = 8, α = 45°

59. ‖**v**‖ = 14, α = 120°

60. ‖**v**‖ = 3, α = 240°

61. ‖**v**‖ = 25, α = 330°

62. ‖**v**‖ = 15, α = 315°

In Problems 63–70, find the direction angle of **v** *for each vector.*

63. **v** = 3**i** + 3**j**

64. **v** = **i** + $\sqrt{3}$**j**

65. **v** = −3$\sqrt{3}$**i** + 3**j**

66. **v** = −5**i** − 5**j**

67. **v** = 4**i** − 2**j**

68. **v** = 6**i** − 4**j**

69. **v** = −**i** − 5**j**

70. **v** = −**i** + 3**j**

Applications and Extensions

71. Computer Graphics The field of computer graphics utilizes vectors to compute translations of points. For example, if the point (−3, 2) is to be translated by **v** = ⟨5, 2⟩, then the new location will be **u′** = **u** + **v** = ⟨−3, 2⟩ + ⟨5, 2⟩ = ⟨2, 4⟩. As illustrated in the figure, the point (−3, 2) is translated to (2, 4) by **v**.

Source: Phil Dadd, Vectors and Matrices: A Primer.
www.gamedev.net/reference/articles/article1832.asp

(a) Determine the new coordinates of (3, −1) if it is translated by **v** = ⟨−4, 5⟩.

(b) Illustrate this translation graphically.

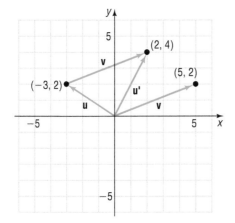

72. Computer Graphics Refer to Problem 71. The points (−3, 0), (−1, −2), (3, 1), and (1, 3) are the vertices of a parallelogram ABCD.

(a) Find the new vertices of a parallelogram A′B′C′D′ if it is translated by **v** = ⟨3, −2⟩.

(b) Find the new vertices of a parallelogram A′B′C′D′ if it is translated by $-\frac{1}{2}$**v**.

73. Force Vectors A child pulls a wagon with a force of 40 pounds. The handle of the wagon makes an angle of 30° with the ground. Express the force vector **F** in terms of **i** and **j**.

74. Force Vectors A man pushes a wheelbarrow up an incline of 20° with a force of 100 pounds. Express the force vector **F** in terms of **i** and **j**.

75. Resultant Force Two forces of magnitude 40 newtons (N) and 60 N act on an object at angles of 30° and −45° with the positive x-axis, as shown in the figure. Find the direction and magnitude of the resultant force; that is, find **F**₁ + **F**₂.

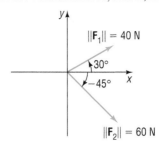

76. Resultant Force Two forces of magnitude 30 newtons (N) and 70 N act on an object at angles of 45° and 120° with the positive x-axis, as shown in the figure. Find the direction and magnitude of the resultant force; that is, find **F**₁ + **F**₂.

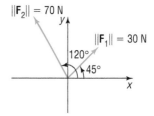

77. Finding the Actual Speed and Direction of an Aircraft A Boeing 747 jumbo jet maintains a constant airspeed of 550 miles per hour (mi/hr) headed due north. The jet stream is 100 mi/hr in the northeasterly direction.

(a) Express the velocity **v**ₐ of the 747 relative to the air and the velocity **v**ᵥᵥ of the jet stream in terms of **i** and **j**.

(b) Find the velocity of the 747 relative to the ground.

(c) Find the acutal speed and direction of the 747 relative to the ground.

78. Finding the Actual Speed and Direction of an Aircraft An Airbus A320 jet maintains a constant airspeed of 500 mi/hr headed due west. The jet stream is 100 mi/hr in the southeasterly direction.

(a) Express the velocity **v**ₐ of the A320 relative to the air and the velocity **v**ᵥᵥ of the jet stream in terms of **i** and **j**.

(b) Find the velocity of the A320 relative to the ground.

(c) Find the actual speed and direction of the A320 relative to the ground.

79. Ground Speed and Direction of an Airplane An airplane has an airspeed of 500 kilometers per hour (km/hr) bearing N45°E. The wind velocity is 60 km/hr in the direction N30°W. Find the resultant vector representing the path of the plane relative to the ground. What is the ground speed of the plane? What is its direction?

80. Ground Speed and Direction of an Airplane An airplane has an airspeed of 600 km/hr bearing S30°E. The wind velocity is 40 km/hr in the direction S45°E. Find the resultant vector representing the path of the plane relative to the ground. What is the ground speed of the plane? What is its direction?

81. Weight of a Boat A magnitude of 700 pounds of force is required to hold a boat and its trailer in place on a ramp whose incline is 10° to the horizontal. What is the combined weight of the boat and its trailer?

82. Weight of a Car A magnitude of 1200 pounds of force is required to prevent a car from rolling down a hill whose incline is 15° to the horizontal. What is the weight of the car?

83. Correct Direction for Crossing a River A river has a constant current of 3 km/hr. At what angle to a boat dock should a motorboat capable of maintaining a constant speed of 20 km/hr be headed in order to reach a point directly opposite the dock? If the river is $\frac{1}{2}$ kilometer wide, how long will it take to cross?

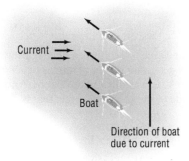

84. Finding the Correct Compass Heading The pilot of an aircraft wishes to head directly east, but is faced with a wind speed of 40 mi/hr from the northwest. If the pilot maintains an airspeed of 250 mi/hr, what compass heading should be maintained to head directly east? What is the actual speed of the aircarft

85. Static Equilibrium A weight of 1000 pounds is suspended from two cables as shown in the figure. What are the tensions in the two cables?

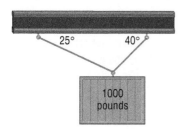

86. Static Equilibrium A weight of 800 pounds is suspended from two cables, as shown in the figure. What are the tensions in the two cables?

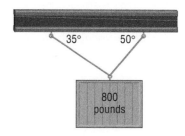

87. Static Equilibrium A tightrope walker located at a certain point deflects the rope as indicated in the figure. If the weight of the tightrope walker is 150 pounds, how much tension is in each part of the rope?

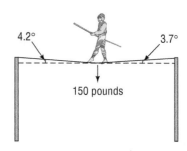

88. Static Equilibrium Repeat Problem 87 if the angle on the left is 3.8°, the angle on the right is 2.6°, and the weight of the tightrope walker is 135 pounds.

89. Truck Pull At a county fair truck pull, two pickup trucks are attached to the back end of a monster truck as illustrated in the figure. One of the pickups pulls with a force of 2000 pounds and the other pulls with a force of 3000 pounds with an angle of 45° between them. With how much force must the monster truck pull in order to remain unmoved?

[Hint: Find the resultant force of the two trucks.]

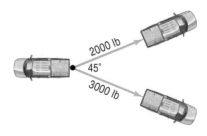

90. Removing a Stump A farmer wishes to remove a stump from a field by pulling it out with his tractor. Having removed many stumps before, he estimates that he will need 6 tons (12,000 pounds) of force to remove the stump. However, his tractor is only capable of pulling with a force of 7000 pounds, so he asks his neighbor to help. His neighbor's tractor can pull with a force of 5500 pounds. They attach the two tractors to the stump with a 40° angle between the forces as shown in the figure.

(a) Assuming the farmer's estimate of a needed 6-ton force is correct, will the farmer be successful in removing the stump? Explain.

(b) Had the farmer arranged the tractors with a 25° angle between the forces, would he have been successful in removing the stump? Explain.

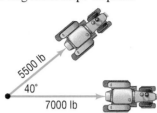

5500 lb
40°
7000 lb

91. Static Equilibrium Show on the following graph the force needed for the object at P to be in static equilibrium.

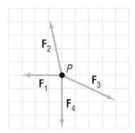

Interactive Exercises

Visualizing Vectors

92. *Open the Vectors applet.* Draw the directed line segment from $P_1 = (1, 2)$ to $P_2 = (5, 4)$. Then draw the position vector $\mathbf{v} = \overrightarrow{P_1P_2}$.

93. *Open the Vectors applet.* Suppose $\mathbf{v} = 2\mathbf{i} + 3\mathbf{j}$ and $\mathbf{w} = 4\mathbf{i} - 3\mathbf{j}$.

(a) Draw $\mathbf{v}$ and then use the red vector to show $3\mathbf{v}$.
(b) Use the red vector to show $-\mathbf{v}$.
(c) Draw $\mathbf{v}$ and $\mathbf{w}$. Then use the red vector to show $\mathbf{v} + \mathbf{w}$.
(d) Use the red vector to show $\mathbf{v} - \mathbf{w}$.
(e) Use the red vector to show $2\mathbf{v} + \mathbf{w}$.

Explaining Concepts: Discussion and Writing

94. Explain in your own words what a vector is. Give an example of a vector.

95. Write a brief paragraph comparing the algebra of complex numbers and the algebra of vectors.

96. Explain the difference between an algebraic vector and a position vector.

9.5 The Dot Product

PREPARING FOR THIS SECTION *Before getting started, review the following:*

- Law of Cosines (Section 8.3, p. 528)

Now Work the 'Are You Prepared?' problem on page 609.

OBJECTIVES   **1** Find the Dot Product of Two Vectors (p. 603)
              2 Find the Angle between Two Vectors (p. 604)
              3 Determine Whether Two Vectors Are Parallel (p. 605)
              4 Determine Whether Two Vectors Are Orthogonal (p. 605)
              5 Decompose a Vector into Two Orthogonal Vectors (p. 606)
              6 Compute Work (p. 608)

1 Find the Dot Product of Two Vectors

The definition for a product of two vectors is somewhat unexpected. However, such a product has meaning in many geometric and physical applications.

DEFINITION If $\mathbf{v} = a_1\mathbf{i} + b_1\mathbf{j}$ and $\mathbf{w} = a_2\mathbf{i} + b_2\mathbf{j}$ are two vectors, the **dot product** $\mathbf{v} \cdot \mathbf{w}$ is defined as

$$\mathbf{v} \cdot \mathbf{w} = a_1a_2 + b_1b_2 \qquad \textbf{(1)}$$

EXAMPLE 1   **Finding Dot Products**

If $\mathbf{v} = 2\mathbf{i} - 3\mathbf{j}$ and $\mathbf{w} = 5\mathbf{i} + 3\mathbf{j}$, find:

(a) $\mathbf{v} \cdot \mathbf{w}$ (b) $\mathbf{w} \cdot \mathbf{v}$ (c) $\mathbf{v} \cdot \mathbf{v}$ (d) $\mathbf{w} \cdot \mathbf{w}$ (e) $\|\mathbf{v}\|$ (f) $\|\mathbf{w}\|$

Solution

(a) $\mathbf{v} \cdot \mathbf{w} = 2(5) + (-3)3 = 1$
(b) $\mathbf{w} \cdot \mathbf{v} = 5(2) + 3(-3) = 1$
(c) $\mathbf{v} \cdot \mathbf{v} = 2(2) + (-3)(-3) = 13$
(d) $\mathbf{w} \cdot \mathbf{w} = 5(5) + 3(3) = 34$
(e) $\|\mathbf{v}\| = \sqrt{2^2 + (-3)^2} = \sqrt{13}$
(f) $\|\mathbf{w}\| = \sqrt{5^2 + 3^2} = \sqrt{34}$

COMMENT A scalar multiple $\alpha\mathbf{v}$ is a vector. A dot product $\mathbf{u} \cdot \mathbf{v}$ is a scalar (real number). ■

Since the dot product $\mathbf{v} \cdot \mathbf{w}$ of two vectors $\mathbf{v}$ and $\mathbf{w}$ is a real number (scalar), we sometimes refer to it as the **scalar product.**

The results obtained in Example 1 suggest some general properties.

THEOREM

Properties of the Dot Product

If $\mathbf{u}$, $\mathbf{v}$, and $\mathbf{w}$ are vectors, then

Commutative Property

$$\mathbf{u} \cdot \mathbf{v} = \mathbf{v} \cdot \mathbf{u} \qquad (2)$$

Distributive Property

$$\mathbf{u} \cdot (\mathbf{v} + \mathbf{w}) = \mathbf{u} \cdot \mathbf{v} + \mathbf{u} \cdot \mathbf{w} \qquad (3)$$

$$\mathbf{v} \cdot \mathbf{v} = \|\mathbf{v}\|^2 \qquad (4)$$

$$\mathbf{0} \cdot \mathbf{v} = 0 \qquad (5)$$

Proof We prove properties (2) and (4) here and leave properties (3) and (5) as exercises (see Problems 34 and 35).

To prove property (2), let $\mathbf{u} = a_1\mathbf{i} + b_1\mathbf{j}$ and $\mathbf{v} = a_2\mathbf{i} + b_2\mathbf{j}$. Then

$$\mathbf{u} \cdot \mathbf{v} = a_1a_2 + b_1b_2 = a_2a_1 + b_2b_1 = \mathbf{v} \cdot \mathbf{u}$$

To prove property (4), let $\mathbf{v} = a\mathbf{i} + b\mathbf{j}$. Then

$$\mathbf{v} \cdot \mathbf{v} = a^2 + b^2 = \|\mathbf{v}\|^2 \qquad ■$$

2 Find the Angle between Two Vectors

One use of the dot product is to calculate the angle between two vectors. We proceed as follows.

Let $\mathbf{u}$ and $\mathbf{v}$ be two vectors with the same initial point A. Then the vectors $\mathbf{u}$, $\mathbf{v}$, and $\mathbf{u} - \mathbf{v}$ form a triangle. The angle θ at vertex A of the triangle is the angle between the vectors $\mathbf{u}$ and $\mathbf{v}$. See Figure 64. We wish to find a formula for calculating the angle θ.

Figure 64

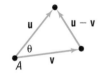

The sides of the triangle have lengths $\|\mathbf{v}\|$, $\|\mathbf{u}\|$, and $\|\mathbf{u} - \mathbf{v}\|$, and θ is the included angle between the sides of length $\|\mathbf{v}\|$ and $\|\mathbf{u}\|$. The Law of Cosines (Section 8.3) can be used to find the cosine of the included angle.

$$\|\mathbf{u} - \mathbf{v}\|^2 = \|\mathbf{u}\|^2 + \|\mathbf{v}\|^2 - 2\|\mathbf{u}\|\|\mathbf{v}\| \cos \theta$$

Now use property (4) to rewrite this equation in terms of dot products.

$$(\mathbf{u} - \mathbf{v}) \cdot (\mathbf{u} - \mathbf{v}) = \mathbf{u} \cdot \mathbf{u} + \mathbf{v} \cdot \mathbf{v} - 2\|\mathbf{u}\|\|\mathbf{v}\| \cos \theta \qquad (6)$$

Then apply the distributive property (3) twice on the left side of (6) to obtain

$$(\mathbf{u} - \mathbf{v}) \cdot (\mathbf{u} - \mathbf{v}) = \mathbf{u} \cdot (\mathbf{u} - \mathbf{v}) - \mathbf{v} \cdot (\mathbf{u} - \mathbf{v})$$
$$= \mathbf{u} \cdot \mathbf{u} - \mathbf{u} \cdot \mathbf{v} - \mathbf{v} \cdot \mathbf{u} + \mathbf{v} \cdot \mathbf{v}$$
$$= \mathbf{u} \cdot \mathbf{u} + \mathbf{v} \cdot \mathbf{v} - 2\,\mathbf{u} \cdot \mathbf{v} \qquad (7)$$
$$\underset{\underset{\text{Property (2)}}{\uparrow}}{}$$

Combining equations (6) and (7), we have

$$\mathbf{u} \cdot \mathbf{u} + \mathbf{v} \cdot \mathbf{v} - 2\,\mathbf{u} \cdot \mathbf{v} = \mathbf{u} \cdot \mathbf{u} + \mathbf{v} \cdot \mathbf{v} - 2\,\|\mathbf{u}\|\|\mathbf{v}\|\cos\theta$$
$$\mathbf{u} \cdot \mathbf{v} = \|\mathbf{u}\|\|\mathbf{v}\|\cos\theta$$

THEOREM

Angle between Vectors

If $\mathbf{u}$ and $\mathbf{v}$ are two nonzero vectors, the angle θ, $0 \le \theta \le \pi$, between $\mathbf{u}$ and $\mathbf{v}$ is determined by the formula

$$\cos\theta = \frac{\mathbf{u} \cdot \mathbf{v}}{\|\mathbf{u}\|\|\mathbf{v}\|} \qquad (8)$$

EXAMPLE 2

Finding the Angle θ between Two Vectors

Find the angle θ between $\mathbf{u} = 4\mathbf{i} - 3\mathbf{j}$ and $\mathbf{v} = 2\mathbf{i} + 5\mathbf{j}$.

Solution

Find $\mathbf{u} \cdot \mathbf{v}$, $\|\mathbf{u}\|$, and $\|\mathbf{v}\|$.

Figure 65

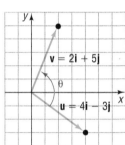

$$\mathbf{u} \cdot \mathbf{v} = 4(2) + (-3)(5) = -7$$
$$\|\mathbf{u}\| = \sqrt{4^2 + (-3)^2} = 5$$
$$\|\mathbf{v}\| = \sqrt{2^2 + 5^2} = \sqrt{29}$$

By formula (8), if θ is the angle between $\mathbf{u}$ and $\mathbf{v}$, then

$$\cos\theta = \frac{\mathbf{u} \cdot \mathbf{v}}{\|\mathbf{u}\|\|\mathbf{v}\|} = \frac{-7}{5\sqrt{29}} \approx -0.26$$

We find that $\theta \approx 105°$. See Figure 65.

────Now Work   PROBLEMS 7(a) AND (b)

3 Determine Whether Two Vectors Are Parallel

Two vectors $\mathbf{v}$ and $\mathbf{w}$ are said to be **parallel** if there is a nonzero scalar α so that $\mathbf{v} = \alpha\mathbf{w}$. In this case, the angle θ between $\mathbf{v}$ and $\mathbf{w}$ is 0 or π.

EXAMPLE 3

Determining Whether Vectors Are Parallel

The vectors $\mathbf{v} = 3\mathbf{i} - \mathbf{j}$ and $\mathbf{w} = 6\mathbf{i} - 2\mathbf{j}$ are parallel, since $\mathbf{v} = \frac{1}{2}\mathbf{w}$. Furthermore, since

$$\cos\theta = \frac{\mathbf{v} \cdot \mathbf{w}}{\|\mathbf{v}\|\|\mathbf{w}\|} = \frac{18 + 2}{\sqrt{10}\,\sqrt{40}} = \frac{20}{\sqrt{400}} = 1$$

the angle θ between $\mathbf{v}$ and $\mathbf{w}$ is 0.

4 Determine Whether Two Vectors Are Orthogonal

Figure 66
v is orthogonal to **w**.

If the angle θ between two nonzero vectors $\mathbf{v}$ and $\mathbf{w}$ is $\frac{\pi}{2}$, the vectors $\mathbf{v}$ and $\mathbf{w}$ are called **orthogonal**.* See Figure 66.

Since $\cos\frac{\pi}{2} = 0$, it follows from formula (8) that if $\mathbf{v}$ and $\mathbf{w}$ are orthogonal then $\mathbf{v} \cdot \mathbf{w} = 0$.

---

* *Orthogonal, perpendicular,* and *normal* are all terms that mean "meet at a right angle." It is customary to refer to two vectors as being *orthogonal*, two lines as being *perpendicular*, and a line and a plane or a vector and a plane as being *normal*.

On the other hand, if $\mathbf{v} \cdot \mathbf{w} = 0$, then $\mathbf{v} = \mathbf{0}$ or $\mathbf{w} = \mathbf{0}$ or $\cos \theta = 0$. If $\cos \theta = 0$, then $\theta = \dfrac{\pi}{2}$, and $\mathbf{v}$ and $\mathbf{w}$ are orthogonal. If $\mathbf{v}$ or $\mathbf{w}$ is the zero vector, then, since the zero vector has no specific direction, we adopt the convention that the zero vector is orthogonal to every vector.

THEOREM

Two vectors $\mathbf{v}$ and $\mathbf{w}$ are orthogonal if and only if

$$\mathbf{v} \cdot \mathbf{w} = 0$$

$\boxed{\textbf{EXAMPLE 4}}$ **Determining Whether Two Vectors Are Orthogonal**

The vectors

$$\mathbf{v} = 2\mathbf{i} - \mathbf{j} \quad \text{and} \quad \mathbf{w} = 3\mathbf{i} + 6\mathbf{j}$$

are orthogonal, since

$$\mathbf{v} \cdot \mathbf{w} = 6 - 6 = 0$$

See Figure 67.

Figure 67

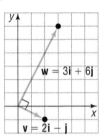

$\mathbf{w} = 3\mathbf{i} + 6\mathbf{j}$

$\mathbf{v} = 2\mathbf{i} - \mathbf{j}$

──── **Now Work** PROBLEM 7(c)

5 Decompose a Vector into Two Orthogonal Vectors

In the last section, we learned how to add two vectors to find the resultant vector. Now, we discuss the reverse problem, decomposing a vector into the sum of two components.

In many physical applications, it is necessary to find "how much" of a vector is applied in a given direction. Look at Figure 68. The force $\mathbf{F}$ due to gravity is pulling straight down (toward the center of Earth) on the block. To study the effect of gravity on the block, it is necessary to determine how much of $\mathbf{F}$ is actually pushing the block down the incline ($\mathbf{F}_1$) and how much is pressing the block against the incline ($\mathbf{F}_2$), at a right angle to the incline. Knowing the **decomposition** of $\mathbf{F}$ often will allow us to determine when friction (the force holding the block in place on the incline) is overcome and the block will slide down the incline.

Figure 68

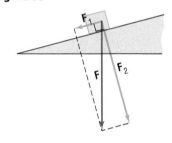

Suppose that $\mathbf{v}$ and $\mathbf{w}$ are two nonzero vectors with the same initial point P. We seek to decompose $\mathbf{v}$ into two vectors: $\mathbf{v}_1$, which is parallel to $\mathbf{w}$, and $\mathbf{v}_2$, which is orthogonal to $\mathbf{w}$. See Figure 69(a) and (b). The vector $\mathbf{v}_1$ is called the **vector projection of v onto w**.

The vector $\mathbf{v}_1$ is obtained as follows: From the terminal point of $\mathbf{v}$, drop a perpendicular to the line containing $\mathbf{w}$. The vector $\mathbf{v}_1$ is the vector from P to the foot of this perpendicular. The vector $\mathbf{v}_2$ is given by $\mathbf{v}_2 = \mathbf{v} - \mathbf{v}_1$. Note that $\mathbf{v} = \mathbf{v}_1 + \mathbf{v}_2$, the vector $\mathbf{v}_1$ is parallel to $\mathbf{w}$, and the vector $\mathbf{v}_2$ is orthogonal to $\mathbf{w}$. This is the decomposition of $\mathbf{v}$ that we wanted.

Figure 69

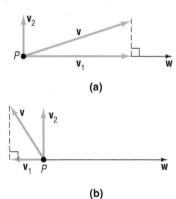

(a)

(b)

Now we seek a formula for $\mathbf{v}_1$ that is based on a knowledge of the vectors $\mathbf{v}$ and $\mathbf{w}$. Since $\mathbf{v} = \mathbf{v}_1 + \mathbf{v}_2$, we have

$$\mathbf{v} \cdot \mathbf{w} = (\mathbf{v}_1 + \mathbf{v}_2) \cdot \mathbf{w} = \mathbf{v}_1 \cdot \mathbf{w} + \mathbf{v}_2 \cdot \mathbf{w} \tag{9}$$

Since $\mathbf{v}_2$ is orthogonal to $\mathbf{w}$, we have $\mathbf{v}_2 \cdot \mathbf{w} = 0$. Since $\mathbf{v}_1$ is parallel to $\mathbf{w}$, we have $\mathbf{v}_1 = \alpha\mathbf{w}$ for some scalar α. Equation (9) can be written as

$$\mathbf{v} \cdot \mathbf{w} = \alpha\mathbf{w} \cdot \mathbf{w} = \alpha\|\mathbf{w}\|^2 \qquad {\scriptstyle \mathbf{v}_1 = \alpha\mathbf{w};\ \mathbf{v}_2 \cdot \mathbf{w} = 0}$$

$$\alpha = \frac{\mathbf{v} \cdot \mathbf{w}}{\|\mathbf{w}\|^2}$$

Then

$$\mathbf{v}_1 = \alpha\mathbf{w} = \frac{\mathbf{v} \cdot \mathbf{w}}{\|\mathbf{w}\|^2}\mathbf{w}$$

THEOREM   If **v** and **w** are two nonzero vectors, the vector projection of **v** onto **w** is

$$\mathbf{v}_1 = \frac{\mathbf{v} \cdot \mathbf{w}}{\|\mathbf{w}\|^2}\mathbf{w} \tag{10}$$

The decomposition of **v** into $\mathbf{v}_1$ and $\mathbf{v}_2$, where $\mathbf{v}_1$ is parallel to **w** and $\mathbf{v}_2$ is orthogonal to **w**, is

$$\mathbf{v}_1 = \frac{\mathbf{v} \cdot \mathbf{w}}{\|\mathbf{w}\|^2}\mathbf{w} \qquad \mathbf{v}_2 = \mathbf{v} - \mathbf{v}_1 \tag{11}$$

EXAMPLE 5   **Decomposing a Vector into Two Orthogonal Vectors**

Find the vector projection of $\mathbf{v} = \mathbf{i} + 3\mathbf{j}$ onto $\mathbf{w} = \mathbf{i} + \mathbf{j}$. Decompose **v** into two vectors, $\mathbf{v}_1$ and $\mathbf{v}_2$, where $\mathbf{v}_1$ is parallel to **w** and $\mathbf{v}_2$ is orthogonal to **w**.

Solution   Use formulas (10) and (11).

Figure 70

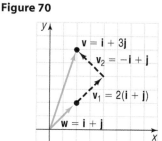

$$\mathbf{v}_1 = \frac{\mathbf{v} \cdot \mathbf{w}}{\|\mathbf{w}\|^2}\mathbf{w} = \frac{1 + 3}{\left(\sqrt{2}\right)^2}\mathbf{w} = 2\mathbf{w} = 2(\mathbf{i} + \mathbf{j})$$

$$\mathbf{v}_2 = \mathbf{v} - \mathbf{v}_1 = (\mathbf{i} + 3\mathbf{j}) - 2(\mathbf{i} + \mathbf{j}) = -\mathbf{i} + \mathbf{j}$$

See Figure 70.

—**Now Work** PROBLEM 19

EXAMPLE 6   **Finding the Force Required to Hold a Wagon on a Hill**

A wagon with two small children as occupants that weighs 100 pounds is on a hill with a grade of 20°. What is the magnitude of the force that is required to keep the wagon from rolling down the hill?

Solution   See Figure 71. We wish to find the magnitude of the force **v** that is causing the wagon to roll down the hill. A force with the same magnitude in the opposite direction of **v** will keep the wagon from rolling down the hill. The force of gravity is orthogonal to the level ground, so we can represent the force of the wagon due to gravity by the vector

Figure 71

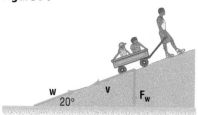

$$\mathbf{F}_w = -100\mathbf{j}$$

We need to determine the vector projection of $\mathbf{F}_w$ onto **w**, which is the force parallel to the hill. The vector **w** is given by

$$\mathbf{w} = \cos 20°\mathbf{i} + \sin 20°\mathbf{j}$$

The vector projection of $\mathbf{F}_w$ onto **w** is

$$\mathbf{v} = \frac{\mathbf{F}_w \cdot \mathbf{w}}{\|\mathbf{w}\|^2}\mathbf{w}$$

$$= \frac{-100(\sin 20°)}{\left(\sqrt{\cos^2 20° + \sin^2 20°}\right)^2}(\cos 20°\mathbf{i} + \sin 20°\mathbf{j})$$

$$= -34.2(\cos 20°\mathbf{i} + \sin 20°\mathbf{j})$$

The magnitude of **v** is 34.2 pounds, so the magnitude of the force required to keep the wagon from rolling down the hill is 34.2 pounds.

6 Compute Work

Figure 72

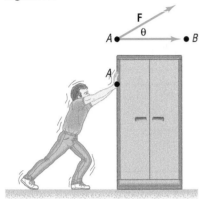

In elementary physics, the **work** W done by a constant force $\mathbf{F}$ in moving an object from a point A to a point B is defined as

$$W = (\text{magnitude of force})(\text{distance}) = \|\mathbf{F}\|\|\overrightarrow{AB}\|$$

Work is commonly measured in foot-pounds or in newton-meters (joules).

In this definition, it is assumed that the force $\mathbf{F}$ is applied along the line of motion. If the constant force $\mathbf{F}$ is not along the line of motion, but, instead, is at an angle θ to the direction of the motion, as illustrated in Figure 72, the **work** W **done by** $\mathbf{F}$ in moving an object from A to B is defined as

$$W = \mathbf{F} \cdot \overrightarrow{AB} \qquad \qquad \textbf{(12)}$$

This definition is compatible with the force times distance definition, since

$$W = (\text{amount of force in the direction of } \overrightarrow{AB})(\text{distance})$$

$$= \|\text{projection of } \mathbf{F} \text{ on } AB\|\|\overrightarrow{AB}\| = \frac{\mathbf{F} \cdot \overrightarrow{AB}}{\|\overrightarrow{AB}\|^2} \|\overrightarrow{AB}\|\|\overrightarrow{AB}\| = \mathbf{F} \cdot \overrightarrow{AB}$$

$$\uparrow$$
Use formula (10).

EXAMPLE 7 | **Computing Work**

Figure 73(a) shows a girl pulling a wagon with a force of 50 pounds. How much work is done in moving the wagon 100 feet if the handle makes an angle of 30° with the ground?

Figure 73

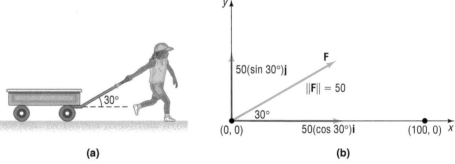

(a) (b)

Solution We position the vectors in a coordinate system in such a way that the wagon is moved from $(0, 0)$ to $(100, 0)$. The motion is from $A = (0, 0)$ to $B = (100, 0)$, so $\overrightarrow{AB} = 100\mathbf{i}$. The force vector $\mathbf{F}$, as shown in Figure 73(b), is

$$\mathbf{F} = 50(\cos 30°\mathbf{i} + \sin 30°\mathbf{j}) = 50\left(\frac{\sqrt{3}}{2}\mathbf{i} + \frac{1}{2}\mathbf{j}\right) = 25\left(\sqrt{3}\mathbf{i} + \mathbf{j}\right)$$

By formula (12), the work done is

$$W = \mathbf{F} \cdot \overrightarrow{AB} = 25\left(\sqrt{3}\mathbf{i} + \mathbf{j}\right) \cdot 100\mathbf{i} = 2500\sqrt{3} \text{ foot-pounds}$$

◀

Now Work PROBLEM 25

Historical Feature

We stated in an earlier Historical Feature that complex numbers were used as vectors in the plane before the general notion of a vector was clarified. Suppose that we make the correspondence

Vector ↔ Complex number
$ai + bj \leftrightarrow a + bi$
$ci + dj \leftrightarrow c + di$

Show that

$$(ai + bj) \cdot (ci + dj) = \text{real part } [\overline{(a + bi)}(c + di)]$$

This is how the dot product was found originally. The imaginary part is also interesting. It is a determinant (see Section 11.3) and represents the area of the parallelogram whose edges are the vectors. This is close to some of Hermann Grassmann's ideas and is also connected with the scalar triple product of three-dimensional vectors.

9.5 Assess Your Understanding

'Are You Prepared?' *The answer is given at the end of these exercises. If you get the wrong answer, read the page listed in red.*

1. In a triangle with sides a, b, c and angles A, B, C, the Law of Cosines states that _____. (p. 528)

Concepts and Vocabulary

2. If $\mathbf{v} = a_1\mathbf{i} + b_1\mathbf{j}$ and $\mathbf{w} = a_2\mathbf{i} + b_2\mathbf{j}$ are two vectors, the _____ is defined as $\mathbf{v} \cdot \mathbf{w} = a_1a_2 + b_1b_2$.

3. If $\mathbf{v} \cdot \mathbf{w} = 0$, then the two vectors $\mathbf{v}$ and $\mathbf{w}$ are _____.

4. If $\mathbf{v} = 3\mathbf{w}$, then the two vectors $\mathbf{v}$ and $\mathbf{w}$ are _____.

5. *True or False* Given two nonzero vectors $\mathbf{v}$ and $\mathbf{w}$, it is always possible to decompose $\mathbf{v}$ into two vectors, one parallel to $\mathbf{w}$ and the other perpendicular to $\mathbf{w}$.

6. *True or False* Work is a physical example of a vector.

Skill Building

In Problems 7–16, (a) find the dot product $\mathbf{v} \cdot \mathbf{w}$; (b) find the angle between $\mathbf{v}$ and $\mathbf{w}$; (c) state whether the vectors are parallel, orthogonal, or neither.

7. $\mathbf{v} = \mathbf{i} - \mathbf{j}, \quad \mathbf{w} = \mathbf{i} + \mathbf{j}$

8. $\mathbf{v} = \mathbf{i} + \mathbf{j}, \quad \mathbf{w} = -\mathbf{i} + \mathbf{j}$

9. $\mathbf{v} = 2\mathbf{i} + \mathbf{j}, \quad \mathbf{w} = \mathbf{i} - 2\mathbf{j}$

10. $\mathbf{v} = 2\mathbf{i} + 2\mathbf{j}, \quad \mathbf{w} = \mathbf{i} + 2\mathbf{j}$

11. $\mathbf{v} = \sqrt{3}\mathbf{i} - \mathbf{j}, \quad \mathbf{w} = \mathbf{i} + \mathbf{j}$

12. $\mathbf{v} = \mathbf{i} + \sqrt{3}\mathbf{j}, \quad \mathbf{w} = \mathbf{i} - \mathbf{j}$

13. $\mathbf{v} = 3\mathbf{i} + 4\mathbf{j}, \quad \mathbf{w} = -6\mathbf{i} - 8\mathbf{j}$

14. $\mathbf{v} = 3\mathbf{i} - 4\mathbf{j}, \quad \mathbf{w} = 9\mathbf{i} - 12\mathbf{j}$

15. $\mathbf{v} = 4\mathbf{i}, \quad \mathbf{w} = \mathbf{j}$

16. $\mathbf{v} = \mathbf{i}, \quad \mathbf{w} = -3\mathbf{j}$

17. Find a so that the vectors $\mathbf{v} = \mathbf{i} - a\mathbf{j}$ and $\mathbf{w} = 2\mathbf{i} + 3\mathbf{j}$ are orthogonal.

18. Find b so that the vectors $\mathbf{v} = \mathbf{i} + \mathbf{j}$ and $\mathbf{w} = \mathbf{i} + b\mathbf{j}$ are orthogonal.

In Problems 19–24, decompose $\mathbf{v}$ into two vectors $\mathbf{v}_1$ and $\mathbf{v}_2$, where $\mathbf{v}_1$ is parallel to $\mathbf{w}$ and $\mathbf{v}_2$ is orthogonal to $\mathbf{w}$.

19. $\mathbf{v} = 2\mathbf{i} - 3\mathbf{j}, \quad \mathbf{w} = \mathbf{i} - \mathbf{j}$

20. $\mathbf{v} = -3\mathbf{i} + 2\mathbf{j}, \quad \mathbf{w} = 2\mathbf{i} + \mathbf{j}$

21. $\mathbf{v} = \mathbf{i} - \mathbf{j}, \quad \mathbf{w} = -\mathbf{i} - 2\mathbf{j}$

22. $\mathbf{v} = 2\mathbf{i} - \mathbf{j}, \quad \mathbf{w} = \mathbf{i} - 2\mathbf{j}$

23. $\mathbf{v} = 3\mathbf{i} + \mathbf{j}, \quad \mathbf{w} = -2\mathbf{i} - \mathbf{j}$

24. $\mathbf{v} = \mathbf{i} - 3\mathbf{j}, \quad \mathbf{w} = 4\mathbf{i} - \mathbf{j}$

Applications and Extensions

25. Computing Work Find the work done by a force of 3 pounds acting in the direction 60° to the horizontal in moving an object 6 feet from $(0, 0)$ to $(6, 0)$.

26. Computing Work A wagon is pulled horizontally by exerting a force of 20 pounds on the handle at an angle of 30° with the horizontal. How much work is done in moving the wagon 100 feet?

27. Solar Energy The amount of energy collected by a solar panel depends on the intensity of the sun's rays and the area of the panel. Let the vector $\mathbf{I}$ represent the intensity, in watts per square centimeter, having the direction of the sun's rays. Let the vector $\mathbf{A}$ represent the area, in square centimeters, whose direction is the orientation of a solar panel. See the figure. The total number of watts collected by the panel is given by $W = |\mathbf{I} \cdot \mathbf{A}|$.

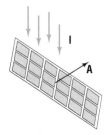

Suppose that $\mathbf{I} = \langle -0.02, -0.01 \rangle$ and $\mathbf{A} = \langle 300, 400 \rangle$.

(a) Find $\|\mathbf{I}\|$ and $\|\mathbf{A}\|$ and interpret the meaning of each.

(b) Compute W and interpret its meaning.

(c) If the solar panel is to collect the maximum number of watts, what must be true about $\mathbf{I}$ and $\mathbf{A}$?

28. Rainfall Measurement Let the vector $\mathbf{R}$ represent the amount of rainfall, in inches, whose direction is the inclination of the rain to a rain gauge. Let the vector $\mathbf{A}$ represent the area, in square inches, whose direction is the orientation of the opening of the rain gauge. See the figure. The volume of rain collected in the gauge, in cubic inches, is given by $V = |\mathbf{R} \cdot \mathbf{A}|$, even when the rain falls in a slanted direction or the gauge is not perfectly vertical.

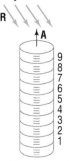

Suppose that $\mathbf{R} = \langle 0.75, -1.75 \rangle$ and $\mathbf{A} = \langle 0.3, 1 \rangle$.

(a) Find $\|\mathbf{R}\|$ and $\|\mathbf{A}\|$ and interpret the meaning of each.

(b) Compute V and interpret its meaning.

(c) If the gauge is to collect the maximum volume of rain, what must be true about $\mathbf{R}$ and $\mathbf{A}$?

29. Braking Load A Toyota Sienna with a gross weight of 5300 pounds is parked on a street with an 8° grade. See the figure.

Weight = 5300 pounds

Find the magnitude of the force required to keep the Sienna from rolling down the hill. What is the magnitude of the force perpendicular to the hill?

30. Braking Load A Pontiac Bonneville with a gross weight of 4500 pounds is parked on a street with a 10° grade. Find the magnitude of the force required to keep the Bonneville from rolling down the hill. What is the magnitude of the force perpendicular to the hill?

31. Ramp Angle Billy and Timmy are using a ramp to load furniture into a truck. While rolling a 250-pound piano up the ramp, they discover that the truck is too full of other furniture for the piano to fit. Timmy holds the piano in place on the ramp while Billy repositions other items to make room for it in the truck. If the angle of inclination of the ramp is 20°, how many pounds of force must Timmy exert to hold the piano in position?

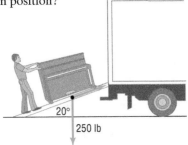

20°

250 lb

32. Incline Angle A bulldozer exerts 1000 pounds of force to prevent a 5000-pound boulder from rolling down a hill. Determine the angle of inclination of the hill.

33. Find the acute angle that a constant unit force vector makes with the positive x-axis if the work done by the force in moving a particle from $(0, 0)$ to $(4, 0)$ equals 2.

34. Prove the distributive property:
$$\mathbf{u} \cdot (\mathbf{v} + \mathbf{w}) = \mathbf{u} \cdot \mathbf{v} + \mathbf{u} \cdot \mathbf{w}$$

35. Prove property (5), $\mathbf{0} \cdot \mathbf{v} = 0$.

36. If $\mathbf{v}$ is a unit vector and the angle between $\mathbf{v}$ and $\mathbf{i}$ is α, show that $\mathbf{v} = \cos \alpha \mathbf{i} + \sin \alpha \mathbf{j}$.

37. Suppose that $\mathbf{v}$ and $\mathbf{w}$ are unit vectors. If the angle between $\mathbf{v}$ and $\mathbf{i}$ is α and that between $\mathbf{w}$ and $\mathbf{i}$ is β, use the idea of the dot product $\mathbf{v} \cdot \mathbf{w}$ to prove that
$$\cos(\alpha - \beta) = \cos \alpha \cos \beta + \sin \alpha \sin \beta$$

38. Show that the projection of $\mathbf{v}$ onto $\mathbf{i}$ is $(\mathbf{v} \cdot \mathbf{i})\mathbf{i}$. Then show that we can always write a vector $\mathbf{v}$ as
$$\mathbf{v} = (\mathbf{v} \cdot \mathbf{i})\mathbf{i} + (\mathbf{v} \cdot \mathbf{j})\mathbf{j}$$

39. (a) If $\mathbf{u}$ and $\mathbf{v}$ have the same magnitude, show that $\mathbf{u} + \mathbf{v}$ and $\mathbf{u} - \mathbf{v}$ are orthogonal.
  (b) Use this to prove that an angle inscribed in a semicircle is a right angle (see the figure).

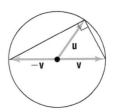

40. Let $\mathbf{v}$ and $\mathbf{w}$ denote two nonzero vectors. Show that the vector $\mathbf{v} - \alpha\mathbf{w}$ is orthogonal to $\mathbf{w}$ if $\alpha = \dfrac{\mathbf{v} \cdot \mathbf{w}}{\|\mathbf{w}\|^2}$.

41. Let $\mathbf{v}$ and $\mathbf{w}$ denote two nonzero vectors. Show that the vectors $\|\mathbf{w}\|\mathbf{v} + \|\mathbf{v}\|\mathbf{w}$ and $\|\mathbf{w}\|\mathbf{v} - \|\mathbf{v}\|\mathbf{w}$ are orthogonal.

42. In the definition of work given in this section, what is the work done if $\mathbf{F}$ is orthogonal to $\overrightarrow{AB}$?

43. Prove the **polarization identity,**
$$\|\mathbf{u} + \mathbf{v}\|^2 - \|\mathbf{u} - \mathbf{v}\|^2 = 4(\mathbf{u} \cdot \mathbf{v})$$

Explaining Concepts: Discussion and Writing

44. Create an application different from any found in the text that requires a dot product.

'Are You Prepared?' Answer

1. $c^2 = a^2 + b^2 - 2ab \cos C$

9.6 Vectors in Space

PREPARING FOR THIS SECTION *Before getting started, review the following:*

- Distance Formula (Section 1.1, p. 3)

Now Work the 'Are You Prepared?' problem on page 618.

Figure 74

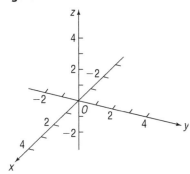

Rectangular Coordinates in Space

In the plane, each point is associated with an ordered pair of real numbers. In space, each point is associated with an ordered triple of real numbers. Through a fixed point, called the **origin** O, draw three mutually perpendicular lines, the x-axis, the y-axis, and the z-axis. On each of these axes, select an appropriate scale and the positive direction. See Figure 74.

The direction chosen for the positive z-axis in Figure 74 makes the system *right-handed*. This conforms to the *right-hand rule,* which states that, if the index finger of the right hand points in the direction of the positive x-axis and the middle finger points in the direction of the positive y-axis, then the thumb will point in the direction of the positive z-axis. See Figure 75.

We associate with each point P an ordered triple (x, y, z) of real numbers, the **coordinates of P.** For example, the point $(2, 3, 4)$ is located by starting at the origin and moving 2 units along the positive x-axis, 3 units in the direction of the positive y-axis, and 4 units in the direction of the positive z-axis. See Figure 76.

Figure 75

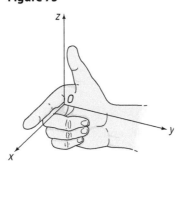

Figure 76

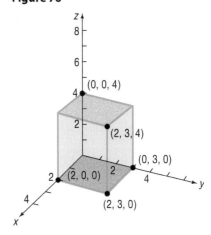

Figure 76 also shows the location of the points $(2, 0, 0)$, $(0, 3, 0)$, $(0, 0, 4)$, and $(2, 3, 0)$. Points of the form $(x, 0, 0)$ lie on the x-axis, while points of the form $(0, y, 0)$ and $(0, 0, z)$ lie on the y-axis and z-axis, respectively. Points of the form $(x, y, 0)$ lie in a plane, called the **xy-plane.** Its equation is $z = 0$. Similarly, points of the form $(x, 0, z)$ lie in the **xz-plane** (equation $y = 0$) and points of the form $(0, y, z)$ lie in the **yz-plane** (equation $x = 0$). See Figure 77(a). By extension of these ideas, all points obeying the equation $z = 3$ will lie in a plane parallel to and 3 units above the xy-plane. The equation $y = 4$ represents a plane parallel to the xz-plane and 4 units to the right of the plane $y = 0$. See Figure 77(b).

Figure 77

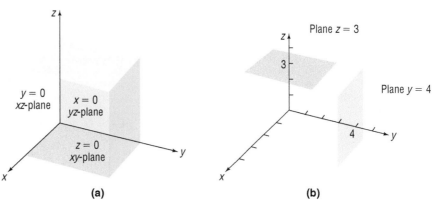

(a)   (b)

--Now Work   PROBLEM 9

1 Find the Distance between Two Points in Space

The formula for the distance between two points in space is an extension of the Distance Formula for points in the plane given in Chapter 1.

THEOREM | **Distance Formula in Space**

If $P_1 = (x_1, y_1, z_1)$ and $P_2 = (x_2, y_2, z_2)$ are two points in space, the distance d from P_1 to P_2 is

$$d = \sqrt{(x_2 - x_1)^2 + (y_2 - y_1)^2 + (z_2 - z_1)^2} \tag{1}$$

The proof, which we omit, utilizes a double application of the Pythagorean Theorem.

EXAMPLE 1 | **Using the Distance Formula**

Find the distance from $P_1 = (-1, 3, 2)$ to $P_2 = (4, -2, 5)$.

Solution $d = \sqrt{[4 - (-1)]^2 + [-2 - 3]^2 + [5 - 2]^2} = \sqrt{25 + 25 + 9} = \sqrt{59}$

Now Work PROBLEM 15

2 Find Position Vectors in Space

To represent vectors in space, we introduce the unit vectors $\mathbf{i}$, $\mathbf{j}$, and $\mathbf{k}$ whose directions are along the positive x-axis, positive y-axis, and positive z-axis, respectively. If $\mathbf{v}$ is a vector with initial point at the origin O and terminal point at $P = (a, b, c)$, we can represent $\mathbf{v}$ in terms of the vectors $\mathbf{i}$, $\mathbf{j}$, and $\mathbf{k}$ as

$$\mathbf{v} = a\mathbf{i} + b\mathbf{j} + c\mathbf{k}$$

Figure 78

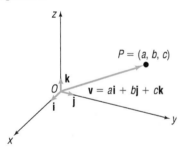

See Figure 78.

The scalars a, b, and c are called the **components** of the vector $\mathbf{v} = a\mathbf{i} + b\mathbf{j} + c\mathbf{k}$, with a being the component in the direction $\mathbf{i}$, b the component in the direction $\mathbf{j}$, and c the component in the direction $\mathbf{k}$.

A vector whose initial point is at the origin is called a **position vector.** The next result states that any vector whose initial point is not at the origin is equal to a unique position vector.

THEOREM   Suppose that $\mathbf{v}$ is a vector with initial point $P_1 = (x_1, y_1, z_1)$, not necessarily the origin, and terminal point $P_2 = (x_2, y_2, z_2)$. If $\mathbf{v} = \overrightarrow{P_1 P_2}$, then $\mathbf{v}$ is equal to the position vector

$$\mathbf{v} = (x_2 - x_1)\mathbf{i} + (y_2 - y_1)\mathbf{j} + (z_2 - z_1)\mathbf{k} \tag{2}$$

Figure 79 illustrates this result.

Figure 79

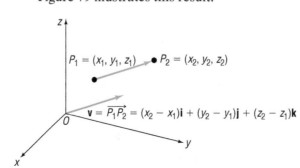

EXAMPLE 2

Finding a Position Vector

Find the position vector of the vector $\mathbf{v} = \overrightarrow{P_1P_2}$ if $P_1 = (-1, 2, 3)$ and $P_2 = (4, 6, 2)$.

Solution

By equation (2), the position vector equal to $\mathbf{v}$ is

$$\mathbf{v} = [4 - (-1)]\mathbf{i} + (6 - 2)\mathbf{j} + (2 - 3)\mathbf{k} = 5\mathbf{i} + 4\mathbf{j} - \mathbf{k}$$

══════Now Work PROBLEM 29

3 Perform Operations on Vectors

We can define equality, addition, subtraction, scalar product, and magnitude in terms of the components of a vector.

DEFINITION

Let $\mathbf{v} = a_1\mathbf{i} + b_1\mathbf{j} + c_1\mathbf{k}$ and $\mathbf{w} = a_2\mathbf{i} + b_2\mathbf{j} + c_2\mathbf{k}$ be two vectors, and let α be a scalar. Then

$$\mathbf{v} = \mathbf{w} \quad \text{if and only if} \quad a_1 = a_2, b_1 = b_2, \text{ and } c_1 = c_2$$

$$\mathbf{v} + \mathbf{w} = (a_1 + a_2)\mathbf{i} + (b_1 + b_2)\mathbf{j} + (c_1 + c_2)\mathbf{k}$$

$$\mathbf{v} - \mathbf{w} = (a_1 - a_2)\mathbf{i} + (b_1 - b_2)\mathbf{j} + (c_1 - c_2)\mathbf{k}$$

$$\alpha\mathbf{v} = (\alpha a_1)\mathbf{i} + (\alpha b_1)\mathbf{j} + (\alpha c_1)\mathbf{k}$$

$$\|\mathbf{v}\| = \sqrt{a_1^2 + b_1^2 + c_1^2}$$

These definitions are compatible with the geometric definitions given for vectors in the plane earlier in Section 9.4.

EXAMPLE 3

Adding and Subtracting Vectors

If $\mathbf{v} = 2\mathbf{i} + 3\mathbf{j} - 2\mathbf{k}$ and $\mathbf{w} = 3\mathbf{i} - 4\mathbf{j} + 5\mathbf{k}$, find:

(a) $\mathbf{v} + \mathbf{w}$ (b) $\mathbf{v} - \mathbf{w}$

Solution

(a) $\mathbf{v} + \mathbf{w} = (2\mathbf{i} + 3\mathbf{j} - 2\mathbf{k}) + (3\mathbf{i} - 4\mathbf{j} + 5\mathbf{k})$
$$= (2 + 3)\mathbf{i} + (3 - 4)\mathbf{j} + (-2 + 5)\mathbf{k}$$
$$= 5\mathbf{i} - \mathbf{j} + 3\mathbf{k}$$

(b) $\mathbf{v} - \mathbf{w} = (2\mathbf{i} + 3\mathbf{j} - 2\mathbf{k}) - (3\mathbf{i} - 4\mathbf{j} + 5\mathbf{k})$
$$= (2 - 3)\mathbf{i} + [3 - (-4)]\mathbf{j} + [-2 - 5]\mathbf{k}$$
$$= -\mathbf{i} + 7\mathbf{j} - 7\mathbf{k}$$

EXAMPLE 4

Finding Scalar Products and Magnitudes

If $\mathbf{v} = 2\mathbf{i} + 3\mathbf{j} - 2\mathbf{k}$ and $\mathbf{w} = 3\mathbf{i} - 4\mathbf{j} + 5\mathbf{k}$, find:

(a) $3\mathbf{v}$ (b) $2\mathbf{v} - 3\mathbf{w}$ (c) $\|\mathbf{v}\|$

Solution

(a) $3\mathbf{v} = 3(2\mathbf{i} + 3\mathbf{j} - 2\mathbf{k}) = 6\mathbf{i} + 9\mathbf{j} - 6\mathbf{k}$

(b) $2\mathbf{v} - 3\mathbf{w} = 2(2\mathbf{i} + 3\mathbf{j} - 2\mathbf{k}) - 3(3\mathbf{i} - 4\mathbf{j} + 5\mathbf{k})$
$$= 4\mathbf{i} + 6\mathbf{j} - 4\mathbf{k} - 9\mathbf{i} + 12\mathbf{j} - 15\mathbf{k} = -5\mathbf{i} + 18\mathbf{j} - 19\mathbf{k}$$

(c) $\|\mathbf{v}\| = \|2\mathbf{i} + 3\mathbf{j} - 2\mathbf{k}\| = \sqrt{2^2 + 3^2 + (-2)^2} = \sqrt{17}$

══════Now Work PROBLEMS 33 AND 39

Recall that a unit vector **u** is one for which $\|\mathbf{u}\| = 1$. In many applications, it is useful to be able to find a unit vector **u** that has the same direction as a given vector **v**.

THEOREM

Unit Vector in the Direction of v

For any nonzero vector **v**, the vector

$$\mathbf{u} = \frac{\mathbf{v}}{\|\mathbf{v}\|}$$

is a unit vector that has the same direction as **v**.

As a consequence of this theorem, if **u** is a unit vector in the same direction as a vector **v**, then **v** may be expressed as

$$\mathbf{v} = \|\mathbf{v}\|\mathbf{u}$$

EXAMPLE 5

Finding a Unit Vector

Find the unit vector in the same direction as $\mathbf{v} = 2\mathbf{i} - 3\mathbf{j} - 6\mathbf{k}$.

Solution Find $\|\mathbf{v}\|$ first.

$$\|\mathbf{v}\| = \|2\mathbf{i} - 3\mathbf{j} - 6\mathbf{k}\| = \sqrt{4 + 9 + 36} = \sqrt{49} = 7$$

Now multiply **v** by the scalar $\dfrac{1}{\|\mathbf{v}\|} = \dfrac{1}{7}$. The result is the unit vector

$$\mathbf{u} = \frac{\mathbf{v}}{\|\mathbf{v}\|} = \frac{2\mathbf{i} - 3\mathbf{j} - 6\mathbf{k}}{7} = \frac{2}{7}\mathbf{i} - \frac{3}{7}\mathbf{j} - \frac{6}{7}\mathbf{k}$$

━━━━━**Now Work** PROBLEM 47

4 Find the Dot Product

The definition of *dot product* is an extension of the definition given for vectors in the plane.

DEFINITION

If $\mathbf{v} = a_1\mathbf{i} + b_1\mathbf{j} + c_1\mathbf{k}$ and $\mathbf{w} = a_2\mathbf{i} + b_2\mathbf{j} + c_2\mathbf{k}$ are two vectors, the **dot product $\mathbf{v} \cdot \mathbf{w}$** is defined as

$$\mathbf{v} \cdot \mathbf{w} = a_1 a_2 + b_1 b_2 + c_1 c_2 \qquad \textbf{(3)}$$

EXAMPLE 6

Finding Dot Products

If $\mathbf{v} = 2\mathbf{i} - 3\mathbf{j} + 6\mathbf{k}$ and $\mathbf{w} = 5\mathbf{i} + 3\mathbf{j} - \mathbf{k}$, find:

(a) $\mathbf{v} \cdot \mathbf{w}$ (b) $\mathbf{w} \cdot \mathbf{v}$ (c) $\mathbf{v} \cdot \mathbf{v}$
(d) $\mathbf{w} \cdot \mathbf{w}$ (e) $\|\mathbf{v}\|$ (f) $\|\mathbf{w}\|$

Solution (a) $\mathbf{v} \cdot \mathbf{w} = 2(5) + (-3)3 + 6(-1) = -5$
(b) $\mathbf{w} \cdot \mathbf{v} = 5(2) + 3(-3) + (-1)(6) = -5$
(c) $\mathbf{v} \cdot \mathbf{v} = 2(2) + (-3)(-3) + 6(6) = 49$
(d) $\mathbf{w} \cdot \mathbf{w} = 5(5) + 3(3) + (-1)(-1) = 35$
(e) $\|\mathbf{v}\| = \sqrt{2^2 + (-3)^2 + 6^2} = \sqrt{49} = 7$
(f) $\|\mathbf{w}\| = \sqrt{5^2 + 3^2 + (-1)^2} = \sqrt{35}$

The dot product in space has the same properties as the dot product in the plane.

THEOREM   **Properties of the Dot Product**

If **u**, **v**, and **w** are vectors, then

Commutative Property

$$\mathbf{u} \cdot \mathbf{v} = \mathbf{v} \cdot \mathbf{u}$$

Distributive Property

$$\mathbf{u} \cdot (\mathbf{v} + \mathbf{w}) = \mathbf{u} \cdot \mathbf{v} + \mathbf{u} \cdot \mathbf{w}$$

$$\mathbf{v} \cdot \mathbf{v} = \|\mathbf{v}\|^2$$
$$\mathbf{0} \cdot \mathbf{v} = 0$$

5 Find the Angle between Two Vectors

The angle θ between two vectors in space follows the same formula as for two vectors in the plane.

THEOREM   **Angle between Vectors**

If **u** and **v** are two nonzero vectors, the angle $\theta, 0 \le \theta \le \pi$, between **u** and **v** is determined by the formula

$$\cos \theta = \frac{\mathbf{u} \cdot \mathbf{v}}{\|\mathbf{u}\| \, \|\mathbf{v}\|} \tag{4}$$

EXAMPLE 7   **Finding the Angle θ between Two Vectors**

Find the angle θ between $\mathbf{u} = 2\mathbf{i} - 3\mathbf{j} + 6\mathbf{k}$ and $\mathbf{v} = 2\mathbf{i} + 5\mathbf{j} - \mathbf{k}$.

Solution   Compute the quantities $\mathbf{u} \cdot \mathbf{v}$, $\|\mathbf{u}\|$, and $\|\mathbf{v}\|$.

$$\mathbf{u} \cdot \mathbf{v} = 2(2) + (-3)(5) + 6(-1) = -17$$
$$\|\mathbf{u}\| = \sqrt{2^2 + (-3)^2 + 6^2} = \sqrt{49} = 7$$
$$\|\mathbf{v}\| = \sqrt{2^2 + 5^2 + (-1)^2} = \sqrt{30}$$

By formula (4), if θ is the angle between **u** and **v**, then

$$\cos \theta = \frac{\mathbf{u} \cdot \mathbf{v}}{\|\mathbf{u}\| \, \|\mathbf{v}\|} = \frac{-17}{7\sqrt{30}} \approx -0.443$$

We find that $\theta \approx 116.3°$.

────**Now Work** PROBLEM 51

6 Find the Direction Angles of a Vector

A nonzero vector **v** in space can be described by specifying its magnitude and its three **direction angles** α, β, and γ. These direction angles are defined as

α = the angle between **v** and **i**, the positive x-axis, $0 \le \alpha \le \pi$

β = the angle between **v** and **j**, the positive y-axis, $0 \le \beta \le \pi$

γ = the angle between **v** and **k**, the positive z-axis, $0 \le \gamma \le \pi$

See Figure 80.

Figure 80

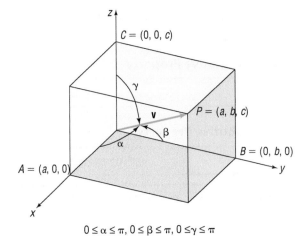

$$0 \le \alpha \le \pi, 0 \le \beta \le \pi, 0 \le \gamma \le \pi$$

Our first goal is to find expressions for α, β, and γ in terms of the components of a vector. Let $\mathbf{v} = a\mathbf{i} + b\mathbf{j} + c\mathbf{k}$ denote a nonzero vector. The angle α between $\mathbf{v}$ and $\mathbf{i}$, the positive x-axis, obeys

$$\cos \alpha = \frac{\mathbf{v} \cdot \mathbf{i}}{\|\mathbf{v}\| \, \|\mathbf{i}\|} = \frac{a}{\|\mathbf{v}\|}$$

Similarly,

$$\cos \beta = \frac{b}{\|\mathbf{v}\|} \qquad \cos \gamma = \frac{c}{\|\mathbf{v}\|}$$

Since $\|\mathbf{v}\| = \sqrt{a^2 + b^2 + c^2}$, we have the following result:

THEOREM

Direction Angles

If $\mathbf{v} = a\mathbf{i} + b\mathbf{j} + c\mathbf{k}$ is a nonzero vector in space, the direction angles α, β, and γ obey

$$\cos \alpha = \frac{a}{\sqrt{a^2 + b^2 + c^2}} = \frac{a}{\|\mathbf{v}\|} \qquad \cos \beta = \frac{b}{\sqrt{a^2 + b^2 + c^2}} = \frac{b}{\|\mathbf{v}\|}$$

$$\cos \gamma = \frac{c}{\sqrt{a^2 + b^2 + c^2}} = \frac{c}{\|\mathbf{v}\|} \qquad \qquad \textbf{(5)}$$

The numbers $\cos \alpha$, $\cos \beta$, and $\cos \gamma$ are called the **direction cosines** of the vector $\mathbf{v}$.

EXAMPLE 8

Finding the Direction Angles of a Vector

Find the direction angles of $\mathbf{v} = -3\mathbf{i} + 2\mathbf{j} - 6\mathbf{k}$.

Solution

$$\|\mathbf{v}\| = \sqrt{(-3)^2 + 2^2 + (-6)^2} = \sqrt{49} = 7$$

Using the formulas in equation (5), we have

$$\cos \alpha = \frac{-3}{7} \qquad \cos \beta = \frac{2}{7} \qquad \cos \gamma = \frac{-6}{7}$$

$$\alpha \approx 115.4° \qquad \beta \approx 73.4° \qquad \gamma \approx 149.0°$$

THEOREM   **Property of the Direction Cosines**

If α, β, and γ are the direction angles of a nonzero vector **v** in space, then

$$\cos^2 \alpha + \cos^2 \beta + \cos^2 \gamma = 1 \qquad\qquad (6)$$

The proof is a direct consequence of the equations in (5).

Based on equation (6), when two direction cosines are known, the third is determined up to its sign. Knowing two direction cosines is not sufficient to uniquely determine the direction of a vector in space.

EXAMPLE 9   **Finding the Direction Angle of a Vector**

The vector **v** makes an angle of $\alpha = \dfrac{\pi}{3}$ with the positive x-axis, an angle of $\beta = \dfrac{\pi}{3}$ with the positive y-axis, and an acute angle γ with the positive z-axis. Find γ.

Solution   By equation (6), we have

$$\cos^2\left(\frac{\pi}{3}\right) + \cos^2\left(\frac{\pi}{3}\right) + \cos^2 \gamma = 1 \qquad 0 < \gamma < \frac{\pi}{2}$$

$$\left(\frac{1}{2}\right)^2 + \left(\frac{1}{2}\right)^2 + \cos^2 \gamma = 1$$

$$\cos^2 \gamma = \frac{1}{2}$$

$$\cos \gamma = \frac{\sqrt{2}}{2} \quad \text{or} \quad \cos \gamma = -\frac{\sqrt{2}}{2}$$

$$\gamma = \frac{\pi}{4} \qquad \text{or} \quad \gamma = \frac{3\pi}{4}$$

Since we are requiring that γ be acute, $\gamma = \dfrac{\pi}{4}$.

The direction cosines of a vector give information about only the direction of the vector; they provide no information about its magnitude. For example, *any* vector parallel to the xy-plane and making an angle of $\dfrac{\pi}{4}$ radian with the positive x-axis and y-axis has direction cosines

$$\cos \alpha = \frac{\sqrt{2}}{2} \qquad \cos \beta = \frac{\sqrt{2}}{2} \qquad \cos \gamma = 0$$

However, if the direction angles *and* the magnitude of a vector are known, the vector is uniquely determined.

EXAMPLE 10   **Writing a Vector in Terms of Its Magnitude and Direction Cosines**

Show that any nonzero vector **v** in space can be written in terms of its magnitude and direction cosines as

$$\mathbf{v} = \|\mathbf{v}\|[(\cos \alpha)\mathbf{i} + (\cos \beta)\mathbf{j} + (\cos \gamma)\mathbf{k}] \qquad\qquad (7)$$

Solution   Let $\mathbf{v} = a\mathbf{i} + b\mathbf{j} + c\mathbf{k}$. From the equations in (5), we see that

$$a = \|\mathbf{v}\| \cos \alpha \qquad b = \|\mathbf{v}\| \cos \beta \qquad c = \|\mathbf{v}\| \cos \gamma$$

Substituting, we find that

$$\mathbf{v} = a\mathbf{i} + b\mathbf{j} + c\mathbf{k} = \|\mathbf{v}\|(\cos \alpha)\mathbf{i} + \|\mathbf{v}\|(\cos \beta)\mathbf{j} + \|\mathbf{v}\|(\cos \gamma)\mathbf{k}$$
$$= \|\mathbf{v}\|[(\cos \alpha)\mathbf{i} + (\cos \beta)\mathbf{j} + (\cos \gamma)\mathbf{k}]$$

Now Work PROBLEM 59

Example 10 shows that the direction cosines of a vector **v** are also the components of the unit vector in the direction of **v**.

9.6 Assess Your Understanding

'Are You Prepared?' *Answer is given at the end of these exercises. If you get the wrong answer, read the page listed in* red.

1. The distance d from $P_1 = (x_1, y_1)$ to $P_2 = (x_2, y_2)$ is $d =$ _____ . (p. 3)

Concepts and Vocabulary

2. In space, points of the form $(x, y, 0)$ lie in a plane called the _____.

3. If $\mathbf{v} = a\mathbf{i} + b\mathbf{j} + c\mathbf{k}$ is a vector in space, the scalars a, b, c are called the _____ of **v**.

4. The sum of the squares of the direction cosines of a vector in space add up to _____ .

5. *True or False* In space, the dot product of two vectors is a positive number.

6. *True or False* A vector in space may be described by specifying its magnitude and its direction angles.

Skill Building

In Problems 7– 14, describe the set of points (x, y, z) defined by the equation(s).

7. $y = 0$

8. $x = 0$

9. $z = 2$

10. $y = 3$

11. $x = -4$

12. $z = -3$

13. $x = 1$ and $y = 2$

14. $x = 3$ and $z = 1$

In Problems 15– 20, find the distance from P_1 to P_2.

15. $P_1 = (0, 0, 0)$ and $P_2 = (4, 1, 2)$

16. $P_1 = (0, 0, 0)$ and $P_2 = (1, -2, 3)$

17. $P_1 = (-1, 2, -3)$ and $P_2 = (0, -2, 1)$

18. $P_1 = (-2, 2, 3)$ and $P_2 = (4, 0, -3)$

19. $P_1 = (4, -2, -2)$ and $P_2 = (3, 2, 1)$

20. $P_1 = (2, -3, -3)$ and $P_2 = (4, 1, -1)$

In Problems 21– 26, opposite vertices of a rectangular box whose edges are parallel to the coordinate axes are given. List the coordinates of the other six vertices of the box.

21. $(0, 0, 0)$; $(2, 1, 3)$

22. $(0, 0, 0)$; $(4, 2, 2)$

23. $(1, 2, 3)$; $(3, 4, 5)$

24. $(5, 6, 1)$; $(3, 8, 2)$

25. $(-1, 0, 2)$; $(4, 2, 5)$

26. $(-2, -3, 0)$; $(-6, 7, 1)$

*In Problems 27– 32, the vector **v** has initial point P and terminal point Q. Write **v** in the form $a\mathbf{i} + b\mathbf{j} + c\mathbf{k}$; that is, find its position vector.*

27. $P = (0, 0, 0)$; $Q = (3, 4, -1)$

28. $P = (0, 0, 0)$; $Q = (-3, -5, 4)$

29. $P = (3, 2, -1)$; $Q = (5, 6, 0)$

30. $P = (-3, 2, 0)$; $Q = (6, 5, -1)$

31. $P = (-2, -1, 4)$; $Q = (6, -2, 4)$

32. $P = (-1, 4, -2)$; $Q = (6, 2, 2)$

In Problems 33– 38, find $\|\mathbf{v}\|$.

33. $\mathbf{v} = 3\mathbf{i} - 6\mathbf{j} - 2\mathbf{k}$

34. $\mathbf{v} = -6\mathbf{i} + 12\mathbf{j} + 4\mathbf{k}$

35. $\mathbf{v} = \mathbf{i} - \mathbf{j} + \mathbf{k}$

36. $\mathbf{v} = -\mathbf{i} - \mathbf{j} + \mathbf{k}$

37. $\mathbf{v} = -2\mathbf{i} + 3\mathbf{j} - 3\mathbf{k}$

38. $\mathbf{v} = 6\mathbf{i} + 2\mathbf{j} - 2\mathbf{k}$

In Problems 39– 44, find each quantity if $\mathbf{v} = 3\mathbf{i} - 5\mathbf{j} + 2\mathbf{k}$ and $\mathbf{w} = -2\mathbf{i} + 3\mathbf{j} - 2\mathbf{k}$.

39. $2\mathbf{v} + 3\mathbf{w}$

40. $3\mathbf{v} - 2\mathbf{w}$

41. $\|\mathbf{v} - \mathbf{w}\|$

42. $\|\mathbf{v} + \mathbf{w}\|$

43. $\|\mathbf{v}\| - \|\mathbf{w}\|$

44. $\|\mathbf{v}\| + \|\mathbf{w}\|$

In Problems 45–50, find the unit vector in the same direction as **v**.

45. $\mathbf{v} = 5\mathbf{i}$

46. $\mathbf{v} = -3\mathbf{j}$

47. $\mathbf{v} = 3\mathbf{i} - 6\mathbf{j} - 2\mathbf{k}$

48. $\mathbf{v} = -6\mathbf{i} + 12\mathbf{j} + 4\mathbf{k}$

49. $\mathbf{v} = \mathbf{i} + \mathbf{j} + \mathbf{k}$

50. $\mathbf{v} = 2\mathbf{i} - \mathbf{j} + \mathbf{k}$

In Problems 51–58, find the dot product **v** • **w** *and the angle between* **v** *and* **w**.

51. $\mathbf{v} = \mathbf{i} - \mathbf{j}, \quad \mathbf{w} = \mathbf{i} + \mathbf{j} + \mathbf{k}$

52. $\mathbf{v} = \mathbf{i} + \mathbf{j}, \quad \mathbf{w} = -\mathbf{i} + \mathbf{j} - \mathbf{k}$

53. $\mathbf{v} = 2\mathbf{i} + \mathbf{j} - 3\mathbf{k}, \quad \mathbf{w} = \mathbf{i} + 2\mathbf{j} + 2\mathbf{k}$

54. $\mathbf{v} = 2\mathbf{i} + 2\mathbf{j} - \mathbf{k}, \quad \mathbf{w} = \mathbf{i} + 2\mathbf{j} + 3\mathbf{k}$

55. $\mathbf{v} = 3\mathbf{i} - \mathbf{j} + 2\mathbf{k}, \quad \mathbf{w} = \mathbf{i} + \mathbf{j} - \mathbf{k}$

56. $\mathbf{v} = \mathbf{i} + 3\mathbf{j} + 2\mathbf{k}, \quad \mathbf{w} = \mathbf{i} - \mathbf{j} + \mathbf{k}$

57. $\mathbf{v} = 3\mathbf{i} + 4\mathbf{j} + \mathbf{k}, \quad \mathbf{w} = 6\mathbf{i} + 8\mathbf{j} + 2\mathbf{k}$

58. $\mathbf{v} = 3\mathbf{i} - 4\mathbf{j} + \mathbf{k}, \quad \mathbf{w} = 6\mathbf{i} - 8\mathbf{j} + 2\mathbf{k}$

In Problems 59–66, find the direction angles of each vector. Write each vector in the form of equation (7).

59. $\mathbf{v} = 3\mathbf{i} - 6\mathbf{j} - 2\mathbf{k}$

60. $\mathbf{v} = -6\mathbf{i} + 12\mathbf{j} + 4\mathbf{k}$

61. $\mathbf{v} = \mathbf{i} + \mathbf{j} + \mathbf{k}$

62. $\mathbf{v} = \mathbf{i} - \mathbf{j} - \mathbf{k}$

63. $\mathbf{v} = \mathbf{i} + \mathbf{j}$

64. $\mathbf{v} = \mathbf{j} + \mathbf{k}$

65. $\mathbf{v} = 3\mathbf{i} - 5\mathbf{j} + 2\mathbf{k}$

66. $\mathbf{v} = 2\mathbf{i} + 3\mathbf{j} - 4\mathbf{k}$

Applications and Extensions

67. Robotic Arm Consider the double-jointed robotic arm shown in the figure. Let the lower arm be modeled by $\mathbf{a} = \langle 2, 3, 4 \rangle$, the middle arm be modeled by $\mathbf{b} = \langle 1, -1, 3 \rangle$, and the upper arm by $\mathbf{c} = \langle 4, -1, -2 \rangle$, where units are in feet.

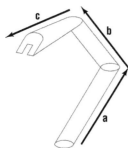

(a) Find a vector **d** that represents the position of the hand.
(b) Determine the distance of the hand from the origin.

68. The Sphere In space, the collection of all points that are the same distance from some fixed point is called a **sphere.** See the illustration. The constant distance is called the **radius,** and the fixed point is the **center** of the sphere. Show that the equation of a sphere with center at (x_0, y_0, z_0) and radius r is

$$(x - x_0)^2 + (y - y_0)^2 + (z - z_0)^2 = r^2$$

[**Hint:** Use the Distance Formula (1).]

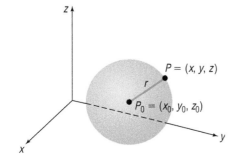

In Problems 69 and 70, find the equation of a sphere with radius r and center P_0.

69. $r = 1; \quad P_0 = (3, 1, 1)$

70. $r = 2; \quad P_0 = (1, 2, 2)$

In Problems 71–76, find the radius and center of each sphere.
[**Hint:** *Complete the square in each variable.*]

71. $x^2 + y^2 + z^2 + 2x - 2y = 2$

72. $x^2 + y^2 + z^2 + 2x - 2z = -1$

73. $x^2 + y^2 + z^2 - 4x + 4y + 2z = 0$

74. $x^2 + y^2 + z^2 - 4x = 0$

75. $2x^2 + 2y^2 + 2z^2 - 8x + 4z = -1$

76. $3x^2 + 3y^2 + 3z^2 + 6x - 6y = 3$

The **work** *W done by a constant force* **F** *in moving an object from a point A in space to a point B in space is defined as* $W = \mathbf{F} \cdot \overrightarrow{AB}$. *Use this definition in Problems 77–79.*

77. Work Find the work done by a force of 3 newtons acting in the direction $2\mathbf{i} + \mathbf{j} + 2\mathbf{k}$ in moving an object 2 meters from $(0, 0, 0)$ to $(0, 2, 0)$.

78. Work Find the work done by a force of 1 newton acting in the direction $2\mathbf{i} + 2\mathbf{j} + \mathbf{k}$ in moving an object 3 meters from $(0, 0, 0)$ to $(1, 2, 2)$.

79. Work Find the work done in moving an object along a vector $\mathbf{u} = 3\mathbf{i} + 2\mathbf{j} - 5\mathbf{k}$ if the applied force is $\mathbf{F} = 2\mathbf{i} - \mathbf{j} - \mathbf{k}$. Use meters for distance and newtons for force.

'Are You Prepared?' Answer

1. $\sqrt{(x_2 - x_1)^2 + (y_2 - y_1)^2}$

9.7 The Cross Product

OBJECTIVES 1 Find the Cross Product of Two Vectors (p. 620)
2 Know Algebraic Properties of the Cross Product (p. 621)
3 Know Geometric Properties of the Cross Product (p. 622)
4 Find a Vector Orthogonal to Two Given Vectors (p. 622)
5 Find the Area of a Parallelogram (p. 623)

1 Find the Cross Product of Two Vectors

For vectors in space, and only for vectors in space, a second product of two vectors is defined, called the *cross product*. The cross product of two vectors in space is, in fact, also a vector that has applications in both geometry and physics.

DEFINITION If $\mathbf{v} = a_1\mathbf{i} + b_1\mathbf{j} + c_1\mathbf{k}$ and $\mathbf{w} = a_2\mathbf{i} + b_2\mathbf{j} + c_2\mathbf{k}$ are two vectors in space, the **cross product** $\mathbf{v} \times \mathbf{w}$ is defined as the vector

$$\mathbf{v} \times \mathbf{w} = (b_1c_2 - b_2c_1)\mathbf{i} - (a_1c_2 - a_2c_1)\mathbf{j} + (a_1b_2 - a_2b_1)\mathbf{k} \quad \textbf{(1)}$$

Notice that the cross product $\mathbf{v} \times \mathbf{w}$ of two vectors is a vector. Because of this, it is sometimes referred to as the **vector product.**

EXAMPLE 1 **Finding Cross Products Using Equation (1)**

If $\mathbf{v} = 2\mathbf{i} + 3\mathbf{j} + 5\mathbf{k}$ and $\mathbf{w} = \mathbf{i} + 2\mathbf{j} + 3\mathbf{k}$, an application of equation (1) gives

$$\begin{aligned}
\mathbf{v} \times \mathbf{w} &= (3 \cdot 3 - 2 \cdot 5)\mathbf{i} - (2 \cdot 3 - 1 \cdot 5)\mathbf{j} + (2 \cdot 2 - 1 \cdot 3)\mathbf{k} \\
&= (9 - 10)\mathbf{i} - (6 - 5)\mathbf{j} + (4 - 3)\mathbf{k} \\
&= -\mathbf{i} - \mathbf{j} + \mathbf{k}
\end{aligned}$$

Determinants* may be used as an aid in computing cross products. A **2 by 2 determinant,** symbolized by

$$\begin{vmatrix} a_1 & b_1 \\ a_2 & b_2 \end{vmatrix}$$

has the value $a_1b_2 - a_2b_1$; that is,

$$\begin{vmatrix} a_1 & b_1 \\ a_2 & b_2 \end{vmatrix} = a_1b_2 - a_2b_1$$

A **3 by 3 determinant** has the value

$$\begin{vmatrix} A & B & C \\ a_1 & b_1 & c_1 \\ a_2 & b_2 & c_2 \end{vmatrix} = \begin{vmatrix} b_1 & c_1 \\ b_2 & c_2 \end{vmatrix} A - \begin{vmatrix} a_1 & c_1 \\ a_2 & c_2 \end{vmatrix} B + \begin{vmatrix} a_1 & b_1 \\ a_2 & b_2 \end{vmatrix} C$$

EXAMPLE 2 **Evaluating Determinants**

(a) $\begin{vmatrix} 2 & 3 \\ 1 & 2 \end{vmatrix} = 2 \cdot 2 - 1 \cdot 3 = 4 - 3 = 1$

(b) $\begin{vmatrix} A & B & C \\ 2 & 3 & 5 \\ 1 & 2 & 3 \end{vmatrix} = \begin{vmatrix} 3 & 5 \\ 2 & 3 \end{vmatrix} A - \begin{vmatrix} 2 & 5 \\ 1 & 3 \end{vmatrix} B + \begin{vmatrix} 2 & 3 \\ 1 & 2 \end{vmatrix} C$

$\qquad\qquad\qquad = (9 - 10)A - (6 - 5)B + (4 - 3)C$

$\qquad\qquad\qquad = -A - B + C$

Now Work PROBLEM 7

*Determinants are discussed in detail in Section 11.3.

The cross product of the vectors $\mathbf{v} = a_1\mathbf{i} + b_1\mathbf{j} + c_1\mathbf{k}$ and $\mathbf{w} = a_2\mathbf{i} + b_2\mathbf{j} + c_2\mathbf{k}$, that is,

$$\mathbf{v} \times \mathbf{w} = (b_1c_2 - b_2c_1)\mathbf{i} - (a_1c_2 - a_2c_1)\mathbf{j} + (a_1b_2 - a_2b_1)\mathbf{k}$$

may be written symbolically using determinants as

$$\mathbf{v} \times \mathbf{w} = \begin{vmatrix} \mathbf{i} & \mathbf{j} & \mathbf{k} \\ a_1 & b_1 & c_1 \\ a_2 & b_2 & c_2 \end{vmatrix} = \begin{vmatrix} b_1 & c_1 \\ b_2 & c_2 \end{vmatrix}\mathbf{i} - \begin{vmatrix} a_1 & c_1 \\ a_2 & c_2 \end{vmatrix}\mathbf{j} + \begin{vmatrix} a_1 & b_1 \\ a_2 & b_2 \end{vmatrix}\mathbf{k}$$

EXAMPLE 3   **Using Determinants to Find Cross Products**

If $\mathbf{v} = 2\mathbf{i} + 3\mathbf{j} + 5\mathbf{k}$ and $\mathbf{w} = \mathbf{i} + 2\mathbf{j} + 3\mathbf{k}$, find:

(a) $\mathbf{v} \times \mathbf{w}$ (b) $\mathbf{w} \times \mathbf{v}$ (c) $\mathbf{v} \times \mathbf{v}$ (d) $\mathbf{w} \times \mathbf{w}$

Solution   (a) $\mathbf{v} \times \mathbf{w} = \begin{vmatrix} \mathbf{i} & \mathbf{j} & \mathbf{k} \\ 2 & 3 & 5 \\ 1 & 2 & 3 \end{vmatrix} = \begin{vmatrix} 3 & 5 \\ 2 & 3 \end{vmatrix}\mathbf{i} - \begin{vmatrix} 2 & 5 \\ 1 & 3 \end{vmatrix}\mathbf{j} + \begin{vmatrix} 2 & 3 \\ 1 & 2 \end{vmatrix}\mathbf{k} = -\mathbf{i} - \mathbf{j} + \mathbf{k}$

(b) $\mathbf{w} \times \mathbf{v} = \begin{vmatrix} \mathbf{i} & \mathbf{j} & \mathbf{k} \\ 1 & 2 & 3 \\ 2 & 3 & 5 \end{vmatrix} = \begin{vmatrix} 2 & 3 \\ 3 & 5 \end{vmatrix}\mathbf{i} - \begin{vmatrix} 1 & 3 \\ 2 & 5 \end{vmatrix}\mathbf{j} + \begin{vmatrix} 1 & 2 \\ 2 & 3 \end{vmatrix}\mathbf{k} = \mathbf{i} + \mathbf{j} - \mathbf{k}$

(c) $\mathbf{v} \times \mathbf{v} = \begin{vmatrix} \mathbf{i} & \mathbf{j} & \mathbf{k} \\ 2 & 3 & 5 \\ 2 & 3 & 5 \end{vmatrix}$

$= \begin{vmatrix} 3 & 5 \\ 3 & 5 \end{vmatrix}\mathbf{i} - \begin{vmatrix} 2 & 5 \\ 2 & 5 \end{vmatrix}\mathbf{j} + \begin{vmatrix} 2 & 3 \\ 2 & 3 \end{vmatrix}\mathbf{k} = 0\mathbf{i} - 0\mathbf{j} + 0\mathbf{k} = \mathbf{0}$

(d) $\mathbf{w} \times \mathbf{w} = \begin{vmatrix} \mathbf{i} & \mathbf{j} & \mathbf{k} \\ 1 & 2 & 3 \\ 1 & 2 & 3 \end{vmatrix}$

$= \begin{vmatrix} 2 & 3 \\ 2 & 3 \end{vmatrix}\mathbf{i} - \begin{vmatrix} 1 & 3 \\ 1 & 3 \end{vmatrix}\mathbf{j} + \begin{vmatrix} 1 & 2 \\ 1 & 2 \end{vmatrix}\mathbf{k} = 0\mathbf{i} - 0\mathbf{j} + 0\mathbf{k} = \mathbf{0}$

═══ **Now Work**   PROBLEM 15

2 Know Algebraic Properties of the Cross Product

Notice in Examples 3(a) and (b) that $\mathbf{v} \times \mathbf{w}$ and $\mathbf{w} \times \mathbf{v}$ are negatives of one another. From Examples 3(c) and (d), we might conjecture that the cross product of a vector with itself is the zero vector. These and other algebraic properties of the cross product are given next.

THEOREM   **Algebraic Properties of the Cross Product**

If $\mathbf{u}, \mathbf{v}$, and $\mathbf{w}$ are vectors in space and if α is a scalar, then

$\mathbf{u} \times \mathbf{u} = \mathbf{0}$	(2)
$\mathbf{u} \times \mathbf{v} = -(\mathbf{v} \times \mathbf{u})$	(3)
$\alpha(\mathbf{u} \times \mathbf{v}) = (\alpha\mathbf{u}) \times \mathbf{v} = \mathbf{u} \times (\alpha\mathbf{v})$	(4)
$\mathbf{u} \times (\mathbf{v} + \mathbf{w}) = (\mathbf{u} \times \mathbf{v}) + (\mathbf{u} \times \mathbf{w})$	(5)

Proof   We will prove properties (2) and (4) here and leave properties (3) and (5) as exercises (see Problems 60 and 61).

To prove property (2), we let $\mathbf{u} = a_1\mathbf{i} + b_1\mathbf{j} + c_1\mathbf{k}$. Then

$$\mathbf{u} \times \mathbf{u} = \begin{vmatrix} \mathbf{i} & \mathbf{j} & \mathbf{k} \\ a_1 & b_1 & c_1 \\ a_1 & b_1 & c_1 \end{vmatrix} = \begin{vmatrix} b_1 & c_1 \\ b_1 & c_1 \end{vmatrix}\mathbf{i} - \begin{vmatrix} a_1 & c_1 \\ a_1 & c_1 \end{vmatrix}\mathbf{j} + \begin{vmatrix} a_1 & b_1 \\ a_1 & b_1 \end{vmatrix}\mathbf{k}$$

$$= 0\mathbf{i} - 0\mathbf{j} + 0\mathbf{k} = \mathbf{0}$$

To prove property (4), we let $\mathbf{u} = a_1\mathbf{i} + b_1\mathbf{j} + c_1\mathbf{k}$ and $\mathbf{v} = a_2\mathbf{i} + b_2\mathbf{j} + c_2\mathbf{k}$. Then

$$\alpha(\mathbf{u} \times \mathbf{v}) = \alpha[(b_1c_2 - b_2c_1)\mathbf{i} - (a_1c_2 - a_2c_1)\mathbf{j} + (a_1b_2 - a_2b_1)\mathbf{k}]$$

↑
Apply (1).

$$= \alpha(b_1c_2 - b_2c_1)\mathbf{i} - \alpha(a_1c_2 - a_2c_1)\mathbf{j} + \alpha(a_1b_2 - a_2b_1)\mathbf{k} \quad \textbf{(6)}$$

Since $\alpha\mathbf{u} = \alpha a_1\mathbf{i} + \alpha b_1\mathbf{j} + \alpha c_1\mathbf{k}$, we have

$$(\alpha\mathbf{u}) \times \mathbf{v} = (\alpha b_1c_2 - b_2\alpha c_1)\mathbf{i} - (\alpha a_1c_2 - a_2\alpha c_1)\mathbf{j} + (\alpha a_1b_2 - a_2\alpha b_1)\mathbf{k}$$

$$= \alpha(b_1c_2 - b_2c_1)\mathbf{i} - \alpha(a_1c_2 - a_2c_1)\mathbf{j} + \alpha(a_1b_2 - a_2b_1)\mathbf{k} \quad \textbf{(7)}$$

Based on equations (6) and (7), the first part of property (4) follows. The second part can be proved in like fashion. ∎

Now Work PROBLEM 17

3 Know Geometric Properties of the Cross Product

THEOREM

Geometric Properties of the Cross Product

Let $\mathbf{u}$ and $\mathbf{v}$ be vectors in space.

$\mathbf{u} \times \mathbf{v}$ is orthogonal to both $\mathbf{u}$ and $\mathbf{v}$.	**(8)**
$\|\mathbf{u} \times \mathbf{v}\| = \|\mathbf{u}\|\,\|\mathbf{v}\|\sin\theta$, where θ is the angle between $\mathbf{u}$ and $\mathbf{v}$.	**(9)**
$\|\mathbf{u} \times \mathbf{v}\|$ is the area of the parallelogram having $\mathbf{u} \neq \mathbf{0}$ and $\mathbf{v} \neq \mathbf{0}$ as adjacent sides.	**(10)**
$\mathbf{u} \times \mathbf{v} = \mathbf{0}$ if and only if $\mathbf{u}$ and $\mathbf{v}$ are parallel.	**(11)**

Figure 81

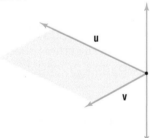

Proof of Property (8) Let $\mathbf{u} = a_1\mathbf{i} + b_1\mathbf{j} + c_1\mathbf{k}$ and $\mathbf{v} = a_2\mathbf{i} + b_2\mathbf{j} + c_2\mathbf{k}$. Then

$$\mathbf{u} \times \mathbf{v} = (b_1c_2 - b_2c_1)\mathbf{i} - (a_1c_2 - a_2c_1)\mathbf{j} + (a_1b_2 - a_2b_1)\mathbf{k}$$

Now we compute the dot product $\mathbf{u} \cdot (\mathbf{u} \times \mathbf{v})$.

$$\mathbf{u} \cdot (\mathbf{u} \times \mathbf{v}) = (a_1\mathbf{i} + b_1\mathbf{j} + c_1\mathbf{k}) \cdot [(b_1c_2 - b_2c_1)\mathbf{i} - (a_1c_2 - a_2c_1)\mathbf{j} + (a_1b_2 - a_2b_1)\mathbf{k}]$$

$$= a_1(b_1c_2 - b_2c_1) - b_1(a_1c_2 - a_2c_1) + c_1(a_1b_2 - a_2b_1) = 0$$

Since two vectors are orthogonal if their dot product is zero, it follows that $\mathbf{u}$ and $\mathbf{u} \times \mathbf{v}$ are orthogonal. Similarly, $\mathbf{v} \cdot (\mathbf{u} \times \mathbf{v}) = 0$, so $\mathbf{v}$ and $\mathbf{u} \times \mathbf{v}$ are orthogonal. ∎

Figure 82

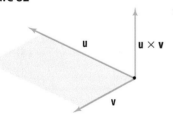

4 Find a Vector Orthogonal to Two Given Vectors

As long as the vectors $\mathbf{u}$ and $\mathbf{v}$ are not parallel, they will form a plane in space. See Figure 81. Based on property (8), the vector $\mathbf{u} \times \mathbf{v}$ is normal to this plane. As Figure 81 illustrates, there are essentially (without regard to magnitude) two vectors normal to the plane containing $\mathbf{u}$ and $\mathbf{v}$. It can be shown that the vector $\mathbf{u} \times \mathbf{v}$ is the one determined by the thumb of the right hand when the other fingers of the right hand are cupped so that they point in a direction from $\mathbf{u}$ to $\mathbf{v}$. See Figure 82.*

*This is a consequence of using a right-handed coordinate system.

EXAMPLE 4

Finding a Vector Orthogonal to Two Given Vectors

Find a vector that is orthogonal to $\mathbf{u} = 3\mathbf{i} - 2\mathbf{j} + \mathbf{k}$ and $\mathbf{v} = -\mathbf{i} + 3\mathbf{j} - \mathbf{k}$.

Solution

Based on property (8), such a vector is $\mathbf{u} \times \mathbf{v}$.

$$\mathbf{u} \times \mathbf{v} = \begin{vmatrix} \mathbf{i} & \mathbf{j} & \mathbf{k} \\ 3 & -2 & 1 \\ -1 & 3 & -1 \end{vmatrix} = (2 - 3)\mathbf{i} - [-3 - (-1)]\mathbf{j} + (9 - 2)\mathbf{k} = -\mathbf{i} + 2\mathbf{j} + 7\mathbf{k}$$

The vector $-\mathbf{i} + 2\mathbf{j} + 7\mathbf{k}$ is orthogonal to both $\mathbf{u}$ and $\mathbf{v}$.

✓**Check:** Two vectors are orthogonal if their dot product is zero.

$$\mathbf{u} \cdot (-\mathbf{i} + 2\mathbf{j} + 7\mathbf{k}) = (3\mathbf{i} - 2\mathbf{j} + \mathbf{k}) \cdot (-\mathbf{i} + 2\mathbf{j} + 7\mathbf{k}) = -3 - 4 + 7 = 0$$
$$\mathbf{v} \cdot (-\mathbf{i} + 2\mathbf{j} + 7\mathbf{k}) = (-\mathbf{i} + 3\mathbf{j} - \mathbf{k}) \cdot (-\mathbf{i} + 2\mathbf{j} + 7\mathbf{k}) = 1 + 6 - 7 = 0$$

⬤══►**Now Work** PROBLEM 41

The proof of property (9) is left as an exercise. See Problem 62.

5 Find the Area of a Parallelogram

Figure 83

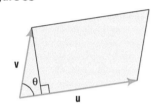

Proof of Property (10) Suppose that $\mathbf{u}$ and $\mathbf{v}$ are adjacent sides of a parallelogram. See Figure 83. Then the lengths of these sides are $\|\mathbf{u}\|$ and $\|\mathbf{v}\|$. If θ is the angle between $\mathbf{u}$ and $\mathbf{v}$, then the height of the parallelogram is $\|\mathbf{v}\| \sin\theta$ and its area is

$$\text{Area of parallelogram} = \text{Base} \times \text{Height} = \|\mathbf{u}\|[\|\mathbf{v}\| \sin\theta] = \|\mathbf{u} \times \mathbf{v}\|$$
$$\uparrow$$
$$\textit{Property (9)}$$
■

EXAMPLE 5

Finding the Area of a Parallelogram

Find the area of the parallelogram whose vertices are $P_1 = (0, 0, 0)$, $P_2 = (3, -2, 1)$, $P_3 = (-1, 3, -1)$, and $P_4 = (2, 1, 0)$.

Solution

Two adjacent sides of this parallelogram are

$$\mathbf{u} = \overrightarrow{P_1P_2} = 3\mathbf{i} - 2\mathbf{j} + \mathbf{k} \quad \text{and} \quad \mathbf{v} = \overrightarrow{P_1P_3} = -\mathbf{i} + 3\mathbf{j} - \mathbf{k}$$

WARNING Not all pairs of vertices give rise to a side. For example, $\overrightarrow{P_1P_4}$ is a diagonal of the parallelogram since $\overrightarrow{P_1P_3} + \overrightarrow{P_3P_4} = \overrightarrow{P_1P_4}$. Also, $\overrightarrow{P_1P_3}$ and $\overrightarrow{P_2P_4}$ are not adjacent sides; they are parallel sides. ■

Since $\mathbf{u} \times \mathbf{v} = -\mathbf{i} + 2\mathbf{j} + 7\mathbf{k}$ (Example 4), the area of the parallelogram is

$$\text{Area of parallelogram} = \|\mathbf{u} \times \mathbf{v}\| = \sqrt{1 + 4 + 49} = \sqrt{54} = 3\sqrt{6} \text{ square units}$$

⬤══►**Now Work** PROBLEM 49

Proof of Property (11) The proof requires two parts. If $\mathbf{u}$ and $\mathbf{v}$ are parallel, then there is a scalar α such that $\mathbf{u} = \alpha\mathbf{v}$. Then

$$\mathbf{u} \times \mathbf{v} = (\alpha\mathbf{v}) \times \mathbf{v} = \alpha(\mathbf{v} \times \mathbf{v}) = 0$$
$$\uparrow \qquad\qquad \uparrow$$
$$\textit{Property (4)} \quad \textit{Property (2)}$$

If $\mathbf{u} \times \mathbf{v} = \mathbf{0}$, then, by property (9), we have

$$\|\mathbf{u} \times \mathbf{v}\| = \|\mathbf{u}\| \|\mathbf{v}\| \sin\theta = 0$$

Since $\mathbf{u} \neq \mathbf{0}$ and $\mathbf{v} \neq \mathbf{0}$, we must have $\sin\theta = 0$, so $\theta = 0$ or $\theta = \pi$. In either case, since θ is the angle between $\mathbf{u}$ and $\mathbf{v}$, then $\mathbf{u}$ and $\mathbf{v}$ are parallel. ■

9.7 Assess Your Understanding

Concepts and Vocabulary

1. **True or False** If **u** and **v** are parallel vectors, then $\mathbf{u} \times \mathbf{v} = \mathbf{0}$.

2. **True or False** For any vector **v**, $\mathbf{v} \times \mathbf{v} = \mathbf{0}$.

3. **True or False** If **u** and **v** are vectors, then $\mathbf{u} \times \mathbf{v} + \mathbf{v} \times \mathbf{u} = \mathbf{0}$.

4. **True or False** $\mathbf{u} \times \mathbf{v}$ is a vector that is parallel to both **u** and **v**.

5. **True or False** $\|\mathbf{u} \times \mathbf{v}\| = \|\mathbf{u}\| \, \|\mathbf{v}\| \cos \theta$, where θ is the angle between **u** and **v**.

6. **True or False** The area of the parallelogram having **u** and **v** as adjacent sides is the magnitude of the cross product of **u** and **v**.

Skill Building

In Problems 7–14, find the value of each determinant.

7. $\begin{vmatrix} 3 & 4 \\ 1 & 2 \end{vmatrix}$

8. $\begin{vmatrix} -2 & 5 \\ 2 & -3 \end{vmatrix}$

9. $\begin{vmatrix} 6 & 5 \\ -2 & -1 \end{vmatrix}$

10. $\begin{vmatrix} -4 & 0 \\ 5 & 3 \end{vmatrix}$

11. $\begin{vmatrix} A & B & C \\ 2 & 1 & 4 \\ 1 & 3 & 1 \end{vmatrix}$

12. $\begin{vmatrix} A & B & C \\ 0 & 2 & 4 \\ 3 & 1 & 3 \end{vmatrix}$

13. $\begin{vmatrix} A & B & C \\ -1 & 3 & 5 \\ 5 & 0 & -2 \end{vmatrix}$

14. $\begin{vmatrix} A & B & C \\ 1 & -2 & -3 \\ 0 & 2 & -2 \end{vmatrix}$

In Problems 15–22, find (a) $\mathbf{v} \times \mathbf{w}$, (b) $\mathbf{w} \times \mathbf{v}$, (c) $\mathbf{w} \times \mathbf{w}$, and (d) $\mathbf{v} \times \mathbf{v}$.

15. $\mathbf{v} = 2\mathbf{i} - 3\mathbf{j} + \mathbf{k}$
    $\mathbf{w} = 3\mathbf{i} - 2\mathbf{j} - \mathbf{k}$

16. $\mathbf{v} = -\mathbf{i} + 3\mathbf{j} + 2\mathbf{k}$
    $\mathbf{w} = 3\mathbf{i} - 2\mathbf{j} - \mathbf{k}$

17. $\mathbf{v} = \mathbf{i} + \mathbf{j}$
    $\mathbf{w} = 2\mathbf{i} + \mathbf{j} + \mathbf{k}$

18. $\mathbf{v} = \mathbf{i} - 4\mathbf{j} + 2\mathbf{k}$
    $\mathbf{w} = 3\mathbf{i} + 2\mathbf{j} + \mathbf{k}$

19. $\mathbf{v} = 2\mathbf{i} - \mathbf{j} + 2\mathbf{k}$
    $\mathbf{w} = \mathbf{j} - \mathbf{k}$

20. $\mathbf{v} = 3\mathbf{i} + \mathbf{j} + 3\mathbf{k}$
    $\mathbf{w} = \mathbf{i} - \mathbf{k}$

21. $\mathbf{v} = \mathbf{i} - \mathbf{j} - \mathbf{k}$
    $\mathbf{w} = 4\mathbf{i} - 3\mathbf{k}$

22. $\mathbf{v} = 2\mathbf{i} - 3\mathbf{j}$
    $\mathbf{w} = 3\mathbf{j} - 2\mathbf{k}$

*In Problems 23–44, use the given vectors **u**, **v**, and **w** to find each expression.*

$$\mathbf{u} = 2\mathbf{i} - 3\mathbf{j} + \mathbf{k} \qquad \mathbf{v} = -3\mathbf{i} + 3\mathbf{j} + 2\mathbf{k} \qquad \mathbf{w} = \mathbf{i} + \mathbf{j} + 3\mathbf{k}$$

23. $\mathbf{u} \times \mathbf{v}$

24. $\mathbf{v} \times \mathbf{w}$

25. $\mathbf{v} \times \mathbf{u}$

26. $\mathbf{w} \times \mathbf{v}$

27. $\mathbf{v} \times \mathbf{v}$

28. $\mathbf{w} \times \mathbf{w}$

29. $(3\mathbf{u}) \times \mathbf{v}$

30. $\mathbf{v} \times (4\mathbf{w})$

31. $\mathbf{u} \times (2\mathbf{v})$

32. $(-3\mathbf{v}) \times \mathbf{w}$

33. $\mathbf{u} \cdot (\mathbf{u} \times \mathbf{v})$

34. $\mathbf{v} \cdot (\mathbf{v} \times \mathbf{w})$

35. $\mathbf{u} \cdot (\mathbf{v} \times \mathbf{w})$

36. $(\mathbf{u} \times \mathbf{v}) \cdot \mathbf{w}$

37. $\mathbf{v} \cdot (\mathbf{u} \times \mathbf{w})$

38. $(\mathbf{v} \times \mathbf{u}) \cdot \mathbf{w}$

39. $\mathbf{u} \times (\mathbf{v} \times \mathbf{v})$

40. $(\mathbf{w} \times \mathbf{w}) \times \mathbf{v}$

41. Find a vector orthogonal to both **u** and **v**.

42. Find a vector orthogonal to both **u** and **w**.

43. Find a vector orthogonal to both **u** and $\mathbf{i} + \mathbf{j}$.

44. Find a vector orthogonal to both **u** and $\mathbf{j} + \mathbf{k}$.

In Problems 45–48, find the area of the parallelogram with one corner at P_1 and adjacent sides $\overrightarrow{P_1P_2}$ and $\overrightarrow{P_1P_3}$.

45. $P_1 = (0, 0, 0)$, $P_2 = (1, 2, 3)$, $P_3 = (-2, 3, 0)$

46. $P_1 = (0, 0, 0)$, $P_2 = (2, 3, 1)$, $P_3 = (-2, 4, 1)$

47. $P_1 = (1, 2, 0)$, $P_2 = (-2, 3, 4)$, $P_3 = (0, -2, 3)$

48. $P_1 = (-2, 0, 2)$, $P_2 = (2, 1, -1)$, $P_3 = (2, -1, 2)$

In Problems 49–52, find the area of the parallelogram with vertices P_1, P_2, P_3, and P_4.

49. $P_1 = (1, 1, 2)$, $P_2 = (1, 2, 3)$, $P_3 = (-2, 3, 0)$,
    $P_4 = (-2, 4, 1)$

50. $P_1 = (2, 1, 1)$, $P_2 = (2, 3, 1)$, $P_3 = (-2, 4, 1)$,
    $P_4 = (-2, 6, 1)$

51. $P_1 = (1, 2, -1)$, $P_2 = (4, 2, -3)$, $P_3 = (6, -5, 2)$,
    $P_4 = (9, -5, 0)$

52. $P_1 = (-1, 1, 1)$, $P_2 = (-1, 2, 2)$, $P_3 = (-3, 4, -5)$,
    $P_4 = (-3, 5, -4)$

Applications and Extensions

53. Find a unit vector normal to the plane containing $\mathbf{v} = \mathbf{i} + 3\mathbf{j} - 2\mathbf{k}$ and $\mathbf{w} = -2\mathbf{i} + \mathbf{j} + 3\mathbf{k}$.

54. Find a unit vector normal to the plane containing $\mathbf{v} = 2\mathbf{i} + 3\mathbf{j} - \mathbf{k}$ and $\mathbf{w} = -2\mathbf{i} - 4\mathbf{j} - 3\mathbf{k}$.

55. Volume of a Parallelepiped A **parallelepiped** is a prism whose faces are all parallelograms. Let **A**, **B**, and **C** be the vectors that define the parallelepiped shown in the figure. The volume V of the parallelepiped is given by the formula $V = |(\mathbf{A} \times \mathbf{B}) \cdot \mathbf{C}|$.

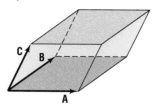

Find the volume of a parallelepiped if the defining vectors are $\mathbf{A} = 3\mathbf{i} - 2\mathbf{j} + 4\mathbf{k}$, $\mathbf{B} = 2\mathbf{i} + \mathbf{j} - 2\mathbf{k}$, and $\mathbf{C} = 3\mathbf{i} - 6\mathbf{j} - 2\mathbf{k}$.

56. Volume of a Parallelepiped Refer to Problem 55. Find the volume of a parallelepiped whose defining vectors are $\mathbf{A} = \langle 1, 0, 6 \rangle$, $\mathbf{B} = \langle 2, 3, -8 \rangle$, and $\mathbf{C} = \langle 8, -5, 6 \rangle$.

57. Prove for vectors **u** and **v** that

$$\|\mathbf{u} \times \mathbf{v}\|^2 = \|\mathbf{u}\|^2 \|\mathbf{v}\|^2 - (\mathbf{u} \cdot \mathbf{v})^2$$

[**Hint:** Proceed as in the proof of property (4), computing first the left side and then the right side.]

58. Show that if **u** and **v** are orthogonal then

$$\|\mathbf{u} \times \mathbf{v}\| = \|\mathbf{u}\| \, \|\mathbf{v}\|$$

59. Show that if **u** and **v** are orthogonal unit vectors then $\mathbf{u} \times \mathbf{v}$ is also a unit vector.

60. Prove property (3).

61. Prove property (5).

62. Prove property (9).

[**Hint:** Use the result of Problem 57 and the fact that if θ is the angle between **u** and **v** then $\mathbf{u} \cdot \mathbf{v} = \|\mathbf{u}\| \, \|\mathbf{v}\| \cos \theta$.]

Explaining Concepts: Discussion and Writing

63. If $\mathbf{u} \cdot \mathbf{v} = 0$ and $\mathbf{u} \times \mathbf{v} = \mathbf{0}$, what, if anything, can you conclude about **u** and **v**?

CHAPTER REVIEW

Things to Know

Polar Coordinates (pp. 558–565)

Relationship between polar coordinates (r, θ) and rectangular coordinates (x, y) (pp. 560 and 563)	$x = r \cos \theta$, $y = r \sin \theta$
	$r^2 = x^2 + y^2$, $\tan \theta = \dfrac{y}{x}$, $x \neq 0$
Polar form of a complex number (p. 583)	If $z = x + yi$, then $z = r(\cos \theta + i \sin \theta)$, where $r = |z| = \sqrt{x^2 + y^2}$, $\sin \theta = \dfrac{y}{r}$, $\cos \theta = \dfrac{x}{r}$, $0 \leq \theta < 2\pi$.
De Moivre's Theorem (p. 585)	If $z = r(\cos \theta + i \sin \theta)$, then $z^n = r^n[\cos(n\theta) + i \sin(n\theta)]$, where $n \geq 1$ is a positive integer.
nth root of a complex number $w = r(\cos \theta_0 + i \sin \theta_0)$ (p. 586)	$z_k = \sqrt[n]{r}\left[\cos\left(\dfrac{\theta_0}{n} + \dfrac{2k\pi}{n}\right) + i \sin\left(\dfrac{\theta_0}{n} + \dfrac{2k\pi}{n}\right)\right]$, $k = 0, \ldots, n-1$, where $n \geq 2$ is an integer

Vectors (pp. 589–599)

	Quantity having magnitude and direction; equivalent to a directed line segment $\overrightarrow{PQ}$
Position vector (pp. 593 and 612)	Vector whose initial point is at the origin
Unit vector (pp. 592 and 614)	Vector whose magnitude is 1
Dot product (pp. 603 and 614)	If $\mathbf{v} = a_1\mathbf{i} + b_1\mathbf{j}$ and $\mathbf{w} = a_2\mathbf{i} + b_2\mathbf{j}$, then $\mathbf{v} \cdot \mathbf{w} = a_1 a_2 + b_1 b_2$.
	If $\mathbf{v} = a_1\mathbf{i} + b_1\mathbf{j} + c_1\mathbf{k}$ and $\mathbf{w} = a_2\mathbf{i} + b_2\mathbf{j} + c_2\mathbf{k}$, then $\mathbf{v} \cdot \mathbf{w} = a_1 a_2 + b_1 b_2 + c_1 c_2$.
Angle θ between two nonzero vectors **u** and **v** (pp. 605 and 615)	$\cos \theta = \dfrac{\mathbf{u} \cdot \mathbf{v}}{\|\mathbf{u}\| \, \|\mathbf{v}\|}$
Direction angles of a vector in space (p. 616)	If $\mathbf{v} = a\mathbf{i} + b\mathbf{j} + c\mathbf{k}$, then $\mathbf{v} = \|\mathbf{v}\|[(\cos \alpha)\mathbf{i} + (\cos \beta)\mathbf{j} + (\cos \gamma)\mathbf{k}]$, where $\cos \alpha = \dfrac{a}{\|\mathbf{v}\|}$, $\cos \beta = \dfrac{b}{\|\mathbf{v}\|}$, $\cos \gamma = \dfrac{c}{\|\mathbf{v}\|}$.
Cross product (p. 620)	If $\mathbf{v} = a_1\mathbf{i} + b_1\mathbf{j} + c_1\mathbf{k}$ and $\mathbf{w} = a_2\mathbf{i} + b_2\mathbf{j} + c_2\mathbf{k}$, then $\mathbf{v} \times \mathbf{w} = [b_1 c_2 - b_2 c_1]\mathbf{i} - [a_1 c_2 - a_2 c_1]\mathbf{j} + [a_1 b_2 - a_2 b_1]\mathbf{k}$.
Area of a parallelogram (p. 622)	$\|\mathbf{u} \times \mathbf{v}\| = \|\mathbf{u}\| \, \|\mathbf{v}\| \sin \theta$, where θ is the angle between the two adjacent sides **u** and **v**.

Objectives

Section		You should be able to . . .	Example(s)	Review Exercises
9.1	1	Plot points using polar coordinates (p. 558)	1–3	1–6
	2	Convert from polar coordinates to rectangular coordinates (p. 560)	4	1–6
	3	Convert from rectangular coordinates to polar coordinates (p. 562)	5–7	7–12
	4	Transform equations between polar and rectangular forms (p. 564)	8, 9	13(a)–18(a)
9.2	1	Graph and identify polar equations by converting to rectangular equations (p. 568)	1–6	13(b)–18(b)
	2	Test polar equations for symmetry (p. 571)	7–10	19–24
	3	Graph polar equations by plotting points (p. 572)	7–12	19–24
9.3	1	Plot points in the complex plane (p. 582)	1	29–34
	2	Convert a complex number between rectangular form and polar form (p. 583)	2, 3	25–34
	3	Find products and quotients of complex numbers in polar form (p. 584)	4	35–40
	4	Use De Moivre's Theorem (p. 585)	5, 6	41–48
	5	Find complex roots (p. 586)	7	49–50
9.4	1	Graph vectors (p. 592)	1	51–54
	2	Find a position vector (p. 592)	2	55–58
	3	Add and subtract vectors algebraically (p. 594)	3	59, 60
	4	Find a scalar multiple and the magnitude of a vector (p. 595)	4	55–58, 61–66
	5	Find a unit vector (p. 595)	5	67, 68
	6	Find a vector from its direction and magnitude (p. 596)	6	69, 70
	7	Model with vectors (p. 597)	8–10	111–113
9.5	1	Find the dot product of two vectors (p. 603)	1	87–90
	2	Find the angle between two vectors (p. 604)	2	87–90
	3	Determine whether two vectors are parallel (p. 605)	3	95–100
	4	Determine whether two vectors are orthogonal (p. 605)	4	95–100
	5	Decompose a vector into two orthogonal vectors (p. 606)	5, 6	101–104, 115
	6	Compute work (p. 608)	7	114
9.6	1	Find the distance between two points in space (p. 612)	1	73, 74
	2	Find position vectors in space (p. 612)	2	75, 76
	3	Perform operations on vectors (p. 613)	3–5	77–82, 85
	4	Find the dot product (p. 614)	6	91–94
	5	Find the angle between two vectors (p. 615)	7	91–94
	6	Find the direction angles of a vector (p. 615)	8–10	105, 106
9.7	1	Find the cross product of two vectors (p. 620)	1–3	83, 84
	2	Know algebraic properties of the cross product (p. 621)	p. 621	109, 110
	3	Know geometric properties of the cross product (p. 622)	p. 622	107, 108
	4	Find a vector orthogonal to two given vectors (p. 622)	4	86
	5	Find the area of a parallelogram (p. 623)	5	107, 108

Review Exercises

In Problems 1–6, plot each point given in polar coordinates, and find its rectangular coordinates.

1. $\left(3, \dfrac{\pi}{6}\right)$ **2.** $\left(4, \dfrac{2\pi}{3}\right)$ **3.** $\left(-2, \dfrac{4\pi}{3}\right)$ **4.** $\left(-1, \dfrac{5\pi}{4}\right)$ **5.** $\left(-3, -\dfrac{\pi}{2}\right)$ **6.** $\left(-4, -\dfrac{\pi}{4}\right)$

In Problems 7–12, the rectangular coordinates of a point are given. Find two pairs of polar coordinates (r, θ) for each point, one with $r > 0$ and the other with $r < 0$. Express θ in radians.

7. $(-3, 3)$ **8.** $(1, -1)$ **9.** $(0, -2)$ **10.** $(2, 0)$ **11.** $(3, 4)$ **12.** $(-5, 12)$

In Problems 13– 18, the variables r and θ represent polar coordinates. (a) Write each polar equation as an equation in rectangular coordinates (x, y). (b) Identify the equation and graph it.

13. $r = 2 \sin \theta$

14. $3r = \sin \theta$

15. $r = 5$

16. $\theta = \dfrac{\pi}{4}$

17. $r \cos \theta + 3r \sin \theta = 6$

18. $r^2 + 4r \sin \theta - 8r \cos \theta = 5$

In Problems 19– 24, sketch the graph of each polar equation. Be sure to test for symmetry.

19. $r = 4 \cos \theta$

20. $r = 3 \sin \theta$

21. $r = 3 - 3 \sin \theta$

22. $r = 2 + \cos \theta$

23. $r = 4 - \cos \theta$

24. $r = 1 - 2 \sin \theta$

In Problems 25– 28, write each complex number in polar form. Express each argument in degrees.

25. $-1 - i$

26. $-\sqrt{3} + i$

27. $4 - 3i$

28. $3 - 2i$

In Problems 29– 34, write each complex number in the standard form a + bi and plot each in the complex plane.

29. $2(\cos 150° + i \sin 150°)$

30. $3(\cos 60° + i \sin 60°)$

31. $3\left(\cos \dfrac{2\pi}{3} + i \sin \dfrac{2\pi}{3}\right)$

32. $4\left(\cos \dfrac{3\pi}{4} + i \sin \dfrac{3\pi}{4}\right)$

33. $0.1(\cos 350° + i \sin 350°)$

34. $0.5(\cos 160° + i \sin 160°)$

In Problems 35– 40, find zw and $\dfrac{z}{w}$. Leave your answers in polar form.

35. $z = \cos 80° + i \sin 80°$
$w = \cos 50° + i \sin 50°$

36. $z = \cos 205° + i \sin 205°$
$w = \cos 85° + i \sin 85°$

37. $z = 3\left(\cos \dfrac{9\pi}{5} + i \sin \dfrac{9\pi}{5}\right)$
$w = 2\left(\cos \dfrac{\pi}{5} + i \sin \dfrac{\pi}{5}\right)$

38. $z = 2\left(\cos \dfrac{5\pi}{3} + i \sin \dfrac{5\pi}{3}\right)$
$w = 3\left(\cos \dfrac{\pi}{3} + i \sin \dfrac{\pi}{3}\right)$

39. $z = 5(\cos 10° + i \sin 10°)$
$w = \cos 355° + i \sin 355°$

40. $z = 4(\cos 50° + i \sin 50°)$
$w = \cos 340° + i \sin 340°$

In Problems 41– 48, write each expression in the standard form a + bi.

41. $[3(\cos 20° + i \sin 20°)]^3$

42. $[2(\cos 50° + i \sin 50°)]^3$

43. $\left[\sqrt{2}\left(\cos \dfrac{5\pi}{8} + i \sin \dfrac{5\pi}{8}\right)\right]^4$

44. $\left[2\left(\cos \dfrac{5\pi}{16} + i \sin \dfrac{5\pi}{16}\right)\right]^4$

45. $\left(1 - \sqrt{3}i\right)^6$

46. $(2 - 2i)^8$

47. $(3 + 4i)^4$

48. $(1 - 2i)^4$

49. Find all the complex cube roots of 27.

50. Find all the complex fourth roots of −16.

In Problems 51–54, use the figure to graph each of the following:

51. u + v

52. v + w

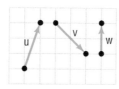

53. 2u + 3v

54. 5v − 2w

In Problems 55–58, the vector $\mathbf{v}$ is represented by the directed line segment $\overrightarrow{PQ}$. Write $\mathbf{v}$ in the form $a\mathbf{i} + b\mathbf{j}$ and find $\|\mathbf{v}\|$.

55. $P = (1, -2); \quad Q = (3, -6)$

56. $P = (-3, 1); \quad Q = (4, -2)$

57. $P = (0, -2); \quad Q = (-1, 1)$

58. $P = (3, -4); \quad Q = (-2, 0)$

In Problems 59– 68, use the vectors $\mathbf{v} = -2\mathbf{i} + \mathbf{j}$ and $\mathbf{w} = 4\mathbf{i} - 3\mathbf{j}$ to find:

59. v + w

60. v − w

61. 4v − 3w

62. −v + 2w

63. $\|\mathbf{v}\|$

64. $\|\mathbf{v} + \mathbf{w}\|$

65. $\|\mathbf{v}\| + \|\mathbf{w}\|$

66. $\|2\mathbf{v}\| - 3\|\mathbf{w}\|$

67. Find a unit vector in the same direction as $\mathbf{v}$.

68. Find a unit vector in the opposite direction of $\mathbf{w}$.

69. Find the vector **v** in the *xy*-plane with magnitude 3 if the angle between **v** and **i** is 60°.

70. Find the vector **v** in the *xy*-plane with magnitude 5 if the angle between **v** and **i** is 150°.

71. Find the direction angle between **i** and **v** = −**i** + $\sqrt{3}$ **j**.

72. Find the direction angle between **i** and **v** = 2**i** − 6**j**.

73. Find the distance from $P_1 = (1, 3, −2)$ to $P_2 = (4, −2, 1)$.

74. Find the distance from $P_1 = (0, −4, 3)$ to $P_2 = (6, −5, −1)$.

75. A vector **v** has initial point $P = (1, 3, −2)$ and terminal point $Q = (4, −2, 1)$. Write **v** in the form **v** = a**i** + b**j** + c**k**.

76. A vector **v** has initial point $P = (0, −4, 3)$ and terminal point $Q = (6, −5, −1)$. Write **v** in the form **v** = a**i** + b**j** + c**k**.

In Problems 77–86, use the vectors **v** = 3**i** + **j** − 2**k** *and* **w** = −3**i** + 2**j** − **k** *to find each expression.*

77. 4**v** − 3**w**

78. −**v** + 2**w**

79. $\|\mathbf{v} − \mathbf{w}\|$

80. $\|\mathbf{v} + \mathbf{w}\|$

81. $\|\mathbf{v}\| − \|\mathbf{w}\|$

82. $\|\mathbf{v}\| + \|\mathbf{w}\|$

83. **v** × **w**

84. **v** · (**v** × **w**)

85. Find a unit vector in the same direction as **v** and then in the opposite direction of **v**.

86. Find a unit vector orthogonal to both **v** and **w**.

In Problems 87–94, find the dot product **v** · **w** *and the angle between* **v** *and* **w**.

87. **v** = −2**i** + **j**, **w** = 4**i** − 3**j**

88. **v** = 3**i** − **j**, **w** = **i** + **j**

89. **v** = **i** − 3**j**, **w** = −**i** + **j**

90. **v** = **i** + 4**j**, **w** = 3**i** − 2**j**

91. **v** = **i** + **j** + **k**, **w** = **i** − **j** + **k**

92. **v** = **i** − **j** + **k**, **w** = 2**i** + **j** + **k**

93. **v** = 4**i** − **j** + 2**k**, **w** = **i** − 2**j** − 3**k**

94. **v** = −**i** − 2**j** + 3**k**, **w** = 5**i** + **j** + **k**

In Problems 95–100, determine whether **v** *and* **w** *are parallel, orthogonal, or neither.*

95. **v** = 2**i** + 3**j**; **w** = −4**i** − 6**j**

96. **v** = −2**i** − **j**; **w** = 2**i** + **j**

97. **v** = 3**i** − 4**j**; **w** = −3**i** + 4**j**

98. **v** = −2**i** + 2**j**; **w** = −3**i** + 2**j**

99. **v** = 3**i** − 2**j**; **w** = 4**i** + 6**j**

100. **v** = −4**i** + 2**j**; **w** = 2**i** + 4**j**

In Problems 101–104, decompose **v** *into two vectors, one parallel to* **w** *and the other orthogonal to* **w**.

101. **v** = 2**i** + **j**; **w** = −4**i** + 3**j**

102. **v** = −3**i** + 2**j**; **w** = −2**i** + **j**

103. **v** = 2**i** + 3**j**; **w** = 3**i** + **j**

104. **v** = −**i** + 2**j**; **w** = 3**i** − **j**

---

105. Find the direction angles of the vector **v** = 3**i** − 4**j** + 2**k**.

106. Find the direction angles of the vector **v** = **i** − **j** + 2**k**.

107. Find the area of the parallelogram with vertices $P_1 = (1, 1, 1)$, $P_2 = (2, 3, 4)$, $P_3 = (6, 5, 2)$, and $P_4 = (7, 7, 5)$.

108. Find the area of the parallelogram with vertices $P_1 = (2, −1, 1)$, $P_2 = (5, 1, 4)$, $P_3 = (0, 1, 1)$, and $P_4 = (3, 3, 4)$.

109. If **u** × **v** = 2**i** − 3**j** + **k**, what is **v** × **u**?

110. Suppose that **u** = 3**v**. What is **u** × **v**?

111. Actual Speed and Direction of a Swimmer A swimmer can maintain a constant speed of 5 miles per hour. If the swimmer heads directly across a river that has a current moving at the rate of 2 miles per hour, what is the actual speed of the swimmer? (See the figure.) If the river is 1 mile wide, how far downstream will the swimmer end up from the point directly across the river from the starting point?

112. Actual Speed and Direction of an Airplane An airplane has an airspeed of 500 kilometers per hour (k/hr) in a northerly direction. The wind velocity is 60 (k/hr) in a southeasterly direction. Find the actual speed and direction of the plane relative to the ground.

113. Static Equilibrium A weight of 2000 pounds is suspended from two cables, as shown in the figure. What are the tensions in each cable?

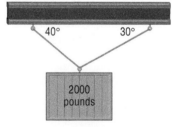

114. Computing Work Find the work done by a force of 5 pounds acting in the direction 60° to the horizontal in moving an object 20 feet from $(0, 0)$ to $(20, 0)$.

115. Braking Load A moving van with a gross weight of 8000 pounds is parked on a street with a 5° grade. Find the magnitude of the force required to keep the van from rolling down the hill. What is the magnitude of the force perpendicular to the hill?

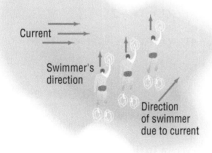

CHAPTER TEST

CHAPTER
Test Prep
VIDEOS

The Chapter Test Prep Videos are step-by-step test solutions available in the Video Resources DVD, in *MyMathLab*, or on this text's You Tube Channel. Flip back to the Student Resources page to see the exact web address for this text's YouTube channel.

In Problems 1–3, plot each point given in polar coordinates.

1. $\left(2, \dfrac{3\pi}{4}\right)$

2. $\left(3, -\dfrac{\pi}{6}\right)$

3. $\left(-4, \dfrac{\pi}{3}\right)$

4. Convert $\left(2, 2\sqrt{3}\right)$ from rectangular coordinates to polar coordinates (r, θ), where $r > 0$ and $0 \le \theta < 2\pi$.

In Problems 5–7, convert the polar equation to a rectangular equation. Graph the equation.

5. $r = 7$

6. $\tan \theta = 3$

7. $r \sin^2 \theta + 8 \sin \theta = r$

In Problems 8 and 9, test the polar equation for symmetry with respect to the pole, the polar axis, and the line $\theta = \dfrac{\pi}{2}$.

8. $r^2 \cos \theta = 5$

9. $r = 5 \sin \theta \cos^2 \theta$

In Problems 10–12, perform the given operation, where $z = 2(\cos 85° + i \sin 85°)$ and $w = 3(\cos 22° + i \sin 22°)$. Write your answer in polar form.

10. $z \cdot w$

11. $\dfrac{w}{z}$

12. w^5

13. Find all the complex cube roots of $-8 + 8\sqrt{3}i$. Then plot them in rectangular coordinates.

In Problems 14–18, $P_1 = \left(3\sqrt{2}, 7\sqrt{2}\right)$ and $P_2 = \left(8\sqrt{2}, 2\sqrt{2}\right)$.

14. Find the position vector $\mathbf{v}$ equal to $\overrightarrow{P_1 P_2}$.

15. Find $\|\mathbf{v}\|$.

16. Find the unit vector in the direction of $\mathbf{v}$.

17. Find the angle between $\mathbf{v}$ and $\mathbf{i}$.

18. Decompose $\mathbf{v}$ into its vertical and horizontal components.

In Problems 19–22, $\mathbf{v}_1 = \langle 4, 6 \rangle$, $\mathbf{v}_2 = \langle -3, -6 \rangle$, $\mathbf{v}_3 = \langle -8, 4 \rangle$, and $\mathbf{v}_4 = \langle 10, 15 \rangle$.

19. Find the vector $\mathbf{v}_1 + 2\mathbf{v}_2 - \mathbf{v}_3$.

20. Which two vectors are parallel?

21. Which two vectors are orthogonal?

22. Find the angle between vectors $\mathbf{v}_1$ and $\mathbf{v}_2$.

In Problems 23–25, use the vectors $\mathbf{u} = 2\mathbf{i} - 3\mathbf{j} + \mathbf{k}$ and $\mathbf{v} = -\mathbf{i} + 3\mathbf{j} + 2\mathbf{k}$.

23. Find $\mathbf{u} \times \mathbf{v}$.

24. Find the direction angles for $\mathbf{u}$.

25. Find the area of the parallelogram that has $\mathbf{u}$ and $\mathbf{v}$ as adjacent sides.

26. A 1200-pound chandelier is to be suspended over a large ballroom; the chandelier will be hung on two cables of equal length whose ends will be attached to the ceiling, 16 feet apart. The chandelier will be free hanging so that the ends of the cable will make equal angles with the ceiling. If the top of the chandelier is to be 16 feet from the ceiling, what is the minimum tension each cable must be able to endure?

CUMULATIVE REVIEW

1. Find the real solutions, if any, of the equation $e^{x^2-9} = 1$.

2. Find an equation for the line containing the origin that makes an angle of $30°$ with the positive x-axis.

3. Find an equation for the circle with center at the point $(0, 1)$ and radius 3. Graph this circle.

4. What is the domain of the function $f(x) = \ln(1 - 2x)$?

5. Test the equation $x^2 + y^3 = 2x^4$ for symmetry with respect to the x-axis, the y-axis, and the origin.

6. Graph the function $y = |\ln x|$.

7. Graph the function $y = |\sin x|$.

8. Graph the function $y = \sin|x|$.

9. Find the exact value of $\sin^{-1}\left(-\dfrac{1}{2}\right)$.

10. Graph the equations $x = 3$ and $y = 4$ on the same set of rectangular coordinates.

11. Graph the equations $r = 2$ and $\theta = \dfrac{\pi}{3}$ on the same set of polar coordinates.

12. What is the amplitude and period of $y = -4\cos(\pi x)$?

CHAPTER PROJECTS

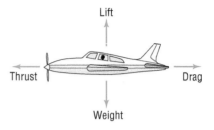

Source: *www.aeromuseum.org/eduHowtoFly.html*

I. Modeling Aircraft Motion Four aerodynamic forces act on an airplane in flight: lift, weight, thrust, and drag. While an aircraft is in flight, these four forces continuously battle each other. Weight opposes lift and drag opposes thrust. See the figure. In balanced flight at constant speed, both the lift and weight are equal and the thrust and drag are equal.

1. What will happen to the aircraft if the lift is held constant while the weight is decreased (say from burning off fuel)?

2. What will happen to the aircraft if the lift is decreased while the weight is held constant?

3. What will happen to the aircraft if the thrust is increased while the drag is held constant?

4. What will happen to the aircraft if the drag is increased while the thrust is held constant?

In 1903 the Wright brothers made the first controlled powered flight. The weight of their plane was approximately 700 pounds (lb). Newton's Second Law of motion states that force = mass × acceleration ($F = ma$). If the mass is measured in kilograms (kg) and acceleration in meters per second squared (m/sec^2), then the force will be measured in newtons (N). [**Note:** $1 \text{ N} = 1 \text{ kg} \cdot \text{m/sec}^2$.]

5. If $1 \text{ kg} = 2.205 \text{ lb}$, convert the weight of the Wright brothers' plane to kilograms.

6. If acceleration due to gravity is $a = 9.80 \text{ m/sec}^2$, determine the force due to weight on the Wright brothers' plane.

7. What must be true about the lift force of the Wright brothers' plane for it to get off the ground?

8. The weight of a fully loaded Cessna 170B is 2200 lb. What lift force is required to get this plane off the ground?

9. The maximum gross weight of a Boeing 747 is 255,000 lb. What lift force is required to get this jet off the ground?

The following projects are available at the Instructors' Resource Center (IRC):

II. Project at Motorola *Signal Fades due to Interference* Complex trigonometric functions are used to assure that a cellphone has optimal reception as the user travels up and down an elevator.

III. Compound Interest The effect of continuously compounded interest is analyzed using polar coordinates.

IV. Complex Equations Analysis of complex equations illustrates the connections between complex and real equations. At times, using complex equations is more efficient for proving mathematical theorems.

Appendix A
Review

Outline

A.1 Algebra Essentials

PREPARING FOR THIS SECTION *Before getting started, read "To the Student" on page ii at the beginning of this book.*

OBJECTIVES
1 Work with Sets (p. A1)
2 Graph Inequalities (p. A4)
3 Find Distance on the Real Number Line (p. A5)
4 Evaluate Algebraic Expressions (p. A6)
5 Determine the Domain of a Variable (p. A7)
6 Use the Laws of Exponents (p. A7)
7 Evaluate Square Roots (p. A9)
8 Use a Calculator to Evaluate Exponents (p. A10)

1 Work with Sets

A **set** is a well-defined collection of distinct objects. The objects of a set are called its **elements.** By **well-defined,** we mean that there is a rule that enables us to determine whether a given object is an element of the set. If a set has no elements, it is called the **empty set,** or **null set,** and is denoted by the symbol $\varnothing$.

For example, the set of *digits* consists of the collection of numbers 0, 1, 2, 3, 4, 5, 6, 7, 8, and 9. If we use the symbol D to denote the set of digits, then we can write

$$D = \{0, 1, 2, 3, 4, 5, 6, 7, 8, 9\}$$

In this notation, the braces $\{\ \}$ are used to enclose the objects, or **elements,** in the set. This method of denoting a set is called the **roster method.** A second way to denote a set is to use **set-builder notation,** where the set D of digits is written as

$$D = \{\quad x \quad | \quad x \text{ is a digit}\}$$

Read as "D is the set of all x such that x is a digit."

A1

EXAMPLE 1

Using Set-builder Notation and the Roster Method

(a) $E = \{x | x \text{ is an even digit}\} = \{0, 2, 4, 6, 8\}$
(b) $O = \{x | x \text{ is an odd digit}\} = \{1, 3, 5, 7, 9\}$

Because the elements of a set are distinct, we never repeat elements. For example, we would never write $\{1, 2, 3, 2\}$; the correct listing is $\{1, 2, 3\}$. Because a set is a collection, the order in which the elements are listed is immaterial. $\{1, 2, 3\}$, $\{1, 3, 2\}$, $\{2, 1, 3\}$, and so on, all represent the same set.

If every element of a set A is also an element of a set B, then we say that A is a **subset** of B and write $A \subseteq B$. If two sets A and B have the same elements, then we say that A **equals** B and write $A = B$.

For example, $\{1, 2, 3\} \subseteq \{1, 2, 3, 4, 5\}$ and $\{1, 2, 3\} = \{2, 3, 1\}$.

DEFINITION

If A and B are sets, the **intersection** of A with B, denoted $A \cap B$, is the set consisting of elements that belong to both A and B. The **union** of A with B, denoted $A \cup B$, is the set consisting of elements that belong to either A or B, or both.

EXAMPLE 2

Finding the Intersection and Union of Sets

Let $A = \{1, 3, 5, 8\}$, $B = \{3, 5, 7\}$, and $C = \{2, 4, 6, 8\}$. Find:

(a) $A \cap B$ (b) $A \cup B$ (c) $B \cap (A \cup C)$

Solution

(a) $A \cap B = \{1, 3, 5, 8\} \cap \{3, 5, 7\} = \{3, 5\}$
(b) $A \cup B = \{1, 3, 5, 8\} \cup \{3, 5, 7\} = \{1, 3, 5, 7, 8\}$
(c) $B \cap (A \cup C) = \{3, 5, 7\} \cap (\{1, 3, 5, 8\} \cup \{2, 4, 6, 8\})$
$= \{3, 5, 7\} \cap \{1, 2, 3, 4, 5, 6, 8\} = \{3, 5\}$

Now Work PROBLEM 13

Usually, in working with sets, we designate a **universal set** U, the set consisting of all the elements that we wish to consider. Once a universal set has been designated, we can consider elements of the universal set not found in a given set.

DEFINITION

If A is a set, the **complement** of A, denoted $\overline{A}$, is the set consisting of all the elements in the universal set that are not in A.*

EXAMPLE 3

Finding the Complement of a Set

If the universal set is $U = \{1, 2, 3, 4, 5, 6, 7, 8, 9\}$ and if $A = \{1, 3, 5, 7, 9\}$, then $\overline{A} = \{2, 4, 6, 8\}$.

It follows from the definition of complement that $A \cup \overline{A} = U$ and $A \cap \overline{A} = \emptyset$. Do you see why?

Now Work PROBLEM 17

It is often helpful to draw pictures of sets. Such pictures, called **Venn diagrams,** represent sets as circles enclosed in a rectangle, which represents the universal set. Such diagrams often help us to visualize various relationships among sets. See Figure 1.

Figure 1

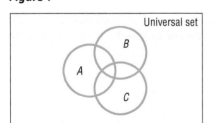

Universal set

---

* Some books use the notation A' or A^c for the complement of A.

If we know that $A \subseteq B$, we might use the Venn diagram in Figure 2(a). If we know that A and B have no elements in common, that is, if $A \cap B = \varnothing$, we might use the Venn diagram in Figure 2(b). The sets A and B in Figure 2(b) are said to be **disjoint.**

Figure 2

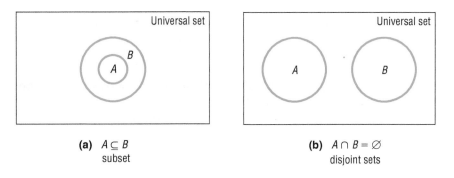

(a) $A \subseteq B$
subset

(b) $A \cap B = \varnothing$
disjoint sets

Figures 3(a), 3(b), and 3(c) use Venn diagrams to illustrate the definitions of intersection, union, and complement, respectively.

Figure 3

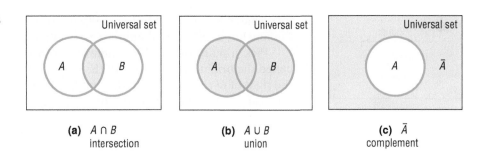

(a) $A \cap B$
intersection

(b) $A \cup B$
union

(c) $\bar{A}$
complement

Real Numbers

Real numbers are represented by symbols such as

$$25, \quad 0, \quad -3, \quad \frac{1}{2}, \quad -\frac{5}{4}, \quad 0.125, \quad \sqrt{2}, \quad \pi, \quad \sqrt[3]{-2}, \quad 0.666\ldots$$

The set of **counting numbers,** or **natural numbers,** contains the numbers in the set $\{1, 2, 3, 4, \ldots\}$. (The three dots, called an **ellipsis,** indicate that the pattern continues indefinitely.) The set of **integers** contains the numbers in the set $\{\ldots, -3, -2, -1, 0, 1, 2, 3, \ldots\}$. A **rational number** is a number that can be expressed as a *quotient* $\frac{a}{b}$ of two integers, where the integer b cannot be 0. Examples of rational numbers are $\frac{3}{4}, \frac{5}{2}, \frac{0}{4}$, and $-\frac{2}{3}$. Since $\frac{a}{1} = a$ for any integer a, every integer is also a rational number. Real numbers that are not rational are called **irrational.** Examples of irrational numbers are $\sqrt{2}$ and π (the Greek letter pi), which equals the constant ratio of the circumference to the diameter of a circle. See Figure 4.

Figure 4 $\pi = \dfrac{C}{d}$

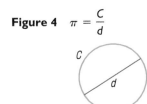

Real numbers can be represented as **decimals.** Rational real numbers have decimal representations that either **terminate** or are nonterminating with **repeating** blocks of digits. For example, $\frac{3}{4} = 0.75$, which terminates; and $\frac{2}{3} = 0.666\ldots$, in which the digit 6 repeats indefinitely. Irrational real numbers have decimal representations that neither repeat nor terminate. For example, $\sqrt{2} = 1.414213\ldots$ and $\pi = 3.14159\ldots$. In practice, the decimal representation of an irrational number is given as an approximation. We use the symbol $\approx$ (read as "approximately equal to") to write $\sqrt{2} \approx 1.4142$ and $\pi \approx 3.1416$.

Two properties of real numbers that we shall use often are given next. Suppose that a, b, and c are real numbers.

Distributive Property

$$a \cdot (b + c) = ab + ac$$

Zero-Product Property

If $ab = 0$, then either $a = 0$ or $b = 0$ or both equal 0.

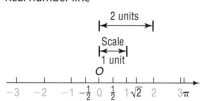

In Words

If a product equals 0, then one or both of the factors is 0.

The Distributive Property can be used to remove parentheses:

$$2(x + 3) = 2x + 2 \cdot 3 = 2x + 6$$

The Zero-Product Property will be used to solve equations (Section A.6). For example, if $2x = 0$, then $2 = 0$ or $x = 0$. Since $2 \neq 0$, it follows that $x = 0$.

The Real Number Line

The real numbers can be represented by points on a line called the **real number line.** There is a one-to-one correspondence between real numbers and points on a line. That is, every real number corresponds to a point on the line, and each point on the line has a unique real number associated with it.

Pick a point on the line somewhere in the center, and label it O. This point, called the **origin,** corresponds to the real number 0. See Figure 5. The point 1 unit to the right of O corresponds to the number 1. The distance between 0 and 1 determines the **scale** of the number line. For example, the point associated with the number 2 is twice as far from O as 1. Notice that an arrowhead on the right end of the line indicates the direction in which the numbers increase. Points to the left of the origin correspond to the real numbers -1, -2, and so on. Figure 5 also shows the points associated with the rational numbers $-\dfrac{1}{2}$ and $\dfrac{1}{2}$ and with the irrational numbers $\sqrt{2}$ and π.

Figure 5
Real number line

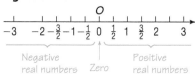

DEFINITION

The real number associated with a point P is called the **coordinate** of P, and the line whose points have been assigned coordinates is called the **real number line.**

The real number line consists of three classes of real numbers, as shown in Figure 6.

Figure 6

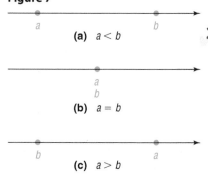

1. The **negative real numbers** are the coordinates of points to the left of the origin O.
2. The real number **zero** is the coordinate of the origin O.
3. The **positive real numbers** are the coordinates of points to the right of the origin O.

Figure 7

(a) $a < b$

(b) $a = b$

(c) $a > b$

— **Now Work** PROBLEM **21**

2 Graph Inequalities

An important property of the real number line follows from the fact that, given two numbers (points) a and b, either a is to the left of b, or a is at the same location as b, or a is to the right of b. See Figure 7.

If a is to the left of b, we say that "a is less than b" and write $a < b$. If a is to the right of b, we say that "a is greater than b" and write $a > b$. If a is at the same location as b, then $a = b$. If a is either less than or equal to b, we write $a \leq b$. Similarly, $a \geq b$ means that a is either greater than or equal to b. Collectively, the symbols $<$, $>$, $\leq$, and $\geq$ are called **inequality symbols.**

Note that $a < b$ and $b > a$ mean the same thing. It does not matter whether we write $2 < 3$ or $3 > 2$.

Furthermore, if $a < b$ or if $b > a$, then the difference $b - a$ is positive. Do you see why?

An **inequality** is a statement in which two expressions are related by an inequality symbol. The expressions are referred to as the **sides** of the inequality. Statements of the form $a < b$ or $b > a$ are called **strict inequalities,** whereas statements of the form $a \le b$ or $b \ge a$ are called **nonstrict inequalities.**

Based on the discussion so far, we conclude that

$a > 0$ is equivalent to a is positive
$a < 0$ is equivalent to a is negative

We sometimes read $a > 0$ by saying that "a is positive." If $a \ge 0$, then either $a > 0$ or $a = 0$, and we may read this as "a is nonnegative."

—— **Now Work** PROBLEMS **25** AND **35**

EXAMPLE 4 | **Graphing Inequalities**

(a) On the real number line, graph all numbers x for which $x > 4$.
(b) On the real number line, graph all numbers x for which $x \le 5$.

Solution

(a) See Figure 8. Notice that we use a left parenthesis to indicate that the number 4 is *not* part of the graph.

(b) See Figure 9. Notice that we use a right bracket to indicate that the number 5 *is* part of the graph.

Figure 8

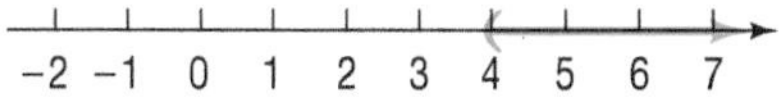

Figure 9

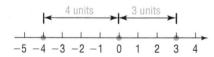

—— **Now Work** PROBLEM **41**

3 Find Distance on the Real Number Line

The *absolute value* of a number a is the distance from 0 to a on the number line. For example, -4 is 4 units from 0, and 3 is 3 units from 0. See Figure 10. Thus, the absolute value of -4 is 4, and the absolute value of 3 is 3.

A more formal definition of absolute value is given next.

Figure 10

4 units   3 units

$-5\ -4\ -3\ -2\ -1\ \ 0\ \ 1\ \ 2\ \ 3\ \ 4$

DEFINITION

The **absolute value** of a real number a, denoted by the symbol $|a|$, is defined by the rules

$\|a\| = a$ if $a \ge 0$ and $\|a\| = -a$ if $a < 0$

For example, since $-4 < 0$, the second rule must be used to get $|-4| = -(-4) = 4$.

EXAMPLE 5 | **Computing Absolute Value**

(a) $|8| = 8$ $\qquad$ (b) $|0| = 0$ $\qquad$ (c) $|-15| = -(-15) = 15$

Look again at Figure 10. The distance from -4 to 3 is 7 units. This distance is the difference $3 - (-4)$, obtained by subtracting the smaller coordinate from the larger. However, since $|3 - (-4)| = |7| = 7$ and $|-4 - 3| = |-7| = 7$, we can use absolute value to calculate the distance between two points without being concerned about which is smaller.

DEFINITION

If P and Q are two points on a real number line with coordinates a and b, respectively, the **distance between P and Q,** denoted by $d(P, Q)$, is

$$d(P, Q) = |b - a|$$

Since $|b - a| = |a - b|$, it follows that $d(P, Q) = d(Q, P)$.

EXAMPLE 6

Finding Distance on a Number Line

Let P, Q, and R be points on a real number line with coordinates -5, 7, and -3, respectively. Find the distance

(a) between P and Q (b) between Q and R

Solution

See Figure 11.

Figure 11

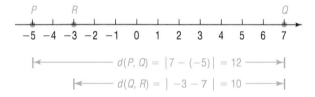

(a) $d(P, Q) = |7 - (-5)| = |12| = 12$
(b) $d(Q, R) = |-3 - 7| = |-10| = 10$

Now Work PROBLEM 47

4 Evaluate Algebraic Expressions

In algebra we use letters such as x, y, a, b, and c to represent numbers. If the letter used is to represent *any* number from a given set of numbers, it is called a **variable.** A **constant** is either a fixed number, such as 5 or $\sqrt{3}$, or a letter that represents a fixed (possibly unspecified) number.

Constants and variables are combined using the operations of addition, subtraction, multiplication, and division to form *algebraic expressions*. Examples of algebraic expressions include

$$x + 3 \qquad \frac{3}{1 - t} \qquad 7x - 2y$$

To evaluate an algebraic expression, substitute for each variable its numerical value.

EXAMPLE 7

Evaluating an Algebraic Expression

Evaluate each expression if $x = 3$ and $y = -1$.

(a) $x + 3y$ (b) $5xy$ (c) $\dfrac{3y}{2 - 2x}$ (d) $|-4x + y|$

Solution

(a) Substitute 3 for x and -1 for y in the expression $x + 3y$.

$$x + 3y = 3 + 3(-1) = 3 + (-3) = 0$$

$$\underset{\uparrow}{}$$

$$x = 3, y = -1$$

(b) If $x = 3$ and $y = -1$, then

$$5xy = 5(3)(-1) = -15$$

(c) If $x = 3$ and $y = -1$, then

$$\frac{3y}{2 - 2x} = \frac{3(-1)}{2 - 2(3)} = \frac{-3}{2 - 6} = \frac{-3}{-4} = \frac{3}{4}$$

(d) If $x = 3$ and $y = -1$, then

$$\left|-4x + y\right| = \left|-4(3) + (-1)\right| = \left|-12 + (-1)\right| = \left|-13\right| = 13$$

Now Work PROBLEMS 49 AND 57

5 Determine the Domain of a Variable

In working with expressions or formulas involving variables, the variables may be allowed to take on values from only a certain set of numbers. For example, in the formula for the area A of a circle of radius r, $A = \pi r^2$, the variable r is necessarily restricted to the positive real numbers. In the expression $\frac{1}{x}$, the variable x cannot take on the value 0, since division by 0 is not defined.

DEFINITION

The set of values that a variable may assume is called the **domain of the variable.**

EXAMPLE 8

Finding the Domain of a Variable

The domain of the variable x in the expression

$$\frac{5}{x - 2}$$

is $\{x | x \neq 2\}$, since, if $x = 2$, the denominator becomes 0, which is not defined.

EXAMPLE 9

Circumference of a Circle

In the formula for the circumference C of a circle of radius r,

$$C = 2\pi r$$

the domain of the variable r, representing the radius of the circle, is the set of positive real numbers. The domain of the variable C, representing the circumference of the circle, is also the set of positive real numbers.

In describing the domain of a variable, we may use either set notation or words, whichever is more convenient.

Now Work PROBLEM 67

6 Use the Laws of Exponents

Integer exponents provide a shorthand notation for representing repeated multiplications of a real number. For example,

$$2^3 = 2 \cdot 2 \cdot 2 = 8 \qquad 3^4 = 3 \cdot 3 \cdot 3 \cdot 3 = 81$$

DEFINITION

If a is a real number and n is a positive integer, then the symbol a^n represents the product of n factors of a. That is,

$$a^n = \underbrace{a \cdot a \cdot \ldots \cdot a}_{n \text{ factors}} \qquad (1)$$

Here it is understood that $a^1 = a$.

Then $a^2 = a \cdot a$, $a^3 = a \cdot a \cdot a$, and so on. In the expression a^n, a is called the **base** and n is called the **exponent,** or **power.** We read a^n as "a raised to the power n" or as "a to the nth power." We usually read a^2 as "a squared" and a^3 as "a cubed."

In working with exponents, the operation of *raising to a power* is performed before any other operation. As examples,

$$4 \cdot 3^2 = 4 \cdot 9 = 36 \qquad 2^2 + 3^2 = 4 + 9 = 13$$
$$-2^4 = -16 \qquad 5 \cdot 3^2 + 2 \cdot 4 = 5 \cdot 9 + 2 \cdot 4 = 45 + 8 = 53$$

Parentheses are used to indicate operations to be performed first. For example,

$$(-2)^4 = (-2)(-2)(-2)(-2) = 16 \qquad (2 + 3)^2 = 5^2 = 25$$

DEFINITION

If $a \neq 0$, we define

$$a^0 = 1 \quad \text{if } a \neq 0$$

DEFINITION

If $a \neq 0$ and if n is a positive integer, then we define

$$a^{-n} = \frac{1}{a^n} \quad \text{if } a \neq 0$$

Whenever you encounter a negative exponent, think "reciprocal."

EXAMPLE 10

Evaluating Expressions Containing Negative Exponents

(a) $2^{-3} = \dfrac{1}{2^3} = \dfrac{1}{8}$ (b) $x^{-4} = \dfrac{1}{x^4}$ (c) $\left(\dfrac{1}{5}\right)^{-2} = \dfrac{1}{\left(\dfrac{1}{5}\right)^2} = \dfrac{1}{\dfrac{1}{25}} = 25$

Now Work PROBLEMS 85 AND 105

The following properties, called the **Laws of Exponents,** can be proved using the preceding definitions. In the list, a and b are real numbers, and m and n are integers.

THEOREM

Laws of Exponents

$$a^m a^n = a^{m+n} \qquad (a^m)^n = a^{mn} \qquad (ab)^n = a^n b^n$$

$$\frac{a^m}{a^n} = a^{m-n} = \frac{1}{a^{n-m}} \quad \text{if } a \neq 0 \qquad \left(\frac{a}{b}\right)^n = \frac{a^n}{b^n} \quad \text{if } b \neq 0$$

EXAMPLE 11

Using the Laws of Exponents

Write each expression so that all exponents are positive.

(a) $\dfrac{x^5 y^{-2}}{x^3 y}$ $x \neq 0, \quad y \neq 0$ (b) $\left(\dfrac{x^{-3}}{3y^{-1}} \right)^{-2}$ $x \neq 0, \quad y \neq 0$

Solution   (a) $\dfrac{x^5 y^{-2}}{x^3 y} = \dfrac{x^5}{x^3} \cdot \dfrac{y^{-2}}{y} = x^{5-3} \cdot y^{-2-1} = x^2 y^{-3} = x^2 \cdot \dfrac{1}{y^3} = \dfrac{x^2}{y^3}$

(b) $\left(\dfrac{x^{-3}}{3y^{-1}} \right)^{-2} = \dfrac{(x^{-3})^{-2}}{(3y^{-1})^{-2}} = \dfrac{x^6}{3^{-2}(y^{-1})^{-2}} = \dfrac{x^6}{\dfrac{1}{9} y^2} = \dfrac{9x^6}{y^2}$

────── **Now Work** PROBLEMS 87 AND 97

7 Evaluate Square Roots

A real number is squared when it is raised to the power 2. The inverse of squaring is finding a **square root.** For example, since $6^2 = 36$ and $(-6)^2 = 36$, the numbers 6 and -6 are square roots of 36.

The symbol $\sqrt{}$, called a **radical sign,** is used to denote the **principal,** or nonnegative, square root. For example, $\sqrt{36} = 6$.

DEFINITION

If a is a nonnegative real number, the nonnegative number b, such that $b^2 = a$, is the **principal square root** of a and is denoted by $b = \sqrt{a}$.

The following comments are noteworthy:

1. Negative numbers do not have square roots (in the real number system), because the square of any real number is *nonnegative.* For example, $\sqrt{-4}$ is not a real number, because there is no real number whose square is -4.

2. The principal square root of 0 is 0, since $0^2 = 0$. That is, $\sqrt{0} = 0$.

3. The principal square root of a positive number is positive.

4. If $c \geq 0$, then $(\sqrt{c})^2 = c$. For example, $(\sqrt{2})^2 = 2$ and $(\sqrt{3})^2 = 3$.

EXAMPLE 12

Evaluating Square Roots

(a) $\sqrt{64} = 8$ (b) $\sqrt{\dfrac{1}{16}} = \dfrac{1}{4}$ (c) $\left(\sqrt{1.4} \right)^2 = 1.4$

Examples 12(a) and (b) are examples of square roots of perfect squares, since

$64 = 8^2$ and $\dfrac{1}{16} = \left(\dfrac{1}{4} \right)^2$.

Consider the expression $\sqrt{a^2}$. Since $a^2 \geq 0$, the principal square root of a^2 is defined whether $a > 0$ or $a < 0$. However, since the principal square root is nonnegative, we need an absolute value to ensure the nonnegative result. That is,

$$\sqrt{a^2} = |a| \qquad a \text{ any real number} \qquad (2)$$

EXAMPLE 13   **Simplifying Expressions Using Equation 2**

(a) $\sqrt{(2.3)^2} = |2.3| = 2.3$ (b) $\sqrt{(-2.3)^2} = |-2.3| = 2.3$ (c) $\sqrt{x^2} = |x|$

Now Work PROBLEM 93

Calculators

Calculators are finite machines. As a result, they are incapable of displaying decimals that contain a large number of digits. For example, some calculators are capable of displaying only eight digits. When a number requires more than eight digits, the calculator either truncates or rounds. To see how your calculator handles decimals, divide 2 by 3. How many digits do you see? Is the last digit a 6 or a 7? If it is a 6, your calculator truncates; if it is a 7, your calculator rounds.

There are different kinds of calculators. An **arithmetic** calculator can only add, subtract, multiply, and divide numbers; therefore, this type is not adequate for this course. **Scientific** calculators have all the capabilities of arithmetic calculators and also contain **function keys** labeled ln, log, sin, cos, tan, x^y, inv, and so on. **Graphing** calculators have all the capabilities of scientific calculators and contain a screen on which graphs can be displayed. We use the ⬚ symbol whenever a graphing calculator needs to be used. In this book the use of a graphing calculator is optional.

8 Use a Calculator to Evaluate Exponents

Your calculator has either a caret key, ⌃, or an x^y key, which is used for computations involving exponents.

EXAMPLE 14   **Exponents on a Graphing Calculator**

Evaluate: $(2.3)^5$

Solution   Figure 12 shows the result using a TI-84 graphing calculator.

Figure 12

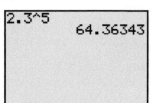

Now Work PROBLEM 123

A.1 Assess Your Understanding

Concepts and Vocabulary

1. A(n) _____ is a letter used in algebra to represent any number from a given set of numbers.

2. On the real number line, the real number zero is the coordinate of the _____.

3. An inequality of the form $a > b$ is called a(n) _____ inequality.

4. In the expression 2^4, the number 2 is called the _____ and 4 is called the _____.

5. **True or False** The product of two negative real numbers is always greater than zero.

6. **True or False** The distance between two distinct points on the real number line is always greater than zero.

7. **True or False** The absolute value of a real number is always greater than zero.

8. **True or False** To multiply two expressions having the same base, retain the base and multiply the exponents.

Skill Building

In Problems 9–20, use U = universal set = {0, 1, 2, 3, 4, 5, 6, 7, 8, 9}, A = {1, 3, 4, 5, 9}, B = {2, 4, 6, 7, 8}, and C = {1, 3, 4, 6} to find each set.

9. $A \cup B$

10. $A \cup C$

11. $A \cap B$

12. $A \cap C$

13. $(A \cup B) \cap C$

14. $(A \cap B) \cup C$

15. $\overline{A}$

16. $\overline{C}$

17. $\overline{A \cap B}$

18. $\overline{B \cup C}$

19. $\overline{A} \cup \overline{B}$

20. $\overline{B} \cap \overline{C}$

21. On the real number line, label the points with coordinates $0, 1, -1, \frac{5}{2}, -2.5, \frac{3}{4}$, and 0.25.

22. On the real number line, label the points with coordinates $0, -2, 2, -1.5, \frac{3}{2}, \frac{1}{3}$, and $\frac{2}{3}$.

In Problems 23–32, replace the question mark by <, >, or =, whichever is correct.

23. $\frac{1}{2} ? 0$

24. $5 ? 6$

25. $-1 ? -2$

26. $-3 ? -\frac{5}{2}$

27. $\pi ? 3.14$

28. $\sqrt{2} ? 1.41$

29. $\frac{1}{2} ? 0.5$

30. $\frac{1}{3} ? 0.33$

31. $\frac{2}{3} ? 0.67$

32. $\frac{1}{4} ? 0.25$

In Problems 33–38, write each statement as an inequality.

33. x is positive

34. z is negative

35. x is less than 2

36. y is greater than -5

37. x is less than or equal to 1

38. x is greater than or equal to 2

In Problems 39–42, graph the numbers x on the real number line.

39. $x \geq -2$

40. $x < 4$

41. $x > -1$

42. $x \leq 7$

In Problems 43–48, use the given real number line to compute each distance.

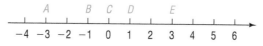

43. $d(C, D)$

44. $d(C, A)$

45. $d(D, E)$

46. $d(C, E)$

47. $d(A, E)$

48. $d(D, B)$

In Problems 49–56, evaluate each expression if x = −2 and y = 3.

49. $x + 2y$

50. $3x + y$

51. $5xy + 2$

52. $-2x + xy$

53. $\frac{2x}{x - y}$

54. $\frac{x + y}{x - y}$

55. $\frac{3x + 2y}{2 + y}$

56. $\frac{2x - 3}{y}$

In Problems 57–66, find the value of each expression if x = 3 and y = −2.

57. $|x + y|$

58. $|x - y|$

59. $|x| + |y|$

60. $|x| - |y|$

61. $\frac{|x|}{x}$

62. $\frac{|y|}{y}$

63. $|4x - 5y|$

64. $|3x + 2y|$

65. $||4x| - |5y||$

66. $3|x| + 2|y|$

In Problems 67–74, determine which of the value(s) (a) through (d), if any, must be excluded from the domain of the variable in each expression:

   (a) $x = 3$ *(b)* $x = 1$ *(c)* $x = 0$ *(d)* $x = -1$

67. $\frac{x^2 - 1}{x}$

68. $\frac{x^2 + 1}{x}$

69. $\frac{x}{x^2 - 9}$

70. $\frac{x}{x^2 + 9}$

71. $\frac{x^2}{x^2 + 1}$

72. $\frac{x^3}{x^2 - 1}$

73. $\frac{x^2 + 5x - 10}{x^3 - x}$

74. $\frac{-9x^2 - x + 1}{x^3 + x}$

In Problems 75–78, determine the domain of the variable x in each expression.

75. $\dfrac{4}{x-5}$

76. $\dfrac{-6}{x+4}$

77. $\dfrac{x}{x+4}$

78. $\dfrac{x-2}{x-6}$

In Problems 79–82, use the formula $C = \dfrac{5}{9}(F-32)$ for converting degrees Fahrenheit into degrees Celsius to find the Celsius measure of each Fahrenheit temperature.

79. $F = 32°$

80. $F = 212°$

81. $F = 77°$

82. $F = -4°$

In Problems 83–94, simplify each expression.

83. $(-4)^2$

84. -4^2

85. 4^{-2}

86. -4^{-2}

87. $3^{-6} \cdot 3^4$

88. $4^{-2} \cdot 4^3$

89. $(3^{-2})^{-1}$

90. $(2^{-1})^{-3}$

91. $\sqrt{25}$

92. $\sqrt{36}$

93. $\sqrt{(-4)^2}$

94. $\sqrt{(-3)^2}$

In Problems 95–104, simplify each expression. Express the answer so that all exponents are positive. Whenever an exponent is 0 or negative, we assume that the base is not 0.

95. $(8x^3)^2$

96. $(-4x^2)^{-1}$

97. $(x^2y^{-1})^2$

98. $(x^{-1}y)^3$

99. $\dfrac{x^2y^3}{xy^4}$

100. $\dfrac{x^{-2}y}{xy^2}$

101. $\dfrac{(-2)^3x^4(yz)^2}{3^2xy^3z}$

102. $\dfrac{4x^{-2}(yz)^{-1}}{2^3x^4y}$

103. $\left(\dfrac{3x^{-1}}{4y^{-1}}\right)^{-2}$

104. $\left(\dfrac{5x^{-2}}{6y^{-2}}\right)^{-3}$

In Problems 105–116, find the value of each expression if $x = 2$ and $y = -1$.

105. $2xy^{-1}$

106. $-3x^{-1}y$

107. $x^2 + y^2$

108. x^2y^2

109. $(xy)^2$

110. $(x+y)^2$

111. $\sqrt{x^2}$

112. $\left(\sqrt{x}\right)^2$

113. $\sqrt{x^2 + y^2}$

114. $\sqrt{x^2} + \sqrt{y^2}$

115. x^y

116. y^x

117. Find the value of the expression $2x^3 - 3x^2 + 5x - 4$ if $x = 2$. What is the value if $x = 1$?

118. Find the value of the expression $4x^3 + 3x^2 - x + 2$ if $x = 1$. What is the value if $x = 2$?

119. What is the value of $\dfrac{(666)^4}{(222)^4}$?

120. What is the value of $(0.1)^3(20)^3$?

In Problems 121–128, use a calculator to evaluate each expression. Round your answer to three decimal places.

121. $(8.2)^6$

122. $(3.7)^5$

123. $(6.1)^{-3}$

124. $(2.2)^{-5}$

125. $(-2.8)^6$

126. $-(2.8)^6$

127. $(-8.11)^{-4}$

128. $-(8.11)^{-4}$

Applications and Extensions

In Problems 129–138, express each statement as an equation involving the indicated variables.

129. Area of a Rectangle The area A of a rectangle is the product of its length l and its width w.

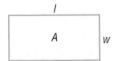

131. Circumference of a Circle The circumference C of a circle is the product of π and its diameter d.

130. Perimeter of a Rectangle The perimeter P of a rectangle is twice the sum of its length l and its width w.

132. Area of a Triangle The area A of a triangle is one-half the product of its base b and its height h.

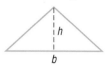

133. Area of an Equilateral Triangle The area A of an equilateral triangle is $\dfrac{\sqrt{3}}{4}$ times the square of the length x of one side.

134. Perimeter of an Equilateral Triangle The perimeter P of an equilateral triangle is 3 times the length x of one side.

135. Volume of a Sphere The volume V of a sphere is $\dfrac{4}{3}$ times π times the cube of the radius r.

136. Surface Area of a Sphere The surface area S of a sphere is 4 times π times the square of the radius r.

137. Volume of a Cube The volume V of a cube is the cube of the length x of a side.

138. Surface Area of a Cube The surface area S of a cube is 6 times the square of the length x of a side.

139. Manufacturing Cost The weekly production cost C of manufacturing x watches is given by the formula $C = 4000 + 2x$, where the variable C is in dollars.
(a) What is the cost of producing 1000 watches?
(b) What is the cost of producing 2000 watches?

140. Balancing a Checkbook At the beginning of the month, Mike had a balance of $210 in his checking account. During the next month, he deposited $80, wrote a check for $120, made another deposit of $25, and wrote two checks: one for $60 and the other for $32. He was also assessed a monthly service charge of $5. What was his balance at the end of the month?

In Problems 141 and 142, write an inequality using an absolute value to describe each statement.

141. x is at least 6 units from 4.

142. x is more than 5 units from 2.

143. U.S. Voltage In the United States, normal household voltage is 110 volts. It is acceptable for the actual voltage x to differ from normal by at most 5 volts. A formula that describes this is
$$|x - 110| \le 5$$
(a) Show that a voltage of 108 volts is acceptable.
(b) Show that a voltage of 104 volts is not acceptable.

144. Foreign Voltage In some countries, normal household voltage is 220 volts. It is acceptable for the actual voltage x to differ from normal by at most 8 volts. A formula that describes this is
$$|x - 220| \le 8$$
(a) Show that a voltage of 214 volts is acceptable.
(b) Show that a voltage of 209 volts is not acceptable.

145. Making Precision Ball Bearings The FireBall Company manufactures ball bearings for precision equipment. One of its products is a ball bearing with a stated radius of 3 centimeters (cm). Only ball bearings with a radius within 0.01 cm of this stated radius are acceptable. If x is the radius of a ball bearing, a formula describing this situation is
$$|x - 3| \le 0.01$$
(a) Is a ball bearing of radius $x = 2.999$ acceptable?
(b) Is a ball bearing of radius $x = 2.89$ acceptable?

146. Body Temperature Normal human body temperature is 98.6°F. A temperature x that differs from normal by at least 1.5°F is considered unhealthy. A formula that describes this is
$$|x - 98.6| \ge 1.5$$
(a) Show that a temperature of 97°F is unhealthy.
(b) Show that a temperature of 100°F is not unhealthy.

147. Does $\dfrac{1}{3}$ equal 0.333? If not, which is larger? By how much?

148. Does $\dfrac{2}{3}$ equal 0.666? If not, which is larger? By how much?

Explaining Concepts: Discussion and Writing

149. Is there a positive real number "closest" to 0?

150. Number Game I'm thinking of a number! It lies between 1 and 10; its square is rational and lies between 1 and 10. The number is larger than π. Correct to two decimal places (that is, truncated to two decimal places) name the number. Now think of your own number, describe it, and challenge a fellow student to name it.

151. Write a brief paragraph that illustrates the similarities and differences between "less than" ($<$) and "less than or equal to" ($\le$).

152. Give a reason why the statement $5 < 8$ is true.

A.2 Geometry Essentials

OBJECTIVES **1** Use the Pythagorean Theorem and Its Converse (p. A14)

2 Know Geometry Formulas (p. A15)

3 Understand Congruent Triangles and Similar Triangles (p. A16)

1 Use the Pythagorean Theorem and Its Converse

Figure 13

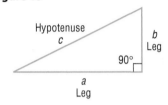

The *Pythagorean Theorem* is a statement about *right triangles*. A **right triangle** is one that contains a **right angle,** that is, an angle of 90°. The side of the triangle opposite the 90° angle is called the **hypotenuse;** the remaining two sides are called **legs.** In Figure 13 we have used c to represent the length of the hypotenuse and a and b to represent the lengths of the legs. Notice the use of the symbol ⌐ to show the 90° angle. We now state the Pythagorean Theorem.

PYTHAGOREAN THEOREM

In a right triangle, the square of the length of the hypotenuse is equal to the sum of the squares of the lengths of the legs. That is, in the right triangle shown in Figure 13,

$$c^2 = a^2 + b^2 \qquad (1)$$

EXAMPLE 1 | **Finding the Hypotenuse of a Right Triangle**

In a right triangle, one leg has length 4 and the other has length 3. What is the length of the hypotenuse?

Solution Since the triangle is a right triangle, we use the Pythagorean Theorem with $a = 4$ and $b = 3$ to find the length c of the hypotenuse. From equation (1), we have

$$c^2 = a^2 + b^2$$
$$c^2 = 4^2 + 3^2 = 16 + 9 = 25$$
$$c = \sqrt{25} = 5$$

Now Work PROBLEM 13

The converse of the Pythagorean Theorem is also true.

CONVERSE OF THE PYTHAGOREAN THEOREM

In a triangle, if the square of the length of one side equals the sum of the squares of the lengths of the other two sides, the triangle is a right triangle. The 90° angle is opposite the longest side.

EXAMPLE 2 | **Verifying That a Triangle Is a Right Triangle**

Show that a triangle whose sides are of lengths 5, 12, and 13 is a right triangle. Identify the hypotenuse.

Solution We square the lengths of the sides.

$$5^2 = 25, \qquad 12^2 = 144, \qquad 13^2 = 169$$

Figure 14

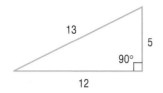

Notice that the sum of the first two squares (25 and 144) equals the third square (169). Hence, the triangle is a right triangle. The longest side, 13, is the hypotenuse. See Figure 14.

Now Work PROBLEM 21

EXAMPLE 3

Applying the Pythagorean Theorem

The tallest building in the world is Burj Khalifa in Dubai, United Arab Emirates, at 2717 feet and 160 floors. The observation deck is 1450 feet above ground level. How far can a person standing on the observation deck see (with the aid of a telescope)? Use 3960 miles for the radius of Earth.

Source: Wikipedia 2010

Solution From the center of Earth, draw two radii: one through Burj Khalifa and the other to the farthest point a person can see from the observation deck. See Figure 15. Apply the Pythagorean Theorem to the right triangle.

Since 1 mile = 5280 feet, then 1450 feet = $\dfrac{1450}{5280}$ mile. So we have

$$d^2 + (3960)^2 = \left(3960 + \frac{1450}{5280}\right)^2$$

$$d^2 = \left(3960 + \frac{1450}{5280}\right)^2 - (3960)^2 \approx 2175.08$$

$$d \approx 46.64$$

A person can see almost 47 miles from the observation tower.

Figure 15

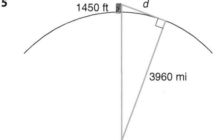

1450 ft d

3960 mi

Now Work PROBLEM 53

2 Know Geometry Formulas

Certain formulas from geometry are useful in solving algebra problems.

For a rectangle of length l and width w,

$$\text{Area} = lw \qquad \text{Perimeter} = 2l + 2w$$

For a triangle with base b and altitude h,

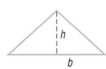

$$\text{Area} = \frac{1}{2}bh$$

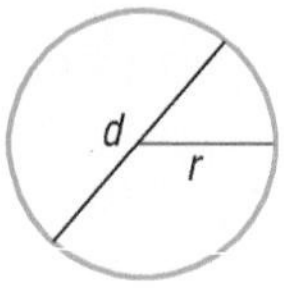

For a circle of radius r (diameter $d = 2r$),

$$\text{Area} = \pi r^2 \qquad \text{Circumference} = 2\pi r = \pi d$$

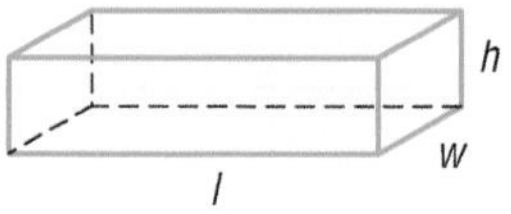

For a closed rectangular box of length l, width w, and height h,

$$\text{Volume} = lwh \qquad \text{Surface area} = 2lh + 2wh + 2lw$$

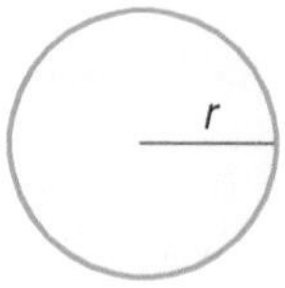

For a sphere of radius r,

$$\text{Volume} = \frac{4}{3}\pi r^3 \qquad \text{Surface area} = 4\pi r^2$$

For a right circular cylinder of height h and radius r,

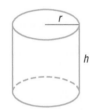

$$\text{Volume} = \pi r^2 h \qquad \text{Surface area} = 2\pi r^2 + 2\pi rh$$

Now Work PROBLEM 29

| **EXAMPLE 4** | **Using Geometry Formulas** |

A Christmas tree ornament is in the shape of a semicircle on top of a triangle. How many square centimeters (cm) of copper is required to make the ornament if the height of the triangle is 6 cm and the base is 4 cm?

Solution

Figure 16

See Figure 16. The amount of copper required equals the shaded area. This area is the sum of the areas of the triangle and the semicircle. The triangle has height $h = 6$ and base $b = 4$. The semicircle has diameter $d = 4$, so its radius is $r = 2$.

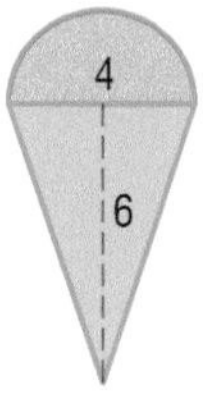

$$\text{Area} = \text{Area of triangle} + \text{Area of semicircle}$$
$$= \frac{1}{2}bh + \frac{1}{2}\pi r^2 = \frac{1}{2}(4)(6) + \frac{1}{2}\pi \cdot 2^2 \qquad b = 4; h = 6; r = 2$$
$$= 12 + 2\pi \approx 18.28 \text{ cm}^2$$

About 18.28 cm^2 of copper is required.

Now Work PROBLEM 47

---

3 Understand Congruent Triangles and Similar Triangles

Throughout the text we will make reference to triangles. We begin with a discussion of *congruent* triangles. According to dictionary.com, the word **congruent** means coinciding exactly when superimposed. For example, two angles are congruent if they have the same measure and two line segments are congruent if they have the same length.

> **In Words**
> Two triangles are congruent if they have the same size and shape.

DEFINITION

Two triangles are **congruent** if each of the corresponding angles is the same measure and each of the corresponding sides is the same length.

In Figure 17, corresponding angles are equal and the lengths of the corresponding sides are equal: $a = d$, $b = e$, and $c = f$. We conclude that these triangles are congruent.

Figure 17 Congruent triangles

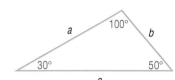 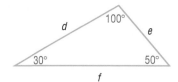

It is not necessary to verify that all three angles and all three sides are the same measure to determine whether two triangles are congruent.

Determining Congruent Triangles

1. **Angle–Side–Angle Case**   Two triangles are congruent if two of the angles are equal and the lengths of the corresponding sides between the two angles are equal.

   For example, in Figure 18(a), the two triangles are congruent because two angles and the included side are equal.

2. **Side–Side–Side Case**   Two triangles are congruent if the lengths of the corresponding sides of the triangles are equal.

   For example, in Figure 18(b), the two triangles are congruent because the three corresponding sides are all equal.

3. **Side–Angle–Side Case**   Two triangles are congruent if the lengths of two corresponding sides are equal and the angles between the two sides are the same.

   For example, in Figure 18(c), the two triangles are congruent because two sides and the included angle are equal.

Figure 18

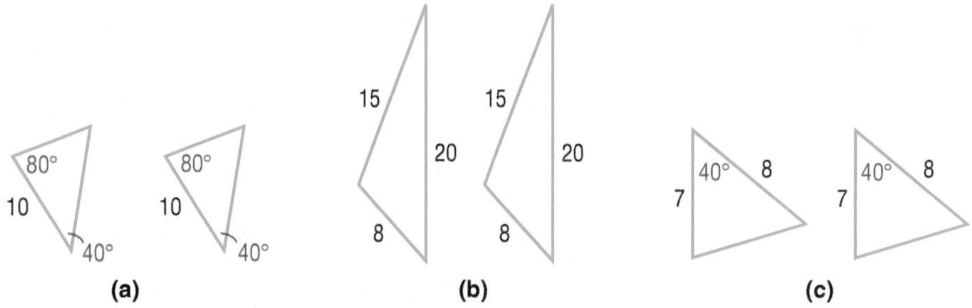

(a)   (b)   (c)

We contrast congruent triangles with *similar* triangles.

DEFINITION   Two triangles are **similar** if the corresponding angles are equal and the lengths of the corresponding sides are proportional.

In Words

Two triangles are similar if they have the same shape, but (possibly) different sizes.

For example, the triangles in Figure 19 are similar because the corresponding angles are equal. In addition, the lengths of the corresponding sides are proportional because each side in the triangle on the right is twice as long as each corresponding side in the triangle on the left. That is, the ratio of the corresponding sides is a constant: $\dfrac{d}{a} = \dfrac{e}{b} = \dfrac{f}{c} = 2$.

Figure 19

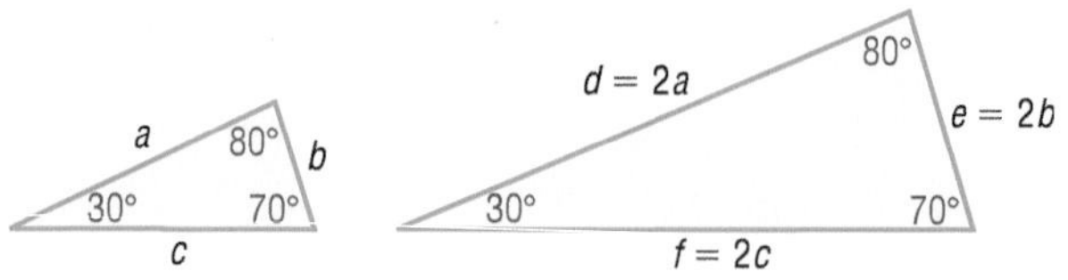

It is not necessary to verify that all three angles are equal and all three sides are proportional to determine whether two triangles are congruent.

Determining Similar Triangles

1. **Angle–Angle Case** Two triangles are similar if two of the corresponding angles are equal.

   For example, in Figure 20(a), the two triangles are similar because two angles are equal.

2. **Side–Side–Side Case** Two triangles are similar if the lengths of all three sides of each triangle are proportional.

   For example, in Figure 20(b), the two triangles are similar because

   $$\frac{10}{30} = \frac{5}{15} = \frac{6}{18} = \frac{1}{3}.$$

3. **Side–Angle–Side Case** Two triangles are similar if two corresponding sides are proportional and the angles between the two sides are equal.

   For example, in Figure 20(c), the two triangles are similar because $\frac{4}{6} = \frac{12}{18} = \frac{2}{3}$ and the angles between the sides are equal.

Figure 20

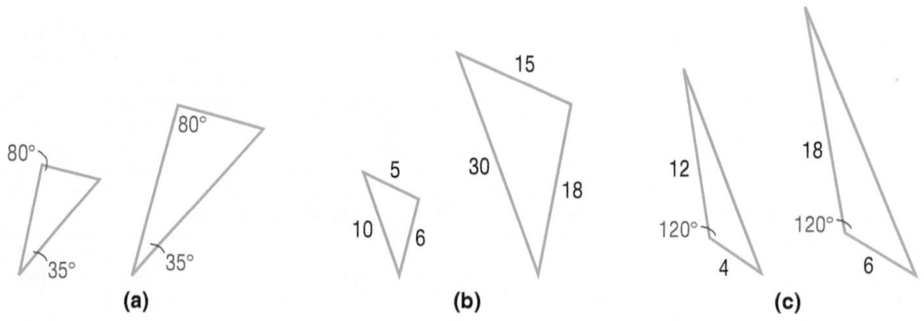

(a)	(b)	(c)

EXAMPLE 5

Using Similar Triangles

Given that the triangles in Figure 21 are similar, find the missing length x and the angles A, B, and C.

Figure 21

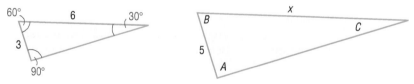

Solution Because the triangles are similar, corresponding angles are equal. So $A = 90°$, $B = 60°$, and $C = 30°$. Also, the corresponding sides are proportional. That is, $\dfrac{3}{5} = \dfrac{6}{x}$. We solve this equation for x.

$$\frac{3}{5} = \frac{6}{x}$$
$$5x \cdot \frac{3}{5} = 5x \cdot \frac{6}{x} \qquad \text{Multiply both sides by 5x.}$$
$$3x = 30 \qquad \text{Simplify.}$$
$$x = 10 \qquad \text{Divide both sides by 3.}$$

The missing length is 10 units.

Now Work PROBLEM 41

A.2 Assess Your Understanding

Concepts and Vocabulary

1. A(n) _____ triangle is one that contains an angle of 90 degrees. The longest side is called the _____.

2. For a triangle with base b and altitude h, a formula for the area A is _____.

3. The formula for the circumference C of a circle of radius r is _____.

4. Two triangles are _____ if corresponding angles are equal and the lengths of the corresponding sides are proportional.

5. *True or False* In a right triangle, the square of the length of the longest side equals the sum of the squares of the lengths of the other two sides.

6. *True or False* The triangle with sides of length 6, 8, and 10 is a right triangle.

7. *True or False* The volume of a sphere of radius r is $\dfrac{4}{3}\pi r^2$.

8. *True or False* The triangles shown are congruent.

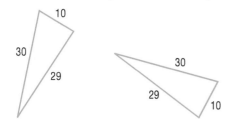

9. *True or False* The triangles shown are similar.

10. *True or False* The triangles shown are similar.

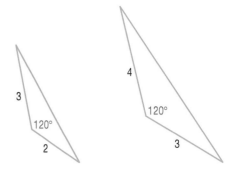

Skill Building

In Problems 11–16, the lengths of the legs of a right triangle are given. Find the hypotenuse.

11. $a = 5, \quad b = 12$

12. $a = 6, \quad b = 8$

13. $a = 10, \quad b = 24$

14. $a = 4, \quad b = 3$

15. $a = 7, \quad b = 24$

16. $a = 14, \quad b = 48$

In Problems 17–24, the lengths of the sides of a triangle are given. Determine which are right triangles. For those that are, identify the hypotenuse.

17. 3, 4, 5   **18.** 6, 8, 10   **19.** 4, 5, 6   **20.** 2, 2, 3

21. 7, 24, 25   **22.** 10, 24, 26   **23.** 6, 4, 3   **24.** 5, 4, 7

25. Find the area A of a rectangle with length 4 inches and width 2 inches.

26. Find the area A of a rectangle with length 9 centimeters and width 4 centimeters.

27. Find the area A of a triangle with height 4 inches and base 2 inches.

28. Find the area A of a triangle with height 9 centimeters and base 4 centimeters.

29. Find the area A and circumference C of a circle of radius 5 meters.

30. Find the area A and circumference C of a circle of radius 2 feet.

31. Find the volume V and surface area S of a rectangular box with length 8 feet, width 4 feet, and height 7 feet.

32. Find the volume V and surface area S of a rectangular box with length 9 inches, width 4 inches, and height 8 inches.

33. Find the volume V and surface area S of a sphere of radius 4 centimeters.

34. Find the volume V and surface area S of a sphere of radius 3 feet.

35. Find the volume V and surface area S of a right circular cylinder with radius 9 inches and height 8 inches.

36. Find the volume V and surface area S of a right circular cylinder with radius 8 inches and height 9 inches.

In Problems 37–40, find the area of the shaded region.

37.

38.

39.

40.

In Problems 41–44, each pair of triangles is similar. Find the missing length x and the missing angles A, B, and C.

41.
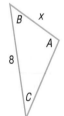

42.
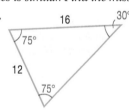

43.
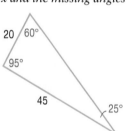
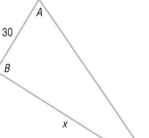

44.
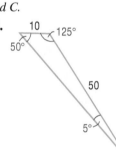

Applications and Extensions

45. How many feet does a wheel with a diameter of 16 inches travel after four revolutions?

46. How many revolutions will a circular disk with a diameter of 4 feet have completed after it has rolled 20 feet?

47. In the figure shown, *ABCD* is a square, with each side of length 6 feet. The width of the border (shaded portion) between the outer square *EFGH* and *ABCD* is 2 feet. Find the area of the border.

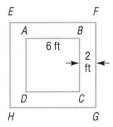

48. Refer to the figure. Square *ABCD* has an area of 100 square feet; square *BEFG* has an area of 16 square feet. What is the area of the triangle *CGF*?

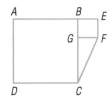

49. Architecture A **Norman window** consists of a rectangle surmounted by a semicircle. Find the area of the Norman window shown in the illustration. How much wood frame is needed to enclose the window?

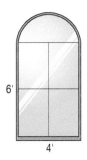

50. Construction A circular swimming pool, 20 feet in diameter, is enclosed by a wooden deck that is 3 feet wide. What is the area of the deck? How much fence is required to enclose the deck?

51. How Tall Is the Great Pyramid? The ancient Greek philosopher Thales of Miletus is reported on one occasion to have visited Egypt and calculated the height of the Great Pyramid of Cheops by means of shadow reckoning. Thales knew that each side of the base of the pyramid was 252 paces and that his own height was 2 paces. He measured the length of the pyramid's shadow to be 114 paces and determined the length of his shadow to be 3 paces. See the illustration. Using similar triangles, determine the height of the Great Pyramid in terms of the number of paces.

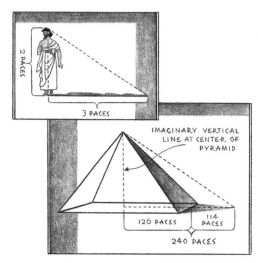

Source: Diggins, Julia E., illustrations by Corydon Bell, *String, Straightedge and Shadow: The Story of Geometry*, 2003 Whole Spirit Press, http://wholespiritpress.com.

52. The Bermuda Triangle Karen is doing research on the Bermuda Triangle, which she defines roughly by Hamilton, Bermuda; San Juan, Puerto Rico; and Fort Lauderdale, Florida. On her atlas Karen measures the straight-line distances from Hamilton to Fort Lauderdale, Fort Lauderdale to San Juan, and San Juan to Hamilton to be approximately 57 millimeters (mm), 58 mm, and 53.5 mm, respectively. If the actual distance from Fort Lauderdale to San Juan is 1046 miles, approximate the actual distances from San Juan to Hamilton and from Hamilton to Fort Lauderdale.

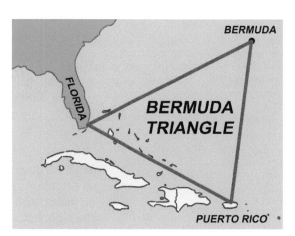

Source: Reprinted with permission from Red River Press, Inc., Winnipeg, Canada.

In Problems 53–55, use the facts that the radius of Earth is 3960 miles and 1 mile = 5280 feet.

53. **How Far Can You See?** The conning tower of the U.S.S. *Silversides,* a World War II submarine now permanently stationed in Muskegon, Michigan, is approximately 20 feet above sea level. How far can you see from the conning tower?

54. **How Far Can You See?** A person who is 6 feet tall is standing on the beach in Fort Lauderdale, Florida, and looks out onto the Atlantic Ocean. Suddenly, a ship appears on the horizon. How far is the ship from shore?

55. **How Far Can You See?** The deck of a destroyer is 100 feet above sea level. How far can a person see from the deck?

How far can a person see from the bridge, which is 150 feet above sea level?

56. Suppose that m and n are positive integers with $m > n$. If $a = m^2 - n^2$, $b = 2mn$, and $c = m^2 + n^2$, show that a, b, and c are the lengths of the sides of a right triangle. (This formula can be used to find the sides of a right triangle that are integers, such as 3, 4, 5; 5, 12, 13; and so on. Such triplets of integers are called **Pythagorean triples.**)

Explaining Concepts: Discussion and Writing

57. You have 1000 feet of flexible pool siding and wish to construct a swimming pool. Experiment with rectangular-shaped pools with perimeters of 1000 feet. How do their areas vary? What is the shape of the rectangle with the largest area? Now compute the area enclosed by a circular pool with a perimeter (circumference) of 1000 feet. What would be your choice of shape for the pool? If rectangular, what is your preference for dimensions? Justify your choice. If your only consideration is to have a pool that encloses the most area, what shape should you use?

58. **The Gibb's Hill Lighthouse, Southampton, Bermuda,** in operation since 1846, stands 117 feet high on a hill 245 feet high, so its beam of light is 362 feet above sea level. A brochure states that the light itself can be seen on the horizon about 26 miles from the lighthouse. Verify the correctness of this information. The brochure further states that ships 40 miles away can see the light and planes flying at 10,000 feet can see it 120 miles away. Verify the accuracy of these statements. What assumption did the brochure make about the height of the ship?

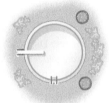

120 miles

40 miles

A.3 Polynomials

OBJECTIVES **1** Recognize Monomials (p. A23)
2 Recognize Polynomials (p. A23)
3 Know Formulas for Special Products (p. A24)
4 Divide Polynomials Using Long Division (p. A25)
5 Factor Polynomials (p. A28)
6 Complete the Square (p. A29)

We have described algebra as a generalization of arithmetic in which letters are used to represent real numbers. From now on, we shall use the letters at the end of the alphabet, such as x, y, and z, to represent variables and the letters at the beginning of the alphabet, such as a, b, and c, to represent constants. In the expressions $3x + 5$ and $ax + b$, it is understood that x is a variable and that a and b are constants, even though the constants a and b are unspecified. As you will find out, the context usually makes the intended meaning clear.

1 Recognize Monomials

DEFINITION

A **monomial** in one variable is the product of a constant and a variable raised to a nonnegative integer power. A monomial is of the form

$$ax^k$$

COMMENT The nonnegative integers are the integers 0, 1, 2, 3, … . ∎

where a is a constant, x is a variable, and $k \geq 0$ is an integer. The constant a is called the **coefficient** of the monomial. If $a \neq 0$, then k is the **degree** of the monomial.

EXAMPLE 1

Examples of Monomials

Monomial	Coefficient	Degree	
(a) $6x^2$	6	2	
(b) $-\sqrt{2}x^3$	$-\sqrt{2}$	3	
(c) 3	3	0	Since $3 = 3 \cdot 1 = 3x^0, x \neq 0$
(d) $-5x$	-5	1	Since $-5x = -5x^1$
(e) x^4	1	4	Since $x^4 = 1 \cdot x^4$

Now let's look at some expressions that are not monomials.

EXAMPLE 2

Examples of Nonmonomial Expressions

(a) $3x^{1/2}$ is not a monomial, since the exponent of the variable x is $\frac{1}{2}$ and $\frac{1}{2}$ is not a nonnegative integer.

(b) $4x^{-3}$ is not a monomial, since the exponent of the variable x is -3 and -3 is not a nonnegative integer.

Now Work PROBLEM 11

2 Recognize Polynomials

Two monomials with the same variable raised to the same power are called **like terms.** For example, $2x^4$ and $-5x^4$ are like terms. In contrast, the monomials $2x^3$ and $2x^5$ are not like terms.

We can add or subtract like terms using the Distributive Property. For example,

$$2x^2 + 5x^2 = (2 + 5)x^2 = 7x^2 \quad \text{and} \quad 8x^3 - 5x^3 = (8 - 5)x^3 = 3x^3$$

The sum or difference of two monomials having different degrees is called a **binomial.** The sum or difference of three monomials with three different degrees is called a **trinomial.** For example,

$x^2 - 2$ is a binomial.
$x^3 - 3x + 5$ is a trinomial.
$2x^2 + 5x^2 + 2 = 7x^2 + 2$ is a binomial.

DEFINITION

A **polynomial** in one variable is an algebraic expression of the form

$$a_n x^n + a_{n-1} x^{n-1} + \cdots + a_1 x + a_0 \qquad (1)$$

where $a_n, a_{n-1}, \ldots, a_1, a_0$ are constants,* called the **coefficients** of the polynomial, $n \geq 0$ is an integer, and x is a variable. If $a_n \neq 0$, it is the **leading coefficient,** and n is the **degree** of the polynomial.

The monomials that make up a polynomial are called its **terms.** If all the coefficients are 0, the polynomial is called the **zero polynomial,** which has no degree.

Polynomials are usually written in **standard form,** beginning with the nonzero term of highest degree and continuing with terms in descending order according to degree. If a power of x is missing, it is because its coefficient is zero.

EXAMPLE 3

Examples of Polynomials

Polynomial	Coefficients	Degree
$-8x^3 + 4x^2 + 6x + 2$	$-8, 4, 6, 2$	3
$3x^2 - 5 = 3x^2 + 0 \cdot x + (-5)$	$3, 0, -5$	2
$8 - 2x + x^2 = 1 \cdot x^2 + (-2)x + 8$	$1, -2, 8$	2
$5x + \sqrt{2} = 5x^1 + \sqrt{2}$	$5, \sqrt{2}$	1
$3 = 3 \cdot 1 = 3 \cdot x^0$	3	0
0	0	No degree

Although we have been using x to represent the variable, letters such as y or z are also commonly used.

$3x^4 - x^2 + 2$ is a polynomial (in x) of degree 4.

$9y^3 - 2y^2 + y - 3$ is a polynomial (in y) of degree 3.

$z^5 + \pi$ is a polynomial (in z) of degree 5.

Algebraic expressions such as

$$\frac{1}{x} \quad \text{and} \quad \frac{x^2 + 1}{x + 5}$$

are not polynomials. The first is not a polynomial because $\dfrac{1}{x} = x^{-1}$ has an exponent that is not a nonnegative integer. Although the second expression is the quotient of two polynomials, the polynomial in the denominator has degree greater than 0, so the expression cannot be a polynomial.

Now Work PROBLEM 21

---

3 Know Formulas for Special Products

Certain products, which we call **special products,** occur frequently in algebra. For example, we can find the product of two binomials using the **FOIL** (*F*irst, *O*uter, *I*nner, *L*ast) method.

---

* The notation a_n is read as "a sub n." The number n is called a **subscript** and should not be confused with an exponent. We use subscripts to distinguish one constant from another when a large or undetermined number of constants is required.

$$(ax + b)(cx + d) = ax(cx + d) + b(cx + d)$$

$$= \overbrace{ax \cdot cx}^{\text{First}} + \overbrace{ax \cdot d}^{\text{Outer}} + \overbrace{b \cdot cx}^{\text{Inner}} + \overbrace{b \cdot d}^{\text{Last}}$$

$$= acx^2 + adx + bcx + bd$$

$$= acx^2 + (ad + bc)x + bd$$

EXAMPLE 4 **Using FOIL**

(a) $(x - 3)(x + 3) = x^2 + 3x - 3x - 9 = x^2 - 9$

(b) $(x + 2)^2 = (x + 2)(x + 2) = x^2 + 2x + 2x + 4 = x^2 + 4x + 4$

(c) $(x - 3)^2 = (x - 3)(x - 3) = x^2 - 3x - 3x + 9 = x^2 - 6x + 9$

(d) $(x + 3)(x + 1) = x^2 + x + 3x + 3 = x^2 + 4x + 3$

(e) $(2x + 1)(3x + 4) = 6x^2 + 8x + 3x + 4 = 6x^2 + 11x + 4$

Now Work PROBLEM 41

Some products have been given special names because of their form. In the list that follows, x, a, and b are real numbers.

Difference of Two Squares

$$(x - a)(x + a) = x^2 - a^2 \qquad \text{(2)}$$

Squares of Binomials, or Perfect Squares

$$(x + a)^2 = x^2 + 2ax + a^2 \qquad \text{(3a)}$$

$$(x - a)^2 = x^2 - 2ax + a^2 \qquad \text{(3b)}$$

Cubes of Binomials, or Perfect Cubes

$$(x + a)^3 = x^3 + 3ax^2 + 3a^2x + a^3 \qquad \text{(4a)}$$

$$(x - a)^3 = x^3 - 3ax^2 + 3a^2x - a^3 \qquad \text{(4b)}$$

Difference of Two Cubes

$$(x - a)(x^2 + ax + a^2) = x^3 - a^3 \qquad \text{(5)}$$

Sum of Two Cubes

$$(x + a)(x^2 - ax + a^2) = x^3 + a^3 \qquad \text{(6)}$$

Now Work PROBLEMS 45, 49, AND 53

4 Divide Polynomials Using Long Division

The procedure for dividing two polynomials is similar to the procedure for dividing two integers.

EXAMPLE 5

Dividing Two Integers

Divide 842 by 15.

Solution

$$
\begin{array}{r}
56 \quad \leftarrow \text{Quotient} \\
\text{Divisor} \rightarrow \quad 15\overline{)842} \quad \leftarrow \text{Dividend} \\
75 \quad \leftarrow 5 \cdot 15 \text{ (subtract)} \\
\hline
92 \\
90 \quad \leftarrow 6 \cdot 15 \text{ (subtract)} \\
\hline
2 \quad \leftarrow \text{Remainder}
\end{array}
$$

So, $\dfrac{842}{15} = 56 + \dfrac{2}{15}$.

In the long division process detailed in Example 5, the number 15 is called the **divisor,** the number 842 is called the **dividend,** the number 56 is called the **quotient,** and the number 2 is called the **remainder.**

To check the answer obtained in a division problem, multiply the quotient by the divisor and add the remainder. The answer should be the dividend.

$$
\boxed{(\text{Quotient})(\text{Divisor}) + \text{Remainder} = \text{Dividend}}
$$

For example, we can check the results obtained in Example 5 as follows:

$$
(56)(15) + 2 = 840 + 2 = 842
$$

To divide two polynomials, we first must write each polynomial in standard form. The process then follows a pattern similar to that of Example 5. The next example illustrates the procedure.

EXAMPLE 6

Dividing Two Polynomials

Find the quotient and the remainder when

$$
3x^3 + 4x^2 + x + 7 \quad \text{is divided by} \quad x^2 + 1
$$

Solution   Each polynomial is in standard form. The dividend is $3x^3 + 4x^2 + x + 7$, and the divisor is $x^2 + 1$.

REMEMBER A polynomial is in standard form when its terms are written according to descending degrees. ■

STEP 1: Divide the leading term of the dividend, $3x^3$, by the leading term of the divisor, x^2. Enter the result, $3x$, over the term $3x^3$, as follows:

$$
\begin{array}{r}
3x \\
x^2 + 1\overline{)3x^3 + 4x^2 + x + 7}
\end{array}
$$

STEP 2: Multiply $3x$ by $x^2 + 1$ and enter the result below the dividend.

$$
\begin{array}{r}
3x \\
x^2 + 1\overline{)3x^3 + 4x^2 + x + 7} \\
3x^3 + 3x \qquad \leftarrow 3x \cdot (x^2 + 1) = 3x^3 + 3x
\end{array}
$$

Notice that we align the 3x term under the x to make the next step easier.

STEP 3: Subtract and bring down the remaining terms.

$$
\begin{array}{r}
3x \\
x^2 + 1\overline{)3x^3 + 4x^2 + x + 7} \\
\underline{3x^3 + 3x} \qquad \leftarrow \text{Subtract (change the signs and add).} \\
4x^2 - 2x + 7 \qquad \leftarrow \text{Bring down the } 4x^2 \text{ and the 7.}
\end{array}
$$

STEP 4: Repeat Steps 1–3 using $4x^2 - 2x + 7$ as the dividend.

$$
\begin{array}{r}
3x + 4 \\
x^2 + 1 \overline{)3x^3 + 4x^2 + x + 7} \\
\underline{3x^3 + 3x} \\
4x^2 - 2x + 7 \\
\underline{4x^2 + 4} \\
-2x + 3
\end{array}
$$

← Divide $4x^2$ by x^2 to get 4.
← Multiply $x^2 + 1$ by 4; subtract.

Since x^2 does not divide $-2x$ evenly (that is, the result is not a monomial), the process ends. The quotient is $3x + 4$, and the remainder is $-2x + 3$.

✓ **Check:** (Quotient)(Divisor) + Remainder

$$= (3x + 4)(x^2 + 1) + (-2x + 3)$$

$$= 3x^3 + 3x + 4x^2 + 4 + (-2x + 3)$$

$$= 3x^3 + 4x^2 + x + 7 = \text{Dividend}$$

Then

$$\frac{3x^3 + 4x^2 + x + 7}{x^2 + 1} = 3x + 4 + \frac{-2x + 3}{x^2 + 1}$$

The next example combines the steps involved in long division.

EXAMPLE 7   **Dividing Two Polynomials**

Find the quotient and the remainder when

$$x^4 - 3x^3 + 2x - 5 \quad \text{is divided by} \quad x^2 - x + 1$$

Solution   In setting up this division problem, it is necessary to leave a space for the missing x^2 term in the dividend.

$$
\begin{array}{r}
x^2 - 2x - 3 \\
x^2 - x + 1 \overline{)x^4 - 3x^3 + 2x - 5} \\
\underline{x^4 - x^3 + x^2} \\
-2x^3 - x^2 + 2x - 5 \\
\underline{-2x^3 + 2x^2 - 2x} \\
-3x^2 + 4x - 5 \\
\underline{-3x^2 + 3x - 3} \\
x - 2
\end{array}
$$

Divisor → Subtract → Subtract → Subtract →

← Quotient
← Dividend
← Remainder

✓ **Check:** (Quotient)(Divisor) + Remainder

$$= (x^2 - 2x - 3)(x^2 - x + 1) + x - 2$$

$$= x^4 - x^3 + x^2 - 2x^3 + 2x^2 - 2x - 3x^2 + 3x - 3 + x - 2$$

$$= x^4 - 3x^3 + 2x - 5 = \text{Dividend}$$

As a result,

$$\frac{x^4 - 3x^3 + 2x - 5}{x^2 - x + 1} = x^2 - 2x - 3 + \frac{x - 2}{x^2 - x + 1}$$

The process of dividing two polynomials leads to the following result:

THEOREM

Let Q be a polynomial of positive degree and let P be a polynomial whose degree is greater than or equal to the degree of Q. The remainder after dividing P by Q is either the zero polynomial or a polynomial whose degree is less than the degree of the divisor Q.

 **Now Work** PROBLEM 61

5 Factor Polynomials

Consider the following product:

$$(2x + 3)(x - 4) = 2x^2 - 5x - 12$$

The two polynomials on the left side are called **factors** of the polynomial on the right side. Expressing a given polynomial as a product of other polynomials, that is, finding the factors of a polynomial, is called **factoring.**

We shall restrict our discussion here to factoring polynomials in one variable into products of polynomials in one variable, where all coefficients are integers. We call this **factoring over the integers.**

Any polynomial can be written as the product of 1 times itself or as -1 times its additive inverse. If a polynomial cannot be written as the product of two other polynomials (excluding 1 and -1), then the polynomial is said to be **prime.** When a polynomial has been written as a product consisting only of prime factors, it is said to be **factored completely.** Examples of prime polynomials (over the integers) are

COMMENT Over the real numbers, $3x + 4$ factors into $3(x + \frac{4}{3})$. It is the noninteger $\frac{4}{3}$ that causes $3x + 4$ to be prime over the integers. ∎

$$2, \quad 3, \quad 5, \quad x, \quad x + 1, \quad x - 1, \quad 3x + 4 \quad x^2 + 4$$

The first factor to look for in a factoring problem is a common monomial factor present in each term of the polynomial. If one is present, use the Distributive Property to factor it out.

EXAMPLE 8

Identifying Common Monomial Factors

Polynomial	Common Monomial Factor	Remaining Factor	Factored Form
$2x + 4$	2	$x + 2$	$2x + 4 = 2(x + 2)$
$3x - 6$	3	$x - 2$	$3x - 6 = 3(x - 2)$
$2x^2 - 4x + 8$	2	$x^2 - 2x + 4$	$2x^2 - 4x + 8 = 2(x^2 - 2x + 4)$
$8x - 12$	4	$2x - 3$	$8x - 12 = 4(2x - 3)$
$x^2 + x$	x	$x + 1$	$x^2 + x = x(x + 1)$
$x^3 - 3x^2$	x^2	$x - 3$	$x^3 - 3x^2 = x^2(x - 3)$
$6x^2 + 9x$	$3x$	$2x + 3$	$6x^2 + 9x = 3x(2x + 3)$

Notice that, once all common monomial factors have been removed from a polynomial, the remaining factor is either a prime polynomial of degree 1 or a polynomial of degree 2 or higher. (Do you see why?)

The list of special products (2) through (6) given earlier provides a list of factoring formulas when the equations are read from right to left. For example, equation (2) states that if the polynomial is the difference of two squares, $x^2 - a^2$, it can be factored into $(x - a)(x + a)$. The following example illustrates several factoring techniques.

EXAMPLE 9

Factoring Polynomials

Factor completely each polynomial.

(a) $x^4 - 16$

(b) $x^3 - 1$

(c) $9x^2 - 6x + 1$

(d) $x^2 + 4x - 12$

(e) $3x^2 + 10x - 8$

(f) $x^3 - 4x^2 + 2x - 8$

Solution

(a) $x^4 - 16 = (x^2 - 4)(x^2 + 4) = (x - 2)(x + 2)(x^2 + 4)$

             ↑   ↑

     Difference of squares   Difference of squares

(b) $x^3 - 1 = (x - 1)(x^2 + x + 1)$

      ↑

   Difference of cubes

(c) $9x^2 - 6x + 1 = (3x - 1)^2$

           ↑

     Perfect square

(d) $x^2 + 4x - 12 = (x + 6)(x - 2)$

        ↑

  The product of 6 and -2 is -12, and the sum of 6 and -2 is 4.

                         $12x - 2x = 10x$

(e) $3x^2 + 10x - 8 = (3x - 2)(x + 4)$

                   $3x^2$ -8

COMMENT The technique used in part (f) is called **factoring by grouping**. ▪

(f) $x^3 - 4x^2 + 2x - 8 = (x^3 - 4x^2) + (2x - 8)$

               ↑

       Group terms

          $= x^2(x - 4) + 2(x - 4) = (x^2 + 2)(x - 4)$

         ↑   ↑

   Distributive Property   Distributive Property

⌐Now Work▪ **PROBLEMS 81, 97, AND 131**

6 Complete the Square

The idea behind completing the square in one variable is to "adjust" an expression of the form $x^2 + bx$ to make it a perfect square. Perfect squares are trinomials of the form

$$x^2 + 2ax + a^2 = (x + a)^2 \text{ or } x^2 - 2ax + a^2 = (x - a)^2$$

For example, $x^2 + 6x + 9$ is a perfect square because $x^2 + 6x + 9 = (x + 3)^2$. And $p^2 - 12p + 36$ is a perfect square because $p^2 - 12p + 36 = (p - 6)^2$.

So how do we "adjust" $x^2 + bx$ to make it a perfect square? We do it by adding a number. For example, to make $x^2 + 6x$ a perfect square, add 9. But how do we know to add 9? If we divide the coefficient on the first-degree term, 6, by 2, and then square the result, we obtain 9. This approach works in general.

Completing the Square

Identify the coefficient of the first-degree term. Multiply this coefficient by $\frac{1}{2}$ and then square the result. That is, determine the value of b in $x^2 + bx$ and compute $\left(\frac{1}{2}b\right)^2$.

EXAMPLE 10 **Completing the Square**

Determine the number that must be added to each expression to complete the square. Then factor the expression.

Start	Add	Result	Factored Form
$y^2 + 8y$	$\left(\dfrac{1}{2} \cdot 8\right)^2 = 16$	$y^2 + 8y + 16$	$(y + 4)^2$
$x^2 + 12x$	$\left(\dfrac{1}{2} \cdot 12\right)^2 = 36$	$x^2 + 12x + 36$	$(x + 6)^2$
$a^2 - 20a$	$\left(\dfrac{1}{2} \cdot (-20)\right)^2 = 100$	$a^2 - 20a + 100$	$(a - 10)^2$
$p^2 - 5p$	$\left(\dfrac{1}{2} \cdot (-5)\right)^2 = \dfrac{25}{4}$	$p^2 - 5p + \dfrac{25}{4}$	$\left(p - \dfrac{5}{2}\right)^2$

Notice that the factored form of a perfect square is either

Figure 22

$$x^2 + bx + \left(\frac{b}{2}\right)^2 = \left(x + \frac{b}{2}\right)^2 \text{ or } x^2 - bx + \left(\frac{b}{2}\right)^2 = \left(x - \frac{b}{2}\right)^2$$

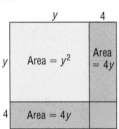

Now Work PROBLEM 121

Are you wondering why we call making an expression a perfect square "completing the square"? Look at the square in Figure 22. Its area is $(y + 4)^2$. The yellow area is y^2 and each orange area is $4y$ (for a total area of $8y$). The sum of these areas is $y^2 + 8y$. To complete the square, we need to add the area of the green region: $4 \cdot 4 = 16$. As a result, $y^2 + 8y + 16 = (y + 4)^2$.

A.3 Assess Your Understanding

Concepts and Vocabulary

1. The polynomial $3x^4 - 2x^3 + 13x^2 - 5$ is of degree _____. The leading coefficient is _____.

2. $(x^2 - 4)(x^2 + 4) = $ _____.

3. $(x - 2)(x^2 + 2x + 4) = $ _____.

4. *True or False* $4x^{-2}$ is a monomial of degree -2.

5. *True or False* $(x + a)(x^2 + ax + a) = x^3 + a^3$.

6. To check division, the expression that is being divided, the dividend, should equal the product of the _____ and the _____ plus the _____.

7. If factored completely, $3x^3 - 12x = $ _____.

8. To complete the square of the expression $x^2 + 5x$, you would _____ the number _____.

9. *True or False* The polynomial $x^2 + 4$ is prime.

10. *True or False* $3x^3 - 2x^2 - 6x + 4 = (3x - 2)(x^2 + 2)$.

Skill Building

In Problems 11–20, tell whether the expression is a monomial. If it is, name the variable(s) and the coefficient and give the degree of the monomial. If it is not a monomial, state why not.

11. $2x^3$

12. $-4x^2$

13. $\dfrac{8}{x}$

14. $-2x^{-3}$

15. $-2x^3 + 5x^2$

16. $6x^5 - 8x^2$

17. $\dfrac{8x}{x^2 - 1}$

18. $-\dfrac{2x^2}{x^3 + 1}$

19. $x^2 + 2x - 5$

20. $3x^2 + 4$

In Problems 21–30, tell whether the expression is a polynomial. If it is, give its degree. If it is not, state why not.

21. $3x^2 - 5$

22. $1 - 4x$

23. 5

24. $-\pi$

25. $3x^2 - \dfrac{5}{x}$

26. $\dfrac{3}{x} + 2$

27. $2y^3 - \sqrt{2}$

28. $10z^2 + z$

29. $\dfrac{x^2 + 5}{x^3 - 1}$

30. $\dfrac{3x^3 + 2x - 1}{x^2 + x + 1}$

In Problems 31–56, add, subtract, or multiply, as indicated. Express your answer as a single polynomial in standard form.

31. $(x^2 + 4x + 5) + (3x - 3)$

32. $(x^3 + 3x^2 + 2) + (x^2 - 4x + 4)$

33. $(x^3 - 2x^2 + 5x + 10) - (2x^2 - 4x + 3)$

34. $(x^2 - 3x - 4) - (x^3 - 3x^2 + x + 5)$

35. $6(x^3 + x^2 - 3) - 4(2x^3 - 3x^2)$

36. $8(4x^3 - 3x^2 - 1) - 6(4x^3 + 8x - 2)$

37. $9(y^2 - 3y + 4) - 6(1 - y^2)$

38. $8(1 - y^3) + 4(1 + y + y^2 + y^3)$

39. $x(x^2 + x - 4)$

40. $4x^2(x^3 - x + 2)$

41. $(x + 2)(x + 4)$

42. $(x + 3)(x + 5)$

43. $(2x + 5)(x + 2)$

44. $(3x + 1)(2x + 1)$

45. $(x - 7)(x + 7)$

46. $(x - 1)(x + 1)$

47. $(2x + 3)(2x - 3)$

48. $(3x + 2)(3x - 2)$

49. $(x + 4)^2$

50. $(x - 5)^2$

51. $(2x - 3)^2$

52. $(3x - 4)^2$

53. $(x - 2)^3$

54. $(x + 1)^3$

55. $(2x + 1)^3$

56. $(3x - 2)^3$

In Problems 57–72, find the quotient and the remainder. Check your work by verifying that

$$(Quotient)(Divisor) + Remainder = Dividend$$

57. $4x^3 - 3x^2 + x + 1$ divided by $x + 2$

58. $3x^3 - x^2 + x - 2$ divided by $x + 2$

59. $4x^3 - 3x^2 + x + 1$ divided by x^2

60. $3x^3 - x^2 + x - 2$ divided by x^2

61. $5x^4 - 3x^2 + x + 1$ divided by $x^2 + 2$

62. $5x^4 - x^2 + x - 2$ divided by $x^2 + 2$

63. $4x^5 - 3x^2 + x + 1$ divided by $2x^3 - 1$

64. $3x^5 - x^2 + x - 2$ divided by $3x^3 - 1$

65. $2x^4 - 3x^3 + x + 1$ divided by $2x^2 + x + 1$

66. $3x^4 - x^3 + x - 2$ divided by $3x^2 + x + 1$

67. $-4x^3 + x^2 - 4$ divided by $x - 1$

68. $-3x^4 - 2x - 1$ divided by $x - 1$

69. $1 - x^2 + x^4$ divided by $x^2 + x + 1$

70. $1 - x^2 + x^4$ divided by $x^2 - x + 1$

71. $x^3 - a^3$ divided by $x - a$

72. $x^5 - a^5$ divided by $x - a$

In Problems 73–120, factor completely each polynomial. If the polynomial cannot be factored, say it is prime.

73. $x^2 - 36$

74. $x^2 - 9$

75. $2 - 8x^2$

76. $3 - 27x^2$

77. $x^2 + 11x + 10$

78. $x^2 + 5x + 4$

79. $x^2 - 10x + 21$

80. $x^2 - 6x + 8$

81. $4x^2 - 8x + 32$

82. $3x^2 - 12x + 15$

83. $x^2 + 4x + 16$

84. $x^2 + 12x + 36$

85. $15 + 2x - x^2$

86. $14 + 6x - x^2$

87. $3x^2 - 12x - 36$

88. $x^3 + 8x^2 - 20x$

89. $y^4 + 11y^3 + 30y^2$

90. $3y^3 - 18y^2 - 48y$

91. $4x^2 + 12x + 9$

92. $9x^2 - 12x + 4$

93. $6x^2 + 8x + 2$

94. $8x^2 + 6x - 2$

95. $x^4 - 81$

96. $x^4 - 1$

97. $x^6 - 2x^3 + 1$

98. $x^6 + 2x^3 + 1$

99. $x^7 - x^5$

100. $x^8 - x^5$

101. $16x^2 + 24x + 9$

102. $9x^2 - 24x + 16$

103. $5 + 16x - 16x^2$

104. $5 + 11x - 16x^2$

105. $4y^2 - 16y + 15$

106. $9y^2 + 9y - 4$

107. $1 - 8x^2 - 9x^4$

108. $4 - 14x^2 - 8x^4$

109. $x(x + 3) - 6(x + 3)$

110. $5(3x - 7) + x(3x - 7)$

111. $(x + 2)^2 - 5(x + 2)$

112. $(x - 1)^2 - 2(x - 1)$

113. $(3x - 2)^3 - 27$

114. $(5x + 1)^3 - 1$

115. $3(x^2 + 10x + 25) - 4(x + 5)$

116. $7(x^2 - 6x + 9) + 5(x - 3)$

117. $x^3 + 2x^2 - x - 2$

118. $x^3 - 3x^2 - x + 3$

119. $x^4 - x^3 + x - 1$

120. $x^4 + x^3 + x + 1$

In Problems 121–126, determine the number that should be added to complete the square of each expression. Then factor each expression.

121. $x^2 + 10x$

122. $p^2 + 14p$

123. $y^2 - 6y$

124. $x^2 - 4x$

125. $x^2 - \dfrac{1}{2}x$

126. $x^2 + \dfrac{1}{3}x$

Applications and Extensions

In Problems 127–136, expressions that occur in calculus are given. Factor completely each expression.

127. $2(3x + 4)^2 + (2x + 3) \cdot 2(3x + 4) \cdot 3$

128. $5(2x + 1)^2 + (5x - 6) \cdot 2(2x + 1) \cdot 2$

129. $2x(2x + 5) + x^2 \cdot 2$

130. $3x^2(8x - 3) + x^3 \cdot 8$

131. $2(x + 3)(x - 2)^3 + (x + 3)^2 \cdot 3(x - 2)^2$

132. $4(x + 5)^3(x - 1)^2 + (x + 5)^4 \cdot 2(x - 1)$

133. $(4x - 3)^2 + x \cdot 2(4x - 3) \cdot 4$

134. $3x^2(3x + 4)^2 + x^3 \cdot 2(3x + 4) \cdot 3$

135. $2(3x - 5) \cdot 3(2x + 1)^3 + (3x - 5)^2 \cdot 3(2x + 1)^2 \cdot 2$

136. $3(4x + 5)^2 \cdot 4(5x + 1)^2 + (4x + 5)^3 \cdot 2(5x + 1) \cdot 5$

137. Show that $x^2 + 4$ is prime.

138. Show that $x^2 + x + 1$ is prime.

Explaining Concepts: Discussion and Writing

139. Explain why the degree of the product of two nonzero polynomials equals the sum of their degrees.

140. Explain why the degree of the sum of two polynomials of different degrees equals the larger of their degrees.

141. Give a careful statement about the degree of the sum of two polynomials of the same degree.

142. Do you prefer to memorize the rule for the square of a binomial $(x + a)^2$ or to use FOIL to obtain the product? Write a brief position paper defending your choice.

143. Make up a polynomial that factors into a perfect square.

144. Explain to a fellow student what you look for first when presented with a factoring problem. What do you do next?

A.4 Synthetic Division

> **OBJECTIVE** **1** Divide Polynomials Using Synthetic Division (p. A32)

1 Divide Polynomials Using Synthetic Division

To find the quotient as well as the remainder when a polynomial of degree 1 or higher is divided by $x - c$, a shortened version of long division, called **synthetic division,** makes the task simpler.

To see how synthetic division works, we will use long division to divide the polynomial $2x^3 - x^2 + 3$ by $x - 3$.

$$
\begin{array}{r}
2x^2 + 5x + 15 \quad \leftarrow \text{Quotient} \\
x - 3 \overline{)\ 2x^3 - x^2 \qquad\quad + 3} \\
\underline{2x^3 - 6x^2} \\
5x^2 \\
\underline{5x^2 - 15x} \\
15x + 3 \\
\underline{15x - 45} \\
48 \quad \leftarrow \text{Remainder}
\end{array}
$$

✓ **Check:** (Divisor) $\cdot$ (Quotient) $+$ Remainder

$$= (x - 3)(2x^2 + 5x + 15) + 48$$
$$= 2x^3 + 5x^2 + 15x - 6x^2 - 15x - 45 + 48$$
$$= 2x^3 - x^2 + 3$$

The process of synthetic division arises from rewriting the long division in a more compact form, using simpler notation. For example, in the long division on the previous page, the terms in blue are not really necessary because they are identical to the terms directly above them. With these terms removed, we have

$$
\begin{array}{r}
2x^2 + 5x\ + 15 \\
x - 3\overline{)2x^3 - x^2\qquad\ + 3} \\
-6x^2 \\
\overline{5x^2} \\
-15x \\
\overline{15x} \\
-45 \\
\overline{48}
\end{array}
$$

Most of the x's that appear in this process can also be removed, provided that we are careful about positioning each coefficient. In this regard, we will need to use 0 as the coefficient of x in the dividend, because that power of x is missing. Now we have

$$
\begin{array}{r}
2x^2 + 5x + 15 \\
x - 3\overline{)2\quad -1\quad 0\quad 3} \\
-6 \\
\overline{5} \\
-15 \\
\overline{15} \\
-45 \\
\overline{48}
\end{array}
$$

We can make this display more compact by moving the lines up until the numbers in blue align horizontally.

$$
\begin{array}{rl}
2x^2 + 5x + 15 & \text{Row 1} \\
x - 3\overline{)2\quad -1\quad 0\quad 3} & \text{Row 2} \\
\underline{\qquad -6\ -15\ -45} & \text{Row 3} \\
\bigcirc\quad 5\quad 15\quad 48 & \text{Row 4}
\end{array}
$$

Because the leading coefficient of the divisor is always 1, we know that the leading coefficient of the dividend will also be the leading coefficient of the quotient. So we place the leading coefficient of the dividend, 2, in the circled position. Now, the first three numbers in row 4 are precisely the coefficients of the quotient, and the last number in row 4 is the remainder. Thus, row 1 is not really needed, so we can compress the process to three rows, where the bottom row contains both the coefficients of the quotient and the remainder.

$$
\begin{array}{rl}
x - 3\overline{)2\quad -1\quad 0\quad 3} & \text{Row 1} \\
\underline{\qquad -6\ -15\ -45} & \text{Row 2 (subtract)} \\
2\quad\ 5\quad 15\quad 48 & \text{Row 3}
\end{array}
$$

Recall that the entries in row 3 are obtained by subtracting the entries in row 2 from those in row 1. Rather than subtracting the entries in row 2, we can change the sign of each entry and add. With this modification, our display will look like this:

$$
\begin{array}{rl}
x - 3\overline{)2\quad -1\quad 0\quad 3} & \text{Row 1} \\
\underline{\qquad\ \ 6\quad 15\quad 45} & \text{Row 2 (add)} \\
2\quad\ 5\quad 15\quad 48 & \text{Row 3}
\end{array}
$$

Notice that the entries in row 2 are three times the prior entries in row 3. Our last modification to the display replaces the $x - 3$ by 3. The entries in row 3 give the quotient and the remainder, as shown next.

$$\begin{array}{r}
3\overline{)2 \quad -1 \quad\ \ 0 \quad\ \ 3} \quad \text{Row 1} \\
\underline{6 \quad\ 15 \quad 45} \quad \text{Row 2 (add)} \\
2 \quad\ \ 5 \quad\ 15 \quad 48 \quad \text{Row 3}
\end{array}$$

Quotient   Remainder

$$2x^2 + 5x + 15 \qquad 48$$

EXAMPLE 1   **Using Synthetic Division to Find the Quotient and Remainder**

Use synthetic division to find the quotient and remainder when

$$x^3 - 4x^2 - 5 \quad \text{is divided by} \quad x - 3$$

Solution   **STEP 1:** Write the dividend in descending powers of x. Then copy the coefficients, remembering to insert a 0 for any missing powers of x.

$$1 \quad -4 \quad 0 \quad -5 \quad \text{Row 1}$$

STEP 2: Insert the usual division symbol. In synthetic division, the divisor is of the form $x - c$, and c is the number placed to the left of the division symbol. Here, since the divisor is $x - 3$, we insert 3 to the left of the division symbol.

$$3\overline{)1 \quad -4 \quad 0 \quad -5} \quad \text{Row 1}$$

STEP 3: Bring the 1 down two rows, and enter it in row 3.

$$\begin{array}{r}
3\overline{)1 \quad -4 \quad 0 \quad -5} \quad \text{Row 1} \\
\downarrow \qquad\qquad\qquad\qquad \text{Row 2} \\
1 \qquad\qquad\qquad\qquad \text{Row 3}
\end{array}$$

STEP 4: Multiply the latest entry in row 3 by 3, and place the result in row 2, one column over to the right.

$$\begin{array}{r}
3\overline{)1 \quad -4 \quad 0 \quad -5} \quad \text{Row 1} \\
3 \qquad\qquad\qquad \text{Row 2} \\
1 \qquad\qquad\qquad\qquad \text{Row 3}
\end{array}$$

STEP 5: Add the entry in row 2 to the entry above it in row 1, and enter the sum in row 3.

$$\begin{array}{r}
3\overline{)1 \quad -4 \quad 0 \quad -5} \quad \text{Row 1} \\
3 \qquad\qquad\qquad \text{Row 2} \\
1 \quad -1 \qquad\qquad\quad \text{Row 3}
\end{array}$$

STEP 6: Repeat Steps 4 and 5 until no more entries are available in row 1.

$$\begin{array}{r}
3\overline{)1 \quad -4 \quad\ \ 0 \quad -5} \quad \text{Row 1} \\
\underline{3 \quad -3 \quad -9} \quad \text{Row 2} \\
1 \quad -1 \quad -3 \quad -14 \quad \text{Row 3}
\end{array}$$

STEP 7: The final entry in row 3, the -14, is the remainder; the other entries in row 3, the $1, -1$, and -3, are the coefficients (in descending order) of a polynomial whose degree is 1 less than that of the dividend. This is the quotient. Thus,

$$\text{Quotient} = x^2 - x - 3 \qquad \text{Remainder} = -14$$

✓ **Check:** (Divisor)(Quotient) + Remainder

$$= (x - 3)(x^2 - x - 3) + (-14)$$
$$= (x^3 - x^2 - 3x - 3x^2 + 3x + 9) + (-14)$$
$$= x^3 - 4x^2 - 5 = \text{Dividend}$$

The next example combines all the steps.

EXAMPLE 2   **Using Synthetic Division to Verify a Factor**

Use synthetic division to show that $x + 3$ is a factor of

$$2x^5 + 5x^4 - 2x^3 + 2x^2 - 2x + 3$$

Solution   The divisor is $x + 3 = x - (-3)$, so we place -3 to the left of the division symbol. Then the row 3 entries will be multiplied by -3, entered in row 2, and added to row 1.

$$
\begin{array}{r|rrrrrr}
-3 & 2 & 5 & -2 & 2 & -2 & 3 \\
 & & -6 & 3 & -3 & 3 & -3 \\
\hline
 & 2 & -1 & 1 & -1 & 1 & 0
\end{array}
\quad
\begin{array}{l}
\text{Row 1} \\
\text{Row 2} \\
\text{Row 3}
\end{array}
$$

Because the remainder is 0, we have

(Divisor)(Quotient) + Remainder

$$= (x + 3)(2x^4 - x^3 + x^2 - x + 1) = 2x^5 + 5x^4 - 2x^3 + 2x^2 - 2x + 3$$

As we see, $x + 3$ is a factor of $2x^5 + 5x^4 - 2x^3 + 2x^2 - 2x + 3$.   ⏎

As Example 2 illustrates, the remainder after division gives information about whether the divisor is, or is not, a factor. We shall have more to say about this in Chapter 4.

━━━━━ **Now Work** PROBLEMS 7 AND 17

A.4 Assess Your Understanding

Concepts and Vocabulary

1. To check division, the expression that is being divided, the dividend, should equal the product of the _____ and the _____ plus the _____ .

2. To divide $2x^3 - 5x + 1$ by $x + 3$ using synthetic division, the first step is to write ____)_____ .

3. **True or False**   In using synthetic division, the divisor is always a polynomial of degree 1, whose leading coefficient is 1.

4. **True or False**
$$
\begin{array}{r|rrrr}
-2 & 5 & 3 & 2 & 1 \\
 & & -10 & 14 & -32 \\
\hline
 & 5 & -7 & 16 & -31
\end{array}
$$
means $\dfrac{5x^3 + 3x^2 + 2x + 1}{x + 2} = 5x^2 - 7x + 16 + \dfrac{-31}{x + 2}$.

Skill Building

In Problems 5–16, use synthetic division to find the quotient and remainder when:

5. $x^3 - x^2 + 2x + 4$ is divided by $x - 2$

6. $x^3 + 2x^2 - 3x + 1$ is divided by $x + 1$

7. $3x^3 + 2x^2 - x + 3$ is divided by $x - 3$

8. $-4x^3 + 2x^2 - x + 1$ is divided by $x + 2$

9. $x^5 - 4x^3 + x$ is divided by $x + 3$

10. $x^4 + x^2 + 2$ is divided by $x - 2$

11. $4x^6 - 3x^4 + x^2 + 5$ is divided by $x - 1$

12. $x^5 + 5x^3 - 10$ is divided by $x + 1$

13. $0.1x^3 + 0.2x$ is divided by $x + 1.1$

14. $0.1x^2 - 0.2$ is divided by $x + 2.1$

15. $x^5 - 1$ is divided by $x - 1$

16. $x^5 + 1$ is divided by $x + 1$

In Problems 17–26, use synthetic division to determine whether $x - c$ is a factor of the given polynomial.

17. $4x^3 - 3x^2 - 8x + 4;$ $x - 2$

18. $-4x^3 + 5x^2 + 8;$ $x + 3$

19. $3x^4 - 6x^3 - 5x + 10;$ $x - 2$

20. $4x^4 - 15x^2 - 4;$ $x - 2$

21. $3x^6 + 82x^3 + 27;$ $x + 3$

22. $2x^6 - 18x^4 + x^2 - 9;$ $x + 3$

23. $4x^6 - 64x^4 + x^2 - 15;$ $x + 4$

24. $x^6 - 16x^4 + x^2 - 16;$ $x + 4$

25. $2x^4 - x^3 + 2x - 1;$ $x - \dfrac{1}{2}$

26. $3x^4 + x^3 - 3x + 1;$ $x + \dfrac{1}{3}$

Applications and Extensions

27. Find the sum of $a, b, c,$ and d if

$$\frac{x^3 - 2x^2 + 3x + 5}{x + 2} = ax^2 + bx + c + \frac{d}{x + 2}$$

Explaining Concepts: Discussion and Writing

28. When dividing a polynomial by $x - c$, do you prefer to use long division or synthetic division? Does the value of c make a difference to you in choosing? Give reasons.

A.5 Rational Expressions

OBJECTIVES **1** Reduce a Rational Expression to Lowest Terms (p. A36)

2 Multiply and Divide Rational Expressions (p. A37)

3 Add and Subtract Rational Expressions (p. A38)

4 Use the Least Common Multiple Method (p. A39)

5 Simplify Complex Rational Expressions (p. A40)

1 Reduce a Rational Expression to Lowest Terms

If we form the quotient of two polynomials, the result is called a **rational expression.** Some examples of rational expressions are

(a) $\dfrac{x^3 + 1}{x}$ (b) $\dfrac{3x^2 + x - 2}{x^2 + 5}$ (c) $\dfrac{x}{x^2 - 1}$ (d) $\dfrac{xy^2}{(x - y)^2}$

Expressions (a), (b), and (c) are rational expressions in one variable, x, whereas (d) is a rational expression in two variables, x and y.

Rational expressions are described in the same manner as rational numbers. In expression (a), the polynomial $x^3 + 1$ is called the **numerator,** and x is called the **denominator.** When the numerator and denominator of a rational expression contain no common factors (except 1 and -1), we say that the rational expression is **reduced to lowest terms,** or **simplified.**

The polynomial in the denominator of a rational expression cannot be equal to 0 because division by 0 is not defined. For example, for the expression $\dfrac{x^3 + 1}{x}$, x cannot take on the value 0. The domain of the variable x is $\{x | x \neq 0\}$.

WARNING Apply   the   Cancellation Property only to rational expressions written in factored form. Be sure to cancel only common factors! ■

A rational expression is reduced to lowest terms by factoring completely the numerator and the denominator and canceling any common factors by using the Cancellation Property:

$$\frac{a\cancel{c}}{b\cancel{c}} = \frac{a}{b} \qquad \text{if } b \neq 0, c \neq 0 \tag{1}$$

EXAMPLE 1	**Reducing a Rational Expression to Lowest Terms**

Reduce each rational expression to lowest terms.

(a) $\dfrac{x^2 + 4x + 4}{x^2 + 3x + 2}$ (b) $\dfrac{x^3 - 8}{x^3 - 2x^2}$ (c) $\dfrac{8 - 2x}{x^2 - x - 12}$

Solution (a) $\dfrac{x^2 + 4x + 4}{x^2 + 3x + 2} = \dfrac{\cancel{(x + 2)}(x + 2)}{\cancel{(x + 2)}(x + 1)} = \dfrac{x + 2}{x + 1}$ $x \neq -2, -1$

(b) $\dfrac{x^3 - 8}{x^3 - 2x^2} = \dfrac{\cancel{(x - 2)}(x^2 + 2x + 4)}{x^2\cancel{(x - 2)}} = \dfrac{x^2 + 2x + 4}{x^2}$ $x \neq 0, 2$

(c) $\dfrac{8 - 2x}{x^2 - x - 12} = \dfrac{2(4 - x)}{(x - 4)(x + 3)} = \dfrac{2(-1)\cancel{(x - 4)}}{\cancel{(x - 4)}(x + 3)} = -\dfrac{2}{x + 3}$ $x \neq -3, 4$

↵

━━━━━ **Now Work** PROBLEM 5

2 Multiply and Divide Rational Expressions

The rules for multiplying and dividing rational expressions are the same as the rules for multiplying and dividing rational numbers. If $\dfrac{a}{b}$ and $\dfrac{c}{d}$, $b \neq 0$, $d \neq 0$, are two rational expressions, then

$$\frac{a}{b} \cdot \frac{c}{d} = \frac{ac}{bd} \qquad \text{if } b \neq 0, d \neq 0 \tag{2}$$

$$\frac{\dfrac{a}{b}}{\dfrac{c}{d}} = \frac{a}{b} \cdot \frac{d}{c} = \frac{ad}{bc} \qquad \text{if } b \neq 0, c \neq 0, d \neq 0 \tag{3}$$

In using equations (2) and (3) with rational expressions, be sure first to factor each polynomial completely so that common factors can be canceled. Leave your answer in factored form.

EXAMPLE 2 **Multiplying and Dividing Rational Expressions**

Perform the indicated operation and simplify the result. Leave your answer in factored form.

(a) $\dfrac{x^2 - 2x + 1}{x^3 + x} \cdot \dfrac{4x^2 + 4}{x^2 + x - 2}$

(b) $\dfrac{\dfrac{x + 3}{x^2 - 4}}{\dfrac{x^2 - x - 12}{x^3 - 8}}$

Solution (a) $\dfrac{x^2 - 2x + 1}{x^3 + x} \cdot \dfrac{4x^2 + 4}{x^2 + x - 2} = \dfrac{(x - 1)^2}{x(x^2 + 1)} \cdot \dfrac{4(x^2 + 1)}{(x + 2)(x - 1)}$

$= \dfrac{(x - 1)^{\cancel{2}}(4)\cancel{(x^2 + 1)}}{x\cancel{(x^2 + 1)}(x + 2)\cancel{(x - 1)}}$

$= \dfrac{4(x - 1)}{x(x + 2)}$ $x \neq -2, 0, 1$

(b) $\dfrac{\dfrac{x+3}{x^2-4}}{\dfrac{x^2-x-12}{x^3-8}} = \dfrac{x+3}{x^2-4} \cdot \dfrac{x^3-8}{x^2-x-12}$

$$= \frac{x+3}{(x-2)(x+2)} \cdot \frac{(x-2)(x^2+2x+4)}{(x-4)(x+3)}$$

$$= \frac{(x+3)\,(x-2)(x^2+2x+4)}{(x-2)(x+2)(x-4)(x+3)}$$

$$= \frac{x^2+2x+4}{(x+2)(x-4)} \qquad x \neq -3, -2, 2, 4$$

Now Work PROBLEM 13

3 Add and Subtract Rational Expressions

The rules for adding and subtracting rational expressions are the same as the rules for adding and subtracting rational numbers. So, if the denominators of two rational expressions to be added (or subtracted) are equal, we add (or subtract) the numerators and keep the common denominator.

In Words

To add (or subtract) two rational expressions with the same denominator, keep the common denominator and add (or subtract) the numerators.

If $\dfrac{a}{b}$ and $\dfrac{c}{b}$ are two rational expressions, then

$$\frac{a}{b} + \frac{c}{b} = \frac{a+c}{b} \qquad \frac{a}{b} - \frac{c}{b} = \frac{a-c}{b} \qquad \text{if } b \neq 0 \tag{4}$$

EXAMPLE 3

Adding Rational Expressions with Equal Denominators

Perform the indicated operation and simplify the result. Leave your answer in factored form.

$$\frac{2x^2-4}{2x+5} + \frac{x+3}{2x+5} \qquad x \neq -\frac{5}{2}$$

Solution

$$\frac{2x^2-4}{2x+5} + \frac{x+3}{2x+5} = \frac{(2x^2-4)+(x+3)}{2x+5}$$

$$= \frac{2x^2+x-1}{2x+5} = \frac{(2x-1)(x+1)}{2x+5}$$

Now Work PROBLEM 21

If the denominators of two rational expressions to be added or subtracted are not equal, we can use the general formulas for adding and subtracting quotients.

$$\frac{a}{b} + \frac{c}{d} = \frac{a \cdot d}{b \cdot d} + \frac{b \cdot c}{b \cdot d} = \frac{ad+bc}{bd} \qquad \text{if } b \neq 0, d \neq 0 \tag{5a}$$

$$\frac{a}{b} - \frac{c}{d} = \frac{a \cdot d}{b \cdot d} - \frac{b \cdot c}{b \cdot d} = \frac{ad-bc}{bd} \qquad \text{if } b \neq 0, d \neq 0 \tag{5b}$$

EXAMPLE 4   **Subtracting Rational Expressions with Unequal Denominators**

Perform the indicated operation and simplify the result. Leave your answer in factored form.

$$\frac{x^2}{x^2 - 4} - \frac{1}{x} \qquad x \neq -2, 0, 2$$

Solution $\dfrac{x^2}{x^2 - 4} - \dfrac{1}{x} = \dfrac{x^2}{x^2 - 4} \cdot \dfrac{x}{x} - \dfrac{x^2 - 4}{x^2 - 4} \cdot \dfrac{1}{x} = \dfrac{x^2(x) - (x^2 - 4)(1)}{(x^2 - 4)(x)}$

(5b)

$$= \frac{x^3 - x^2 + 4}{(x - 2)(x + 2)(x)}$$

⤶

━━━ **Now Work** PROBLEM 23

4 Use the Least Common Multiple Method

If the denominators of two rational expressions to be added (or subtracted) have common factors, we usually do not use the general rules given by equations (5a) and (5b). Just as with fractions, we apply the **least common multiple (LCM) method.** The LCM method uses the polynomial of least degree that has each denominator polynomial as a factor.

The LCM Method for Adding or Subtracting Rational Expressions

The Least Common Multiple (LCM) Method requires four steps:

Step 1: Factor completely the polynomial in the denominator of each rational expression.

Step 2: The LCM of the denominator is the product of each of these factors raised to a power equal to the greatest number of times that the factor occurs in the polynomials.

Step 3: Write each rational expression using the LCM as the common denominator.

Step 4: Add or subtract the rational expressions using equation (4).

We begin with an example that goes through Steps 1 and 2.

EXAMPLE 5   **Finding the Least Common Multiple**

Find the least common multiple of the following pair of polynomials:

$$x(x - 1)^2(x + 1) \quad \text{and} \quad 4(x - 1)(x + 1)^3$$

Solution   **Step 1:** The polynomials are already factored completely as
$$x(x - 1)^2(x + 1) \quad \text{and} \quad 4(x - 1)(x + 1)^3$$

Step 2: Start by writing the factors of the left-hand polynomial. (Or you could start with the one on the right.)
$$x(x - 1)^2(x + 1)$$

Now look at the right-hand polynomial. Its first factor, 4, does not appear in our list, so we insert it.
$$4x(x - 1)^2(x + 1)$$

The next factor, $x - 1$, is already in our list, so no change is necessary. The final factor is $(x + 1)^3$. Since our list has $x + 1$ to the first power only, we replace $x + 1$ in the list by $(x + 1)^3$. The LCM is

$$4x(x - 1)^2(x + 1)^3$$

Notice that the LCM is, in fact, the polynomial of least degree that contains $x(x - 1)^2(x + 1)$ and $4(x - 1)(x + 1)^3$ as factors.

| EXAMPLE 6 | **Using the Least Common Multiple to Add Rational Expressions** |

Perform the indicated operation and simplify the result. Leave your answer in factored form.

$$\frac{x}{x^2 + 3x + 2} + \frac{2x - 3}{x^2 - 1} \qquad x \neq -2, -1, 1$$

Solution   **STEP 1:** Factor completely the polynomials in the denominators.

$$x^2 + 3x + 2 = (x + 2)(x + 1)$$
$$x^2 - 1 = (x - 1)(x + 1)$$

STEP 2: The LCM is $(x + 2)(x + 1)(x - 1)$. Do you see why?
STEP 3: Write each rational expression using the LCM as the denominator.

$$\frac{x}{x^2 + 3x + 2} = \frac{x}{(x + 2)(x + 1)} = \frac{x}{(x + 2)(x + 1)} \cdot \frac{x - 1}{x - 1} = \frac{x(x - 1)}{(x + 2)(x + 1)(x - 1)}$$

↑ Multiply numerator and denominator by x − 1 to get the LCM in the denominator.

$$\frac{2x - 3}{x^2 - 1} = \frac{2x - 3}{(x - 1)(x + 1)} = \frac{2x - 3}{(x - 1)(x + 1)} \cdot \frac{x + 2}{x + 2} = \frac{(2x - 3)(x + 2)}{(x - 1)(x + 1)(x + 2)}$$

↑ Multiply numerator and denominator by x + 2 to get the LCM in the denominator.

STEP 4: Now add by using equation (4).

$$\frac{x}{x^2 + 3x + 2} + \frac{2x - 3}{x^2 - 1} = \frac{x(x - 1)}{(x + 2)(x + 1)(x - 1)} + \frac{(2x - 3)(x + 2)}{(x + 2)(x + 1)(x - 1)}$$

$$= \frac{(x^2 - x) + (2x^2 + x - 6)}{(x + 2)(x + 1)(x - 1)}$$

$$= \frac{3x^2 - 6}{(x + 2)(x + 1)(x - 1)} = \frac{3(x^2 - 2)}{(x + 2)(x + 1)(x - 1)}$$

— **Now Work** PROBLEM 27

5 Simplify Complex Rational Expressions

When sums and/or differences of rational expressions appear as the numerator and/or denominator of a quotient, the quotient is called a **complex rational expression.*** For example,

$$\frac{1 + \dfrac{1}{x}}{1 - \dfrac{1}{x}} \quad \text{and} \quad \frac{\dfrac{x^2}{x^2 - 4} - 3}{\dfrac{x - 3}{x + 2} - 1}$$

* Some texts use the term **complex fraction.**

are complex rational expressions. To **simplify** a complex rational expression means to write it as a rational expression reduced to lowest terms. This can be accomplished in either of two ways.

Simplifying a Complex Rational Expression

METHOD 1: Treat the numerator and denominator of the complex rational expression separately, performing whatever operations are indicated and simplifying the results. Follow this by simplifying the resulting rational expression.

METHOD 2: Find the LCM of the denominators of all rational expressions that appear in the complex rational expression. Multiply the numerator and denominator of the complex rational expression by the LCM and simplify the result.

We use both methods in the next example. By carefully studying each method, you can discover situations in which one method may be easier to use than the other.

EXAMPLE 7 **Simplifying a Complex Rational Expression**

Simplify: $\dfrac{\dfrac{1}{2} + \dfrac{3}{x}}{\dfrac{x+3}{4}}$ $x \neq -3, 0$

Solution *Method 1:* First, perform the indicated operation in the numerator, and then divide.

$$\dfrac{\dfrac{1}{2} + \dfrac{3}{x}}{\dfrac{x+3}{4}} = \dfrac{\dfrac{1 \cdot x + 2 \cdot 3}{2 \cdot x}}{\dfrac{x+3}{4}} = \dfrac{\dfrac{x+6}{2x}}{\dfrac{x+3}{4}} = \dfrac{x+6}{2x} \cdot \dfrac{4}{x+3}$$

Rule for adding quotients   Rule for dividing quotients

$$= \dfrac{(x+6) \cdot 4}{2 \cdot x \cdot (x+3)} = \dfrac{2 \cdot 2 \cdot (x+6)}{2 \cdot x \cdot (x+3)} = \dfrac{2(x+6)}{x(x+3)}$$

Rule for multiplying quotients

Method 2: The rational expressions that appear in the complex rational expression are

$$\dfrac{1}{2}, \quad \dfrac{3}{x}, \quad \dfrac{x+3}{4}$$

The LCM of their denominators is $4x$. Multiply the numerator and denominator of the complex rational expression by $4x$ and then simplify.

$$\dfrac{\dfrac{1}{2} + \dfrac{3}{x}}{\dfrac{x+3}{4}} = \dfrac{4x \cdot \left(\dfrac{1}{2} + \dfrac{3}{x}\right)}{4x \cdot \left(\dfrac{x+3}{4}\right)} = \dfrac{4x \cdot \dfrac{1}{2} + 4x \cdot \dfrac{3}{x}}{\dfrac{4x \cdot (x+3)}{4}}$$

Multiply the numerator and denominator by 4x.   Use the Distributive Property in the numerator.

$$= \dfrac{2 \cdot 2x \cdot \dfrac{1}{2} + 4x \cdot \dfrac{3}{x}}{\dfrac{4x \cdot (x+3)}{4}} = \dfrac{2x + 12}{x(x+3)} = \dfrac{2(x+6)}{x(x+3)}$$

Simplify.   Factor.

EXAMPLE 8   **Simplifying a Complex Rational Expression**

Simplify: $\dfrac{\dfrac{x^2}{x-4}+2}{\dfrac{2x-2}{x}-1}$ $x \ne 0, 2, 4$

Solution   We will use Method 1.

$$\dfrac{\dfrac{x^2}{x-4}+2}{\dfrac{2x-2}{x}-1} = \dfrac{\dfrac{x^2}{x-4}+\dfrac{2(x-4)}{x-4}}{\dfrac{2x-2}{x}-\dfrac{x}{x}} = \dfrac{\dfrac{x^2+2x-8}{x-4}}{\dfrac{2x-2-x}{x}}$$

$$= \dfrac{\dfrac{(x+4)(x-2)}{x-4}}{\dfrac{x-2}{x}} = \dfrac{(x+4)\cancel{(x-2)}}{x-4}\cdot\dfrac{x}{\cancel{x-2}}$$

$$= \dfrac{(x+4)\cdot x}{x-4}$$

────── **Now Work** PROBLEM 31

A.5 Assess Your Understanding

Concepts and Vocabulary

1. When the numerator and denominator of a rational expression contain no common factors (except 1 and −1), the rational expression is in _____ _____.

2. LCM is an abbreviation for _____ _____ _____.

3. *True or False*   The rational expression $\dfrac{2x^3-4x}{x-2}$ is reduced to lowest terms.

4. *True or False*   The LCM of $2x^3+6x^2$ and $6x^4+4x^3$ is $4x^3(x+1)$.

Skill Building

In Problems 5–12, reduce each rational expression to lowest terms.

5. $\dfrac{3x+9}{x^2-9}$

6. $\dfrac{4x^2+8x}{12x+24}$

7. $\dfrac{x^2-2x}{3x-6}$

8. $\dfrac{15x^2+24x}{3x^2}$

9. $\dfrac{24x^2}{12x^2-6x}$

10. $\dfrac{x^2+4x+4}{x^2-4}$

11. $\dfrac{y^2-25}{2y^2-8y-10}$

12. $\dfrac{3y^2-y-2}{3y^2+5y+2}$

In Problems 13–34, perform the indicated operation and simplify the result. Leave your answer in factored form.

13. $\dfrac{3x+6}{5x^2}\cdot\dfrac{x}{x^2-4}$

14. $\dfrac{3}{2x}\cdot\dfrac{x^2}{6x+10}$

15. $\dfrac{4x^2}{x^2-16}\cdot\dfrac{x^3-64}{2x}$

16. $\dfrac{12}{x^2+x}\cdot\dfrac{x^3+1}{4x-2}$

17. $\dfrac{\dfrac{8x}{x^2-1}}{\dfrac{10x}{x+1}}$

18. $\dfrac{\dfrac{x-2}{4x}}{\dfrac{x^2-4x+4}{12x}}$

19. $\dfrac{\dfrac{4-x}{4+x}}{\dfrac{4x}{x^2-16}}$

20. $\dfrac{\dfrac{3+x}{3-x}}{\dfrac{x^2-9}{9x^3}}$

21. $\dfrac{x^2}{2x-3}-\dfrac{4}{2x-3}$

22. $\dfrac{3x^2}{2x-1}-\dfrac{9}{2x-1}$

23. $\dfrac{x}{x^2-4}+\dfrac{1}{x}$

24. $\dfrac{x-1}{x^3}+\dfrac{x}{x^2+1}$

25. $\dfrac{x}{x^2 - 7x + 6} - \dfrac{x}{x^2 - 2x - 24}$

26. $\dfrac{x}{x - 3} - \dfrac{x + 1}{x^2 + 5x - 24}$

27. $\dfrac{4x}{x^2 - 4} - \dfrac{2}{x^2 + x - 6}$

28. $\dfrac{3x}{x - 1} - \dfrac{x - 4}{x^2 - 2x + 1}$

29. $\dfrac{3}{(x - 1)^2(x + 1)} + \dfrac{2}{(x - 1)(x + 1)^2}$

30. $\dfrac{2}{(x + 2)^2(x - 1)} - \dfrac{6}{(x + 2)(x - 1)^2}$

31. $\dfrac{1 + \dfrac{1}{x}}{1 - \dfrac{1}{x}}$

32. $\dfrac{4 + \dfrac{1}{x^2}}{3 - \dfrac{1}{x^2}}$

33. $\dfrac{\dfrac{x - 2}{x + 2} + \dfrac{x - 1}{x + 1}}{\dfrac{x}{x + 1} - \dfrac{2x - 3}{x}}$

34. $\dfrac{\dfrac{2x + 5}{x} - \dfrac{x}{x - 3}}{\dfrac{x^2}{x - 3} - \dfrac{(x + 1)^2}{x + 3}}$

Applications and Extensions

In Problems 35–42, expressions that occur in calculus are given. Reduce each expression to lowest terms.

35. $\dfrac{(2x + 3) \cdot 3 - (3x - 5) \cdot 2}{(3x - 5)^2}$

36. $\dfrac{(4x + 1) \cdot 5 - (5x - 2) \cdot 4}{(5x - 2)^2}$

37. $\dfrac{x \cdot 2x - (x^2 + 1) \cdot 1}{(x^2 + 1)^2}$

38. $\dfrac{x \cdot 2x - (x^2 - 4) \cdot 1}{(x^2 - 4)^2}$

39. $\dfrac{(3x + 1) \cdot 2x - x^2 \cdot 3}{(3x + 1)^2}$

40. $\dfrac{(2x - 5) \cdot 3x^2 - x^3 \cdot 2}{(2x - 5)^2}$

41. $\dfrac{(x^2 + 1) \cdot 3 - (3x + 4) \cdot 2x}{(x^2 + 1)^2}$

42. $\dfrac{(x^2 + 9) \cdot 2 - (2x - 5) \cdot 2x}{(x^2 + 9)^2}$

43. The Lensmaker's Equation The focal length f of a lens with index of refraction n is

$$\frac{1}{f} = (n - 1)\left[\frac{1}{R_1} + \frac{1}{R_2}\right]$$

where R_1 and R_2 are the radii of curvature of the front and back surfaces of the lens. Express f as a rational expression. Evaluate the rational expression for $n = 1.5$, $R_1 = 0.1$ meter, and $R_2 = 0.2$ meter.

44. Electrical Circuits An electrical circuit contains three resistors connected in parallel. If the resistance of each is R_1, R_2, and R_3 ohms, respectively, their combined resistance R is given by the formula

$$\frac{1}{R} = \frac{1}{R_1} + \frac{1}{R_2} + \frac{1}{R_3}$$

Express R as a rational expression. Evaluate R for $R_1 = 5$ ohms, $R_2 = 4$ ohms, and $R_3 = 10$ ohms.

Explaining Concepts: Discussion and Writing

45. The following expressions are called **continued fractions:**

$$1 + \frac{1}{x}, \quad 1 + \cfrac{1}{1 + \cfrac{1}{x}}, \quad 1 + \cfrac{1}{1 + \cfrac{1}{1 + \cfrac{1}{x}}}, \quad 1 + \cfrac{1}{1 + \cfrac{1}{1 + \cfrac{1}{1 + \cfrac{1}{x}}}}, \quad \ldots$$

Each simplifies to an expression of the form

$$\frac{ax + b}{bx + c}$$

Trace the successive values of a, b, and c as you "continue" the fraction. Can you discover the patterns that these values follow? Go to the library and research Fibonacci numbers. Write a report on your findings.

46. Explain to a fellow student when you would use the LCM method to add two rational expressions. Give two examples of adding two rational expressions, one in which you use the LCM and the other in which you do not.

47. Which of the two methods given in the text for simplifying complex rational expressions do you prefer? Write a brief paragraph stating the reasons for your choice.

A.6 Solving Equations

PREPARING FOR THIS SECTION *Before getting started, review the following:*

- Factoring Polynomials (Appendix A, Section A.3, pp. A28–A29)
- Zero-Product Property (Appendix A, Section A.1, p. A4)
- Square Roots (Appendix A, Section A.1, pp. A9–A10)
- Absolute Value (Appendix A, Section A.1, pp. A5–A6)

Now Work the 'Are You Prepared?' problems on page A51.

OBJECTIVES 1 Solve Equations by Factoring (p. A46)
2 Solve Equations Involving Absolute Value (p. A46)
3 Solve a Quadratic Equation by Factoring (p. A47)
4 Solve a Quadratic Equation by Completing the Square (p. A48)
5 Solve a Quadratic Equation Using the Quadratic Formula (p. A49)

An **equation in one variable** is a statement in which two expressions, at least one containing the variable, are equal. The expressions are called the **sides** of the equation. Since an equation is a statement, it may be true or false, depending on the value of the variable. Unless otherwise restricted, the admissible values of the variable are those in the domain of the variable. The admissible values of the variable, if any, that result in a true statement are called **solutions,** or **roots,** of the equation. To **solve an equation** means to find all the solutions of the equation.

For example, the following are all equations in one variable, x:

$$x + 5 = 9 \qquad x^2 + 5x = 2x - 2 \qquad \frac{x^2 - 4}{x + 1} = 0 \qquad \sqrt{x^2 + 9} = 5$$

The first of these statements, $x + 5 = 9$, is true when $x = 4$ and false for any other choice of x. That is, 4 is a solution of the equation $x + 5 = 9$. We also say that 4 **satisfies** the equation $x + 5 = 9$, because, when we substitute 4 for x, a true statement results.

Sometimes an equation will have more than one solution. For example, the equation

$$\frac{x^2 - 4}{x + 1} = 0$$

has $x = -2$ and $x = 2$ as solutions.

Usually, we will write the solution of an equation in set notation. This set is called the **solution set** of the equation. For example, the solution set of the equation $x^2 - 9 = 0$ is $\{-3, 3\}$.

Some equations have no real solution. For example, $x^2 + 9 = 5$ has no real solution, because there is no real number whose square when added to 9 equals 5.

An equation that is satisfied for every value of the variable for which both sides are defined is called an **identity.** For example, the equation

$$3x + 5 = x + 3 + 2x + 2$$

is an identity, because this statement is true for any real number x.

One method for solving an equation is to replace the original equation by a succession of equivalent equations until an equation with an obvious solution is obtained.

For example, all the following equations are equivalent.

$$2x + 3 = 13$$
$$2x = 10$$
$$x = 5$$

We conclude that the solution set of the original equation is $\{5\}$.

How do we obtain equivalent equations? In general, there are five ways.

Procedures That Result in Equivalent Equations

1. Interchange the two sides of the equation:
   $$\text{Replace} \quad 3 = x \quad \text{by} \quad x = 3$$

2. Simplify the sides of the equation by combining like terms, eliminating parentheses, and so on:
   $$\text{Replace} \quad (x + 2) + 6 = 2x + (x + 1)$$
   $$\text{by} \quad x + 8 = 3x + 1$$

3. Add or subtract the same expression on both sides of the equation:
   $$\text{Replace} \quad 3x - 5 = 4$$
   $$\text{by} \quad (3x - 5) + 5 = 4 + 5$$

4. Multiply or divide both sides of the equation by the same nonzero expression:
   $$\text{Replace} \quad \frac{3x}{x - 1} = \frac{6}{x - 1} \quad x \neq 1$$
   $$\text{by} \quad \frac{3x}{x - 1} \cdot (x - 1) = \frac{6}{x - 1} \cdot (x - 1)$$

5. If one side of the equation is 0 and the other side can be factored, then we may use the Zero-Product Property* and set each factor equal to 0:
   $$\text{Replace} \quad x(x - 3) = 0$$
   $$\text{by} \quad x = 0 \quad \text{or} \quad x - 3 = 0$$

WARNING Squaring both sides of an equation does not necessarily lead to an equivalent equation. ∎

Whenever it is possible to solve an equation in your head, do so. For example,

The solution of $2x = 8$ is $x = 4$.

The solution of $3x - 15 = 0$ is $x = 5$.

Now Work PROBLEM 13

Often, though, some rearrangement is necessary.

EXAMPLE 1 | **Solving an Equation**

Solve the equation: $3x - 5 = 4$

Solution Replace the original equation by a succession of equivalent equations.

$$3x - 5 = 4$$
$$(3x - 5) + 5 = 4 + 5 \qquad \text{Add 5 to both sides.}$$
$$3x = 9 \qquad \text{Simplify.}$$
$$\frac{3x}{3} = \frac{9}{3} \qquad \text{Divide both sides by 3.}$$
$$x = 3 \qquad \text{Simplify.}$$

The last equation, $x = 3$, has the single solution 3. All these equations are equivalent, so 3 is the only solution of the original equation, $3x - 5 = 4$.

---

* The Zero-Product Property says that if $ab = 0$, then $a = 0$ or $b = 0$ or both equal 0.

✓**Check:** It is a good practice to check the solution by substituting 3 for x in the original equation.

$$3x - 5 = 3(3) - 5 = 9 - 5 = 4$$

The solution checks.

↵

━━━━ **Now Work** PROBLEMS 27 AND 33

1 Solve Equations by Factoring

EXAMPLE 2

Solving Equations by Factoring

Solve the equations: (a) $x^3 = 4x$ (b) $x^3 - x^2 - 4x + 4 = 0$

Solution

(a) Begin by collecting all terms on one side. This results in 0 on one side and an expression to be factored on the other.

$$\begin{aligned} x^3 &= 4x \\ x^3 - 4x &= 0 \\ x(x^2 - 4) &= 0 \quad \text{Factor.} \\ x(x - 2)(x + 2) &= 0 \quad \text{Factor again.} \\ x = 0 \quad \text{or} \quad x - 2 = 0 \quad \text{or} \quad x + 2 &= 0 \quad \text{Apply the Zero-Product Property.} \\ x = 0 \quad \text{or} \qquad x = 2 \quad \text{or} \qquad x &= -2 \quad \text{Solve for x.} \end{aligned}$$

The solution set is $\{-2, 0, 2\}$.

✓**Check:** $x = -2$: $(-2)^3 = -8$ and $4(-2) = -8$ −2 is a solution.

             $x = 0$: $0^3 = 0$ and $4 \cdot 0 = 0$ 0 is a solution.

             $x = 2$: $2^3 = 8$ and $4 \cdot 2 = 8$ 4 is a solution.

(b) Group the terms of $x^3 - x^2 - 4x + 4 = 0$ as follows:

$$(x^3 - x^2) - (4x - 4) = 0$$

Factor out x^2 from the first grouping and 4 from the second.

$$x^2(x - 1) - 4(x - 1) = 0$$

This reveals the common factor $(x - 1)$, so we have

$$\begin{aligned} (x^2 - 4)(x - 1) &= 0 \\ (x - 2)(x + 2)(x - 1) &= 0 \qquad \text{Factor again.} \\ x - 2 = 0 \quad \text{or} \quad x + 2 = 0 \quad x - 1 &= 0 \qquad \text{Apply the Zero-Product Property.} \\ x = 2 \qquad\qquad x = -2 \qquad x &= 1 \qquad \text{Solve for x.} \end{aligned}$$

The solution set is $\{-2, 1, 2\}$.

✓**Check:**

$x = -2$: $(-2)^3 - (-2)^2 - 4(-2) + 4 = -8 - 4 + 8 + 4 = 0$ −2 is a solution

$x = 1$: $1^3 - 1^2 - 4(1) + 4 = 1 - 1 - 4 + 4 = 0$ 1 is a solution.

$x = 2$: $2^3 - 2^2 - 4(2) + 4 = 8 - 4 - 8 + 4 = 0$ 2 is a solution.

↵

━━━━ **Now Work** PROBLEM 37

2 Solve Equations Involving Absolute Value

On the real number line, there are two points whose distance from the origin is 5 units, −5 and 5, so the equation $|x| = 5$ will have the solution set $\{-5, 5\}$.

EXAMPLE 3

Solving an Equation Involving Absolute Value

Solve the equation: $|x + 4| = 13$

Solution

There are two possibilities.

$$x + 4 = 13 \quad \text{or} \quad x + 4 = -13$$
$$x = 9 \quad \text{or} \quad x = -17$$

The solution set is $\{-17, 9\}$.

Now Work PROBLEM 49

3 Solve a Quadratic Equation by Factoring

DEFINITION

A **quadratic equation** is an equation equivalent to one of the form

$$ax^2 + bx + c = 0 \tag{1}$$

where a, b, and c are real numbers and $a \neq 0$.

A quadratic equation written in the form $ax^2 + bx + c = 0$ is said to be in **standard form.**

Sometimes, a quadratic equation is called a **second-degree equation,** because the left side is a polynomial of degree 2.

When a quadratic equation is written in standard form $ax^2 + bx + c = 0$, it may be possible to factor the expression on the left side into the product of two first-degree polynomials. Then, by using the Zero-Product Property and setting each factor equal to 0, we can solve the resulting linear equations and obtain the solutions of the quadratic equation.

EXAMPLE 4

Solving a Quadratic Equation by Factoring

Solve the equation: $2x^2 = x + 3$

Solution

Put the equation $2x^2 = x + 3$ in standard form by adding $-x - 3$ to both sides.

$$2x^2 = x + 3$$
$$2x^2 - x - 3 = 0 \qquad \text{Add } -x - 3 \text{ to both sides.}$$

The left side may now be factored as

$$(2x - 3)(x + 1) = 0 \qquad \text{Factor.}$$

so that

$$2x - 3 = 0 \quad \text{or} \quad x + 1 = 0 \qquad \text{Apply the Zero-Product Property.}$$
$$x = \frac{3}{2} \qquad\qquad x = -1 \qquad \text{Solve.}$$

The solution set is $\left\{-1, \dfrac{3}{2}\right\}$.

When the left side factors into two linear equations with the same solution, the quadratic equation is said to have a **repeated solution.** We also call this solution a **root of multiplicity 2,** or a **double root.**

| EXAMPLE 5 | **Solving a Quadratic Equation by Factoring** |

Solve the equation: $9x^2 - 6x + 1 = 0$

Solution This equation is already in standard form, and the left side can be factored.

$$9x^2 - 6x + 1 = 0$$
$$(3x - 1)(3x - 1) = 0 \quad \text{Factor.}$$

so

$$x = \frac{1}{3} \quad \text{or} \quad x = \frac{1}{3} \quad \text{Solve for } x.$$

This equation has only the repeated solution $\frac{1}{3}$. The solution set is $\left\{\frac{1}{3}\right\}$.

➤ **Now Work** PROBLEM 67

The Square Root Method

Suppose that we wish to solve the quadratic equation

$$x^2 = p \tag{2}$$

where $p \geq 0$ is a nonnegative number. Proceed as in the earlier examples.

$$x^2 - p = 0 \qquad \text{Put in standard form.}$$
$$(x - \sqrt{p})(x + \sqrt{p}) = 0 \qquad \text{Factor (over the real numbers).}$$
$$x = \sqrt{p} \quad \text{or} \quad x = -\sqrt{p} \qquad \text{Solve.}$$

We have the following result:

> If $x^2 = p$ and $p \geq 0$, then $x = \sqrt{p}$ or $x = -\sqrt{p}$. $\qquad$ (3)

When statement (3) is used, it is called the **Square Root Method.** In statement (3), note that if $p > 0$ the equation $x^2 = p$ has two solutions, $x = \sqrt{p}$ and $x = -\sqrt{p}$. We usually abbreviate these solutions as $x = \pm\sqrt{p}$, read as "x equals plus or minus the square root of p."

For example, the two solutions of the equation

$$x^2 = 4$$

are

$$x = \pm\sqrt{4} \quad \text{Use the Square Root Method.}$$

and, since $\sqrt{4} = 2$, we have

$$x = \pm 2$$

The solution set is $\{-2, 2\}$.

➤ **Now Work** PROBLEM 81

4 Solve a Quadratic Equation by Completing the Square

| EXAMPLE 6 | **Solving a Quadratic Equation by Completing the Square** |

Solve by completing the square: $2x^2 - 8x - 5 = 0$

Solution First, rewrite the equation as follows:

$$2x^2 - 8x - 5 = 0$$
$$2x^2 - 8x = 5$$

Next, divide both sides by 2 so that the coefficient of x^2 is 1. (This enables us to complete the square at the next step.)

$$x^2 - 4x = \frac{5}{2}$$

Finally, complete the square by adding $\left[\frac{1}{2}(-4)\right]^2 = 4$ to both sides.

$$x^2 - 4x + 4 = \frac{5}{2} + 4$$

$$(x - 2)^2 = \frac{13}{2}$$

$$x - 2 = \pm\sqrt{\frac{13}{2}} \quad \text{Use the Square Root Method.}$$

$$x - 2 = \pm\frac{\sqrt{26}}{2} \quad \sqrt{\frac{13}{2}} = \frac{\sqrt{13}}{\sqrt{2}} = \frac{\sqrt{13}}{\sqrt{2}} \cdot \frac{\sqrt{2}}{\sqrt{2}} = \frac{\sqrt{26}}{2}$$

$$x = 2 \pm \frac{\sqrt{26}}{2}$$

COMMENT If we wanted an approximation, say rounded to two decimal places, of these solutions, we would use a calculator to get $\{-0.55, 4.55\}$. ■

The solution set is $\left\{2 - \dfrac{\sqrt{26}}{2}, 2 + \dfrac{\sqrt{26}}{2}\right\}$

━━ **Now Work** PROBLEM 8 5

5 Solve a Quadratic Equation Using the Quadratic Formula

We can use the method of completing the square to obtain a general formula for solving any quadratic equation

$$ax^2 + bx + c = 0 \qquad a \neq 0$$

COMMENT There is no loss in generality to assume that $a > 0$, since if $a < 0$ we can multiply by -1 to obtain an equivalent equation with a positive leading coefficient. ■

As in Example 6, we rearrange the terms as

$$ax^2 + bx = -c \quad a > 0$$

Since $a > 0$, we can divide both sides by a to get

$$x^2 + \frac{b}{a}x = -\frac{c}{a}$$

Now the coefficient of x^2 is 1. To complete the square on the left side, add the square of $\frac{1}{2}$ of the coefficient of x; that is, add

$$\left(\frac{1}{2} \cdot \frac{b}{a}\right)^2 = \frac{b^2}{4a^2}$$

to both sides. Then

$$x^2 + \frac{b}{a}x + \frac{b^2}{4a^2} = \frac{b^2}{4a^2} - \frac{c}{a}$$

$$\left(x + \frac{b}{2a}\right)^2 = \frac{b^2 - 4ac}{4a^2} \quad \frac{b^2}{4a^2} - \frac{c}{a} = \frac{b^2}{4a^2} - \frac{4ac}{4a^2} = \frac{b^2 - 4ac}{4a^2} \quad \textbf{(4)}$$

Provided that $b^2 - 4ac \geq 0$, we now can use the Square Root Method to get

$$x + \frac{b}{2a} = \pm\sqrt{\frac{b^2 - 4ac}{4a^2}}$$

$$x + \frac{b}{2a} = \frac{\pm\sqrt{b^2 - 4ac}}{2a}$$

The square root of a quotient equals the quotient of the square roots.

Also, $\sqrt{4a^2} = 2a$ since $a > 0$.

$$x = -\frac{b}{2a} \pm \frac{\sqrt{b^2 - 4ac}}{2a}$$

Add $-\dfrac{b}{2a}$ to both sides.

$$= \frac{-b \pm \sqrt{b^2 - 4ac}}{2a}$$

Combine the quotients on the right.

What if $b^2 - 4ac$ is negative? Then equation (4) states that the left expression (a real number squared) equals the right expression (a negative number). Since this occurrence is impossible for real numbers, we conclude that if $b^2 - 4ac < 0$ the quadratic equation has no *real* solution. (We discuss quadratic equations for which the quantity $b^2 - 4ac < 0$ in detail in the next section.)

We now state the *quadratic formula*.

THEOREM

Consider the quadratic equation

$$\boxed{ax^2 + bx + c = 0 \qquad a \neq 0}$$

If $b^2 - 4ac < 0$, this equation has no real solution.

If $b^2 - 4ac \geq 0$, the real solution(s) of this equation is (are) given by the **quadratic formula.**

Quadratic Formula

$$x = \frac{-b \pm \sqrt{b^2 - 4ac}}{2a} \tag{5}$$

The quantity $b^2 - 4ac$ is called the **discriminant** of the quadratic equation, because its value tells us whether the equation has real solutions. In fact, it also tells us how many solutions to expect.

Discriminant of a Quadratic Equation

For a quadratic equation $ax^2 + bx + c = 0$:

1. If $b^2 - 4ac > 0$, there are two unequal real solutions.
2. If $b^2 - 4ac = 0$, there is a repeated solution, a root of multiplicity 2.
3. If $b^2 - 4ac < 0$, there is no real solution.

When asked to find the real solutions, if any, of a quadratic equation, always evaluate the discriminant first to see how many real solutions there are.

EXAMPLE 7

Solving a Quadratic Equation Using the Quadratic Formula

Use the quadratic formula to find the real solutions, if any, of the equation

$$3x^2 - 5x + 1 = 0$$

Solution

The equation is in standard form, so we compare it to $ax^2 + bx + c = 0$ to find a, b, and c.

$$3x^2 - 5x + 1 = 0$$
$$ax^2 + bx + c = 0 \quad \text{$a = 3, b = -5, c = 1$}$$

With $a = 3$, $b = -5$, and $c = 1$, evaluate the discriminant $b^2 - 4ac$.

$$b^2 - 4ac = (-5)^2 - 4(3)(1) = 25 - 12 = 13$$

Since $b^2 - 4ac > 0$, there are two real solutions, which can be found using the quadratic formula.

$$x = \frac{-b \pm \sqrt{b^2 - 4ac}}{2a} = \frac{-(-5) \pm \sqrt{13}}{2(3)} = \frac{5 \pm \sqrt{13}}{6}$$

The solution set is $\left\{ \dfrac{5 - \sqrt{13}}{6}, \dfrac{5 + \sqrt{13}}{6} \right\}$.

EXAMPLE 8   **Solving a Quadratic Equation Using the Quadratic Formula**

Use the quadratic formula to find the real solutions, if any, of the equation

$$3x^2 + 2 = 4x$$

Solution   The equation, as given, is not in standard form.

$$3x^2 + 2 = 4x$$
$$3x^2 - 4x + 2 = 0 \qquad \text{Put in standard form.}$$
$$ax^2 + bx + c = 0 \qquad \text{Compare to standard form.}$$

With $a = 3$, $b = -4$, and $c = 2$, we find

$$b^2 - 4ac = (-4)^2 - 4(3)(2) = 16 - 24 = -8$$

Since $b^2 - 4ac < 0$, the equation has no real solution.

Now Work PROBLEMS 91 AND 97

SUMMARY   **Procedure for Solving a Quadratic Equation**

To solve a quadratic equation, first put it in standard form:

$$ax^2 + bx + c = 0$$

Then:

STEP 1: Identify a, b, and c.

STEP 2: Evaluate the discriminant, $b^2 - 4ac$.

STEP 3: (a) If the discriminant is negative, the equation has no real solution.
(b) If the discriminant is zero, the equation has one real solution, a repeated root.
(c) If the discriminant is positive, the equation has two distinct real solutions.

If you can easily spot factors, use the factoring method to solve the equation. Otherwise, use the quadratic formula or the method of completing the square.

A.6 Assess Your Understanding

'Are You Prepared?' *Answers are given at the end of these exercises. If you get a wrong answer, read the pages listed in red.*

1. Factor $x^2 - 5x - 6$. (pp. A28–A29)

2. Factor $2x^2 - x - 3$. (pp. A28–A29)

3. The solution set of the equation $(x - 3)(3x + 5) = 0$ is
_____ . (p. A4)

4. *True or False* $\sqrt{x^2} = |x|$. (pp. A9–A10)

Concepts and Vocabulary

5. *True or False* Squaring both sides of an equation results in an equivalent equation.

6. An equation that is satisfied for every choice of the variable for which both sides are defined is called a(n) _____.

7. *True or False* The solution of the equation $3x - 8 = 0$ is $\frac{3}{8}$.

8. *True or False* Some equations have no solution.

9. To solve the equation $x^2 + 5x = 0$ by completing the square, you would _____ the number _____ to both sides.

10. The quantity $b^2 - 4ac$ is called the _____ of a quadratic equation. If it is _____, the equation has no real solution.

11. *True or False* Quadratic equations always have two real solutions.

12. *True or False* If the discriminant of a quadratic equation is positive, then the equation has two solutions that are negatives of one another.

Skill Building

In Problems 13–78, solve each equation.

13. $3x = 21$

14. $3x = -24$

15. $5x + 15 = 0$

16. $3x + 18 = 0$

17. $2x - 3 = 5$

18. $3x + 4 = -8$

19. $\frac{1}{3}x = \frac{5}{12}$

20. $\frac{2}{3}x = \frac{9}{2}$

21. $6 - x = 2x + 9$

22. $3 - 2x = 2 - x$

23. $2(3 + 2x) = 3(x - 4)$

24. $3(2 - x) = 2x - 1$

25. $8x - (2x + 1) = 3x - 10$

26. $5 - (2x - 1) = 10$

27. $\frac{1}{2}x - 4 = \frac{3}{4}x$

28. $1 - \frac{1}{2}x = 5$

29. $0.9t = 0.4 + 0.1t$

30. $0.9t = 1 + t$

31. $\frac{2}{y} + \frac{4}{y} = 3$

32. $\frac{4}{y} - 5 = \frac{5}{2y}$

33. $(x + 7)(x - 1) = (x + 1)^2$

34. $(x + 2)(x - 3) = (x - 3)^2$

35. $z(z^2 + 1) = 3 + z^3$

36. $w(4 - w^2) = 8 - w^3$

37. $x^2 = 9x$

38. $x^3 = x^2$

39. $t^3 - 9t^2 = 0$

40. $4z^3 - 8z^2 = 0$

41. $\frac{3}{2x - 3} = \frac{2}{x + 5}$

42. $\frac{-2}{x + 4} = \frac{-3}{x + 1}$

43. $(x + 2)(3x) = (x + 2)(6)$

44. $(x - 5)(2x) = (x - 5)(4)$

45. $\frac{2}{x - 2} = \frac{3}{x + 5} + \frac{10}{(x + 5)(x - 2)}$

46. $\frac{1}{2x + 3} + \frac{1}{x - 1} = \frac{1}{(2x + 3)(x - 1)}$

47. $|2x| = 6$

48. $|3x| = 12$

49. $|2x + 3| = 5$

50. $|3x - 1| = 2$

51. $|1 - 4t| = 5$

52. $|1 - 2z| = 3$

53. $|-2x| = 8$

54. $|-x| = 1$

55. $|-2|x = 4$

56. $|3|x = 9$

57. $|x - 2| = -\frac{1}{2}$

58. $|2 - x| = -1$

59. $|x^2 - 4| = 0$

60. $|x^2 - 9| = 0$

61. $|x^2 - 2x| = 3$

62. $|x^2 + x| = 12$

63. $|x^2 + x - 1| = 1$

64. $|x^2 + 3x - 2| = 2$

65. $x^2 = 4x$

66. $x^2 = -8x$

67. $z^2 + 4z - 12 = 0$

68. $v^2 + 7v + 12 = 0$

69. $2x^2 - 5x - 3 = 0$

70. $3x^2 + 5x + 2 = 0$

71. $x(x - 7) + 12 = 0$

72. $x(x + 1) = 12$

73. $4x^2 + 9 = 12x$

74. $25x^2 + 16 = 40x$

75. $6x - 5 = \frac{6}{x}$

76. $x + \frac{12}{x} = 7$

77. $\frac{4(x - 2)}{x - 3} + \frac{3}{x} = \frac{-3}{x(x - 3)}$

78. $\frac{5}{x + 4} = 4 + \frac{3}{x - 2}$

In Problems 79–84, solve each equation by the Square Root Method.

79. $x^2 = 25$

80. $x^2 = 36$

81. $(x - 1)^2 = 4$

82. $(x + 2)^2 = 1$

83. $(2y + 3)^2 = 9$

84. $(3x - 2)^2 = 4$

In Problems 85–90, solve each equation by completing the square.

85. $x^2 + 4x = 21$

86. $x^2 - 6x = 13$

87. $x^2 - \frac{1}{2}x - \frac{3}{16} = 0$

88. $x^2 + \frac{2}{3}x - \frac{1}{3} = 0$

89. $3x^2 + x - \frac{1}{2} = 0$

90. $2x^2 - 3x - 1 = 0$

In Problems 91–102, find the real solutions, if any, of each equation. Use the quadratic formula.

91. $x^2 - 4x + 2 = 0$

92. $x^2 + 4x + 2 = 0$

93. $x^2 - 5x - 1 = 0$

94. $x^2 + 5x + 3 = 0$

95. $2x^2 - 5x + 3 = 0$

96. $2x^2 + 5x + 3 = 0$

97. $4y^2 - y + 2 = 0$

98. $4t^2 + t + 1 = 0$

99. $4x^2 = 1 - 2x$

100. $2x^2 = 1 - 2x$

101. $x^2 + \sqrt{3}x - 3 = 0$

102. $x^2 + \sqrt{2}x - 2 = 0$

In Problems 103–108, use the discriminant to determine whether each quadratic equation has two unequal real solutions, a repeated real solution, or no real solution without solving the equation.

103. $x^2 - 5x + 7 = 0$

104. $x^2 + 5x + 7 = 0$

105. $9x^2 - 30x + 25 = 0$

106. $25x^2 - 20x + 4 = 0$

107. $3x^2 + 5x - 8 = 0$

108. $2x^2 - 3x - 4 = 0$

Applications and Extensions

In Problems 109–114, solve each equation. The letters a, b, and c are constants.

109. $ax - b = c, \quad a \neq 0$

110. $1 - ax = b, \quad a \neq 0$

111. $\dfrac{x}{a} + \dfrac{x}{b} = c, \quad a \neq 0, b \neq 0, a \neq -b$

112. $\dfrac{a}{x} + \dfrac{b}{x} = c, \quad c \neq 0$

113. $\dfrac{1}{x - a} + \dfrac{1}{x + a} = \dfrac{2}{x - 1}$

114. $\dfrac{b + c}{x + a} = \dfrac{b - c}{x - a}, \quad c \neq 0, a \neq 0$

Problems 115–120 list some formulas that occur in applications. Solve each formula for the indicated variable.

115. Electricity $\dfrac{1}{R} = \dfrac{1}{R_1} + \dfrac{1}{R_2}$ for R

116. Finance $A = P(1 + rt)$ for r

117. Mechanics $F = \dfrac{mv^2}{R}$ for R

118. Chemistry $PV = nRT$ for T

119. Mathematics $S = \dfrac{a}{1 - r}$ for r

120. Mechanics $v = -gt + v_0$ for t

---

121. Show that the sum of the roots of a quadratic equation is $-\dfrac{b}{a}$.

122. Show that the product of the roots of a quadratic equation is $\dfrac{c}{a}$.

123. Find k such that the equation $kx^2 + x + k = 0$ has a repeated real solution.

124. Find k such that the equation $x^2 - kx + 4 = 0$ has a repeated real solution.

125. Show that the real solutions of the equation $ax^2 + bx + c = 0$ are the negatives of the real solutions of the equation $ax^2 - bx + c = 0$. Assume that $b^2 - 4ac \geq 0$.

126. Show that the real solutions of the equation $ax^2 + bx + c = 0$ are the reciprocals of the real solutions of the equation $cx^2 + bx + a = 0$. Assume that $b^2 - 4ac \geq 0$.

Explaining Concepts: Discussion and Writing

127. Which of the following pairs of equations are equivalent? Explain.

(a) $x^2 = 9; \quad x = 3$

(b) $x = \sqrt{9}; \quad x = 3$

(c) $(x - 1)(x - 2) = (x - 1)^2; \quad x - 2 = x - 1$

128. The equation

$$\frac{5}{x + 3} + 3 = \frac{8 + x}{x + 3}$$

has no solution, yet when we go through the process of solving it we obtain $x = -3$. Write a brief paragraph to explain what causes this to happen.

129. Make up an equation that has no solution and give it to a fellow student to solve. Ask the fellow student to write a critique of your equation.

130. Describe three ways you might solve a quadratic equation. State your preferred method; explain why you chose it.

131. Explain the benefits of evaluating the discriminant of a quadratic equation before attempting to solve it.

132. Make up three quadratic equations: one having two distinct solutions, one having no real solution, and one having exactly one real solution.

133. The word *quadratic* seems to imply four (*quad*), yet a quadratic equation is an equation that involves a polynomial of degree 2. Investigate the origin of the term *quadratic* as it is used in the expression *quadratic equation*. Write a brief essay on your findings.

'Are You Prepared?' Answers

1. $(x - 6)(x + 1)$

2. $(2x - 3)(x + 1)$

3. $\left\{ -\dfrac{5}{3}, 3 \right\}$

4. True

A.7 Complex Numbers; Quadratic Equations in the Complex Number System

OBJECTIVES **1** Add, Subtract, Multiply, and Divide Complex Numbers (p. A54)

2 Solve Quadratic Equations in the Complex Number System (p. A58)

Complex Numbers

One property of a real number is that its square is nonnegative. For example, there is no real number x for which

$$x^2 = -1$$

To remedy this situation, we introduce a new number called the *imaginary unit.*

DEFINITION

The **imaginary unit,** which we denote by i, is the number whose square is -1. That is,

$$i^2 = -1$$

This should not surprise you. If our universe were to consist only of integers, there would be no number x for which $2x = 1$. This unfortunate circumstance was remedied by introducing numbers such as $\dfrac{1}{2}$ and $\dfrac{2}{3}$, the *rational numbers.* If our universe were to consist only of rational numbers, there would be no x whose square equals 2. That is, there would be no number x for which $x^2 = 2$. To remedy this, we introduced numbers such as $\sqrt{2}$ and $\sqrt[3]{5}$, the *irrational numbers.* The *real numbers,* you will recall, consist of the rational numbers and the irrational numbers. Now, if our universe were to consist only of real numbers, then there would be no number x whose square is -1. To remedy this, we introduce a number i, whose square is -1.

In the progression outlined, each time we encountered a situation that was unsuitable, we introduced a new number system to remedy this situation. And each new number system contained the earlier number system as a subset. The number system that results from introducing the number i is called the **complex number system.**

DEFINITION

Complex numbers are numbers of the form $a + bi$, where a and b are real numbers. The real number a is called the **real part** of the number $a + bi$; the real number b is called the **imaginary part** of $a + bi$; and i is the imaginary unit, so $i^2 = -1$.

For example, the complex number $-5 + 6i$ has the real part -5 and the imaginary part 6.

When a complex number is written in the form $a + bi$, where a and b are real numbers, we say it is in **standard form.** However, if the imaginary part of a complex number is negative, such as in the complex number $3 + (-2)i$, we agree to write it instead in the form $3 - 2i$.

Also, the complex number $a + 0i$ is usually written merely as a. This serves to remind us that the real numbers are a subset of the complex numbers. The complex number $0 + bi$ is usually written as bi. Sometimes the complex number bi is called a **pure imaginary number.**

1 Add, Subtract, Multiply, and Divide Complex Numbers

Equality, addition, subtraction, and multiplication of complex numbers are defined so as to preserve the familiar rules of algebra for real numbers. Two complex numbers are equal if and only if their real parts are equal and their imaginary parts are equal. That is,

Equality of Complex Numbers

$$a + bi = c + di \quad \text{if and only if } a = c \text{ and } b = d \qquad \textbf{(1)}$$

Two complex numbers are added by forming the complex number whose real part is the sum of the real parts and whose imaginary part is the sum of the imaginary parts. That is,

Sum of Complex Numbers

$$(a + bi) + (c + di) = (a + c) + (b + d)i \qquad \textbf{(2)}$$

To subtract two complex numbers, we use this rule:

Difference of Complex Numbers

$$(a + bi) - (c + di) = (a - c) + (b - d)i \qquad \textbf{(3)}$$

EXAMPLE 1   **Adding and Subtracting Complex Numbers**

(a) $(3 + 5i) + (-2 + 3i) = [3 + (-2)] + (5 + 3)i = 1 + 8i$

(b) $(6 + 4i) - (3 + 6i) = (6 - 3) + (4 - 6)i = 3 + (-2)i = 3 - 2i$

Now Work PROBLEM 13

Products of complex numbers are calculated as illustrated in Example 2.

EXAMPLE 2   **Multiplying Complex Numbers**

$$(5 + 3i) \cdot (2 + 7i) = 5 \cdot (2 + 7i) + 3i(2 + 7i) = 10 + 35i + 6i + 21i^2$$

$\uparrow$ Distributive Property $\uparrow$ Distributive Property

$$= 10 + 41i + 21(-1)$$

$\uparrow$ $i^2 = -1$

$$= -11 + 41i$$

Based on the procedure of Example 2, we define the **product** of two complex numbers as follows:

Product of Complex Numbers

$$(a + bi) \cdot (c + di) = (ac - bd) + (ad + bc)i \qquad \textbf{(4)}$$

Do not bother to memorize formula (4). Instead, whenever it is necessary to multiply two complex numbers, follow the usual rules for multiplying two binomials, as in Example 2, remembering that $i^2 = -1$. For example,

$$(2i)(2i) = 4i^2 = -4$$

$$(2 + i)(1 - i) = 2 - 2i + i - i^2 = 3 - i$$

Now Work PROBLEM 19

Algebraic properties for addition and multiplication, such as the commutative, associative, and distributive properties, hold for complex numbers. The property that every nonzero complex number has a multiplicative inverse, or reciprocal, requires a closer look.

DEFINITION

If $z = a + bi$ is a complex number, then its **conjugate,** denoted by $\bar{z}$, is defined as

$$\bar{z} = \overline{a + bi} = a - bi$$

For example, $\overline{2 + 3i} = 2 - 3i$ and $\overline{-6 - 2i} = -6 + 2i$.

EXAMPLE 3 **Multiplying a Complex Number by Its Conjugate**

Find the product of the complex number $z = 3 + 4i$ and its conjugate $\bar{z}$.

Solution Since $\bar{z} = 3 - 4i$, we have

$$z\bar{z} = (3 + 4i)(3 - 4i) = 9 - 12i + 12i - 16i^2 = 9 + 16 = 25$$

The result obtained in Example 3 has an important generalization.

THEOREM

The product of a complex number and its conjugate is a nonnegative real number. That is, if $z = a + bi$, then

$$z\bar{z} = a^2 + b^2 \qquad\qquad \textbf{(5)}$$

Proof If $z = a + bi$, then

$$z\bar{z} = (a + bi)(a - bi) = a^2 - (bi)^2 = a^2 - b^2i^2 = a^2 + b^2 \qquad\blacksquare$$

To express the reciprocal of a nonzero complex number z in standard form, multiply the numerator and denominator of $\dfrac{1}{z}$ by $\bar{z}$. That is, if $z = a + bi$ is a nonzero complex number, then

$$\frac{1}{a + bi} = \frac{1}{z} = \frac{1}{z} \cdot \frac{\bar{z}}{\bar{z}} = \frac{\bar{z}}{z\bar{z}} = \frac{a - bi}{a^2 + b^2}$$

$$\uparrow$$
Use (5).

$$= \frac{a}{a^2 + b^2} - \frac{b}{a^2 + b^2}i$$

EXAMPLE 4 **Writing the Reciprocal of a Complex Number in Standard Form**

Write $\dfrac{1}{3 + 4i}$ in standard form $a + bi$; that is, find the reciprocal of $3 + 4i$.

Solution The idea is to multiply the numerator and denominator by the conjugate of $3 + 4i$, that is, by the complex number $3 - 4i$. The result is

$$\frac{1}{3 + 4i} = \frac{1}{3 + 4i} \cdot \frac{3 - 4i}{3 - 4i} = \frac{3 - 4i}{9 + 16} = \frac{3}{25} - \frac{4}{25}i$$

To express the quotient of two complex numbers in standard form, multiply the numerator and denominator of the quotient by the conjugate of the denominator.

| EXAMPLE 5 | **Writing the Quotient of Two Complex Numbers in Standard Form** |

Write each of the following in standard form.

(a) $\dfrac{1 + 4i}{5 - 12i}$ (b) $\dfrac{2 - 3i}{4 - 3i}$

Solution

(a) $\dfrac{1 + 4i}{5 - 12i} = \dfrac{1 + 4i}{5 - 12i} \cdot \dfrac{5 + 12i}{5 + 12i} = \dfrac{5 + 12i + 20i + 48i^2}{25 + 144}$

$= \dfrac{-43 + 32i}{169} = -\dfrac{43}{169} + \dfrac{32}{169}i$

(b) $\dfrac{2 - 3i}{4 - 3i} = \dfrac{2 - 3i}{4 - 3i} \cdot \dfrac{4 + 3i}{4 + 3i} = \dfrac{8 + 6i - 12i - 9i^2}{16 + 9}$

$= \dfrac{17 - 6i}{25} = \dfrac{17}{25} - \dfrac{6}{25}i$

✏️— **Now Work** PROBLEM 27

| EXAMPLE 6 | **Writing Other Expressions in Standard Form** |

If $z = 2 - 3i$ and $w = 5 + 2i$, write each of the following expressions in standard form.

(a) $\dfrac{z}{w}$ (b) $\overline{z + w}$ (c) $z + \overline{z}$

Solution

(a) $\dfrac{z}{w} = \dfrac{z \cdot \overline{w}}{w \cdot \overline{w}} = \dfrac{(2 - 3i)(5 - 2i)}{(5 + 2i)(5 - 2i)} = \dfrac{10 - 4i - 15i + 6i^2}{25 + 4}$

$= \dfrac{4 - 19i}{29} = \dfrac{4}{29} - \dfrac{19}{29}i$

(b) $\overline{z + w} = \overline{(2 - 3i) + (5 + 2i)} = \overline{7 - i} = 7 + i$

(c) $z + \overline{z} = (2 - 3i) + (2 + 3i) = 4$

The conjugate of a complex number has certain general properties that we shall find useful later.

For a real number $a = a + 0i$, the conjugate is $\overline{a} = \overline{a + 0i} = a - 0i = a$. That is,

THEOREM

The conjugate of a real number is the real number itself.

Other properties of the conjugate that are direct consequences of the definition are given next. In each statement, z and w represent complex numbers.

THEOREM

The conjugate of the conjugate of a complex number is the complex number itself.

$$\overline{(\overline{z})} = z \tag{6}$$

The conjugate of the sum of two complex numbers equals the sum of their conjugates.

$$\overline{z + w} = \overline{z} + \overline{w} \tag{7}$$

The conjugate of the product of two complex numbers equals the product of their conjugates.

$$\overline{z \cdot w} = \overline{z} \cdot \overline{w} \tag{8}$$

We leave the proofs of equations (6), (7), and (8) as exercises.

Powers of i

The **powers of i** follow a pattern that is useful to know.

$$i^1 = i$$
$$i^2 = -1$$
$$i^3 = i^2 \cdot i = -1 \cdot i = -i$$
$$i^4 = i^2 \cdot i^2 = (-1)(-1) = 1$$

$$i^5 = i^4 \cdot i = 1 \cdot i = i$$
$$i^6 = i^4 \cdot i^2 = -1$$
$$i^7 = i^4 \cdot i^3 = -i$$
$$i^8 = i^4 \cdot i^4 = 1$$

And so on. The powers of i repeat with every fourth power.

EXAMPLE 7

Evaluating Powers of i

(a) $i^{27} = i^{24} \cdot i^3 = (i^4)^6 \cdot i^3 = 1^6 \cdot i^3 = -i$

(b) $i^{101} = i^{100} \cdot i^1 = (i^4)^{25} \cdot i = 1^{25} \cdot i = i$

EXAMPLE 8

Writing the Power of a Complex Number in Standard Form

Write $(2 + i)^3$ in standard form.

Solution   Use the special product formula for $(x + a)^3$.

$$(x + a)^3 = x^3 + 3ax^2 + 3a^2x + a^3$$

COMMENT Another way to find $(2 + i)^3$ is to multiply out $(2 + i)^2(2 + i)$. ∎

Using this special product formula,

$$(2 + i)^3 = 2^3 + 3 \cdot i \cdot 2^2 + 3 \cdot i^2 \cdot 2 + i^3$$
$$= 8 + 12i + 6(-1) + (-i)$$
$$= 2 + 11i.$$

Now Work PROBLEM 41

---

2 Solve Quadratic Equations in the Complex Number System

Quadratic equations with a negative discriminant have no real number solution. However, if we extend our number system to allow complex numbers, quadratic equations will always have a solution. Since the solution to a quadratic equation involves the square root of the discriminant, we begin with a discussion of square roots of negative numbers.

DEFINITION   If N is a positive real number, we define the **principal square root of $-N$,** denoted by $\sqrt{-N}$, as

$$\sqrt{-N} = \sqrt{N}\, i$$

WARNING In writing $\sqrt{-N} = \sqrt{N}i$ be sure to place i outside the $\sqrt{}$ symbol. ∎

where i is the imaginary unit and $i^2 = -1$.

EXAMPLE 9

Evaluating the Square Root of a Negative Number

(a) $\sqrt{-1} = \sqrt{1}\, i = i$

(b) $\sqrt{-4} = \sqrt{4}\, i = 2i$

(c) $\sqrt{-8} = \sqrt{8}\, i = 2\sqrt{2}\, i$

EXAMPLE 10 **Solving Equations**

Solve each equation in the complex number system.
(a) $x^2 = 4$ (b) $x^2 = -9$

Solution (a) $x^2 = 4$

$$x = \pm\sqrt{4} = \pm 2$$

The equation has two solutions, -2 and 2. The solution set is $\{-2, 2\}$.

(b) $x^2 = -9$

$$x = \pm\sqrt{-9} = \pm\sqrt{9}i = \pm 3i$$

The equation has two solutions, $-3i$ and $3i$. The solution set is $\{-3i, 3i\}$.

Now Work PROBLEMS 49 AND 53

WARNING When working with square roots of negative numbers, do not set the square root of a product equal to the product of the square roots (which can be done with positive numbers). To see why, look at this calculation: We know that $\sqrt{100} = 10$. However, it is also true that $100 = (-25)(-4)$, so

$$10 = \sqrt{100} = \sqrt{(-25)(-4)} \neq \sqrt{-25}\sqrt{-4} = \left(\sqrt{25}i\right)\left(\sqrt{4}i\right) = (5i)(2i) = 10i^2 = -10$$

$\uparrow$
Here is the error. ■

Because we have defined the square root of a negative number, we can now restate the quadratic formula without restriction.

THEOREM **Quadratic Formula**

In the complex number system, the solutions of the quadratic equation $ax^2 + bx + c = 0$, where $a, b,$ and c are real numbers and $a \neq 0$, are given by the formula

$$x = \frac{-b \pm \sqrt{b^2 - 4ac}}{2a} \tag{9}$$

EXAMPLE 11 **Solving Quadratic Equations in the Complex Number System**

Solve the equation $x^2 - 4x + 8 = 0$ in the complex number system.

Solution Here $a = 1, b = -4, c = 8,$ and $b^2 - 4ac = 16 - 4(1)(8) = -16$. Using equation (9), we find that

$$x = \frac{-(-4) \pm \sqrt{-16}}{2(1)} = \frac{4 \pm \sqrt{16}i}{2} = \frac{4 \pm 4i}{2} = 2 \pm 2i$$

The equation has two solutions, $2 - 2i$ and $2 + 2i$. The solution set is $\{2 - 2i, 2 + 2i\}$.

✓ Check: $2 + 2i$: $(2 + 2i)^2 - 4(2 + 2i) + 8 = 4 + 8i + 4i^2 - 8 - 8i + 8$
$$= 4 - 4 = 0$$

$2 - 2i$: $(2 - 2i)^2 - 4(2 - 2i) + 8 = 4 - 8i + 4i^2 - 8 + 8i + 8$
$$= 4 - 4 = 0$$

Now Work PROBLEM 59

The discriminant $b^2 - 4ac$ of a quadratic equation still serves as a way to determine the character of the solutions.

Character of the Solutions of a Quadratic Equation

In the complex number system, consider a quadratic equation $ax^2 + bx + c = 0$ with real coefficients.

1. If $b^2 - 4ac > 0$, the equation has two unequal real solutions.
2. If $b^2 - 4ac = 0$, the equation has a repeated real solution, a double root.
3. If $b^2 - 4ac < 0$, the equation has two complex solutions that are not real. The solutions are conjugates of each other.

The third conclusion in the display is a consequence of the fact that if $b^2 - 4ac = -N < 0$ then, by the quadratic formula, the solutions are

$$x = \frac{-b + \sqrt{b^2 - 4ac}}{2a} = \frac{-b + \sqrt{-N}}{2a} = \frac{-b + \sqrt{N}\,i}{2a} = \frac{-b}{2a} + \frac{\sqrt{N}}{2a}i$$

and

$$x = \frac{-b - \sqrt{b^2 - 4ac}}{2a} = \frac{-b - \sqrt{-N}}{2a} = \frac{-b - \sqrt{N}\,i}{2a} = \frac{-b}{2a} - \frac{\sqrt{N}}{2a}i$$

which are conjugates of each other.

EXAMPLE 12

Determining the Character of the Solution of a Quadratic Equation

Without solving, determine the character of the solution of each equation.

(a) $3x^2 + 4x + 5 = 0$ (b) $2x^2 + 4x + 1 = 0$ (c) $9x^2 - 6x + 1 = 0$

Solution (a) Here $a = 3, b = 4$, and $c = 5$, so $b^2 - 4ac = 16 - 4(3)(5) = -44$. The solutions are two complex numbers that are not real and are conjugates of each other.
(b) Here $a = 2, b = 4$, and $c = 1$, so $b^2 - 4ac = 16 - 8 = 8$. The solutions are two unequal real numbers.
(c) Here $a = 9, b = -6$, and $c = 1$, so $b^2 - 4ac = 36 - 4(9)(1) = 0$. The solution is a repeated real number, that is, a double root.

--- **Now Work** PROBLEM 73

A.7 Assess Your Understanding

Concepts and Vocabulary

1. **True or False** The square of a complex number is sometimes negative.

2. $(2 + i)(2 - i) = $ _____.

3. **True or False** In the complex number system, a quadratic equation has four solutions.

4. In the complex number $5 + 2i$, the number 5 is called the _____ part; the number 2 is called the _____ part; the number i is called the _____ _____.

5. The equation $x^2 = -4$ has the solution set _____.

6. **True or False** The conjugate of $2 + 5i$ is $-2 - 5i$.

7. **True or False** All real numbers are complex numbers.

8. **True or False** If $2 - 3i$ is a solution of a quadratic equation with real coefficients, then $-2 + 3i$ is also a solution.

Skill Building

In Problems 9–46, write each expression in the standard form $a + bi$.

9. $(2 - 3i) + (6 + 8i)$
10. $(4 + 5i) + (-8 + 2i)$
11. $(-3 + 2i) - (4 - 4i)$
12. $(3 - 4i) - (-3 - 4i)$
13. $(2 - 5i) - (8 + 6i)$
14. $(-8 + 4i) - (2 - 2i)$
15. $3(2 - 6i)$
16. $-4(2 + 8i)$
17. $2i(2 - 3i)$
18. $3i(-3 + 4i)$
19. $(3 - 4i)(2 + i)$
20. $(5 + 3i)(2 - i)$

21. $(-6 + i)(-6 - i)$ **22.** $(-3 + i)(3 + i)$ **23.** $\dfrac{10}{3 - 4i}$ **24.** $\dfrac{13}{5 - 12i}$

25. $\dfrac{2 + i}{i}$ **26.** $\dfrac{2 - i}{-2i}$ **27.** $\dfrac{6 - i}{1 + i}$ **28.** $\dfrac{2 + 3i}{1 - i}$

29. $\left(\dfrac{1}{2} + \dfrac{\sqrt{3}}{2}i\right)^2$ **30.** $\left(\dfrac{\sqrt{3}}{2} - \dfrac{1}{2}i\right)^2$ **31.** $(1 + i)^2$ **32.** $(1 - i)^2$

33. i^{23} **34.** i^{14} **35.** i^{-15} **36.** i^{-23}

37. $i^6 - 5$ **38.** $4 + i^3$ **39.** $6i^3 - 4i^5$ **40.** $4i^3 - 2i^2 + 1$

41. $(1 + i)^3$ **42.** $(3i)^4 + 1$ **43.** $i^7(1 + i^2)$ **44.** $2i^4(1 + i^2)$

45. $i^6 + i^4 + i^2 + 1$ **46.** $i^7 + i^5 + i^3 + i$

In Problems 47–52, perform the indicated operations and express your answer in the form $a + bi$.

47. $\sqrt{-4}$ **48.** $\sqrt{-9}$ **49.** $\sqrt{-25}$

50. $\sqrt{-64}$ **51.** $\sqrt{(3 + 4i)(4i - 3)}$ **52.** $\sqrt{(4 + 3i)(3i - 4)}$

In Problems 53–72, solve each equation in the complex number system.

53. $x^2 + 4 = 0$ **54.** $x^2 - 4 = 0$ **55.** $x^2 - 16 = 0$ **56.** $x^2 + 25 = 0$

57. $x^2 - 6x + 13 = 0$ **58.** $x^2 + 4x + 8 = 0$ **59.** $x^2 - 6x + 10 = 0$ **60.** $x^2 - 2x + 5 = 0$

61. $8x^2 - 4x + 1 = 0$ **62.** $10x^2 + 6x + 1 = 0$ **63.** $5x^2 + 1 = 2x$ **64.** $13x^2 + 1 = 6x$

65. $x^2 + x + 1 = 0$ **66.** $x^2 - x + 1 = 0$ **67.** $x^3 - 8 = 0$ **68.** $x^3 + 27 = 0$

69. $x^4 = 16$ **70.** $x^4 = 1$ **71.** $x^4 + 13x^2 + 36 = 0$ **72.** $x^4 + 3x^2 - 4 = 0$

In Problems 73–78, without solving, determine the character of the solutions of each equation in the complex number system.

73. $3x^2 - 3x + 4 = 0$ **74.** $2x^2 - 4x + 1 = 0$ **75.** $2x^2 + 3x = 4$

76. $x^2 + 6 = 2x$ **77.** $9x^2 - 12x + 4 = 0$ **78.** $4x^2 + 12x + 9 = 0$

79. $2 + 3i$ is a solution of a quadratic equation with real coefficients. Find the other solution.

80. $4 - i$ is a solution of a quadratic equation with real coefficients. Find the other solution.

In Problems 81–84, $z = 3 - 4i$ and $w = 8 + 3i$. Write each expression in the standard form $a + bi$.

81. $z + \bar{z}$ **82.** $w - \bar{w}$ **83.** $z\bar{z}$ **84.** $\overline{z - w}$

Applications and Extensions

85. Electrical Circuits The impedance Z, in ohms, of a circuit element is defined as the ratio of the phasor voltage V, in volts, across the element to the phasor current I, in amperes, through the elements. That is, $Z = \dfrac{V}{I}$. If the voltage across a circuit element is $18 + i$ volts and the current through the element is $3 - 4i$ amperes, determine the impedance.

86. Parallel Circuits In an ac circuit with two parallel pathways, the total impedance Z, in ohms, satisfies the formula $\dfrac{1}{Z} = \dfrac{1}{Z_1} + \dfrac{1}{Z_2}$, where Z_1 is the impedance of the first pathway and Z_2 is the impedance of the second pathway. Determine the total impedance if the impedances of the two pathways are $Z_1 = 2 + i$ ohms and $Z_2 = 4 - 3i$ ohms.

87. Use $z = a + bi$ to show that $z + \bar{z} = 2a$ and $z - \bar{z} = 2bi$.

88. Use $z = a + bi$ to show that $\bar{\bar{z}} = z$.

89. Use $z = a + bi$ and $w = c + di$ to show that $\overline{z + w} = \bar{z} + \bar{w}$.

90. Use $z = a + bi$ and $w = c + di$ to show that $\overline{z \cdot w} = \bar{z} \cdot \bar{w}$.

Explaining Concepts: Discussion and Writing

91. Explain to a friend how you would add two complex numbers and how you would multiply two complex numbers. Explain any differences in the two explanations.

92. Write a brief paragraph that compares the method used to rationalize the denominator of a radical expression and the method used to write the quotient of two complex numbers in standard form.

93. Use an Internet search engine to investigate the origins of complex numbers. Write a paragraph describing what you find and present it to the class.

94. What Went Wrong? A student multiplied $\sqrt{-9}$ and $\sqrt{-9}$ as follows:

$$\sqrt{-9} \cdot \sqrt{-9} = \sqrt{(-9)(-9)} = \sqrt{81} = 9$$

The instructor marked the problem incorrect. Why?

A.8 Problem Solving: Interest, Mixture, Uniform Motion, Constant Rate Job Applications

OBJECTIVES   1 Translate Verbal Descriptions into Mathematical Expressions (p. A62)

2 Solve Interest Problems (p. A63)

3 Solve Mixture Problems (p. A64)

4 Solve Uniform Motion Problems (p. A65)

5 Solve Constant Rate Job Problems (p. A67)

The icon is a Model It! icon.

It indicates that the discussion or problem involves modeling.

Applied (word) problems do not come in the form "Solve the equation. . . ." Instead, they supply information using words, a verbal description of the real problem. So, to solve applied problems, we must be able to translate the verbal description into the language of mathematics. We do this by using variables to represent unknown quantities and then finding relationships (such as equations) that involve these variables. The process of doing all this is called **mathematical modeling.**

Any solution to the mathematical problem must be checked against the mathematical problem, the verbal description, and the real problem. See Figure 23 for an illustration of the **modeling process.**

Figure 23

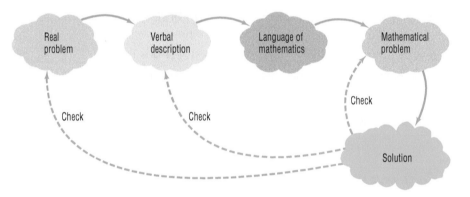

1 Translate Verbal Descriptions into Mathematical Expressions

Let's look at a few examples that will help you to translate certain words into mathematical symbols.

EXAMPLE 1

Translating Verbal Descriptions into Mathematical Expressions

(a) The (average) speed of an object equals the distance traveled divided by the time required.

Translation: If r is the speed, d the distance, and t the time, then $r = \dfrac{d}{t}$.

(b) Let x denote a number.

The number 5 times as large as x is $5x$.

The number 3 less than x is $x - 3$.

The number that exceeds x by 4 is $x + 4$.

The number that, when added to x, gives 5 is $5 - x$.

Now Work PROBLEM 7

Always check the units used to measure the variables of an applied problem. In Example 1(a), if v is measured in miles per hour, then the distance s must be expressed in miles and the time t must be expressed in hours. It is a good practice to check units to be sure that they are consistent and make sense.

Steps for Solving Applied Problems

Step 1: Read the problem carefully, perhaps two or three times. Pay particular attention to the question being asked in order to identify what you are looking for. If you can, determine realistic possibilities for the answer.

Step 2: Assign a letter (variable) to represent what you are looking for, and, if necessary, express any remaining unknown quantities in terms of this variable.

Step 3: Make a list of all the known facts, and translate them into mathematical expressions. These may take the form of an equation or an inequality involving the variable. If possible, draw an appropriately labeled diagram to assist you. Sometimes a table or chart helps.

Step 4: Solve the equation for the variable, and then answer the question.

Step 5: Check the answer with the facts in the problem. If it agrees, congratulations! If it does not agree, try again.

2 Solve Interest Problems

Interest is money paid for the use of money. The total amount borrowed (whether by an individual from a bank in the form of a loan or by a bank from an individual in the form of a savings account) is called the **principal.** The **rate of interest,** expressed as a percent, is the amount charged for the use of the principal for a given period of time, usually on a yearly (that is, on a per annum) basis.

Simple Interest Formula

If a principal of P dollars is borrowed for a period of t years at a per annum interest rate r, expressed as a decimal, the interest I charged is

$$I = Prt \tag{1}$$

Interest charged according to formula (1) is called **simple interest.** When using formula (1), be sure to express r as a decimal. For example, if the rate of interest is 4%, then $r = 0.04$.

EXAMPLE 2

Finance: Computing Interest on a Loan

Suppose that Juanita borrows $500 for 6 months at the simple interest rate of 9% per annum. What is the interest that Juanita will be charged on the loan? How much does Juanita owe after 6 months?

Solution The rate of interest is given per annum, so the actual time that the money is borrowed must be expressed in years. The interest charged would be the principal, $500, times the rate of interest (9% = 0.09) times the time in years, $\frac{1}{2}$:

$$\text{Interest charged} = I = Prt = (500)(0.09)\left(\frac{1}{2}\right) = \$22.50$$

After 6 months, Juanita will owe what she borrowed plus the interest:

$$\$500 + \$22.50 = \$522.50$$

EXAMPLE 3	**Financial Planning**

Candy has $70,000 to invest and wants an annual return of $2800, which requires an overall rate of return of 4%. She can invest in a safe, government-insured certificate of deposit, but it only pays 2%. To obtain 4%, she agrees to invest some of her money in noninsured corporate bonds paying 7%. How much should be placed in each investment to achieve her goal?

Solution   **STEP 1:** The question is asking for two dollar amounts: the principal to invest in the corporate bonds and the principal to invest in the certificate of deposit.

STEP 2: Let x represent the amount (in dollars) to be invested in the bonds. Then $70,000 - x$ is the amount that will be invested in the certificate. (Do you see why?)

STEP 3: Now set up Table 1:

Table 1

	Principal ($)	Rate	Time (yr)	Interest ($)
Bonds	x	7% = 0.07	1	$0.07x$
Certificate	$70,000 - x$	2% = 0.02	1	$0.02(70,000 - x)$
Total	70,000	4% = 0.04	1	$0.04(70,000) = 2800$

Since the total interest from the investments is equal to $0.04(70,000) = 2800$, we have the equation

$$0.07x + 0.02(70,000 - x) = 2800$$

(Note that the units are consistent: the unit is dollars on each side.)

STEP 4:
$$0.07x + 1400 - 0.02x = 2800$$
$$0.05x = 1400 \quad \text{Simplify.}$$
$$x = 28,000 \quad \text{Divide both sides by 0.05.}$$

Candy should place $28,000 in the bonds and $70,000 - \$28,000 = \$42,000$ in the certificate.

STEP 5: The interest on the bonds after 1 year is $0.07(\$28,000) = \$1960$; the interest on the certificate after 1 year is $0.02(\$42,000) = \$840$. The total annual interest is $2800, the required amount. ⏎

━━━━━━ **Now Work** PROBLEM 17

3 Solve Mixture Problems

Oil refineries sometimes produce gasoline that is a blend of two or more types of fuel; bakeries occasionally blend two or more types of flour for their bread. These problems are referred to as **mixture problems** because they combine two or more quantities to form a mixture.

EXAMPLE 4	**Blending Coffees**

The manager of a local coffee shop decides to experiment with a new blend of coffee. She will mix some B grade Colombian coffee that sells for $5 per pound with some A grade Arabica coffee that sells for $10 per pound to get 100 pounds of the new blend. The selling price of the new blend is to be $7 per pound, and there is to be no difference in revenue from selling the new blend versus selling the other types. How many pounds of the B grade Colombian and A grade Arabica coffees are required?

Solution   **STEP 1:** The question is asking how many pounds of Colombian coffee and how many pounds of Arabica coffee are needed to make 100 pounds of the mixture.

STEP 2: Let x represent the number of pounds of the B grade Colombian coffee. Then $100 - x$ equals the number of pounds of the A grade Arabica coffee.

STEP 3: See Figure 24.

Figure 24

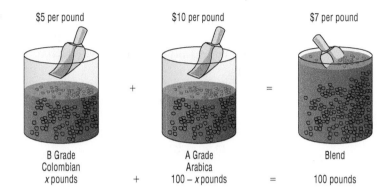

B Grade		A Grade		Blend
Colombian		Arabica		
x pounds	+	100 − x pounds	=	100 pounds

Since there is to be no difference in revenue between selling the A and B grades separately versus the blend, we have

$$\left\{ \begin{array}{c} \text{Price per pound} \\ \text{of B grade} \end{array} \right\} \left\{ \begin{array}{c} \text{\# Pounds} \\ \text{B grade} \end{array} \right\} + \left\{ \begin{array}{c} \text{Price per pound} \\ \text{of A grade} \end{array} \right\} \left\{ \begin{array}{c} \text{\# Pounds} \\ \text{A grade} \end{array} \right\} = \left\{ \begin{array}{c} \text{Price per pound} \\ \text{of blend} \end{array} \right\} \left\{ \begin{array}{c} \text{\# Pounds} \\ \text{blend} \end{array} \right\}$$

$$\$5 \quad \cdot \quad x \quad + \quad \$10 \quad \cdot (100 - x) \quad = \quad \$7 \quad \cdot \quad 100$$

STEP 4: Solve the equation

$$5x + 10(100 - x) = 700$$
$$5x + 1000 - 10x = 700$$
$$-5x = -300$$
$$x = 60$$

The manager should blend 60 pounds of B grade Colombian coffee with $100 - 60 = 40$ pounds of A grade Arabica coffee to get the desired blend.

STEP 5: ✓ **Check:** The 60 pounds of B grade coffee would sell for $(\$5)(60) = \$300$, and the 40 pounds of A grade coffee would sell for $(\$10)(40) = \$400$; the total revenue, \$700, equals the revenue obtained from selling the blend, as desired. ⌐

Now Work PROBLEM 21

4 Solve Uniform Motion Problems

Objects that move at a constant speed are said to be in **uniform motion.** When the average speed of an object is known, it can be interpreted as its constant speed. For example, a bicyclist traveling at an average speed of 25 miles per hour can be modeled as uniform motion with a constant speed of 25 miles per hour.

Uniform Motion Formula

If an object moves at an average speed (rate) r, the distance d covered in time t is given by the formula

$$d = rt \tag{2}$$

That is, Distance = Rate · Time.

> [!NOTE]
> **EXAMPLE 5**

Physics: Uniform Motion

Tanya, who is a long-distance runner, runs at an average speed of 8 miles per hour (mi/hr). Two hours after Tanya leaves your house, you leave in your Honda and follow the same route. If your average speed is 40 mi/hr, how long will it be before you catch up to Tanya? How far will each of you be from your home?

Solution

Refer to Figure 25. Use t to represent the time (in hours) that it takes the Honda to catch up to Tanya. When this occurs, the total time elapsed for Tanya is $t + 2$ hours.

Figure 25

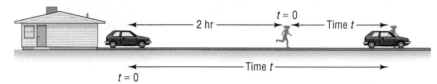

Set up Table 2:

Table 2

	Rate (mi/hr)	Time (hr)	Distance (mi)
Tanya	8	$t + 2$	$8(t + 2)$
Honda	40	t	$40t$

Since the distance traveled is the same, we are led to the following equation:

$$8(t + 2) = 40t$$
$$8t + 16 = 40t$$
$$32t = 16$$
$$t = \frac{1}{2} \text{ hour}$$

It will take the Honda $\frac{1}{2}$ hour to catch up to Tanya. Each will have gone 20 miles.

✓**Check:** In 2.5 hours, Tanya travels a distance of $(2.5)(8) = 20$ miles. In $\frac{1}{2}$ hour, the Honda travels a distance of $\left(\frac{1}{2}\right)(40) = 20$ miles.

> [!NOTE]
> **EXAMPLE 6**

Physics: Uniform Motion

A motorboat heads upstream a distance of 24 miles on a river whose current is running at 3 miles per hour (mi/hr). The trip up and back takes 6 hours. Assuming that the motorboat maintained a constant speed relative to the water, what was its speed?

Solution

See Figure 26. We use r to represent the constant speed of the motorboat relative to the water. Then the true speed going upstream is $r - 3$ mi/hr, and the true speed going downstream is $r + 3$ mi/hr. Since Distance = Rate × Time, then Time = $\dfrac{\text{Distance}}{\text{Rate}}$. Set up Table 3.

Figure 26

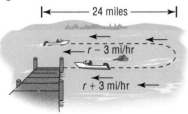

Table 3

	Rate (mi/hr)	Distance (mi)	Time = $\dfrac{\text{Distance}}{\text{Rate}}$ (hr)
Upstream	$r - 3$	24	$\dfrac{24}{r - 3}$
Downstream	$r + 3$	24	$\dfrac{24}{r + 3}$

Since the total time up and back is 6 hours, we have

$$\frac{24}{r-3} + \frac{24}{r+3} = 6$$

$$\frac{24(r+3) + 24(r-3)}{(r-3)(r+3)} = 6 \qquad \text{Add the quotients on the left.}$$

$$\frac{48r}{r^2 - 9} = 6 \qquad \text{Simplify.}$$

$$48r = 6(r^2 - 9) \qquad \text{Multiply both sides by } r^2 - 9.$$

$$6r^2 - 48r - 54 = 0 \qquad \text{Place in standard form.}$$

$$r^2 - 8r - 9 = 0 \qquad \text{Divide by 6.}$$

$$(r-9)(r+1) = 0 \qquad \text{Factor.}$$

$$r = 9 \quad \text{or} \quad r = -1 \qquad \text{Apply the Zero-Product Property and solve.}$$

Discard the solution $r = -1$ mi/hr, so the speed of the motorboat relative to the water is 9 mi/hr.

Now Work PROBLEM 27

5 Solve Constant Rate Job Problems

This section involves jobs that are performed at a **constant rate.** Our assumption is that, if a job can be done in t units of time, then $\frac{1}{t}$ of the job is done in 1 unit of time.

EXAMPLE 7

Working Together to Do a Job

At 10 AM Danny is asked by his father to weed the garden. From past experience, Danny knows that this will take him 4 hours, working alone. His older brother, Mike, when it is his turn to do this job, requires 6 hours. Since Mike wants to go golfing with Danny and has a reservation for 1 PM, he agrees to help Danny. Assuming no gain or loss of efficiency, when will they finish if they work together? Can they make the golf date?

Solution

We set up Table 4. In 1 hour, Danny does $\frac{1}{4}$ of the job, and in 1 hour, Mike does $\frac{1}{6}$ of the job. Let t be the time (in hours) that it takes them to do the job together. In 1 hour, then, $\frac{1}{t}$ of the job is completed. We reason as follows:

$$\left(\begin{array}{c} \text{Part done by Danny} \\ \text{in 1 hour} \end{array} \right) + \left(\begin{array}{c} \text{Part done by Mike} \\ \text{in 1 hour} \end{array} \right) = \left(\begin{array}{c} \text{Part done together} \\ \text{in 1 hour} \end{array} \right)$$

From Table 4,

$$\frac{1}{4} + \frac{1}{6} = \frac{1}{t}$$

$$\frac{3}{12} + \frac{2}{12} = \frac{1}{t}$$

$$\frac{5}{12} = \frac{1}{t}$$

$$5t = 12$$

$$t = \frac{12}{5}$$

Table 4

	Hours to Do Job	Part of Job Done in 1 Hour
Danny	4	$\frac{1}{4}$
Mike	6	$\frac{1}{6}$
Together	t	$\frac{1}{t}$

Working together, the job can be done in $\dfrac{12}{5}$ hours, or 2 hours, 24 minutes. They should make the golf date, since they will finish at 12:24 PM.

Now Work PROBLEM 33

 The next example is one that you will probably see again in a slightly different form if you study calculus.

EXAMPLE 8 **Constructing a Box**

From each corner of a square piece of sheet metal, remove a square of side 9 centimeters. Turn up the edges to form an open box. If the box is to hold 144 cubic centimeters (cm^3), what should be the dimensions of the piece of sheet metal?

Solution We use Figure 27 as a guide. We have labeled by x the length of a side of the square piece of sheet metal. The box will be of height 9 centimeters, and its square base will measure $x - 18$ on each side. The volume V (Length $\times$ Width $\times$ Height) of the box is therefore

$$V = (x - 18)(x - 18) \cdot 9 = 9(x - 18)^2$$

Figure 27

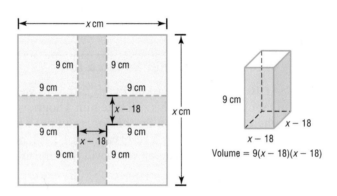

Since the volume of the box is to be 144 cm^3, we have

$$9(x - 18)^2 = 144 \qquad {\color{gray} V = 144}$$
$$(x - 18)^2 = 16 \qquad {\color{gray} \text{Divide each side by 9.}}$$
$$x - 18 = \pm 4 \qquad {\color{gray} \text{Use the Square Root Method.}}$$
$$x = 18 \pm 4$$
$$x = 22 \quad \text{or} \quad x = 14$$

We discard the solution $x = 14$ (do you see why?) and conclude that the sheet metal should be 22 centimeters by 22 centimeters.

✓ **Check:** If we begin with a piece of sheet metal 22 centimeters by 22 centimeters, cut out a 9-centimeter square from each corner, and fold up the edges, we get a box whose dimensions are 9 by 4 by 4, with volume $9 \times 4 \times 4 = 144 \ cm^3$, as required.

Now Work PROBLEM 55

A.8 Assess Your Understanding

Concepts and Vocabulary

1. The process of using variables to represent unknown quantities and then finding relationships that involve these variables is referred to as _____ _____.

2. The money paid for the use of money is _____.

3. Objects that move at a constant rate are said to be in _____ _____.

4. *True or False*   The amount charged for the use of principal for a given period of time is called the rate of interest.

5. *True or False*   If an object moves at an average speed r, the distance d covered in time t is given by the formula $d = rt$.

6. Suppose that you want to mix two coffees in order to obtain 100 pounds of the blend. If x represents the number of pounds of coffee A, write an algebraic expression that represents the number of pounds of coffee B.

Applications and Extensions

In Problems 7–16, translate each sentence into a mathematical equation. Be sure to identify the meaning of all symbols.

7. Geometry   The area of a circle is the product of the number π and the square of the radius.

8. Geometry   The circumference of a circle is the product of the number π and twice the radius.

9. Geometry   The area of a square is the square of the length of a side.

10. Geometry   The perimeter of a square is four times the length of a side.

11. Physics   Force equals the product of mass and acceleration.

12. Physics   Pressure is force per unit area.

13. Physics   Work equals force times distance.

14. Physics   Kinetic energy is one-half the product of the mass and the square of the velocity.

15. Business   The total variable cost of manufacturing x dishwashers is $150 per dishwasher times the number of dishwashers manufactured.

16. Business   The total revenue derived from selling x dishwashers is $250 per dishwasher times the number of dishwashers sold.

17. Financial Planning   Betsy, a recent retiree, requires $6000 per year in extra income. She has $50,000 to invest and can invest in B-rated bonds paying 15% per year or in a certificate of deposit (CD) paying 7% per year. How much money should be invested in each to realize exactly $6000 in interest per year?

18. Financial Planning   After 2 years, Betsy (see Problem 17) finds that she will now require $7000 per year. Assuming that the remaining information is the same, how should the money be reinvested?

19. Banking   A bank loaned out $12,000, part of it at the rate of 8% per year and the rest at the rate of 18% per year. If the interest received totaled $1000, how much was loaned at 8%?

20. Banking   Wendy, a loan officer at a bank, has $1,000,000 to lend and is required to obtain an average return of 18% per year. If she can lend at the rate of 19% or at the rate of 16%, how much can she lend at the 16% rate and still meet her requirement?

21. Blending Teas   The manager of a store that specializes in selling tea decides to experiment with a new blend. She will mix some Earl Grey tea that sells for $5 per pound with some Orange Pekoe tea that sells for $3 per pound to get 100 pounds of the new blend. The selling price of the new blend is to be $4.50 per pound, and there is to be no difference in revenue from selling the new blend versus selling the other types. How many pounds of the Earl Grey tea and Orange Pekoe tea are required?

22. Business: Blending Coffee   A coffee manufacturer wants to market a new blend of coffee that sells for $3.90 per pound by mixing two coffees that sell for $2.75 and $5 per pound, respectively. What amounts of each coffee should be blended to obtain the desired mixture?

[**Hint:** Assume that the total weight of the desired blend is 100 pounds.]

23. Business: Mixing Nuts   A nut store normally sells cashews for $9.00 per pound and almonds for $3.50 per pound. But at the end of the month the almonds had not sold well, so, in order to sell 60 pounds of almonds, the manager decided to mix the 60 pounds of almonds with some cashews and sell the mixture for $7.50 per pound. How many pounds of cashews should be mixed with the almonds to ensure no change in the profit?

24. Business: Mixing Candy   A candy store sells boxes of candy containing caramels and cremes. Each box sells for $12.50 and holds 30 pieces of candy (all pieces are the same size). If the caramels cost $0.25 to produce and the cremes cost $0.45 to produce, how many of each should be in a box to make a profit of $3?

25. Physics: Uniform Motion   A motorboat can maintain a constant speed of 16 miles per hour relative to the water. The boat makes a trip upstream to a certain point in 20 minutes; the return trip takes 15 minutes. What is the speed of the current? See the figure.

26. Physics: Uniform Motion   A motorboat heads upstream on a river that has a current of 3 miles per hour. The trip upstream takes 5 hours, and the return trip takes 2.5 hours. What is the speed of the motorboat? (Assume that the motorboat maintains a constant speed relative to the water.)

27. Physics: Uniform Motion   A motorboat maintained a constant speed of 15 miles per hour relative to the water in going 10 miles upstream and then returning. The total time for the trip was 1.5 hours. Use this information to find the speed of the current.

28. **Physics: Uniform Motion** Two cars enter the Florida Turnpike at Commercial Boulevard at 8:00 AM, each heading for Wildwood. One car's average speed is 10 miles per hour more than the other's. The faster car arrives at Wildwood at 11:00 AM, $\frac{1}{2}$ hour before the other car. What was the average speed of each car? How far did each travel?

29. **Moving Walkways** The speed of a moving walkway is typically about 2.5 feet per second. Walking on such a moving walkway, it takes Karen a total of 40 seconds to travel 50 feet with the movement of the walkway and then back again against the movement of the walkway. What is Karen's normal walking speed?

    Source: Answers.com

30. **Moving Walkways** The Gare Montparnasse train station in Paris has a high-speed version of a moving walkway. If he walks while riding this moving walkway, Jean Claude can travel 200 meters in 30 seconds less time than if he stands still on the moving walkway. If Jean Claude walks at a normal rate of 1.5 meters per second, what is the speed of the Gare Montparnasse walkway?

    Source: Answers.com

31. **Tennis** A regulation doubles tennis court has an area of 2808 square feet. If it is 6 feet longer than twice its width, determine the dimensions of the court.

    Source: United States Tennis Association

32. **Laser Printers** It takes an HP LaserJet 1300 laser printer 10 minutes longer to complete a 600-page print job by itself than it takes an HP LaserJet 2420 to complete the same job by itself. Together the two printers can complete the job in 12 minutes. How long does it take each printer to complete the print job alone? What is the speed of each printer?

    Source: Hewlett-Packard

33. **Working Together on a Job** Trent can deliver his newspapers in 30 minutes. It takes Lois 20 minutes to do the same route. How long would it take them to deliver the newspapers if they work together?

34. **Working Together on a Job** Patrick, by himself, can paint four rooms in 10 hours. If he hires April to help, they can do the same job together in 6 hours. If he lets April work alone, how long will it take her to paint four rooms?

35. **Enclosing a Garden** A gardener has 46 feet of fencing to be used to enclose a rectangular garden that has a border 2 feet wide surrounding it. See the figure.
    (a) If the length of the garden is to be twice its width, what will be the dimensions of the garden?
    (b) What is the area of the garden?
    (c) If the length and width of the garden are to be the same, what would be the dimensions of the garden?
    (d) What would be the area of the square garden?

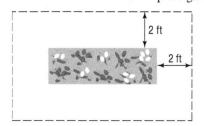

36. **Construction** A pond is enclosed by a wooden deck that is 3 feet wide. The fence surrounding the deck is 100 feet long.
    (a) If the pond is square, what are its dimensions?
    (b) If the pond is rectangular and the length of the pond is to be three times its width, what are its dimensions?
    (c) If the pond is circular, what is its diameter?
    (d) Which pond has the most area?

37. **Football** A tight end can run the 100-yard dash in 12 seconds. A defensive back can do it in 10 seconds. The tight end catches a pass at his own 20-yard line with the defensive back at the 15-yard line. (See the figure.) If no other players are nearby, at what yard line will the defensive back catch up to the tight end?

    [**Hint:** At time $t = 0$, the defensive back is 5 yards behind the tight end.]

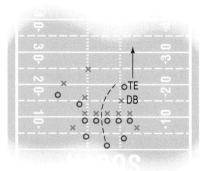

38. **Computing Business Expense** Therese, an outside salesperson, uses her car for both business and pleasure. Last year, she traveled 30,000 miles, using 900 gallons of gasoline. Her car gets 40 miles per gallon on the highway and 25 in the city. She can deduct all highway travel, but no city travel, on her taxes. How many miles should Therese be allowed as a business expense?

39. **Mixing Water and Antifreeze** How much water should be added to 1 gallon of pure antifreeze to obtain a solution that is 60% antifreeze?

40. **Mixing Water and Antifreeze** The cooling system of a certain foreign-made car has a capacity of 15 liters. If the system is filled with a mixture that is 40% antifreeze, how much of this mixture should be drained and replaced by pure antifreeze so that the system is filled with a solution that is 60% antifreeze?

41. **Chemistry: Salt Solutions** How much water must be evaporated from 32 ounces of a 4% salt solution to make a 6% salt solution?

42. **Chemistry: Salt Solutions** How much water must be evaporated from 240 gallons of a 3% salt solution to produce a 5% salt solution?

43. **Purity of Gold** The purity of gold is measured in karats, with pure gold being 24 karats. Other purities of gold are expressed as proportional parts of pure gold. Thus, 18-karat gold is $\frac{18}{24}$, or 75% pure gold; 12-karat gold is $\frac{12}{24}$, or 50% pure gold; and so on. How much 12-karat gold should be mixed with pure gold to obtain 60 grams of 16-karat gold?

44. **Chemistry: Sugar Molecules** A sugar molecule has twice as many atoms of hydrogen as it does oxygen and one

more atom of carbon than oxygen. If a sugar molecule has a total of 45 atoms, how many are oxygen? How many are hydrogen?

45. Running a Race Mike can run the mile in 6 minutes, and Dan can run the mile in 9 minutes. If Mike gives Dan a head start of 1 minute, how far from the start will Mike pass Dan? How long does it take? See the figure.

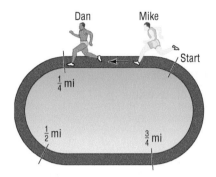

46. Range of an Airplane An air rescue plane averages 300 miles per hour in still air. It carries enough fuel for 5 hours of flying time. If, upon takeoff, it encounters a head wind of 30 mi/hr, how far can it fly and return safely? (Assume that the wind speed remains constant.)

47. Emptying Oil Tankers An oil tanker can be emptied by the main pump in 4 hours. An auxiliary pump can empty the tanker in 9 hours. If the main pump is started at 9 AM, when is the latest the auxiliary pump can be started so that the tanker is emptied by noon?

48. Cement Mix A 20-pound bag of Economy brand cement mix contains 25% cement and 75% sand. How much pure cement must be added to produce a cement mix that is 40% cement?

49. Emptying a Tub A bathroom tub will fill in 15 minutes with both faucets open and the stopper in place. With both faucets closed and the stopper removed, the tub will empty in 20 minutes. How long will it take for the tub to fill if both faucets are open and the stopper is removed?

50. Using Two Pumps A 5-horsepower (hp) pump can empty a pool in 5 hours. A smaller, 2-hp pump empties the same pool in 8 hours. The pumps are used together to begin emptying this pool. After two hours, the 2-hp pump breaks down. How long will it take the larger pump to empty the pool?

51. A Biathlon Suppose that you have entered an 87-mile biathlon that consists of a run and a bicycle race. During your run, your average speed is 6 miles per hour, and during your bicycle race, your average speed is 25 miles per hour. You finish the race in 5 hours. What is the distance of the run? What is the distance of the bicycle race?

52. Cyclists Two cyclists leave a city at the same time, one going east and the other going west. The westbound cyclist bikes 5 mph faster than the eastbound cyclist. After 6 hours they are 246 miles apart. How fast is each cyclist riding?

53. Comparing Olympic Heroes In the 1984 Olympics, C. Lewis of the United States won the gold medal in the 100-meter race with a time of 9.99 seconds. In the 1896 Olympics, Thomas Burke, also of the United States, won the gold medal in the 100-meter race in 12.0 seconds. If they ran in the same race repeating their respective times, by how many meters would Lewis beat Burke?

54. Constructing a Coffee Can A 39-ounce can of Hills Bros.® coffee requires 188.5 square inches of aluminum. If its height is 7 inches, what is its radius? [**Hint:** The surface area S of a right cylinder is $S = 2\pi r^2 + 2\pi r h$, where r is the radius and h is the height.]

55. Constructing a Box An open box is to be constructed from a square piece of sheet metal by removing a square of side 1 foot from each corner and turning up the edges. If the box is to hold 4 cubic feet, what should be the dimension of the sheet metal?

56. Constructing a Box Rework Problem 55 if the piece of sheet metal is a rectangle whose length is twice its width.

Explaining Concepts: Discussion and Writing

57. Critical Thinking You are the manager of a clothing store and have just purchased 100 dress shirts for $20.00 each. After 1 month of selling the shirts at the regular price, you plan to have a sale giving 40% off the original selling price. However, you still want to make a profit of $4 on each shirt at the sale price. What should you price the shirts at initially to ensure this? If, instead of 40% off at the sale, you give 50% off, by how much is your profit reduced?

58. Critical Thinking Make up a word problem that requires solving a linear equation as part of its solution. Exchange problems with a friend. Write a critique of your friend's problem.

59. Critical Thinking Without solving, explain what is wrong with the following mixture problem: How many liters of 25% ethanol should be added to 20 liters of 48% ethanol to obtain a solution of 58% ethanol? Now go through an algebraic solution. What happens?

60. Computing Average Speed In going from Chicago to Atlanta, a car averages 45 miles per hour, and in going from Atlanta to Miami, it averages 55 miles per hour. If Atlanta is halfway between Chicago and Miami, what is the average speed from Chicago to Miami? Discuss an intuitive solution. Write a paragraph defending your intuitive solution. Then solve the problem algebraically. Is your intuitive solution the same as the algebraic one? If not, find the flaw.

61. Speed of a Plane On a recent flight from Phoenix to Kansas City, a distance of 919 nautical miles, the plane arrived 20 minutes early. On leaving the aircraft, I asked the captain, "What was our tail wind?" He replied, "I don't know, but our ground speed was 550 knots." How can you determine if enough information is provided to find the tail wind? If possible, find the tail wind. (1 knot = 1 nautical mile per hour)

A.9 Interval Notation; Solving Inequalities

PREPARING FOR THIS SECTION *Before getting started, review the following:*

- Algebra Essentials (Appendix A, Section A.1, pp. A1–A10)

Now Work the 'Are You Prepared?' problems on page A78.

OBJECTIVES 1 Use Interval Notation (p. A72)
           2 Use Properties of Inequalities (p. A73)
           3 Solve Inequalities (p. A75)
           4 Solve Combined Inequalities (p. A76)
           5 Solve Inequalities Involving Absolute Value (p. A77)

Suppose that a and b are two real numbers and $a < b$. We use the notation $a < x < b$ to mean that x is a number *between* a and b. The expression $a < x < b$ is equivalent to the two inequalities $a < x$ and $x < b$. Similarly, the expression $a \le x \le b$ is equivalent to the two inequalities $a \le x$ and $x \le b$. The remaining two possibilities, $a \le x < b$ and $a < x \le b$, are defined similarly.

Although it is acceptable to write $3 \ge x \ge 2$, it is preferable to reverse the inequality symbols and write instead $2 \le x \le 3$ so that, as you read from left to right, the values go from smaller to larger.

A statement such as $2 \le x \le 1$ is false because there is no number x for which $2 \le x$ and $x \le 1$. Finally, we never mix inequality symbols, as in $2 \le x \ge 3$.

1 Use Interval Notation

DEFINITION

Let a and b represent two real numbers with $a < b$.
A **closed interval**, denoted by **[a, b]**, consists of all real numbers x for which $a \le x \le b$.
An **open interval**, denoted by **(a, b)**, consists of all real numbers x for which $a < x < b$.
The **half-open**, or **half-closed**, **intervals** are **(a, b]**, consisting of all real numbers x for which $a < x \le b$, and **[a, b)**, consisting of all real numbers x for which $a \le x < b$.

In each of these definitions, a is called the **left endpoint** and b the **right endpoint** of the interval.

The symbol ∞ (read as "infinity") is not a real number, but a notational device used to indicate unboundedness in the positive direction. The symbol $-\infty$ (read as "negative infinity") also is not a real number, but a notational device used to indicate unboundedness in the negative direction. Using the symbols ∞ and $-\infty$, we can define five other kinds of intervals:

[a, ∞)   Consists of all real numbers x for which $x \ge a$
(a, ∞)   Consists of all real numbers x for which $x > a$
(−∞, a]   Consists of all real numbers x for which $x \le a$
(−∞, a)   Consists of all real numbers x for which $x < a$
(−∞, ∞) Consists of all real numbers x

Note that ∞ and $-\infty$ are never included as endpoints, since neither is a real number.

Table 5 summarizes interval notation, corresponding inequality notation, and their graphs.

Table 5

Interval	Inequality	Graph
The open interval (a, b)	$a < x < b$	
The closed interval $[a, b]$	$a \leq x \leq b$	
The half-open interval $[a, b)$	$a \leq x < b$	
The half-open interval $(a, b]$	$a < x \leq b$	
The interval $[a, \infty)$	$x \geq a$	
The interval (a, ∞)	$x > a$	
The interval $(-\infty, a]$	$x \leq a$	
The interval $(-\infty, a)$	$x < a$	
The interval $(-\infty, \infty)$	All real numbers	

EXAMPLE 1

Writing Inequalities Using Interval Notation

Write each inequality using interval notation.

(a) $1 \leq x \leq 3$ (b) $-4 < x < 0$ (c) $x > 5$ (d) $x \leq 1$

Solution

(a) $1 \leq x \leq 3$ describes all numbers x between 1 and 3, inclusive. In interval notation, we write $[1, 3]$.

(b) In interval notation, $-4 < x < 0$ is written $(-4, 0)$.

(c) $x > 5$ consists of all numbers x greater than 5. In interval notation, we write $(5, \infty)$.

(d) In interval notation, $x \leq 1$ is written $(-\infty, 1]$.

EXAMPLE 2

Writing Intervals Using Inequality Notation

Write each interval as an inequality involving x.

(a) $[1, 4)$ (b) $(2, \infty)$ (c) $[2, 3]$ (d) $(-\infty, -3]$

Solution

(a) $[1, 4)$ consists of all numbers x for which $1 \leq x < 4$.

(b) $(2, \infty)$ consists of all numbers x for which $x > 2$.

(c) $[2, 3]$ consists of all numbers x for which $2 \leq x \leq 3$.

(d) $(-\infty, -3]$ consists of all numbers x for which $x \leq -3$.

 Now Work PROBLEMS 11, 23, AND 31

2 Use Properties of Inequalities

The product of two positive real numbers is positive, the product of two negative real numbers is positive, and the product of 0 and 0 is 0. For any real number a, the value of a^2 is 0 or positive; that is, a^2 is nonnegative. This is called the **nonnegative property.**

In Words

The square of a real number is never negative.

Nonnegative Property

For any real number a,

$$a^2 \geq 0 \qquad (1)$$

If we add the same number to both sides of an inequality, we obtain an equivalent inequality. For example, since $3 < 5$, then $3 + 4 < 5 + 4$ or $7 < 9$. This is called the **addition property** of inequalities.

Addition Property of Inequalities

For real numbers a, b, and c,

$$\text{If } a < b, \text{ then } a + c < b + c. \tag{2a}$$
$$\text{If } a > b, \text{ then } a + c > b + c. \tag{2b}$$

The addition property states that the sense, or direction, of an inequality remains unchanged if the same number is added to each side.

Now let's see what happens if we multiply each side of an inequality by a nonzero number. We begin with $3 < 7$ and multiply each side by 2. The numbers 6 and 14 that result obey the inequality $6 < 14$.

Now start with $9 > 2$ and multiply each side by -4. The numbers -36 and -8 that result obey the inequality $-36 < -8$.

Note that the effect of multiplying both sides of $9 > 2$ by the negative number -4 is that the direction of the inequality symbol is reversed. We are led to the following general **multiplication properties** for inequalities:

Multiplication Properties for Inequalities

For real numbers a, b, and c,

$$\text{If } a < b \text{ and if } c > 0, \text{ then } ac < bc.$$
$$\text{If } a < b \text{ and if } c < 0, \text{ then } ac > bc. \tag{3a}$$

$$\text{If } a > b \text{ and if } c > 0, \text{ then } ac > bc.$$
$$\text{If } a > b \text{ and if } c < 0, \text{ then } ac < bc. \tag{3b}$$

> **In Words**
>
> Multiplying by a negative number reverses the inequality.

The multiplication properties state that the sense, or direction, of an inequality *remains the same* if each side is multiplied by a *positive* real number, whereas the direction is *reversed* if each side is multiplied by a *negative* real number.

EXAMPLE 3

Multiplication Property of Inequalities

(a) If $2x < 6$, then $\dfrac{1}{2}(2x) < \dfrac{1}{2}(6)$ or $x < 3$.

(b) If $\dfrac{x}{-3} > 12$, then $-3\left(\dfrac{x}{-3}\right) < -3(12)$ or $x < -36$.

(c) If $-4x < -8$, then $\dfrac{-4x}{-4} > \dfrac{-8}{-4}$ or $x > 2$.

(d) If $-x > 8$, then $(-1)(-x) < (-1)(8)$ or $x < -8$.

Now Work PROBLEM 45

The **reciprocal property** states that the reciprocal of a positive real number is positive and that the reciprocal of a negative real number is negative.

> **In Words**
>
> The reciprocal property states that the reciprocal of a positive real number is positive and that the reciprocal of a negative real number is negative.

Reciprocal Property for Inequalities

$$\text{If } a > 0, \text{ then } \dfrac{1}{a} > 0 \qquad \text{If } \dfrac{1}{a} > 0, \text{ then } a > 0 \tag{4a}$$

$$\text{If } a < 0, \text{ then } \dfrac{1}{a} < 0 \qquad \text{If } \dfrac{1}{a} < 0, \text{ then } a < 0 \tag{4b}$$

3 Solve Inequalities

An **inequality in one variable** is a statement involving two expressions, at least one containing the variable, separated by one of the inequality symbols $<$, $\leq$, $>$, or $\geq$. To **solve an inequality** means to find all values of the variable for which the statement is true. These values are called **solutions** of the inequality.

For example, the following are all inequalities involving one variable x:

$$x + 5 < 8 \qquad 2x - 3 \geq 4 \qquad x^2 - 1 \leq 3 \qquad \frac{x + 1}{x - 2} > 0$$

As with equations, one method for solving an inequality is to replace it by a series of equivalent inequalities until an inequality with an obvious solution, such as $x < 3$, is obtained. We obtain equivalent inequalities by applying some of the same properties as those used to find equivalent equations. The addition property and the multiplication properties form the basis for the following procedures.

Procedures That Leave the Inequality Symbol Unchanged

1. Simplify both sides of the inequality by combining like terms and eliminating parentheses:

$$\begin{array}{ll} \text{Replace} & (x + 2) + 6 > 2x + 5(x + 1) \\ \text{by} & x + 8 > 7x + 5 \end{array}$$

2. Add or subtract the same expression on both sides of the inequality:

$$\begin{array}{ll} \text{Replace} & 3x - 5 < 4 \\ \text{by} & (3x - 5) + 5 < 4 + 5 \end{array}$$

3. Multiply or divide both sides of the inequality by the same positive expression:

$$\text{Replace} \qquad 4x > 16 \quad \text{by} \quad \frac{4x}{4} > \frac{16}{4}$$

Procedures That Reverse the Sense or Direction of the Inequality Symbol

1. Interchange the two sides of the inequality:

$$\text{Replace} \qquad 3 < x \quad \text{by} \quad x > 3$$

2. Multiply or divide both sides of the inequality by the same *negative* expression:

$$\text{Replace} \qquad -2x > 6 \quad \text{by} \quad \frac{-2x}{-2} < \frac{6}{-2}$$

As the examples that follow illustrate, we solve inequalities using many of the same steps that we would use to solve equations. In writing the solution of an inequality, we may use either set notation or interval notation, whichever is more convenient.

EXAMPLE 4

Solving an Inequality

Solve the inequality: $4x + 7 \geq 2x - 3$
Graph the solution set.

Solution

$$4x + 7 \geq 2x - 3$$
$$4x + 7 - 7 \geq 2x - 3 - 7 \qquad \text{Subtract 7 from both sides.}$$
$$4x \geq 2x - 10 \qquad \text{Simplify.}$$

$$\begin{aligned} 4x - 2x &\geq 2x - 10 - 2x && \text{Subtract } 2x \text{ from both sides.} \\ 2x &\geq -10 && \text{Simplify.} \\ \frac{2x}{2} &\geq \frac{-10}{2} && \text{Divide both sides by 2. (The direction of the inequality symbol is unchanged.)} \\ x &\geq -5 && \text{Simplify.} \end{aligned}$$

Figure 28

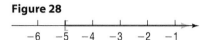

The solution set is $\{x | x \geq -5\}$ or, using interval notation, all numbers in the interval $[-5, \infty)$. See Figure 28 for the graph.

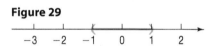

Now Work PROBLEM 57

4 Solve Combined Inequalities

EXAMPLE 5 **Solving Combined Inequalities**

Solve the inequality: $-5 < 3x - 2 < 1$
Graph the solution set.

Solution Recall that the inequality

$$-5 < 3x - 2 < 1$$

is equivalent to the two inequalities

$$-5 < 3x - 2 \quad \text{and} \quad 3x - 2 < 1$$

We solve each of these inequalities separately.

$$\begin{aligned} -5 &< 3x - 2 & & & 3x - 2 &< 1 \\ -5 + 2 &< 3x - 2 + 2 & & \text{Add 2 to both sides.} & 3x - 2 + 2 &< 1 + 2 \\ -3 &< 3x & & \text{Simplify.} & 3x &< 3 \\ \frac{-3}{3} &< \frac{3x}{3} & & \text{Divide both sides by 3.} & \frac{3x}{3} &< \frac{3}{3} \\ -1 &< x & & \text{Simplify.} & x &< 1 \end{aligned}$$

The solution set of the original pair of inequalities consists of all x for which

$$-1 < x \quad \text{and} \quad x < 1$$

Figure 29

This may be written more compactly as $\{x | -1 < x < 1\}$. In interval notation, the solution is $(-1, 1)$. See Figure 29 for the graph.

Observe in the preceding process that the two inequalities we solved required exactly the same steps. A shortcut to solving the original inequality algebraically is to deal with the two inequalities at the same time, as follows:

$$\begin{aligned} -5 < \quad & 3x - 2 && < 1 \\ -5 + 2 < \; & 3x - 2 + 2 && < 1 + 2 && \text{Add 2 to each part.} \\ -3 < \quad & 3x && < 3 && \text{Simplify.} \\ \frac{-3}{3} < \quad & \frac{3x}{3} && < \frac{3}{3} && \text{Divide each part by 3.} \\ -1 < \quad & x && < 1 && \text{Simplify.} \end{aligned}$$

Now Work PROBLEM 73

| EXAMPLE 6 | **Using the Reciprocal Property to Solve an Inequality** |

Solve the inequality: $(4x - 1)^{-1} > 0$
Graph the solution set.

Solution Since $(4x - 1)^{-1} = \dfrac{1}{4x - 1}$ and since the Reciprocal Property states that when $\dfrac{1}{a} > 0$ then $a > 0$, we have

$$(4x - 1)^{-1} > 0$$
$$\frac{1}{4x - 1} > 0$$
$$4x - 1 > 0 \qquad \textit{Reciprocal Property}$$
$$4x > 1$$
$$x > \frac{1}{4}$$

Figure 30

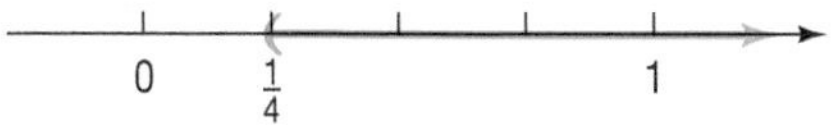

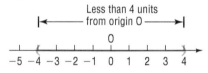

The solution set is $\left\{ x \middle| x > \dfrac{1}{4} \right\}$, that is, all x in the interval $\left(\dfrac{1}{4}, \infty \right)$. Figure 30 illustrates the graph.

━━━ **Now Work** PROBLEM 83

5 Solve Inequalities Involving Absolute Value

| EXAMPLE 7 | **Solving an Inequality Involving Absolute Value** |

Solve the inequality $|x| < 4$, and graph the solution set.

Solution We are looking for all points whose coordinate x is a distance less than 4 units from the origin. See Figure 31 for an illustration. Because any x between -4 and 4 satisfies the condition $|x| < 4$, the solution set consists of all numbers x for which $-4 < x < 4$, that is, all x in the interval $(-4, 4)$.

Figure 31

Less than 4 units from origin 0

0

−5 −4 −3 −2 −1 0 1 2 3 4

| EXAMPLE 8 | **Solving an Inequality Involving Absolute Value** |

Solve the inequality $|x| > 3$, and graph the solution set.

Solution We are looking for all points whose coordinate x is a distance greater than 3 units from the origin. Figure 32 illustrates the situation. We conclude that any x less than -3 or greater than 3 satisfies the condition $|x| > 3$. The solution set consists of all numbers x for which $x < -3$ or $x > 3$, that is, all x in $(-\infty, -3) \cup (3, \infty)$.*

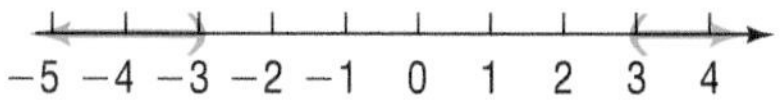

We are led to the following results:

Figure 32

−5 −4 −3 −2 −1 0 1 2 3 4

THEOREM If a is any positive number, then

$\lvert u \rvert < a$ is equivalent to $-a < u < a$		**(5)**
$\lvert u \rvert \le a$ is equivalent to $-a \le u \le a$		**(6)**
$\lvert u \rvert > a$ is equivalent to $u < -a$ or $u > a$		**(7)**
$\lvert u \rvert \ge a$ is equivalent to $u \le -a$ or $u \ge a$		**(8)**

* The symbol $\cup$ stands for the union of two sets. Refer to page A2 if necessary.

EXAMPLE 9 **Solving an Inequality Involving Absolute Value**

Solve the inequality $|2x + 4| \leq 3$, and graph the solution set.

Solution

$$|2x + 4| \leq 3 \quad \text{This follows the form of statement (6); the expression}$$
$$u = 2x + 4 \text{ is inside the absolute value bars.}$$

$$-3 \leq \quad 2x + 4 \quad \leq 3 \quad \text{Apply statement (6).}$$

$$-3 - 4 \leq 2x + 4 - 4 \leq 3 - 4 \quad \text{Subtract 4 from each part.}$$

$$-7 \leq \quad 2x \quad \leq -1 \quad \text{Simplify.}$$

$$\frac{-7}{2} \leq \quad \frac{2x}{2} \quad \leq \frac{-1}{2} \quad \text{Divide each part by 2.}$$

$$-\frac{7}{2} \leq \quad x \quad \leq -\frac{1}{2} \quad \text{Simplify.}$$

Figure 33

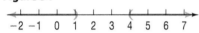

The solution set is $\left\{ x \left| -\frac{7}{2} \leq x \leq -\frac{1}{2} \right. \right\}$, that is, all x in the interval $\left[-\frac{7}{2}, -\frac{1}{2} \right]$. See Figure 33 for a graph of the solution set.

Now Work PROBLEM 89

EXAMPLE 10 **Solving an Inequality Involving Absolute Value**

Solve the inequality $|2x - 5| > 3$, and graph the solution set.

Solution

$$|2x - 5| > 3 \quad \text{This follows the form of statement (7); the expression}$$
$$u = 2x - 5 \text{ is inside the absolute value bars.}$$

$$2x - 5 < -3 \qquad \text{or} \qquad 2x - 5 > 3 \quad \text{Apply statement (7).}$$

$$2x - 5 + 5 < -3 + 5 \quad \text{or} \quad 2x - 5 + 5 > 3 + 5 \quad \text{Add 5 to each part.}$$

$$2x < 2 \qquad \text{or} \qquad 2x > 8 \quad \text{Simplify.}$$

$$\frac{2x}{2} < \frac{2}{2} \qquad \text{or} \qquad \frac{2x}{2} > \frac{8}{2} \quad \text{Divide each part by 2.}$$

$$x < 1 \qquad \text{or} \qquad x > 4 \quad \text{Simplify.}$$

Figure 34

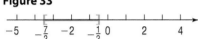

The solution set is $\{x | x < 1 \text{ or } x > 4\}$, that is, all x in $(-\infty, 1) \cup (4, \infty)$. See Figure 34 for a graph of the solution set.

WARNING A common error to be avoided is to attempt to write the solution $x < 1$ or $x > 4$ as the combined inequality $1 > x > 4$, which is incorrect, since there are no numbers x for which $x < 1$ and $x > 4$. Another common error is to "mix" the symbols and write $1 < x > 4$, which makes no sense. ∎

Now Work PROBLEM 95

A.9 Assess Your Understanding

'Are You Prepared?' *Answers are given at the end of these exercises. If you get a wrong answer, read the pages listed in* red.

1. Graph the inequality: $x \geq -2$. (pp. A4–A5)

2. *True or False* $-5 > -3$ (pp. A4–A5)

3. $|-2| = $ _____. (p. A5)

4. *True or False* $|x| \geq 0$ for any real number x. (pp. A5–A6)

Concepts and Vocabulary

5. If each side of an inequality is multiplied by a(n) _____ number, then the sense of the inequality symbol is reversed.

6. A(n) _____ _____, denoted $[a, b]$, consists of all real numbers x for which $a \leq x \leq b$.

7. The solution set of the equation $|x| = 5$ is { _____ }.

8. The solution set of the inequality $|x| < 5$ is $\{x | $ _____ $\}$

9. *True or False* The equation $|x| = -2$ has no solution.

10. *True or False* The inequality $|x| \geq -2$ has the set of real numbers as solution set.

Skill Building

In Problems 11–16, express the graph shown in blue using interval notation. Also express each as an inequality involving x.

11.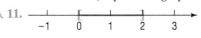

12.

13.

14.

15.

16.

In Problems 17–22, an inequality is given. Write the inequality obtained by:
  (a) Adding 3 to each side of the given inequality.
  (b) Subtracting 5 from each side of the given inequality.
  (c) Multiplying each side of the given inequality by 3.
  (d) Multiplying each side of the given inequality by −2.

17. $3 < 5$ **18.** $2 > 1$ **19.** $4 > -3$ **20.** $-3 > -5$ **21.** $2x + 1 < 2$ **22.** $1 - 2x > 5$

In Problems 23–30, write each inequality using interval notation, and illustrate each inequality using the real number line.

23. $0 \leq x \leq 4$ **24.** $-1 < x < 5$ **25.** $4 \leq x < 6$ **26.** $-2 < x < 0$

27. $x \geq 4$ **28.** $x \leq 5$ **29.** $x < -4$ **30.** $x > 1$

In Problems 31–38, write each interval as an inequality involving x, and illustrate each inequality using the real number line.

31. $[2, 5]$ **32.** $(1, 2)$ **33.** $(-3, -2)$ **34.** $[0, 1)$

35. $[4, \infty)$ **36.** $(-\infty, 2]$ **37.** $(-\infty, -3)$ **38.** $(-8, \infty)$

In Problems 39–52, fill in the blank with the correct inequality symbol.

39. If $x < 5$, then $x - 5$ _____ 0.

40. If $x < -4$, then $x + 4$ _____ 0.

41. If $x > -4$, then $x + 4$ _____ 0.

42. If $x > 6$, then $x - 6$ _____ 0.

43. If $x \geq -4$, then $3x$ _____ -12.

44. If $x \leq 3$, then $2x$ _____ 6.

45. If $x > 6$, then $-2x$ _____ -12.

46. If $x > -2$, then $-4x$ _____ 8.

47. If $x \geq 5$, then $-4x$ _____ -20.

48. If $x \leq -4$, then $-3x$ _____ 12.

49. If $2x > 6$, then x _____ 3.

50. If $3x \leq 12$, then x _____ 4.

51. If $-\dfrac{1}{2}x \leq 3$, then x _____ -6.

52. If $-\dfrac{1}{4}x > 1$, then x _____ -4.

In Problems 53–100, solve each inequality. Express your answer using set notation or interval notation. Graph the solution set.

53. $x + 1 < 5$ **54.** $x - 6 < 1$ **55.** $1 - 2x \leq 3$

56. $2 - 3x \leq 5$ **57.** $3x - 7 > 2$ **58.** $2x + 5 > 1$

59. $3x - 1 \geq 3 + x$ **60.** $2x - 2 \geq 3 + x$ **61.** $-2(x + 3) < 8$

62. $-3(1 - x) < 12$ **63.** $4 - 3(1 - x) \leq 3$ **64.** $8 - 4(2 - x) \leq -2x$

65. $\dfrac{1}{2}(x - 4) > x + 8$ **66.** $3x + 4 > \dfrac{1}{3}(x - 2)$ **67.** $\dfrac{x}{2} \geq 1 - \dfrac{x}{4}$

68. $\dfrac{x}{3} \geq 2 + \dfrac{x}{6}$ **69.** $0 \leq 2x - 6 \leq 4$ **70.** $4 \leq 2x + 2 \leq 10$

71. $-5 \leq 4 - 3x \leq 2$ **72.** $-3 \leq 3 - 2x \leq 9$ **73.** $-3 < \dfrac{2x - 1}{4} < 0$

74. $0 < \dfrac{3x + 2}{2} < 4$ **75.** $1 < 1 - \dfrac{1}{2}x < 4$ **76.** $0 < 1 - \dfrac{1}{3}x < 1$

77. $(x + 2)(x - 3) > (x - 1)(x + 1)$ **78.** $(x - 1)(x + 1) > (x - 3)(x + 4)$ **79.** $x(4x + 3) \le (2x + 1)^2$

80. $x(9x - 5) \le (3x - 1)^2$ **81.** $\dfrac{1}{2} \le \dfrac{x + 1}{3} < \dfrac{3}{4}$ **82.** $\dfrac{1}{3} < \dfrac{x + 1}{2} \le \dfrac{2}{3}$

83. $(4x + 2)^{-1} < 0$ **84.** $(2x - 1)^{-1} > 0$ **85.** $0 < \dfrac{2}{x} < \dfrac{3}{5}$

86. $0 < \dfrac{4}{x} < \dfrac{2}{3}$ **87.** $0 < (2x - 4)^{-1} < \dfrac{1}{2}$ **88.** $0 < (3x + 6)^{-1} < \dfrac{1}{3}$

89. $|2x| < 8$ **90.** $|3x| < 12$ **91.** $|3x| > 12$

92. $|2x| > 6$ **93.** $|2x - 1| \le 1$ **94.** $|2x + 5| \le 7$

95. $|1 - 2x| > 3$ **96.** $|2 - 3x| > 1$ **97.** $|-4x| + |-5| \le 9$

98. $|-x| - |4| \le 2$ **99.** $|-2x| \ge |-4|$ **100.** $|-x - 2| \ge 1$

Applications and Extensions

101. Express the fact that x differs from 2 by less than $\dfrac{1}{2}$ as an inequality involving an absolute value. Solve for x.

102. Express the fact that x differs from -1 by less than 1 as an inequality involving an absolute value. Solve for x.

103. Express the fact that x differs from -3 by more than 2 as an inequality involving an absolute value. Solve for x.

104. Express the fact that x differs from 2 by more than 3 as an inequality involving an absolute value. Solve for x.

105. What is the domain of the variable in the expression $\sqrt{3x + 6}$?

106. What is the domain of the variable in the expression $\sqrt{8 + 2x}$?

107. A young adult may be defined as someone older than 21, but less than 30 years of age. Express this statement using inequalities.

108. Middle-aged may be defined as being 40 or more and less than 60. Express this statement using inequalities.

109. Life Expectancy The Social Security Administration determined that an average 30-year-old male in 2005 could expect to live at least 46.60 more years and an average 30-year-old female in 2005 could expect to live at least 51.03 more years.
  (a) To what age can an average 30-year-old male expect to live? Express your answer as an inequality.
  (b) To what age can an average 30-year-old female expect to live? Express your answer as an inequality.
  (c) Who can expect to live longer, a male or a female? By how many years?

  Source: Social Security Administration, Period Life Table, 2005

110. General Chemistry For a certain ideal gas, the volume V (in cubic centimeters) equals 20 times the temperature T (in degrees Celsius). If the temperature varies from 80° to 120° C inclusive, what is the corresponding range of the volume of the gas?

111. Real Estate A real estate agent agrees to sell an apartment complex according to the following commission schedule: $45,000 plus 25% of the selling price in excess of $900,000. Assuming that the complex will sell at some price between $900,000 and $1,100,000 inclusive, over what range does the agent's commission vary? How does the commission vary as a percent of selling price?

112. Sales Commission A used car salesperson is paid a commission of $25 plus 40% of the selling price in excess of owner's cost. The owner claims that used cars typically sell for at least owner's cost plus $200 and at most owner's cost plus $3000. For each sale made, over what range can the salesperson expect the commission to vary?

113 Federal Tax Withholding The percentage method of withholding for federal income tax (2010) states that a single person whose weekly wages, after subtracting withholding allowances, are over $693, but not over $1302, shall have $82.35 plus 25% of the excess over $693 withheld. Over what range does the amount withheld vary if the weekly wages vary from $700 to $900 inclusive?

Source: Employer's Tax Guide. Department of the Treasury, Internal Revenue Service, Publication 2010.

114. Exercising Sue wants to lose weight. For healthy weight loss, the American College of Sports Medicine (ACSM) recommends 200 to 300 minutes of exercise per week. For the first six days of the week, Sue exercised 40, 45, 0, 50, 25, and 35 minutes. How long should Sue exercise on the seventh day in order to stay within the ACSM guidelines?

115. Electricity Rates Commonwealth Edison Company's charge for electricity in January 2010 is 9.44¢ per kilowatt-hour. In addition, each monthly bill contains a customer charge of $12.55. If last year's bills ranged from a low of $76.27 to a high of $248.55, over what range did usage vary (in kilowatt-hours)?

Source: Commonwealth Edison Co., Chicago, Illinois, 2010.

116. Water Bills The Village of Oak Lawn charges homeowners $37.62 per quarter-year plus $3.86 per 1000 gallons for water usage in excess of 10,000 gallons. In 2010 one homeowner's quarterly bill ranged from a high of \$122.54 to a low of \$68.50. Over what range did water usage vary?

Source: Village of Oak Lawn, Illinois, April 2010.

117. Markup of a New Car The markup over dealer's cost of a new car ranges from 12% to 18%. If the sticker price is \$18,000, over what range will the dealer's cost vary?

118. IQ Tests A standard intelligence test has an average score of 100. According to statistical theory, of the people who take the test, the 2.5% with the highest scores will have scores of more than 1.96σ above the average, where σ (sigma, a number called the **standard deviation**) depends on the nature of the test. If $\sigma = 12$ for this test and there is (in principle) no upper limit to the score possible on the test, write the interval of possible test scores of the people in the top 2.5%.

119. Computing Grades In your Economics 101 class, you have scores of 68, 82, 87, and 89 on the first four of five tests. To get a grade of B, the average of the first five test scores must be greater than or equal to 80 and less than 90.

(a) Solve an inequality to find the range of the score that you need on the last test to get a B.

(b) What score do you need if the fifth test counts double?

What do I need to get a B?

120. "Light" Foods For food products to be labeled "light," the U.S. Food and Drug Administration requires that the altered product must either contain one-third or fewer calories than the regular product or it must contain one-half or less fat than the regular product. If a serving of Miracle Whip® Light contains 20 calories and 1.5 grams of fat, then what must be true about either the number of calories or the grams of fat in a serving of regular Miracle Whip®?

121. Arithmetic Mean If $a < b$, show that $a < \dfrac{a+b}{2} < b$. The number $\dfrac{a+b}{2}$ is called the **arithmetic mean** of a and b.

122. Refer to Problem 121. Show that the arithmetic mean of a and b is equidistant from a and b.

123. Geometric Mean If $0 < a < b$, show that $a < \sqrt{ab} < b$. The number $\sqrt{ab}$ is called the **geometric mean** of a and b.

124. Refer to Problems 121 and 123. Show that the geometric mean of a and b is less than the arithmetic mean of a and b.

125. Harmonic Mean For $0 < a < b$, let h be defined by

$$\frac{1}{h} = \frac{1}{2}\left(\frac{1}{a} + \frac{1}{b}\right)$$

Show that $a < h < b$. The number h is called the **harmonic mean** of a and b.

126. Refer to Problems 121, 123, and 125. Show that the harmonic mean of a and b equals the geometric mean squared divided by the arithmetic mean.

127. Another Reciprocal Property Prove that if $0 < a < b$, then $0 < \dfrac{1}{b} < \dfrac{1}{a}$.

Explaining Concepts: Discussion and Writing

128. Make up an inequality that has no solution. Make up one that has exactly one solution.

129. The inequality $x^2 + 1 < -5$ has no real solution. Explain why.

130. Do you prefer to use inequality notation or interval notation to express the solution to an inequality? Give your reasons. Are there particular circumstances when you prefer one to the other? Cite examples.

131. How would you explain to a fellow student the underlying reason for the multiplication properties for inequalities (page A74), that is, the sense or direction of an inequality remains the same if each side is multiplied by a positive real number, whereas the direction is reversed if each side is multiplied by a negative real number?

'Are You Prepared?' Answers

1. 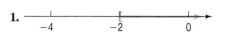   **2.** False   **3.** 2   **4.** True

A.10 *nth* Roots; Rational Exponents

PREPARING FOR THIS SECTION *Before getting started, review the following:*

- Exponents, Square Roots (Appendix A, Section A.1, pp. A7–A10)

Now Work the 'Are You Prepared?' problems on page A87.

OBJECTIVES   **1** Work with *nth* Roots (p. A82)

         2 Simplify Radicals (p. A82)

         3 Rationalize Denominators (p. A84)

         4 Solve Radical Equations (p. A84)

         5 Simplify Expressions with Rational Exponents (p. A85)

1 Work with *n*th Roots

DEFINITION

The **principal *n*th root of a real number *a*,** $n \geq 2$ an integer, symbolized by $\sqrt[n]{a}$, is defined as follows:

$$\sqrt[n]{a} = b \quad \text{means} \quad a = b^n$$

where $a \geq 0$ and $b \geq 0$ if *n* is even and *a*, *b* are any real numbers if *n* is odd.

> **In Words**
> The symbol $\sqrt[n]{a}$ means "give me the number, which when raised to the power *n*, equals *a*."

Notice that if *a* is negative and *n* is even, then $\sqrt[n]{a}$ is not defined as a real number. When it is defined, the principal *n*th root of a number is unique.

The symbol $\sqrt[n]{a}$ for the principal *n*th root of *a* is called a **radical;** the integer *n* is called the **index,** and *a* is called the **radicand.** If the index of a radical is 2, we call $\sqrt[2]{a}$ the **square root** of *a* and omit the index 2 by simply writing $\sqrt{a}$. If the index is 3, we call $\sqrt[3]{a}$ the **cube root** of *a*.

EXAMPLE 1   **Simplifying Principal *n*th Roots**

(a) $\sqrt[3]{8} = \sqrt[3]{2^3} = 2$

(b) $\sqrt[3]{-64} = \sqrt[3]{(-4)^3} = -4$

(c) $\sqrt[4]{\dfrac{1}{16}} = \sqrt[4]{\left(\dfrac{1}{2}\right)^4} = \dfrac{1}{2}$

(d) $\sqrt[6]{(-2)^6} = |-2| = 2$

These are examples of **perfect roots,** since each simplifies to a rational number. Notice the absolute value in Example 1(d). If *n* is even, the principal *n*th root must be nonnegative.

In general, if $n \geq 2$ is an integer and *a* is a real number, we have

$$\sqrt[n]{a^n} = a \qquad \text{if } n \geq 3 \text{ is odd} \qquad \textbf{(1a)}$$
$$\sqrt[n]{a^n} = |a| \qquad \text{if } n \geq 2 \text{ is even} \qquad \textbf{(1b)}$$

—— **Now Work** PROBLEM 7

Radicals provide a way of representing many irrational real numbers. For example, there is no rational number whose square is 2. Using radicals, we can say that $\sqrt{2}$ is the positive number whose square is 2.

EXAMPLE 2   **Using a Calculator to Approximate Roots**

Use a calculator to approximate $\sqrt[5]{16}$.

Solution   Figure 35 shows the result using a TI-84 Plus graphing calculator.

Figure 35

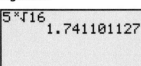
```
5ˣ√16
        1.741101127
```

—— **Now Work** PROBLEM 81

2 Simplify Radicals

Let $n \geq 2$ and $m \geq 2$ denote positive integers, and let *a* and *b* represent real numbers. Assuming that all radicals are defined, we have the following properties:

Properties of Radicals

$$\sqrt[n]{ab} = \sqrt[n]{a}\,\sqrt[n]{b} \qquad\qquad \textbf{(2a)}$$

$$\sqrt[n]{\dfrac{a}{b}} = \dfrac{\sqrt[n]{a}}{\sqrt[n]{b}} \qquad\qquad \textbf{(2b)}$$

$$\sqrt[n]{a^m} = \left(\sqrt[n]{a}\right)^m \qquad\qquad \textbf{(2c)}$$

When used in reference to radicals, the direction to "simplify" will mean to remove from the radicals any perfect roots that occur as factors. Let's look at some examples of how the preceding rules are applied to simplify radicals.

EXAMPLE 3   **Simplifying Radicals**

(a) $\sqrt{32} = \sqrt{16 \cdot 2} = \sqrt{16} \cdot \sqrt{2} = 4\sqrt{2}$

     Factor out 16,   (2a)
     a perfect square.

(b) $\sqrt[3]{16} = \sqrt[3]{8 \cdot 2} = \sqrt[3]{8} \cdot \sqrt[3]{2} = \sqrt[3]{2^3} \cdot \sqrt[3]{2} = 2\sqrt[3]{2}$

     Factor out 8,   (2a)
     a perfect cube.

(c) $\sqrt[3]{-16x^4} = \sqrt[3]{-8 \cdot 2 \cdot x^3 \cdot x} = \sqrt[3]{(-8x^3)(2x)}$

     Factor perfect   Group perfect
     cubes inside radical. cubes.

$$= \sqrt[3]{(-2x)^3 \cdot 2x} = \sqrt[3]{(-2x)^3} \cdot \sqrt[3]{2x} = -2x\sqrt[3]{2x}$$

                           (2a)

(d) $\sqrt[4]{\dfrac{16x^5}{81}} = \sqrt[4]{\dfrac{2^4 x^4 x}{3^4}} = \sqrt[4]{\left(\dfrac{2x}{3}\right)^4 \cdot x} = \sqrt[4]{\left(\dfrac{2x}{3}\right)^4} \cdot \sqrt[4]{x} = \left|\dfrac{2x}{3}\right| \sqrt[4]{x}$

Now Work PROBLEMS 11 AND 17

Two or more radicals can be combined, provided that they have the same index and the same radicand. Such radicals are called **like radicals.**

EXAMPLE 4   **Combining Like Radicals**

(a) $-8\sqrt{12} + \sqrt{3} = -8\sqrt{4 \cdot 3} + \sqrt{3}$

$\qquad\qquad\qquad\quad = -8 \cdot \sqrt{4}\,\sqrt{3} + \sqrt{3}$

$\qquad\qquad\qquad\quad = -16\sqrt{3} + \sqrt{3} = -15\sqrt{3}$

(b) $\sqrt[3]{8x^4} + \sqrt[3]{-x} + 4\sqrt[3]{27x} = \sqrt[3]{2^3 x^3 x} + \sqrt[3]{-1 \cdot x} + 4\sqrt[3]{3^3 x}$

$\qquad\qquad\qquad\qquad\qquad = \sqrt[3]{(2x)^3} \cdot \sqrt[3]{x} + \sqrt[3]{-1} \cdot \sqrt[3]{x} + 4\sqrt[3]{3^3} \cdot \sqrt[3]{x}$

$\qquad\qquad\qquad\qquad\qquad = 2x\sqrt[3]{x} - 1 \cdot \sqrt[3]{x} + 12\sqrt[3]{x}$

$\qquad\qquad\qquad\qquad\qquad = (2x + 11)\sqrt[3]{x}$

Now Work PROBLEM 33

3 Rationalize Denominators

When radicals occur in the denominator of a quotient, it is customary to rewrite the quotient so that the new denominator contains no radicals. This process is referred to as **rationalizing the denominator.**

The idea is to multiply by an appropriate expression so that the new denominator contains no radicals. For example:

If a Denominator Contains the Factor	Multiply by	To Obtain a Denominator Free of Radicals
$\sqrt{3}$	$\sqrt{3}$	$\left(\sqrt{3}\right)^2 = 3$
$\sqrt{3} + 1$	$\sqrt{3} - 1$	$\left(\sqrt{3}\right)^2 - 1^2 = 3 - 1 = 2$
$\sqrt{2} - 3$	$\sqrt{2} + 3$	$\left(\sqrt{2}\right)^2 - 3^2 = 2 - 9 = -7$
$\sqrt{5} - \sqrt{3}$	$\sqrt{5} + \sqrt{3}$	$\left(\sqrt{5}\right)^2 - \left(\sqrt{3}\right)^2 = 5 - 3 = 2$
$\sqrt[3]{4}$	$\sqrt[3]{2}$	$\sqrt[3]{4} \cdot \sqrt[3]{2} = \sqrt[3]{8} = 2$

In rationalizing the denominator of a quotient, be sure to multiply both the numerator and the denominator by the expression.

EXAMPLE 5   **Rationalizing Denominators**

Rationalize the denominator of each expression.

(a) $\dfrac{4}{\sqrt{2}}$ (b) $\dfrac{\sqrt{3}}{\sqrt[3]{2}}$ (c) $\dfrac{\sqrt{x} - 2}{\sqrt{x} + 2}, \quad x \geq 0$

Solution   (a) $\dfrac{4}{\sqrt{2}} = \dfrac{4}{\sqrt{2}} \cdot \dfrac{\sqrt{2}}{\sqrt{2}} = \dfrac{4\sqrt{2}}{\left(\sqrt{2}\right)^2} = \dfrac{4\sqrt{2}}{2} = 2\sqrt{2}$

Multiply by $\dfrac{\sqrt{2}}{\sqrt{2}}$.

(b) $\dfrac{\sqrt{3}}{\sqrt[3]{2}} = \dfrac{\sqrt{3}}{\sqrt[3]{2}} \cdot \dfrac{\sqrt[3]{4}}{\sqrt[3]{4}} = \dfrac{\sqrt{3}\,\sqrt[3]{4}}{\sqrt[3]{8}} = \dfrac{\sqrt{3}\,\sqrt[3]{4}}{2}$

Multiply by $\dfrac{\sqrt[3]{4}}{\sqrt[3]{4}}$.

(c) $\dfrac{\sqrt{x} - 2}{\sqrt{x} + 2} = \dfrac{\sqrt{x} - 2}{\sqrt{x} + 2} \cdot \dfrac{\sqrt{x} - 2}{\sqrt{x} - 2} = \dfrac{\left(\sqrt{x} - 2\right)^2}{\left(\sqrt{x}\right)^2 - 2^2}$

$= \dfrac{\left(\sqrt{x}\right)^2 - 4\sqrt{x} + 4}{x - 4} = \dfrac{x - 4\sqrt{x} + 4}{x - 4}$

Now Work PROBLEM 47

4 Solve Radical Equations

When the variable in an equation occurs in a square root, cube root, and so on, that is, when it occurs under a radical, the equation is called a **radical equation.** Sometimes a suitable operation will change a radical equation to one that is linear or quadratic. The most commonly used procedure is to isolate the most complicated radical on one side of the equation and then eliminate it by raising each side to a power equal to the index of the radical. Care must be taken because extraneous solutions may result. Thus, when working with radical equations, we always check apparent solutions. Let's look at an example.

EXAMPLE 6 **Solving Radical Equations**

Solve the equation: $\sqrt[3]{2x - 4} - 2 = 0$

Solution The equation contains a radical whose index is 3. We isolate it on the left side.

$$\sqrt[3]{2x - 4} - 2 = 0$$
$$\sqrt[3]{2x - 4} = 2$$

Now raise each side to the third power (since the index of the radical is 3) and solve.

$$\left(\sqrt[3]{2x - 4}\right)^3 = 2^3 \quad \text{Raise each side to the third power.}$$
$$2x - 4 = 8 \quad \text{Simplify.}$$
$$2x = 12 \quad \text{Simplify.}$$
$$x = 6 \quad \text{Solve for } x.$$

✓ Check: $\sqrt[3]{2(6) - 4} - 2 = \sqrt[3]{12 - 4} - 2 = \sqrt[3]{8} - 2 = 2 - 2 = 0.$

The solution is $x = 6$.

Now Work PROBLEM 55

5 Simplify Expressions with Rational Exponents

Radicals are used to define rational exponents.

DEFINITION If a is a real number and $n \geq 2$ is an integer, then

$$a^{1/n} = \sqrt[n]{a} \tag{3}$$

provided that $\sqrt[n]{a}$ exists.

Note that if n is even and $a < 0$, then $\sqrt[n]{a}$ and $a^{1/n}$ do not exist as real numbers.

EXAMPLE 7 **Writing Expressions Containing Fractional Exponents as Radicals**

(a) $4^{1/2} = \sqrt{4} = 2$ (b) $8^{1/2} = \sqrt{8} = 2\sqrt{2}$

(c) $(-27)^{1/3} = \sqrt[3]{-27} = -3$ (d) $16^{1/3} = \sqrt[3]{16} = 2\sqrt[3]{2}$

DEFINITION If a is a real number and m and n are integers containing no common factors, with $n \geq 2$, then

$$a^{m/n} = \sqrt[n]{a^m} = \left(\sqrt[n]{a}\right)^m \tag{4}$$

provided that $\sqrt[n]{a}$ exists.

We have two comments about equation (4):

1. The exponent $\dfrac{m}{n}$ must be in lowest terms and n must be positive.

2. In simplifying the rational expression $a^{m/n}$, either $\sqrt[n]{a^m}$ or $\left(\sqrt[n]{a}\right)^m$ may be used, the choice depending on which is easier to simplify. Generally, taking the root first, as in $\left(\sqrt[n]{a}\right)^m$, is easier.

EXAMPLE 8

Using Equation (4)

(a) $4^{3/2} = \left(\sqrt{4}\right)^3 = 2^3 = 8$ (b) $(-8)^{4/3} = \left(\sqrt[3]{-8}\right)^4 = (-2)^4 = 16$

(c) $(32)^{-2/5} = \left(\sqrt[5]{32}\right)^{-2} = 2^{-2} = \dfrac{1}{4}$ (d) $25^{6/4} = 25^{3/2} = \left(\sqrt{25}\right)^3 = 5^3 = 125$

═══ **Now Work** PROBLEM 59

It can be shown that the Laws of Exponents hold for rational exponents. The next example illustrates using the Laws of Exponents to simplify.

EXAMPLE 9

Simplifying Expressions Containing Rational Exponents

Simplify each expression. Express your answer so that only positive exponents occur. Assume that the variables are positive.

(a) $\left(x^{2/3}y\right)\left(x^{-2}y\right)^{1/2}$ (b) $\left(\dfrac{2x^{1/3}}{y^{2/3}}\right)^{-3}$ (c) $\left(\dfrac{9x^2y^{1/3}}{x^{1/3}y}\right)^{1/2}$

Solution   (a) $\left(x^{2/3}y\right)\left(x^{-2}y\right)^{1/2} = \left(x^{2/3}y\right)\left[\left(x^{-2}\right)^{1/2}y^{1/2}\right]$

$= x^{2/3}yx^{-1}y^{1/2}$

$= \left(x^{2/3}\cdot x^{-1}\right)\left(y\cdot y^{1/2}\right)$

$= x^{-1/3}y^{3/2}$

$= \dfrac{y^{3/2}}{x^{1/3}}$

(b) $\left(\dfrac{2x^{1/3}}{y^{2/3}}\right)^{-3} = \left(\dfrac{y^{2/3}}{2x^{1/3}}\right)^3 = \dfrac{\left(y^{2/3}\right)^3}{\left(2x^{1/3}\right)^3} = \dfrac{y^2}{2^3\left(x^{1/3}\right)^3} = \dfrac{y^2}{8x}$

(c) $\left(\dfrac{9x^2y^{1/3}}{x^{1/3}y}\right)^{1/2} = \left(\dfrac{9x^{2-(1/3)}}{y^{1-(1/3)}}\right)^{1/2} = \left(\dfrac{9x^{5/3}}{y^{2/3}}\right)^{1/2} = \dfrac{9^{1/2}\left(x^{5/3}\right)^{1/2}}{\left(y^{2/3}\right)^{1/2}} = \dfrac{3x^{5/6}}{y^{1/3}}$

═══ **Now Work** PROBLEM 75

The next two examples illustrate some algebra that you will need to know for certain calculus problems.

EXAMPLE 10

Writing an Expression as a Single Quotient

Write the following expression as a single quotient in which only positive exponents appear.

$$\left(x^2 + 1\right)^{1/2} + x\cdot\frac{1}{2}\left(x^2 + 1\right)^{-1/2}\cdot 2x$$

Solution $\left(x^2 + 1\right)^{1/2} + x\cdot\dfrac{1}{2}\left(x^2 + 1\right)^{-1/2}\cdot 2x = \left(x^2 + 1\right)^{1/2} + \dfrac{x^2}{\left(x^2 + 1\right)^{1/2}}$

$= \dfrac{\left(x^2 + 1\right)^{1/2}\left(x^2 + 1\right)^{1/2} + x^2}{\left(x^2 + 1\right)^{1/2}}$

$= \dfrac{\left(x^2 + 1\right) + x^2}{\left(x^2 + 1\right)^{1/2}}$

$= \dfrac{2x^2 + 1}{\left(x^2 + 1\right)^{1/2}}$

═══ **Now Work** PROBLEM 89

EXAMPLE 11   **Factoring an Expression Containing Rational Exponents**

Factor: $\dfrac{4}{3}x^{1/3}(2x + 1) + 2x^{4/3}$

Solution   We begin by writing $2x^{4/3}$ as a fraction with 3 as denominator.

$$\frac{4}{3}x^{1/3}(2x + 1) + 2x^{4/3} = \frac{4x^{1/3}(2x + 1)}{3} + \frac{6x^{4/3}}{3} = \frac{4x^{1/3}(2x + 1) + 6x^{4/3}}{3}$$

Add the two fractions.

$$= \frac{2x^{1/3}[2(2x + 1) + 3x]}{3} = \frac{2x^{1/3}(7x + 2)}{3}$$

2 and $x^{1/3}$ are common factors.   Simplify.

Now Work PROBLEM 101

A.10 Assess Your Understanding

'Are You Prepared?' *Answers are given at the end of these exercises. If you get a wrong answer, read the pages listed in red.*

1. $(-3)^2 = $ _____; $-3^2 = $ _____ (pp. A7–A9)

2. $\sqrt{16} = $ _____; $\sqrt{(-4)^2} = $ _____ (pp. A9–A10)

Concepts and Vocabulary

3. In the symbol $\sqrt[n]{a}$, the integer n is called the _____.

4. **True or False** $\sqrt[5]{-32} = -2$

5. We call $\sqrt[3]{a}$ the _____ _____ of a.

6. **True or False** $\sqrt[4]{(-3)^4} = -3$

Skill Building

In Problems 7–42, simplify each expression. Assume that all variables are positive when they appear.

7. $\sqrt[3]{27}$

8. $\sqrt[4]{16}$

9. $\sqrt[3]{-8}$

10. $\sqrt[3]{-1}$

11. $\sqrt{8}$

12. $\sqrt[3]{54}$

13. $\sqrt[3]{-8x^4}$

14. $\sqrt[4]{48x^5}$

15. $\sqrt[4]{x^{12}y^8}$

16. $\sqrt[5]{x^{10}y^5}$

17. $\sqrt[4]{\dfrac{x^9y^7}{xy^3}}$

18. $\sqrt[3]{\dfrac{3xy^2}{81x^4y^2}}$

19. $\sqrt{36x}$

20. $\sqrt{9x^5}$

21. $\sqrt{3x^2}\sqrt{12x}$

22. $\sqrt{5x}\sqrt{20x^3}$

23. $\left(\sqrt{5}\sqrt[3]{9}\right)^2$

24. $\left(\sqrt[3]{3}\sqrt{10}\right)^4$

25. $\left(3\sqrt{6}\right)\left(2\sqrt{2}\right)$

26. $\left(5\sqrt{8}\right)\left(-3\sqrt{3}\right)$

27. $3\sqrt{2} + 4\sqrt{2}$

28. $6\sqrt{5} - 4\sqrt{5}$

29. $-\sqrt{18} + 2\sqrt{8}$

30. $2\sqrt{12} - 3\sqrt{27}$

31. $\left(\sqrt{3} + 3\right)\left(\sqrt{3} - 1\right)$

32. $\left(\sqrt{5} - 2\right)\left(\sqrt{5} + 3\right)$

33. $5\sqrt[3]{2} - 2\sqrt[3]{54}$

34. $9\sqrt[3]{24} - \sqrt[3]{81}$

35. $\left(\sqrt{x} - 1\right)^2$

36. $\left(\sqrt{x} + \sqrt{5}\right)^2$

37. $\sqrt[3]{16x^4} - \sqrt[3]{2x}$

38. $\sqrt[4]{32x} + \sqrt[4]{2x^5}$

39. $\sqrt{8x^3} - 3\sqrt{50x}$

40. $3x\sqrt{9y} + 4\sqrt{25y}$

41. $\sqrt[3]{16x^4y} - 3x\sqrt[3]{2xy} + 5\sqrt[3]{-2xy^4}$

42. $8xy - \sqrt{25x^2y^2} + \sqrt[3]{8x^3y^3}$

In Problems 43–54, rationalize the denominator of each expression. Assume that all variables are positive when they appear.

43. $\dfrac{1}{\sqrt{2}}$

44. $\dfrac{2}{\sqrt{3}}$

45. $\dfrac{-\sqrt{3}}{\sqrt{5}}$

46. $\dfrac{-\sqrt{3}}{\sqrt{8}}$

47. $\dfrac{\sqrt{3}}{5 - \sqrt{2}}$

48. $\dfrac{\sqrt{2}}{\sqrt{7} + 2}$

49. $\dfrac{2 - \sqrt{5}}{2 + 3\sqrt{5}}$

50. $\dfrac{\sqrt{3} - 1}{2\sqrt{3} + 3}$

51. $\dfrac{5}{\sqrt[3]{2}}$

52. $\dfrac{-2}{\sqrt[3]{9}}$

53. $\dfrac{\sqrt{x + h} - \sqrt{x}}{\sqrt{x + h} + \sqrt{x}}$

54. $\dfrac{\sqrt{x + h} + \sqrt{x - h}}{\sqrt{x + h} - \sqrt{x - h}}$

In Problems 55–58, solve each equation.

55. $\sqrt[3]{2t - 1} = 2$

56. $\sqrt[3]{3t + 1} = -2$

57. $\sqrt{15 - 2x} = x$

58. $\sqrt{12 - x} = x$

In Problems 59–70, simplify each expression.

59. $8^{2/3}$

60. $4^{3/2}$

61. $(-27)^{1/3}$

62. $16^{3/4}$

63. $16^{3/2}$

64. $25^{3/2}$

65. $9^{-3/2}$

66. $16^{-3/2}$

67. $\left(\dfrac{9}{8}\right)^{3/2}$

68. $\left(\dfrac{27}{8}\right)^{2/3}$

69. $\left(\dfrac{8}{9}\right)^{-3/2}$

70. $\left(\dfrac{8}{27}\right)^{-2/3}$

In Problems 71–78, simplify each expression. Express your answer so that only positive exponents occur. Assume that the variables are positive.

71. $x^{3/4}x^{1/3}x^{-1/2}$

72. $x^{2/3}x^{1/2}x^{-1/4}$

73. $(x^3 y^6)^{1/3}$

74. $(x^4 y^8)^{3/4}$

75. $\dfrac{(x^2 y)^{1/3}(xy^2)^{2/3}}{x^{2/3}y^{2/3}}$

76. $\dfrac{(xy)^{1/4}(x^2 y^2)^{1/2}}{(x^2 y)^{3/4}}$

77. $\dfrac{(16x^2 y^{-1/3})^{3/4}}{(xy^2)^{1/4}}$

78. $\dfrac{(4x^{-1} y^{1/3})^{3/2}}{(xy)^{3/2}}$

In Problems 79–86, use a calculator to approximate each radical. Round your answer to two decimal places.

79. $\sqrt{2}$

80. $\sqrt{7}$

81. $\sqrt[3]{4}$

82. $\sqrt[3]{-5}$

83. $\dfrac{2 + \sqrt{3}}{3 - \sqrt{5}}$

84. $\dfrac{\sqrt{5} - 2}{\sqrt{2} + 4}$

85. $\dfrac{3\sqrt[3]{5} - \sqrt{2}}{\sqrt{3}}$

86. $\dfrac{2\sqrt{3} - \sqrt[3]{4}}{\sqrt{2}}$

Applications and Extensions

In Problems 87–100, expressions that occur in calculus are given. Write each expression as a single quotient in which only positive exponents and/or radicals appear.

87. $\dfrac{x}{(1 + x)^{1/2}} + 2(1 + x)^{1/2}$ $x > -1$

88. $\dfrac{1 + x}{2x^{1/2}} + x^{1/2}$ $x > 0$

89. $2x(x^2 + 1)^{1/2} + x^2 \cdot \dfrac{1}{2}(x^2 + 1)^{-1/2} \cdot 2x$

90. $(x + 1)^{1/3} + x \cdot \dfrac{1}{3}(x + 1)^{-2/3}$ $x \neq -1$

91. $\sqrt{4x + 3} \cdot \dfrac{1}{2\sqrt{x - 5}} + \sqrt{x - 5} \cdot \dfrac{1}{5\sqrt{4x + 3}}$ $x > 5$

92. $\dfrac{\sqrt[3]{8x + 1}}{3\sqrt[3]{(x - 2)^2}} + \dfrac{\sqrt[3]{x - 2}}{24\sqrt[3]{(8x + 1)^2}}$ $x \neq 2, x \neq -\dfrac{1}{8}$

93. $\dfrac{\sqrt{1 + x} - x \cdot \dfrac{1}{2\sqrt{1 + x}}}{1 + x}$ $x > -1$

94. $\dfrac{\sqrt{x^2 + 1} - x \cdot \dfrac{2x}{2\sqrt{x^2 + 1}}}{x^2 + 1}$

95. $\dfrac{(x + 4)^{1/2} - 2x(x + 4)^{-1/2}}{x + 4}$ $x > -4$

96. $\dfrac{(9 - x^2)^{1/2} + x^2(9 - x^2)^{-1/2}}{9 - x^2}$ $-3 < x < 3$

97. $\dfrac{\dfrac{x^2}{(x^2 - 1)^{1/2}} - (x^2 - 1)^{1/2}}{x^2}$ $x < -1$ or $x > 1$

98. $\dfrac{(x^2 + 4)^{1/2} - x^2(x^2 + 4)^{-1/2}}{x^2 + 4}$

99. $\dfrac{\dfrac{1 + x^2}{2\sqrt{x}} - 2x\sqrt{x}}{(1 + x^2)^2}$ $x > 0$

100. $\dfrac{2x(1 - x^2)^{1/3} + \dfrac{2}{3}x^3(1 - x^2)^{-2/3}}{(1 - x^2)^{2/3}}$ $x \neq -1, x \neq 1$

In Problems 101–110, expressions that occur in calculus are given. Factor each expression. Express your answer so that only positive exponents occur.

101. $(x + 1)^{3/2} + x \cdot \dfrac{3}{2}(x + 1)^{1/2}$ $x \geq -1$

102. $(x^2 + 4)^{4/3} + x \cdot \dfrac{4}{3}(x^2 + 4)^{1/3} \cdot 2x$

103. $6x^{1/2}(x^2 + x) - 8x^{3/2} - 8x^{1/2}$ $x \geq 0$

104. $6x^{1/2}(2x + 3) + x^{3/2} \cdot 8$ $x \geq 0$

105. $3(x^2 + 4)^{4/3} + x \cdot 4(x^2 + 4)^{1/3} \cdot 2x$

106. $2x(3x + 4)^{4/3} + x^2 \cdot 4(3x + 4)^{1/3}$

107. $4(3x + 5)^{1/3}(2x + 3)^{3/2} + 3(3x + 5)^{4/3}(2x + 3)^{1/2}$ $x \geq -\dfrac{3}{2}$

108. $6(6x + 1)^{1/3}(4x - 3)^{3/2} + 6(6x + 1)^{4/3}(4x - 3)^{1/2}$ $x \geq \dfrac{3}{4}$

109. $3x^{-1/2} + \dfrac{3}{2}x^{1/2}$ $x > 0$

110. $8x^{1/3} - 4x^{-2/3}$ $x \neq 0$

111. Calculating the Amount of Gasoline in a Tank   A Shell station stores its gasoline in underground tanks that are right circular cylinders lying on their sides. See the illustration. The volume V of gasoline in the tank (in gallons) is given by the formula

$$V = 40h^2\sqrt{\dfrac{96}{h} - 0.608}$$

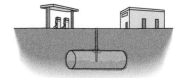

where h is the height of the gasoline (in inches) as measured on a depth stick.
(a) If $h = 12$ inches, how many gallons of gasoline are in the tank?
(b) If $h = 1$ inch, how many gallons of gasoline are in the tank?

112. Inclined Planes   The final velocity v of an object in feet per second (ft/sec) after it slides down a frictionless inclined plane of height h feet is

$$v = \sqrt{64h + v_0^2}$$

where v_0 is the initial velocity (in ft/sec) of the object.
(a) What is the final velocity v of an object that slides down a frictionless inclined plane of height 4 feet? Assume that the initial velocity is 0.
(b) What is the final velocity v of an object that slides down a frictionless inclined plane of height 16 feet? Assume that the initial velocity is 0.
(c) What is the final velocity v of an object that slides down a frictionless inclined plane of height 2 feet with an initial velocity of 4 ft/sec?

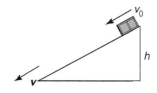

Problems 113–116 require the following information.

Period of a Pendulum *The period T, in seconds, of a pendulum of length l, in feet, may be approximated using the formula*

$$T = 2\pi\sqrt{\frac{l}{32}}$$

In Problems 113–116, express your answer both as a square root and as a decimal.

113. Find the period T of a pendulum whose length is 64 feet.

114. Find the period T of a pendulum whose length is 16 feet.

115. Find the period T of a pendulum whose length is 8 inches.

116. Find the period T of a pendulum whose length is 4 inches.

Explaining Concepts: Discussion and Writing

117. Give an example to show that $\sqrt{a^2}$ is not equal to a. Use it to explain why $\sqrt{a^2} = |a|$.

'Are you Prepared?' Answers

1. 9; −9   **2.** 4; 4

Appendix B
Graphing Utilities

Outline

B.1 The Viewing Rectangle

Figure 1
$y = 2x$

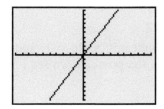

Figure 2

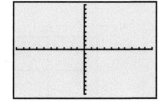

All graphing utilities, that is, all graphing calculators and all computer software graphing packages, graph equations by plotting points on a screen. The screen itself actually consists of small rectangles, called **pixels.** The more pixels the screen has, the better the resolution. Most graphing calculators have 2048 pixels per square inch; most computer screens have 4096 to 8192 pixels per square inch. When a point to be plotted lies inside a pixel, the pixel is turned on (lights up). The graph of an equation is a collection of pixels. Figure 1 shows how the graph of $y = 2x$ looks on a TI-84 Plus graphing calculator.

The screen of a graphing utility will display the coordinate axes of a rectangular coordinate system. However, you must set the scale on each axis. You must also include the smallest and largest values of x and y that you want included in the graph. This is called **setting the viewing rectangle** or **viewing window.** Figure 2 illustrates a typical viewing window.

To select the viewing window, we must give values to the following expressions:

Xmin: the smallest value of x
Xmax: the largest value of x
Xscl: the number of units per tick mark on the x-axis
Ymin: the smallest value of y
Ymax: the largest value of y
Yscl: the number of units per tick mark on the y-axis

Figure 3 illustrates these settings and their relation to the Cartesian coordinate system.

Figure 3

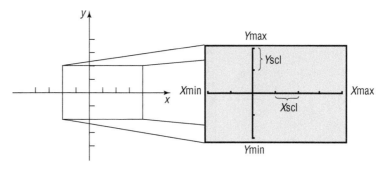

If the scale used on each axis is known, we can determine the minimum and maximum values of x and y shown on the screen by counting the tick marks. Look again at Figure 2. For a scale of 1 on each axis, the minimum and maximum values of x are -10 and 10, respectively; the minimum and maximum values of y are also -10 and 10. If the scale is 2 on each axis, then the minimum and maximum values of x are -20 and 20, respectively; and the minimum and maximum values of y are -20 and 20, respectively.

Conversely, if we know the minimum and maximum values of x and y, we can determine the scales being used by counting the tick marks displayed. We shall follow the practice of showing the minimum and maximum values of x and y in our illustrations so that you will know how the viewing window was set. See Figure 4.

Figure 4

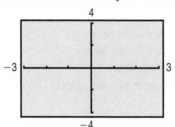

means

$$X\text{min} = -3 \qquad Y\text{min} = -4$$
$$X\text{max} = 3 \qquad Y\text{max} = 4$$
$$X\text{scl} = 1 \qquad Y\text{scl} = 2$$

EXAMPLE 1 **Finding the Coordinates of a Point Shown on a Graphing Utility Screen**

Find the coordinates of the point shown in Figure 5. Assume that the coordinates are integers.

Figure 5

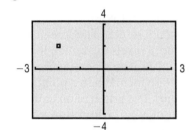

Solution First we note that the viewing window used in Figure 5 is

$$X\text{min} = -3 \qquad Y\text{min} = -4$$
$$X\text{max} = 3 \qquad Y\text{max} = 4$$
$$X\text{scl} = 1 \qquad Y\text{scl} = 2$$

The point shown is 2 tick units to the left on the horizontal axis (scale $= 1$) and 1 tick up on the vertical axis (scale $= 2$). The coordinates of the point shown are $(-2, 2)$.

B.1 Exercises

In Problems 1–4, determine the coordinates of the points shown. Tell in which quadrant each point lies. Assume that the coordinates are integers.

1.

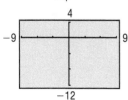

2.

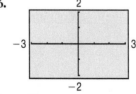

3.

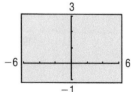

4.

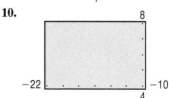

In Problems 5–10, determine the viewing window used.

5.

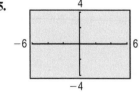

6.

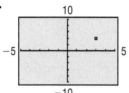

7.

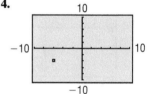

8.

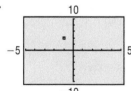

9.

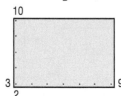

10.

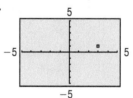

In Problems 11–16, select a setting so that each of the given points will lie within the viewing rectangle.

11. $(-10, 5), (3, -2), (4, -1)$

12. $(5, 0), (6, 8), (-2, -3)$

13. $(40, 20), (-20, -80), (10, 40)$

14. $(-80, 60), (20, -30), (-20, -40)$

15. $(0, 0), (100, 5), (5, 150)$

16. $(0, -1), (100, 50), (-10, 30)$

B.2 Using a Graphing Utility to Graph Equations

From Examples 2 and 3 in Chapter 1, Section 1.2, we see that a graph can be obtained by plotting points in a rectangular coordinate system and connecting them. Graphing utilities perform these same steps when graphing an equation. For example, the TI-84 Plus determines 95 evenly spaced input values,* starting at Xmin and ending at Xmax, uses the equation to determine the output values, plots these points on the screen, and finally (if in the connected mode) draws a line between consecutive points.

To graph an equation in two variables x and y using a graphing utility requires that the equation be written in the form $y = \{expression\ in\ x\}$. If the original equation is not in this form, replace it by equivalent equations until the form $y = \{expression\ in\ x\}$ is obtained.

Steps for Graphing an Equation Using a Graphing Utility

STEP 1: Solve the equation for y in terms of x.

STEP 2: Get into the graphing mode of your graphing utility. The screen will usually display $Y_1 = \quad$, prompting you to enter the expression involving x that you found in Step 1. (Consult your manual for the correct way to enter the expression; for example, $y = x^2$ might be entered as $x^\wedge 2$ or as $x*x$ or as $x\ x^Y\ 2$).

STEP 3: Select the viewing window. Without prior knowledge about the behavior of the graph of the equation, it is common to select the **standard viewing window**** initially. The viewing window is then adjusted based on the graph that appears. In this text the standard viewing window is

$$X\text{min} = -10 \qquad Y\text{min} = -10$$
$$X\text{max} = 10 \qquad Y\text{max} = 10$$
$$X\text{scl} = 1 \qquad Y\text{scl} = 1$$

STEP 4: Graph.

STEP 5: Adjust the viewing window until a complete graph is obtained.

EXAMPLE 1   **Graphing an Equation on a Graphing Utility**

Graph the equation: $6x^2 + 3y = 36$

Solution   **STEP 1:** Solve for y in terms of x.

$$6x^2 + 3y = 36$$
$$3y = -6x^2 + 36 \quad \text{Subtract } 6x^2 \text{ from both sides of the equation.}$$
$$y = -2x^2 + 12 \quad \text{Divide both sides of the equation by 3 and simplify.}$$

---

*These input values depend on the values of Xmin and Xmax. For example, if Xmin $= -10$ and Xmax $= 10$, then the first input value will be -10 and the next input value will be $-10 + \dfrac{10 - (-10)}{94} = -9.7872$, and so on.

**Some graphing utilities have a ZOOM-STANDARD feature that automatically sets the viewing window to the standard viewing window and graphs the equation.

STEP 2: From the $Y_1 = $ screen, enter the expression $-2x^2 + 12$ after the prompt.

STEP 3: Set the viewing window to the standard viewing window.

STEP 4: Graph. The screen should look like Figure 6.

STEP 5: The graph of $y = -2x^2 + 12$ is not complete. The value of Ymax must be increased so that the top portion of the graph is visible. After increasing the value of Ymax to 12, we obtain the graph in Figure 7. The graph is now complete.

Figure 6

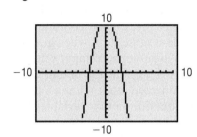

Figure 7

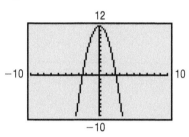

Figure 8

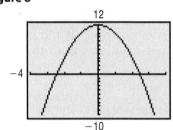

Look again at Figure 7. Although a complete graph is shown, the graph might be improved by adjusting the values of Xmin and Xmax. Figure 8 shows the graph of $y = -2x^2 + 12$ using Xmin $= -4$ and Xmax $= 4$. Do you think this is a better choice for the viewing window?

EXAMPLE 2 **Creating a Table and Graphing an Equation**

Create a table and graph the equation: $y = x^3$

Solution Most graphing utilities have the capability of creating a table of values for an equation. (Check your manual to see if your graphing utility has this capability.) Table 1 illustrates a table of values for $y = x^3$ on a TI-84 Plus. See Figure 9 for the graph.

Table 1

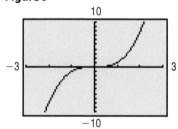

Figure 9

B.2 Exercises

In Problems 1–16, graph each equation using the following viewing windows:

(a) Xmin $= -5$
   Xmax $= 5$
   Xscl $= 1$
   Ymin $= -4$
   Ymax $= 4$
   Yscl $= 1$

(b) Xmin $= -10$
   Xmax $= 10$
   Xscl $= 2$
   Ymin $= -8$
   Ymax $= 8$
   Yscl $= 2$

1. $y = x + 2$ **2.** $y = x - 2$ **3.** $y = -x + 2$ **4.** $y = -x - 2$

5. $y = 2x + 2$ **6.** $y = 2x - 2$ **7.** $y = -2x + 2$ **8.** $y = -2x - 2$

9. $y = x^2 + 2$ **10.** $y = x^2 - 2$ **11.** $y = -x^2 + 2$ **12.** $y = -x^2 - 2$

13. $3x + 2y = 6$ **14.** $3x - 2y = 6$ **15.** $-3x + 2y = 6$ **16.** $-3x - 2y = 6$

17–32. *For each of the above equations, create a table, $-3 \le x \le 3$, and list points on the graph.*

B.3 Using a Graphing Utility to Locate Intercepts and Check for Symmetry

Value and Zero (or Root)

Most graphing utilities have an eVALUEate feature that, given a value of x, determines the value of y for an equation. We can use this feature to evaluate an equation at $x = 0$ to determine the y-intercept. Most graphing utilities also have a ZERO (or ROOT) feature that can be used to determine the x-intercept(s) of an equation.

EXAMPLE 1

Finding Intercepts Using a Graphing Utility

Use a graphing utility to find the intercepts of the equation $y = x^3 - 8$.

Solution   Figure 10(a) shows the graph of $y = x^3 - 8$.

Figure 10

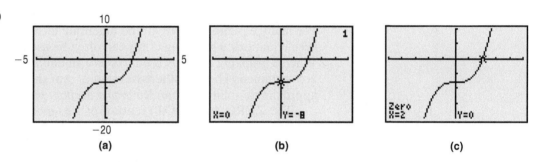

(a)   (b)   (c)

The eVALUEate feature of a TI-84 Plus graphing calculator accepts as input a value of x and determines the value of y. If we let $x = 0$, we find that the y-intercept is -8. See Figure 10(b).

The ZERO feature of a TI-84 Plus is used to find the x-intercept(s). See Figure 10(c). The x-intercept is 2.

EXAMPLE 2

Graphing the Equation $y = \dfrac{1}{x}$

Graph the equation $y = \dfrac{1}{x}$. Based on the graph, infer information about intercepts and symmetry.

Solution   Figure 11 illustrates the graph. We infer from the graph that there are no intercepts; we may also infer that symmetry with respect to the origin is a possibility. The TABLE feature on a graphing utility can provide further evidence of symmetry with respect to the origin. Using a TABLE, we observe that for any ordered pair (x, y) the ordered pair $(-x, -y)$ is also a point on the graph.

Figure 11

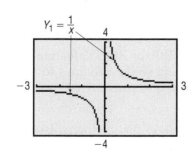

B.3 Exercises

In Problems 1–6, use ZERO (or ROOT) to approximate the smaller of the two x-intercepts of each equation. Express the answer rounded to two decimal places.

1. $y = x^2 + 4x + 2$

2. $y = x^2 + 4x - 3$

3. $y = 2x^2 + 4x + 1$

4. $y = 3x^2 + 5x + 1$

5. $y = 2x^2 - 3x - 1$

6. $y = 2x^2 - 4x - 1$

*In Problems 7–12, use ZERO (or ROOT) to approximate the **positive** x-intercepts of each equation. Express each answer rounded to two decimal places.*

7. $y = x^3 + 3.2x^2 - 16.83x - 5.31$

8. $y = x^3 + 3.2x^2 - 7.25x - 6.3$

9. $y = x^4 - 1.4x^3 - 33.71x^2 + 23.94x + 292.41$

10. $y = x^4 + 1.2x^3 - 7.46x^2 - 4.692x + 15.2881$

11. $y = x^3 + 19.5x^2 - 1021x + 1000.5$

12. $y = x^3 + 14.2x^2 - 4.8x - 12.4$

B.4 Using a Graphing Utility to Solve Equations

For many equations, there are no algebraic techniques that lead to a solution. For such equations, a graphing utility can often be used to investigate possible solutions. When a graphing utility is used to solve an equation, usually *approximate* solutions are obtained. Unless otherwise stated, we shall follow the practice of giving approximate solutions *rounded to two decimal places*.

The ZERO (or ROOT) feature of a graphing utility can be used to find the solutions of an equation when one side of the equation is 0. In using this feature to solve equations, we make use of the fact that the *x*-intercepts (or zeros) of the graph of an equation are found by letting $y = 0$ and solving the equation for *x*. Solving an equation for *x* when one side of the equation is 0 is equivalent to finding where the graph of the corresponding equation crosses or touches the *x*-axis.

EXAMPLE 1 **Using ZERO (or ROOT) to Approximate Solutions of an Equation**

Find the solution(s) of the equation $x^2 - 6x + 7 = 0$. Round answers to two decimal places.

Solution The solutions of the equation $x^2 - 6x + 7 = 0$ are the same as the *x*-intercepts of the graph of $Y_1 = x^2 - 6x + 7$. We begin by graphing the equation. See Figure 12(a).

From the graph there appear to be two *x*-intercepts (solutions to the equation): one between 1 and 2, the other between 4 and 5.

Figure 12

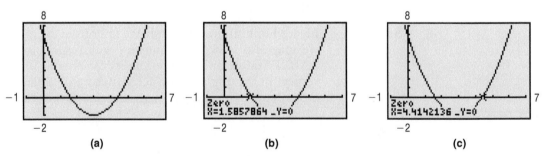

(a)   (b)   (c)

Using the ZERO (or ROOT) feature of our graphing utility, we determine that the *x*-intercepts, and so the solutions to the equation, are $x = 1.59$ and $x = 4.41$, rounded to two decimal places. See Figures 12(b) and (c). ↵

A second method for solving equations using a graphing utility involves the INTERSECT feature of the graphing utility. This feature is used most effectively when one side of the equation is not 0.

EXAMPLE 2   **Using INTERSECT to Approximate Solutions of an Equation**

Find the solution(s) to the equation $3(x - 2) = 5(x - 1)$.

Solution   Begin by graphing each side of the equation as follows: graph $Y_1 = 3(x - 2)$ and $Y_2 = 5(x - 1)$. See Figure 13(a).

Figure 13

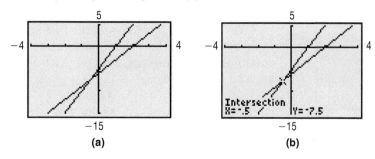

(a)   (b)

At the point of intersection of the graphs, the value of the y-coordinate is the same. We conclude that the x-coordinate of the point of intersection represents the solution to the equation. Do you see why? The INTERSECT feature on a graphing utility determines the point of intersection of the graphs. Using this feature, we find that the graphs intersect at $(-0.5, -7.5)$. See Figure 13(b). The solution of the equation is therefore $x = -0.5$.

SUMMARY

The steps to follow for approximating solutions of equations are given next.

Steps for Approximating Solutions of Equations Using ZERO (or ROOT)

STEP 1:   Write the equation in the form $\{expression\ in\ x\} = 0$.

STEP 2:   Graph $Y_1 = \{expression\ in\ x\}$.

Be sure that the graph is complete. That is, be sure that all the intercepts are shown on the screen.

STEP 3:   Use ZERO (or ROOT) to determine each x-intercept of the graph.

Steps for Approximating Solutions of Equations Using INTERSECT

STEP 1:   Graph $Y_1 = \{expression\ in\ x\ on\ the\ left\ side\ of\ the\ equation\}$.

Graph $Y_2 = \{expression\ in\ x\ on\ the\ right\ side\ of\ the\ equation\}$.

STEP 2:   Use INTERSECT to determine each x-coordinate of the point(s) of intersection, if any.

Be sure that the graphs are complete. That is, be sure that all the points of intersection are shown on the screen.

EXAMPLE 3   **Solving a Radical Equation**

Find the real solutions of the equation $\sqrt[3]{2x - 4} - 2 = 0$.

Solution   Figure 14 shows the graph of the equation $Y_1 = \sqrt[3]{2x - 4} - 2$. From the graph, we see one x-intercept near 6. Using ZERO (or ROOT), we find that the x-intercept is 6. The only solution is $x = 6$.

Figure 14

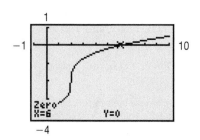

B.5 Square Screens

Figure 15

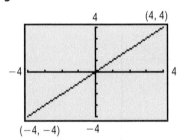

Most graphing utilities have a rectangular screen. Because of this, using the same settings for both x and y will result in a distorted view. For example, Figure 15 shows the graph of the line $y = x$ connecting the points $(-4, -4)$ and $(4, 4)$.

We expect the line to bisect the first and third quadrants, but it doesn't. We need to adjust the selections for Xmin, Xmax, Ymin, and Ymax so that a **square screen** results. On most graphing utilities, this is accomplished by setting the ratio of x to y at $3:2$.* For example, if

$$X\text{min} = -6 \qquad Y\text{min} = -4$$
$$X\text{max} = 6 \qquad Y\text{max} = 4$$

then the ratio of x to y is

$$\frac{X\text{max} - X\text{min}}{Y\text{max} - Y\text{min}} = \frac{6 - (-6)}{4 - (-4)} = \frac{12}{8} = \frac{3}{2}$$

for a ratio of $3:2$, resulting in a square screen.

EXAMPLE 1 **Examples of Viewing Rectangles That Result in Square Screens**

Figure 16

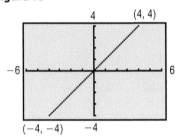

(a) Xmin $= -3$
  Xmax $=$ 3
  Xscl $=$ 1
  Ymin $= -2$
  Ymax $=$ 2
  Yscl $=$ 1

(b) Xmin $= -6$
  Xmax $=$ 6
  Xscl $=$ 1
  Ymin $= -4$
  Ymax $=$ 4
  Yscl $=$ 1

(c) Xmin $= -12$
  Xmax $=$ 12
  Xscl $=$ 1
  Ymin $= -8$
  Ymax $=$ 8
  Yscl $=$ 2

Figure 16 shows the graph of the line $y = x$ on a square screen using the viewing rectangle given in part (b). Notice that the line now bisects the first and third quadrants. Compare this illustration to Figure 15.

B.5 Exercises

In Problems 1–8, determine which of the given viewing rectangles result in a square screen.

1. Xmin $= -3$
  Xmax $=$ 3
  Xscl $=$ 2
  Ymin $= -2$
  Ymax $=$ 2
  Yscl $=$ 2

2. Xmin $= -5$
  Xmax $=$ 5
  Xscl $=$ 1
  Ymin $= -4$
  Ymax $=$ 4
  Yscl $=$ 1

3. Xmin $=$ 0
  Xmax $=$ 9
  Xscl $=$ 3
  Ymin $= -2$
  Ymax $=$ 4
  Yscl $=$ 2

4. Xmin $= -6$
  Xmax $=$ 6
  Xscl $=$ 1
  Ymin $= -4$
  Ymax $=$ 4
  Yscl $=$ 2

5. Xmin $= -6$
  Xmax $=$ 6
  Xscl $=$ 1
  Ymin $= -2$
  Ymax $=$ 2
  Yscl $= 0.5$

6. Xmin $= -6$
  Xmax $=$ 6
  Xscl $=$ 2
  Ymin $= -4$
  Ymax $=$ 4
  Yscl $=$ 1

7. Xmin $=$ 0
  Xmax $=$ 9
  Xscl $=$ 1
  Ymin $= -2$
  Ymax $=$ 4
  Yscl $=$ 1

8. Xmin $= -6$
  Xmax $=$ 6
  Xscl $=$ 2
  Ymin $= -4$
  Ymax $=$ 4
  Yscl $=$ 2

9. If Xmin $= -4$, Xmax $= 8$, and Xscl $= 1$, how should Ymin, Ymax, and Yscl be selected so that the viewing rectangle contains the point $(4, 8)$ and the screen is square?

10. If Xmin $= -6$, Xmax $= 12$, and Xscl $= 2$, how should Ymin, Ymax, and Yscl be selected so that the viewing rectangle contains the point $(4, 8)$ and the screen is square?

*Some graphing utilities have a built-in function that automatically squares the screen. For example, the TI-84 has a ZSquare function that does this. Some graphing utilities require a ratio other than $3:2$ to square the screen. For example, the HP 48G requires the ratio of x to y to be $2:1$ for a square screen. Consult your manual.

B.6 Using a Graphing Utility to Graph Inequalities

EXAMPLE 1 **Graphing an Inequality Using a Graphing Utility**

Use a graphing utility to graph: $3x + y - 6 \leq 0$

Solution We begin by graphing the equation $3x + y - 6 = 0$ ($Y_1 = -3x + 6$). See Figure 17.

As with graphing by hand, we need to test points selected from each region and determine whether they satisfy the inequality. To test the point $(-1, 2)$, for example, enter $3(-1) + 2 - 6 \leq 0$. See Figure 18(a). The 1 that appears indicates that the statement entered (the inequality) is true. When the point $(5, 5)$ is tested, a 0 appears, indicating that the statement entered is false. Thus, $(-1, 2)$ is a part of the graph of the inequality and $(5, 5)$ is not. Figure 18(b) shows the graph of the inequality on a TI-84 Plus.*

Figure 17

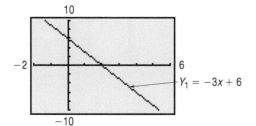

Figure 18

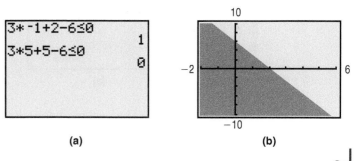

(a)   (b)

Steps for Graphing an Inequality Using a Graphing Utility

STEP 1: Replace the inequality symbol by an equal sign, solve the equation for y, and graph the equation.

STEP 2: In each region, select a test point P and determine if the coordinates of P satisfy the inequality.

(a) If the test point satisfies the inequality, then so do all the points in the region. Indicate this by using the graphing utility to shade the region.

(b) If the coordinates of P do not satisfy the inequality, then none of the points in that region do.

B.7 Using a Graphing Utility to Solve Systems of Linear Equations

Most graphing utilities have the capability to put the augmented matrix of a system of linear equations in row echelon form. The next example, Example 6 from Section 11.2, demonstrates this feature using a TI-84 Plus graphing calculator.

* Consult your owner's manual for shading techniques.

EXAMPLE 1

Solving a System of Linear Equations Using a Graphing Utility

Solve: $\begin{cases} x - y + z = 8 & (1) \\ 2x + 3y - z = -2 & (2) \\ 3x - 2y - 9z = 9 & (3) \end{cases}$

Solution The augmented matrix of the system is

$$\begin{bmatrix} 1 & -1 & 1 & | & 8 \\ 2 & 3 & -1 & | & -2 \\ 3 & -2 & -9 & | & 9 \end{bmatrix}$$

Enter this matrix into a graphing utility and name it A. See Figure 19(a). Using the REF (row echelon form) command on matrix A, we obtain the results shown in Figure 19(b). Since the entire matrix does not fit on the screen, you need to scroll right to see the rest of it. See Figure 19(c).

Figure 19

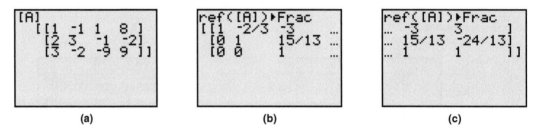

(a)   (b)   (c)

The system of equations represented by the matrix in row echelon form is

$$\begin{bmatrix} 1 & -\dfrac{2}{3} & -3 & | & 3 \\ 0 & 1 & \dfrac{15}{13} & | & -\dfrac{24}{13} \\ 0 & 0 & 1 & | & 1 \end{bmatrix} \quad \begin{cases} x - \dfrac{2}{3}y - 3z = 3 & (1) \\ y + \dfrac{15}{13}z = -\dfrac{24}{13} & (2) \\ z = 1 & (3) \end{cases}$$

Using $z = 1$, back-substitute to get

$$\begin{cases} x - \dfrac{2}{3}y - 3(1) = 3 & (1) \\ y + \dfrac{15}{13}(1) = -\dfrac{24}{13} & (2) \end{cases} \xrightarrow[\text{Simplify.}]{} \begin{cases} x - \dfrac{2}{3}y = 6 & (1) \\ y = \dfrac{-39}{13} = -3 & (2) \end{cases}$$

Solving the second equation for y, we find that $y = -3$. Back-substituting $y = -3$ into $x - \dfrac{2}{3}y = 6$, we find that $x = 4$. The solution of the system is $x = 4$, $y = -3$, $z = 1$. ↵

Notice that the row echelon form of the augmented matrix using the graphing utility differs from the row echelon form in Chapter 11 (p. 718), yet both matrices provide the same solution! This is because the two solutions used different row operations to obtain the row echelon form. In all likelihood, the two solutions parted ways in Step 4 of the algebraic solution, where we avoided introducing fractions by interchanging rows 2 and 3.

Figure 20

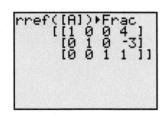

Most graphing utilities also have the ability to put a matrix in reduced row echelon form. Figure 20 shows the reduced row echelon form of the augmented matrix from Example 1 using the RREF command on a TI-84 Plus graphing calculator. Using this command, we see that the solution of the system is $x = 4$, $y = -3$, $z = 1$.

B.8 Using a Graphing Utility to Graph a Polar Equation

Most graphing utilities require the following steps in order to obtain the graph of a polar equation. Be sure to be in POLar mode.

Graphing a Polar Equation Using a Graphing Utility

STEP 1: Set the mode to POLar. Solve the equation for r in terms of θ.

STEP 2: Select the viewing rectangle in polar mode. Besides setting Xmin, Xmax, Xscl, and so forth, the viewing rectangle in polar mode requires setting the minimum and maximum values for θ and an increment setting for θ (θstep). In addition, a square screen and radian measure should be used.

STEP 3: Enter the expression involving θ that you found in Step 1. (Consult your manual for the correct way to enter the expression.)

STEP 4: Graph.

| EXAMPLE 1 | **Graphing a Polar Equation Using a Graphing Utility** |

Use a graphing utility to graph the polar equation $r \sin \theta = 2$.

Solution   **STEP 1:** Solve the equation for r in terms of θ.

$$r \sin \theta = 2$$

$$r = \frac{2}{\sin \theta}$$

STEP 2: From the POLar mode, select the viewing rectangle. We will use the one given next.

$$\theta\text{min} = 0 \qquad X\text{min} = -9 \qquad Y\text{min} = -6$$
$$\theta\text{max} = 2\pi \qquad X\text{max} = 9 \qquad Y\text{max} = 6$$
$$\theta\text{step} = \frac{\pi}{24} \qquad X\text{scl} = 1 \qquad Y\text{scl} = 1$$

θstep determines the number of points that the graphing utility will plot. For example, if θstep is $\dfrac{\pi}{24}$, the graphing utility will evaluate r at $\theta = 0(\theta\text{min})$, $\dfrac{\pi}{24}, \dfrac{2\pi}{24}, \dfrac{3\pi}{24}$, and so forth, up to $2\pi(\theta\text{max})$. The smaller θstep is, the more points that the graphing utility will plot. You are encouraged to experiment with different values for θmin, θmax, and θstep to see how the graph is affected.

Figure 21

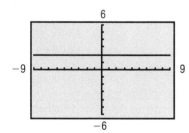

STEP 3: Enter the expression $\dfrac{2}{\sin \theta}$ after the prompt $r_1 =$ ___ .

STEP 4: Graph.

The graph is shown in Figure 21.   ♩

B.9 Using a Graphing Utility to Graph Parametric Equations

Most graphing utilities have the capability of graphing parametric equations. The following steps are usually required to obtain the graph of parametric equations. Check your owner's manual to see how yours works.

Graphing Parametric Equations Using a Graphing Utility

STEP 1: Set the mode to PARametric. Enter $x(t)$ and $y(t)$.

STEP 2: Select the viewing window. In addition to setting Xmin, Xmax, Xscl, and so on, the viewing window in parametric mode requires setting minimum and maximum values for the parameter t and an increment setting for t (Tstep).

STEP 3: Graph.

EXAMPLE 1 **Graphing a Curve Defined by Parametric Equations Using a Graphing Utility**

Graph the curve defined by the parametric equations

$$x = 3t^2, \qquad y = 2t, \qquad -2 \le t \le 2$$

Solution **STEP 1:** Enter the equations $x(t) = 3t^2$, $y(t) = 2t$ with the graphing utility in PARametric mode.

STEP 2: Select the viewing window. The interval is $-2 \le t \le 2$, so we select the following square viewing window:

$$T\text{min} = -2 \qquad X\text{min} = 0 \qquad Y\text{min} = -5$$
$$T\text{max} = 2 \qquad X\text{max} = 15 \qquad Y\text{max} = 5$$
$$T\text{step} = 0.1 \qquad X\text{scl} = 1 \qquad Y\text{scl} = 1$$

We choose Tmin $= -2$ and Tmax $= 2$ because $-2 \le t \le 2$. Finally, the choice for Tstep will determine the number of points that the graphing utility will plot. For example, with Tstep at 0.1, the graphing utility will evaluate x and y at $t = -2, -1.9, -1.8$, and so on. The smaller the Tstep, the more points the graphing utility will plot. The reader is encouraged to experiment with different values of Tstep to see how the graph is affected.

STEP 3: Graph. Notice the direction in which the graph is drawn. This direction shows the orientation of the curve.

The graph shown in Figure 22 is complete.

Figure 22

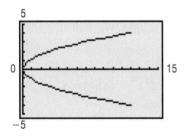

Exploration

Graph the following parametric equations using a graphing utility with Xmin = 0, Xmax = 15, Ymin = −5, Ymax = 5, and Tstep = 0.1.

1. $x = \dfrac{3t^2}{4}, \quad y = t, \quad -4 \le t \le 4$

2. $x = 3t^2 + 12t + 12, \quad y = 2t + 4, \quad -4 \le t \le 0$

3. $x = 3t^{2/3}, \quad y = 2\sqrt[3]{t}, \quad -8 \le t \le 8$

Compare these graphs to the graph in Figure 22. Conclude that parametric equations defining a curve are not unique; that is, different parametric equations can represent the same graph.

Exploration

In FUNCtion mode, graph $x = \dfrac{3y^2}{4}$ $\left(Y_1 = \sqrt{\dfrac{4x}{3}} \text{ and } Y_2 = -\sqrt{\dfrac{4x}{3}}\right)$ with Xmin = 0, Xmax = 15, Ymin = −5, Ymax = 5. Compare this graph with Figure 22. Why do the graphs differ?

Answers

CHAPTER 1 Graphs

1.1 Assess Your Understanding *(page 6)*

7. *x*-coordinate or abscissa; *y*-coordinate or ordinate **8.** quadrants **9.** midpoint **10.** F **11.** F **12.** T
13. (a) Quadrant II **(b)** *x*-axis **15.** The points will be on a **17.** $\sqrt{5}$ **29.** $d(A,B) = \sqrt{13}$
(c) Quadrant III **(d)** Quadrant I vertical line that is 2 units **19.** $\sqrt{10}$ $d(B,C) = \sqrt{13}$
(e) *y*-axis **(f)** Quadrant IV to the right of the *y*-axis. **21.** $2\sqrt{17}$ $d(A,C) = \sqrt{26}$
23. $\sqrt{85}$ $(\sqrt{13})^2 + (\sqrt{13})^2 = (\sqrt{26})^2$
25. $\sqrt{53}$ Area $= \dfrac{13}{2}$ square units
27. $\sqrt{a^2 + b^2}$

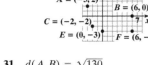

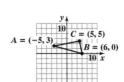

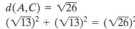
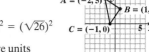

31. $d(A,B) = \sqrt{130}$ **33.** $d(A,B) = 4$
$d(B,C) = \sqrt{26}$ $d(B,C) = \sqrt{41}$
$d(A,C) = 2\sqrt{26}$ $d(A,C) = 5$
$(\sqrt{26})^2 + (2\sqrt{26})^2 = (\sqrt{130})^2$ $4^2 + 5^2 = (\sqrt{41})^2$
Area $= 26$ square units Area $= 10$ square units

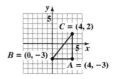

35. $(4,0)$ **37.** $\left(\dfrac{3}{2}, 1\right)$ **39.** $(5, -1)$ **41.** $\left(\dfrac{a}{2}, \dfrac{b}{2}\right)$ **43.** $(5,3)$ **45.** $(3, -13), (3, 11)$

47. $(4 + 3\sqrt{3}, 0); (4 - 3\sqrt{3}, 0)$ **49.** $(1,2)$ **51.** $\sqrt{17}; 2\sqrt{5}; \sqrt{29}$ **53.** $\left(\dfrac{s}{2}, \dfrac{s}{2}\right)$ **55.** $d(P_1, P_2) = 6; d(P_2, P_3) = 4; d(P_1, P_3) = 2\sqrt{13}$; right triangle

57. $d(P_1, P_2) = 2\sqrt{17}; d(P_2, P_3) = \sqrt{34}; d(P_1, P_3) = \sqrt{34}$; isosceles right triangle **59.** $90\sqrt{2} \approx 127.28$ ft **61. (a)** $(90, 0), (90, 90), (0, 90)$
(b) $5\sqrt{2161} \approx 232.43$ ft **(c)** $30\sqrt{149} \approx 366.20$ ft **63.** $d = 50t$ mi **65. (a)** $(2.65, 1.6)$ **(b)** Approximately 1.285 units

1.2 Assess Your Understanding *(page 16)*

3. intercepts **4.** $y = 0$ **5.** *y*-axis **6.** 4 **7.** $(-3, 4)$ **8.** T **9.** F **10.** F **11.** $(0, 0)$ is on the graph. **13.** $(0, 3)$ is on the graph.
15. $(0, 2)$ and $(\sqrt{2}, \sqrt{2})$ are on the graph.

17. $(-2, 0), (0, 2)$ **19.** $(-4, 0), (0, 8)$ **21.** $(-1, 0), (1, 0), (0, -1)$ **23.** $(-2, 0), (2, 0), (0, 4)$ **25.** $(3, 0), (0, 2)$

27. $(-2, 0), (2, 0), (0, 9)$ **29.** **31.** **33.** **35.**

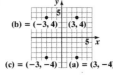

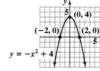

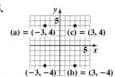

37. **39. (a)** $(-1, 0), (1, 0)$ **41. (a)** $\left(-\dfrac{\pi}{2}, 0\right), (0, 1), \left(\dfrac{\pi}{2}, 0\right)$ **43. (a)** $(0, 0)$
(b) Symmetric with respect to the **(b)** Symmetric with respect to the *y*-axis **(b)** Symmetric with respect to
x-axis, the *y*-axis, and the origin the *x*-axis

45. (a) $(-2, 0), (0, 0), (2, 0)$ **47. (a)** $(x, 0), -2 \leq x \leq 1$ **49. (a)** No intercepts
(b) Symmetric with respect to the origin **(b)** No symmetry **(b)** Symmetric with respect to the origin

51. **53.** **55.** $(-4, 0), (0, -2), (0, 2)$; symmetric with respect to the *x*-axis **57.** $(0, 0)$; symmetric with
respect to the origin **59.** $(0, 9), (3, 0), (-3, 0)$; symmetric with respect to the *y*-axis
61. $(-2, 0), (2, 0), (0, -3), (0, 3)$; symmetric with respect to the *x*-axis, *y*-axis, and origin
63. $(0, -27), (3, 0)$; no symmetry **65.** $(0, -4), (4, 0), (-1, 0)$; no symmetry **67.** $(0, 0)$;
symmetric with respect to the origin **69.** $(0, 0)$; symmetric with respect to the origin

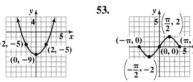

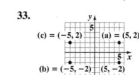

71.   **73.**   **75.** $b = 13$ **77.** $a = -4$ or $a = 1$ **79.** $(-1, -2)$ **81.** 4 **83. (a)** $(0,0), (2,0), (0,1), (0,-1)$
(b) x-axis symmetry **85. (a)** $y = \sqrt{x^2}$ and $y = |x|$ have the same graph. **(b)** $\sqrt{x^2} = |x|$
(c) $x \geq 0$ for $y = (\sqrt{x})^2$, while x can be any real number for $y = x$.
(d) $y \geq 0$ for $y = \sqrt{x^2}$

1.3 Assess Your Understanding *(page 30)*

1. undefined; 0 **2.** $3; 2$ **3.** $y = b$; y-intercept **4.** T **5.** F **6.** T **7.** $m_1 = m_2$; y-intercepts; $m_1 m_2 = -1$ **8.** 2 **9.** $-\dfrac{1}{2}$ **10.** False

11. (a) Slope $= \dfrac{1}{2}$ **13. (a)** Slope $= -\dfrac{1}{3}$ **15.** Slope $= -\dfrac{3}{2}$ **17.** Slope $= -\dfrac{1}{2}$ **19.** Slope $= 0$ **21.** Slope undefined
(b) If x increases by 2 units, y will increase by 1 unit. **(b)** If x increases by 3 units, y will decrease by 1 unit.

23. **25.** **27.** **29.**

31. $(2,6); (3,10); (4,14)$
33. $(4,-7); (6,-10); (8,-13)$
35. $(-1,-5); (0,-7); (1,-9)$
37. $x - 2y = 0$ or $y = \dfrac{1}{2}x$

39. $x + y = 2$ or $y = -x + 2$ **41.** $2x - y = 3$ or $y = 2x - 3$ **43.** $x + 2y = 5$ or $y = -\dfrac{1}{2}x + \dfrac{5}{2}$ **45.** $3x - y = -9$ or $y = 3x + 9$

47. $2x + 3y = -1$ or $y = -\dfrac{2}{3}x - \dfrac{1}{3}$ **49.** $x - 2y = -5$ or $y = \dfrac{1}{2}x + \dfrac{5}{2}$ **51.** $3x + y = 3$ or $y = -3x + 3$ **53.** $x - 2y = 2$ or $y = \dfrac{1}{2}x - 1$

55. $x = 2$; no slope–intercept form **57.** $y = 2$ **59.** $2x - y = -4$ or $y = 2x + 4$ **61.** $2x - y = 0$ or $y = 2x$ **63.** $x = 4$; no slope–intercept form

65. $2x + y = 0$ or $y = -2x$ **67.** $x - 2y = -3$ or $y = \dfrac{1}{2}x + \dfrac{3}{2}$ **69.** $y = 4$

71. Slope $= 2$; y-intercept $= 3$ **73.** Slope $= 2$; y-intercept $= -2$ **75.** Slope $= \dfrac{1}{2}$; y-intercept $= 2$ **77.** Slope $= -\dfrac{1}{2}$; y-intercept $= 2$

 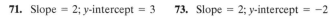 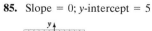

79. Slope $= \dfrac{2}{3}$; y-intercept $= -2$ **81.** Slope $= -1$; y-intercept $= 1$ **83.** Slope undefined; no y-intercept **85.** Slope $= 0$; y-intercept $= 5$

 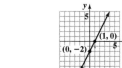 

87. Slope $= 1$; y-intercept $= 0$ **89.** Slope $= \dfrac{3}{2}$; y-intercept $= 0$ **91. (a)** x-intercept: 3; y-intercept: 2 **93. (a)** x-intercept: -10; y-intercept: 8
(b) **(b)**

   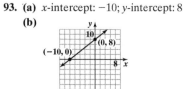

95. (a) x-intercept: 3; y-intercept: $\dfrac{21}{2}$ **97. (a)** x-intercept: 2; y-intercept: 3 **99. (a)** x-intercept: 5; y-intercept: -2 **101.** $y = 0$
(b) **(b)** **(b)** **103.** Parallel
105. Neither
107. $x - y = -2$ or $y = x + 2$
 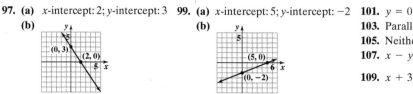 **109.** $x + 3y = 3$ or $y = -\dfrac{1}{3}x + 1$

111. $P_1 = (-2,5), P_2 = (1,3), m_1 = -\dfrac{2}{3}; P_2 = (1,3), P_3 = (-1,0), m_2 = \dfrac{3}{2};$ because $m_1 m_2 = -1,$ the lines are perpendicular and the

points $(-2,5), (1,3),$ and $(-1,0)$ are the vertices of a right triangle; thus, the points $P_1, P_2,$ and P_3 are the vertices of a right triangle.

113. $P_1 = (-1,0), P_2 = (2,3), m = 1; P_3 = (1,-2), P_4 = (4,1), m = 1; P_1 = (-1,0), P_3 = (1,-2), m = -1; P_2 = (2,3), P_4 = (4,1), m = -1;$
opposite sides are parallel, and adjacent sides are perpendicular; the points are the vertices of a rectangle.

115. $C = 0.20x + 29; \$51.00; \$75.00$ **117.** $C = 0.15x + 1289$

119. (a) $C = 0.0944x + 10.55, 0 \le x \le 600$
(b)

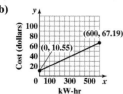

(c) $\$29.43$ **(d)** $\$57.75$
(e) Each additional kW-hr used adds
$\$0.0944$ to the bill.

121. $^\circ C = \dfrac{5}{9}(^\circ F - 32);$ approximately $21.1^\circ C$ **123. (a)** $y = -\dfrac{2}{25}x + 30$ **(b)** x-intercept: 375;
The ramp meets the floor 375 in. (31.25 ft) from the base of the platform.   **(c)** The ramp does not
meet design requirements. It has a run of 31.25 ft long.   **(d)** The only slope possible for the ramp to
comply with the requirement is for it to drop 1 in. for every 12-in. run.

125. (a) $A = \dfrac{1}{5}x + 20,000$ **(b)** $\$80,000$ **(c)** Each additional box sold requires an
additional $\$0.20$ in advertising.   **127.** All have the same slope, 2; the lines are parallel.

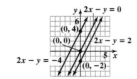

129. (b),(c),(e),(g)   **131.** (c)   **137.** No; no
139. They are the same line.   **141.** Yes, if the y-intercept is 0.

1.4 Assess Your Understanding (page 37)

3. F   **4.** radius   **5.** T   **6.** F   **7.** Center $(2,1);$ radius $= 2; (x-2)^2 + (y-1)^2 = 4$ **9.** Center $\left(\dfrac{5}{2}, 2\right);$ radius $= \dfrac{3}{2}; \left(x - \dfrac{5}{2}\right)^2 + (y-2)^2 = \dfrac{9}{4}$

11. $x^2 + y^2 = 4;$
$x^2 + y^2 - 4 = 0$

13. $x^2 + (y-2)^2 = 4;$
$x^2 + y^2 - 4y = 0$

15. $(x-4)^2 + (y+3)^2 = 25;$
$x^2 + y^2 - 8x + 6y = 0$

17. $(x+2)^2 + (y-1)^2 = 16;$
$x^2 + y^2 + 4x - 2y - 11 = 0$

19. $\left(x - \dfrac{1}{2}\right)^2 + y^2 = \dfrac{1}{4};$
$x^2 + y^2 - x = 0$

21. (a) $(h,k) = (0,0); r = 2$
(b)

(c) $(\pm 2, 0); (0, \pm 2)$

23. (a) $(h,k) = (3,0); r = 2$
(b)

(c) $(1,0); (5,0)$

25. (a) $(h,k) = (1,2); r = 3$
(b)

(c) $(1 \pm \sqrt{5}, 0); (0, 2 \pm 2\sqrt{2})$

27. (a) $(h,k) = (-2,2); r = 3$
(b)

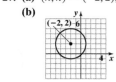

(c) $(-2 \pm \sqrt{5}, 0); (0, 2 \pm \sqrt{5})$

29. (a) $(h,k) = \left(\dfrac{1}{2}, -1\right); r = \dfrac{1}{2}$
(b)

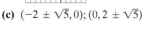

(c) $(0, -1)$

31. (a) $(h,k) = (3,-2); r = 5$
(b)

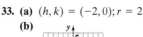

(c) $(3 \pm \sqrt{21}, 0); (0,-6), (0,2)$

33. (a) $(h,k) = (-2,0); r = 2$
(b)

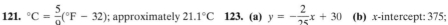

(c) $(0,0), (-4,0)$

35. $x^2 + y^2 = 13$ **37.** $(x-2)^2 + (y-3)^2 = 9$ **39.** $(x+1)^2 + (y-3)^2 = 5$ **41.** $(x+1)^2 + (y-3)^2 = 1$ **43.** (c)   **45.** (b)   **47.** 18 units^2
49. $x^2 + (y-139)^2 = 15,625$ **51.** $x^2 + y^2 + 2x + 4y - 4168.16 = 0$ **53.** $\sqrt{2}x + 4y - 9\sqrt{2} = 0$ **55.** $(1,0)$ **57.** $y = 2$ **59.** (b),(c),(e),(g)

Review Exercises *(page 42)*

1. (a) $2\sqrt{5}$ **(b)** $(2,1)$ **(c)** $\dfrac{1}{2}$ **(d)** For each run of 2, there is a rise of 1. **3. (a)** 5 **(b)** $\left(-\dfrac{1}{2},1\right)$ **(c)** $-\dfrac{4}{3}$ **(d)** For each run of 3, there is a rise of -4.

5. (a) 12 **(b)** $(4,2)$ **(c)** undefined **(d)** no change in x

7. 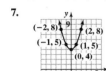 **9.** $(0,0)$; symmetric with respect to the x-axis **11.** $(\pm4,0),(0,\pm2)$; symmetric with respect to the x-axis, y-axis, and origin

13. $(0,1)$; symmetric with respect to the y-axis **15.** $(0,0),(-1,0),(0,-2)$; no symmetry

17. $(x+2)^2+(y-3)^2=16$ **19.** $(x+1)^2+(y+2)^2=1$

21. Center $(0,1)$; radius $=2$ **23.** Center $(1,-2)$; radius $=3$ **25.** Center $(1,-2)$; radius $=\sqrt{5}$

27. $2x+y=5$ or $y=-2x+5$

29. $x=-3$; no slope–intercept form

31. $x+5y=-10$ or $y=-\dfrac{1}{5}x-2$

33. $2x-3y=-19$ or $y=\dfrac{2}{3}x+\dfrac{19}{3}$

Intercepts: $(-\sqrt{3},0),(\sqrt{3},0),$ Intercepts: $(1-\sqrt{5},0),(1+\sqrt{5},0),$ Intercepts: $(0,0),(2,0),(0,-4)$ **35.** $x-y=7$ or $y=x-7$
$(0,-1),(0,3)$ $(0,-2-2\sqrt{2}),(0,-2+2\sqrt{2})$

37. Slope $=\dfrac{4}{5}$; y-intercept $=4$ **39.** Slope $=\dfrac{3}{2}$; y-intercept $=\dfrac{1}{2}$ **41.** Intercepts: $(6,0),(0,-4)$ **43.** Intercepts: $(4,0),(0,6)$ **45.**

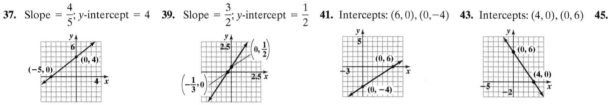

47. 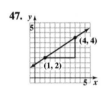   **49. (a)** $d(A,B)=2\sqrt{5}; d(B,C)=\sqrt{145}; d(A,C)=5\sqrt{5}; [d(A,B)]^2+[d(A,C)]^2=(2\sqrt{5})^2+(5\sqrt{5})^2=$
$20+125=145=[d(B,C)]^2$ **(b)** Slope from A to B is -2; slope from A to C is $\dfrac{1}{2}$. Since $(-2)\left(\dfrac{1}{2}\right)=-1,$
the lines are perpendicular. **51.** Slope from A to B is -1; slope from A to C is -1.

Chapter Test *(page 43)*

1. $d=2\sqrt{13}$ **2.** $(2,1)$ **3. (a)** $m=-\dfrac{2}{3}$ **(b)** For every 3-unit change in x, y will change by -2 units.

4.   **5.**   **6.** Intercepts:
$(-3,0),(3,0),(0,9)$;
symmetric with
respect to the y-axis

7. $y=-2x+2$ **8.** $x^2+y^2-8x+6y=0$ **9.** Center: $(-2,1)$; radius: 3

10. Parallel line: $y=-\dfrac{2}{3}x-\dfrac{1}{3}$; perpendicular line: $y=\dfrac{3}{2}x+3$

CHAPTER 2 Functions and Their Graphs

2.1 Assess Your Understanding *(page 56)*

5. independent; dependent **6.** range **7.** $[0,5]$ **8.** $\neq; f,g$ **9.** $(g-f)(x)$ **10.** F **11.** T **12.** T **13** F **14.** F

15. Function; Domain: {Elvis, Colleen, Kaleigh, Marissa}; Range: {January 8, March 15, September 17} **17.** Not a function **19.** Not a function

21. Function; Domain: {1, 2, 3, 4}; Range: {3} **23.** Not a function **25.** Function; Domain: {$-2,-1,0,1$}; Range: {0, 1, 4} **27.** Function **29.** Function

31. Not a function **33.** Not a function **35.** Function **37.** Not a function **39. (a)** -4 **(b)** 1 **(c)** -3 **(d)** $3x^2-2x-4$ **(e)** $-3x^2-2x+4$

(f) $3x^2+8x+1$ **(g)** $12x^2+4x-4$ **(h)** $3x^2+6xh+3h^2+2x+2h-4$ **41. (a)** 0 **(b)** $\dfrac{1}{2}$ **(c)** $-\dfrac{1}{2}$ **(d)** $\dfrac{-x}{x^2+1}$ **(e)** $\dfrac{-x}{x^2+1}$

(f) $\dfrac{x+1}{x^2+2x+2}$ **(g)** $\dfrac{2x}{4x^2+1}$ **(h)** $\dfrac{x+h}{x^2+2xh+h^2+1}$ **43. (a)** 4 **(b)** 5 **(c)** 5 **(d)** $|x|+4$ **(e)** $-|x|-4$ **(f)** $|x+1|+4$ **(g)** $2|x|+4$

(h) $|x+h|+4$ **45. (a)** $-\dfrac{1}{5}$ **(b)** $-\dfrac{3}{2}$ **(c)** $\dfrac{1}{8}$ **(d)** $\dfrac{2x-1}{3x+5}$ **(e)** $\dfrac{-2x-1}{3x-5}$ **(f)** $\dfrac{2x+3}{3x-2}$ **(g)** $\dfrac{4x+1}{6x-5}$ **(h)** $\dfrac{2x+2h+1}{3x+3h-5}$ **47.** All real numbers

49. All real numbers **51.** {$x|x\neq-4,x\neq4$} **53.** {$x|x\neq0$} **55.** {$x|x\geq4$} **57.** {$x|x>9$} **59.** {$x|x>1$} **61.** {$t|t\geq4,t\neq7$}

63. (a) $(f + g)(x) = 5x + 1$; All real numbers **(b)** $(f - g)(x) = x + 7$; All real numbers **(c)** $(f \cdot g)(x) = 6x^2 - x - 12$; All real numbers

(d) $\left(\dfrac{f}{g}\right)(x) = \dfrac{3x + 4}{2x - 3}$; $\left\{x \middle| x \neq \dfrac{3}{2}\right\}$ **(e)** 16 **(f)** 11 **(g)** 10 **(h)** -7 **65. (a)** $(f + g)(x) = 2x^2 + x - 1$; All real numbers

(b) $(f - g)(x) = -2x^2 + x - 1$; All real numbers **(c)** $(f \cdot g)(x) = 2x^3 - 2x^2$; All real numbers **(d)** $\left(\dfrac{f}{g}\right)(x) = \dfrac{x - 1}{2x^2}$; $\{x | x \neq 0\}$

(e) 20 **(f)** -29 **(g)** 8 **(h)** 0 **67. (a)** $(f + g)(x) = \sqrt{x} + 3x - 5$; $\{x | x \geq 0\}$ **(b)** $(f - g)(x) = \sqrt{x} - 3x + 5$; $\{x | x \geq 0\}$

(c) $(f \cdot g)(x) = 3x\sqrt{x} - 5\sqrt{x}$; $\{x | x \geq 0\}$ **(d)** $\left(\dfrac{f}{g}\right)(x) = \dfrac{\sqrt{x}}{3x - 5}$; $\left\{x \middle| x \geq 0, x \neq \dfrac{5}{3}\right\}$ **(e)** $\sqrt{3} + 4$ **(f)** -5 **(g)** $\sqrt{2}$ **(h)** $-\dfrac{1}{2}$

69. (a) $(f + g)(x) = 1 + \dfrac{2}{x}$; $\{x | x \neq 0\}$ **(b)** $(f - g)(x) = 1$; $\{x | x \neq 0\}$ **(c)** $(f \cdot g)(x) = \dfrac{1}{x} + \dfrac{1}{x^2}$; $\{x | x \neq 0\}$ **(d)** $\left(\dfrac{f}{g}\right)(x) = x + 1$; $\{x | x \neq 0\}$

(e) $\dfrac{5}{3}$ **(f)** 1 **(g)** $\dfrac{3}{4}$ **(h)** 2 **71. (a)** $(f + g)(x) = \dfrac{6x + 3}{3x - 2}$; $\left\{x \middle| x \neq \dfrac{2}{3}\right\}$ **(b)** $(f - g)(x) = \dfrac{-2x + 3}{3x - 2}$; $\left\{x \middle| x \neq \dfrac{2}{3}\right\}$

(c) $(f \cdot g)(x) = \dfrac{8x^2 + 12x}{(3x - 2)^2}$; $\left\{x \middle| x \neq \dfrac{2}{3}\right\}$ **(d)** $\left(\dfrac{f}{g}\right)(x) = \dfrac{2x + 3}{4x}$; $\left\{x \middle| x \neq 0, x \neq \dfrac{2}{3}\right\}$ **(e)** 3 **(f)** $-\dfrac{1}{2}$ **(g)** $\dfrac{7}{2}$ **(h)** $\dfrac{5}{4}$ **73.** $g(x) = 5 - \dfrac{7}{2}x$

75. 4 **77.** $2x + h - 1$ **79.** $\dfrac{-(2x + h)}{x^2(x + h)^2}$ **81.** $\dfrac{1}{\sqrt{x + h} + \sqrt{x}}$ **83.** $A = -\dfrac{7}{2}$ **85.** $A = -4$ **87.** $A = 8$; undefined at $x = 3$ **89.** $A(x) = \dfrac{1}{2}x^2$

91. $G(x) = 10x$ **93. (a)** P is the dependent variable; a is the independent variable. **(b)** $P(20) = 197.34$ million; In 2005, there were 197.34 million people 20 years of age or older. **(c)** $P(0) = 290.580$ million; In 2005, there were 290.580 million people. **95. (a)** 15.1 m, 14.071 m, 12.944 m, 11.719 m

(b) 1.01 sec, 1.43 sec, 1.75 sec **(c)** 2.02 sec **97. (a)** $222 **(b)** $225 **(c)** $220 **(d)** $230 **99.** $R(x) = \dfrac{L(x)}{P(x)}$ **101.** $H(x) = P(x) \cdot I(x)$

103. (a) $P(x) = -0.05x^3 + 0.8x^2 + 155x - 500$ **(b)** $P(15) = 1836.25 **(c)** When 15 hundred cellphones are sold, the profit is $1836.25.

105. Only $h(x) = 2x$

2.2 Assess Your Understanding *(page 64)*

3. vertical **4.** 5; -3 **5.** $a = -2$ **6.** F **7.** F **8.** T **9. (a)** $f(0) = 3$; $f(-6) = -3$ **(b)** $f(6) = 0$; $f(11) = 1$ **(c)** Positive **(d)** Negative
(e) $-3, 6$, and 10 **(f)** $-3 < x < 6$; $10 < x \leq 11$ **(g)** $\{x | -6 \leq x \leq 11\}$ **(h)** $\{y | -3 \leq y \leq 4\}$ **(i)** $-3, 6, 10$ **(j)** 3 **(k)** 3 times **(l)** Once
(m) $0, 4$ **(n)** $-5, 8$ **11.** Not a function **13.** Function **(a)** Domain: $\{x | -\pi \leq x \leq \pi\}$; Range: $\{y | -1 \leq y \leq 1\}$ **(b)** $\left(-\dfrac{\pi}{2}, 0\right), \left(\dfrac{\pi}{2}, 0\right), (0, 1)$
(c) y-axis **15.** Not a function **17.** Function **(a)** Domain: $\{x | x > 0\}$; Range: all real numbers **(b)** $(1, 0)$ **(c)** None **19.** Function
(a) Domain: all real numbers; Range: $\{y | y \leq 2\}$ **(b)** $(-3, 0), (3, 0), (0, 2)$ **(c)** y-axis **21.** Function **(a)** Domain: all real numbers; Range:
$\{y | y \geq -3\}$ **(b)** $(1, 0), (3, 0), (0, 9)$ **(c)** None **23. (a)** Yes **(b)** $f(-2) = 9$; $(-2, 9)$ **(c)** $0, \dfrac{1}{2}$; $(0, -1), \left(\dfrac{1}{2}, -1\right)$ **(d)** All real numbers
(e) $-\dfrac{1}{2}, 1$ **(f)** -1 **25. (a)** No **(b)** $f(4) = -3$; $(4, -3)$ **(c)** 14; $(14, 2)$ **(d)** $\{x | x \neq 6\}$ **(e)** -2 **(f)** $-\dfrac{1}{3}$ **27. (a)** Yes
(b) $f(2) = \dfrac{8}{17}$; $\left(2, \dfrac{8}{17}\right)$ **(c)** $-1, 1$; $(-1, 1), (1, 1)$ **(d)** All real numbers **(e)** 0 **(f)** 0

29. (a) Approximately 10.4 ft high
(b) Approximately 9.9 ft high
(c)

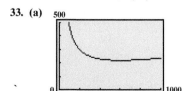

(d) The ball will not go through the hoop; $h(15) \approx 8.4$ ft.
If $v = 30$ ft/sec, $h(15) = 10$ ft.

33. (a)

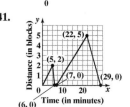

41.

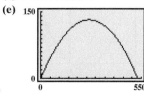

31. (a) About 81.07 ft **(b)** About 129.59 ft **(c)** About 26.63 ft
(d) About 528.13 ft
(e)

(f) About 115.07 ft and 413.05 ft **(g)** 275 ft; maximum height shown in the
table is 131.8 ft **(h)** 264 ft

(b)

(c) 600 mi/hr

35. (a) 3 **(b)** -2 **(c)** -1 **(d)** 1 **(e)** 2 **(f)** $-\dfrac{1}{3}$

37. The x-intercepts can number anywhere from 0 to infinitely many.
There is at most one y-intercept.

39. (a) III **(b)** IV **(c)** I **(d)** V **(e)** II

43. (a) 2 hr elapsed during which Kevin was between 0 and 3 mi from home **(b)** 0.5 hr elapsed during
which Kevin was 3 mi from home **(c)** 0.3 hr elapsed during which Kevin was between 0 and 3 mi
from home **(d)** 0.2 hr elapsed during which Kevin was 0 mi from home **(e)** 0.9 hr elapsed
during which Kevin was between 0 and 2.8 mi from home **(f)** 0.3 hr elapsed during which Kevin
was 2.8 mi from home **(g)** 1.1 hr elapsed during which Kevin was between 0 and 2.8 mi from home
(h) 3 mi **(i)** 2 times **45.** No points whose x-coordinate is 5 or whose y-coordinate is 0 can be on
the graph.

2.3 Assess Your Understanding *(page 76)*

6. increasing **7.** even; odd **8.** T **9.** T **10.** F **11.** Yes **13.** No **15.** $(-8, -2)$; $(0, 2)$; $(5, \infty)$ **17.** Yes; 10 **19.** $-2, 2; 6, 10$
21. (a) $(-2, 0), (0, 3), (2, 0)$ **(b)** Domain: $\{x | -4 \le x \le 4\}$ or $[-4, 4]$; Range: $\{y | 0 \le y \le 3\}$ or $[0, 3]$ **(c)** Increasing on $(-2, 0)$ and $(2, 4)$;
Decreasing on $(-4, -2)$ and $(0, 2)$ **(d)** Even **23. (a)** $(0, 1)$ **(b)** Domain: all real numbers; Range: $\{y | y > 0\}$ or $(0, \infty)$ **(c)** Increasing on
$(-\infty, \infty)$ **(d)** Neither **25. (a)** $(-\pi, 0), (0, 0), (\pi, 0)$ **(b)** Domain: $\{x | -\pi \le x \le \pi\}$ or $[-\pi, \pi]$; Range: $\{y | -1 \le y \le 1\}$ or $[-1, 1]$
(c) Increasing on $\left(-\dfrac{\pi}{2}, \dfrac{\pi}{2}\right)$; Decreasing on $\left(-\pi, -\dfrac{\pi}{2}\right)$ and $\left(\dfrac{\pi}{2}, \pi\right)$ **(d)** Odd **27. (a)** $\left(0, \dfrac{1}{2}\right), \left(\dfrac{1}{3}, 0\right), \left(\dfrac{5}{2}, 0\right)$ **(b)** Domain: $\{x | -3 \le x \le 3\}$ or
$[-3, 3]$; Range: $\{y | -1 \le y \le 2\}$ or $[-1, 2]$ **(c)** Increasing on $(2, 3)$; Decreasing on $(-1, 1)$; Constant on $(-3, -1)$ and $(1, 2)$ **(d)** Neither
29. (a) $0; 3$ **(b)** $-2, 2; 0, 0$ **31. (a)** $\dfrac{\pi}{2}; 1$ **(b)** $-\dfrac{\pi}{2}; -1$ **33.** Odd **35.** Even **37.** Odd **39.** Neither **41.** Even **43.** Odd **45.** Absolute
maximum: $f(1) = 4$; absolute minimum: $f(5) = 1$ **47.** Absolute maximum: $f(3) = 4$; absolute minimum: $f(1) = 1$ **49.** Absolute maximum:
none; absolute minimum: $f(0) = 0$ **51.** Absolute maximum: none; absolute minimum: none

53.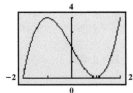
Increasing: $(-2, -1), (1, 2)$
Decreasing: $(-1, 1)$
Local maximum: $(-1, 4)$
Local minimum: $(1, 0)$

55.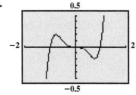
Increasing: $(-2, -0.77), (0.77, 2)$
Decreasing: $(-0.77, 0.77)$
Local maximum: $(-0.77, 0.19)$
Local minimum: $(0.77, -0.19)$

57.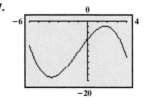
Increasing: $(-3.77, 1.77)$
Decreasing: $(-6, -3.77), (1.77, 4)$
Local maximum: $(-1.77, -1.91)$
Local minimum: $(-3.77, -18.89)$

59.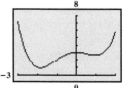
Increasing: $(-1.87, 0), (0.97, 2)$
Decreasing: $(-3, -1.87), (0, 0.97)$
Local maximum: $(0, 3)$
Local minima: $(-1.87, 0.95), (0.97, 2.65)$

61. (a) -4 **(b)** -8 **(c)** -10 **63. (a)** 17 **(b)** -1 **(c)** 11 **65. (a)** 5 **(b)** $y = 5x - 2$ **67. (a)** -1 **(b)** $y = -x$ **69. (a)** 4 **(b)** $y = 4x - 8$
71. (a) Odd **(b)** Local maximum value: 54 at $x = -3$ **73. (a)** Even **(b)** Local maximum value: 24 at $x = -2$ **(c)** 47.4 sq. units

75. (a)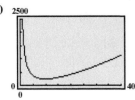
(b) 10 riding lawn mowers/hr
(c) \$239/mower

77. (a) On average, the population is increasing at a rate of 0.036 g/hr from 0 to 2.5 hr.
(b) On average, from 4.5 to 6 hr, the population is increasing at a rate of 0.1 g/hr. **(c)** The average rate of change is increasing over time.

79. (a) 1 **(b)** 0.5 **(c)** 0.1 **(d)** 0.01
(e) 0.001
(f)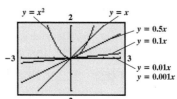

(g) They are getting closer to the tangent line at $(0, 0)$.
(h) They are getting closer to 0.

81. (a) 2
(b) $2; 2; 2; 2$
(c) $y = 2x + 5$
(d)

83. (a) $2x + h + 2$
(b) $4.5; 4.1; 4.01; 4$
(c) $y = 4.01x - 1.01$
(d)

85. (a) $4x + 2h - 3$
(b) $2; 1.2; 1.02; 1$
(c) $y = 1.02x - 1.02$
(d)

87. (a) $-\dfrac{1}{(x + h)x}$
(b) $-\dfrac{2}{3}, -\dfrac{10}{11}, -\dfrac{100}{101}, -1$
(c) $y = -\dfrac{100}{101}x + \dfrac{201}{101}$
(d)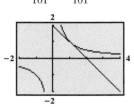

91. At most one **93.** Yes; the function $f(x) = 0$ is both even and odd. **95.** Not necessarily. It just means $f(5) > f(2)$.

2.4 Assess Your Understanding *(page 87)*

4. $(-\infty, 0)$ **5.** piecewise-defined **6.** T **7.** F **8.** F **9.** C **11.** E **13.** B **15.** F

17.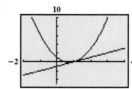

19.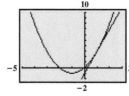

21.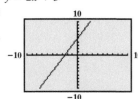

23.

25. (a) 4 **(b)** 2 **(c)** 5 **27. (a)** -4 **(b)** -2 **(c)** 0 **(d)** 25

29. (a) All real numbers
(b) $(0, 1)$
(c)

(d) $\{y | y \neq 0\}$; $(-\infty, 0) \cup (0, \infty)$
(e) Discontinuous at $x = 0$

31. (a) All real numbers
(b) $(0, 3)$
(c)

(d) $\{y | y \geq 1\}$; $[1, \infty)$
(e) Continuous

33. (a) $\{x | x \geq -2\}$; $[-2, \infty)$
(b) $(0, 3)$, $(2, 0)$
(c)

(d) $\{y | y < 4, y = 5\}$; $(-\infty, 4) \cup \{5\}$
(e) Discontinuous at $x = 1$

35. (a) All real numbers
(b) $(-1, 0)$, $(0, 0)$
(c)
(d) All real numbers
(e) Discontinuous at $x = 0$

37. (a) $\{x | x \geq -2, x \neq 0\}$; $[-2, 0) \cup (0, \infty)$
(b) No intercepts
(c)
(d) $\{y | y > 0\}$; $(0, \infty)$
(e) Discontinuous at $x = 0$

39. (a) All real numbers
(b) $(x, 0)$ for $0 \leq x < 1$
(c)

(d) Set of even integers
(e) Discontinuous at $\{x | x \text{ is an integer}\}$

41. $f(x) = \begin{cases} -x & \text{if } -1 \leq x \leq 0 \\ \frac{1}{2}x & \text{if } 0 < x \leq 2 \end{cases}$ (Other answers are possible.)

43. $f(x) = \begin{cases} -x & \text{if } x \leq 0 \\ -x + 2 & \text{if } 0 < x \leq 2 \end{cases}$ (Other answers are possible.)

45. (a) 2 **(b)** 3 **(c)** -4 **47. (a)** \$39.99 **(b)** \$46.74 **(c)** \$40.44

49. (a) \$52.45 **(b)** \$277.36
(c) $C(x) = \begin{cases} 0.73006x + 15.95 & \text{if } 0 \leq x \leq 50 \\ 0.4998x + 27.463 & \text{if } x > 50 \end{cases}$
(d)

51. For schedule X: $f(x) = \begin{cases} 0.10x & \text{if} & 0 < x \leq 8350 \\ 835 + 0.15(x - 8350) & \text{if} & 8350 < x \leq 33{,}950 \\ 4675 + 0.25(x - 33{,}950) & \text{if} & 33{,}950 < x \leq 82{,}250 \\ 16{,}750 + 0.28(x - 82{,}250) & \text{if} & 82{,}250 < x \leq 171{,}550 \\ 41{,}754 + 0.33(x - 171{,}550) & \text{if} & 171{,}550 < x \leq 372{,}950 \\ 108{,}216 + 0.35(x - 372{,}950) & \text{if} & x > 372{,}950 \end{cases}$

53. (a)
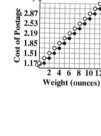
(b) $C(x) = 10 + 0.4x$ **(c)** $C(x) = 70 + 0.25x$

55. $f(x) = \begin{cases} x & \text{if} & 0 \leq x < 10 \\ 10 & \text{if} & 10 \leq x < 500 \\ 30 & \text{if} & 500 \leq x < 1000 \\ 50 & \text{if} & 1000 \leq x < 1500 \\ 70 & \text{if} & x \geq 1500 \end{cases}$

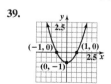

57. (a) 10°C **(b)** 4°C
(c) -3°C **(d)** -4°C
(e) The wind chill is equal to the air temperature.
(f) At wind speed greater than 20 m/s, the wind chill factor depends only on the air temperature.

59.
$C(x) = \begin{cases} 1.17 & 0 < x \leq 1 \\ 1.34 & 1 < x \leq 2 \\ 1.51 & 2 < x \leq 3 \\ 1.68 & 3 < x \leq 4 \\ 1.85 & 4 < x \leq 5 \\ 2.02 & 5 < x \leq 6 \\ 2.19 & 6 < x \leq 7 \\ 2.36 & 7 < x \leq 8 \\ 2.53 & 8 < x \leq 9 \\ 2.70 & 9 < x \leq 10 \\ 2.87 & 10 < x \leq 11 \\ 3.04 & 11 < x \leq 12 \\ 3.21 & 12 < x \leq 13 \end{cases}$

61. Each graph is that of $y = x^2$, but shifted horizontally. If $y = (x - k)^2$, $k > 0$, the shift is right k units; if $y = (x + k)^2$, $k > 0$, the shift is left k units.
63. The graph of $y = -f(x)$ is the reflection about the x-axis of the graph of $y = f(x)$. **65.** Yes. The graph of $y = (x - 1)^3 + 2$ is the graph of $y = x^3$ shifted right 1 unit and up 2 units. **67.** They all have the same general shape. All three go through the points $(-1, -1)$, $(0, 0)$, and $(1, 1)$. As the exponent increases, the steepness of the curve increases (except near $x = 0$).

2.5 Assess Your Understanding (page 99)

1. horizontal; right **2.** y **3.** vertical; up **4.** T **5.** F **6.** T **7.** B **9.** H **11.** I **13.** L **15.** F **17.** G **19.** $y = (x - 4)^3$ **21.** $y = x^3 + 4$
23. $y = -x^3$ **25.** $y = 4x^3$ **27.** $y = -(\sqrt{-x} + 2)$ **29.** $y = -\sqrt{x + 3} + 2$ **31.** (c) **33.** (c) **35. (a)** -7 and 1 **(b)** -3 and 5 **(c)** -5 and 3
(d) -3 and 5 **37. (a)** $(-3, 3)$ **(b)** $(4, 10)$ **(c)** Decreasing on $(-1, 5)$ **(d)** Decreasing on $(-5, 1)$

39.
Domain: $(-\infty, \infty)$;
Range: $[-1, \infty)$

41.
Domain: $(-\infty, \infty)$;
Range: $(-\infty, \infty)$

43.
Domain: $[2, \infty)$;
Range: $[0, \infty)$

45.
Domain: $(-\infty, \infty)$;
Range: $(-\infty, \infty)$

47.
Domain: $[0, \infty)$;
Range: $[0, \infty)$

49.
Domain: $(-\infty, \infty)$;
Range: $(-\infty, \infty)$

51.
Domain: $(-\infty, \infty)$;
Range: $[-3, \infty)$

53.
Domain: $[2, \infty)$;
Range: $[1, \infty)$

55.
Domain: $(-\infty, 0]$;
Range: $[-2, \infty)$

57.
Domain: $(-\infty, \infty)$;
Range: $(-\infty, \infty)$

59.
Domain: $(-\infty, \infty)$;
Range: $[0, \infty)$

61.
Domain: $(-\infty, \infty)$;
Range: $\{y | y \text{ is an even integer}\}$

63. (a) $F(x) = f(x) + 3$
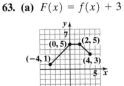

(b) $G(x) = f(x + 2)$

(c) $P(x) = -f(x)$

(d) $H(x) = f(x + 1) - 2$

(e) $Q(x) = \frac{1}{2}f(x)$

(f) $g(x) = f(-x)$

(g) $h(x) = f(2x)$

65. (a) $F(x) = f(x) + 3$

(b) $G(x) = f(x + 2)$
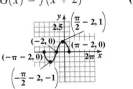

(c) $P(x) = -f(x)$

(d) $H(x) = f(x + 1) - 2$
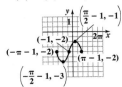

(e) $Q(x) = \frac{1}{2}f(x)$
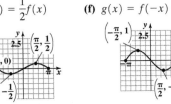

(f) $g(x) = f(-x)$

(g) $h(x) = f(2x)$

67. $f(x) = (x + 1)^2 - 1$

69. $f(x) = (x - 4)^2 - 15$

71. $f(x) = 2(x - 3)^2 + 1$

73. $f(x) = -3(x + 2)^2 - 5$

75.

77. (a) $72°F$; $65°F$
(b) The temperature decreases by 2° to 70°F during the day and 63°F overnight.

(c) The time at which the temperature adjusts between the daytime and overnight settings is moved to 1 hr sooner. It begins warming up at 5:00 AM instead of 6:00 AM, and it begins cooling down at 8:00 PM instead of 9:00 PM.

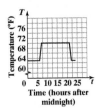

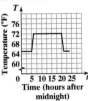

79.

81. (a)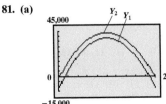

(b) 10% tax
(c) Y_1 is the graph of $p(x)$ shifted down vertically 10,000 units. Y_2 is the graph of $p(x)$ vertically compressed by a factor of 0.9.
(d) 10% tax

83. (a)

(b)

85. (a) $(-4, 2)$ **(b)** $(1, -12)$ **(c)** $(-4, 5)$

87. The graph of $y = f(x) - 2$ is the graph of $y = f(x)$ shifted down 2 units. The graph of $y = f(x - 2)$ is the graph of $y = f(x)$ shifted right 2 units.

2.6 Assess Your Understanding (page 106)

1. (a) $d(x) = \sqrt{x^4 - 15x^2 + 64}$
(b) $d(0) = 8$ (c) $d(1) = \sqrt{50} \approx 7.07$
(d)
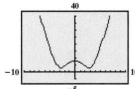
(e) d is smallest when $x \approx -2.74$ or $x \approx 2.74$.

3. (a) $d(x) = \sqrt{x^2 - x + 1}$
(b)
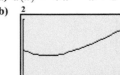
(c) d is smallest when $x = 0.5$.

5. $A(x) = \dfrac{1}{2}x^4$ **7.** (a) $A(x) = x(16 - x^2)$
(b) Domain: $\{x | 0 < x < 4\}$
(c) The area is largest when $x \approx 2.31$.
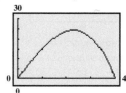

9. (a) $A(x) = 4x\sqrt{4 - x^2}$
(c) A is largest when $x \approx 1.41$.

(b) $p(x) = 4x + 4\sqrt{4 - x^2}$
(d) p is largest when $x \approx 1.41$.
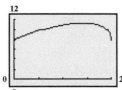

11. (a) $A(x) = x^2 + \dfrac{25 - 20x + 4x^2}{\pi}$
(b) Domain: $\{x | 0 < x < 2.5\}$
(c) A is smallest when $x \approx 1.40$ m.
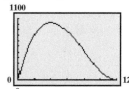

13. (a) $C(x) = x$ (b) $A(x) = \dfrac{x^2}{4\pi}$ **15.** (a) $A(r) = 2r^2$ (b) $p(r) = 6r$ **17.** $A(x) = \left(\dfrac{\pi}{3} - \dfrac{\sqrt{3}}{4}\right)x^2$

19. (a) $d(t) = \sqrt{2500t^2 - 360t + 13}$ **21.** $V(r) = \dfrac{\pi H(R - r)r^2}{R}$ **23.** (a) $T(x) = \dfrac{12 - x}{5} + \dfrac{\sqrt{x^2 + 4}}{3}$ **25.** (a) $V(x) = x(24 - 2x)^2$
(b) d is smallest when $t \approx 0.07$ hr.
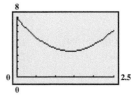
(b) $\{x | 0 \le x \le 12\}$
(c) 3.09 hr
(d) 3.55 hr
(b) 972 in.^{3} (c) 160 in.^{3}
(d) V is largest when $x = 4$.

Review Exercises (page 111)

1. Function; domain $\{-1, 2, 4\}$, range $\{0, 3\}$ **3.** (a) 2 (b) -2 (c) $-\dfrac{3x}{x^2 - 1}$ (d) $-\dfrac{3x}{x^2 - 1}$ (e) $\dfrac{3(x - 2)}{x^2 - 4x + 3}$ (f) $\dfrac{6x}{4x^2 - 1}$ **5.** (a) 0 (b) 0

(c) $\sqrt{x^2 - 4}$ (d) $-\sqrt{x^2 - 4}$ (e) $\sqrt{x^2 - 4x}$ (f) $2\sqrt{x^2 - 1}$ **7.** (a) 0 (b) 0 (c) $\dfrac{x^2 - 4}{x^2}$ (d) $-\dfrac{x^2 - 4}{x^2}$ (e) $\dfrac{x(x - 4)}{(x - 2)^2}$ (f) $\dfrac{x^2 - 1}{x^2}$

9. $\{x | x \ne -3, x \ne 3\}$ **11.** $\{x | x \le 2\}$ **13.** $\{x | x > 0\}$ **15.** $\{x | x \ne -3, x \ne 1\}$

17. $(f + g)(x) = 2x + 3$; Domain: all real numbers
$(f - g)(x) = -4x + 1$; Domain: all real numbers
$(f \cdot g)(x) = -3x^2 + 5x + 2$; Domain: all real numbers
$\left(\dfrac{f}{g}\right)(x) = \dfrac{2 - x}{3x + 1}$; Domain: $\left\{x | x \ne -\dfrac{1}{3}\right\}$

19. $(f + g)(x) = 3x^2 + 4x + 1$; Domain: all real numbers
$(f - g)(x) = 3x^2 - 2x + 1$; Domain: all real numbers
$(f \cdot g)(x) = 9x^3 + 3x^2 + 3x$; Domain: all real numbers
$\left(\dfrac{f}{g}\right)(x) = \dfrac{3x^2 + x + 1}{3x}$; Domain: $\{x | x \ne 0\}$

21. $(f + g)(x) = \dfrac{x^2 + 2x - 1}{x(x - 1)}$; Domain: $\{x | x \ne 0, x \ne 1\}$

$(f - g)(x) = \dfrac{x^2 + 1}{x(x - 1)}$; Domain: $\{x | x \ne 0, x \ne 1\}$

$(f \cdot g)(x) = \dfrac{x + 1}{x(x - 1)}$; Domain: $\{x | x \ne 0, x \ne 1\}$

$\left(\dfrac{f}{g}\right)(x) = \dfrac{x(x + 1)}{x - 1}$; Domain: $\{x | x \ne 0, x \ne 1\}$

23. $-4x + 1 - 2h$ **25.** (a) Domain: $\{x | -4 \le x \le 3\}$; Range: $\{y | -3 \le y \le 3\}$
(b) $(0, 0)$ (c) -1 (d) -4 (e) $\{x | 0 < x \le 3\}$
(f)
(g)
(h)

27. (a) Domain: $\{x | -4 \le x \le 4\}$ or $[-4, 4]$
Range: $\{y | -3 \le y \le 1\}$ or $[-3, 1]$
(b) Increasing on $(-4, -1)$ and $(3, 4)$; Decreasing on $(-1, 3)$
(c) Local maximum value is 1 and occurs at $x = -1$.
Local minimum value is -3 and occurs at $x = 3$.

(d) Absolute maximum: $f(-1) = 1$
Absolute minimum: $f(3) = -3$
(e) No symmetry (f) Neither
(g) x-intercepts: $-2, 0, 4$; y-intercept: 0
29. Odd **31.** Even **33.** Neither **35.** Odd

37.

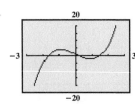

39.

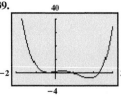

41. (a) 23   **(b)** 7   **(c)** 47   **43.** −5   **45.** −17   **47.** No   **49.** Yes

51.

53.

Local maximum value: 4.04 at $x = -0.91$
Local minimum value: −2.04 at $x = 0.91$
Increasing: $(-3, -0.91); (0.91, 3)$
Decreasing: $(-0.91, 0.91)$

Local maximum value: 1.53 at $x = 0.41$
Local minima values: −0.54 at $x = -0.34$
and −3.56 at $x = 1.80$
Increasing: $(-0.34, 0.41); (1.80, 3)$
Decreasing: $(-2, -0.34); (0.41, 1.80)$

55.

Intercepts: $(-4, 0), (4, 0), (0, -4)$
Domain: all real numbers
Range: $\{y | y \geq -4\}$ or $[-4, \infty)$

57.

Intercept: $(0, 0)$
Domain: all real numbers
Range: $\{y | y \leq 0\}$ or $(-\infty, 0]$

59.

Intercept: $(1, 0)$
Domain: $\{x | x \geq 1\}$ or $[1, \infty)$
Range: $\{y | y \geq 0\}$ or $[0, \infty)$

61.

Intercepts: $(0, 1), (1, 0)$
Domain: $\{x | x \leq 1\}$ or $(-\infty, 1]$
Range: $\{y | y \geq 0\}$ or $[0, \infty)$

63.

Intercept: $(0, 3)$
Domain: all real numbers
Range: $\{y | y \geq 2\}$ or $[2, \infty)$

65.

Intercepts: $(0, -2),$
$\left(1 - \dfrac{\sqrt[3]{9}}{3}, 0\right)$ or about $(0.3, 0)$
Domain: all real numbers
Range: all real numbers

67. (a) $\{x | x > -2\}$ or $(-2, \infty)$
   (b) $(0, 0)$
   (c)

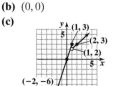

   (d) $\{y | y > -6\}$ or $(-6, \infty)$
   (e) Discontinuous at $x = 1$

69. (a) $\{x | x \geq -4\}$ or $[-4, \infty)$
   (b) $(0, 1)$
   (c)

   (d) $\{y | -4 \leq y < 0$ or $y > 0\}$
     or $[-4, 0) \cup (0, \infty)$
   (e) Discontinuous at $x = 0$

71. $A = 11$ **73. (a)** $A(x) = (8.5 - 2x)(11 - 2x)$
     (b) $0 \leq x < 4.25, 0 < A \leq 93.5$
     (c) $A(1) = 58.5$ in.^{2}, $A(1.2) = 52.46$ in.^{2}, $A(1.5) = 44$ in.^{2}
     (d)

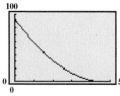

75. (a) $A(x) = 10x - x^3$
     (b) The largest area that can be enclosed by the
     rectangle is approximately 12.17 square units.

Chapter Test *(page 114)*

1. (a) Function; domain: $\{2, 4, 6, 8\}$; range: $\{5, 6, 7, 8\}$ **(b)** Not a function   **(c)** Not a function   **(d)** Function; domain; all real numbers;
range: $\{y | y \geq 2\}$ **2.** Domain: $\left\{x \middle| x \leq \dfrac{4}{5}\right\}$; $f(-1) = 3$ **3.** Domain: $\{x | x \neq -2\}$; $g(-1) = 1$ **4.** Domain: $\{x | x \neq -9, x \neq 4\}$; $h(-1) = \dfrac{1}{8}$

5. (a) Domain: $\{x | -5 \leq x \leq 5\}$; range: $\{y | -3 \leq y \leq 3\}$ **(b)** $(0, 2), (-2, 0),$ and $(2, 0)$ **(c)** $f(1) = 3$ **(d)** $x = -5$ and $x = 3$
(e) $\{x | -5 \leq x < -2$ or $2 < x \leq 5\}$ or $[-5, -2) \cup (2, 5]$ **6.** Local maxima values: $f(-0.85) \approx -0.86; f(2.35) \approx 15.55;$ local minima values: $f(0) = -2;$
the function is increasing on the intervals $(-5, -0.85)$ and $(0, 2.35)$ and decreasing on the intervals $(-0.85, 0)$ and $(2.35, 5)$.
7. (a)

   (b) $(0, -4), (4, 0)$ **8.** 19   **9. (a)** $(f - g)(x) = 2x^2 - 3x + 3$ **10. (a)**

   (b)

   (c) $g(-5) = -9$ **(b)** $(f \cdot g)(x) = 6x^3 - 4x^2 + 3x - 2$
   (d) $g(2) = -2$ **(c)** $f(x + h) - f(x) = 4xh + 2h^2$

11. (a) 8.67% occurring in 1997 $(x \approx 5)$ **(b)** The model predicts that the interest rate will be −10.343%. This is not reasonable.

12. (a) $V(x) = \dfrac{x^2}{8} - \dfrac{5x}{4} + \dfrac{\pi x^2}{64}$ **(b)** 1297.61 ft^3

Cumulative Review *(page 115)*

1. $\{6\}$ **2.** $\left\{0, \dfrac{1}{3}\right\}$ **3.** $\{-1, 9\}$ **4.** $\left\{\dfrac{1}{3}, \dfrac{1}{2}\right\}$ **5.** $\left\{-\dfrac{7}{2}, \dfrac{1}{2}\right\}$ **6.** $\left\{\dfrac{1}{2}\right\}$

7. $\left\{x \mid x < -\dfrac{4}{3}\right\}; \left(-\infty, -\dfrac{4}{3}\right)$ **8.** $\{x \mid 1 < x < 4\}; (1, 4)$ **9.** $\left\{x \mid x \le -2 \text{ or } x \ge \dfrac{3}{2}\right\}; (-\infty, -2] \cup \left[\dfrac{3}{2}, \infty\right)$

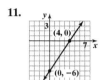   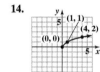

10. **(a)** distance: $\sqrt{29}$ **(b)** midpoint: $\left(\dfrac{1}{2}, -4\right)$ **(c)** slope: $-\dfrac{2}{5}$

11. 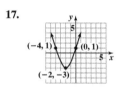 **12.**   **13.** 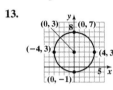   **14.** **15.** Intercepts: $(0, -3), (-2, 0), (2, 0)$; symmetry with respect to the y-axis

16. $y = \dfrac{1}{2}x + 5$

17. 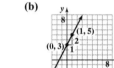 **18.**   **19.**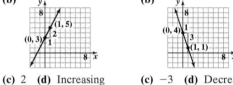

CHAPTER 3 Linear and Quadratic Functions

3.1 Assess Your Understanding *(page 124)*

7. slope; y-intercept **8.** -4; 3 **9.** positive **10.** T **11.** F **12.** F

13. **(a)** $m = 2$; $b = 3$
(b)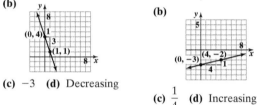
(c) 2 **(d)** Increasing

15. **(a)** $m = -3$; $b = 4$
(b)
(c) -3 **(d)** Decreasing

17. **(a)** $m = \dfrac{1}{4}$; $b = -3$
(b)
(c) $\dfrac{1}{4}$ **(d)** Increasing

19. **(a)** $m = 0$; $b = 4$
(b)
(c) 0 **(d)** Constant

21. Linear; -3 **23.** Nonlinear
25. Nonlinear **27.** Linear; 0

29. **(a)** $\dfrac{1}{4}$ **(b)** $\left\{x \mid x > \dfrac{1}{4}\right\}$ or $\left(\dfrac{1}{4}, \infty\right)$
(c) 1 **(d)** $\{x \mid x \le 1\}$ or $(-\infty, 1]$
(e)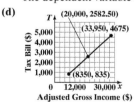

31. **(a)** 40 **(b)** 88 **(c)** -40 **(d)** $\{x \mid x > 40\}$ or $(40, \infty)$ **(e)** $\{x \mid x \le 88\}$ or $(-\infty, 88]$
(f) $\{x \mid -40 < x < 88\}$ or $(-40, 88)$ **33.** **(a)** -4 **(b)** $\{x \mid x < -4\}$ or $(-\infty, -4)$
35. **(a)** -6 **(b)** $\{x \mid -6 \le x < 5\}$ or $[-6, 5)$ **37.** **(a)** \$45 **(b)** 180 mi **(c)** 260 mi
(d) $\{x \mid x \ge 0\}$ or $[0, \infty)$ **39.** **(a)** \$16; 600 T-shirts **(b)** \$0 \le p < \$16 **(c)** The price will increase.

41. **(a)** $\{x \mid 8350 \le x \le 33{,}950\}$ or $[8350, 33{,}950]$
(b) \$2582.50
(c) The independent variable is adjusted gross income, x.
The dependent variable is the tax bill, T.
(d)

43. **(a)** $x = 5000$
(b) $x > 5000$

45. **(a)** $V(x) = -1000x + 3000$
(b) $\{x \mid 0 \le x \le 3\}$ or $[0, 3]$
(c)

(d) \$1000
(e) After 1 year

47. **(a)** $C(x) = 90x + 1800$
(b)

(c) \$3060
(d) 22 bicycles

(e) \$27,500

49. (a) $C(x) = 0.07x + 29$ **(b)** $36.70; $45.10

51. (a)

(e)

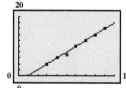

53. (d), (e) **55.** $b = 0$; yes, $f(x) = b$

(b) Since each input (price) corresponds to a single output (quantity demanded), we know that quantity demanded is a function of price. Also, because the average rate of change is a constant -0.4 24″ LCD monitor per dollar, the function is linear.

(c) $q(p) = -0.4p + 160$

(d) $\{p | 0 \le p \le 400\}$ or $[0, 400]$

(f) If price increases by $1, quantity demanded of 24″ LCD monitors decreases by 0.4 monitor.

(g) q-intercept: When the price is $0, 160 24″ LCD monitors will be demanded. p-intercept: There will be 0 24″ LCD monitors demanded when the price is $400.

3.2 Assess Your Understanding *(page 131)*

3. scatter diagram **4.** T **5.** Linear relation, $m > 0$ **7.** Linear relation, $m < 0$ **9.** Nonlinear relation

11. (a)

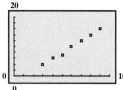

(c)

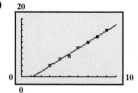

(e)

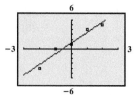

(b) Answers vary. Using $(4, 6)$ and $(8, 14)$, $y = 2x - 2$. **(d)** $y = 2.0357x - 2.3571$

13. (a)

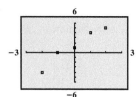

(c)

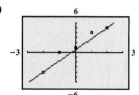

(e)

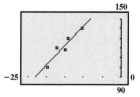

(b) Answers will vary. Using $(-2, -4)$ and $(2, 5)$, $y = \dfrac{9}{4}x + \dfrac{1}{2}$. **(d)** $y = 2.2x + 1.2$

15. (a)

(c)

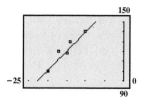

(e)

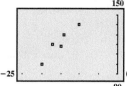

(b) Answers will vary. Using $(-20, 100)$ and $(-10, 140)$, $y = 4x + 180$. **(d)** $y = 3.8613x + 180.2920$

17. (a)

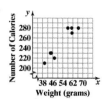

(c) Answers will vary. Using the points $(39.52, 210)$ and $(66.45, 280)$, $y = 2.599x + 107.288$.

(d)

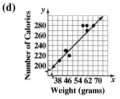

(e) 269 calories

(f) If the weight of a candy bar is increased by 1 gram, the number of calories will increase by 2.599, on average.

(b) Linear with positive slope

19. (a) The independent variable is the number of hours spent playing video games and cumulative grade-point average is the dependent variable because we are using number of hours playing video games to predict (or explain) cumulative grade-point average.

(b)

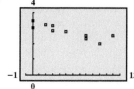

(c) $G(h) = -0.0942h + 3.2763$

(d) If the number of hours playing video games in a week increases by 1 hour, the cumulative grade-point average decreases 0.09, on average.

(e) 2.52

(f) Approximately 9.3 hours

21. (a) No

(b)

(c) $D = -1.3355p + 86.1974$

(d) If the price increases $1, the quantity sold per day decreases by about 1.34 pairs of jeans, on average.

(e) $D(p) = -1.3355p + 86.1974$

(f) $\{p \mid 0 < p \le 64\}$

(g) About 49 pairs

23.
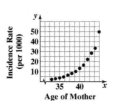

No, the data do not follow a linear pattern.

25. No linear relation   **27.** 34.8 hours; A student whose GPA is 0 spends 34.8 hours each week playing video games.; $G(0) = 3.28$; The average GPA of a student who does not play video games is 3.28.

3.3 Assess Your Understanding (page 143)

5. parabola   **6.** axis or axis of symmetry   **7.** $-\dfrac{b}{2a}$ **8.** T   **9.** T   **10.** T   **11.** C   **13.** F   **15.** G   **17.** H

19.
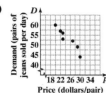

21.

23. $f(x) = (x + 2)^2 - 2$ **25.** $f(x) = 2(x - 1)^2 - 1$ **27.** $f(x) = -(x + 1)^2 + 1$

29. $f(x) = \dfrac{1}{2}(x + 1)^2 - \dfrac{3}{2}$

31. (a)

(b) Domain: $(-\infty, \infty)$
Range: $[-1, \infty)$
(c) Decreasing: $(-\infty, -1)$
Increasing: $(-1, \infty)$

33. (a)

(b) Domain: $(-\infty, \infty)$
Range: $(-\infty, 9]$
(c) Increasing: $(-\infty, -3)$
Decreasing: $(-3, \infty)$

35. (a)

(b) Domain: $(-\infty, \infty)$
Range: $[-9, \infty)$
(c) Decreasing: $(-\infty, -1)$
Increasing: $(-1, \infty)$

37. (a)

(b) Domain: $(-\infty, \infty)$
Range: $[0, \infty)$
(c) Decreasing: $(-\infty, -1)$
Increasing: $(-1, \infty)$

39. (a)

(b) Domain: $(-\infty, \infty)$
Range: $\left[\dfrac{15}{8}, \infty\right)$
(c) Decreasing: $\left(-\infty, \dfrac{1}{4}\right)$
Increasing: $\left(\dfrac{1}{4}, \infty\right)$

41. (a)
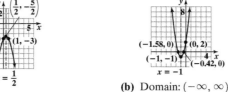

(b) Domain: $(-\infty, \infty)$
Range: $\left(-\infty, -\dfrac{5}{2}\right]$
(c) Increasing: $\left(-\infty, \dfrac{1}{2}\right)$
Decreasing: $\left(\dfrac{1}{2}, \infty\right)$

43. (a)
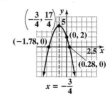

(b) Domain: $(-\infty, \infty)$
Range: $[-1, \infty)$
(c) Decreasing: $(-\infty, -1)$
Increasing: $(-1, \infty)$

45. (a)

(b) Domain: $(-\infty, \infty)$
Range: $\left(-\infty, \dfrac{17}{4}\right]$
(c) Increasing: $\left(-\infty, -\dfrac{3}{4}\right)$
Decreasing: $\left(-\dfrac{3}{4}, \infty\right)$

47. $f(x) = (x + 1)^2 - 2 = x^2 + 2x - 1$ **49.** $f(x) = -(x + 3)^2 + 5 = -x^2 - 6x - 4$ **51.** $f(x) = 2(x - 1)^2 - 3 = 2x^2 - 4x - 1$
53. Minimum value; -18 **55.** Minimum value; -21 **57.** Maximum value; 21   **59.** Maximum value; 13   **61.** $a = 6, b = 0, c = 2$

63. (a), (c), (d)

(b) $\{-1, 3\}$

65. (a), (c), (d)

(b) $\{-1, 3\}$

67. (a), (c), (d)

(b) $\{-1, 2\}$

69. (a) $a = 1: f(x) = (x + 3)(x - 1) = x^2 + 2x - 3$
$a = 2: f(x) = 2(x + 3)(x - 1) = 2x^2 + 4x - 6$
$a = -2: f(x) = -2(x + 3)(x - 1) = -2x^2 - 4x + 6$
$a = 5: f(x) = 5(x + 3)(x - 1) = 5x^2 + 10x - 15$

(b) The value of a does not affect the x-intercepts, but it changes the y-intercept by a factor of a.
(c) The value of a does not affect the axis of symmetry. It is $x = -1$ for all values of a.
(d) The value of a does not affect the x-coordinate of the vertex. However, the y-coordinate of the vertex is multiplied by a.
(e) The mean of the x-intercepts is the x-coordinate of the vertex.

71. (a) $(-2, -25)$
(b) $-7, 3$
(c) $-4, 0; (-4, -21), (0, -21)$
(d)

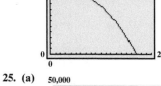

73. $(2, 2)$ **75.** $500; $1,000,000   **77. (a)** 70,000 mp3 players   **(b)** $2500   **79. (a)** 187 or 188 watches; $7031.20
(b) $P(x) = -0.2x^2 + 43x - 1750$ **(c)** 107 or 108 watches; $561.20   **81. (a)** 171 ft   **(b)** 49 mph
(c) Reaction time   **83.** $f(x) = 2(x + 4)(x - 2)$ **85.** If x is even, then ax^2 and bx are even and $ax^2 + bx$ is
even, which means that $ax^2 + bx + c$ is odd. If x is odd, then ax^2 and bx are odd and $ax^2 + bx$ is even, which
means that $ax^2 + bx + c$ is odd. In either case, $f(x)$ is odd.
87.

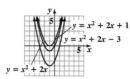

89. $b^2 - 4ac < 0$ **91.** No

3.4 Assess Your Understanding (page 151)

3. (a) $R(x) = -\dfrac{1}{6}x^2 + 100x$ **(b)** $\{x \mid 0 \le x \le 600\}$ **(c)** $13,333.33   **(d)** 300; $15,000   **(e)** $50   **5. (a)** $R(x) = -\dfrac{1}{5}x^2 + 20x$ **(b)** $255

(c) 50; $500   **(d)** $10   **(e)** Between $8 and $12   **7. (a)** $A(w) = -w^2 + 200w$ **(b)** A is largest when $w = 100$ yd.   **(c)** 10,000 yd^2 **9.** 2,000,000 m^2

11. (a) $\dfrac{625}{16} \approx 39$ ft   **(b)** $\dfrac{7025}{32} \approx 219.5$ ft   **(c)** About 170 ft   **13.** 18.75 m   **15. (a)** 3 in.   **(b)** Between 2 in. and 4 in.

(d)

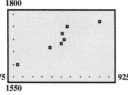

(f) When the height is 100 ft, the projectile is about 135.7 ft from the cliff.

17. $\dfrac{750}{\pi} \approx 238.73$ m by 375 m

19. $x = \dfrac{a}{2}$ **21.** $\dfrac{38}{3}$ **23.** $\dfrac{248}{3}$

25. (a)

(b) $I(x) = -45.466x^2 + 4314.374x - 55,961.675$ **(e)**
(c) About 47.4 years of age
(d) Approximately $46,388

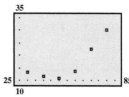

The data appear to follow a quadratic relation with $a < 0$.

27. (a)

29. (a)

The data appear to be linearly related with positive slope.
(b) $R(x) = 0.836x + 1032.273$ **(c)** $1743

The data appear to follow a quadratic relation with $a > 0$.
(b) $P(a) = 0.015a^2 - 1.332a + 39.823$ **(c)** 11.6%

3.5 Assess Your Understanding (page 158)

3. (a) $\{x \mid x < -2 \text{ or } x > 2\}; (-\infty, -2) \text{ or } (2, \infty)$ **(b)** $\{x \mid -2 \le x \le 2\}; [-2, 2]$
5. (a) $\{x \mid -2 \le x \le 1\}; [-2, 1]$ **(b)** $\{x \mid x < -2 \text{ or } x > 1\}; (-\infty, -2) \text{ or } (1, \infty)$
7. $\{x \mid -2 < x < 5\}; (-2, 5)$ **9.** $\{x \mid x < 0 \text{ or } x > 4\}; (-\infty, 0) \text{ or } (4, \infty)$ **11.** $\{x \mid -3 < x < 3\}; (-3, 3)$

13. $\{x \mid x < -4 \text{ or } x > 3\}; (-\infty, -4) \text{ or } (3, \infty)$ **15.** $\left\{x \mid -\dfrac{1}{2} < x < 3\right\}; \left(-\dfrac{1}{2}, 3\right)$ **17.** No real solution   **19.** No real solution

21. $\left\{x \mid x < -\dfrac{2}{3} \text{ or } x > \dfrac{3}{2}\right\}; \left(-\infty, -\dfrac{2}{3}\right) \text{ or } \left(\dfrac{3}{2}, \infty\right)$ **23.** $\{x \mid x \le -4 \text{ or } x \ge 4\}; (-\infty, -4] \text{ or } [4, \infty)$ **25. (a)** $\{-1, 1\}$ **(b)** $\{-1\}$ **(c)** $\{-1, 4\}$
(d) $\{x \mid x < -1 \text{ or } x > 1\}; (-\infty, -1) \text{ or } (1, \infty)$ **(e)** $\{x \mid x \le -1\} \text{ or } (-\infty, -1]$ **(f)** $\{x \mid x < -1 \text{ or } x > 4\}; (-\infty, -1) \text{ or } (4, \infty)$
(g) $\left\{x \mid x \le -\sqrt{2} \text{ or } x \ge \sqrt{2}\right\}; \left(-\infty, -\sqrt{2}\right] \text{ or } \left[\sqrt{2}, \infty\right)$

27. (a) $\{-1, 1\}$ **(b)** $\left\{-\dfrac{1}{4}\right\}$ **(c)** $\{-4, 0\}$ **(d)** $\{x \mid -1 < x < 1\}; (-1, 1)$ **(e)** $\left\{x \mid x \le -\dfrac{1}{4}\right\} \text{ or } \left(-\infty, -\dfrac{1}{4}\right]$ **(f)** $\{x \mid -4 < x < 0\}; (-4, 0)$ **(g)** $\{0\}$

29. (a) $\{-2, 2\}$ **(b)** $\{-2, 2\}$ **(c)** $\{-2, 2\}$ **(d)** $\{x \mid x < -2 \text{ or } x > 2\}; (-\infty, -2) \text{ or } (2, \infty)$ **(e)** $\{x \mid x \le -2 \text{ or } x \ge 2\}; (-\infty, -2] \text{ or } [2, \infty)$
(f) $\{x \mid x < -2 \text{ or } x > 2\}; (-\infty, -2) \text{ or } (2, \infty)$ **(g)** $\left\{x \mid x \le -\sqrt{5} \text{ or } x \ge \sqrt{5}\right\}; \left(-\infty, -\sqrt{5}\right] \text{ or } \left[\sqrt{5}, \infty\right)$

31. (a) $\{-1, 2\}$ **(b)** $\{-2, 1\}$ **(c)** $\{0\}$ **(d)** $\{x \mid x < -1 \text{ or } x > 2\}; (-\infty, -1) \text{ or } (2, \infty)$ **(e)** $\{x \mid -2 \le x \le 1\}; [-2, 1]$ **(f)** $\{x \mid x < 0\}; (-\infty, 0)$

(g) $\left\{x \mid x \le \dfrac{1 - \sqrt{13}}{2} \text{ or } x \ge \dfrac{1 + \sqrt{13}}{2}\right\}; \left(-\infty, \dfrac{1 - \sqrt{13}}{2}\right] \text{ or } \left[\dfrac{1 + \sqrt{13}}{2}, \infty\right)$ **33. (a)** 5 sec   **(b)** The ball is more than 96 ft above the ground
for time t between 2 and 3 sec, $2 < t < 3$.   **35. (a)** $0, $1000   **(b)** The revenue is more than $800,000 for prices between $276.39 and $723.61,
$276.39 < p < $723.61.   **37. (a)** $\{c \mid 0.112 < c < 81.907\}; (0.112, 81.907)$ **(b)** It is possible to hit a target 75 km away if $c = 0.651$ or $c = 1.536$.

Review Exercises *(page 160)*

1. (a) $m = 2; b = -5$ **(b)** 2   **3. (a)** $m = \dfrac{4}{5}; b = -6$ **(b)** $\dfrac{4}{5}$ **5. (a)** $m = 0; b = 4$ **(b)** 0   **7.** Linear; Slope: 5

(c)
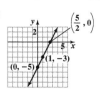

(c)

(c)

(d) Increasing   **(d)** Increasing   **(d)** Constant

9.
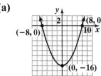

11.

13.

15. (a)

(b) Domain: $(-\infty, \infty)$
Range: $[2, \infty)$
(c) Decreasing: $(-\infty, 2)$
Increasing: $(2, \infty)$

17. (a)

19. (a)
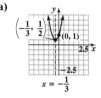

21. (a)

23. (a)

(b) Domain: $(-\infty, \infty)$

Range: $[-16, \infty)$

(c) Decreasing: $(-\infty, 0)$

Increasing: $(0, \infty)$

(b) Domain: $(-\infty, \infty)$

Range: $(-\infty, 1]$

(c) Increasing: $\left(-\infty, \dfrac{1}{2}\right)$

Decreasing: $\left(\dfrac{1}{2}, \infty\right)$

(b) Domain: $(-\infty, \infty)$

Range: $\left[\dfrac{1}{2}, \infty\right)$

(c) Decreasing: $\left(-\infty, -\dfrac{1}{3}\right)$

Increasing: $\left(-\dfrac{1}{3}, \infty\right)$

(b) Domain: $(-\infty, \infty)$

Range: $\left[-\dfrac{7}{3}, \infty\right)$

(c) Decreasing: $\left(-\infty, -\dfrac{2}{3}\right)$

Increasing: $\left(-\dfrac{2}{3}, \infty\right)$

25. Minimum value; 1   **27.** Maximum value; 12   **29.** Maximum value; 16   **31.** $\{x | -8 < x < 2\}; (-8, -2)$

33. $\left\{ x \,\middle|\, x \le -\dfrac{1}{3} \text{ or } x \ge 5 \right\}; \left(-\infty, -\dfrac{1}{3}\right] \text{ or } [5, \infty)$ **35.** $y = x^2 + 2x + 3$

37. (a) Company A: $C(x) = 0.06x + 7$; Company B: $C(x) = 0.08x$ **(b)** 350 min   **(c)** $0 \le x < 350$

39. (a) $R(x) = -\dfrac{1}{10}x^2 + 150x$ **(b)** \$14,000   **(c)** 750; \$56,250   **(d)** \$75   **41.** 4,166,666.7 m²   **43. (a)** 63 clubs   **(b)** \$151.90   **45.** 3.6 ft

47. (a) Quadratic, $a < 0$ **(b)** About \$26.5 thousand
(c) \$6408 thousand
(e)

Chapter Test *(page 162)*

1. (a) Slope: -4; y-intercept: 3
(b) -4 **(c)** Decreasing
(d)

2. $\left(-\dfrac{4}{3}, 0\right)$, $(2, 0)$, $(0, -8)$

3. $\left(\dfrac{2 - \sqrt{6}}{2}, 0\right)$, $\left(\dfrac{2 + \sqrt{6}}{2}, 0\right)$, $(0, 1)$

4. $\{-1, 3\}$

5.

6. (a) Opens up
(b) $(2, -8)$
(c) $x = 2$
(d) x-intercepts: $\dfrac{6 - 2\sqrt{6}}{3}$, $\dfrac{6 + 2\sqrt{6}}{3}$;
y-intercept: 4

(e)

7. Maximum value; 21   **8.** $\{x | x \le 4 \text{ or } x \ge 6\}; (-\infty, 4] \text{ or } [6, \infty)$
9. (a) $C(m) = 0.15m + 129.50$ **(b)** \$258.50   **(c)** 562 miles

Cumulative Review *(page 163)*

1. $5\sqrt{2}; \left(\dfrac{3}{2}, \dfrac{1}{2}\right)$ **2.** $(-2, -1)$ and $(2, 3)$ are on the graph.

3. $\left\{x \,\middle|\, x \geq -\dfrac{3}{5}\right\}$ or $\left[-\dfrac{3}{5}, \infty\right)$ **4.** $y = -2x + 2$ **5.** $y = -\dfrac{1}{2}x + \dfrac{13}{2}$ **6.** $(x - 2)^2 + (y + 4)^2 = 25$

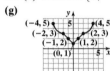   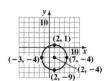

7. Yes   **8. (a)** -3 **(b)** $x^2 - 4x - 2$ **(c)** $x^2 + 4x + 1$ **(d)** $-x^2 + 4x - 1$ **(e)** $x^2 - 3$ **(f)** $2x + h - 4$ **9.** $\left\{z \,\middle|\, z \neq \dfrac{7}{6}\right\}$

10. Yes   **11. (a)** No   **(b)** $-1; (-2, -1)$ is on the graph.   **(c)** $-8; (-8, 2)$ is on the graph.   **12.** Neither   **13.** Local maximum value is 5.30 and occurs at $x = -1.29$. Local minimum value is -3.30 and occurs at $x = 1.29$. Increasing: $(-4, -1.29)$ and $(1.29, 4)$; Decreasing: $(-1.29, 1.29)$

14. (a) -4 **(b)** $\{x \,|\, x > -4\}$ or $(-4, \infty)$

15. (a) Domain: $\{x \,|\, -4 \leq x \leq 4\}$; Range: $\{y \,|\, -1 \leq y \leq 3\}$ **(b)** $(-1, 0), (0, -1), (1, 0)$ **(c)** y-axis   **(d)** 1   **(e)** -4 and 4   **(f)** $\{x \,|\, -1 < x < 1\}$

(g) 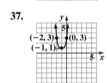   **(h)** 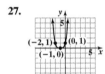   **(i)**   **(j)** Even   **(k)** $(0, 4)$

CHAPTER 4   Polynomial and Rational Functions

4.1 Assess Your Understanding *(page 183)*

7. smooth; continuous   **8.** touches   **9.** $(-1, 1); (0, 0); (1, 1)$ **10.** r is a real zero of f; r is an x-intercept of the graph of f; $x - r$ is a factor of f.
11. turning points   **12.** $y = 3x^4$ **13.** $\infty; -\infty$ **14.** As x increases in the positive direction, $f(x)$ decreases without bound.   **15.** Yes; degree 3

17. Yes; degree 2   **19.** No; x is raised to the -1 power.   **21.** No; x is raised to the $\dfrac{3}{2}$ power.   **23.** Yes; degree 4   **25.** Yes; degree 4

27. 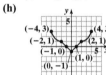   **29.**   **31.** 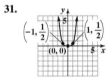   **33.**   **35.**

37.   **39.**   **41.** $f(x) = x^3 - 3x^2 - x + 3$ for $a = 1$ **43.** $f(x) = x^3 - x^2 - 12x$ for $a = 1$
45. $f(x) = x^4 - 15x^2 + 10x + 24$ for $a = 1$ **47.** $f(x) = x^3 - 5x^2 + 3x + 9$ for $a = 1$
49. (a) 7, multiplicity 1; -3, multiplicity 2   **(b)** Graph touches the x-axis at -3 and crosses it at 7.   **(c)** Near -3: $f(x) \approx -30(x + 3)^2$; Near 7: $f(x) \approx 300(x - 7)$
(d) 2   **(e)** $y = 3x^3$

51. (a) 2, multiplicity 3   **(b)** Graph crosses the x-axis at 2.   **(c)** Near 2: $f(x) \approx 20(x - 2)^3$ **(d)** 4   **(e)** $y = 4x^5$ **53. (a)** $-\dfrac{1}{2}$, multiplicity 2; -4,
multiplicity 3   **(b)** Graph touches the x-axis at $-\dfrac{1}{2}$ and crosses at -4 **(c)** Near $-\dfrac{1}{2}$: $f(x) \approx -85.75\left(x + \dfrac{1}{2}\right)^2$; Near -4: $f(x) \approx -24.5(x + 4)^3$

(d) 4   **(e)** $y = -2x^5$ **55. (a)** 5, multiplicity 3; -4, multiplicity 2   **(b)** Graph touches the x-axis at -4 and crosses it at 5.
(c) Near -4: $f(x) \approx -729(x + 4)^2$; Near 5: $f(x) \approx 81(x - 5)^3$ **(d)** 4   **(e)** $y = x^5$ **57. (a)** No real zeros   **(b)** Graph neither crosses nor touches
the x-axis.   **(c)** No real zeros   **(d)** 5   **(e)** $y = 3x^6$ **59. (a)** 0, multiplicity 2; $-\sqrt{2}, \sqrt{2}$, multiplicity 1   **(b)** Graph touches the x-axis at 0 and
crosses at $-\sqrt{2}$ and $\sqrt{2}$.   **(c)** Near $-\sqrt{2}$: $f(x) \approx 11.31(x + \sqrt{2})$; Near 0: $f(x) \approx 4x^2$; Near $\sqrt{2}$: $f(x) \approx -11.31(x - \sqrt{2})$ **(d)** 3   **(e)** $y = -2x^4$
61. Could be; zeros: $-1, 1, 2$; Least degree is 3.   **63.** Cannot be the graph of a polynomial; gap at $x = -1$ **65.** $f(x) = x(x - 1)(x - 2)$

67. $f(x) = -\dfrac{1}{2}(x + 1)(x - 1)^2(x - 2)$

69. Step 1: $y = x^3$
    Step 2: x-intercepts: $0, 3$; y-intercept: 0
    Step 3: 0: multiplicity 2, touches; 3: multiplicity 1, crosses
    Step 4: At most 2 turning points
    Step 5: Near 0: $f(x) \approx -3x^2$; Near 3: $f(x) \approx 9(x - 3)$
    Step 6:
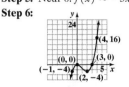

71. Step 1: $y = x^3$
    Step 2: x-intercepts: $-4, 2$; y-intercept: 16
    Step 3: -4: multiplicity 1, crosses; 2: multiplicity 2, touches
    Step 4: At most 2 turning points
    Step 5: Near -4: $f(x) \approx 36(x + 4)$; Near 2: $f(x) \approx 6(x - 2)^2$
    Step 6:

73. Step 1: $y = -2x^4$
Step 2: x-intercepts: $-2, 2$; y-intercept: 32
Step 3: -2: multiplicity 1, crosses; 2: multiplicity 3, crosses
Step 4: At most 3 turning points
Step 5: Near -2: $f(x) \approx 128(x + 2)$; Near 2: $f(x) \approx -8(x - 2)^3$
Step 6:

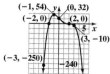

75. Step 1: $y = x^3$
Step 2: x-intercepts: $-4, -1, 2$; y-intercept: -8
Step 3: $-4, -1, 2$: multiplicity 1, crosses
Step 4: At most 2 turning points
Step 5: Near -4: $f(x) \approx 18(x + 4)$; Near -1: $f(x) \approx -9(x + 1)$;
Near 2: $f(x) \approx 18(x - 2)$
Step 6:

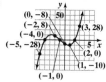

77. Step 1: $y = x^4$
Step 2: x-intercepts: $-2, 0, 2$; y-intercept: 0
Step 3: $-2, 2$, multiplicity 1, crosses; 0, multiplicity 2, touches
Step 4: At most 3 turning points
Step 5: Near -2: $f(x) \approx -16(x + 2)$; Near 0: $f(x) \approx -4x^2$;
Near 2: $f(x) \approx 16(x - 2)$
Step 6:

79. Step 1: $y = x^4$
Step 2: x-intercepts: $-1, 2$; y-intercept: 4
Step 3: $-1, 2$: multiplicity 2, touches
Step 4: At most 3 turning points
Step 5: Near -1: $f(x) \approx 9(x + 1)^2$; Near 2: $f(x) \approx 9(x - 2)^2$
Step 6:

81. Step 1: $y = x^4$
Step 2: x-intercepts: $-1, 0, 3$; y-intercept: 0
Step 3: $-1, 3$: multiplicity 1, crosses; 0: multiplicity 2, touches
Step 4: At most 3 turning points
Step 5: Near -1: $f(x) \approx -4(x + 1)$; Near 0: $f(x) \approx -3x^2$;
Near 3: $f(x) \approx 36(x - 3)$
Step 6:

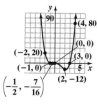

83. Step 1: $y = x^4$
Step 2: x-intercepts: $-2, 4$; y-intercept: 64
Step 3: $-2, 4$, multiplicity 2, touches
Step 4: At most 3 turning points
Step 5: Near -2: $f(x) \approx 36(x + 2)^2$; Near 4: $f(x) \approx 36(x - 4)^2$
Step 6:

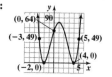

85. Step 1: $y = x^5$
Step 2: x-intercepts: $0, 2$; y-intercept: 0
Step 3: 2, multiplicity 1, crosses;
0, multiplicity 2, touches
Step 4: At most 4 turning points
Step 5: Near 0: $f(x) \approx -6x^2$;
Near 2: $f(x) \approx 28(x - 2)$
Step 6:

87. Step 1: $y = x^3$
Step 2:

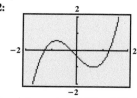

Step 3: x-intercepts: $-1.26, -0.20, 1.26$
y-intercept: -0.31752
Step 4:

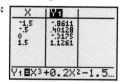

Step 5: $(-0.80, 0.57)$; $(0.66, -0.99)$
Step 6:

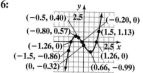

Step 7: Domain: $(-\infty, \infty)$;
Range: $(-\infty, \infty)$
Step 8: Increasing on $(-\infty, -0.80)$
and $(0.66, \infty)$
Decreasing on $(-0.80, 0.66)$

89. Step 1: $y = x^3$
Step 2:

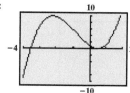

Step 3: x-intercepts: $-3.56, 0.50$
y-intercept: 0.89

Step 4:

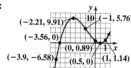

Step 5: $(-2.21, 9.91)$; $(0.50, 0)$

Step 6:

Step 7: Domain: $(-\infty, \infty)$;
Range: $(-\infty, \infty)$
Step 8: Increasing on $(-\infty, -2.21)$
and $(0.50, \infty)$
Decreasing on $(-2.21, 0.50)$

91. Step 1: $y = x^4$
    Step 2:

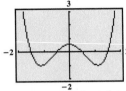

Step 3: x-intercepts: $-1.5, -0.5, 0.5, 1.5$
      y-intercept: 0.5625

Step 4:

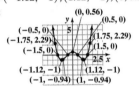

Step 5: $(-1.12, -1); (1.12, -1), (0, 0.56)$
Step 6:

Step 7: Domain: $(-\infty, \infty)$;
      Range: $[-1, \infty)$
Step 8: Increasing on $(-1.12, 0)$ and $(1.12, \infty)$
      Decreasing on $(-\infty, -1.12)$
      and $(0, 1.12)$

93. Step 1: $y = 2x^4$
    Step 2:

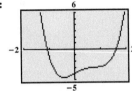

Step 3: x-intercepts: $-1.07, 1.62$;
      y-intercept: -4

Step 4:

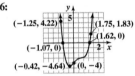

Step 5: $(-0.42, -4.64)$
Step 6:

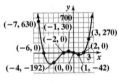

Step 7: Domain: $(-\infty, \infty)$;
      Range: $[-4.64, \infty)$
Step 8: Increasing on $(-0.42, \infty)$
      Decreasing on $(-\infty, -0.42)$

95. $f(x) = -x(x + 2)(x - 2)$
    Step 1: $y = -x^3$
    Step 2: x-intercepts: $-2, 0, 2$; y-intercept: 0
    Step 3: $-2, 0, 2$: multiplicity 1, crosses
    Step 4: At most 2 turning points
    Step 5: Near -2: $f(x) \approx -8(x + 2)$;
        Near 0: $f(x) \approx 4x$;
        Near 2: $f(x) \approx -8(x - 2)$
    Step 6:

97. $f(x) = x(x + 4)(x - 3)$
    Step 1: $y = x^3$
    Step 2: x-intercepts: $-4, 0, 3$; y-intercept: 0
    Step 3: $-4, 0, 3$: multiplicity 1, crosses
    Step 4: At most 2 turning points
    Step 5: Near -4: $f(x) \approx 28(x + 4)$;
        Near 0: $f(x) \approx -12x$;
        Near 3: $f(x) \approx 21(x - 3)$
    Step 6:

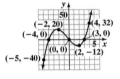

99. $f(x) = 2x(x + 6)(x - 2)(x + 2)$
    Step 1: $y = 2x^4$
    Step 2: x-intercepts: $-6, -2, 0, 2$;
      y-intercept: 0
    Step 3: $-6, -2, 0, 2$: multiplicity 1, crosses
    Step 4: At most 3 turning points
    Step 5: Near -6: $f(x) \approx -384(x + 6)$;
        Near -2: $f(x) \approx 64(x + 2)$;
        Near 0: $f(x) \approx -48x$;
        Near 2: $f(x) \approx 128(x - 2)$

    Step 6:

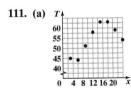

101. $f(x) = -x^2(x + 1)^2(x - 1)$
    Step 1: $y = -x^5$
    Step 2: x-intercepts: $-1, 0, 1$;
      y-intercept: 0
    Step 3: 1: multiplicity 1, crosses;
        $-1, 0$: multiplicity 2, touches
    Step 4: At most 4 turning points
    Step 5: Near -1: $f(x) \approx 2(x + 1)^2$;
        Near 0: $f(x) \approx x^2$;
        Near 1: $-4(x - 1)$

Step 6:

103. $f(x) = 3(x + 3)(x - 1)(x - 4)$
105. $f(x) = -2(x + 5)^2(x - 2)(x - 4)$
107. (a) $-3, 2$ **(b)** $-6, -1$

109. (a)

The relation appears to be cubic.

(b) $H(x) = 0.1591x^3 - 2.3203x^2 + 9.3301x - 2.2143$
(c) About 6 major hurricanes

(d)

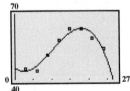

(e) Approximately 10 major hurricanes

111. (a)

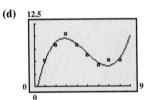

The relation appears to be cubic.

(b) Average rate of change: $2.27°/h$
(c) Average rate of change: $0°/h$
(d) $T(x) = -0.0103x^3 + 0.3174x^2 - 1.3742x + 45.3929$; The predicted temperature at 5 PM is $63.2°F$.

(e)

(f) The y-intercept, $45.4°$, is the predicted temperature at midnight.

113. (a)

(b)

(c)

(d) As more terms are added, the values of the polynomial function get closer to the values of f. The approximations near 0 are better than those near -1 or 1.

119. (a)–(d)

4.2 Assess Your Understanding *(page 196)*

5. F   **6.** horizontal asymptote   **7.** vertical asymptote   **8.** proper   **9.** T   **10.** F   **11.** $y = 0$ **12.** T   **13.** All real numbers except 3; $\{x \mid x \neq 3\}$

15. All real numbers except 2 and -4; $\{x \mid x \neq 2, x \neq -4\}$ **17.** All real numbers except $-\frac{1}{2}$ and 3; $\left\{x \mid x \neq -\frac{1}{2}, x \neq 3\right\}$

19. All real numbers except 2; $\{x \mid x \neq 2\}$ **21.** All real numbers   **23.** All real numbers except -3 and 3; $\{x \mid x \neq -3, x \neq 3\}$

25. (a) Domain: $\{x \mid x \neq 2\}$; Range: $\{y \mid y \neq 1\}$ **(b)** $(0,0)$ **(c)** $y = 1$ **(d)** $x = 2$ **(e)** None

27. (a) Domain: $\{x \mid x \neq 0\}$; Range: all real numbers   **(b)** $(-1,0),(1,0)$ **(c)** None   **(d)** $x = 0$ **(e)** $y = 2x$

29. (a) Domain: $\{x \mid x \neq -2, x \neq 2\}$; Range: $\{y \mid y \leq 0, y > 1\}$ **(b)** $(0,0)$ **(c)** $y = 1$ **(d)** $x = -2, x = 2$ **(e)** None

31.   **33.**   **35.**   **37.**   **39.**   **41.**

43. Vertical asymptote: $x = -4$; horizontal asymptote: $y = 3$ **45.** Vertical asymptote: $x = 3$; oblique asymptote: $y = x + 5$

47. Vertical asymptotes: $x = 1, x = -1$; horizontal asymptote: $y = 0$ **49.** Vertical asymptote: $x = -\frac{1}{3}$; horizontal asymptote: $y = \frac{2}{3}$

51. Vertical asymptote: none; oblique asymptote: $y = 2x - 1$ **53.** Vertical asymptote: $x = 0$; no horizontal or oblique asymptote

55. (a) 9.8208 m/sec^2 **(b)** 9.8195 m/sec^2 **(c)** 9.7936 m/sec^2 **(d)** h-axis   **(e)** $\varnothing$

57. (a) 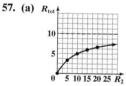   **(b)** Horizontal: $R_{tot} = 10$; as the resistance of R_2 increases without bound, the total resistance approaches 10 ohms, the resistance R_1.   **(c)** $R_1 \approx 103.5$ ohms

4.3 Assess Your Understanding *(page 211)*

2. in lowest terms   **3.** vertical   **4.** True   **5.** True   **6. (a)** $\{x \mid x \neq 2\}$ **(b)** 0

7. 1. Domain: $\{x \mid x \neq 0, x \neq -4\}$ **2.** R is in lowest terms   **3.** no y-intercept; x-intercept: -1
   4. R is in lowest terms; vertical asymptotes: $x = 0, x = -4$ **5.** Horizontal asymptote: $y = 0$, intersected at $(-1,0)$

6.

Interval	$(-\infty, -4)$	$(-4, -1)$	$(-1, 0)$	$(0, \infty)$
Number Chosen	-5	-2	$-\frac{1}{2}$	1
Value of R	$R(-5) = -\frac{4}{5}$	$R(-2) = \frac{1}{4}$	$R\left(-\frac{1}{2}\right) = -\frac{2}{7}$	$R(1) = \frac{2}{5}$
Location of Graph	Below x-axis	Above x-axis	Below x-axis	Above x-axis
Point on Graph	$\left(-5, -\frac{4}{5}\right)$	$\left(-2, \frac{1}{4}\right)$	$\left(-\frac{1}{2}, -\frac{2}{7}\right)$	$\left(1, \frac{2}{5}\right)$

7/8.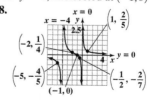

9. 1. $R(x) = \dfrac{3(x+1)}{2(x+2)}$; domain: $\{x \mid x \neq -2\}$ **2.** R is in lowest terms   **3.** y-intercept: $\dfrac{3}{4}$; x-intercept: -1

  4. R is in lowest terms; vertical asymptote: $x = -2$ **5.** Horizontal asymptote: $y = \dfrac{3}{2}$, not intersected

6.

Interval	$(-\infty, -2)$	$(-2, -1)$	$(-1, \infty)$
Number Chosen	-3	$-\frac{3}{2}$	0
Value of R	$R(-3) = 3$	$R\left(-\frac{3}{2}\right) = -\frac{3}{2}$	$R(0) = \frac{3}{4}$
Location of Graph	Above x-axis	Below x-axis	Above x-axis
Point on Graph	$(-3, 3)$	$\left(-\frac{3}{2}, -\frac{3}{2}\right)$	$\left(0, \frac{3}{4}\right)$

7/8.

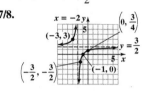

11. 1. $R(x) = \dfrac{3}{(x+2)(x-2)}$; domain: $\{x \mid x \neq -2, x \neq 2\}$ **2.** R is in lowest terms   **3.** y-intercept: $-\dfrac{3}{4}$; no x-intercept

  4. R is in lowest terms; vertical asymptotes: $x = 2, x = -2$ **5.** Horizontal asymptote: $y = 0$, not intersected

6.

Interval	$(-\infty, -2)$	$(-2, 2)$	$(2, \infty)$
Number Chosen	-3	0	3
Value of R	$R(-3) = \frac{3}{5}$	$R(0) = -\frac{3}{4}$	$R(3) = \frac{3}{5}$
Location of Graph	Above x-axis	Below x-axis	Above x-axis
Point on Graph	$\left(-3, \frac{3}{5}\right)$	$\left(0, -\frac{3}{4}\right)$	$\left(3, \frac{3}{5}\right)$

7/8.

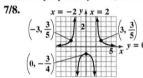

13. 1. $P(x) = \dfrac{(x^2 + x + 1)(x^2 - x + 1)}{(x+1)(x-1)}$; domain: $\{x \mid x \neq -1, x \neq 1\}$ **2.** P is in lowest terms   **3.** y-intercept: -1; no x-intercept

  4. P is in lowest terms; vertical asymptotes: $x = -1, x = 1$ **5.** No horizontal or oblique asymptote

6.

Interval	$(-\infty, -1)$	$(-1, 1)$	$(1, \infty)$
Number Chosen	-2	0	2
Value of P	$P(-2) = 7$	$P(0) = -1$	$P(2) = 7$
Location of Graph	Above x-axis	Below x-axis	Above x-axis
Point on Graph	$(-2, 7)$	$(0, -1)$	$(2, 7)$

7/8.

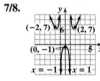

15. 1. $H(x) = \dfrac{(x-1)(x^2 + x + 1)}{(x+3)(x-3)}$; domain: $\{x \mid x \neq -3, x \neq 3\}$ **2.** H is in lowest terms   **3.** y-intercept: $\dfrac{1}{9}$; x-intercept: 1

  4. H is in lowest terms; vertical asymptotes: $x = 3, x = -3$ **5.** Oblique asymptote: $y = x$, intersected at $\left(\dfrac{1}{9}, \dfrac{1}{9}\right)$

6.

Interval	$(-\infty, -3)$	$(-3, 1)$	$(1, 3)$	$(3, \infty)$
Number Chosen	-4	0	2	4
Value of H	$H(-4) \approx -9.3$	$H(0) = \frac{1}{9}$	$H(2) = -1.4$	$H(4) = 9$
Location of Graph	Below x-axis	Above x-axis	Below x-axis	Above x-axis
Point on Graph	$(-4, -9.3)$	$\left(0, \frac{1}{9}\right)$	$(2, -1.4)$	$(4, 9)$

7/8.

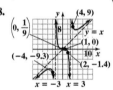

17. 1. $R(x) = \dfrac{x^2}{(x+3)(x-2)}$; domain: $\{x \neq -3, x \neq 2\}$ **2.** R is in lowest terms   **3.** y-intercept: 0; x-intercept: 0

  4. R is in lowest terms; vertical asymptotes: $x = 2, x = -3$ **5.** Horizontal asymptote: $y = 1$, intersected at $(6, 1)$

6.

Interval	$(-\infty, -3)$	$(-3, 0)$	$(0, 2)$	$(2, \infty)$
Number Chosen	-6	-1	1	3
Value of R	$R(-6) = 1.5$	$R(-1) = -\frac{1}{6}$	$R(1) = -0.25$	$R(3) = 1.5$
Location of Graph	Above x-axis	Below x-axis	Below x-axis	Above x-axis
Point on Graph	$(-6, 1.5)$	$\left(-1, -\frac{1}{6}\right)$	$(1, -0.25)$	$(3, 1.5)$

7/8.

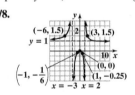

19. 1. $G(x) = \dfrac{x}{(x+2)(x-2)}$; domain: $\{x \mid x \neq -2, x \neq 2\}$ **2.** G is in lowest terms   **3.** y-intercept: 0; x-intercept: 0

  4. G is in lowest terms; vertical asymptotes: $x = -2, x = 2$ **5.** Horizontal asymptote: $y = 0$, intersected at $(0, 0)$

6.

Interval	$(-\infty, -2)$	$(-2, 0)$	$(0, 2)$	$(2, \infty)$
Number Chosen	-3	-1	1	3
Value of G	$G(-3) = -\frac{3}{5}$	$G(-1) = \frac{1}{3}$	$G(1) = -\frac{1}{3}$	$G(3) = \frac{3}{5}$
Location of Graph	Below x-axis	Above x-axis	Below x-axis	Above x-axis
Point on Graph	$\left(-3, -\frac{3}{5}\right)$	$\left(-1, \frac{1}{3}\right)$	$\left(1, -\frac{1}{3}\right)$	$\left(3, \frac{3}{5}\right)$

7/8.

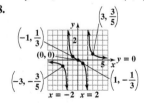

21. **1.** $R(x) = \dfrac{3}{(x-1)(x+2)(x-2)}$; domain: $\{x|x \neq 1, x \neq -2, x \neq 2\}$ **2.** R is in lowest terms **3.** y-intercept: $\dfrac{3}{4}$; no x-intercept

4. R is in lowest terms; vertical asymptotes: $x = -2, x = 1, x = 2$ **5.** Horizontal asymptote: $y = 0$, not intersected

6.

Interval	$(-\infty, -2)$	$(-2, 1)$	$(1, 2)$	$(2, \infty)$
Number Chosen	-3	0	1.5	3
Value of R	$R(-3) = -\frac{3}{20}$	$R(0) = \frac{3}{4}$	$R(1.5) = -\frac{24}{7}$	$R(3) = \frac{3}{10}$
Location of Graph	Below x-axis	Above x-axis	Below x-axis	Above x-axis
Point on Graph	$\left(-3, -\frac{3}{20}\right)$	$\left(0, \frac{3}{4}\right)$	$\left(1.5, -\frac{24}{7}\right)$	$\left(3, \frac{3}{10}\right)$

7/8.

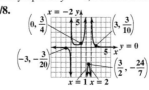

23. **1.** $H(x) = \dfrac{(x+1)(x-1)}{(x^2+4)(x+2)(x-2)}$; domain: $\{x|x \neq -2, x \neq 2\}$ **2.** H is in lowest terms **3.** y-intercept: $\dfrac{1}{16}$; x-intercepts: $-1, 1$

4. H is in lowest terms; vertical asymptotes: $x = -2, x = 2$ **5.** Horizontal asymptote: $y = 0$, intersected at $(-1, 0)$ and $(1, 0)$

6.

Interval	$(-\infty, -2)$	$(-2, -1)$	$(-1, 1)$	$(1, 2)$	$(2, \infty)$
Number Chosen	-3	-1.5	0	1.5	3
Value of H	$H(-3) \approx 0.12$	$H(-1.5) \approx -0.11$	$H(0) = \frac{1}{16}$	$H(1.5) \approx -0.11$	$H(3) \approx 0.12$
Location of Graph	Above x-axis	Below x-axis	Above x-axis	Below x-axis	Above x-axis
Point on Graph	$(-3, 0.12)$	$(-1.5, -0.11)$	$\left(0, \frac{1}{16}\right)$	$(1.5, -0.11)$	$(3, 0.12)$

7/8.

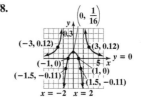

25. **1.** $F(x) = \dfrac{(x+1)(x-4)}{x+2}$; domain: $\{x|x \neq -2\}$ **2.** F is in lowest terms **3.** y-intercept: -2; x-intercepts: $-1, 4$

4. F is in lowest terms; vertical asymptote: $x = -2$ **5.** Oblique asymptote: $y = x - 5$, not intersected

6.

Interval	$(-\infty, -2)$	$(-2, -1)$	$(-1, 4)$	$(4, \infty)$
Number Chosen	-3	-1.5	0	5
Value of F	$F(-3) = -14$	$F(-1.5) = 5.5$	$F(0) = -2$	$F(5) \approx 0.86$
Location of Graph	Below x-axis	Above x-axis	Below x-axis	Above x-axis
Point on Graph	$(-3, -14)$	$(-1.5, 5.5)$	$(0, -2)$	$(5, 0.86)$

7/8.

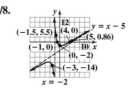

27. **1.** $R(x) = \dfrac{(x+4)(x-3)}{x-4}$; domain: $\{x|x \neq 4\}$ **2.** R is in lowest terms **3.** y-intercept: 3; x-intercepts: $-4, 3$

4. R is in lowest terms; vertical asymptote: $x = 4$ **5.** Oblique asymptote: $y = x + 5$, not intersected

6.

Interval	$(-\infty, -4)$	$(-4, 3)$	$(3, 4)$	$(4, \infty)$
Number Chosen	-5	0	3.5	5
Value of R	$R(-5) = -\frac{8}{9}$	$R(0) = 3$	$R(3.5) = -7.5$	$R(5) = 18$
Location of Graph	Below x-axis	Above x-axis	Below x-axis	Above x-axis
Point on Graph	$\left(-5, -\frac{8}{9}\right)$	$(0, 3)$	$(3.5, -7.5)$	$(5, 18)$

7/8.

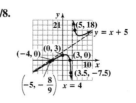

29. **1.** $F(x) = \dfrac{(x+4)(x-3)}{x+2}$; domain: $\{x|x \neq -2\}$ **2.** F is in lowest terms **3.** y-intercept: -6; x-intercepts: $-4, 3$

4. F is in lowest terms; vertical asymptote: $x = -2$ **5.** Oblique asymptote: $y = x - 1$, not intersected

6.

Interval	$(-\infty, -4)$	$(-4, -2)$	$(-2, 3)$	$(3, \infty)$
Number Chosen	-5	-3	0	4
Value of F	$F(-5) = -\frac{8}{3}$	$F(-3) = 6$	$F(0) = -6$	$F(4) = \frac{4}{3}$
Location of Graph	Below x-axis	Above x-axis	Below x-axis	Above x-axis
Point on Graph	$\left(-5, -\frac{8}{3}\right)$	$(-3, 6)$	$(0, -6)$	$\left(4, \frac{4}{3}\right)$

7/8.

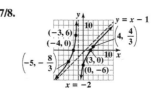

31. **1.** Domain: $\{x|x \neq -3\}$ **2.** R is in lowest terms **3.** y-intercept: 0; x-intercepts: $0, 1$ **4.** Vertical asymptote: $x = -3$
5. Horizontal asymptote: $y = 1$, not intersected

6.

Interval	$(-\infty, -3)$	$(-3, 0)$	$(0, 1)$	$(1, \infty)$
Number Chosen	-4	-1	$\frac{1}{2}$	2
Value of R	$R(-4) = 100$	$R(-1) = -0.5$	$R\left(\frac{1}{2}\right) \approx 0.003$	$R(2) = 0.016$
Location of Graph	Above x-axis	Below x-axis	Above x-axis	Above x-axis
Point on Graph	$(-4, 100)$	$(-1, -0.5)$	$\left(\frac{1}{2}, 0.003\right)$	$(2, 0.016)$

7/8.

See enlarged view at right.

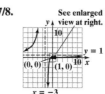

Enlarged view

33. 1. $R(x) = \dfrac{(x+4)(x-3)}{(x+2)(x-3)}$; domain: $\{x \mid x \neq -2, x \neq 3\}$ **2.** In lowest terms, $R(x) = \dfrac{x+4}{x+2}$ **3.** y-intercept: 2; x-intercept: -4

4. Vertical asymptote: $x = -2$; hole at $\left(3, \dfrac{7}{5}\right)$ **5.** Horizontal asymptote: $y = 1$, not intersected

6.

Interval	$(-\infty, -4)$	$(-4, -2)$	$(-2, 3)$	$(3, \infty)$
Number Chosen	-5	-3	0	4
Value of R	$R(-5) = \frac{1}{3}$	$R(-3) = -1$	$R(0) = 2$	$R(4) = \frac{4}{3}$
Location of Graph	Above x-axis	Below x-axis	Above x-axis	Above x-axis
Point on Graph	$\left(-5, \frac{1}{3}\right)$	$(-3, -1)$	$(0, 2)$	$\left(4, \frac{4}{3}\right)$

7/8.

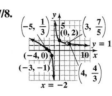

35. 1. $R(x) = \dfrac{(3x+1)(2x-3)}{(x-2)(2x-3)}$; domain: $\left\{x \mid x \neq \dfrac{3}{2}, x \neq 2\right\}$ **2.** In lowest terms, $R(x) = \dfrac{3x+1}{x-2}$ **3.** y-intercept: $-\dfrac{1}{2}$; x-intercept: $-\dfrac{1}{3}$

4. Vertical asymptote: $x = 2$; hole at $\left(\dfrac{3}{2}, -11\right)$ **5.** Horizontal asymptote: $y = 3$, not intersected

6.

Interval	$\left(-\infty, -\frac{1}{3}\right)$	$\left(-\frac{1}{3}, \frac{3}{2}\right)$	$\left(\frac{3}{2}, 2\right)$	$(2, \infty)$
Number Chosen	-1	0	1.7	6
Value of R	$R(-1) = \frac{2}{3}$	$R(0) = -\frac{1}{2}$	$R(1.7) \approx -20.3$	$R(6) = 4.75$
Location of Graph	Above x-axis	Below x-axis	Below x-axis	Above x-axis
Point on Graph	$\left(-1, \frac{2}{3}\right)$	$\left(0, -\frac{1}{2}\right)$	$(1.7, -20.3)$	$(6, 4.75)$

7/8.

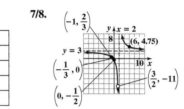

37. 1. $R(x) = \dfrac{(x+3)(x+2)}{x+3}$; domain: $\{x \mid x \neq -3\}$ **2.** In lowest terms, $R(x) = x + 2$ **3.** y-intercept: 2; x-intercept: -2

4. Vertical asymptote: none; hole at $(-3, -1)$ **5.** Oblique asymptote: $y = x + 2$ intersected at all points except $x = -3$

6.

Interval	$(-\infty, -3)$	$(-3, -2)$	$(-2, \infty)$
Number Chosen	-4	$-\frac{5}{2}$	0
Value of R	$R(-4) = -2$	$R\left(-\frac{5}{2}\right) = -\frac{1}{2}$	$R(0) = 2$
Location of Graph	Below x-axis	Below x-axis	Above x-axis
Point on Graph	$(-4, -2)$	$\left(-\frac{5}{2}, -\frac{1}{2}\right)$	$(0, 2)$

7/8.

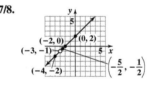

39. 1. $f(x) = \dfrac{x^2 + 1}{x}$; domain: $\{x \mid x \neq 0\}$ **2.** f is in lowest terms   **3.** no y-intercept; no x-intercepts

4. f is in lowest terms; vertical asymptote: $x = 0$ **5.** Oblique asymptote: $y = x$, not intersected

6.

Interval	$(-\infty, 0)$	$(0, \infty)$
Number Chosen	-1	1
Value of f	$f(-1) = -2$	$f(1) = 2$
Location of Graph	Below x-axis	Above x-axis
Point on Graph	$(-1, -2)$	$(1, 2)$

7/8.

41. 1. $f(x) = \dfrac{x^3 + 1}{x} = \dfrac{(x+1)(x^2 - x + 1)}{x}$; domain: $\{x \mid x \neq 0\}$ **2.** f is in lowest terms   **3.** no y-intercept; x-intercept: -1

4. f is in lowest terms; vertical asymptote: $x = 0$ **5.** No horizontal or oblique asymptote

6.

Interval	$(-\infty, -1)$	$(-1, 0)$	$(0, \infty)$
Number Chosen	-2	$-\frac{1}{2}$	1
Value of f	$f(-2) = \frac{7}{2}$	$f\left(-\frac{1}{2}\right) = -\frac{7}{4}$	$f(1) = 2$
Location of Graph	Above x-axis	Below x-axis	Above x-axis
Point on Graph	$\left(-2, \frac{7}{2}\right)$	$\left(-\frac{1}{2}, -\frac{7}{4}\right)$	$(1, 2)$

7/8.

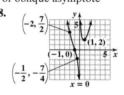

43. 1. $f(x) = \dfrac{x^4 + 1}{x^3}$; domain: $\{x \mid x \neq 0\}$ **2.** f is in lowest terms   **3.** no y-intercept; no x-intercepts

4. f is in lowest terms; vertical asymptote: $x = 0$ **5.** Oblique asymptote: $y = x$, not intersected

6.

Interval	$(-\infty, 0)$	$(0, \infty)$
Number Chosen	-1	1
Value of f	$f(-1) = -2$	$f(1) = 2$
Location of Graph	Below x-axis	Above x-axis
Point on Graph	$(-1, -2)$	$(1, 2)$

7/8.

45. One possibility: $R(x) = \dfrac{x^2}{x^2 - 4}$ **47.** One possibility: $R(x) = \dfrac{(x-1)(x-3)\left(x^2 + \dfrac{4}{3}\right)}{(x+1)^2(x-2)^2}$

49. (a) t-axis; $C(t) \to 0$

(b)
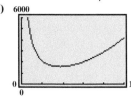

(c) 0.71 h after injection

51. (a) $C(x) = 16x + \dfrac{5000}{x} + 100$

(b) $x > 0$

(c)
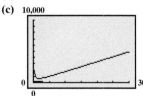

(d) Approximately 17.7 ft by 56.6 ft (longer side parallel to river)

53. (a) $S(x) = 2x^2 + \dfrac{40{,}000}{x}$

(b)
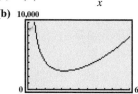

(c) 2784.95 in.^{2}

(d) 21.54 in. $\times$ 21.54 in. $\times$ 21.54 in.

(e) To minimize the cost of materials needed for construction

55. (a) $C(r) = 12\pi r^2 + \dfrac{4000}{r}$

(b)
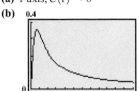

The cost is smallest when $r = 3.76$ cm.

57. No. Each function is a quotient of polynomials, but it is not written in lowest terms. Each function is undefined for $x = 1$; each graph has a hole at $x = 1$.

63. If there is a common factor between the numerator and the denominator, and the factor yields a real zero, then the graph will have a hole.

4.4 Assess Your Understanding *(page 217)*

3. T   **4.** F   **5. (a)** $\{x | 0 < x < 1 \text{ or } x > 2\}$; $(0,1) \cup (2,\infty)$ **(b)** $\{x | x \le 0 \text{ or } 1 \le x \le 2\}$; $(-\infty,0] \cup [1,2]$

7. (a) $\{x | -1 < x < 0 \text{ or } x > 1\}$; $(-1,0) \cup (1,\infty)$ **(b)** $\{x | x < -1 \text{ or } 0 \le x < 1\}$; $(-\infty,-1) \cup [0,1)$

9. $\{x | x < 0 \text{ or } 0 < x < 3\}$; $(-\infty,0) \cup (0,3)$ **11.** $\{x | x \ge -4\}$; $[-4,\infty)$ **13.** $\{x | x \le -2 \text{ or } x \ge 2\}$; $(-\infty,-2] \cup [2,\infty)$

15. $\{x | -4 < x < -1 \text{ or } x > 0\}$; $(-4,-1) \cup (0,\infty)$ **17.** $\{x | -2 < x \le -1\}$; $(-2,-1]$ **19.** $\{x | x < -2\}$; $(-\infty,-2)$ **21.** $\{x | x > 4\}$; $(4,\infty)$

23. $\{x | -4 < x < 0 \text{ or } x > 0\}$; $(-4,0) \cup (0,\infty)$ **25.** $\{x | x \le 1 \text{ or } 2 \le x \le 3\}$; $(-\infty,1] \cup [2,3]$ **27.** $\{x | -1 < x < 0 \text{ or } x > 3\}$; $(-1,0) \cup (3,\infty)$

29. $\{x | x < -1 \text{ or } x > 1\}$; $(-\infty,-1) \cup (1,\infty)$ **31.** $\{x | x < -1 \text{ or } x > 1\}$; $(-\infty,-1) \cup (1,\infty)$ **33.** $\{x | x < -1 \text{ or } x > 1\}$; $(-\infty,-1) \cup (1,\infty)$

35. $\{x | x \le -1 \text{ or } 0 < x \le 1\}$; $(-\infty,-1] \cup (0,1]$ **37.** $\{x | x < -1 \text{ or } x > 1\}$; $(-\infty,-1) \cup (1,\infty)$ **39.** $\{x | x < 2\}$; $(-\infty,2)$

41. $\{x | -2 < x \le 9\}$; $(-2,9]$ **43.** $\{x | x < 2 \text{ or } 3 < x < 5\}$; $(-\infty,2) \cup (3,5)$ **45.** $\{x | x < -5 \text{ or } -4 \le x \le -3 \text{ or } x = 0 \text{ or } x > 1\}$;

$(-\infty,-5) \cup [-4,-3] \cup \{0\} \cup (1,\infty)$ **47.** $\left\{x \left| -\dfrac{1}{2} < x < 1 \text{ or } x > 3\right.\right\}$; $\left(-\dfrac{1}{2},1\right) \cup (3,\infty)$ **49.** $\{x | -1 < x < 3 \text{ or } x > 5\}$; $(-1,3) \cup (5,\infty)$

51. $\left\{x \left| x \le -4 \text{ or } x \ge \dfrac{1}{2}\right.\right\}$; $(-\infty,-4] \cup \left[\dfrac{1}{2},\infty\right)$ **53.** $\{x | x < 3 \text{ or } x \ge 7\}$; $(-\infty,3) \cup [7,\infty)$ **55.** $\{x | x < 2\}$; $(-\infty,2)$

57. $\left\{x \left| x < -\dfrac{2}{3} \text{ or } 0 < x < \dfrac{3}{2}\right.\right\}$; $\left(-\infty,-\dfrac{2}{3}\right) \cup \left(0,\dfrac{3}{2}\right)$ **59.** $\{x | x \le -3 \text{ or } 0 \le x \le 3\}$; $(-\infty,-3] \cup [0,3]$ **61.** $\{x | x > 4\}$; $(4,\infty)$

63. $\{x | x \le -2 \text{ or } x \ge 2\}$; $(-\infty,-2] \cup [2,\infty)$ **65.** $\{x | x < -4 \text{ or } x \ge 2\}$; $(-\infty,-4) \cup [2,\infty)$

67.
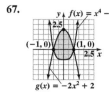

$f(x) \le g(x)$ if $-1 \le x \le 1$

69.
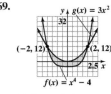

$f(x) \le g(x)$ if $-2 \le x \le 2$

71. Produce at least 250 bicycles

73. (a) The stretch is less than 39 ft.

(b) The ledge should be at least 84 ft above the ground for a 150-lb jumper.

75. At least 50 students must attend.

Historical Problems *(page 230)*

1.
$$\left(x - \frac{b}{3}\right)^3 + b\left(x - \frac{b}{3}\right)^2 + c\left(x - \frac{b}{3}\right) + d = 0$$
$$x^3 - bx^2 + \frac{b^2x}{3} - \frac{b^3}{27} + bx^2 - \frac{2b^2x}{3} + \frac{b^3}{9} + cx - \frac{bc}{3} + d = 0$$
$$x^3 + \left(c - \frac{b^2}{3}\right)x + \left(\frac{2b^3}{27} - \frac{bc}{3} + d\right) = 0$$

Let $p = c - \dfrac{b^2}{3}$ and $q = \dfrac{2b^3}{27} - \dfrac{bc}{3} + d$. Then $x^3 + px + q = 0$.

2.
$$(H + K)^3 + p(H + K) + q = 0$$
$$H^3 + 3H^2K + 3HK^2 + K^3 + pH + pK + q = 0$$

Let $3HK = -p$.
$$H^3 - pH - pK + K^3 + pH + pK + q = 0, \quad H^3 + K^3 = -q$$

3.
$$3HK = -p$$
$$K = -\frac{p}{3H}$$
$$H^3 + \left(-\frac{p}{3H}\right)^3 = -q$$
$$H^3 - \frac{p^3}{27H^3} = -q$$
$$27H^6 - p^3 = -27qH^3$$
$$27H^6 + 27qH^3 - p^3 = 0$$
$$H^3 = \frac{-27q \pm \sqrt{(27q)^2 - 4(27)(-p^3)}}{2 \cdot 27}$$
$$H^3 = \frac{-q}{2} \pm \sqrt{\frac{27^2 q^2}{2^2(27^2)} + \frac{4(27)p^3}{2^2(27^2)}}$$
$$H^3 = \frac{-q}{2} \pm \sqrt{\frac{q^2}{4} + \frac{p^3}{27}}$$
$$H = \sqrt[3]{\frac{-q}{2} + \sqrt{\frac{q^2}{4} + \frac{p^3}{27}}}$$

Choose the positive root for now.

4. $H^3 + K^3 = -q$
$$K^3 = -q - H^3$$
$$K^3 = -q - \left[\frac{-q}{2} + \sqrt{\frac{q^2}{4} + \frac{p^3}{27}}\right]$$
$$K^3 = \frac{-q}{2} - \sqrt{\frac{q^2}{4} + \frac{p^3}{27}}$$
$$K = \sqrt[3]{\frac{-q}{2} - \sqrt{\frac{q^2}{4} + \frac{p^3}{27}}}$$

5. $x = H + K$
$$x = \sqrt[3]{\frac{-q}{2} + \sqrt{\frac{q^2}{4} + \frac{p^3}{27}}} + \sqrt[3]{\frac{-q}{2} - \sqrt{\frac{q^2}{4} + \frac{p^3}{27}}}$$

(Note that had we used the negative root in 3 the result would be the same.)

6. $x = 3$ **7.** $x = 2$ **8.** $x = 2$

4.5 Assess Your Understanding (page 230)

5. Remainder; dividend **6.** $f(c)$ **7.** -4 **8.** F **9.** 0 **10.** T **11.** $R = f(2) = 8$; no **13.** $R = f(2) = 0$; yes **15.** $R = f(-3) = 0$; yes

17. $R = f(-4) = 1$; no **19.** $R = f\left(\frac{1}{2}\right) = 0$; yes **21.** 7 **23.** 6 **25.** 3 **27.** 4 **29.** 5 **31.** 6 **33.** $\pm 1, \pm\frac{1}{3}$ **35.** $\pm 1, \pm 3$

37. $\pm 1, \pm 2, \pm\frac{1}{4}, \pm\frac{1}{2}$ **39.** $\pm 1, \pm 3, \pm 9, \pm\frac{1}{2}, \pm\frac{1}{3}, \pm\frac{1}{6}, \pm\frac{3}{2}, \pm\frac{9}{2}$ **41.** $\pm 1, \pm 2, \pm 3, \pm 4, \pm 6, \pm 12, \pm\frac{1}{2}, \pm\frac{3}{2}$

43. $\pm 1, \pm 2, \pm 4, \pm 5, \pm 10, \pm 20, \pm\frac{1}{2}, \pm\frac{5}{2}, \pm\frac{1}{3}, \pm\frac{2}{3}, \pm\frac{4}{3}, \pm\frac{5}{3}, \pm\frac{10}{3}, \pm\frac{20}{3}, \pm\frac{1}{6}, \pm\frac{5}{6}$ **45.** $-3, -1, 2; f(x) = (x + 3)(x + 1)(x - 2)$

47. $\frac{1}{2}; f(x) = 2\left(x - \frac{1}{2}\right)(x^2 + 1)$ **49.** $2, \sqrt{5}, -\sqrt{5}; f(x) = 2(x - 2)(x - \sqrt{5})(x + \sqrt{5})$

51. $-1, \frac{1}{2}, \sqrt{3}, -\sqrt{3}; f(x) = 2(x + 1)\left(x - \frac{1}{2}\right)(x - \sqrt{3})(x + \sqrt{3})$ **53.** 1, multiplicity 2; $-2, -1; f(x) = (x + 2)(x + 1)(x - 1)^2$

55. $-1, -\frac{1}{4}; f(x) = 4(x + 1)\left(x + \frac{1}{4}\right)(x^2 + 2)$ **57.** $\{-1, 2\}$ **59.** $\left\{\frac{2}{3}, -1 + \sqrt{2}, -1 - \sqrt{2}\right\}$ **61.** $\left\{\frac{1}{3}, \sqrt{5}, -\sqrt{5}\right\}$ **63.** $\{-3, -2\}$ **65.** $\left\{-\frac{1}{3}\right\}$

67. $\left\{\frac{1}{2}, 2, 5\right\}$ **69.** 5 **71.** 2 **73.** 5 **75.** $\frac{3}{2}$ **77.** $f(0) = -1; f(1) = 10$ **79.** $f(-5) = -58; f(-4) = 2$ **81.** $f(1.4) = -0.17536; f(1.5) = 1.40625$

83. 0.21 **85.** -4.04 **87.** 1.15 **89.** 2.53

91.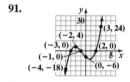

93.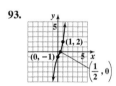

95.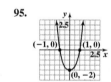

97.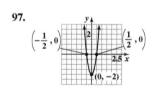

99.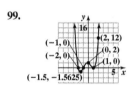

101.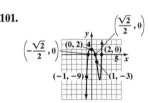

103. $k = 5$ **105.** -7 **107.** If $f(x) = x^n - c^n$, then $f(c) = c^n - c^n = 0$, so $x - c$ is a factor of f. **109.** 5 **111.** 7 in. **113.** All the potential rational zeros are integers, so r is either an integer or is not a rational zero (and is therefore irrational).

115. 0.215 **117.** No; by the Rational Zeros Theorem, $\frac{1}{3}$ is not a potential rational zero.

119. No; by the Rational Zeros Theorem, $\frac{2}{3}$ is not a potential rational zero.

4.6 Assess Your Understanding (page 238)

3. one **4.** $3 - 4i$ **5.** T **6.** F **7.** $4 + i$ **9.** $-i, 1 - i$ **11.** $-i, -2i$ **13.** $-i$ **15.** $2 - i, -3 + i$ **17.** $f(x) = x^4 - 14x^3 + 77x^2 - 200x + 208; a = 1$

19. $f(x) = x^5 - 4x^4 + 7x^3 - 8x^2 + 6x - 4; a = 1$ **21.** $f(x) = x^4 - 6x^3 + 10x^2 - 6x + 9; a = 1$ **23.** $-2i, 4$ **25.** $2i, -3, \frac{1}{2}$

27. $3 + 2i, -2, 5$ **29.** $4i, -\sqrt{11}, \sqrt{11}, -\frac{2}{3}$ **31.** $1, -\frac{1}{2} - \frac{\sqrt{3}}{2}i, -\frac{1}{2} + \frac{\sqrt{3}}{2}i; f(x) = (x - 1)\left(x + \frac{1}{2} + \frac{\sqrt{3}}{2}i\right)\left(x + \frac{1}{2} - \frac{\sqrt{3}}{2}i\right)$

33. $2, 3 - 2i, 3 + 2i; f(x) = (x - 2)(x - 3 + 2i)(x - 3 - 2i)$ **35.** $-i, i, -2i, 2i; f(x) = (x + i)(x - i)(x + 2i)(x - 2i)$

37. $-5i, 5i, -3, 1; f(x) = (x + 5i)(x - 5i)(x + 3)(x - 1)$ **39.** $-4, \dfrac{1}{3}, 2 - 3i, 2 + 3i; f(x) = 3(x + 4)\left(x - \dfrac{1}{3}\right)(x - 2 + 3i)(x - 2 - 3i)$

41. Zeros that are complex numbers must occur in conjugate pairs; or a polynomial with real coefficients of odd degree must have at least one real zero.
43. If the remaining zero were a complex number, its conjugate would also be a zero, creating a polynomial of degree 5.

Review Exercises *(page 240)*

1. Polynomial of degree 5   **3.** Neither

5.

7.

9.

11. 1. $y = x^3$
   2. x-intercepts: $-4, -2, 0$; y-intercept: 0
   3. $-4, -2, 0$, multiplicity 1, crosses
   4. 2
   5. Near -4: $f(x) \approx 8(x + 4)$
      Near -2: $f(x) \approx -4(x + 2)$
      Near 0: $f(x) \approx 8x$
   6.
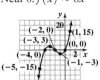

13. 1. $y = x^3$
   2. x-intercepts: $-4, 2$; y-intercept: 16
   3. -4, multiplicity 1, crosses; 2, multiplicity 2, touches
   4. 2
   5. Near -4: $f(x) \approx 36(x + 4)$
      Near 2: $f(x) \approx 6(x - 2)^2$
   6.

15. 1. $y = -2x^3$
   2. $f(x) = -2x^2(x - 2)$
      x-intercepts: $0, 2$; y-intercept: 0
   3. 0, multiplicity 2, touches; 2, multiplicity 1, crosses
   4. 2
   5. Near 0: $f(x) \approx 4x^2$
      Near 2: $f(x) \approx -8(x - 2)$
   6.

17. 1. $y = x^4$
   2. x-intercepts: $-3, -1, 1$; y-intercept: 3
   3. $-3, -1$, multiplicity 1, crosses; 1, multiplicity 2, touches
   4. 3
   5. Near -3: $f(x) \approx -32(x + 3)$
      Near -1: $f(x) \approx 8(x + 1)$; Near 1: $f(x) \approx 8(x - 1)^2$

6.
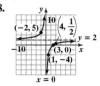

19. Domain: $\{x \mid x \neq -3, x \neq 3\}$: horizontal asymptote: $y = 0$; vertical asymptotes: $x = -3, x = 3$

21. Domain: $\{x \mid x \neq -2\}$; horizontal asymptote: $y = 1$; vertical asymptote: $x = -2$

23. 1. $R(x) = \dfrac{2(x - 3)}{x}$; domain: $\{x \mid x \neq 0\}$ **2.** R is in lowest terms   **3.** no y-intercept; x-intercept: 3
   4. R is in lowest terms; vertical asymptote: $x = 0$ **5.** Horizontal asymptote: $y = 2$; not intersected

6.

Interval	$(-\infty, 0)$	$(0, 3)$	$(3, \infty)$
Number Chosen	-2	1	4
Value of R	$R(-2) = 5$	$R(1) = -4$	$R(4) = \dfrac{1}{2}$
Location of Graph	Above x-axis	Below x-axis	Above x-axis
Point on Graph	$(-2, 5)$	$(1, -4)$	$\left(4, \dfrac{1}{2}\right)$

7/8.
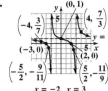

25. 1. Domain: $\{x \mid x \neq 0, x \neq 2\}$ **2.** H is in lowest terms   **3.** no y-intercept; x-intercept: -2
   4. H is in lowest terms; vertical asymptote: $x = 0, x = 2$ **5.** Horizontal asymptote: $y = 0$; intersected at $(-2, 0)$

6.

Interval	$(-\infty, -2)$	$(-2, 0)$	$(0, 2)$	$(2, \infty)$
Number Chosen	-3	-1	1	3
Value of H	$H(-3) = -\dfrac{1}{15}$	$H(-1) = \dfrac{1}{3}$	$H(1) = -3$	$H(3) = \dfrac{5}{3}$
Location of Graph	Below x-axis	Above x-axis	Below x-axis	Above x-axis
Point on Graph	$\left(-3, -\dfrac{1}{15}\right)$	$\left(-1, \dfrac{1}{3}\right)$	$(1, -3)$	$\left(3, \dfrac{5}{3}\right)$

7/8.
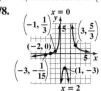

27. 1. $R(x) = \dfrac{(x + 3)(x - 2)}{(x - 3)(x + 2)}$; domain: $\{x \mid x \neq -2, x \neq 3\}$ **2.** R is in lowest terms   **3.** y-intercept: 1; x-intercepts: $-3, 2$
   4. R is in lowest terms; vertical asymptotes: $x = -2, x = 3$ **5.** Horizontal asymptote: $y = 1$; intersected at $(0, 1)$

6.

Interval	$(-\infty, -3)$	$(-3, -2)$	$(-2, 2)$	$(2, 3)$	$(3, \infty)$
Number Chosen	-4	$-\dfrac{5}{2}$	0	$\dfrac{5}{2}$	4
Value of R	$R(-4) = \dfrac{3}{7}$	$R\left(-\dfrac{5}{2}\right) = -\dfrac{9}{11}$	$R(0) = 1$	$R\left(\dfrac{5}{2}\right) = -\dfrac{11}{9}$	$R(4) = \dfrac{7}{3}$
Location of Graph	Above x-axis	Below x-axis	Above x-axis	Below x-axis	Above x-axis
Point on Graph	$\left(-4, \dfrac{3}{7}\right)$	$\left(-\dfrac{5}{2}, -\dfrac{9}{11}\right)$	$(0, 1)$	$\left(\dfrac{5}{2}, -\dfrac{11}{9}\right)$	$\left(4, \dfrac{7}{3}\right)$

7/8.

29. 1. $F(x) = \dfrac{x^3}{(x+2)(x-2)}$; domain: $\{x \mid x \neq -2, x \neq 2\}$ **2.** F is in lowest terms **3.** y-intercept: 0; x-intercept: 0

4. F is in lowest terms; vertical asymptotes: $x = -2, x = 2$ **5.** Oblique asymptote: $y = x$; intersected at $(0, 0)$

6.

Interval	$(-\infty, -2)$	$(-2, 0)$	$(0, 2)$	$(2, \infty)$
Number Chosen	-3	-1	1	3
Value of F	$F(-3) = -\frac{27}{5}$	$F(-1) = \frac{1}{3}$	$F(1) = -\frac{1}{3}$	$F(3) = \frac{27}{5}$
Location of Graph	Below x-axis	Above x-axis	Below x-axis	Above x-axis
Point on Graph	$\left(-3, -\frac{27}{5}\right)$	$\left(-1, \frac{1}{3}\right)$	$\left(1, -\frac{1}{3}\right)$	$\left(3, \frac{27}{5}\right)$

7/8.

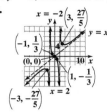

31. 1. Domain: $\{x \mid x \neq 1\}$ **2.** R is in lowest terms **3.** y-intercept: 0; x-intercept: 0 **4.** R is in lowest terms; vertical asymptote: $x = 1$
5. No oblique or horizontal asymptote

6.

Interval	$(-\infty, 0)$	$(0, 1)$	$(1, \infty)$
Number Chosen	-2	$\frac{1}{2}$	2
Value of R	$R(-2) = \frac{32}{9}$	$R\left(\frac{1}{2}\right) = \frac{1}{2}$	$R(2) = 32$
Location of Graph	Above x-axis	Above x-axis	Above x-axis
Point on Graph	$\left(-2, \frac{32}{9}\right)$	$\left(\frac{1}{2}, \frac{1}{2}\right)$	$(2, 32)$

7/8.

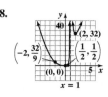

33. 1. $G(x) = \dfrac{(x+2)(x-2)}{(x+1)(x-2)}$; domain: $\{x \mid x \neq -1, x \neq 2\}$ **2.** In lowest terms, $G(x) = \dfrac{x+2}{x+1}$ **3.** y-intercept: 2; x-intercept: -2

4. Vertical asymptote: $x = -1$; hole at $\left(2, \frac{4}{3}\right)$ **5.** Horizontal asymptote: $y = 1$, not intersected

6.

Interval	$(-\infty, -2)$	$(-2, -1)$	$(-1, 2)$	$(2, \infty)$
Number Chosen	-3	$-\frac{3}{2}$	0	3
Value of G	$G(-3) = \frac{1}{2}$	$G\left(-\frac{3}{2}\right) = -1$	$G(0) = 2$	$G(3) = \frac{5}{4}$
Location of Graph	Above x-axis	Below x-axis	Above x-axis	Above x-axis
Point on Graph	$\left(-3, \frac{1}{2}\right)$	$\left(-\frac{3}{2}, -1\right)$	$(0, 2)$	$\left(3, \frac{5}{4}\right)$

7/8.

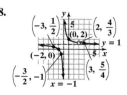

35. $\{x \mid x < -2 \text{ or } -1 < x < 2\}$; $(-\infty, -2) \cup (-1, 2)$

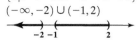

37. $\{x \mid -3 < x \leq 3\}$; $(-3, 3]$

39. $\{x \mid x < 1 \text{ or } x > 2\}$; $(-\infty, 1) \cup (2, \infty)$

41. $\{x \mid 1 \leq x \leq 2 \text{ or } x > 3\}$; $[1, 2] \cup (3, \infty)$

43. $\{x \mid x < -4 \text{ or } 2 < x < 4 \text{ or } x > 6\}$; $(-\infty, -4) \cup (2, 4) \cup (6, \infty)$

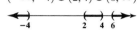

45. $R = 10$; g is not a factor of f. **47.** $R = 0$; g is a factor of f. **49.** $f(4) = 47{,}105$ **51.** $\pm 1, \pm 3, \pm\frac{1}{2}, \pm\frac{3}{2}, \pm\frac{1}{3}, \pm\frac{1}{4}, \pm\frac{3}{4}, \pm\frac{1}{6}, \pm\frac{1}{12}$

53. $-2, 1, 4$; $f(x) = (x+2)(x-1)(x-4)$ **55.** $\frac{1}{2}$, multiplicity 2; -2; $f(x) = 4\left(x - \frac{1}{2}\right)^2(x+2)$ **57.** 2, multiplicity 2; $f(x) = (x-2)^2(x^2+5)$

59. $\{-3, 2\}$ **61.** $\left\{-3, -1, -\frac{1}{2}, 1\right\}$ **63.** 5 **65.** $\frac{37}{2}$ **67.** $f(0) = -1; f(1) = 1$ **69.** $f(0) = -1; f(1) = 1$ **71.** 1.52 **73.** 0.93

75. $4 - i$; $f(x) = x^3 - 14x^2 + 65x - 102$ **77.** $-i, 1 - i$; $f(x) = x^4 - 2x^3 + 3x^2 - 2x + 2$ **79.** $-2, 1, 4$; $f(x) = (x+2)(x-1)(x-4)$

81. $-2, \frac{1}{2}$ (multiplicity 2); $f(x) = 4(x+2)\left(x - \frac{1}{2}\right)^2$ **83.** 2 (multiplicity 2), $-\sqrt{5}i, \sqrt{5}i$; $f(x) = (x + \sqrt{5}i)(x - \sqrt{5}i)(x-2)^2$

85. $-3, 2, -\frac{\sqrt{2}}{2}i, \frac{\sqrt{2}}{2}i$; $f(x) = 2(x+3)(x-2)\left(x + \frac{\sqrt{2}}{2}i\right)\left(x - \frac{\sqrt{2}}{2}i\right)$

87. (a) $A(r) = 2\pi r^2 + \dfrac{500}{r}$

(b) 223.22 cm^2 **(c)** 257.08 cm^2

(d)

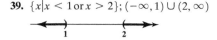

A is smallest when $r \approx 3.41$ cm.

91. (a) Even
(b) Positive
(c) Even
(d) The graph touches the x-axis at $x = 0$, but does not cross it there.
(e) 8

Chapter Test *(page 243)*

1.

2. (a) 3

(b) Every zero of g lies between -15 and 15.

(c) $\dfrac{p}{q}: \pm\dfrac{1}{2}, \pm 1, \pm\dfrac{3}{2}, \pm\dfrac{5}{2}, \pm 3, \pm 5, \pm\dfrac{15}{2}, \pm 15$

(d) $-5, -\dfrac{1}{2}, 3; g(x) = (x + 5)(2x + 1)(x - 3)$

(e) y-intercept: -15; x-intercepts: $-5, -\dfrac{1}{2}, 3$

(f) Crosses at $-5, -\dfrac{1}{2}, 3$

(g) $y = 2x^3$

(h) Near $-5: g(x) \approx 72(x + 5)$

Near $-\dfrac{1}{2}: g(x) \approx -\dfrac{63}{4}(2x + 1)$

Near $3: g(x) \approx 56(x - 3)$

(i)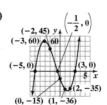

3. $4, -5i, 5i$ **4.** $\left\{1, \dfrac{5 - \sqrt{61}}{6}, \dfrac{5 + \sqrt{61}}{6}\right\}$ **5.** Domain: $\{x \mid x \neq -10, x \neq 4\}$; asymptotes: $x = -10, y = 2$

6. Domain: $\{x \mid x \neq -1\}$; asymptotes: $x = -1, y = x + 1$

7.

9. Answers may vary. One possibility is $r(x) = \dfrac{2(x - 9)(x - 1)}{(x - 4)(x - 9)}$.

10. $f(0) = 8; f(4) = -36$

Since $f(0) = 8 > 0$ and $f(4) = -36 < 0$, the Intermediate Value Theorem guarantees that there is at least one real zero between 0 and 4.

11. $\{x \mid x < 3 \text{ or } x > 8\}; (-\infty, 3) \cup (8, \infty)$

8. Answers may vary. One possibility is
$f(x) = x^4 - 4x^3 - 2x^2 + 20x$.

Cumulative Review *(page 243)*

1. $\sqrt{26}$ **2.** $\{x \mid x \leq 0 \text{ or } x \geq 1\}$; $(-\infty, 0]$ or $[1, \infty)$

3. $\{x \mid -1 < x < 4\}; (-1, 4)$

4. $f(x) = -3x + 1$ **5.** $y = 2x - 1$ **6.**

7. Not a function; 3 has two images. **8.** $\{0, 2, 4\}$ **9.** $\left\{x \mid x \geq \dfrac{3}{2}\right\}; \left[\dfrac{3}{2}, \infty\right)$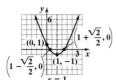

10. Center: $(-2, 1)$; radius: 3

11. x-intercepts: $-3, 0, 3$; y-intercept: 0; symmetric with respect to the origin

12. $y = -\dfrac{2}{3}x + \dfrac{17}{3}$

13. Not a function; it fails the Vertical Line Test.

14. (a) 22 **(b)** $x^2 - 5x - 2$ **(c)** $-x^2 - 5x + 2$ **(d)** $9x^2 + 15x - 2$ **(e)** $2x + h + 5$

15. (a) $\{x \mid x \neq 1\}$ **(b)** No; $(2, 7)$ is on the graph. **(c)** $4; (3, 4)$ is on the graph. **(d)** $\dfrac{7}{4}; \left(\dfrac{7}{4}, 9\right)$ is on the graph. **(e)** Rational

16.

17.

18. $6; y = 6x - 1$

19. (a) x-intercepts: $-5, -1, 5$; y-intercept: -3
(b) No symmetry
(c) Neither
(d) Increasing: $(-\infty, -3)$ and $(2, \infty)$; decreasing: $(-3, 2)$
(e) Local maximum value is 5 and occurs at $x = -3$.
(f) Local minimum value is -6 and occurs at $x = 2$.

20. Odd

21. (a) Domain: $\{x \mid x > -3\}$ or $(-3, \infty)$

(b) x-intercept: $-\dfrac{1}{2}$; y-intercept: 1

(c)

(d) Range: $\{y \mid y < 5\}$ or $(-\infty, 5)$

22.

23. (a) $(f + g)(x) = x^2 - 9x - 6$; domain: all real numbers

(b) $\left(\dfrac{f}{g}\right)(x) = \dfrac{x^2 - 5x + 1}{-4x - 7}$; domain: $\left\{x \mid x \neq -\dfrac{7}{4}\right\}$

24. (a) $R(x) = -\dfrac{1}{10}x^2 + 150x$

(b) \$14,000

(c) 750, \$56,250

(d) \$75

CHAPTER 5 Exponential and Logarithmic Functions

5.1 Assess Your Understanding *(page 252)*

4. composite function; $f(g(x))$ **5.** F **6.** F **7. (a)** -1 **(b)** -1 **(c)** 8 **(d)** 0 **(e)** 8 **(f)** -7 **9. (a)** 4 **(b)** 5 **(c)** -1 **(d)** -2 **11. (a)** 98

(b) 49 **(c)** 4 **(d)** 4 **13. (a)** 97 **(b)** $-\dfrac{163}{2}$ **(c)** 1 **(d)** $-\dfrac{3}{2}$ **15. (a)** $2\sqrt{2}$ **(b)** $2\sqrt{2}$ **(c)** 1 **(d)** 0 **17. (a)** $\dfrac{1}{17}$ **(b)** $\dfrac{1}{5}$ **(c)** 1 **(d)** $\dfrac{1}{2}$

19. (a) $\dfrac{3}{\sqrt[3]{4}+1}$ **(b)** 1 **(c)** $\dfrac{6}{5}$ **(d)** 0 **21.** $\{x|x \neq 0,\ x \neq 2\}$ **23.** $\{x|x \neq -4,\ x \neq 0\}$ **25.** $\left\{x\,\middle|\,x \geq -\dfrac{3}{2}\right\}$ **27.** $\{x|x \geq 1\}$

29. (a) $(f \circ g)(x) = 6x + 3$; all real numbers
(b) $(g \circ f)(x) = 6x + 9$; all real numbers
(c) $(f \circ f)(x) = 4x + 9$; all real numbers
(d) $(g \circ g)(x) = 9x$; all real numbers

31. (a) $(f \circ g)(x) = 3x^2 + 1$; all real numbers
(b) $(g \circ f)(x) = 9x^2 + 6x + 1$; all real numbers
(c) $(f \circ f)(x) = 9x + 4$; all real numbers
(d) $(g \circ g)(x) = x^4$; all real numbers

33. (a) $(f \circ g)(x) = x^4 + 8x^2 + 16$; all real numbers
(b) $(g \circ f)(x) = x^4 + 4$; all real numbers
(c) $(f \circ f)(x) = x^4$; all real numbers
(d) $(g \circ g)(x) = x^4 + 8x^2 + 20$; all real numbers

35. (a) $(f \circ g)(x) = \dfrac{3x}{2 - x}$; $\{x|x \neq 0,\ x \neq 2\}$ **(b)** $(g \circ f)(x) = \dfrac{2(x - 1)}{3}$; $\{x|x \neq 1\}$ **(c)** $(f \circ f)(x) = \dfrac{3(x - 1)}{4 - x}$; $\{x|x \neq 1,\ x \neq 4\}$

(d) $(g \circ g)(x) = x$; $\{x|x \neq 0\}$ **37. (a)** $(f \circ g)(x) = \dfrac{4}{4 + x}$; $\{x|x \neq -4,\ x \neq 0\}$ **(b)** $(g \circ f)(x) = \dfrac{-4(x - 1)}{x}$; $\{x|x \neq 0,\ x \neq 1\}$

(c) $(f \circ f)(x) = x$; $\{x|x \neq 1\}$ **(d)** $(g \circ g)(x) = x$; $\{x|x \neq 0\}$ **39. (a)** $(f \circ g)(x) = \sqrt{2x + 3}$; $\left\{x\,\middle|\,x \geq -\dfrac{3}{2}\right\}$

(b) $(g \circ f)(x) = 2\sqrt{x} + 3$; $\{x|x \geq 0\}$ **(c)** $(f \circ f)(x) = \sqrt[4]{x}$; $\{x|x \geq 0\}$ **(d)** $(g \circ g)(x) = 4x + 9$; all real numbers
41. (a) $(f \circ g)(x) = x$; $\{x|x \geq 1\}$ **(b)** $(g \circ f)(x) = |x|$; all real numbers **(c)** $(f \circ f)(x) = x^4 + 2x^2 + 2$; all real numbers

(d) $(g \circ g)(x) = \sqrt{\sqrt{x - 1} - 1}$; $\{x|x \geq 2\}$ **43. (a)** $(f \circ g)(x) = -\dfrac{4x - 17}{2x - 1}$; $\left\{x\,\middle|\,x \neq 3;\ x \neq \dfrac{1}{2}\right\}$

(b) $(g \circ f)(x) = -\dfrac{3x - 3}{2x + 8}$; $\{x|x \neq -4;\ x \neq -1\}$ **(c)** $(f \circ f)(x) = -\dfrac{2x + 5}{x - 2}$; $\{x|x \neq -1;\ x \neq 2\}$

(d) $(g \circ g)(x) = -\dfrac{3x - 4}{2x - 11}$; $\left\{x\,\middle|\,x \neq \dfrac{11}{2};\ x \neq 3\right\}$ **45.** $(f \circ g)(x) = f(g(x)) = f\left(\dfrac{1}{2}x\right) = 2\left(\dfrac{1}{2}x\right) = x$; $(g \circ f)(x) = g(f(x)) = g(2x) = \dfrac{1}{2}(2x) = x$

47. $(f \circ g)(x) = f(g(x)) = f(\sqrt[3]{x}) = (\sqrt[3]{x})^3 = x$; $(g \circ f)(x) = g(f(x)) = g(x^3) = \sqrt[3]{x^3} = x$

49. $(f \circ g)(x) = f(g(x)) = f\left(\dfrac{1}{2}(x + 6)\right) = 2\left[\dfrac{1}{2}(x + 6)\right] - 6 = x + 6 - 6 = x$;

$(g \circ f)(x) = g(f(x)) = g(2x - 6) = \dfrac{1}{2}(2x - 6 + 6) = \dfrac{1}{2}(2x) = x$

51. $(f \circ g)(x) = f(g(x)) = f\left(\dfrac{1}{a}(x - b)\right) = a\left[\dfrac{1}{a}(x - b)\right] + b = x$; $(g \circ f)(x) = g(f(x)) = g(ax + b) = \dfrac{1}{a}(ax + b - b) = x$
53. $f(x) = x^4$; $g(x) = 2x + 3$ (Other answers are possible.) **55.** $f(x) = \sqrt{x}$; $g(x) = x^2 + 1$ (Other answers are possible.)
57. $f(x) = |x|$; $g(x) = 2x + 1$ (Other answers are possible.) **59.** $(f \circ g)(x) = 11$; $(g \circ f)(x) = 2$ **61.** $-3, 3$
63. (a) $(f \circ g)(x) = acx + ad + b$ **(b)** $(g \circ f)(x) = acx + bc + d$ **(c)** The domains of both $f \circ g$ and $g \circ f$ are all real numbers.

(d) $f \circ g = g \circ f$ when $ad + b = bc + d$ **65.** $S(t) = \dfrac{16}{9}\pi t^6$ **67.** $C(t) = 15{,}000 + 800{,}000t - 40{,}000t^2$

69. $C(p) = \dfrac{2\sqrt{100 - p}}{25} + 600,\ 0 \leq p \leq 100$ **71.** $V(r) = 2\pi r^3$ **73. (a)** $f(x) = 0.7143x$ **(b)** $g(x) = 137.402x$

(c) $g(f(x)) = g(0.7143x) = 98.1462486x$ **(d)** 98,146.2486 yen **75. (a)** $f(p) = p - 200$ **(b)** $g(p) = 0.8p$
(c) $(f \circ g)(p) = 0.8p - 200$; $(g \circ f)(p) = 0.8p - 160$; The 20% discount followed by the \$200 rebate is the better deal.
77. f is an odd function, so $f(-x) = -f(x)$. g is an even function, so $g(-x) = g(x)$. Then $(f \circ g)(-x) = f(g(-x)) = f(g(x)) = (f \circ g)(x)$. So $f \circ g$
is even. Also, $(g \circ f)(-x) = g(f(-x)) = g(-f(x)) = g(f(x)) = (g \circ f)(x)$, so $g \circ f$ is even.

5.2 Assess Your Understanding (page 263)

5. $f(x_1) \neq f(x_2)$ **6.** one-to-one **7.** 3 **8.** $y = x$ **9.** $[4, \infty)$ **10.** T **11.** one-to-one **13.** not one-to-one **15.** not one-to-one **17.** one-to-one
19. one-to-one **21.** not one-to-one **23.** one-to-one

25.

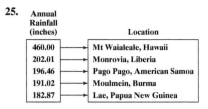

Domain: $\{460.00, 202.01, 196.46, 191.02, 182.87\}$
Range: $\{$Mt Waialeale, Monrovia, Pago Pago, Moulmein, Lae$\}$

27.

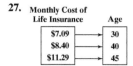

Domain: $\{\$7.09, \$8.40, \$11.29\}$
Range: $\{30, 40, 45\}$

29. $\{(5, -3), (9, -2), (2, -1), (11, 0), (-5, 1)\}$ **31.** $\{(1, -2), (2, -3), (0, -10), (9, 1), (4, 2)\}$
Domain: $\{5, 9, 2, 11, -5\}$ Domain: $\{1, 2, 0, 9, 4\}$
Range: $\{-3, -2, -1, 0, 1\}$ Range: $\{-2, -3, -10, 1, 2\}$

33. $f(g(x)) = f\left(\dfrac{1}{3}(x - 4)\right) = 3\left[\dfrac{1}{3}(x - 4)\right] + 4 = (x - 4) + 4 = x$ **35.** $f(g(x)) = f\left(\dfrac{x}{4} + 2\right) = 4\left[\dfrac{x}{4} + 2\right] - 8 = (x + 8) - 8 = x$

$g(f(x)) = g(3x + 4) = \dfrac{1}{3}[(3x + 4) - 4] = \dfrac{1}{3}(3x) = x$ $g(f(x)) = g(4x - 8) = \dfrac{4x - 8}{4} + 2 = (x - 2) + 2 = x$

37. $f(g(x)) = f(\sqrt[3]{x+8}) = (\sqrt[3]{x+8})^3 - 8 = (x+8) - 8 = x$
$g(f(x)) = g(x^3 - 8) = \sqrt[3]{(x^3 - 8) + 8} = \sqrt[3]{x^3} = x$

39. $f(g(x)) = f\left(\dfrac{1}{x}\right) = \dfrac{1}{\left(\dfrac{1}{x}\right)} = x;\ x \neq 0,\ g(f(x)) = g\left(\dfrac{1}{x}\right) = \dfrac{1}{\left(\dfrac{1}{x}\right)} = x,\ x \neq 0$

41. $f(g(x)) = f\left(\dfrac{4x - 3}{2 - x}\right) = \dfrac{2\left(\dfrac{4x-3}{2-x}\right) + 3}{\dfrac{4x-3}{2-x} + 4}$

$= \dfrac{2(4x - 3) + 3(2 - x)}{4x - 3 + 4(2 - x)} = \dfrac{5x}{5} = x,\ x \neq 2$

$g(f(x)) = g\left(\dfrac{2x + 3}{x + 4}\right) = \dfrac{4\left(\dfrac{2x+3}{x+4}\right) - 3}{2 - \dfrac{2x+3}{x+4}}$

$= \dfrac{4(2x + 3) - 3(x + 4)}{2(x + 4) - (2x + 3)} = \dfrac{5x}{5} = x,\ x \neq -4$

43.

45.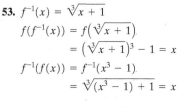

47.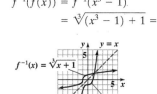

49. $f^{-1}(x) = \dfrac{1}{3}x$

$f(f^{-1}(x)) = f\left(\dfrac{1}{3}x\right) = 3\left(\dfrac{1}{3}x\right) = x$

$f^{-1}(f(x)) = f^{-1}(3x) = \dfrac{1}{3}(3x) = x$

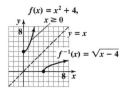

51. $f^{-1}(x) = \dfrac{x}{4} - \dfrac{1}{2}$

$f(f^{-1}(x)) = f\left(\dfrac{x}{4} - \dfrac{1}{2}\right) = 4\left(\dfrac{x}{4} - \dfrac{1}{2}\right) + 2$

$= (x - 2) + 2 = x$

$f^{-1}(f(x)) = f^{-1}(4x + 2) = \dfrac{4x + 2}{4} - \dfrac{1}{2}$

$= \left(x + \dfrac{1}{2}\right) - \dfrac{1}{2} = x$

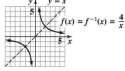

53. $f^{-1}(x) = \sqrt[3]{x + 1}$

$f(f^{-1}(x)) = f(\sqrt[3]{x + 1})$
$= (\sqrt[3]{x + 1})^3 - 1 = x$

$f^{-1}(f(x)) = f^{-1}(x^3 - 1)$
$= \sqrt[3]{(x^3 - 1) + 1} = x$

55. $f^{-1}(x) = \sqrt{x - 4},\ x \geq 4$

$f(f^{-1}(x)) = f(\sqrt{x - 4}) = (\sqrt{x - 4})^2 + 4 = x$

$f^{-1}(f(x)) = f^{-1}(x^2 + 4) = \sqrt{(x^2 + 4) - 4} = \sqrt{x^2} = x,\ x \geq 0$

57. $f^{-1}(x) = \dfrac{4}{x}$

$f(f^{-1}(x)) = f\left(\dfrac{4}{x}\right) = \dfrac{4}{\left(\dfrac{4}{x}\right)} = x$

$f^{-1}(f(x)) = f^{-1}\left(\dfrac{4}{x}\right) = \dfrac{4}{\left(\dfrac{4}{x}\right)} = x$

59. $f^{-1}(x) = \dfrac{2x + 1}{x}$

$f(f^{-1}(x)) = f\left(\dfrac{2x + 1}{x}\right) = \dfrac{1}{\dfrac{2x+1}{x} - 2} = \dfrac{x}{(2x + 1) - 2x} = x$

$f^{-1}(f(x)) = f^{-1}\left(\dfrac{1}{x - 2}\right) = \dfrac{2\left(\dfrac{1}{x-2}\right) + 1}{\dfrac{1}{x-2}} = \dfrac{2 + (x - 2)}{1} = x$

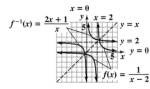

61. $f^{-1}(x) = \dfrac{2 - 3x}{x}$

$f(f^{-1}(x)) = f\left(\dfrac{2 - 3x}{x}\right) = \dfrac{2}{3 + \dfrac{2 - 3x}{x}} = \dfrac{2x}{3x + 2 - 3x} = \dfrac{2x}{2} = x$

$f^{-1}(f(x)) = f^{-1}\left(\dfrac{2}{3 + x}\right) = \dfrac{2 - 3\left(\dfrac{2}{3+x}\right)}{\dfrac{2}{3+x}} = \dfrac{2(3 + x) - 3 \cdot 2}{2} = \dfrac{2x}{2} = x$

63. $f^{-1}(x) = \dfrac{-2x}{x-3}$

$$f(f^{-1}(x)) = f\left(\dfrac{-2x}{x-3}\right) = \dfrac{3\left(\dfrac{-2x}{x-3}\right)}{\dfrac{-2x}{x-3}+2}$$

$$= \dfrac{3(-2x)}{-2x+2(x-3)} = \dfrac{-6x}{-6} = x$$

$$f^{-1}(f(x)) = f^{-1}\left(\dfrac{3x}{x+2}\right) = \dfrac{-2\left(\dfrac{3x}{x+2}\right)}{\dfrac{3x}{x+2}-3}$$

$$= \dfrac{-2(3x)}{3x-3(x+2)} = \dfrac{-6x}{-6} = x$$

65. $f^{-1}(x) = \dfrac{x}{3x-2}$

$$f(f^{-1}(x)) = f\left(\dfrac{x}{3x-2}\right) = \dfrac{2\left(\dfrac{x}{3x-2}\right)}{3\left(\dfrac{x}{3x-2}\right)-1}$$

$$= \dfrac{2x}{3x-(3x-2)} = \dfrac{2x}{2} = x$$

$$f^{-1}(f(x)) = f^{-1}\left(\dfrac{2x}{3x-1}\right) = \dfrac{\dfrac{2x}{3x-1}}{3\left(\dfrac{2x}{3x-1}\right)-2}$$

$$= \dfrac{2x}{6x-2(3x-1)} = \dfrac{2x}{2} = x$$

67. $f^{-1}(x) = \dfrac{3x+4}{2x-3}$

$$f(f^{-1}(x)) = f\left(\dfrac{3x+4}{2x-3}\right) = \dfrac{3\left(\dfrac{3x+4}{2x-3}\right)+4}{2\left(\dfrac{3x+4}{2x-3}\right)-3}$$

$$= \dfrac{3(3x+4)+4(2x-3)}{2(3x+4)-3(2x-3)}$$

$$= \dfrac{17x}{17} = x$$

$$f^{-1}(f(x)) = f^{-1}\left(\dfrac{3x+4}{2x-3}\right) = \dfrac{3\left(\dfrac{3x+4}{2x-3}\right)+4}{2\left(\dfrac{3x+4}{2x-3}\right)-3}$$

$$= \dfrac{3(3x+4)+4(2x-3)}{2(3x+4)-3(2x-3)}$$

$$= \dfrac{17x}{17} = x$$

69. $f^{-1}(x) = \dfrac{-2x+3}{x-2}$

$$f(f^{-1}(x)) = f\left(\dfrac{-2x+3}{x-2}\right) = \dfrac{2\left(\dfrac{-2x+3}{x-2}\right)+3}{\dfrac{-2x+3}{x-2}+2}$$

$$= \dfrac{2(-2x+3)+3(x-2)}{-2x+3+2(x-2)} = \dfrac{-x}{-1} = x$$

$$f^{-1}(f(x)) = f^{-1}\left(\dfrac{2x+3}{x+2}\right) = \dfrac{-2\left(\dfrac{2x+3}{x+2}\right)+3}{\dfrac{2x+3}{x+2}-2}$$

$$= \dfrac{-2(2x+3)+3(x+2)}{2x+3-2(x+2)} = \dfrac{-x}{-1} = x$$

71. $f^{-1}(x) = \dfrac{2}{\sqrt{1-2x}}$

$$f(f^{-1}(x)) = f\left(\dfrac{2}{\sqrt{1-2x}}\right) = \dfrac{\dfrac{4}{1-2x}-4}{2\cdot\dfrac{4}{1-2x}} = \dfrac{4-4(1-2x)}{2\cdot4}$$

$$= \dfrac{8x}{8} = x$$

$$f^{-1}(f(x)) = f^{-1}\left(\dfrac{x^2-4}{2x^2}\right) = \dfrac{2}{\sqrt{1-2\left(\dfrac{x^2-4}{2x^2}\right)}} = \dfrac{2}{\sqrt{\dfrac{4}{x^2}}} = \sqrt{x^2}$$

$$= x, \text{ since } x > 0$$

73. (a) 0 **(b)** 2 **(c)** 0 **(d)** 1
75. 7 **77.** Domain of f^{-1}: $[-2, \infty)$; range of f^{-1}: $[5, \infty)$
79. Domain of g^{-1}: $[0, \infty)$; range of g^{-1}: $(-\infty, 0]$
81. Increasing on the interval $(f(0), f(5))$
83. $f^{-1}(x) = \dfrac{1}{m}(x-b), m \neq 0$ **85.** Quadrant I
87. Possible answer: $f(x) = |x|, x \geq 0$, is one-to-one; $f^{-1}(x) = x, x \geq 0$
89. (a) $r(d) = \dfrac{d+90.39}{6.97}$

(b) $r(d(r)) = \dfrac{6.97r - 90.39 + 90.39}{6.97} = \dfrac{6.97r}{6.97} = r$

$$d(r(d)) = 6.97\left(\dfrac{d+90.39}{6.97}\right) - 90.39 = d + 90.39 - 90.39 = d$$

(c) 56 miles per hour

91. (a) 77.6 kg

(b) $h(W) = \dfrac{W-50}{2.3} + 60 = \dfrac{W+88}{2.3}$

(c) $h(W(h)) = \dfrac{50+2.3(h-60)+88}{2.3} = \dfrac{2.3h}{2.3} = h$

$$W(h(W)) = 50 + 2.3\left(\dfrac{W+88}{2.3} - 60\right)$$

$$= 50 + W + 88 - 138 = W$$

(d) 73 inches

93. (a) $\{g \mid 33,950 \leq g \leq 82,250\}$
(b) $\{T \mid 4675 \leq T \leq 16,750\}$
(c) $g(T) = \dfrac{T-4675}{0.25} + 33,950$
Domain: $\{T \mid 4675 \leq T \leq 16,750\}$
Range: $\{g \mid 33,950 \leq g \leq 82,250\}$

97. $f^{-1}(x) = \dfrac{-dx+b}{cx-a}; f = f^{-1}$ if $a = -d$ **101.** No

95. (a) t represents time, so $t \geq 0$.

(b) $t(H) = \sqrt{\dfrac{H-100}{-4.9}} = \sqrt{\dfrac{100-H}{4.9}}$

(c) 2.02 seconds

5.3 Assess Your Understanding *(page 278)*

6. Exponential function; growth factor; initial value **7.** a **8.** T **9.** F **10.** T **11.** $\left(-1, \dfrac{1}{a}\right); (0, 1); (1, a)$ **12.** 1 **13.** 4 **14.** F

15. (a) 11.212 **(b)** 11.587 **(c)** 11.664 **(d)** 11.665 **17. (a)** 8.815 **(b)** 8.821 **(c)** 8.824 **(d)** 8.825 **19. (a)** 21.217 **(b)** 22.217 **(c)** 22.440
(d) 22.459 **21.** 3.320 **23.** 0.427 **25.** Neither **27.** Exponential; $H(x) = 4^x$ **29.** Exponential; $f(x) = 3(2^x)$ **31.** Linear; $H(x) = 2x + 4$
33. B **35.** D **37.** A **39.** E

41.

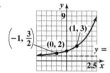

Domain: All real numbers
Range: $\{y|y > 1\}$ or $(1, \infty)$
Horizontal asymptote: $y = 1$

43.

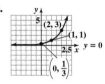

Domain: All real numbers
Range: $\{y|y > 0\}$ or $(0, \infty)$
Horizontal asymptote: $y = 0$

45.

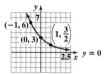

Domain: All real numbers
Range: $\{y|y > 0\}$ or $(0, \infty)$
Horizontal asymptote: $y = 0$

47.

Domain: All real numbers
Range: $\{y|y > -2\}$ or $(-2, \infty)$
Horizontal asymptote: $y = -2$

49.

Domain: All real numbers
Range: $\{y|y > 2\}$ or $(2, \infty)$
Horizontal asymptote: $y = 2$

51.

Domain: All real numbers
Range: $\{y|y > 2\}$ or $(2, \infty)$
Horizontal asymptote: $y = 2$

53.

Domain: All real numbers
Range: $\{y|y > 0\}$ or $(0, \infty)$
Horizontal asymptote: $y = 0$

55.

Domain: All real numbers
Range: $\{y|y > 0\}$ or $(0, \infty)$
Horizontal asymptote: $y = 0$

57.

Domain: All real numbers
Range: $\{y|y < 5\}$ or $(-\infty, 5)$
Horizontal asymptote: $y = 5$

59.

Domain: All real numbers
Range: $\{y|y < 2\}$ or $(-\infty, 2)$
Horizontal asymptote: $y = 2$

61. $\{3\}$ **63.** $\{-4\}$ **65.** $\{2\}$ **67.** $\left\{\dfrac{3}{2}\right\}$ **69.** $\{-\sqrt{2}, 0, \sqrt{2}\}$ **71.** $\{6\}$

73. $\{-1, 7\}$ **75.** $\{-4, 2\}$ **77.** $\{-4\}$ **79.** $\{1, 2\}$ **81.** $\dfrac{1}{49}$ **83.** $\dfrac{1}{4}$

85. $f(x) = 3^x$ **87.** $f(x) = -6^x$ **89.** $f(x) = 3^x + 2$

91. (a) $16; (4, 16)$ **(b)** $-4; \left(-4, \dfrac{1}{16}\right)$ **93. (a)** $\dfrac{9}{4}; \left(-1, \dfrac{9}{4}\right)$

  (b) $3; (3, 66)$ **95. (a)** $60; (-6, 60)$ **(b)** $-4; (-4, 12)$ **(c)** -2

97.

Domain: $(-\infty, \infty)$
Range: $[1, \infty)$
Intercept: $(0, 1)$

99.

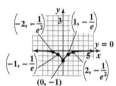

Domain: $(-\infty, \infty)$
Range: $[-1, 0)$
Intercept: $(0, -1)$

101. (a) 74% **(b)** 47%
103. (a) $\$12{,}123$ **(b)** $\$6443$
105. 3.35 mg; 0.45 mg

107. (a) 0.632 **(b)** 0.982 **(c)** 1
  (d)

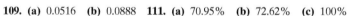

  (e) About 7 min

109. (a) 0.0516 **(b)** 0.0888 **111. (a)** 70.95% **(b)** 72.62% **(c)** 100% **115.** 36
113. (a) 5.41 amp, 7.59 amp, 10.38 amp   **(b)** 12 amp
  (d) 3.34 amp, 5.31 amp, 9.44 amp   **(e)** 24 amp
  (c), (f)

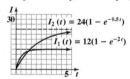

117.

Final Denominator	Value of Expression	Compare Value to $e \approx 2.718281828$
$1 + 1$	2.5	$2.5 < e$
$2 + 2$	2.8	$2.8 > e$
$3 + 3$	2.7	$2.7 < e$
$4 + 4$	2.721649485	$2.721649485 > e$
$5 + 5$	2.717770035	$2.717770035 < e$
$6 + 6$	2.718348855	$2.718348855 > e$

119. $f(A + B) = a^{A+B} = a^A \cdot a^B = f(A) \cdot f(B)$ **121.** $f(\alpha x) = a^{\alpha x} = (a^x)^\alpha = [f(x)]^\alpha$

123. (a) $f(-x) = \dfrac{1}{2}(e^{-x} + e^{-(-x)})$

  $= \dfrac{1}{2}(e^{-x} + e^x)$

  $= \dfrac{1}{2}(e^x + e^{-x})$

  $= f(x)$

  (b)

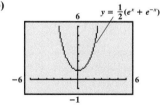

  (c) $(\cosh x)^2 - (\sinh x)^2$

  $= \left[\dfrac{1}{2}(e^x + e^{-x})\right]^2 - \left[\dfrac{1}{2}(e^x - e^{-x})\right]^2$

  $= \dfrac{1}{4}[e^{2x} + 2 + e^{-2x} - e^{2x} + 2 - e^{-2x}]$

  $= \dfrac{1}{4}(4) = 1$

125. 59 minutes

5.4 Assess Your Understanding *(page 292)*

4. $\{x|x > 0\}$ or $(0, \infty)$ **5.** $\left(\dfrac{1}{a}, -1\right)$, $(1, 0)$, $(a, 1)$ **6.** 1 **7.** F   **8.** T   **9.** $2 = \log_3 9$ **11.** $2 = \log_a 1.6$ **13.** $x = \log_2 7.2$ **15.** $x = \ln 8$

17. $2^3 = 8$ **19.** $a^6 = 3$ **21.** $3^x = 2$ **23.** $e^x = 4$ **25.** 0 **27.** 2 **29.** -4 **31.** $\dfrac{1}{2}$ **33.** 4 **35.** $\dfrac{1}{2}$ **37.** $\{x|x > 3\}; (3, \infty)$

39. All real numbers except 0; $\{x | x \neq 0\}$ **41.** $\{x | x > 10\}$; $(10, \infty)$ **43.** $\{x | x > -1\}$; $(-1, \infty)$ **45.** $\{x | x < -1 \text{ or } x > 0\}$; $(-\infty, -1) \cup (0, \infty)$
47. $\{x | x \geq 1\}$; $[1, \infty)$ **49.** 0.511 **51.** 30.099 **53.** 2.303 **55.** -53.991 **57.** $\sqrt{2}$

59.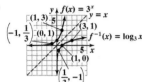

61.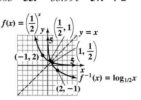

63. B **65.** D **67.** A **69.** E

71. (a) Domain: $(-4, \infty)$
(b)
(c) Range: $(-\infty, \infty)$
Vertical asymptote: $x = -4$
(d) $f^{-1}(x) = e^x - 4$
(e) Domain of f^{-1}: $(-\infty, \infty)$
Range of f^{-1}: $(-4, \infty)$
(f)

73. (a) Domain: $(0, \infty)$
(b)
(c) Range: $(-\infty, \infty)$
Vertical asymptote: $x = 0$
(d) $f^{-1}(x) = e^{x-2}$
(e) Domain of f^{-1}: $(-\infty, \infty)$
Range of f^{-1}: $(0, \infty)$
(f)

75. (a) Domain: $(0, \infty)$
(b)
(c) Range: $(-\infty, \infty)$
Vertical asymptote: $x = 0$
(d) $f^{-1}(x) = \dfrac{1}{2} e^{x+3}$
(e) Domain of f^{-1}: $(-\infty, \infty)$
Range of f^{-1}: $(0, \infty)$
(f)

77. (a) Domain: $(4, \infty)$
(b)
(c) Range: $(-\infty, \infty)$
Vertical asymptote: $x = 4$
(d) $f^{-1}(x) = 10^{x-2} + 4$
(e) Domain of f^{-1}: $(-\infty, \infty)$
Range of f^{-1}: $(4, \infty)$
(f)

79. (a) Domain: $(0, \infty)$
(b)
(c) Range: $(-\infty, \infty)$
Vertical asymptote: $x = 0$
(d) $f^{-1}(x) = \dfrac{1}{2} \cdot 10^{2x}$
(e) Domain of f^{-1}: $(-\infty, \infty)$
Range of f^{-1}: $(0, \infty)$
(f)

81. (a) Domain: $(-2, \infty)$
(b)
(c) Range: $(-\infty, \infty)$
Vertical asymptote: $x = -2$
(d) $f^{-1}(x) = 3^{x-3} - 2$
(e) Domain of f^{-1}: $(-\infty, \infty)$
Range of f^{-1}: $(-2, \infty)$
(f)

83. (a) Domain: $(-\infty, \infty)$
(b)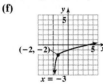
(c) Range: $(-3, \infty)$
Horizontal asymptote: $y = -3$
(d) $f^{-1}(x) = \ln(x + 3) - 2$
(e) Domain of f^{-1}: $(-3, \infty)$
Range of f^{-1}: $(-\infty, \infty)$
(f)

85. (a) Domain: $(-\infty, \infty)$
(b)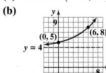
(c) Range: $(4, \infty)$
Horizontal asymptote: $y = 4$
(d) $f^{-1}(x) = 3 \log_2(x - 4)$
(e) Domain of f^{-1}: $(4, \infty)$
Range of f^{-1}: $(-\infty, \infty)$
(f)

87. $\{9\}$ **89.** $\left\{\dfrac{7}{2}\right\}$ **91.** $\{2\}$ **93.** $\{5\}$

95. $\{3\}$ **97.** $\{2\}$ **99.** $\left\{\dfrac{\ln 10}{3}\right\}$

101. $\left\{\dfrac{\ln 8 - 5}{2}\right\}$ **103.** $\{-2\sqrt{2}, 2\sqrt{2}\}$

105. $\{-1\}$ **107.** $\left\{5 \ln \dfrac{7}{5}\right\}$

109. $\left\{2 - \log \dfrac{5}{2}\right\}$

111. (a) $\left\{x \,\middle|\, x > -\dfrac{1}{2}\right\}$; $\left(-\dfrac{1}{2}, \infty\right)$
(b) 2; $(40, 2)$ (c) 121; $(121, 3)$ (d) 4

113.

Domain: $\{x \mid x \neq 0\}$
Range: $(-\infty, \infty)$
Intercepts: $(-1, 0), (1, 0)$

115.

Domain: $\{x \mid x > 0\}$
Range: $\{y \mid y \geq 0\}$
Intercept: $(1, 0)$

117. (a) 1 **(b)** 2 **(c)** 3
(d) It increases. **(e)** 0.000316
(f) 3.981×10^{-8}
119. (a) 5.97 km **(b)** 0.90 km
121. (a) 6.93 min **(b)** 16.09 min
123. $h \approx 2.29$, so the time between injections is about 2 h, 17 min.

125. 0.2695 s
0.8959 s

127. 50 decibels (dB) **129.** 90 dB **131.** 8.1 **133. (a)** $k \approx 11.216$ **(b)** 6.73 **(c)** 0.41% **(d)** 0.14%
135. Because $y = \log_1 x$ means $1^y = 1 = x$, which cannot be true for $x \neq 1$

5.5 Assess Your Understanding (page 303)

1. 0 **2.** 1 **3.** M **4.** r **5.** $\log_a M$; $\log_a N$ **6.** $\log_a M$; $\log_a N$ **7.** $r \log_a M$ **8.** 6 **9.** 7 **10.** F **11.** F **12.** F **13.** 71 **15.** -4 **17.** 7 **19.** 1

21. 1 **23.** 3 **25.** $\dfrac{5}{4}$ **27.** 4 **29.** $a + b$ **31.** $b - a$ **33.** $3a$ **35.** $\dfrac{1}{5}(a + b)$ **37.** $2 + \log_5 x$ **39.** $3 \log_2 z$ **41.** $1 + \ln x$ **43.** $\ln x - x$

45. $2 \log_a u + 3 \log_a v$ **47.** $2 \ln x + \dfrac{1}{2}\ln(1 - x)$ **49.** $3 \log_2 x - \log_2(x - 3)$ **51.** $\log x + \log(x + 2) - 2 \log(x + 3)$

53. $\dfrac{1}{3}\ln(x - 2) + \dfrac{1}{3}\ln(x + 1) - \dfrac{2}{3}\ln(x + 4)$ **55.** $\ln 5 + \ln x + \dfrac{1}{2}\ln(1 + 3x) - 3 \ln(x - 4)$ **57.** $\log_5 u^3 v^4$ **59.** $\log_3\left(\dfrac{1}{x^{5/2}}\right)$ **61.** $\log_4\left[\dfrac{x - 1}{(x + 1)^4}\right]$

63. $-2 \ln(x - 1)$ **65.** $\log_2[x(3x - 2)^4]$ **67.** $\log_a\left(\dfrac{25x^6}{\sqrt{2x + 3}}\right)$ **69.** $\log_2\left[\dfrac{(x + 1)^2}{(x + 3)(x - 1)}\right]$ **71.** 2.771 **73.** -3.880 **75.** 5.615 **77.** 0.874

79. $y = \dfrac{\log x}{\log 4}$

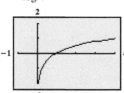

81. $y = \dfrac{\log(x + 2)}{\log 2}$

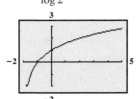

83. $y = \dfrac{\log(x + 1)}{\log(x - 1)}$

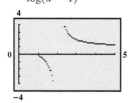

85. (a) $(f \circ g)(x) = x$; $\{x \mid x$ is any real number$\}$ or $(-\infty, \infty)$
(b) $(g \circ f)(x) = x$; $\{x \mid x > 0\}$ or $(0, \infty)$ **(c)** 5
(d) $(f \circ h)(x) = \ln x^2$; $\{x \mid x \neq 0\}$ or $(-\infty, 0) \cup (0, \infty)$ **(e)** 2

87. $y = Cx$ **89.** $y = Cx(x + 1)$ **91.** $y = Ce^{3x}$ **93.** $y = Ce^{-4x} + 3$

95. $y = \dfrac{\sqrt[3]{C}(2x + 1)^{1/6}}{(x + 4)^{1/9}}$ **97.** 3 **99.** 1

101. $\log_a\left(x + \sqrt{x^2 - 1}\right) + \log_a\left(x - \sqrt{x^2 - 1}\right) = \log_a\left[\left(x + \sqrt{x^2 - 1}\right)\left(x - \sqrt{x^2 - 1}\right)\right] = \log_a[x^2 - (x^2 - 1)] = \log_a 1 = 0$
103. $\ln(1 + e^{2x}) = \ln[e^{2x}(e^{-2x} + 1)] = \ln e^{2x} + \ln(e^{-2x} + 1) = 2x + \ln(1 + e^{-2x})$
105. $y = f(x) = \log_a x$; $a^y = x$ implies $a^y = \left(\dfrac{1}{a}\right)^{-y} = x$, so $-y = \log_{1/a} x = -f(x)$.

107. $f(x) = \log_a x$; $f\left(\dfrac{1}{x}\right) = \log_a \dfrac{1}{x} = \log_a 1 - \log_a x = -f(x)$

109. $\log_a \dfrac{M}{N} = \log_a(M \cdot N^{-1}) = \log_a M + \log_a N^{-1} = \log_a M - \log_a N$, since $a^{\log_a N^{-1}} = N^{-1}$ implies $a^{-\log_a N^{-1}} = N$; i.e., $\log_a N = -\log_a N^{-1}$.

5.6 Assess Your Understanding (page 309)

5. $\{16\}$ **7.** $\left\{\dfrac{16}{5}\right\}$ **9.** $\{6\}$ **11.** $\{16\}$ **13.** $\left\{\dfrac{1}{3}\right\}$ **15.** $\{3\}$ **17.** $\{5\}$ **19.** $\left\{\dfrac{21}{8}\right\}$ **21.** $\{-6\}$ **23.** $\{-2\}$ **25.** $\left\{-1 + \sqrt{1 + e^4}\right\} \approx \{6.456\}$

27. $\left\{\dfrac{-5 + 3\sqrt{5}}{2}\right\} \approx \{0.854\}$ **29.** $\{2\}$ **31.** $\left\{\dfrac{9}{2}\right\}$ **33.** $\{8\}$ **35.** $\{\log_2 10\} = \left\{\dfrac{\ln 10}{\ln 2}\right\} \approx \{3.322\}$ **37.** $\{-\log_8 1.2\} = \left\{-\dfrac{\ln 1.2}{\ln 8}\right\} \approx \{-0.088\}$

39. $\left\{\dfrac{1}{3}\log_2 \dfrac{8}{5}\right\} = \left\{\dfrac{\ln\dfrac{8}{5}}{3 \ln 2}\right\} \approx \{0.226\}$ **41.** $\left\{\dfrac{\ln 3}{2 \ln 3 + \ln 4}\right\} \approx \{0.307\}$ **43.** $\left\{\dfrac{\ln 7}{\ln 0.6 + \ln 7}\right\} \approx \{1.356\}$ **45.** $\{0\}$ **47.** $\left\{\dfrac{\ln \pi}{1 + \ln \pi}\right\} \approx \{0.534\}$

49. $\left\{\dfrac{\ln 3}{\ln 2}\right\} \approx \{1.585\}$ **51.** $\{0\}$ **53.** $\left\{\log_4\left(-2 + \sqrt{7}\right)\right\} \approx \{-0.315\}$ **55.** $\{\log_5 4\} \approx \{0.861\}$ **57.** No real solution **59.** $\{\log_4 5\} \approx \{1.161\}$

61. $\{2.79\}$ **63.** $\{-0.57\}$ **65.** $\{-0.70\}$ **67.** $\{0.57\}$ **69.** $\{0.39, 1.00\}$ **71.** $\{1.32\}$ **73.** $\{1.31\}$ **75.** $\{1\}$ **77.** $\{16\}$ **79.** $\left\{-1, \dfrac{2}{3}\right\}$ **81.** $\{0\}$

83. $\left\{\ln\left(2 + \sqrt{5}\right)\right\} \approx \{1.444\}$ **85.** $\left\{\dfrac{\ln 5 \cdot \ln 3}{\ln 15}\right\} \approx \{1.921\}$ **87. (a)** $\{5\}; (5, 3)$ **(b)** $\{5\}; (5, 4)$ **(c)** $\{1\};$ yes, at $(1, 2)$ **(d)** $\{5\}$ **(e)** $\left\{-\dfrac{1}{11}\right\}$

89. (a), (b)

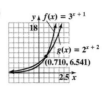

(c) $\{x \mid x > 0.710\}$ or $(0.710, \infty)$

91. (a), (b), (c)

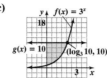

93. (a), (b), (c)

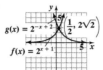

95. (a)

(b) 2

(c) $\{x \mid x < 2\}$ or $(-\infty, 2)$

97. (a) 2025 **(b)** 2043

99. (a) After 3.1 yr

(b) After 7.1 yr

(c) After 10.6 yr

5.7 Assess Your Understanding (page 318)

3. principal **4.** I; Prt; simple interest **5.** 4 **6.** effective rate of interest **7.** $108.29 **9.** $609.50 **11.** $697.09 **13.** $1246.08 **15.** $88.72

17. $860.72 **19.** $554.09 **21.** $59.71 **23.** 5.095% **25.** 5.127% **27.** $6\frac{1}{4}$% compounded annually **29.** 9% compounded monthly **31.** 25.992%

33. 24.573% **35. (a)** About 8.69 yr **(b)** About 8.66 yr **37.** 6.823% **39.** 5.09 yr; 5.07 yr **41.** 15.27 yr or 15 yr, 3 mo **43.** $104,335

45. $12,910.62 **47.** About $30.17 per share or $3017 **49.** Not quite. Jim will have $1057.60. The second bank gives a better deal, since Jim will have $1060.62 after 1 yr. **51.** Will has $11,632.73; Henry has $10,947.89. **53. (a)** $79,129 **(b)** $38,516 **55.** About $1019 billion; about $232 billion

57. $940.90 **59.** 2.53% **61.** 34.31 yr **63. (a)** $1364.62 **(b)** $1353.35 **65.** $4631.93

67. (a) 6.12 yr **(c)** $mP = P\left(1 + \dfrac{r}{n}\right)^{nt}$

(b) 18.45 yr

$$m = \left(1 + \dfrac{r}{n}\right)^{nt}$$

$$\ln m = \ln\left(1 + \dfrac{r}{n}\right)^{nt} = nt \ln\left(1 + \dfrac{r}{n}\right)$$

$$t = \dfrac{\ln m}{n \ln\left(1 + \dfrac{r}{n}\right)}$$

69. (a) 2.82% **(b)** In 2020 or after 12 yr **71.** 22.7 yr

5.8 Assess Your Understanding (page 330)

1. (a) 500 insects **(b)** $0.02 = 2\%$ per day **(c)** About 611 insects **(d)** After about 23.5 days **(e)** After about 34.7 days

3. (a) $-0.0244 = -2.44\%$ per year **(b)** About 391.7 g **(c)** After about 9.1 yr **(d)** 28.4 yr **5. (a)** $N(t) = N_0 e^{kt}$ **(b)** 5832 **(c)** 3.9 days

7. (a) $N(t) = N_0 e^{kt}$ **(b)** 25,198 **9.** 9.797 g **11.** 9727 yr ago **13. (a)** 5:18 PM **(b)** About 14.3 min **(c)** The temperature of the pan approaches 70°F. **15.** 18.63°C; 25.1°C **17.** 1.7 ppm; 7.17 days or 172 hr **19.** 0.26 M; 6.58 hr or 395 min **21.** 26.6 days **23. (a)** 1000 g **(b)** 43.9% **(c)** 30 g

(d) 616.6 g **(e)** After 9.85 h **(f)** About 7.9 h **25. (a)** 9.23×10^{-3}, or about 0 **(b)** 0.81, or about 1 **(c)** 5.01, or about 5

(d) 57.91°, 43.99°, 30.07°

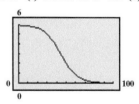

5.9 Assess Your Understanding (page 336)

1. (a)

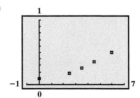

(d)

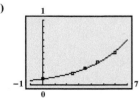

3. (a)

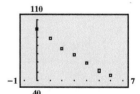

(d)

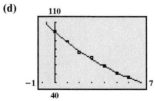

(b) $y = 0.0903(1.3384)^x$

(c) $N(t) = 0.0903 e^{0.2915t}$

(e) 0.69

(f) After about 7.26 hr

(b) $y = 100.326(0.8769)^x$

(c) $A(t) = 100.326 e^{-0.1314t}$

(e) 5.3 weeks **(f)** 0.14 g

(g) After about 12.3 weeks

5. (a) 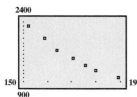 **(b)** $y = 32{,}741.02 - 6070.96 \ln x$ **(c)** 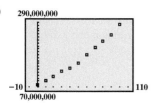 **(d)** Approximately 168 computers

7. (a)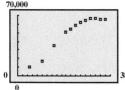

(b) $y = \dfrac{799{,}475{,}916.5}{1 + 9.1968e^{-0.0160x}}$

(c)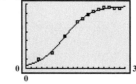

(d) 799,475,917
(e) Approximately 291,599,733
(f) 2006

9. (a)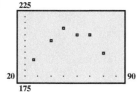

(c)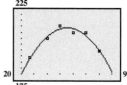

(b) $y = \dfrac{67{,}856.6}{1 + 19.844e^{-0.2029x}}$

(d) About 67,856,600 subscribers
(e) About 67,711,000 subscribers

11. (a)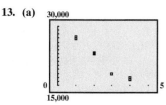

(b) Quadratic with $a < 0$ because of the "upside down U-shape" of the data
(c) $y = -0.0311x^2 + 3.4444x + 118.2493$

(d)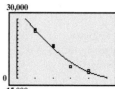

(e) 201

13. (a)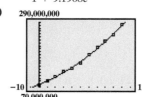

(b) Exponential because depreciation of a car is described by exponential models in the theory of finance.
(c) $y = 31{,}808.51(0.8474)^x$

(d)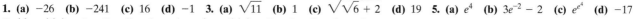

(e) $13,899

Review Exercises *(page 342)*

1. (a) -26 **(b)** -241 **(c)** 16 **(d)** -1 **3. (a)** $\sqrt{11}$ **(b)** 1 **(c)** $\sqrt{\sqrt{6} + 2}$ **(d)** 19 **5. (a)** e^4 **(b)** $3e^{-2} - 2$ **(c)** e^{e^4} **(d)** -17

7. $(f \circ g)(x) = 1 - 3x$, all real numbers; $(g \circ f)(x) = 7 - 3x$, all real numbers;
$(f \circ f)(x) = x$, all real numbers; $(g \circ g)(x) = 9x + 4$, all real numbers

9. $(f \circ g)(x) = 27x^2 + 3|x| + 1$, all real numbers; $(g \circ f)(x) = 3|3x^2 + x + 1|$,
all real numbers; $(f \circ f)(x) = 27x^4 + 18x^3 + 24x^2 + 7x + 5$, all real numbers; $(g \circ g)(x) = 9|x|$, all real numbers

11. $(f \circ g)(x) = \dfrac{1 + x}{1 - x}, \{x \,|\, x \neq 0, x \neq 1\}; (g \circ f)(x) = \dfrac{x - 1}{x + 1}, \{x \,|\, x \neq -1, x \neq 1\}; (f \circ f)(x) = x, \{x \,|\, x \neq 1\}; (g \circ g)(x) = x, \{x \,|\, x \neq 0\}$

13. (a) one-to-one **(b)** $\{(2, 1), (5, 3), (8, 5), (10, 6)\}$

15.

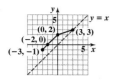

17. $f^{-1}(x) = \dfrac{2x + 3}{5x - 2}$

$$f(f^{-1}(x)) = \dfrac{2\left(\dfrac{2x + 3}{5x - 2}\right) + 3}{5\left(\dfrac{2x + 3}{5x - 2}\right) - 2} = x$$

$$f^{-1}(f(x)) = \dfrac{2\left(\dfrac{2x + 3}{5x - 2}\right) + 3}{5\left(\dfrac{2x + 3}{5x - 2}\right) - 2} = x$$

Domain of f = range of f^{-1} = all real numbers except $\dfrac{2}{5}$

Range of f = domain of f^{-1} = all real numbers except $\dfrac{2}{5}$

19. $f^{-1}(x) = \dfrac{x + 1}{x}$

$$f(f^{-1}(x)) = \dfrac{1}{\dfrac{x + 1}{x} - 1} = x$$

$$f^{-1}(f(x)) = \dfrac{\dfrac{1}{x - 1} + 1}{\dfrac{1}{x - 1}} = x$$

Domain of f = range of f^{-1} = all real numbers except 1
Range of f = domain of f^{-1} = all real numbers except 0

21. $f^{-1}(x) = \dfrac{27}{x^3}$

$$f(f^{-1}(x)) = \dfrac{3}{\left(\dfrac{27}{x^3}\right)^{1/3}} = x$$

$$f^{-1}(f(x)) = \dfrac{27}{\left(\dfrac{3}{x^{1/3}}\right)^3} = x$$

Domain of f = range of f^{-1} = all real numbers except 0
Range of f = domain of f^{-1} = all real numbers except 0

23. (a) 81 **(b)** 2 **(c)** $\dfrac{1}{9}$ **(d)** -3 **25.** $\log_5 z = 2$ **27.** $5^{13} = u$

29. $\left\{x \,\middle|\, x > \dfrac{2}{3}\right\}; \left(\dfrac{2}{3}, \infty\right)$ **31.** $\{x \mid x < 1 \text{ or } x > 2\}; (-\infty, 1) \cup (2, \infty)$

33. -3 **35.** $\sqrt{2}$ **37.** 0.4 **39.** $\log_3 u + 2\log_3 v - \log_3 w$

41. $2\log x + \dfrac{1}{2}\log(x^3 + 1)$ **43.** $\ln x + \dfrac{1}{3}\ln(x^2 + 1) - \ln(x - 3)$ **45.** $\dfrac{25}{4}\log_4 x$

47. $-2\ln(x + 1)$ **49.** $\log\left(\dfrac{4x^3}{[(x + 3)(x - 2)]^{1/2}}\right)$ **51.** 2.124

53.

55. (a) Domain of f: $(-\infty, \infty)$
(b)

(c) Range of f: $(0, \infty)$
Horizontal asymptote: $y = 0$
(d) $f^{-1}(x) = 3 + \log_2 x$
(e) Domain of f^{-1}: $(0, \infty)$
Range of f^{-1}: $(-\infty, \infty)$
(f)

57. (a) Domain of f: $(-\infty, \infty)$
(b)

(c) Range of f: $(0, \infty)$
Horizontal asymptote: $y = 0$
(d) $f^{-1}(x) = -\log_3(2x)$
(e) Domain of f^{-1}: $(0, \infty)$
Range of f^{-1}: $(-\infty, \infty)$
(f)

59. (a) Domain of f: $(-\infty, \infty)$
(b)

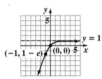

(c) Range of f: $(-\infty, 1)$
Horizontal asymptote: $y = 1$
(d) $f^{-1}(x) = -\ln(1 - x)$
(e) Domain of f^{-1}: $(-\infty, 1)$
Range of f^{-1}: $(-\infty, \infty)$
(f)

61. (a) Domain of f: $(-3, \infty)$
(b)

(c) Range of f: $(-\infty, \infty)$
Vertical asymptote: $x = -3$
(d) $f^{-1}(x) = e^{2x} - 3$
(e) Domain of f^{-1}: $(-\infty, \infty)$
Range of f^{-1}: $(-3, \infty)$
(f)

63. $\left\{\dfrac{1}{4}\right\}$ **65.** $\left\{\dfrac{-1 - \sqrt{3}}{2}, \dfrac{-1 + \sqrt{3}}{2}\right\} \approx \{-1.366, 0.366\}$ **67.** $\left\{\dfrac{1}{4}\right\}$ **69.** $\left\{\dfrac{2\ln 3}{\ln 5 - \ln 3}\right\} \approx \{4.301\}$ **71.** $\left\{\dfrac{12}{5}\right\}$ **73.** $\{83\}$ **75.** $\left\{\dfrac{1}{2}, -3\right\}$

77. $\{-1\}$ **79.** $\{1 - \ln 5\} \approx \{-0.609\}$ **81.** $\left\{\log_3\left(-2 + \sqrt{7}\right)\right\} = \left\{\dfrac{\ln\left(-2 + \sqrt{7}\right)}{\ln 3}\right\} \approx \{-0.398\}$

83. (a), (e)

(b) 3; (6, 3) **(c)** 10; (10, 4)
(d) $\left\{x \,\middle|\, x > \dfrac{5}{2}\right\}$ or $\left(\dfrac{5}{2}, \infty\right)$
(e) $f^{-1}(x) = 2^{x-1} + 2$

85. 3229.5 m **87. (a)** 37.3 W **(b)** 6.9 dB
89. (a) 9.85 yr **(b)** 4.27 yr **91.** \$41,668.97 **93.** 24,203 yr ago
95. 7,237,271,501 **97.** \$483.67 billion

99. (a)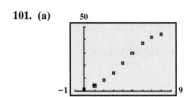

(c)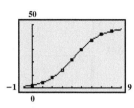

(b) $y = 165.73(0.9951)^x$ **(d)** Approximately 83 s

101. (a)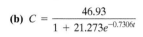

(b) $C = \dfrac{46.93}{1 + 21.273e^{-0.7306t}}$

(c)

(d) About 47 people; 50 people
(e) 2.4 days; during the tenth hour of day 3
(f) 9.5 days

Chapter Test *(page 346)*

1. (a) $f \circ g = \dfrac{2x + 7}{2x + 3}$; domain: $\left\{x \middle| x \neq -\dfrac{3}{2}\right\}$ **(b)** $(g \circ f)(-2) = 5$ **(c)** $(f \circ g)(-2) = -3$

2. (a) The function is not one-to-one.   **(b)** The function is one-to-one.

3. $f^{-1}(x) = \dfrac{2 + 5x}{3x}$; domain of $f = \left\{x \middle| x \neq \dfrac{5}{3}\right\}$, range of $f = \{y | y \neq 0\}$; domain of $f^{-1} = \{x | x \neq 0\}$; range of $f^{-1} = \left\{y \middle| y \neq \dfrac{5}{3}\right\}$

4. The point $(-5, 3)$ must be on the graph of f^{-1}.   **5.** $x = 5$ **6.** $b = 4$ **7.** $x = 625$ **8.** $e^3 + 2 \approx 22.086$ **9.** $\log 20 \approx 1.301$

10. $\log_3 21 = \dfrac{\ln 21}{\ln 3} \approx 2.771$ **11.** $\ln 133 \approx 4.890$

12. (a) Domain of f: $\{x | -\infty < x < \infty\}$ or $(-\infty, \infty)$

(b)

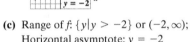
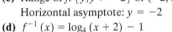

(c) Range of f: $\{y | y > -2\}$ or $(-2, \infty)$; Horizontal asymptote: $y = -2$
(d) $f^{-1}(x) = \log_4(x + 2) - 1$

(e) Domain of f^{-1}: $\{x | x > -2\}$ or $(-2, \infty)$
Range of f^{-1}: $\{y | -\infty < y < \infty\}$ or $(-\infty, \infty)$

(f)

13. (a) Domain of f: $\{x | x > 2\}$ or $(2, \infty)$

(b)

(c) Range of f: $\{y | -\infty < y < \infty\}$ or $(-\infty, \infty)$; vertical asymptote: $x = 2$
(d) $f^{-1}(x) = 5^{1-x} + 2$

(e) Domain of f^{-1}: $\{x | -\infty < x < \infty\}$ or $(-\infty, \infty)$
Range of f^{-1}: $\{y | y > 2\}$ or $(2, \infty)$

(f)

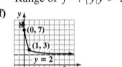

14. $\{1\}$ **15.** $\{91\}$ **16.** $\{-\ln 2\} \approx \{-0.693\}$ **17.** $\left\{\dfrac{1 - \sqrt{13}}{2}, \dfrac{1 + \sqrt{13}}{2}\right\} \approx \{-1.303, 2.303\}$ **18.** $\left\{\dfrac{3\ln 7}{1 - \ln 7}\right\} \approx \{-6.172\}$

19. $\{2\sqrt{6}\} \approx \{4.899\}$ **20.** $2 + 3\log_2 x - \log_2(x - 6) - \log_2(x + 3)$ **21.** About 250.39 days   **22. (a)** \$1033.82   **(b)** \$963.42   **(c)** 11.9 yr

23. (a) About 83 dB   **(b)** The pain threshold will be exceeded if 31,623 people shout at the same time.

Cumulative Review *(page 346)*

1. Yes; no   **2. (a)** 10   **(b)** $2x^2 + 3x + 1$ **(c)** $2x^2 + 4xh + 2h^2 - 3x - 3h + 1$ **3.** $\left(\dfrac{1}{2}, \dfrac{\sqrt{3}}{2}\right)$ is on the graph.   **4.** $\{-26\}$

5.

6. (a)

(b) $\{x | -\infty < x < \infty\}$

7. $f(x) = 2(x - 4)^2 - 8 = 2x^2 - 16x + 24$
8.

9. $f(g(x)) = \dfrac{4}{(x - 3)^2} + 2$; domain: $\{x | x \neq 3\}$; 3

10. (a) Zeros: $-4, -\dfrac{1}{4}, 2$
(b) x-intercepts: $-4, -\dfrac{1}{4}, 2$; y-intercept: -8
(c) Local maximum value of 60.75 occurs at $x = -2.5$. Local minimum value of -25 occurs at $x = 1$.
(d)

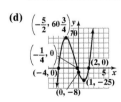

11. (a), (c)

Domain g = range g^{-1} = $(-\infty, \infty)$
Range g = domain g^{-1} = $(2, \infty)$
(b) $g^{-1}(x) = \log_3(x - 2)$

12. $\left\{-\dfrac{3}{2}\right\}$ **13.** $\{2\}$ **14. (a)** $\{-1\}$ **(b)** $\{x \mid x > -1\}$ or $(-1, \infty)$ **(c)** $\{25\}$

15. (a) **(b)** Logarithmic; $y = 49.293 - 10.563 \ln x$ **(c)** Highest value of $|r|$

CHAPTER 6 Trigonometric Functions

6.1 Assess Your Understanding *(page 359)*

3. standard position **4.** central angle **5.** radian **6.** $r\theta; \dfrac{1}{2}r^2\theta$ **7.** π **8.** $\dfrac{s}{t}; \dfrac{\theta}{t}$ **9.** T **10.** F

11.  **13.**  **15.** **17.** 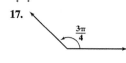 **19.** 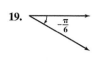 **21.**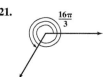

23. $40.17°$ **25.** $1.03°$ **27.** $9.15°$ **29.** $40°19'12''$ **31.** $18°15'18''$ **33.** $19°59'24''$ **35.** $\dfrac{\pi}{6}$ **37.** $\dfrac{4\pi}{3}$ **39.** $-\dfrac{\pi}{3}$ **41.** π **43.** $-\dfrac{3\pi}{4}$ **45.** $-\dfrac{\pi}{2}$ **47.** $60°$

49. $-225°$ **51.** $90°$ **53.** $15°$ **55.** $-90°$ **57.** $-30°$ **59.** 0.30 **61.** -0.70 **63.** 2.18 **65.** $179.91°$ **67.** $114.59°$ **69.** $362.11°$ **71.** 5 m **73.** 6 ft

75. 0.6 radian **77.** $\dfrac{\pi}{3} \approx 1.047$ in. **79.** 25 m^2 **81.** $2\sqrt{3} \approx 3.464$ ft **83.** 0.24 radian **85.** $\dfrac{\pi}{3} \approx 1.047$ in.^{2} **87.** $s = 2.094$ ft; $A = 2.094$ ft^2

89. $s = 14.661$ yd; $A = 87.965$ yd^2 **91.** $3\pi \approx 9.42$ in; $5\pi \approx 15.71$ in. **93.** $2\pi \approx 6.28$ m^2 **95.** $\dfrac{675\pi}{2} \approx 1060.29$ ft^2 **97.** $\omega = \dfrac{1}{60}$ radian/s; $v = \dfrac{1}{12}$ cm/s

99. ≈ 452.5 rpm **101.** ≈ 359 mi **103.** ≈ 898 mi/h **105.** ≈ 2292 mi/h **107.** $\dfrac{3}{4}$ rpm **109.** ≈ 2.86 mi/h **111.** ≈ 31.47 rpm **113.** ≈ 1037 mi/h

115. Radius ≈ 3979 mi; circumference $\approx 25{,}000$ mi **117.** $v_1 = r_1\omega_1, v_2 = r_2\omega_2$, and $v_1 = v_2$, so $r_1\omega_1 = r_2\omega_2$ and $\dfrac{r_1}{r_2} = \dfrac{\omega_2}{\omega_1}$.

6.2 Assess Your Understanding *(page 375)*

7. cosine **8.** $(0, 1)$ **9.** $\left(\dfrac{\sqrt{2}}{2}, \dfrac{\sqrt{2}}{2}\right)$ **10.** $\left(\dfrac{1}{2}, \dfrac{\sqrt{3}}{2}\right)$ **11.** $\dfrac{y}{r}; \dfrac{x}{r}$ **12.** F **13.** $\sin t = \dfrac{1}{2}; \cos t = \dfrac{\sqrt{3}}{2}; \tan t = \dfrac{\sqrt{3}}{3}; \csc t = 2; \sec t = \dfrac{2\sqrt{3}}{3}; \cot t = \sqrt{3}$

15. $\sin t = \dfrac{\sqrt{21}}{5}; \cos t = -\dfrac{2}{5}; \tan t = -\dfrac{\sqrt{21}}{2}; \csc t = \dfrac{5\sqrt{21}}{21}; \sec t = -\dfrac{5}{2}; \cot t = -\dfrac{2\sqrt{21}}{21}$ **17.** $\sin t = \dfrac{\sqrt{2}}{2}; \cos t = -\dfrac{\sqrt{2}}{2};$

$\tan t = -1; \csc t = \sqrt{2}; \sec t = -\sqrt{2}; \cot t = -1$ **19.** $\sin t = -\dfrac{1}{3}; \cos t = \dfrac{2\sqrt{2}}{3}; \tan t = -\dfrac{\sqrt{2}}{4}; \csc t = -3; \sec t = \dfrac{3\sqrt{2}}{4}; \cot t = -2\sqrt{2}$

21. -1 **23.** 0 **25.** -1 **27.** 0 **29.** -1 **31.** $\dfrac{1}{2}\left(\sqrt{2} + 1\right)$ **33.** 2 **35.** $\dfrac{1}{2}$ **37.** $\sqrt{6}$ **39.** 4 **41.** 0 **43.** $2\sqrt{2} + \dfrac{4\sqrt{3}}{3}$ **45.** 1

47. $\sin\dfrac{2\pi}{3} = \dfrac{\sqrt{3}}{2}; \cos\dfrac{2\pi}{3} = -\dfrac{1}{2}; \tan\dfrac{2\pi}{3} = -\sqrt{3}; \csc\dfrac{2\pi}{3} = \dfrac{2\sqrt{3}}{3}; \sec\dfrac{2\pi}{3} = -2; \cot\dfrac{2\pi}{3} = -\dfrac{\sqrt{3}}{3}$

49. $\sin 210° = -\dfrac{1}{2}; \cos 210° = -\dfrac{\sqrt{3}}{2}; \tan 210° = \dfrac{\sqrt{3}}{3}; \csc 210° = -2; \sec 210° = -\dfrac{2\sqrt{3}}{3}; \cot 210° = \sqrt{3}$

51. $\sin\dfrac{3\pi}{4} = \dfrac{\sqrt{2}}{2}; \cos\dfrac{3\pi}{4} = -\dfrac{\sqrt{2}}{2}; \tan\dfrac{3\pi}{4} = -1; \csc\dfrac{3\pi}{4} = \sqrt{2}; \sec\dfrac{3\pi}{4} = -\sqrt{2}; \cot\dfrac{3\pi}{4} = -1$

53. $\sin\dfrac{8\pi}{3} = \dfrac{\sqrt{3}}{2}; \cos\dfrac{8\pi}{3} = -\dfrac{1}{2}; \tan\dfrac{8\pi}{3} = -\sqrt{3}; \csc\dfrac{8\pi}{3} = \dfrac{2\sqrt{3}}{3}; \sec\dfrac{8\pi}{3} = -2; \cot\dfrac{8\pi}{3} = -\dfrac{\sqrt{3}}{3}$

55. $\sin 405° = \dfrac{\sqrt{2}}{2}; \cos 405° = \dfrac{\sqrt{2}}{2}; \tan 405° = 1; \csc 405° = \sqrt{2}; \sec 405° = \sqrt{2}; \cot 405° = 1$

57. $\sin\left(-\dfrac{\pi}{6}\right) = -\dfrac{1}{2}; \cos\left(-\dfrac{\pi}{6}\right) = \dfrac{\sqrt{3}}{2}; \tan\left(-\dfrac{\pi}{6}\right) = -\dfrac{\sqrt{3}}{3}; \csc\left(-\dfrac{\pi}{6}\right) = -2; \sec\left(-\dfrac{\pi}{6}\right) = \dfrac{2\sqrt{3}}{3}; \cot\left(-\dfrac{\pi}{6}\right) = -\sqrt{3}$

59. $\sin(-135°) = -\dfrac{\sqrt{2}}{2}; \cos(-135°) = -\dfrac{\sqrt{2}}{2}; \tan(-135°) = 1; \csc(-135°) = -\sqrt{2}; \sec(-135°) = -\sqrt{2}; \cot(-135°) = 1$

61. $\sin\dfrac{5\pi}{2} = 1; \cos\dfrac{5\pi}{2} = 0; \tan\dfrac{5\pi}{2}$ is undefined; $\csc\dfrac{5\pi}{2} = 1; \sec\dfrac{5\pi}{2}$ is undefined; $\cot\dfrac{5\pi}{2} = 0$

63. $\sin\left(-\dfrac{14\pi}{3}\right) = -\dfrac{\sqrt{3}}{2}$; $\cos\left(-\dfrac{14\pi}{3}\right) = -\dfrac{1}{2}$; $\tan\left(-\dfrac{14\pi}{3}\right) = \sqrt{3}$; $\csc\left(-\dfrac{14\pi}{3}\right) = -\dfrac{2\sqrt{3}}{3}$; $\sec\left(-\dfrac{14\pi}{3}\right) = -2$; $\cot\left(-\dfrac{14\pi}{3}\right) = \dfrac{\sqrt{3}}{3}$

65. 0.47 **67.** 1.07 **69.** 0.32 **71.** 3.73 **73.** 0.84 **75.** 0.02 **77.** $\sin\theta = \dfrac{4}{5}$; $\cos\theta = -\dfrac{3}{5}$; $\tan\theta = -\dfrac{4}{3}$; $\csc\theta = \dfrac{5}{4}$; $\sec\theta = -\dfrac{5}{3}$; $\cot\theta = -\dfrac{3}{4}$

79. $\sin\theta = -\dfrac{3\sqrt{13}}{13}$; $\cos\theta = \dfrac{2\sqrt{13}}{13}$; $\tan\theta = -\dfrac{3}{2}$; $\csc\theta = -\dfrac{\sqrt{13}}{3}$; $\sec\theta = \dfrac{\sqrt{13}}{2}$; $\cot\theta = -\dfrac{2}{3}$

81. $\sin\theta = -\dfrac{\sqrt{2}}{2}$; $\cos\theta = -\dfrac{\sqrt{2}}{2}$; $\tan\theta = 1$; $\csc\theta = -\sqrt{2}$; $\sec\theta = -\sqrt{2}$; $\cot\theta = 1$

83. $\sin\theta = \dfrac{3}{5}$; $\cos\theta = \dfrac{4}{5}$; $\tan\theta = \dfrac{3}{4}$; $\csc\theta = \dfrac{5}{3}$; $\sec\theta = \dfrac{5}{4}$; $\cot\theta = \dfrac{4}{3}$ **85.** 0 **87.** 0 **89.** −0.1 **91.** 3 **93.** 5 **95.** $\dfrac{\sqrt{3}}{2}$ **97.** $\dfrac{1}{2}$ **99.** $\dfrac{3}{4}$ **101.** $\dfrac{\sqrt{3}}{2}$

103. $\sqrt{3}$ **105.** $-\dfrac{\sqrt{3}}{2}$ **107.** $\dfrac{1+\sqrt{3}}{2}$ **109.** $-\dfrac{1}{2}$ **111.** $\dfrac{\sqrt{3}}{2}$ **113.** $\dfrac{\sqrt{2}}{4}$ **115. (a)** $\dfrac{\sqrt{2}}{2}$; $\left(\dfrac{\pi}{4},\dfrac{\sqrt{2}}{2}\right)$ **(b)** $\left(\dfrac{\sqrt{2}}{2},\dfrac{\pi}{4}\right)$ **(c)** $\left(\dfrac{\pi}{4},-2\right)$

117. Answers may vary. One set of possible answers is $-\dfrac{11\pi}{3}, -\dfrac{5\pi}{3}, \dfrac{\pi}{3}, \dfrac{7\pi}{3}, \dfrac{13\pi}{3}$.

119.

θ	0.5	0.4	0.2	0.1	0.01	0.001	0.0001	0.00001
$\sin\theta$	0.4794	0.3894	0.1987	0.0998	0.0100	0.0010	0.0001	0.00001
$\dfrac{\sin\theta}{\theta}$	0.9589	0.9735	0.9933	0.9983	1.0000	1.0000	1.0000	1.0000

$\dfrac{\sin\theta}{\theta}$ approaches 1 as θ approaches 0.

121. $R \approx 310.56$ ft; $H \approx 77.64$ ft **123.** $R \approx 19{,}541.95$ m; $H \approx 2278.14$ m **125. (a)** 1.20 sec **(b)** 1.12 sec **(c)** 1.20 sec
127. (a) 1.9 hr; 0.57 hr **(b)** 1.69 hr; 0.75 hr **(c)** 1.63 hr; 0.86 hr **(d)** 1.67 hr; tan 90° is undefined
129. (a) 16.56 ft **(b)** 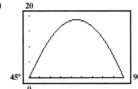 **(c)** 67.5° **131. (a)** values estimated to the nearest tenth:
sin 1 ≈ 0.8; cos 1 ≈ 0.5; tan 1 ≈ 1.6; csc 1 ≈ 1.3; sec 1 ≈ 2.0; cot 1 ≈ 0.6;
actual values to the nearest tenth: sin 1 ≈ 0.8; cos 1 ≈ 0.5; tan 1 ≈ 1.6;
csc 1 ≈ 1.2; sec 1 ≈ 1.9; cot 1 ≈ 0.6
(b) values estimated to the nearest tenth: sin 5.1 ≈ −0.9; cos 5.1 ≈ 0.4;
tan 5.1 ≈ −2.3; csc 5.1 ≈ −1.1; sec 5.1 ≈ 2.5; cot 5.1 ≈ −0.4; actual
values to the nearest tenth: sin 5.1 ≈ −0.9; cos 5.1 ≈ 0.4; tan 5.1 ≈ −2.4;
csc 5.1 ≈ −1.1; sec 5.1 ≈ 2.6; cot 5.1 ≈ −0.4

6.3 Assess Your Understanding *(page 390)*

5. 2π; π **6.** All real numbers except odd multiples of $\dfrac{\pi}{2}$ **7.** $[-1, 1]$ **8.** T **9.** 1 **10.** F **11.** $\dfrac{\sqrt{2}}{2}$ **13.** 1 **15.** 1 **17.** $\sqrt{3}$ **19.** $\dfrac{\sqrt{2}}{2}$ **21.** 0

23. $\sqrt{2}$ **25.** $\dfrac{\sqrt{3}}{3}$ **27.** II **29.** IV **31.** IV **33.** II **35.** $\tan\theta = -\dfrac{3}{4}$; $\cot\theta = -\dfrac{4}{3}$; $\sec\theta = \dfrac{5}{4}$; $\csc\theta = -\dfrac{5}{3}$ **37.** $\tan\theta = 2$; $\cot\theta = \dfrac{1}{2}$; $\sec\theta = \sqrt{5}$;

$\csc\theta = \dfrac{\sqrt{5}}{2}$ **39.** $\tan\theta = \dfrac{\sqrt{3}}{3}$; $\cot\theta = \sqrt{3}$; $\sec\theta = \dfrac{2\sqrt{3}}{3}$; $\csc\theta = 2$ **41.** $\tan\theta = -\dfrac{\sqrt{2}}{4}$; $\cot\theta = -2\sqrt{2}$; $\sec\theta = \dfrac{3\sqrt{2}}{4}$; $\csc\theta = -3$

43. $\cos\theta = -\dfrac{5}{13}$; $\tan\theta = -\dfrac{12}{5}$; $\csc\theta = \dfrac{13}{12}$; $\sec\theta = -\dfrac{13}{5}$; $\cot\theta = -\dfrac{5}{12}$ **45.** $\sin\theta = -\dfrac{3}{5}$; $\tan\theta = \dfrac{3}{4}$; $\csc\theta = -\dfrac{5}{3}$; $\sec\theta = -\dfrac{5}{4}$; $\cot\theta = \dfrac{4}{3}$

47. $\cos\theta = -\dfrac{12}{13}$; $\tan\theta = -\dfrac{5}{12}$; $\csc\theta = \dfrac{13}{5}$; $\sec\theta = -\dfrac{13}{12}$; $\cot\theta = -\dfrac{12}{5}$ **49.** $\sin\theta = \dfrac{2\sqrt{2}}{3}$; $\tan\theta = -2\sqrt{2}$; $\csc\theta = \dfrac{3\sqrt{2}}{4}$; $\sec\theta = -3$; $\cot\theta = -\dfrac{\sqrt{2}}{4}$

51. $\cos\theta = -\dfrac{\sqrt{5}}{3}$; $\tan\theta = -\dfrac{2\sqrt{5}}{5}$; $\csc\theta = \dfrac{3}{2}$; $\sec\theta = -\dfrac{3\sqrt{5}}{5}$; $\cot\theta = -\dfrac{\sqrt{5}}{2}$ **53.** $\sin\theta = -\dfrac{\sqrt{3}}{2}$; $\cos\theta = \dfrac{1}{2}$; $\tan\theta = -\sqrt{3}$;

$\csc\theta = -\dfrac{2\sqrt{3}}{3}$; $\cot\theta = -\dfrac{\sqrt{3}}{3}$ **55.** $\sin\theta = -\dfrac{3}{5}$; $\cos\theta = -\dfrac{4}{5}$; $\csc\theta = -\dfrac{5}{3}$; $\sec\theta = -\dfrac{5}{4}$; $\cot\theta = \dfrac{4}{3}$ **57.** $\sin\theta = \dfrac{\sqrt{10}}{10}$; $\cos\theta = -\dfrac{3\sqrt{10}}{10}$;

$\csc\theta = \sqrt{10}$; $\sec\theta = -\dfrac{\sqrt{10}}{3}$; $\cot\theta = -3$ **59.** $-\dfrac{\sqrt{3}}{2}$ **61.** $-\dfrac{\sqrt{3}}{3}$ **63.** 2 **65.** −1 **67.** −1 **69.** $\dfrac{\sqrt{2}}{2}$ **71.** 0 **73.** $-\sqrt{2}$ **75.** $\dfrac{2\sqrt{3}}{3}$ **77.** 1 **79.** 1

81. 0 **83.** 1 **85.** −1 **87.** 0 **89.** 0.9 **91.** 9 **93.** 0 **95.** All real numbers **97.** Odd multiples of $\dfrac{\pi}{2}$ **99.** Odd multiples of $\dfrac{\pi}{2}$ **101.** $-1 \le y \le 1$

103. All real numbers **105.** $|y| \ge 1$ **107.** Odd; yes; origin **109.** Odd; yes; origin **111.** Even; yes; y-axis **113. (a)** $-\dfrac{1}{3}$ **(b)** 1

115. (a) −2 **(b)** 6 **117. (a)** −4 **(b)** −12 **119.** ≈15.81 min **121.** Let a be a real number and $P = (x, y)$ be the point on the unit circle that

corresponds to t. Consider the equation $\tan t = \dfrac{y}{x} = a$. Then $y = ax$. But $x^2 + y^2 = 1$, so $x^2 + a^2x^2 = 1$. So $x = \pm\dfrac{1}{\sqrt{1+a^2}}$ and $y = \pm\dfrac{a}{\sqrt{1+a^2}}$;

that is, for any real number a, there is a point $P = (x, y)$ on the unit circle for which $\tan t = a$. In other words, the range of the tangent function is the set of all real numbers. **123.** Suppose that there is a number p, $0 < p < 2\pi$, for which $\sin(\theta + p) = \sin \theta$ for all θ. If $\theta = 0$, then

$\sin(0 + p) = \sin p = \sin 0 = 0$, so $p = \pi$. If $\theta = \dfrac{\pi}{2}$, then $\sin\left(\dfrac{\pi}{2} + p\right) = \sin\left(\dfrac{\pi}{2}\right)$. But $p = \pi$. Thus, $\sin\left(\dfrac{3\pi}{2}\right) = -1 = \sin\left(\dfrac{\pi}{2}\right) = 1$. This is

impossible. Therefore, the smallest positive number p for which $\sin(\theta + p) = \sin \theta$ for all θ is 2π. **125.** $\sec \theta = \dfrac{1}{\cos \theta}$; since $\cos \theta$ has period 2π,

so does $\sec \theta$. **127.** If $P = (a, b)$ is the point on the unit circle corresponding to θ, then $Q = (-a, -b)$ is the point on the unit circle corresponding to

$\theta + \pi$. Thus, $\tan(\theta + \pi) = \dfrac{-b}{-a} = \dfrac{b}{a} = \tan \theta$. Suppose that there exists a number p, $0 < p < \pi$, for which $\tan(\theta + p) = \tan \theta$ for all θ. Then, if $\theta = 0$,

then $\tan p = \tan 0 = 0$. But this means that p is a multiple of π. Since no multiple of π exists in the interval $(0, \pi)$, this is a contradiction. Therefore, the period of $f(\theta) = \tan \theta$ is π.

129. Let $P = (a, b)$ be the point on the unit circle corresponding to θ. Then $\csc \theta = \dfrac{1}{b} = \dfrac{1}{\sin \theta}$; $\sec \theta = \dfrac{1}{a} = \dfrac{1}{\cos \theta}$; $\cot \theta = \dfrac{a}{b} = \dfrac{1}{b/a} = \dfrac{1}{\tan \theta}$.

131. $(\sin \theta \cos \phi)^2 + (\sin \theta \sin \phi)^2 + \cos^2 \theta = \sin^2 \theta \cos^2 \phi + \sin^2 \theta \sin^2 \phi + \cos^2 \theta = \sin^2 \theta(\cos^2 \phi + \sin^2 \phi) + \cos^2 \theta = \sin^2 \theta + \cos^2 \theta = 1$

6.4 Assess Your Understanding (page 403)

3. $1; \dfrac{\pi}{2}$ **4.** $3; \pi$ **5.** $3; \dfrac{\pi}{3}$ **6.** T **7.** F **8.** T **9. (a)** 0 **(b)** $-\dfrac{\pi}{2} < x < \dfrac{\pi}{2}$ **(c)** 1 **(d)** $0, \pi, 2\pi$

(e) $f(x) = 1$ for $x = -\dfrac{3\pi}{2}, \dfrac{\pi}{2}$; $f(x) = -1$ for $x = -\dfrac{\pi}{2}, \dfrac{3\pi}{2}$ **(f)** $-\dfrac{5\pi}{6}, -\dfrac{\pi}{6}, \dfrac{7\pi}{6}, \dfrac{11\pi}{6}$ **(g)** $\{x | x = k\pi, k \text{ an integer}\}$ **11.** Amplitude $= 2$; period $= 2\pi$

13. Amplitude $= 4$; period $= \pi$ **15.** Amplitude $= 6$; period $= 2$ **17.** Amplitude $= \dfrac{1}{2}$; period $= \dfrac{4\pi}{3}$ **19.** Amplitude $= \dfrac{5}{3}$; period $= 3$

21. F **23.** A **25.** H **27.** C **29.** J **31.** A **33.** B

35.
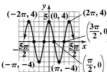
Domain: $(-\infty, \infty)$
Range: $[-4, 4]$

37.
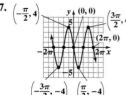
Domain: $(-\infty, \infty)$
Range: $[-4, 4]$

39.
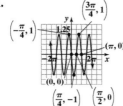
Domain: $(-\infty, \infty)$
Range: $[-1, 1]$

41.
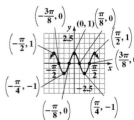
Domain: $(-\infty, \infty)$
Range: $[-1, 1]$

43.
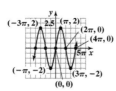
Domain: $(-\infty, \infty)$
Range: $[-2, 2]$

45.
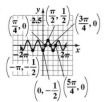
Domain: $(-\infty, \infty)$
Range: $\left[-\dfrac{1}{2}, \dfrac{1}{2}\right]$

47.
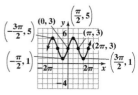
Domain: $(-\infty, \infty)$
Range: $[1, 5]$

49.
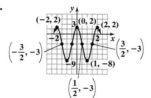
Domain: $(-\infty, \infty)$
Range: $[-8, 2]$

51.
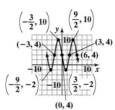
Domain: $(-\infty, \infty)$
Range: $[-2, 10]$

53.
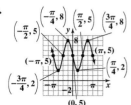
Domain: $(-\infty, \infty)$
Range: $[2, 8]$

55.
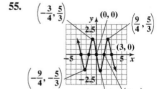
Domain: $(-\infty, \infty)$
Range: $\left[-\dfrac{5}{3}, \dfrac{5}{3}\right]$

57.
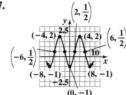
Domain: $(-\infty, \infty)$
Range: $[-1, 2]$

59. $y = \pm 3 \sin(2x)$ **61.** $y = \pm 3 \sin(\pi x)$ **63.** $y = 5 \cos\left(\dfrac{\pi}{4}x\right)$ **65.** $y = -3 \cos\left(\dfrac{1}{2}x\right)$ **67.** $y = \dfrac{3}{4} \sin(2\pi x)$ **69.** $y = -\sin\left(\dfrac{3}{2}x\right)$

71. $y = -\cos\left(\dfrac{4\pi}{3}x\right) + 1$ **73.** $y = 3 \sin\left(\dfrac{\pi}{2}x\right)$ **75.** $y = -4 \cos(3x)$ **77.** $\dfrac{2}{\pi}$ **79.** $\dfrac{\sqrt{2}}{\pi}$

81. $(f \circ g)(x) = \sin(4x)$ **83.** $(f \circ g)(x) = -2 \cos x$ **85.**

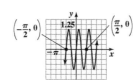

$(g \circ f)(x) = 4 \sin x$

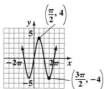

$(g \circ f)(x) = \cos(-2x)$

87. Period $= \dfrac{1}{30}$ s;

amplitude $= 220$ amp

89. (a) Amplitude $= 220$ V; **(c)** $I(t) = 22 \sin(120\pi t)$

period $= \dfrac{1}{60}$ s **(d)** Amplitude $= 22$ amp;

(b), (e) period $= \dfrac{1}{60}$ s

91. (a) $P(t) = \dfrac{[V_0 \sin(2\pi ft)]^2}{R} = \dfrac{V_0^2}{R} \sin^2(2\pi ft)$ **(b)** Since the graph of P has amplitude $\dfrac{V_0^2}{2R}$ and period $\dfrac{1}{2f}$ and is of the form $y = A\cos(\omega t) + B$,

then $A = -\dfrac{V_0^2}{2R}$ and $B = \dfrac{V_0^2}{2R}$. Since $\dfrac{1}{2f} = \dfrac{2\pi}{\omega}$, then $\omega = 4\pi f$. Therefore, $P(t) = -\dfrac{V_0^2}{2R}\cos(4\pi ft) + \dfrac{V_0^2}{2R} = \dfrac{V_0^2}{2R}[1 - \cos(4\pi ft)]$.

93. (a) Physical potential: $\omega = \dfrac{2\pi}{23}$; emotional potential: $\omega = \dfrac{\pi}{14}$; intellectual potential: $\omega = \dfrac{2\pi}{33}$

(b)

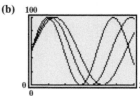

(c) No **(d)** Physical potential peaks at 15 days after 20th birthday. Emotional potential is 50% at 17 days, with a maximum at 10 days and a minimum at 24 days. Intellectual potential starts fairly high, drops to a minimum at 13 days, and rises to a maximum at 29 days.

95.

97. Answers may vary. $\left(-\dfrac{5\pi}{3}, \dfrac{1}{2}\right), \left(-\dfrac{\pi}{3}, \dfrac{1}{2}\right), \left(\dfrac{\pi}{3}, \dfrac{1}{2}\right), \left(\dfrac{5\pi}{3}, \dfrac{1}{2}\right)$ **99.** Answers may vary. $\left(-\dfrac{3\pi}{4}, 1\right), \left(\dfrac{\pi}{4}, 1\right), \left(\dfrac{5\pi}{4}, 1\right), \left(\dfrac{9\pi}{4}, 1\right)$

6.5 Assess Your Understanding (page 413)

3. origin; odd multiples of $\dfrac{\pi}{2}$ **4.** y-axis; odd multiples of $\dfrac{\pi}{2}$ **5.** $y = \cos x$ **6.** T **7.** 0 **9.** 1

11. $\sec x = 1$ for $x = -2\pi, 0, 2\pi$; $\sec x = -1$ for $x = -\pi, \pi$ **13.** $-\dfrac{3\pi}{2}, -\dfrac{\pi}{2}, \dfrac{\pi}{2}, \dfrac{3\pi}{2}$ **15.** $-\dfrac{3\pi}{2}, -\dfrac{\pi}{2}, \dfrac{\pi}{2}, \dfrac{3\pi}{2}$

17.

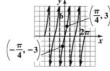

Domain: $\left\{x \,\middle|\, x \neq \dfrac{k\pi}{2}, k \text{ is an odd integer}\right\}$

Range: $(-\infty, \infty)$

19.

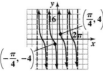

Domain: $\{x \mid x \neq k\pi, k \text{ is an integer}\}$
Range: $(-\infty, \infty)$

21.

Domain: $\{x \mid x \text{ does not equal an odd integer}\}$
Range: $(-\infty, \infty)$

23.

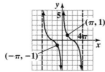

Domain: $\{x \mid x \neq 4k\pi, k \text{ is an integer}\}$
Range: $(-\infty, \infty)$

25.

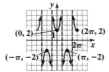

Domain: $\left\{x \,\middle|\, x \neq \dfrac{k\pi}{2}, k \text{ is an odd integer}\right\}$
Range: $\{y \mid y \leq -2 \text{ or } y \geq 2\}$

27.

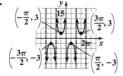

Domain: $\{x \mid x \neq k\pi, k \text{ is an integer}\}$
Range: $\{y \mid y \leq -3 \text{ or } y \geq 3\}$

29.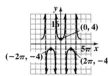

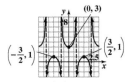

Domain: $\{x | x \neq k\pi, k \text{ is an odd integer}\}$
Range: $\{y | y \leq -4 \text{ or } y \geq 4\}$

31.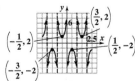

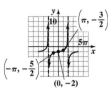

Domain: $\{x | x \text{ does not equal an integer}\}$
Range: $\{y | y \leq -2 \text{ or } y \geq 2\}$

33.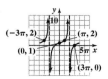

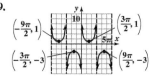

Domain: $\{x | x \neq 2\pi k, k \text{ is an odd integer}\}$
Range: $(-\infty, \infty)$

35.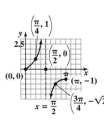

Domain: $\left\{ x \,\middle|\, x \neq \dfrac{3}{4}k, k \text{ is an odd integer} \right\}$
Range: $\{y | y \leq 1 \text{ or } y \geq 3\}$

37.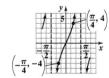

Domain: $\{x | x \neq 2\pi k, k \text{ is an odd integer}\}$
Range: $(-\infty, \infty)$

39.

Domain: $\{x | x \neq 3\pi k, k \text{ is an integer}\}$
Range: $\{y | y \leq -3 \text{ or } y \geq 1\}$

41. $\dfrac{2\sqrt{3}}{\pi}$ **43.** $\dfrac{6\sqrt{3}}{\pi}$ **45.** $(f \circ g)(x) = \tan(4x)$ $(g \circ f)(x) = 4\tan x$ **47.** $(f \circ g)(x) = -2\cot x$ $(g \circ f)(x) = \cot(-2x)$

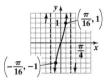   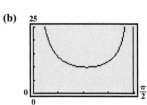   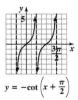

49.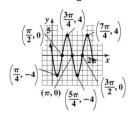

51. (a) $L(\theta) = \dfrac{3}{\cos \theta} + \dfrac{4}{\sin \theta}$
$= 3\sec \theta + 4\csc \theta$

(b)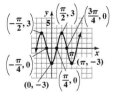

(c) ≈ 0.83 **(d)** $\approx 9.86\,\text{ft}$

53.

$y = \tan x$ $y = -\cot\left(x + \dfrac{\pi}{2}\right)$

6.6 Assess Your Understanding *(page 424)*

1. phase shift   **2.** F
3. Amplitude = 4
   Period = π
   Phase shift = $\dfrac{\pi}{2}$

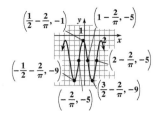

5. Amplitude = 2
   Period = $\dfrac{2\pi}{3}$
   Phase shift = $-\dfrac{\pi}{6}$

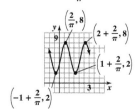

7. Amplitude = 3
   Period = π
   Phase shift = $-\dfrac{\pi}{4}$

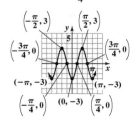

9. Amplitude = 4
   Period = 2
   Phase shift = $-\dfrac{2}{\pi}$

11. Amplitude = 3
   Period = 2
   Phase shift = $\dfrac{2}{\pi}$

13. Amplitude = 3
   Period = π
   Phase shift = $\dfrac{\pi}{4}$

15. $y = 2\sin\left[2\left(x - \dfrac{1}{2}\right)\right]$ or
   $y = 2\sin(2x - 1)$

17. $y = 3\sin\left[\dfrac{2}{3}\left(x + \dfrac{1}{3}\right)\right]$ or
   $y = 3\sin\left(\dfrac{2}{3}x + \dfrac{2}{9}\right)$

10.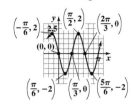

19.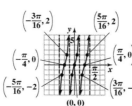

21.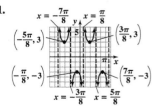

23.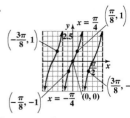

25.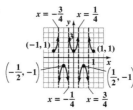

27. Period $= \dfrac{1}{15}$ s;

amplitude $= 120$ amp;

phase shift $= \dfrac{1}{90}$ s

29. (a)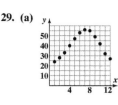

(b) $y = 15.9 \sin\left[\dfrac{\pi}{6}(x-4)\right] + 40.1$ or $y = 15.9\sin\left(\dfrac{\pi}{6}x - \dfrac{2\pi}{3}\right) + 40.1$

(c)

(d) $y = 15.62 \sin(0.517x - 2.096) + 40.377$

(e)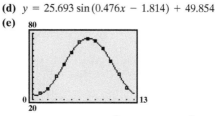

31. (a)

(b) $y = 24.95 \sin\left[\dfrac{\pi}{6}(x-4)\right] + 50.45$ or $y = 24.95\sin\left(\dfrac{\pi}{6}x - \dfrac{2\pi}{3}\right) + 50.45$

(c)

(d) $y = 25.693 \sin(0.476x - 1.814) + 49.854$

(e)

33. (a) 11:55 PM   **(b)** $y = 3.105 \sin\left[\dfrac{24\pi}{149}(x - 8.3958)\right] + 2.735$ or $y = 3.105\sin\left[\dfrac{24\pi}{149}x - 4.2485\right] + 2.735$ **(c)** 2.12 ft

35. (a) $y = 1.6\sin\left(\dfrac{2\pi}{365}x - 1.39\right) + 12.15$

(b) 12.43 h

(c)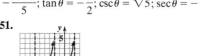

(d) The actual hours of sunlight on April 1, 2010, were 12.43 hours. This is the same as the predicted amount.

37. (a) $y = 6.97\sin\left(\dfrac{2\pi}{365}x - 1.39\right) + 12.45$

(b) 13.67 h

(c)

(d) The actual hours of sunlight on April 1, 2010, were 13.38 hours. This is close to the predicted amount of 13.67 hours.

Review Exercises (page 430)

1. $\dfrac{3\pi}{4}$ **3.** $\dfrac{\pi}{10}$ **5.** $135°$ **7.** $-450°$ **9.** $\dfrac{1}{2}$ **11.** $\dfrac{3\sqrt{2}}{2} - \dfrac{4\sqrt{3}}{3}$ **13.** $-3\sqrt{2} - 2\sqrt{3}$ **15.** 3 **17.** 0 **19.** 0 **21.** 1 **23.** 1 **25.** 1 **27.** -1 **29.** 1

31. $\cos\theta = \dfrac{3}{5}$; $\tan\theta = \dfrac{4}{3}$; $\csc\theta = \dfrac{5}{4}$; $\sec\theta = \dfrac{5}{3}$; $\cot\theta = \dfrac{3}{4}$ **33.** $\sin\theta = -\dfrac{12}{13}$; $\cos\theta = -\dfrac{5}{13}$; $\csc\theta = -\dfrac{13}{12}$; $\sec\theta = -\dfrac{13}{5}$; $\cot\theta = \dfrac{5}{12}$

35. $\sin\theta = \dfrac{3}{5}$; $\cos\theta = -\dfrac{4}{5}$; $\tan\theta = -\dfrac{3}{4}$; $\csc\theta = \dfrac{5}{3}$; $\cot\theta = -\dfrac{4}{3}$ **37.** $\cos\theta = -\dfrac{5}{13}$; $\tan\theta = -\dfrac{12}{5}$; $\csc\theta = \dfrac{13}{12}$; $\sec\theta = -\dfrac{13}{5}$; $\cot\theta = -\dfrac{5}{12}$

39. $\cos\theta = \dfrac{12}{13}$; $\tan\theta = -\dfrac{5}{12}$; $\csc\theta = -\dfrac{13}{5}$; $\sec\theta = \dfrac{13}{12}$; $\cot\theta = -\dfrac{12}{5}$ **41.** $\sin\theta = -\dfrac{\sqrt{10}}{10}$; $\cos\theta = -\dfrac{3\sqrt{10}}{10}$; $\csc\theta = -\sqrt{10}$; $\sec\theta = -\dfrac{\sqrt{10}}{3}$; $\cot\theta = 3$

43. $\sin\theta = -\dfrac{2\sqrt{2}}{3}$; $\cos\theta = \dfrac{1}{3}$; $\tan\theta = -2\sqrt{2}$; $\csc\theta = -\dfrac{3\sqrt{2}}{4}$; $\cot\theta = -\dfrac{\sqrt{2}}{4}$ **45.** $\sin\theta = \dfrac{\sqrt{5}}{5}$; $\cos\theta = -\dfrac{2\sqrt{5}}{5}$; $\tan\theta = -\dfrac{1}{2}$; $\csc\theta = \sqrt{5}$; $\sec\theta = -\dfrac{\sqrt{5}}{2}$

47.

Domain: $(-\infty, \infty)$
Range: $[-2, 2]$

49.

Domain: $(-\infty, \infty)$
Range: $[-2, 2]$

51.

Domain: $\left\{x \,\middle|\, x \neq \dfrac{k\pi}{2},\ k \text{ is an odd integer}\right\}$

Range: $(-\infty, \infty)$

53.

Domain: $\left\{ x \mid x \neq \dfrac{\pi}{6} + k \cdot \dfrac{\pi}{3}, k \text{ is an integer} \right\}$

Range: $(-\infty, \infty)$

55.

Domain: $\left\{ x \mid x \neq -\dfrac{\pi}{4} + k\pi, k \text{ is an integer} \right\}$

Range: $(-\infty, \infty)$

57.

Domain: $\left\{ x \mid x \neq \dfrac{k\pi}{4}, k \text{ is an odd integer} \right\}$

Range: $\{ y \mid y \leq -4 \text{ or } y \geq 4 \}$

59.

Domain: $(-\infty, \infty)$
Range: $[-6, 2]$

61.

Domain: $\left\{ x \mid x \neq \dfrac{\pi}{2} + k \cdot 2\pi, k \text{ is an integer} \right\}$

Range: $(-\infty, \infty)$

63. Amplitude = 4; period = 2π

65. Amplitude = 8; period = 4

67. Amplitude = 4

Period = $\dfrac{2\pi}{3}$

Phase shift = 0

69. Amplitude = 2

Period = π

Phase shift = $\dfrac{\pi}{2}$

71. Amplitude = $\dfrac{1}{2}$

Period = $\dfrac{4\pi}{3}$

Phase shift = $\dfrac{2\pi}{3}$

73. Amplitude = $\dfrac{2}{3}$

Period = 2

Phase shift = $\dfrac{6}{\pi}$

75. $y = 5 \cos \dfrac{x}{4}$ **77.** $y = -6 \cos\left(\dfrac{\pi}{4} x \right)$ **79.** 0.38 **81.** Sine, cosine, cosecant and secant: negative; tangent and cotangent: positive

83. $\sin\theta = \dfrac{2\sqrt{2}}{3}$; $\cos\theta = -\dfrac{1}{3}$; $\tan\theta = -2\sqrt{2}$; $\csc\theta = \dfrac{3\sqrt{2}}{4}$; $\sec\theta = -3$; $\cot\theta = -\dfrac{\sqrt{2}}{4}$

85. Domain: $\left\{ x \mid x \neq \text{odd multiple of } \dfrac{\pi}{2} \right\}$; range: $\{ y \mid |y| \geq 1 \}$; period = 2π **87.** $\dfrac{\pi}{3} \approx 1.05$ ft; $\dfrac{\pi}{3} \approx 1.05$ ft^2 **89.** ≈ 114.59 revolutions/hr

91. 0.1 revolution/sec = $\dfrac{\pi}{5}$ radian/sec

93. (a) 120

(b) $\dfrac{1}{60}$

(c)

95. (a)

(b) $y = 19.5 \sin\left[\dfrac{\pi}{6}(x - 4) \right] + 70.5$ or

$\qquad y = 19.5 \sin\left(\dfrac{\pi}{6}x - \dfrac{2\pi}{3} \right) + 70.5$

(c)

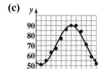

(d) $y = 19.52 \sin(0.54x - 2.28) + 71.01$

(e)

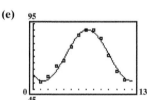

97.

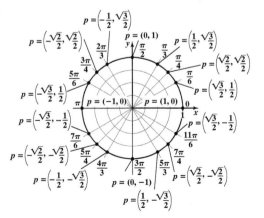

Chapter Test *(page 432)*

1. $\dfrac{13\pi}{9}$ **2.** $-\dfrac{20\pi}{9}$ **3.** $\dfrac{13\pi}{180}$ **4.** $-22.5°$ **5.** $810°$ **6.** $135°$ **7.** $\dfrac{1}{2}$ **8.** 0 **9.** $-\dfrac{1}{2}$ **10.** $-\dfrac{\sqrt{3}}{3}$ **11.** 2 **12.** $\dfrac{3(1-\sqrt{2})}{2}$ **13.** 0.292 **14.** 0.309

15. -1.524 **16.** 2.747 **17.**

	sin θ	cos θ	tan θ	sec θ	csc θ	cot θ
θ in QI	+	+	+	+	+	+
θ in QII	+	−	−	−	+	−
θ in QIII	−	−	+	−	−	+
θ in QIV	−	+	−	+	−	−

18. $-\dfrac{3}{5}$

19. $\cos\theta = -\dfrac{2\sqrt{6}}{7}$; $\tan\theta = -\dfrac{5\sqrt{6}}{12}$; $\csc\theta = \dfrac{7}{5}$; $\sec\theta = -\dfrac{7\sqrt{6}}{12}$; $\cot\theta = -\dfrac{2\sqrt{6}}{5}$ **20.** $\sin\theta = -\dfrac{\sqrt{5}}{3}$; $\tan\theta = -\dfrac{\sqrt{5}}{2}$; $\csc\theta = -\dfrac{3\sqrt{5}}{5}$;

$\sec\theta = \dfrac{3}{2}$; $\cot\theta = -\dfrac{2\sqrt{5}}{5}$ **21.** $\sin\theta = \dfrac{12}{13}$; $\cos\theta = -\dfrac{5}{13}$; $\csc\theta = \dfrac{13}{12}$; $\sec\theta = -\dfrac{13}{5}$; $\cot\theta = -\dfrac{5}{12}$ **22.** $\dfrac{7\sqrt{53}}{53}$ **23.** $-\dfrac{5\sqrt{146}}{146}$ **24.** $-\dfrac{1}{2}$

25.
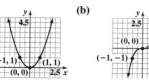

26.

27. $y = -3\sin\left(3x + \dfrac{3\pi}{4}\right)$ **28.** 78.93 ft^2 **29.** 143.5 rpm

Cumulative Review *(page 433)*

1. $\left\{-1, \dfrac{1}{2}\right\}$ **2.** $y - 5 = -3(x + 2)$ or $y = -3x - 1$ **3.** $x^2 + (y + 2)^2 = 16$

4. A line; slope $\dfrac{2}{3}$; intercepts $(6, 0)$ and $(0, -4)$

5. A circle; center $(1, -2)$; radius 3

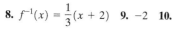

6.
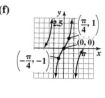

7. (a)
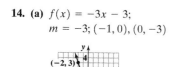
(b)
(c)
(d)
(e)
(f)

8. $f^{-1}(x) = \dfrac{1}{3}(x + 2)$ **9.** -2 **10.**
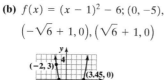

11. $3 - \dfrac{3\sqrt{3}}{2}$ **12.** $y = 2(3^x)$ **13.** $y = 3\cos\left(\dfrac{\pi}{6}x\right)$

14. (a) $f(x) = -3x - 3$;
$m = -3; (-1, 0), (0, -3)$

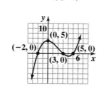

(b) $f(x) = (x - 1)^2 - 6; (0, -5)$,
$\left(-\sqrt{6} + 1, 0\right), \left(\sqrt{6} + 1, 0\right)$

(c) We have that $y = 3$ when $x = -2$ and $y = -6$ when $x = 1$. Both points satisfy $y = ae^x$. Therefore, for $(-2, 3)$ we have $3 = ae^{-2}$, which implies that $a = 3e^2$. But for $(1, -6)$ we have $-6 = ae^1$, which implies that $a = -6e^{-1}$. Therefore, there is no exponential function $y = ae^x$ that contains $(-2, 3)$ and $(1, -6)$.

15. (a) $f(x) = \dfrac{1}{6}(x + 2)(x - 3)(x - 5)$

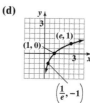

(b) $R(x) = -\dfrac{(x + 2)(x - 3)(x - 5)}{3(x - 2)}$

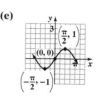

CHAPTER 7   Analytic Trigonometry

7.1 Assess Your Understanding *(page 445)*

7. $x = \sin y$ **8.** $0 \le x \le \pi$ **9.** $-\infty < x < \infty$ **10.** F   **11.** T   **12.** T   **13.** 0   **15.** $-\dfrac{\pi}{2}$ **17.** 0   **19.** $\dfrac{\pi}{4}$ **21.** $\dfrac{\pi}{3}$ **23.** $\dfrac{5\pi}{6}$ **25.** 0. 10   **27.** 1.37

29. 0.51   **31.** −0.38   **33.** −0.12   **35.** 1.08   **37.** $\dfrac{4\pi}{5}$ **39.** $-\dfrac{3\pi}{8}$ **41.** $-\dfrac{\pi}{8}$ **43.** $-\dfrac{\pi}{5}$ **45.** $\dfrac{1}{4}$ **47.** 4   **49.** Not defined   **51.** π

53. $f^{-1}(x) = \sin^{-1}\dfrac{x - 2}{5}$

    Range of f = Domain of $f^{-1} = [-3, 7]$

    Range of $f^{-1} = \left[-\dfrac{\pi}{2}, \dfrac{\pi}{2}\right]$

55. $f^{-1}(x) = \dfrac{1}{3}\cos^{-1}\left(-\dfrac{x}{2}\right)$

    Range of f = Domain of $f^{-1} = [-2, 2]$

    Range of $f^{-1} = \left[0, \dfrac{\pi}{3}\right]$

57. $f^{-1}(x) = -\tan^{-1}(x + 3) - 1$

    Range of f = Domain of $f^{-1} = (-\infty, \infty)$

    Range of $f^{-1} = \left(-1 - \dfrac{\pi}{2}, \dfrac{\pi}{2} - 1\right)$

59. $f^{-1}(x) = \dfrac{1}{2}\left[\sin^{-1}\left(\dfrac{x}{3}\right) - 1\right]$

    Range of f = Domain of $f^{-1} = [-3, 3]$

    Range of $f^{-1} = \left[-\dfrac{1}{2} - \dfrac{\pi}{4}, -\dfrac{1}{2} + \dfrac{\pi}{4}\right]$

61. $\left\{\dfrac{\sqrt{2}}{2}\right\}$ **63.** $\left\{-\dfrac{1}{4}\right\}$ **65.** $\{\sqrt{3}\}$ **67.** $\{-1\}$

69. (a) 13.92 h or 13 h, 55 min   **(b)** 12 h   **(c)** 13.85 h or 13 h, 51 min

71. (a) 13.3 h or 13 h, 18 min   **(b)** 12 h   **(c)** 13.26 h or 13 h, 15 min

73. (a) 12 h   **(b)** 12 h   **(c)** 12 h   **(d)** It is 12 h.   **75.** 3.35 min   **77. (a)** $\dfrac{\pi}{3}$ square units   **(b)** $\dfrac{5\pi}{12}$ square units   **79.** 4250 mi

7.2 Assess Your Understanding *(page 452)*

4. $x = \sec y; \ge 1; 0; \pi$ **5.** cosine   **6.** F   **7.** T   **8.** T   **9.** $\dfrac{\sqrt{2}}{2}$ **11.** $-\dfrac{\sqrt{3}}{3}$ **13.** 2   **15.** $\sqrt{2}$ **17.** $-\dfrac{\sqrt{2}}{2}$ **19.** $\dfrac{2\sqrt{3}}{3}$ **21.** $\dfrac{3\pi}{4}$ **23.** $-\dfrac{\pi}{3}$ **25.** $\dfrac{\sqrt{2}}{4}$

27. $\dfrac{\sqrt{5}}{2}$ **29.** $-\dfrac{\sqrt{14}}{2}$ **31.** $-\dfrac{3\sqrt{10}}{10}$ **33.** $\sqrt{5}$ **35.** $-\dfrac{\pi}{4}$ **37.** $\dfrac{\pi}{6}$ **39.** $-\dfrac{\pi}{2}$ **41.** $\dfrac{\pi}{6}$ **43.** $\dfrac{2\pi}{3}$ **45.** 1.32   **47.** 0.46   **49.** −0.34   **51.** 2.72   **53.** −0.73

55. 2.55   **57.** $\dfrac{1}{\sqrt{1 + u^2}}$ **59.** $\dfrac{u}{\sqrt{1 - u^2}}$ **61.** $\dfrac{\sqrt{u^2 - 1}}{|u|}$ **63.** $\dfrac{\sqrt{u^2 - 1}}{|u|}$ **65.** $\dfrac{1}{u}$ **67.** $\dfrac{5}{13}$ **69.** $\dfrac{3\pi}{4}$ **71.** $-\dfrac{3}{4}$ **73.** $\dfrac{5}{13}$ **75.** $\dfrac{\pi}{6}$ **77.** $-\sqrt{15}$

79. (a) $\theta = 31.89°$ **(b)** 54.64 ft in diameter   **(c)** 37.96 ft high   **81. (a)** $\theta = 22.3°$ **(b)** $v_0 = 2940.23$ ft/s

83.

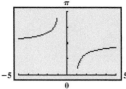

7.3 Assess Your Understanding *(page 460)*

7. $\dfrac{\pi}{6}; \dfrac{5\pi}{6}$ **8.** $\left\{\theta \,\middle|\, \theta = \dfrac{\pi}{6} + 2\pi k, \theta = \dfrac{5\pi}{6} + 2\pi k, k \text{ is any integer}\right\}$ **9.** F   **10.** F   **11.** $\left\{\dfrac{7\pi}{6}, \dfrac{11\pi}{6}\right\}$ **13.** $\left\{\dfrac{\pi}{3}, \dfrac{2\pi}{3}, \dfrac{4\pi}{3}, \dfrac{5\pi}{3}\right\}$ **15.** $\left\{\dfrac{\pi}{4}, \dfrac{3\pi}{4}, \dfrac{5\pi}{4}, \dfrac{7\pi}{4}\right\}$

17. $\left\{\dfrac{\pi}{2}, \dfrac{7\pi}{6}, \dfrac{11\pi}{6}\right\}$ **19.** $\left\{\dfrac{\pi}{3}, \dfrac{2\pi}{3}, \dfrac{4\pi}{3}, \dfrac{5\pi}{3}\right\}$ **21.** $\left\{\dfrac{4\pi}{9}, \dfrac{8\pi}{9}, \dfrac{16\pi}{9}\right\}$ **23.** $\left\{\dfrac{7\pi}{6}, \dfrac{11\pi}{6}\right\}$ **25.** $\left\{\dfrac{3\pi}{4}, \dfrac{7\pi}{4}\right\}$ **27.** $\left\{\dfrac{2\pi}{3}, \dfrac{4\pi}{3}\right\}$ **29.** $\left\{\dfrac{3\pi}{4}, \dfrac{5\pi}{4}\right\}$

31. $\left\{\dfrac{3\pi}{4}, \dfrac{7\pi}{4}\right\}$ **33.** $\left\{\dfrac{11\pi}{6}\right\}$ **35.** $\left\{\theta \,\middle|\, \theta = \dfrac{\pi}{6} + 2k\pi, \theta = \dfrac{5\pi}{6} + 2k\pi\right\}; \dfrac{\pi}{6}, \dfrac{5\pi}{6}, \dfrac{13\pi}{6}, \dfrac{17\pi}{6}, \dfrac{25\pi}{6}, \dfrac{29\pi}{6}$

37. $\left\{\theta \,\middle|\, \theta = \dfrac{5\pi}{6} + k\pi\right\}; \dfrac{5\pi}{6}, \dfrac{11\pi}{6}, \dfrac{17\pi}{6}, \dfrac{23\pi}{6}, \dfrac{29\pi}{6}, \dfrac{35\pi}{6}$ **39.** $\left\{\theta \,\middle|\, \theta = \dfrac{\pi}{2} + 2k\pi, \theta = \dfrac{3\pi}{2} + 2k\pi\right\}; \dfrac{\pi}{2}, \dfrac{3\pi}{2}, \dfrac{5\pi}{2}, \dfrac{7\pi}{2}, \dfrac{9\pi}{2}, \dfrac{11\pi}{2}$

41. $\left\{\theta \,\middle|\, \theta = \dfrac{\pi}{3} + k\pi, \theta = \dfrac{2\pi}{3} + k\pi\right\}; \dfrac{\pi}{3}, \dfrac{2\pi}{3}, \dfrac{4\pi}{3}, \dfrac{5\pi}{3}, \dfrac{7\pi}{3}, \dfrac{8\pi}{3}$ **43.** $\left\{\theta \,\middle|\, \theta = \dfrac{8\pi}{3} + 4k\pi, \theta = \dfrac{10\pi}{3} + 4k\pi\right\}; \dfrac{8\pi}{3}, \dfrac{10\pi}{3}, \dfrac{20\pi}{3}, \dfrac{22\pi}{3}, \dfrac{32\pi}{3}, \dfrac{34\pi}{3}$

45. $\{0.41, 2.73\}$ **47.** $\{1.37, 4.51\}$ **49.** $\{2.69, 3.59\}$ **51.** $\{1.82, 4.46\}$ **53.** $\{2.08, 5.22\}$ **55.** $\{0.73, 2.41\}$ **57.** $\left\{\dfrac{\pi}{2}, \dfrac{2\pi}{3}, \dfrac{4\pi}{3}, \dfrac{3\pi}{2}\right\}$

59. $\left\{\dfrac{\pi}{2}, \dfrac{7\pi}{6}, \dfrac{11\pi}{6}\right\}$ **61.** $\left\{0, \dfrac{\pi}{4}, \dfrac{5\pi}{4}\right\}$ **63.** $\left\{\dfrac{\pi}{2}, \dfrac{2\pi}{3}, \dfrac{4\pi}{3}, \dfrac{3\pi}{2}\right\}$ **65.** $\{\pi\}$ **67.** $\left\{\dfrac{\pi}{4}, \dfrac{5\pi}{4}\right\}$ **69.** $\left\{0, \dfrac{\pi}{3}, \pi, \dfrac{5\pi}{3}\right\}$ **71.** $\left\{\dfrac{\pi}{6}, \dfrac{5\pi}{6}, \dfrac{3\pi}{2}\right\}$ **73.** $\left\{\dfrac{\pi}{2}\right\}$ **75.** $\{0\}$

77. $\left\{\dfrac{\pi}{3}, \dfrac{5\pi}{3}\right\}$ **79.** No real solution   **81.** −1.31, 1.98, 3.84   **83.** 0.52   **85.** 1.26   **87.** −1.02, 1.02   **89.** 0, 2.15   **91.** 0.76, 1.35   **93.** $\dfrac{\pi}{3}, \dfrac{2\pi}{3}, \dfrac{4\pi}{3}, \dfrac{5\pi}{3}$

95. (a) $-2\pi, -\pi, 0, \pi, 2\pi, 3\pi, 4\pi$ **(b)**

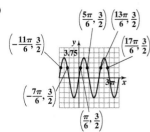

$\left(\dfrac{5\pi}{6}, \dfrac{3}{2}\right)$ $\left(\dfrac{13\pi}{6}, \dfrac{3}{2}\right)$

$\left(-\dfrac{11\pi}{6}, \dfrac{3}{2}\right)$ $\left(\dfrac{17\pi}{6}, \dfrac{3}{2}\right)$

$\left(-\dfrac{7\pi}{6}, \dfrac{3}{2}\right)$

$\left(\dfrac{\pi}{6}, \dfrac{3}{2}\right)$

(c) $\left\{-\dfrac{11\pi}{6}, -\dfrac{7\pi}{6}, \dfrac{\pi}{6}, \dfrac{5\pi}{6}, \dfrac{13\pi}{6}, \dfrac{17\pi}{6}\right\}$

(d) $\left\{x \,\middle|\, -\dfrac{11\pi}{6} < x < -\dfrac{7\pi}{6} \text{ or } \dfrac{\pi}{6} < x < \dfrac{5\pi}{6} \text{ or } \dfrac{13\pi}{6} < x < \dfrac{17\pi}{6}\right\}$

97. (a) $\left\{x \mid x = -\dfrac{\pi}{4} + k\pi, k \text{ is any integer}\right\}$ **(b)** $-\dfrac{\pi}{2} < x < -\dfrac{\pi}{4}$ or $\left(-\dfrac{\pi}{2}, -\dfrac{\pi}{4}\right)$

99. (a), (d)

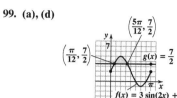

(b) $\left\{\dfrac{\pi}{12}, \dfrac{5\pi}{12}\right\}$

101. (a), (d)

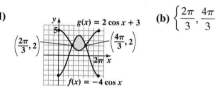

(b) $\left\{\dfrac{2\pi}{3}, \dfrac{4\pi}{3}\right\}$

(c) $\left\{x \mid \dfrac{\pi}{12} < x < \dfrac{5\pi}{12}\right\}$ or $\left(\dfrac{\pi}{12}, \dfrac{5\pi}{12}\right)$

(c) $\left\{x \mid \dfrac{2\pi}{3} < x < \dfrac{4\pi}{3}\right\}$ or $\left(\dfrac{2\pi}{3}, \dfrac{4\pi}{3}\right)$

103. (a) 0 s, 0.43 s, 0.86 s **(b)** 0.21 s
(c) $[0, 0.03] \cup [0.39, 0.43] \cup [0.86, 0.89]$
105. (a) 150 mi **(b)** 6.06, 8.44, 15.72, 18.11 min **(c)** Before 6.06 min, between 8.44 and 15.72 min, and after 18.11 min **(d)** No
107. 2.03, 4.91

109. (a) $30°, 60°$ **(b)** 123.6 m
(c)

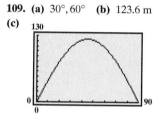

111. 28.90° **113.** Yes; it varies from 1.25 to 1.34. **115.** 1.47
117. If θ is the original angle of incidence and ϕ is the angle of refraction, then $\dfrac{\sin \theta}{\sin \phi} = n_2$. The angle of incidence of the emerging beam is also ϕ, and the index of refraction is $\dfrac{1}{n_2}$. Thus, θ is the angle of refraction of the emerging beam.

7.4 Assess Your Understanding (page 469)

3. identity; conditional **4.** -1 **5.** 0 **6.** T **7.** F **8.** T **9.** $\dfrac{1}{\cos \theta}$ **11.** $\dfrac{1 + \sin \theta}{\cos \theta}$ **13.** $\dfrac{1}{\sin \theta \cos \theta}$ **15.** 2 **17.** $\dfrac{3 \sin \theta + 1}{\sin \theta + 1}$

19. $\csc \theta \cdot \cos \theta = \dfrac{1}{\sin \theta} \cdot \cos \theta = \dfrac{\cos \theta}{\sin \theta} = \cot \theta$ **21.** $1 + \tan^2(-\theta) = 1 + (-\tan \theta)^2 = 1 + \tan^2 \theta = \sec^2 \theta$

23. $\cos \theta(\tan \theta + \cot \theta) = \cos \theta\left(\dfrac{\sin \theta}{\cos \theta} + \dfrac{\cos \theta}{\sin \theta}\right) = \cos \theta\left(\dfrac{\sin^2 \theta + \cos^2 \theta}{\cos \theta \sin \theta}\right) = \cos \theta\left(\dfrac{1}{\cos \theta \sin \theta}\right) = \dfrac{1}{\sin \theta} = \csc \theta$

25. $\tan u \ \cot u - \cos^2 u = \tan u \cdot \dfrac{1}{\tan u} - \cos^2 u = 1 - \cos^2 u = \sin^2 u$ **27.** $(\sec \theta - 1)(\sec \theta + 1) = \sec^2 \theta - 1 = \tan^2 \theta$

29. $(\sec \theta + \tan \theta)(\sec \theta - \tan \theta) = \sec^2 \theta - \tan^2 \theta = 1$ **31.** $\cos^2 \theta(1 + \tan^2 \theta) = \cos^2 \theta \sec^2 \theta = \cos^2 \theta \cdot \dfrac{1}{\cos^2 \theta} = 1$

33. $(\sin \theta + \cos \theta)^2 + (\sin \theta - \cos \theta)^2 = \sin^2 \theta + 2 \sin \theta \cos \theta + \cos^2 \theta + \sin^2 \theta - 2 \sin \theta \cos \theta + \cos^2 \theta$
$= \sin^2 \theta + \cos^2 \theta + \sin^2 \theta + \cos^2 \theta = 1 + 1 = 2$

35. $\sec^4 \theta - \sec^2 \theta = \sec^2 \theta(\sec^2 \theta - 1) = (1 + \tan^2 \theta) \tan^2 \theta = \tan^4 \theta + \tan^2 \theta$

37. $\sec u - \tan u = \dfrac{1}{\cos u} - \dfrac{\sin u}{\cos u} = \dfrac{1 - \sin u}{\cos u} \cdot \dfrac{1 + \sin u}{1 + \sin u} = \dfrac{1 - \sin^2 u}{\cos u(1 + \sin u)} = \dfrac{\cos^2 u}{\cos u(1 + \sin u)} = \dfrac{\cos u}{1 + \sin u}$

39. $3 \sin^2 \theta + 4 \cos^2 \theta = 3 \sin^2 \theta + 3 \cos^2 \theta + \cos^2 \theta = 3(\sin^2 \theta + \cos^2 \theta) + \cos^2 \theta = 3 + \cos^2 \theta$

41. $1 - \dfrac{\cos^2 \theta}{1 + \sin \theta} = 1 - \dfrac{1 - \sin^2 \theta}{1 + \sin \theta} = 1 - \dfrac{(1 + \sin \theta)(1 - \sin \theta)}{1 + \sin \theta} = 1 - (1 - \sin \theta) = \sin \theta$

43. $\dfrac{1 + \tan v}{1 - \tan v} = \dfrac{1 + \dfrac{1}{\cot v}}{1 - \dfrac{1}{\cot v}} = \dfrac{\dfrac{\cot v + 1}{\cot v}}{\dfrac{\cot v - 1}{\cot v}} = \dfrac{\cot v + 1}{\cot v - 1}$ **45.** $\dfrac{\sec \theta}{\csc \theta} + \dfrac{\sin \theta}{\cos \theta} = \dfrac{\dfrac{1}{\cos \theta}}{\dfrac{1}{\sin \theta}} + \tan \theta = \dfrac{\sin \theta}{\cos \theta} + \tan \theta = \tan \theta + \tan \theta = 2 \tan \theta$

47. $\dfrac{1 + \sin \theta}{1 - \sin \theta} = \dfrac{1 + \dfrac{1}{\csc \theta}}{1 - \dfrac{1}{\csc \theta}} = \dfrac{\dfrac{\csc \theta + 1}{\csc \theta}}{\dfrac{\csc \theta - 1}{\csc \theta}} = \dfrac{\csc \theta + 1}{\csc \theta - 1}$

49. $\dfrac{1 - \sin v}{\cos v} + \dfrac{\cos v}{1 - \sin v} = \dfrac{(1 - \sin v)^2 + \cos^2 v}{\cos v(1 - \sin v)} = \dfrac{1 - 2 \sin v + \sin^2 v + \cos^2 v}{\cos v(1 - \sin v)} = \dfrac{2 - 2 \sin v}{\cos v(1 - \sin v)} = \dfrac{2(1 - \sin v)}{\cos v(1 - \sin v)} = \dfrac{2}{\cos v} = 2 \sec v$

51. $\dfrac{\sin \theta}{\sin \theta - \cos \theta} = \dfrac{1}{\dfrac{\sin \theta - \cos \theta}{\sin \theta}} = \dfrac{1}{1 - \dfrac{\cos \theta}{\sin \theta}} = \dfrac{1}{1 - \cot \theta}$

53. $(\sec \theta - \tan \theta)^2 = \sec^2 \theta - 2 \sec \theta \tan \theta + \tan^2 \theta = \dfrac{1}{\cos^2 \theta} - \dfrac{2 \sin \theta}{\cos^2 \theta} + \dfrac{\sin^2 \theta}{\cos^2 \theta} = \dfrac{1 - 2 \sin \theta + \sin^2 \theta}{\cos^2 \theta} = \dfrac{(1 - \sin \theta)^2}{1 - \sin^2 \theta} = \dfrac{(1 - \sin \theta)^2}{(1 - \sin \theta)(1 + \sin \theta)}$
$= \dfrac{1 - \sin \theta}{1 + \sin \theta}$

55. $\dfrac{\cos \theta}{1 - \tan \theta} + \dfrac{\sin \theta}{1 - \cot \theta} = \dfrac{\cos \theta}{1 - \dfrac{\sin \theta}{\cos \theta}} + \dfrac{\sin \theta}{1 - \dfrac{\cos \theta}{\sin \theta}} = \dfrac{\cos \theta}{\dfrac{\cos \theta - \sin \theta}{\cos \theta}} + \dfrac{\sin \theta}{\dfrac{\sin \theta - \cos \theta}{\sin \theta}} = \dfrac{\cos^2 \theta}{\cos \theta - \sin \theta} + \dfrac{\sin^2 \theta}{\sin \theta - \cos \theta}$
$= \dfrac{\cos^2 \theta - \sin^2 \theta}{\cos \theta - \sin \theta} = \dfrac{(\cos \theta - \sin \theta)(\cos \theta + \sin \theta)}{\cos \theta - \sin \theta} = \sin \theta + \cos \theta$

57. $\tan \theta + \dfrac{\cos \theta}{1 + \sin \theta} = \dfrac{\sin \theta}{\cos \theta} + \dfrac{\cos \theta}{1 + \sin \theta} = \dfrac{\sin \theta(1 + \sin \theta) + \cos^2 \theta}{\cos \theta(1 + \sin \theta)} = \dfrac{\sin \theta + \sin^2 \theta + \cos^2 \theta}{\cos \theta(1 + \sin \theta)} = \dfrac{\sin \theta + 1}{\cos \theta(1 + \sin \theta)} = \dfrac{1}{\cos \theta} = \sec \theta$

59. $\dfrac{\tan\theta + \sec\theta - 1}{\tan\theta - \sec\theta + 1} = \dfrac{\tan\theta + (\sec\theta - 1)}{\tan\theta - (\sec\theta - 1)} \cdot \dfrac{\tan\theta + (\sec\theta - 1)}{\tan\theta + (\sec\theta - 1)} = \dfrac{\tan^2\theta + 2\tan\theta(\sec\theta - 1) + \sec^2\theta - 2\sec\theta + 1}{\tan^2\theta - (\sec^2\theta - 2\sec\theta + 1)}$

$= \dfrac{\sec^2\theta - 1 + 2\tan\theta(\sec\theta - 1) + \sec^2\theta - 2\sec\theta + 1}{\sec^2\theta - 1 - \sec^2\theta + 2\sec\theta - 1} = \dfrac{2\sec^2\theta - 2\sec\theta + 2\tan\theta(\sec\theta - 1)}{-2 + 2\sec\theta}$

$= \dfrac{2\sec\theta(\sec\theta - 1) + 2\tan\theta(\sec\theta - 1)}{2(\sec\theta - 1)} = \dfrac{2(\sec\theta - 1)(\sec\theta + \tan\theta)}{2(\sec\theta - 1)} = \tan\theta + \sec\theta$

61. $\dfrac{\tan\theta - \cot\theta}{\tan\theta + \cot\theta} = \dfrac{\dfrac{\sin\theta}{\cos\theta} - \dfrac{\cos\theta}{\sin\theta}}{\dfrac{\sin\theta}{\cos\theta} + \dfrac{\cos\theta}{\sin\theta}} = \dfrac{\dfrac{\sin^2\theta - \cos^2\theta}{\cos\theta\sin\theta}}{\dfrac{\sin^2\theta + \cos^2\theta}{\cos\theta\sin\theta}} = \dfrac{\sin^2\theta - \cos^2\theta}{1} = \sin^2\theta - \cos^2\theta$

63. $\dfrac{\tan u - \cot u}{\tan u + \cot u} + 1 = \dfrac{\dfrac{\sin u}{\cos u} - \dfrac{\cos u}{\sin u}}{\dfrac{\sin u}{\cos u} + \dfrac{\cos u}{\sin u}} + 1 = \dfrac{\dfrac{\sin^2 u - \cos^2 u}{\cos u \sin u}}{\dfrac{\sin^2 u + \cos^2 u}{\cos u \sin u}} + 1 = \sin^2 u - \cos^2 u + 1 = \sin^2 u + (1 - \cos^2 u) = 2\sin^2 u$

65. $\dfrac{\sec\theta + \tan\theta}{\cot\theta + \cos\theta} = \dfrac{\dfrac{1}{\cos\theta} + \dfrac{\sin\theta}{\cos\theta}}{\dfrac{\cos\theta}{\sin\theta} + \cos\theta} = \dfrac{\dfrac{1 + \sin\theta}{\cos\theta}}{\dfrac{\cos\theta + \cos\theta\sin\theta}{\sin\theta}} = \dfrac{1 + \sin\theta}{\cos\theta} \cdot \dfrac{\sin\theta}{\cos\theta(1 + \sin\theta)} = \dfrac{\sin\theta}{\cos\theta} \cdot \dfrac{1}{\cos\theta} = \tan\theta\sec\theta$

67. $\dfrac{1 - \tan^2\theta}{1 + \tan^2\theta} + 1 = \dfrac{1 - \tan^2\theta + 1 + \tan^2\theta}{1 + \tan^2\theta} = \dfrac{2}{1 + \tan^2\theta} = \dfrac{2}{\sec^2\theta} = 2\cos^2\theta$

69. $\dfrac{\sec\theta - \csc\theta}{\sec\theta\csc\theta} = \dfrac{\sec\theta}{\sec\theta\csc\theta} - \dfrac{\csc\theta}{\sec\theta\csc\theta} = \dfrac{1}{\csc\theta} - \dfrac{1}{\sec\theta} = \sin\theta - \cos\theta$

71. $\sec\theta - \cos\theta = \dfrac{1}{\cos\theta} - \cos\theta = \dfrac{1 - \cos^2\theta}{\cos\theta} = \dfrac{\sin^2\theta}{\cos\theta} = \sin\theta \cdot \dfrac{\sin\theta}{\cos\theta} = \sin\theta\tan\theta$

73. $\dfrac{1}{1 - \sin\theta} + \dfrac{1}{1 + \sin\theta} = \dfrac{1 + \sin\theta + 1 - \sin\theta}{(1 + \sin\theta)(1 - \sin\theta)} = \dfrac{2}{1 - \sin^2\theta} = \dfrac{2}{\cos^2\theta} = 2\sec^2\theta$

75. $\dfrac{\sec\theta}{1 - \sin\theta} = \dfrac{\sec\theta}{1 - \sin\theta} \cdot \dfrac{1 + \sin\theta}{1 + \sin\theta} = \dfrac{\sec\theta(1 + \sin\theta)}{1 - \sin^2\theta} = \dfrac{\sec\theta(1 + \sin\theta)}{\cos^2\theta} = \dfrac{1 + \sin\theta}{\cos^3\theta}$

77. $\dfrac{(\sec v - \tan v)^2 + 1}{\csc v(\sec v - \tan v)} = \dfrac{\sec^2 v - 2\sec v\tan v + \tan^2 v + 1}{\dfrac{1}{\sin v}\left(\dfrac{1}{\cos v} - \dfrac{\sin v}{\cos v}\right)} = \dfrac{2\sec^2 v - 2\sec v\tan v}{\dfrac{1}{\sin v}\left(\dfrac{1 - \sin v}{\cos v}\right)} = \dfrac{\dfrac{2}{\cos^2 v} - \dfrac{2\sin v}{\cos^2 v}}{\dfrac{1 - \sin v}{\sin v \cos v}} = \dfrac{2 - 2\sin v}{\cos^2 v} \cdot \dfrac{\sin v\cos v}{1 - \sin v}$

$= \dfrac{2(1 - \sin v)}{\cos v} \cdot \dfrac{\sin v}{1 - \sin v} = \dfrac{2\sin v}{\cos v} = 2\tan v$

79. $\dfrac{\sin\theta + \cos\theta}{\cos\theta} - \dfrac{\sin\theta - \cos\theta}{\sin\theta} = \dfrac{\sin\theta}{\cos\theta} + 1 - 1 + \dfrac{\cos\theta}{\sin\theta} = \dfrac{\sin^2\theta + \cos^2\theta}{\cos\theta\sin\theta} = \dfrac{1}{\cos\theta\sin\theta} = \sec\theta\csc\theta$

81. $\dfrac{\sin^3\theta + \cos^3\theta}{\sin\theta + \cos\theta} = \dfrac{(\sin\theta + \cos\theta)(\sin^2\theta - \sin\theta\cos\theta + \cos^2\theta)}{\sin\theta + \cos\theta} = \sin^2\theta + \cos^2\theta - \sin\theta\cos\theta = 1 - \sin\theta\cos\theta$

83. $\dfrac{\cos^2\theta - \sin^2\theta}{1 - \tan^2\theta} = \dfrac{\cos^2\theta - \sin^2\theta}{1 - \dfrac{\sin^2\theta}{\cos^2\theta}} = \dfrac{\cos^2\theta - \sin^2\theta}{\dfrac{\cos^2\theta - \sin^2\theta}{\cos^2\theta}} = \cos^2\theta$

85. $\dfrac{(2\cos^2\theta - 1)^2}{\cos^4\theta - \sin^4\theta} = \dfrac{[2\cos^2\theta - (\sin^2\theta + \cos^2\theta)]^2}{(\cos^2\theta - \sin^2\theta)(\cos^2\theta + \sin^2\theta)} = \dfrac{(\cos^2\theta - \sin^2\theta)^2}{\cos^2\theta - \sin^2\theta} = \cos^2\theta - \sin^2\theta = (1 - \sin^2\theta) - \sin^2\theta = 1 - 2\sin^2\theta$

87. $\dfrac{1 + \sin\theta + \cos\theta}{1 + \sin\theta - \cos\theta} = \dfrac{(1 + \sin\theta) + \cos\theta}{(1 + \sin\theta) - \cos\theta} \cdot \dfrac{(1 + \sin\theta) + \cos\theta}{(1 + \sin\theta) + \cos\theta} = \dfrac{1 + 2\sin\theta + \sin^2\theta + 2(1 + \sin\theta)\cos\theta + \cos^2\theta}{1 + 2\sin\theta + \sin^2\theta - \cos^2\theta}$

$= \dfrac{1 + 2\sin\theta + \sin^2\theta + 2(1 + \sin\theta)(\cos\theta) + (1 - \sin^2\theta)}{1 + 2\sin\theta + \sin^2\theta - (1 - \sin^2\theta)} = \dfrac{2 + 2\sin\theta + 2(1 + \sin\theta)(\cos\theta)}{2\sin\theta + 2\sin^2\theta}$

$= \dfrac{2(1 + \sin\theta) + 2(1 + \sin\theta)(\cos\theta)}{2\sin\theta(1 + \sin\theta)} = \dfrac{2(1 + \sin\theta)(1 + \cos\theta)}{2\sin\theta(1 + \sin\theta)} = \dfrac{1 + \cos\theta}{\sin\theta}$

89. $(a\sin\theta + b\cos\theta)^2 + (a\cos\theta - b\sin\theta)^2 = a^2\sin^2\theta + 2ab\sin\theta\cos\theta + b^2\cos^2\theta + a^2\cos^2\theta - 2ab\sin\theta\cos\theta + b^2\sin^2\theta$

$= a^2(\sin^2\theta + \cos^2\theta) + b^2(\cos^2\theta + \sin^2\theta) = a^2 + b^2$

91. $\dfrac{\tan\alpha + \tan\beta}{\cot\alpha + \cot\beta} = \dfrac{\tan\alpha + \tan\beta}{\dfrac{1}{\tan\alpha} + \dfrac{1}{\tan\beta}} = \dfrac{\tan\alpha + \tan\beta}{\dfrac{\tan\beta + \tan\alpha}{\tan\alpha\tan\beta}} = (\tan\alpha + \tan\beta) \cdot \dfrac{\tan\alpha\tan\beta}{\tan\alpha + \tan\beta} = \tan\alpha\tan\beta$

93. $(\sin\alpha + \cos\beta)^2 + (\cos\beta + \sin\alpha)(\cos\beta - \sin\alpha) = (\sin^2\alpha + 2\sin\alpha\cos\beta + \cos^2\beta) + (\cos^2\beta - \sin^2\alpha)$

$= 2\cos^2\beta + 2\sin\alpha\cos\beta = 2\cos\beta(\cos\beta + \sin\alpha) = 2\cos\beta(\sin\alpha + \cos\beta)$

95. $\ln|\sec\theta| = \ln|\cos\theta|^{-1} = -\ln|\cos\theta|$

97. $\ln|1 + \cos\theta| + \ln|1 - \cos\theta| = \ln(|1 + \cos\theta||1 - \cos\theta|) = \ln|1 - \cos^2\theta| = \ln|\sin^2\theta| = 2\ln|\sin\theta|$

99. $g(x) = \sec x - \cos x = \dfrac{1}{\cos x} - \cos x = \dfrac{1}{\cos x} - \dfrac{\cos^2 x}{\cos x} = \dfrac{1 - \cos^2 x}{\cos x} = \dfrac{\sin^2 x}{\cos x} = \sin x \cdot \dfrac{\sin x}{\cos x} = \sin x \cdot \tan x = f(x)$

101. $f(\theta) = \dfrac{1 - \sin\theta}{\cos\theta} - \dfrac{\cos\theta}{1 + \sin\theta} = \dfrac{1 - \sin\theta}{\cos\theta} \cdot \dfrac{1 + \sin\theta}{1 + \sin\theta} - \dfrac{\cos\theta}{1 + \sin\theta} \cdot \dfrac{\cos\theta}{\cos\theta} = \dfrac{1 - \sin^2\theta}{\cos\theta(1 + \sin\theta)} - \dfrac{\cos^2\theta}{\cos\theta(1 + \sin\theta)}$

$= \dfrac{\cos^2\theta}{\cos\theta(1 + \sin\theta)} - \dfrac{\cos^2\theta}{\cos\theta(1 + \sin\theta)} = 0 = g(\theta)$

103. $1200\sec\theta\,(2\sec^2\theta - 1) = 1200\,\dfrac{1}{\cos\theta}\left(\dfrac{2}{\cos^2\theta} - 1\right) = 1200\,\dfrac{1}{\cos\theta}\left(\dfrac{2}{\cos^2\theta} - \dfrac{\cos^2\theta}{\cos^2\theta}\right) = 1200\,\dfrac{1}{\cos\theta}\left(\dfrac{2 - \cos^2\theta}{\cos^2\theta}\right) = \dfrac{1200\,(1 + 1 - \cos^2\theta)}{\cos^3\theta}$

$= \dfrac{1200\,(1 + \sin^2\theta)}{\cos^3\theta}$

7.5 Assess Your Understanding *(page 481)*

5. – **6.** – **7.** F **8.** F **9.** F **10.** T **11.** $\dfrac{1}{4}\left(\sqrt{6} + \sqrt{2}\right)$ **13.** $\dfrac{1}{4}\left(\sqrt{2} - \sqrt{6}\right)$ **15.** $-\dfrac{1}{4}\left(\sqrt{2} + \sqrt{6}\right)$ **17.** $2 - \sqrt{3}$ **19.** $-\dfrac{1}{4}\left(\sqrt{6} + \sqrt{2}\right)$

21. $\sqrt{6} - \sqrt{2}$ **23.** $\dfrac{1}{2}$ **25.** 0 **27.** 1 **29.** −1 **31.** $\dfrac{1}{2}$ **33. (a)** $\dfrac{2\sqrt{5}}{25}$ **(b)** $\dfrac{11\sqrt{5}}{25}$ **(c)** $\dfrac{2\sqrt{5}}{5}$ **(d)** 2

35. (a) $\dfrac{4 - 3\sqrt{3}}{10}$ **(b)** $\dfrac{-3 - 4\sqrt{3}}{10}$ **(c)** $\dfrac{4 + 3\sqrt{3}}{10}$ **(d)** $\dfrac{25\sqrt{3} + 48}{39}$ **37. (a)** $-\dfrac{5 + 12\sqrt{3}}{26}$ **(b)** $\dfrac{12 - 5\sqrt{3}}{26}$ **(c)** $\dfrac{-5 + 12\sqrt{3}}{26}$ **(d)** $\dfrac{-240 + 169\sqrt{3}}{69}$

39. (a) $-\dfrac{2\sqrt{2}}{3}$ **(b)** $\dfrac{-2\sqrt{2} + \sqrt{3}}{6}$ **(c)** $\dfrac{-2\sqrt{2} + \sqrt{3}}{6}$ **(d)** $\dfrac{9 - 4\sqrt{2}}{7}$ **41.** $\dfrac{1 - 2\sqrt{6}}{6}$ **43.** $\dfrac{\sqrt{3} - 2\sqrt{2}}{6}$ **45.** $\dfrac{8\sqrt{2} - 9\sqrt{3}}{5}$

47. $\sin\left(\dfrac{\pi}{2} + \theta\right) = \sin\dfrac{\pi}{2}\cos\theta + \cos\dfrac{\pi}{2}\sin\theta = 1\cdot\cos\theta + 0\cdot\sin\theta = \cos\theta$

49. $\sin(\pi - \theta) = \sin\pi\cos\theta - \cos\pi\sin\theta = 0\cdot\cos\theta - (-1)\sin\theta = \sin\theta$

51. $\sin(\pi + \theta) = \sin\pi\cos\theta + \cos\pi\sin\theta = 0\cdot\cos\theta + (-1)\sin\theta = -\sin\theta$

53. $\tan(\pi - \theta) = \dfrac{\tan\pi - \tan\theta}{1 + \tan\pi\tan\theta} = \dfrac{0 - \tan\theta}{1 + 0\cdot\tan\theta} = -\tan\theta$ **55.** $\sin\left(\dfrac{3\pi}{2} + \theta\right) = \sin\dfrac{3\pi}{2}\cos\theta + \cos\dfrac{3\pi}{2}\sin\theta = (-1)\cos\theta + 0\cdot\sin\theta = -\cos\theta$

57. $\sin(\alpha + \beta) + \sin(\alpha - \beta) = \sin\alpha\cos\beta + \cos\alpha\sin\beta + \sin\alpha\cos\beta - \cos\alpha\sin\beta = 2\sin\alpha\cos\beta$

59. $\dfrac{\sin(\alpha + \beta)}{\sin\alpha\cos\beta} = \dfrac{\sin\alpha\cos\beta + \cos\alpha\sin\beta}{\sin\alpha\cos\beta} = \dfrac{\sin\alpha\cos\beta}{\sin\alpha\cos\beta} + \dfrac{\cos\alpha\sin\beta}{\sin\alpha\cos\beta} = 1 + \cot\alpha\tan\beta$

61. $\dfrac{\cos(\alpha + \beta)}{\cos\alpha\cos\beta} = \dfrac{\cos\alpha\cos\beta - \sin\alpha\sin\beta}{\cos\alpha\cos\beta} = \dfrac{\cos\alpha\cos\beta}{\cos\alpha\cos\beta} - \dfrac{\sin\alpha\sin\beta}{\cos\alpha\cos\beta} = 1 - \tan\alpha\tan\beta$

63. $\dfrac{\sin(\alpha + \beta)}{\sin(\alpha - \beta)} = \dfrac{\sin\alpha\cos\beta + \cos\alpha\sin\beta}{\sin\alpha\cos\beta - \cos\alpha\sin\beta} = \dfrac{\dfrac{\sin\alpha\cos\beta + \cos\alpha\sin\beta}{\cos\alpha\cos\beta}}{\dfrac{\sin\alpha\cos\beta - \cos\alpha\sin\beta}{\cos\alpha\cos\beta}} = \dfrac{\dfrac{\sin\alpha\cos\beta}{\cos\alpha\cos\beta} + \dfrac{\cos\alpha\sin\beta}{\cos\alpha\cos\beta}}{\dfrac{\sin\alpha\cos\beta}{\cos\alpha\cos\beta} - \dfrac{\cos\alpha\sin\beta}{\cos\alpha\cos\beta}} = \dfrac{\tan\alpha + \tan\beta}{\tan\alpha - \tan\beta}$

65. $\cot(\alpha + \beta) = \dfrac{\cos(\alpha + \beta)}{\sin(\alpha + \beta)} = \dfrac{\cos\alpha\cos\beta - \sin\alpha\sin\beta}{\sin\alpha\cos\beta + \cos\alpha\sin\beta} = \dfrac{\dfrac{\cos\alpha\cos\beta - \sin\alpha\sin\beta}{\sin\alpha\sin\beta}}{\dfrac{\sin\alpha\cos\beta + \cos\alpha\sin\beta}{\sin\alpha\sin\beta}} = \dfrac{\dfrac{\cos\alpha\cos\beta}{\sin\alpha\sin\beta} - \dfrac{\sin\alpha\sin\beta}{\sin\alpha\sin\beta}}{\dfrac{\sin\alpha\cos\beta}{\sin\alpha\sin\beta} + \dfrac{\cos\alpha\sin\beta}{\sin\alpha\sin\beta}} = \dfrac{\cot\alpha\cot\beta - 1}{\cot\beta + \cot\alpha}$

67. $\sec(\alpha + \beta) = \dfrac{1}{\cos(\alpha + \beta)} = \dfrac{1}{\cos\alpha\cos\beta - \sin\alpha\sin\beta} = \dfrac{\dfrac{1}{\sin\alpha\sin\beta}}{\dfrac{\cos\alpha\cos\beta - \sin\alpha\sin\beta}{\sin\alpha\sin\beta}} = \dfrac{\dfrac{1}{\sin\alpha}\cdot\dfrac{1}{\sin\beta}}{\dfrac{\cos\alpha\cos\beta}{\sin\alpha\sin\beta} - \dfrac{\sin\alpha\sin\beta}{\sin\alpha\sin\beta}} = \dfrac{\csc\alpha\csc\beta}{\cot\alpha\cot\beta - 1}$

69. $\sin(\alpha - \beta)\sin(\alpha + \beta) = (\sin\alpha\cos\beta - \cos\alpha\sin\beta)(\sin\alpha\cos\beta + \cos\alpha\sin\beta) = \sin^2\alpha\cos^2\beta - \cos^2\alpha\sin^2\beta$
$= (\sin^2\alpha)(1 - \sin^2\beta) - (1 - \sin^2\alpha)(\sin^2\beta) = \sin^2\alpha - \sin^2\beta$

71. $\sin(\theta + k\pi) = \sin\theta\cos k\pi + \cos\theta\sin k\pi = (\sin\theta)(-1)^k + (\cos\theta)(0) = (-1)^k\sin\theta$, k any integer

73. $\dfrac{\sqrt{3}}{2}$ **75.** $-\dfrac{24}{25}$ **77.** $-\dfrac{33}{65}$ **79.** $\dfrac{63}{65}$ **81.** $\dfrac{48 + 25\sqrt{3}}{39}$ **83.** $\dfrac{4}{3}$ **85.** $u\sqrt{1 - v^2} - v\sqrt{1 - u^2}; -1 \le u \le 1; -1 \le v \le 1$

87. $\dfrac{u\sqrt{1 - v^2} - v}{\sqrt{1 + u^2}}: -\infty < u < \infty; -1 \le v \le 1$ **89.** $\dfrac{uv - \sqrt{1 - u^2}\sqrt{1 - v^2}}{v\sqrt{1 - u^2} + u\sqrt{1 - v^2}}: -1 \le u \le 1; -1 \le v \le 1$ **91.** $\left\{\dfrac{\pi}{2}, \dfrac{7\pi}{6}\right\}$ **93.** $\left\{\dfrac{\pi}{4}\right\}$ **95.** $\left\{\dfrac{11\pi}{6}\right\}$

97. Let $\alpha = \sin^{-1} v$ and $\beta = \cos^{-1} v$. Then $\sin\alpha = \cos\beta = v$, and since $\sin\alpha = \cos\left(\dfrac{\pi}{2} - \alpha\right)$, $\cos\left(\dfrac{\pi}{2} - \alpha\right) = \cos\beta$.

If $v \ge 0$, then $0 \le \alpha \le \dfrac{\pi}{2}$, so $\left(\dfrac{\pi}{2} - \alpha\right)$ and β both lie on $\left[0, \dfrac{\pi}{2}\right]$. If $v < 0$, then $-\dfrac{\pi}{2} \le \alpha < 0$, so $\left(\dfrac{\pi}{2} - \alpha\right)$ and β both lie on $\left(\dfrac{\pi}{2}, \pi\right]$.

Either way, $\cos\left(\dfrac{\pi}{2} - \alpha\right) = \cos\beta$ implies $\dfrac{\pi}{2} - \alpha = \beta$, or $\alpha + \beta = \dfrac{\pi}{2}$.

99. Let $\alpha = \tan^{-1}\dfrac{1}{v}$ and $\beta = \tan^{-1} v$. Because $v \ne 0$, $\alpha, \beta \ne 0$. Then $\tan\alpha = \dfrac{1}{v} = \dfrac{1}{\tan\beta} = \cot\beta$, and since

$\tan\alpha = \cot\left(\dfrac{\pi}{2} - \alpha\right)$, $\cot\left(\dfrac{\pi}{2} - \alpha\right) = \cot\beta$. Because $v > 0, 0 < \alpha < \dfrac{\pi}{2}$, and so $\left(\dfrac{\pi}{2} - \alpha\right)$ and β both lie on $\left(0, \dfrac{\pi}{2}\right)$.

Then $\cot\left(\dfrac{\pi}{2} - \alpha\right) = \cot\beta$ implies $\dfrac{\pi}{2} - \alpha = \beta$, or $\alpha = \dfrac{\pi}{2} - \beta$.

101. $\sin(\sin^{-1} v + \cos^{-1} v) = \sin(\sin^{-1} v)\cos(\cos^{-1} v) + \cos(\sin^{-1} v)\sin(\cos^{-1} v) = (v)(v) + \sqrt{1 - v^2}\sqrt{1 - v^2} = v^2 + 1 - v^2 = 1$

103. $\dfrac{\sin(x + h) - \sin x}{h} = \dfrac{\sin x \cos h + \cos x \sin h - \sin x}{h} = \dfrac{\cos x \sin h - \sin x(1 - \cos h)}{h} = \cos x \cdot \dfrac{\sin h}{h} - \sin x \cdot \dfrac{1 - \cos h}{h}$

105. (a) $\tan(\tan^{-1} 1 + \tan^{-1} 2 + \tan^{-1} 3) = \tan((\tan^{-1} 1 + \tan^{-1} 2) + \tan^{-1} 3) = \dfrac{\tan(\tan^{-1} 1 + \tan^{-1} 2) + \tan(\tan^{-1} 3)}{1 - \tan(\tan^{-1} 1 + \tan^{-1} 2)\tan(\tan^{-1} 3)}$

$= \dfrac{\dfrac{\tan(\tan^{-1} 1) + \tan(\tan^{-1} 2)}{1 - \tan(\tan^{-1} 1)\tan(\tan^{-1} 2)} + 3}{1 - \dfrac{\tan(\tan^{-1} 1) + \tan(\tan^{-1} 2)}{1 - \tan(\tan^{-1} 1)\tan(\tan^{-1} 2)} \cdot 3} = \dfrac{\dfrac{1 + 2}{1 - 1 \cdot 2} + 3}{1 - \dfrac{1 + 2}{1 - 1 \cdot 2} \cdot 3} = \dfrac{\dfrac{3}{-1} + 3}{1 - \dfrac{3}{-1} \cdot 3} = \dfrac{-3 + 3}{1 + 9} = \dfrac{0}{10} = 0$

(b) From the definition of the inverse tangent function $0 < \tan^{-1} 1 < \dfrac{\pi}{2}$, $0 < \tan^{-1} 2 < \dfrac{\pi}{2}$, and $0 < \tan^{-1} 3 < \dfrac{\pi}{2}$,

so $0 < \tan^{-1} 1 + \tan^{-1} 2 + \tan^{-1} 3 < \dfrac{3\pi}{2}$.

On the interval $\left(0, \dfrac{3\pi}{2}\right)$, $\tan \theta = 0$ if and only if $\theta = \pi$. Therefore, from part (a), $\tan^{-1} 1 + \tan^{-1} 2 + \tan^{-1} 3 = \pi$.

107. $\tan \theta = \tan(\theta_2 - \theta_1) = \dfrac{\tan \theta_2 - \tan \theta_1}{1 + \tan \theta_1 \tan \theta_2} = \dfrac{m_2 - m_1}{1 + m_1 m_2}$

109. $2 \cot(\alpha - \beta) = \dfrac{2}{\tan(\alpha - \beta)} = 2\left(\dfrac{1 + \tan \alpha \tan \beta}{\tan \alpha - \tan \beta}\right) = 2\left(\dfrac{1 + (x + 1)(x - 1)}{(x + 1) - (x - 1)}\right) = 2\left(\dfrac{1 + x^2 - 1}{x + 1 - x + 1}\right) = \dfrac{2x^2}{2} = x^2$

111. $\tan \dfrac{\pi}{2}$ is not defined; $\tan\left(\dfrac{\pi}{2} - \theta\right) = \dfrac{\sin\left(\dfrac{\pi}{2} - \theta\right)}{\cos\left(\dfrac{\pi}{2} - \theta\right)} = \dfrac{\cos \theta}{\sin \theta} = \cot \theta$.

7.6 Assess Your Understanding *(page 491)*

1. $\sin^2 \theta$; $2 \cos^2 \theta$; $2 \sin^2 \theta$ **2.** $1 - \cos \theta$ **3.** $\sin \theta$ **4.** T **5.** F **6.** F **7. (a)** $\dfrac{24}{25}$ **(b)** $\dfrac{7}{25}$ **(c)** $\dfrac{\sqrt{10}}{10}$ **(d)** $\dfrac{3\sqrt{10}}{10}$

9. (a) $\dfrac{24}{25}$ **(b)** $-\dfrac{7}{25}$ **(c)** $\dfrac{2\sqrt{5}}{5}$ **(d)** $-\dfrac{\sqrt{5}}{5}$ **11. (a)** $-\dfrac{2\sqrt{2}}{3}$ **(b)** $\dfrac{1}{3}$ **(c)** $\sqrt{\dfrac{3 + \sqrt{6}}{6}}$ **(d)** $\sqrt{\dfrac{3 - \sqrt{6}}{6}}$

13. (a) $\dfrac{4\sqrt{2}}{9}$ **(b)** $-\dfrac{7}{9}$ **(c)** $\dfrac{\sqrt{3}}{3}$ **(d)** $\dfrac{\sqrt{6}}{3}$ **15. (a)** $-\dfrac{4}{5}$ **(b)** $\dfrac{3}{5}$ **(c)** $\sqrt{\dfrac{5 + 2\sqrt{5}}{10}}$ **(d)** $\sqrt{\dfrac{5 - 2\sqrt{5}}{10}}$

17. (a) $-\dfrac{3}{5}$ **(b)** $-\dfrac{4}{5}$ **(c)** $\dfrac{1}{2}\sqrt{\dfrac{10 - \sqrt{10}}{5}}$ **(d)** $-\dfrac{1}{2}\sqrt{\dfrac{10 + \sqrt{10}}{5}}$ **19.** $\dfrac{\sqrt{2 - \sqrt{2}}}{2}$ **21.** $1 - \sqrt{2}$ **23.** $-\dfrac{\sqrt{2 + \sqrt{3}}}{2}$

25. $\dfrac{2}{\sqrt{2 + \sqrt{2}}} = (2 - \sqrt{2})\sqrt{2 + \sqrt{2}}$ **27.** $-\dfrac{\sqrt{2 - \sqrt{2}}}{2}$ **29.** $-\dfrac{4}{5}$ **31.** $\dfrac{\sqrt{10(5 - \sqrt{5})}}{10}$ **33.** $\dfrac{4}{3}$ **35.** $-\dfrac{7}{8}$ **37.** $\dfrac{\sqrt{10}}{4}$ **39.** $-\dfrac{\sqrt{15}}{3}$

41. $\sin^4 \theta = (\sin^2 \theta)^2 = \left(\dfrac{1 - \cos(2\theta)}{2}\right)^2 = \dfrac{1}{4}[1 - 2\cos(2\theta) + \cos^2(2\theta)] = \dfrac{1}{4} - \dfrac{1}{2}\cos(2\theta) + \dfrac{1}{4}\cos^2(2\theta)$

$= \dfrac{1}{4} - \dfrac{1}{2}\cos(2\theta) + \dfrac{1}{4}\left(\dfrac{1 + \cos(4\theta)}{2}\right) = \dfrac{1}{4} - \dfrac{1}{2}\cos(2\theta) + \dfrac{1}{8} + \dfrac{1}{8}\cos(4\theta) = \dfrac{3}{8} - \dfrac{1}{2}\cos(2\theta) + \dfrac{1}{8}\cos(4\theta)$

43. $\cos(3\theta) = 4\cos^3 \theta - 3\cos \theta$ **45.** $\sin(5\theta) = 16\sin^5 \theta - 20\sin^3 \theta + 5\sin \theta$ **47.** $\cos^4 \theta - \sin^4 \theta = (\cos^2 \theta + \sin^2 \theta)(\cos^2 \theta - \sin^2 \theta) = \cos(2\theta)$

49. $\cot(2\theta) = \dfrac{1}{\tan(2\theta)} = \dfrac{1 - \tan^2 \theta}{2 \tan \theta} = \dfrac{1 - \dfrac{1}{\cot^2 \theta}}{2\left(\dfrac{1}{\cot \theta}\right)} = \dfrac{\dfrac{\cot^2 \theta - 1}{\cot^2 \theta}}{\dfrac{2}{\cot \theta}} = \dfrac{\cot^2 \theta - 1}{\cot^2 \theta} \cdot \dfrac{\cot \theta}{2} = \dfrac{\cot^2 \theta - 1}{2 \cot \theta}$

51. $\sec(2\theta) = \dfrac{1}{\cos(2\theta)} = \dfrac{1}{2\cos^2 \theta - 1} = \dfrac{1}{\dfrac{2}{\sec^2 \theta} - 1} = \dfrac{1}{\dfrac{2 - \sec^2 \theta}{\sec^2 \theta}} = \dfrac{\sec^2 \theta}{2 - \sec^2 \theta}$ **53.** $\cos^2(2u) - \sin^2(2u) = \cos[2(2u)] = \cos(4u)$

55. $\dfrac{\cos(2\theta)}{1 + \sin(2\theta)} = \dfrac{\cos^2 \theta - \sin^2 \theta}{1 + 2\sin \theta \cos \theta} = \dfrac{(\cos \theta - \sin \theta)(\cos \theta + \sin \theta)}{\sin^2 \theta + \cos^2 \theta + 2\sin \theta \cos \theta} = \dfrac{(\cos \theta - \sin \theta)(\cos \theta + \sin \theta)}{(\sin \theta + \cos \theta)(\sin \theta + \cos \theta)} = \dfrac{\cos \theta - \sin \theta}{\cos \theta + \sin \theta}$

$= \dfrac{\dfrac{\cos \theta - \sin \theta}{\sin \theta}}{\dfrac{\cos \theta + \sin \theta}{\sin \theta}} = \dfrac{\dfrac{\cos \theta}{\sin \theta} - \dfrac{\sin \theta}{\sin \theta}}{\dfrac{\cos \theta}{\sin \theta} + \dfrac{\sin \theta}{\sin \theta}} = \dfrac{\cot \theta - 1}{\cot \theta + 1}$

57. $\sec^2 \dfrac{\theta}{2} = \dfrac{1}{\cos^2\left(\dfrac{\theta}{2}\right)} = \dfrac{1}{\dfrac{1 + \cos \theta}{2}} = \dfrac{2}{1 + \cos \theta}$

59. $\cot^2\dfrac{v}{2} = \dfrac{1}{\tan^2\left(\dfrac{v}{2}\right)} = \dfrac{1}{\dfrac{1-\cos v}{1+\cos v}} = \dfrac{1+\cos v}{1-\cos v} = \dfrac{1+\dfrac{1}{\sec v}}{1-\dfrac{1}{\sec v}} = \dfrac{\dfrac{\sec v+1}{\sec v}}{\dfrac{\sec v-1}{\sec v}} = \dfrac{\sec v+1}{\sec v}\cdot\dfrac{\sec v}{\sec v-1} = \dfrac{\sec v+1}{\sec v-1}$

61. $\dfrac{1-\tan^2\left(\dfrac{\theta}{2}\right)}{1+\tan^2\left(\dfrac{\theta}{2}\right)} = \dfrac{1-\dfrac{1-\cos\theta}{1+\cos\theta}}{1+\dfrac{1-\cos\theta}{1+\cos\theta}} = \dfrac{\dfrac{1+\cos\theta-(1-\cos\theta)}{1+\cos\theta}}{\dfrac{1+\cos\theta+1-\cos\theta}{1+\cos\theta}} = \dfrac{2\cos\theta}{1+\cos\theta}\cdot\dfrac{1+\cos\theta}{2} = \cos\theta$

63. $\dfrac{\sin(3\theta)}{\sin\theta} - \dfrac{\cos(3\theta)}{\cos\theta} = \dfrac{\sin(3\theta)\cos\theta - \cos(3\theta)\sin\theta}{\sin\theta\cos\theta} = \dfrac{\sin(3\theta-\theta)}{\frac{1}{2}(2\sin\theta\cos\theta)} = \dfrac{2\sin(2\theta)}{\sin(2\theta)} = 2$

65. $\tan(3\theta) = \tan(\theta+2\theta) = \dfrac{\tan\theta+\tan(2\theta)}{1-\tan\theta\tan(2\theta)} = \dfrac{\tan\theta+\dfrac{2\tan\theta}{1-\tan^2\theta}}{1-\dfrac{\tan\theta(2\tan\theta)}{1-\tan^2\theta}} = \dfrac{\tan\theta-\tan^3\theta+2\tan\theta}{1-\tan^2\theta-2\tan^2\theta} = \dfrac{3\tan\theta-\tan^3\theta}{1-3\tan^2\theta}$

67. $\dfrac{1}{2}(\ln|1-\cos(2\theta)| - \ln 2) = \ln\left(\dfrac{|1-\cos(2\theta)|}{2}\right)^{1/2} = \ln|\sin^2\theta|^{1/2} = \ln|\sin\theta|$ **69.** $\left\{\dfrac{\pi}{3}, \dfrac{2\pi}{3}, \dfrac{4\pi}{3}, \dfrac{5\pi}{3}\right\}$ **71.** $\left\{0, \dfrac{2\pi}{3}, \dfrac{4\pi}{3}\right\}$

73. $\left\{0, \dfrac{\pi}{3}, \dfrac{\pi}{2}, \dfrac{2\pi}{3}, \pi, \dfrac{4\pi}{3}, \dfrac{3\pi}{2}, \dfrac{5\pi}{3}\right\}$ **75.** No real solution   **77.** $\left\{0, \dfrac{\pi}{3}, \pi, \dfrac{5\pi}{3}\right\}$ **79.** $\dfrac{\sqrt{3}}{2}$ **81.** $\dfrac{7}{25}$ **83.** $\dfrac{24}{7}$ **85.** $\dfrac{24}{25}$ **87.** $\dfrac{1}{5}$ **89.** $\dfrac{25}{7}$ **91.** $0, \dfrac{\pi}{3}, \pi, \dfrac{5\pi}{3}$

93. $\dfrac{\pi}{2}, \dfrac{3\pi}{2}$ **95. (a)** $W = 2D(\csc\theta - \cot\theta) = 2D\left(\dfrac{1}{\sin\theta} - \dfrac{\cos\theta}{\sin\theta}\right) = 2D\dfrac{1-\cos\theta}{\sin\theta} = 2D\tan\dfrac{\theta}{2}$ **(b)** $\theta = 24.45°$

97. (a) $R = \dfrac{v_0^2\sqrt{2}}{16}\cos\theta(\sin\theta - \cos\theta)$ **(b)** $\dfrac{3\pi}{8}$ or $67.5°$ **(d)**

$= \dfrac{v_0^2\sqrt{2}}{32}(2\cos\theta\sin\theta - 2\cos^2\theta)$ **(c)** $32(2-\sqrt{2}) \approx 18.75$ ft

$= \dfrac{v_0^2\sqrt{2}}{32}[\sin(2\theta) - \cos(2\theta) - 1]$

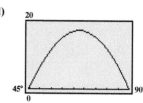

$\theta = 67.5°$
$\left(\dfrac{3\pi}{8}\text{ radians}\right)$ makes R largest.
$R = 18.75$ ft

99. $A = \dfrac{1}{2}h(\text{base}) = h\left(\dfrac{1}{2}\text{base}\right) = s\cos\dfrac{\theta}{2}\cdot s\sin\dfrac{\theta}{2} = \dfrac{1}{2}s^2\sin\theta$ **101.** $\sin(2\theta) = \dfrac{4x}{4+x^2}$ **103.** $-\dfrac{1}{4}$

105. $\dfrac{2z}{1+z^2} = \dfrac{2\tan\left(\dfrac{\alpha}{2}\right)}{1+\tan^2\left(\dfrac{\alpha}{2}\right)} = \dfrac{2\tan\left(\dfrac{\alpha}{2}\right)}{\sec^2\left(\dfrac{\alpha}{2}\right)} = \dfrac{\dfrac{2\sin\left(\dfrac{\alpha}{2}\right)}{\cos\left(\dfrac{\alpha}{2}\right)}}{\dfrac{1}{\cos^2\left(\dfrac{\alpha}{2}\right)}} = 2\sin\left(\dfrac{\alpha}{2}\right)\cos\left(\dfrac{\alpha}{2}\right) = \sin\left(2\cdot\dfrac{\alpha}{2}\right) = \sin\alpha$ **107.**

109. $\sin\dfrac{\pi}{24} = \dfrac{\sqrt{2}}{4}\sqrt{4-\sqrt{6}-\sqrt{2}}$

$\cos\dfrac{\pi}{24} = \dfrac{\sqrt{2}}{4}\sqrt{4+\sqrt{6}+\sqrt{2}}$

111. $\sin^3\theta + \sin^3(\theta+120°) + \sin^3(\theta+240°) = \sin^3\theta + (\sin\theta\cos 120° + \cos\theta\sin 120°)^3 + (\sin\theta\cos 240° + \cos\theta\sin 240°)^3$

$= \sin^3\theta + \left(-\dfrac{1}{2}\sin\theta + \dfrac{\sqrt{3}}{2}\cos\theta\right)^3 + \left(-\dfrac{1}{2}\sin\theta - \dfrac{\sqrt{3}}{2}\cos\theta\right)^3$

$= \sin^3\theta + \dfrac{1}{8}\left(3\sqrt{3}\cos^3\theta - 9\cos^2\theta\sin\theta + 3\sqrt{3}\cos\theta\sin^2\theta - \sin^3\theta\right) - \dfrac{1}{8}\left(\sin^3\theta + 3\sqrt{3}\sin^2\theta\cos\theta + 9\sin\theta\cos^2\theta + 3\sqrt{3}\cos^3\theta\right)$

$= \dfrac{3}{4}\sin^3\theta - \dfrac{9}{4}\cos^2\theta\sin\theta = \dfrac{3}{4}[\sin^3\theta - 3\sin\theta(1-\sin^2\theta)] = \dfrac{3}{4}(4\sin^3\theta - 3\sin\theta) = -\dfrac{3}{4}\sin(3\theta)$ (from Example 2)

7.7 Assess Your Understanding *(page 496)*

1. $\dfrac{1}{2}\left(\dfrac{\sqrt{3}}{2} - 1\right)$ **3.** $-\dfrac{1}{2}\left(\dfrac{\sqrt{3}}{2} + 1\right)$ **5.** $\dfrac{\sqrt{2}}{2}$ **7.** $\dfrac{1}{2}[\cos(2\theta) - \cos(6\theta)]$ **9.** $\dfrac{1}{2}[\sin(6\theta) + \sin(2\theta)]$ **11.** $\dfrac{1}{2}[\cos(2\theta) + \cos(8\theta)]$

13. $\dfrac{1}{2}[\cos\theta - \cos(3\theta)]$ **15.** $\dfrac{1}{2}[\sin(2\theta) + \sin\theta]$ **17.** $2\sin\theta\cos(3\theta)$ **19.** $2\cos(3\theta)\cos\theta$ **21.** $2\sin(2\theta)\cos\theta$ **23.** $2\sin\theta\sin\dfrac{\theta}{2}$

25. $\dfrac{\sin\theta + \sin(3\theta)}{2\sin(2\theta)} = \dfrac{2\sin(2\theta)\cos\theta}{2\sin(2\theta)} = \cos\theta$ **27.** $\dfrac{\sin(4\theta) + \sin(2\theta)}{\cos(4\theta) + \cos(2\theta)} = \dfrac{2\sin(3\theta)\cos\theta}{2\cos(3\theta)\cos\theta} = \dfrac{\sin(3\theta)}{\cos(3\theta)} = \tan(3\theta)$

29. $\dfrac{\cos\theta - \cos(3\theta)}{\sin\theta + \sin(3\theta)} = \dfrac{2\sin(2\theta)\sin\theta}{2\sin(2\theta)\cos\theta} = \dfrac{\sin\theta}{\cos\theta} = \tan\theta$

31. $\sin\theta[\sin\theta + \sin(3\theta)] = \sin\theta[2\sin(2\theta)\cos\theta] = \cos\theta[2\sin(2\theta)\sin\theta] = \cos\theta\left[2\cdot\dfrac{1}{2}[\cos\theta - \cos(3\theta)]\right] = \cos\theta[\cos\theta - \cos(3\theta)]$

33. $\dfrac{\sin(4\theta) + \sin(8\theta)}{\cos(4\theta) + \cos(8\theta)} = \dfrac{2\sin(6\theta)\cos(2\theta)}{2\cos(6\theta)\cos(2\theta)} = \dfrac{\sin(6\theta)}{\cos(6\theta)} = \tan(6\theta)$

35. $\dfrac{\sin(4\theta) + \sin(8\theta)}{\sin(4\theta) - \sin(8\theta)} = \dfrac{2\sin(6\theta)\cos(-2\theta)}{2\sin(-2\theta)\cos(6\theta)} = \dfrac{\sin(6\theta)}{\cos(6\theta)}\cdot\dfrac{\cos(2\theta)}{-\sin(2\theta)} = \tan(6\theta)[-\cot(2\theta)] = -\dfrac{\tan(6\theta)}{\tan(2\theta)}$

37. $\dfrac{\sin\alpha + \sin\beta}{\sin\alpha - \sin\beta} = \dfrac{2\sin\dfrac{\alpha+\beta}{2}\cos\dfrac{\alpha-\beta}{2}}{2\sin\dfrac{\alpha-\beta}{2}\cos\dfrac{\alpha+\beta}{2}} = \dfrac{\sin\dfrac{\alpha+\beta}{2}}{\cos\dfrac{\alpha+\beta}{2}}\cdot\dfrac{\cos\dfrac{\alpha-\beta}{2}}{\sin\dfrac{\alpha-\beta}{2}} = \tan\dfrac{\alpha+\beta}{2}\cot\dfrac{\alpha-\beta}{2}$

39. $\dfrac{\sin\alpha + \sin\beta}{\cos\alpha + \cos\beta} = \dfrac{2\sin\dfrac{\alpha+\beta}{2}\cos\dfrac{\alpha-\beta}{2}}{2\cos\dfrac{\alpha+\beta}{2}\cos\dfrac{\alpha-\beta}{2}} = \dfrac{\sin\dfrac{\alpha+\beta}{2}}{\cos\dfrac{\alpha+\beta}{2}} = \tan\dfrac{\alpha+\beta}{2}$

41. $1 + \cos(2\theta) + \cos(4\theta) + \cos(6\theta) = [1 + \cos(6\theta)] + [\cos(2\theta) + \cos(4\theta)] = 2\cos^2(3\theta) + 2\cos(3\theta)\cos(-\theta)$
$= 2\cos(3\theta)[\cos(3\theta) + \cos\theta] = 2\cos(3\theta)[2\cos(2\theta)\cos\theta] = 4\cos\theta\cos(2\theta)\cos(3\theta)$

43. $\left\{0, \dfrac{\pi}{3}, \dfrac{\pi}{2}, \dfrac{2\pi}{3}, \pi, \dfrac{4\pi}{3}, \dfrac{3\pi}{2}, \dfrac{5\pi}{3}\right\}$ **45.** $\left\{0, \dfrac{\pi}{5}, \dfrac{2\pi}{5}, \dfrac{3\pi}{5}, \dfrac{4\pi}{5}, \pi, \dfrac{6\pi}{5}, \dfrac{7\pi}{5}, \dfrac{8\pi}{5}, \dfrac{9\pi}{5}\right\}$

47. (a) $y = 2\sin(2061\pi t)\cos(357\pi t)$ **49.** $I_u = I_x\cos^2\theta + I_y\sin^2\theta - 2I_{xy}\sin\theta\cos\theta = I_x\cos^2\theta + I_y\sin^2\theta - I_{xy}\sin 2\theta$
(b) $y_{max} = 2$
(c)

$= I_x\left(\dfrac{\cos 2\theta + 1}{2}\right) + I_y\left(\dfrac{1 - \cos 2\theta}{2}\right) - I_{xy}\sin 2\theta$

$= \dfrac{I_x}{2}\cos 2\theta + \dfrac{I_x}{2} + \dfrac{I_y}{2} - \dfrac{I_y}{2}\cos 2\theta - I_{xy}\sin 2\theta$

$= \dfrac{I_x + I_y}{2} + \dfrac{I_x - I_y}{2}\cos 2\theta - I_{xy}\sin 2\theta$

$I_v = I_x\sin^2\theta + I_y\cos^2\theta + 2I_{xy}\sin\theta\cos\theta = I_x\left(\dfrac{1 - \cos 2\theta}{2}\right) + I_y\left(\dfrac{\cos 2\theta + 1}{2}\right) + I_{xy}\sin 2\theta$

$= \dfrac{I_x}{2} - \dfrac{I_x}{2}\cos 2\theta + \dfrac{I_y}{2}\cos 2\theta + \dfrac{I_y}{2} + I_{xy}\sin 2\theta$

$= \dfrac{I_x + I_y}{2} - \dfrac{I_x - I_y}{2}\cos 2\theta + I_{xy}\sin 2\theta$

51. $\sin(2\alpha) + \sin(2\beta) + \sin(2\gamma) = 2\sin(\alpha + \beta)\cos(\alpha - \beta) + \sin(2\gamma) = 2\sin(\alpha + \beta)\cos(\alpha - \beta) + 2\sin\gamma\cos\gamma$
$= 2\sin(\pi - \gamma)\cos(\alpha - \beta) + 2\sin\gamma\cos\gamma = 2\sin\gamma\cos(\alpha - \beta) + 2\sin\gamma\cos\gamma = 2\sin\gamma[\cos(\alpha - \beta) + \cos\gamma]$
$= 2\sin\gamma\left(2\cos\dfrac{\alpha - \beta + \gamma}{2}\cos\dfrac{\alpha - \beta - \gamma}{2}\right) = 4\sin\gamma\cos\dfrac{\pi - 2\beta}{2}\cos\dfrac{2\alpha - \pi}{2} = 4\sin\gamma\cos\left(\dfrac{\pi}{2} - \beta\right)\cos\left(\alpha - \dfrac{\pi}{2}\right)$
$= 4\sin\gamma\sin\beta\sin\alpha = 4\sin\alpha\sin\beta\sin\gamma$

53.
$\sin(\alpha - \beta) = \sin\alpha\cos\beta - \cos\alpha\sin\beta$
$\sin(\alpha + \beta) = \sin\alpha\cos\beta + \cos\alpha\sin\beta$
$\sin(\alpha - \beta) + \sin(\alpha + \beta) = 2\sin\alpha\cos\beta$

$\sin\alpha\cos\beta = \dfrac{1}{2}[\sin(\alpha + \beta) + \sin(\alpha - \beta)]$

55. $2\cos\dfrac{\alpha + \beta}{2}\cos\dfrac{\alpha - \beta}{2} = 2\cdot\dfrac{1}{2}\left[\cos\left(\dfrac{\alpha + \beta}{2} + \dfrac{\alpha - \beta}{2}\right) + \cos\left(\dfrac{\alpha + \beta}{2} - \dfrac{\alpha - \beta}{2}\right)\right] = \cos\dfrac{2\alpha}{2} + \cos\dfrac{2\beta}{2} = \cos\alpha + \cos\beta$

Review Exercises *(page 499)*

1. $\dfrac{\pi}{2}$ **3.** $\dfrac{\pi}{4}$ **5.** $\dfrac{5\pi}{6}$ **7.** $\dfrac{\pi}{4}$ **9.** $\dfrac{3\pi}{8}$ **11.** $-\dfrac{\pi}{3}$ **13.** $\dfrac{\pi}{7}$ **15.** 0.9 **17.** -0.3 **19.** Not defined **21.** $-\dfrac{\pi}{6}$ **23.** $-\dfrac{\pi}{4}$ **25.** $-\sqrt{3}$ **27.** $\dfrac{2\sqrt{3}}{3}$ **29.** $\dfrac{4}{5}$

31. $-\dfrac{4}{3}$ **33.** $f^{-1}(x) = \dfrac{1}{3}\sin^{-1}\left(\dfrac{x}{2}\right)$; Range of f = Domain of $f^{-1} = [-2, 2]$; Range of $f^{-1} = \left[-\dfrac{\pi}{6}, \dfrac{\pi}{6}\right]$ **35.** $f^{-1}(x) = \cos^{-1}(3 - x)$;

Range of f = Domain of $f^{-1} = [2, 4]$; Range of $f^{-1} = [0, \pi]$ **37.** $\sqrt{1 - u^2}$ **39.** $\dfrac{1}{u}$ **41.** $\tan\theta\cot\theta - \sin^2\theta = 1 - \sin^2\theta = \cos^2\theta$

43. $\sin^2\theta(1 + \cot^2\theta) = \sin^2\theta\csc^2\theta = 1$ **45.** $5\cos^2\theta + 3\sin^2\theta = 2\cos^2\theta + 3(\cos^2\theta + \sin^2\theta) = 3 + 2\cos^2\theta$

47. $\dfrac{1 - \cos\theta}{\sin\theta} + \dfrac{\sin\theta}{1 - \cos\theta} = \dfrac{(1 - \cos\theta)^2 + \sin^2\theta}{\sin\theta(1 - \cos\theta)} = \dfrac{1 - 2\cos\theta + \cos^2\theta + \sin^2\theta}{\sin\theta(1 - \cos\theta)} = \dfrac{2(1 - \cos\theta)}{\sin\theta(1 - \cos\theta)} = 2\csc\theta$

49. $\dfrac{\cos\theta}{\cos\theta - \sin\theta} = \dfrac{\dfrac{\cos\theta}{\cos\theta}}{\dfrac{\cos\theta - \sin\theta}{\cos\theta}} = \dfrac{1}{1 - \dfrac{\sin\theta}{\cos\theta}} = \dfrac{1}{1 - \tan\theta}$ **51.** $\dfrac{\csc\theta}{1 + \csc\theta} = \dfrac{\dfrac{1}{\sin\theta}}{1 + \dfrac{1}{\sin\theta}} = \dfrac{1}{1 + \sin\theta} = \dfrac{1}{1 + \sin\theta}\cdot\dfrac{1 - \sin\theta}{1 - \sin\theta} = \dfrac{1 - \sin\theta}{1 - \sin^2\theta} = \dfrac{1 - \sin\theta}{\cos^2\theta}$

53. $\csc\theta - \sin\theta = \dfrac{1}{\sin\theta} - \sin\theta = \dfrac{1 - \sin^2\theta}{\sin\theta} = \dfrac{\cos^2\theta}{\sin\theta} = \cos\theta\cdot\dfrac{\cos\theta}{\sin\theta} = \cos\theta\cot\theta$

55. $\dfrac{1 - \sin\theta}{\sec\theta} = \cos\theta(1 - \sin\theta) \cdot \dfrac{1 + \sin\theta}{1 + \sin\theta} = \dfrac{\cos\theta(1 - \sin^2\theta)}{1 + \sin\theta} = \dfrac{\cos^3\theta}{1 + \sin\theta}$ **57.** $\cot\theta - \tan\theta = \dfrac{\cos\theta}{\sin\theta} - \dfrac{\sin\theta}{\cos\theta} = \dfrac{\cos^2\theta - \sin^2\theta}{\sin\theta\cos\theta} = \dfrac{1 - 2\sin^2\theta}{\sin\theta\cos\theta}$

59. $\dfrac{\cos(\alpha + \beta)}{\cos\alpha\sin\beta} = \dfrac{\cos\alpha\cos\beta - \sin\alpha\sin\beta}{\cos\alpha\sin\beta} = \dfrac{\cos\alpha\cos\beta}{\cos\alpha\sin\beta} - \dfrac{\sin\alpha\sin\beta}{\cos\alpha\sin\beta} = \cot\beta - \tan\alpha$

61. $\dfrac{\cos(\alpha - \beta)}{\cos\alpha\cos\beta} = \dfrac{\cos\alpha\cos\beta + \sin\alpha\sin\beta}{\cos\alpha\cos\beta} = \dfrac{\cos\alpha\cos\beta}{\cos\alpha\cos\beta} + \dfrac{\sin\alpha\sin\beta}{\cos\alpha\cos\beta} = 1 + \tan\alpha\tan\beta$

63. $(1 + \cos\theta)\left(\tan\dfrac{\theta}{2}\right) = (1 + \cos\theta) \cdot \dfrac{\sin\theta}{1 + \cos\theta} = \sin\theta$

65. $2\cot\theta\cot2\theta = 2\left(\dfrac{\cos\theta}{\sin\theta}\right)\left(\dfrac{\cos2\theta}{\sin2\theta}\right) = \dfrac{2\cos\theta(\cos^2\theta - \sin^2\theta)}{2\sin^2\theta\cos\theta} = \dfrac{\cos^2\theta - \sin^2\theta}{\sin^2\theta} = \cot^2\theta - 1$

67. $1 - 8\sin^2\theta\cos^2\theta = 1 - 2(2\sin\theta\cos\theta)^2 = 1 - 2\sin^2(2\theta) = \cos(4\theta)$ **69.** $\dfrac{\sin(2\theta) + \sin(4\theta)}{\cos(2\theta) + \cos(4\theta)} = \dfrac{2\sin(3\theta)\cos(-\theta)}{2\cos(3\theta)\cos(-\theta)} = \tan(3\theta)$

71. $\dfrac{\cos(2\theta) - \cos(4\theta)}{\cos(2\theta) + \cos(4\theta)} - \tan\theta\tan(3\theta) = \dfrac{-2\sin(3\theta)\sin(-\theta)}{2\cos(3\theta)\cos(-\theta)} - \tan\theta\tan(3\theta) = \tan(3\theta)\tan\theta - \tan\theta\tan(3\theta) = 0$ **73.** $\dfrac{1}{4}\left(\sqrt{6} - \sqrt{2}\right)$

75. $\dfrac{1}{4}\left(\sqrt{6} - \sqrt{2}\right)$ **77.** $\dfrac{1}{2}$ **79.** $\sqrt{2} - 1$ **81.** (a) $-\dfrac{33}{65}$ (b) $-\dfrac{56}{65}$ (c) $-\dfrac{63}{65}$ (d) $\dfrac{33}{56}$ (e) $\dfrac{24}{25}$ (f) $\dfrac{119}{169}$ (g) $\dfrac{5\sqrt{26}}{26}$ (h) $\dfrac{2\sqrt{5}}{5}$

83. (a) $-\dfrac{16}{65}$ (b) $-\dfrac{63}{65}$ (c) $-\dfrac{56}{65}$ (d) $\dfrac{16}{63}$ (e) $\dfrac{24}{25}$ (f) $\dfrac{119}{169}$ (g) $\dfrac{\sqrt{26}}{26}$ (h) $-\dfrac{\sqrt{10}}{10}$

85. (a) $-\dfrac{63}{65}$ (b) $\dfrac{16}{65}$ (c) $\dfrac{33}{65}$ (d) $-\dfrac{63}{16}$ (e) $\dfrac{24}{25}$ (f) $-\dfrac{119}{169}$ (g) $\dfrac{2\sqrt{13}}{13}$ (h) $-\dfrac{\sqrt{10}}{10}$

87. (a) $\dfrac{-\sqrt{3} - 2\sqrt{2}}{6}$ (b) $\dfrac{1 - 2\sqrt{6}}{6}$ (c) $\dfrac{-\sqrt{3} + 2\sqrt{2}}{6}$ (d) $\dfrac{8\sqrt{2} + 9\sqrt{3}}{23}$ (e) $-\dfrac{\sqrt{3}}{2}$ (f) $-\dfrac{7}{9}$ (g) $\dfrac{\sqrt{3}}{3}$ (h) $\dfrac{\sqrt{3}}{2}$

89. (a) 1 (b) 0 (c) $-\dfrac{1}{9}$ (d) Not defined (e) $\dfrac{4\sqrt{5}}{9}$ (f) $-\dfrac{1}{9}$ (g) $\dfrac{\sqrt{30}}{6}$ (h) $-\dfrac{\sqrt{6}\sqrt{3 - \sqrt{5}}}{6}$ **91.** $\dfrac{4 + 3\sqrt{3}}{10}$ **93.** $-\dfrac{48 + 25\sqrt{3}}{39}$

95. $-\dfrac{24}{25}$ **97.** $\left\{\dfrac{\pi}{3}, \dfrac{5\pi}{3}\right\}$ **99.** $\left\{\dfrac{3\pi}{4}, \dfrac{5\pi}{4}\right\}$ **101.** $\left\{\dfrac{3\pi}{4}, \dfrac{7\pi}{4}\right\}$ **103.** $\left\{0, \dfrac{\pi}{2}, \pi, \dfrac{3\pi}{2}\right\}$ **105.** $\left\{\dfrac{\pi}{3}, \dfrac{2\pi}{3}, \dfrac{4\pi}{3}, \dfrac{5\pi}{3}\right\}$ **107.** $\{0.25, 2.89\}$

109. $\left\{0, \dfrac{2\pi}{3}, \pi, \dfrac{4\pi}{3}\right\}$ **111.** $\left\{0, \dfrac{\pi}{6}, \dfrac{5\pi}{6}\right\}$ **113.** $\left\{\dfrac{\pi}{6}, \dfrac{\pi}{2}, \dfrac{5\pi}{6}\right\}$ **115.** $\left\{\dfrac{\pi}{3}, \dfrac{5\pi}{3}\right\}$ **117.** $\left\{\dfrac{\pi}{4}, \dfrac{\pi}{2}, \dfrac{3\pi}{4}, \dfrac{3\pi}{2}\right\}$ **119.** $\left\{\dfrac{\pi}{2}, \pi\right\}$ **121.** 0.78 **123.** -1.11

125. 1.23 **127.** $\{1.11\}$ **129.** $\{0.87\}$ **131.** $\{2.22\}$ **133.** $\left\{-\dfrac{\sqrt{3}}{2}\right\}$

135. $\sin 15° = \sqrt{\dfrac{1 - \cos 30°}{2}} = \sqrt{\dfrac{1 - \dfrac{\sqrt{3}}{2}}{2}} = \sqrt{\dfrac{2 - \sqrt{3}}{4}} = \sqrt{\dfrac{2 - \sqrt{3}}{2}}$;

$\sin 15° = \sin(45° - 30°) = \sin 45°\cos 30° - \cos 45°\sin 30° = \dfrac{\sqrt{2}}{2} \cdot \dfrac{\sqrt{3}}{2} - \dfrac{\sqrt{2}}{2} \cdot \dfrac{1}{2} = \dfrac{\sqrt{6}}{4} - \dfrac{\sqrt{2}}{4} = \dfrac{\sqrt{6} - \sqrt{2}}{4}$;

$\left[\dfrac{\sqrt{2 - \sqrt{3}}}{2}\right]^2 = \dfrac{2 - \sqrt{3}}{4} = \dfrac{4(2 - \sqrt{3})}{4 \cdot 4} = \dfrac{8 - 4\sqrt{3}}{16} = \dfrac{6 - 2\sqrt{12} + 2}{16} = \left(\dfrac{\sqrt{6} - \sqrt{2}}{4}\right)^2$

Chapter Test *(page 502)*

1. $\dfrac{\pi}{6}$ **2.** $-\dfrac{\pi}{4}$ **3.** $\dfrac{\pi}{5}$ **4.** $\dfrac{7}{3}$ **5.** 3 **6.** $-\dfrac{4}{3}$ **7.** 0.39 **8.** 0.78 **9.** 1.25 **10.** 0.20

11. $\dfrac{\csc\theta + \cot\theta}{\sec\theta + \tan\theta} = \dfrac{\csc\theta + \cot\theta}{\sec\theta + \tan\theta} \cdot \dfrac{\csc\theta - \cot\theta}{\csc\theta - \cot\theta} = \dfrac{\csc^2\theta - \cot^2\theta}{(\sec\theta + \tan\theta)(\csc\theta - \cot\theta)} = \dfrac{1}{(\sec\theta + \tan\theta)(\csc\theta - \cot\theta)}$

$= \dfrac{1}{(\sec\theta + \tan\theta)(\csc\theta - \cot\theta)} \cdot \dfrac{\sec\theta - \tan\theta}{\sec\theta - \tan\theta} = \dfrac{\sec\theta - \tan\theta}{(\sec^2\theta - \tan^2\theta)(\csc\theta - \cot\theta)} = \dfrac{\sec\theta - \tan\theta}{\csc\theta - \cot\theta}$

12. $\sin\theta\tan\theta + \cos\theta = \sin\theta \cdot \dfrac{\sin\theta}{\cos\theta} + \cos\theta = \dfrac{\sin^2\theta}{\cos\theta} + \dfrac{\cos^2\theta}{\cos\theta} = \dfrac{\sin^2\theta + \cos^2\theta}{\cos\theta} = \dfrac{1}{\cos\theta} = \sec\theta$

13. $\tan\theta + \cot\theta = \dfrac{\sin\theta}{\cos\theta} + \dfrac{\cos\theta}{\sin\theta} = \dfrac{\sin^2\theta}{\sin\theta\cos\theta} + \dfrac{\cos^2\theta}{\sin\theta\cos\theta} = \dfrac{\sin^2\theta + \cos^2\theta}{\sin\theta\cos\theta} = \dfrac{1}{\sin\theta\cos\theta} = \dfrac{2}{2\sin\theta\cos\theta} = \dfrac{2}{\sin(2\theta)} = 2\csc(2\theta)$

14. $\dfrac{\sin(\alpha + \beta)}{\tan\alpha + \tan\beta} = \dfrac{\sin\alpha\cos\beta + \cos\alpha\sin\beta}{\dfrac{\sin\alpha}{\cos\alpha} + \dfrac{\sin\beta}{\cos\beta}} = \dfrac{\sin\alpha\cos\beta + \cos\alpha\sin\beta}{\dfrac{\sin\alpha\cos\beta}{\cos\alpha\cos\beta} + \dfrac{\cos\alpha\sin\beta}{\cos\alpha\cos\beta}} = \dfrac{\sin\alpha\cos\beta + \cos\alpha\sin\beta}{\dfrac{\sin\alpha\cos\beta + \cos\alpha\sin\beta}{\cos\alpha\cos\beta}}$

$= \dfrac{\sin\alpha\cos\beta + \cos\alpha\sin\beta}{1} \cdot \dfrac{\cos\alpha\cos\beta}{\sin\alpha\cos\beta + \cos\alpha\sin\beta} = \cos\alpha\cos\beta$

15. $\sin(3\theta) = \sin(\theta + 2\theta) = \sin\theta\cos(2\theta) + \cos\theta\sin(2\theta) = \sin\theta \cdot (\cos^2\theta - \sin^2\theta) + \cos\theta \cdot 2\sin\theta\cos\theta = \sin\theta\cos^2\theta - \sin^3\theta + 2\sin\theta\cos^2\theta$
$= 3\sin\theta\cos^2\theta - \sin^3\theta = 3\sin\theta(1 - \sin^2\theta) - \sin^3\theta = 3\sin\theta - 3\sin^3\theta - \sin^3\theta = 3\sin\theta - 4\sin^3\theta$

16. $\dfrac{\tan\theta - \cot\theta}{\tan\theta + \cot\theta} = \dfrac{\dfrac{\sin\theta}{\cos\theta} - \dfrac{\cos\theta}{\sin\theta}}{\dfrac{\sin\theta}{\cos\theta} + \dfrac{\cos\theta}{\sin\theta}} = \dfrac{\dfrac{\sin^2\theta - \cos^2\theta}{\sin\theta\cos\theta}}{\dfrac{\sin^2\theta + \cos^2\theta}{\sin\theta\cos\theta}} = \dfrac{\sin^2\theta - \cos^2\theta}{\sin^2\theta + \cos^2\theta} = \dfrac{(1 - \cos^2\theta) - \cos^2\theta}{1} = 1 - 2\cos^2\theta$ **17.** $\dfrac{1}{4}\left(\sqrt{6} + \sqrt{2}\right)$

18. $2 + \sqrt{3}$ **19.** $\dfrac{\sqrt{5}}{5}$ **20.** $\dfrac{12\sqrt{85}}{49}$ **21.** $\dfrac{2\sqrt{13}(\sqrt{5}-3)}{39}$ **22.** $\dfrac{2+\sqrt{3}}{4}$ **23.** $\dfrac{\sqrt{6}}{2}$ **24.** $\dfrac{\sqrt{2}}{2}$ **25.** $\left\{\dfrac{\pi}{3}, \dfrac{2\pi}{3}, \dfrac{4\pi}{3}, \dfrac{5\pi}{3}\right\}$ **26.** $\{0, 1.911, \pi, 4.373\}$

27. $\left\{\dfrac{3\pi}{8}, \dfrac{7\pi}{8}, \dfrac{11\pi}{8}, \dfrac{15\pi}{8}\right\}$ **28.** $\{0.285, 3.427\}$ **29.** $\{0.253, 2.889\}$

Cumulative Review (page 502)

1. $\left\{\dfrac{-1-\sqrt{13}}{6}, \dfrac{-1+\sqrt{13}}{6}\right\}$ **2.** $y + 1 = -1(x - 4)$ or $x + y = 3$; $6\sqrt{2}$; $(1, 2)$ **3.** x-axis symmetry; $(0, -3), (0, 3), (3, 0)$

4.   **5.**   **6.**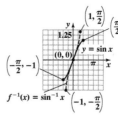

7. (a)   **(b)**   **(c)** **(d)**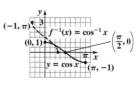

8. (a) $-\dfrac{2\sqrt{2}}{3}$ **(b)** $\dfrac{\sqrt{2}}{4}$ **(c)** $\dfrac{4\sqrt{2}}{9}$ **(d)** $\dfrac{7}{9}$ **(e)** $\sqrt{\dfrac{3+2\sqrt{2}}{6}}$ **(f)** $-\sqrt{\dfrac{3-2\sqrt{2}}{6}}$ **9.** $\dfrac{\sqrt{5}}{5}$ **10. (a)** $-\dfrac{2\sqrt{2}}{3}$ **(b)** $-\dfrac{2\sqrt{2}}{3}$ **(c)** $\dfrac{7}{9}$ **(d)** $\dfrac{4\sqrt{2}}{9}$ **(e)** $\dfrac{\sqrt{6}}{3}$

11. (a) $f(x) = (2x - 1)(x - 1)^2(x + 1)^2$; $\dfrac{1}{2}$ multiplicity 1; 1 and -1 multiplicity 2

(b) $(0, -1)$; $\left(\dfrac{1}{2}, 0\right)$; $(-1, 0)$; $(1, 0)$ **(c)** $y = 2x^5$

(d)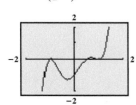

(e) Local minimum value -1.33 at $x = -0.29$,
Local minimum value 0 at $x = 1$
Local maximum value 0 at $x = -1$,
Local maximum value 0.10 at $x = 0.69$

(f)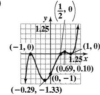

(g) Increasing: $(-\infty, -1), (-0.29, 0.69), (1, \infty)$
Decreasing: $(-1, -0.29), (0.69, 1)$

12. (a) $\left\{-1, -\dfrac{1}{2}\right\}$

(b) $\{-1, 1\}$

(c) $(-\infty, -1) \cup \left(-\dfrac{1}{2}, \infty\right)$

(d) $(-\infty, -1] \cup [1, \infty)$

CHAPTER 8 Applications of Trigonometric Functions

8.1 Assess Your Understanding (page 512)

4. F **5.** T **6.** angle of elevation **7.** T **8.** F **9.** $\sin\theta = \dfrac{5}{13}$; $\cos\theta = \dfrac{12}{13}$; $\tan\theta = \dfrac{5}{12}$; $\cot\theta = \dfrac{12}{5}$; $\sec\theta = \dfrac{13}{12}$; $\csc\theta = \dfrac{13}{5}$

11. $\sin\theta = \dfrac{2\sqrt{13}}{13}$; $\cos\theta = \dfrac{3\sqrt{13}}{13}$; $\tan\theta = \dfrac{2}{3}$; $\cot\theta = \dfrac{3}{2}$; $\sec\theta = \dfrac{\sqrt{13}}{3}$; $\csc\theta = \dfrac{\sqrt{13}}{2}$

13. $\sin\theta = \dfrac{\sqrt{3}}{2}$; $\cos\theta = \dfrac{1}{2}$; $\tan\theta = \sqrt{3}$; $\cot\theta = \dfrac{\sqrt{3}}{3}$; $\sec\theta = 2$; $\csc\theta = \dfrac{2\sqrt{3}}{3}$

15. $\sin\theta = \dfrac{\sqrt{6}}{3}$; $\cos\theta = \dfrac{\sqrt{3}}{3}$; $\tan\theta = \sqrt{2}$; $\cot\theta = \dfrac{\sqrt{2}}{2}$; $\sec\theta = \sqrt{3}$; $\csc\theta = \dfrac{\sqrt{6}}{2}$

17. $\sin\theta = \dfrac{\sqrt{5}}{5}$; $\cos\theta = \dfrac{2\sqrt{5}}{5}$; $\tan\theta = \dfrac{1}{2}$; $\cot\theta = 2$; $\sec\theta = \dfrac{\sqrt{5}}{2}$; $\csc\theta = \sqrt{5}$

19. 0 **21.** 1 **23.** 0 **25.** 0 **27.** 1 **29.** $a \approx 13.74$, $c \approx 14.62$, $A = 70°$ **31.** $b \approx 5.03$, $c \approx 7.83$, $A = 50°$ **33.** $a \approx 0.71$, $c \approx 4.06$, $B = 80°$
35. $b \approx 10.72$, $c \approx 11.83$, $B = 65°$ **37.** $b \approx 3.08$, $a \approx 8.46$, $A = 70°$ **39.** $c \approx 5.83$, $A \approx 59.0°$, $B \approx 31.0°$ **41.** $b \approx 4.58$, $A \approx 23.6°$, $B \approx 66.4°$
43. 23.6° and 66.4° **45.** 4.59 in.; 6.55 in. **47. (a)** 5.52 in. or 11.83 in. **49.** 70.02 ft **51.** 985.91 ft **53.** 137.37 m **55.** 80.5°
57. (a) 111.96 ft/sec or 76.3 mi/hr **(b)** 82.42 ft/sec or 56.2 mi/hr **(c)** Under 18.8° **59. (a)** 2.4898×10^{13} miles **(b)** 0.000214° **61.** 554.52 ft
63. S76.6°E **65.** The embankment is 30.5 m high. **67.** 3.83 mi **69.** 1978.09 ft **71.** 60.27 ft **73.** The buildings are 7984 ft apart. **75.** 69.0°
77. 38.9° **79.** The white ball should hit the top cushion 4.125 ft from the upper left corner.

8.2 Assess Your Understanding (page 524)

4. oblique **5.** $\dfrac{\sin A}{a} = \dfrac{\sin B}{b} = \dfrac{\sin C}{c}$ **6.** F **7.** F **8.** ambiguous case **9.** $a \approx 3.23$, $b \approx 3.55$, $A = 40°$ **11.** $a \approx 3.25$, $c \approx 4.23$, $B = 45°$
13. $C = 95°$, $c \approx 9.86$, $a \approx 6.36$ **15.** $A = 40°$, $a = 2$, $c \approx 3.06$ **17.** $C = 120°$, $b \approx 1.06$, $c \approx 2.69$ **19.** $A = 100°$, $a \approx 5.24$, $c \approx 0.92$

21. $B = 40°, a \approx 5.64, b \approx 3.86$ **23.** $C = 100°, a \approx 1.31, b \approx 1.31$ **25.** One triangle; $B \approx 30.7°, C \approx 99.3°, c \approx 3.86$ **27.** One triangle; $C \approx 36.2°, A \approx 43.8°, a \approx 3.51$ **29.** No triangle   **31.** Two triangles; $C_1 \approx 30.9°, A_1 \approx 129.1°, a_1 \approx 9.07$ or $C_2 \approx 149.1°, A_2 \approx 10.9°, a_2 \approx 2.20$
33. No triangle   **35.** Two triangles; $A_1 \approx 57.7°, B_1 \approx 97.3°, b_1 \approx 2.35$ or $A_2 \approx 122.3°, B_2 \approx 32.7°, b_2 \approx 1.28$ **37. (a)** Station Able is about 143.33 mi from the ship; Station Baker is about 135.58 mi from the ship.   **(b)** Approximately 41 min   **39.** 1490.48 ft   **41.** 381.69 ft   **43.** The tree is 39.4 ft high.
45. Adam receives 100.6 more frequent flyer miles.   **47.** $84.7°; 183.72$ ft   **49.** 2.64 mi   **51.** 38.5 in.   **53.** 449.36 ft   **55.** 187,600,000 km or 101,440,000 km
57. The diameter is 252 ft.

59. $\dfrac{a-b}{c} = \dfrac{a}{c} - \dfrac{b}{c} = \dfrac{\sin A}{\sin C} - \dfrac{\sin B}{\sin C} = \dfrac{\sin A - \sin B}{\sin C} = \dfrac{2\sin\left(\dfrac{A-B}{2}\right)\cos\left(\dfrac{A+B}{2}\right)}{2\sin\dfrac{C}{2}\cos\dfrac{C}{2}} = \dfrac{\sin\left(\dfrac{A-B}{2}\right)\cos\left(\dfrac{\pi}{2} - \dfrac{C}{2}\right)}{\sin\dfrac{C}{2}\cos\dfrac{C}{2}} = \dfrac{\sin\left(\dfrac{A-B}{2}\right)}{\cos\dfrac{C}{2}}$

61. $\dfrac{a-b}{a+b} = \dfrac{\dfrac{a-b}{c}}{\dfrac{a+b}{c}} = \dfrac{\dfrac{\sin\left[\frac{1}{2}(A-B)\right]}{\cos\dfrac{C}{2}}}{\dfrac{\cos\left[\frac{1}{2}(A-B)\right]}{\sin\dfrac{C}{2}}} = \dfrac{\tan\left[\frac{1}{2}(A-B)\right]}{\cot\dfrac{C}{2}} = \dfrac{\tan\left[\frac{1}{2}(A-B)\right]}{\tan\left(\dfrac{\pi}{2} - \dfrac{C}{2}\right)} = \dfrac{\tan\left[\frac{1}{2}(A-B)\right]}{\tan\left[\frac{1}{2}(A+B)\right]}$

8.3 Assess Your Understanding (page 531)

3. Cosines   **4.** Sines   **5.** Cosines   **6.** F   **7.** F   **8.** T   **9.** $b \approx 2.95, A \approx 28.7°, C \approx 106.3°$ **11.** $c \approx 3.75, A \approx 32.1°, B \approx 52.9°$
13. $A \approx 48.5°, B \approx 38.6°, C \approx 92.9°$ **15.** $A \approx 127.2°, B \approx 32.1°, C \approx 20.7°$ **17.** $c \approx 2.57, A \approx 48.6°, B \approx 91.4°$
19. $a \approx 2.99, B \approx 19.2°, C \approx 80.8°$ **21.** $b \approx 4.14, A \approx 43.0°, C \approx 27.0°$ **23.** $c \approx 1.69, A = 65.0°, B = 65.0°$ **25.** $A \approx 67.4°, B = 90°, C \approx 22.6°$
27. $A = 60°, B = 60°, C = 60°$ **29.** $A \approx 33.6°, B \approx 62.2°, C \approx 84.3°$ **31.** $A \approx 97.9°, B \approx 52.4°, C \approx 29.7°$ **33.** $A = 85°, a = 14.56, c = 14.12$
35. $A = 40.8°, B = 60.6°, C = 78.6°$ **37.** $A = 80°, b = 8.74, c = 13.80$ **39.** Two triangles: $B_1 = 35.4°, C_1 = 134.6°, c_1 = 12.29$; $B_2 = 144.6°, C_2 = 25.4°, c_2 = 7.40$ **41.** $B = 24.5°, C = 95.5°, a = 10.44$ **43.** 165 yd   **45. (a)** 26.4°   **(b)** 30.8 h   **47. (a)** 63.7 ft   **(b)** 66.8 ft
(c) 92.8°   **49. (a)** 492.6 ft   **(b)** 269.3 ft   **51.** 342.33 ft   **53.** The footings should be 7.65 ft apart.

55. Suppose $0 < \theta < \pi$. Then, by the Law of Cosines, $d^2 = r^2 + r^2 - 2r^2 \cos\theta = 4r^2\left(\dfrac{1 - \cos\theta}{2}\right) \Rightarrow d = 2r\sqrt{\dfrac{1 - \cos\theta}{2}} = 2r\sin\dfrac{\theta}{2}$.

Since, for any angle in $(0, \pi)$, d is strictly less than the length of the arc subtended by θ, that is, $d < r\theta$, then $2r\sin\dfrac{\theta}{2} < r\theta$, or $2\sin\dfrac{\theta}{2} < \theta$.

Since $\cos\dfrac{\theta}{2} < 1$, then, for $0 < \theta < \pi$, $\sin\theta = 2\sin\dfrac{\theta}{2}\cos\dfrac{\theta}{2} < 2\sin\dfrac{\theta}{2} < \theta$. If $\theta \geq \pi$, then, since $\sin\theta \leq 1$, $\sin\theta < \theta$. Thus $\sin\theta < \theta$ for all $\theta > 0$.

57. $\sin\dfrac{C}{2} = \sqrt{\dfrac{1 - \cos C}{2}} = \sqrt{\dfrac{1 - \dfrac{a^2 + b^2 - c^2}{2ab}}{2}} = \sqrt{\dfrac{2ab - a^2 - b^2 + c^2}{4ab}} = \sqrt{\dfrac{c^2 - (a - b)^2}{4ab}} = \sqrt{\dfrac{(c + a - b)(c + b - a)}{4ab}}$

$= \sqrt{\dfrac{(2s - 2b)(2s - 2a)}{4ab}} = \sqrt{\dfrac{(s - a)(s - b)}{ab}}$

8.4 Assess Your Understanding (page 537)

2. $\frac{1}{2}ab\sin C$ **3.** $\sqrt{s(s-a)(s-b)(s-c)}; \frac{1}{2}(a+b+c)$ **4.** T   **5.** 2.83   **7.** 2.99   **9.** 14.98   **11.** 9.56   **13.** 3.86   **15.** 1.48   **17.** 2.82   **19.** 30

21. 1.73   **23.** 19.90   **25.** $K = \frac{1}{2}ab\sin C = \frac{1}{2}a\sin C\left(\dfrac{a\sin B}{\sin A}\right) = \dfrac{a^2\sin B\sin C}{2\sin A}$ **27.** 0.92   **29.** 2.27   **31.** 5.44   **33.** 9.03 sq ft   **35.** \$5446.38

37. The area of home plate is about 216.5 in.^{2} **39.** $K = \frac{1}{2}r^2(\theta + \sin\theta)$ **41.** The ground area is 7517.4 ft^2.

43. (a) Area $\triangle OAC = \dfrac{1}{2}|OC||AC| = \dfrac{1}{2} \cdot \dfrac{|OC|}{1} \cdot \dfrac{|AC|}{1} = \dfrac{1}{2}\sin\alpha\cos\alpha$

(b) Area $\triangle OCB = \dfrac{1}{2}|BC||OC| = \dfrac{1}{2}|OB|^2\dfrac{|BC|}{|OB|} \cdot \dfrac{|OC|}{|OB|} = \dfrac{1}{2}|OB|^2\sin\beta\cos\beta$

(c) Area $\triangle OAB = \dfrac{1}{2}|BD||OA| = \dfrac{1}{2}|OB|\dfrac{|BD|}{|OB|} = \dfrac{1}{2}|OB|\sin(\alpha + \beta)$

(d) $\dfrac{\cos\alpha}{\cos\beta} = \dfrac{\dfrac{|OC|}{1}}{\dfrac{|OC|}{|OB|}} = |OB|$

(e) Area $\triangle OAB = $ Area $\triangle OAC + $ Area $\triangle OCB$

$\dfrac{1}{2}|OB|\sin(\alpha + \beta) = \dfrac{1}{2}\sin\alpha\cos\alpha + \dfrac{1}{2}|OB|^2\sin\beta\cos\beta$

$\sin(\alpha + \beta) = \dfrac{1}{|OB|}\sin\alpha\cos\alpha + |OB|\sin\beta\cos\beta$

$\sin(\alpha + \beta) = \dfrac{\cos\beta}{\cos\alpha}\sin\alpha\cos\alpha + \dfrac{\cos\alpha}{\cos\beta}\sin\beta\cos\beta$

$\sin(\alpha + \beta) = \sin\alpha\cos\beta + \cos\alpha\sin\beta$

45. 31,145 ft^2 **47. (a)** The perimeter and area are both 36.   **(b)** The perimeter and area are both 60.

49. $K = \dfrac{1}{2}ah = \dfrac{1}{2}ab\sin C \Rightarrow h = b\sin C = \dfrac{a\sin B\sin C}{\sin A}$

51. $\cot\dfrac{C}{2} = \dfrac{\cos\dfrac{C}{2}}{\sin\dfrac{C}{2}} = \dfrac{c\sin\dfrac{A}{2}\sin\dfrac{B}{2}}{r} \Big/ \sqrt{\dfrac{(s-a)(s-b)}{ab}} = c\sqrt{\dfrac{(s-b)(s-c)}{bc}}\sqrt{\dfrac{(s-a)(s-c)}{ac}} \Big/ r\sqrt{\dfrac{(s-a)(s-b)}{ab}} = \dfrac{c}{r}\sqrt{\dfrac{(s-c)^2}{c^2}} = \dfrac{s-c}{r}$

53. $K = $ area of triangle $QOR + $ area of $ROP + $ area of $POQ = \dfrac{1}{2}ar + \dfrac{1}{2}br + \dfrac{1}{2}cr = r\dfrac{1}{2}(a+b+c) = rs$, so

$r = \dfrac{K}{s} = \dfrac{\sqrt{s(s-a)(s-b)(s-c)}}{s} = \sqrt{\dfrac{(s-a)(s-b)(s-c)}{s}}$.

8.5 Assess Your Understanding *(page 547)*

2. Simple harmonic; amplitude   **3.** Simple harmonic motion; damped   **4.** T   **5.** $d = -5\cos(\pi t)$ **7.** $d = -6\cos(2t)$ **9.** $d = -5\sin(\pi t)$

11. $d = -6\sin(2t)$ **13. (a)** Simple harmonic   **(b)** 5 m   **(c)** $\dfrac{2\pi}{3}$ sec   **(d)** $\dfrac{3}{2\pi}$ oscillation/sec   **15. (a)** Simple harmonic   **(b)** 6 m   **(c)** 2 sec

(d) $\dfrac{1}{2}$ oscillation/sec   **17. (a)** Simple harmonic   **(b)** 3 m   **(c)** 4π sec   **(d)** $\dfrac{1}{4\pi}$ oscillation/sec   **19. (a)** Simple harmonic   **(b)** 2 m

(c) 1 sec   **(d)** 1 oscillation/sec

21.   **23.**   **25.** 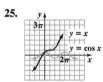   **27.** 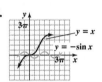   **29.**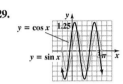

31. 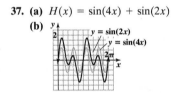   **33. (a)** $f(x) = \dfrac{1}{2}[\cos x - \cos(3x)]$ **35. (a)** $G(x) = \dfrac{1}{2}[\cos(6x) + \cos(2x)]$

(b) 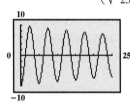   **(b)**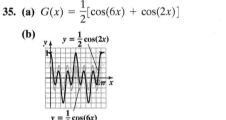

37. (a) $H(x) = \sin(4x) + \sin(2x)$ **39. (a)** $d = -10e^{-0.7t/50}\cos\left(\sqrt{\dfrac{4\pi^2}{25} - \dfrac{0.49}{2500}}\,t\right)$ **41. (a)** $d = -18e^{-0.6t/60}\cos\left(\sqrt{\dfrac{\pi^2}{4} - \dfrac{0.36}{3600}}\,t\right)$

(b)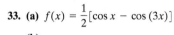

(b) 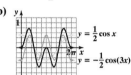   **(b)** 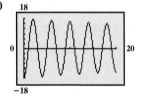   **(b)**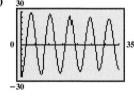

43. (a) $d = -5e^{-0.8t/20}\cos\left(\sqrt{\dfrac{4\pi^2}{9} - \dfrac{0.64}{400}}\,t\right)$ **45. (a)** The motion is damped. The bob has   **47. (a)** The motion is damped. The bob has

(b) mass $m = 20$ kg with a damping factor   mass $m = 40$ kg with a damping factor

of 0.7 kg/sec.   of 0.6 kg/sec.

(b) 20 m leftward   **(b)** 30 m leftward

(c)   **(c)**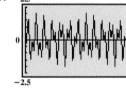

(d) 18.33 m leftward   **(e)** $d \to 0$ **(d)** 28.47 m leftward   **(e)** $d \to 0$

49. (a) The motion is damped. The bob has   **51.** $\omega = 1040\pi$; $d = 0.80\cos(1040\pi t)$ **57.**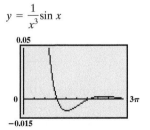

mass $m = 15$ kg with a damping factor   **53.** $\omega = 880\pi$; $d = 0.01\sin(880\pi t)$

of 0.9 kg/sec.   **55. (a)**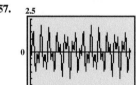

(b) 15 m leftward

(c)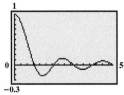

(b) At $t = 0, 2$; at $t = 1, t = 3$

(c) During the approximate intervals

$0.35 < t < 0.67$, $1.29 < t < 1.75$, and

$2.19 < t \le 3$

(d) 12.53 m leftward   **(e)** $d \to 0$

61. **63.** $y = \dfrac{1}{x}\sin x$ $y = \dfrac{1}{x^2}\sin x$ $y = \dfrac{1}{x^3}\sin x$

Review Exercises *(page 551)*

1. $\sin \theta = \dfrac{4}{5}$; $\cos \theta = \dfrac{3}{5}$; $\tan \theta = \dfrac{4}{3}$; $\cot \theta = \dfrac{3}{4}$; $\sec \theta = \dfrac{5}{3}$; $\csc \theta = \dfrac{5}{4}$ **3.** $\sin \theta = \dfrac{\sqrt{3}}{2}$; $\cos \theta = \dfrac{1}{2}$; $\tan \theta = \sqrt{3}$; $\cot \theta = \dfrac{\sqrt{3}}{3}$; $\sec \theta = 2$; $\csc \theta = \dfrac{2\sqrt{3}}{3}$

5. 0 **7.** 1 **9.** 1 **11.** $A = 70°$, $b \approx 3.42$, $a \approx 9.40$ **13.** $a \approx 4.58$, $A \approx 66.4°$, $B \approx 23.6°$ **15.** $C = 100°$, $b \approx 0.65$, $c \approx 1.29$
17. $B \approx 56.8°$, $C \approx 23.2°$, $b \approx 4.25$ **19.** No triangle **21.** $b \approx 3.32$, $A \approx 62.8°$, $C \approx 17.2°$ **23.** No triangle **25.** $c \approx 2.32$, $A \approx 16.1°$, $B \approx 123.9°$
27. $B \approx 36.2°$, $C \approx 63.8°$, $c \approx 4.55$ **29.** $A \approx 39.6°$, $B \approx 18.6°$, $C \approx 121.9°$ **31.** Two triangles: $B_1 \approx 13.4°$, $C_1 \approx 156.6°$, $c_1 \approx 6.86$ or $B_2 \approx 166.6°$,
$C_2 \approx 3.4°$, $c_2 \approx 1.02$ **33.** $a \approx 5.23$, $B \approx 46.0°$, $C \approx 64.0°$ **35.** 1.93 **37.** 18.79 **39.** 6 **41.** 3.80 **43.** 0.32 **45.** 1.92 in^2 **47.** 23.32 ft **49.** 2.15 mi

51. 132.55 ft/min **53.** 29.97 ft **55.** 6.22 mi **57.** 71.12 ft **59.** \$222,983.51 **61.** 76.94 in. **63.** $d = -3 \cos\left(\dfrac{\pi}{2}t\right)$ **65.** (a) Simple harmonic

(b) 6 ft **(c)** π sec **(d)** $\dfrac{1}{\pi}$ oscillation/sec **67. (a)** Simple harmonic **(b)** 2 ft **(c)** 2 sec **(d)** $\dfrac{1}{2}$ oscillation/sec

69. (a) $d = -15e^{-0.75t/80} \cos\left(\sqrt{\dfrac{4\pi^2}{25} - \dfrac{0.5625}{6400}}\, t\right)$

(b)
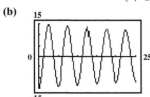

71. (a) The motion is damped. The bob has mass $m = 20$ kg with a damping factor of 0.6 kg/sec.
(b) 15 m leftward
(c)
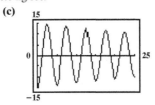
(d) 13.92 m leftward
(d) $d \to 0$

73.
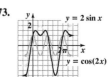

Chapter Test *(page 554)*

1. $\sin \theta = \dfrac{\sqrt{5}}{5}$; $\cos \theta = \dfrac{2\sqrt{5}}{5}$; $\tan \theta = \dfrac{1}{2}$; $\csc \theta = \sqrt{5}$; $\sec \theta = \dfrac{\sqrt{5}}{2}$; $\cot \theta = 2$ **2.** 0 **3.** $a = 15.88$, $B \approx 57.5°$, $C \approx 70.5°$
4. $b \approx 6.85$, $C = 117°$, $C \approx 16.30$ **5.** $A \approx 52.4°$, $B \approx 29.7°$, $C \approx 97.9°$ **6.** $b \approx 4.72$, $c \approx 1.67$, $B = 105°$ **7.** No triangle
8. $c \approx 7.62$, $A \approx 80.5°$, $B \approx 29.5°$ **9.** 15.04 square units **10.** 19.81 square units **11.** 61.0° **12.** 1.3° **13.** The area of the shaded region is 9.26 cm^2.
14. 54.15 square units **15.** Madison will have to swim about 2.23 miles. **16.** 12.63 square units **17.** The length of the sides are 15, 18, and 21.

18. $d = 5(\sin 42°) \sin\left(\dfrac{\pi t}{3}\right)$ or $d \approx 3.346 \sin\left(\dfrac{\pi t}{3}\right)$

Cumulative Review *(page 555)*

1. $\left\{\dfrac{1}{3}, 1\right\}$ **2.** $(x + 5)^2 + (y - 1)^2 = 9$ **3.** $\{x \mid x \le -1 \text{ or } x \ge 4\}$ **4.**
 5.

6. (a) $-\dfrac{2\sqrt{5}}{5}$ **(b)** $\dfrac{\sqrt{5}}{5}$ **(c)** $-\dfrac{4}{5}$ **(d)** $-\dfrac{3}{5}$ **(e)** $\sqrt{\dfrac{5 - \sqrt{5}}{10}}$ **(f)** $-\sqrt{\dfrac{5 + \sqrt{5}}{10}}$

7. (a)
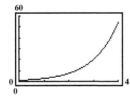 **(b)**
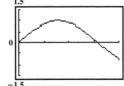 **(c)**
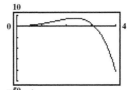 **(d)**
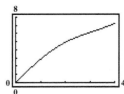

8. (a)
 (b)
 (c)
 (d)

(e)
 (f)
 (g)
 (h)
 (i)

9. Two triangles: $A_1 \approx 59.0°$, $B_1 \approx 81.0°$, $b_1 \approx 23.05$ or $A_2 \approx 121.0°$, $B_2 \approx 19.0°$, $b_2 \approx 7.59$ **10.** $\left\{-2i, 2i, \dfrac{1}{3}, 1, 2\right\}$

11. $R(x) = \dfrac{(2x + 1)(x - 4)}{(x + 5)(x - 3)}$; domain: $\{x \mid x \neq -5, x \neq 3\}$

Intercepts: $\left(-\dfrac{1}{2}, 0\right), (4, 0), \left(0, \dfrac{4}{15}\right)$

No symmetry

Vertical asymptotes: $x = -5, x = 3$

Horizontal asymptote: $y = 2$

Intersects: $\left(\dfrac{26}{11}, 2\right)$

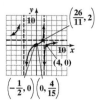

12. $\{2, 26\}$ **13.** $\{1\}$ **14. (a)** $\left\{-\dfrac{5}{4}\right\}$ **(b)** $\{2\}$ **(c)** $\left\{\dfrac{-1 - 3\sqrt{13}}{2}, \dfrac{-1 + 3\sqrt{13}}{2}\right\}$ **(d)** $\left\{x \mid x > -\dfrac{5}{4}\right\}$ or $\left(-\dfrac{5}{4}, \infty\right)$

(e) $\left\{x \mid -8 \leq x \leq 3\right\}$ or $[-8, 3]$ **(f)** **(g)**

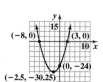

CHAPTER 9 Polar Coordinates; Vectors

9.1 Assess Your Understanding (page 565)

5. pole; polar axis **6.** True **7.** False **8.** $r\cos\theta$; $r\sin\theta$ **9.** A **11.** C **13.** B **15.** A

17. **19.** (−2, 0) O **21.** **23.** **25.** **27.**

$(3, 90°)$

$90°$

O

$\left(6, \dfrac{\pi}{6}\right)$; $\dfrac{\pi}{6}$; O

$135°$; O ; $(-2, 135°)$

O ; $\left(4, -\dfrac{2\pi}{3}\right)$; $-\dfrac{2\pi}{3}$

$\left(-1, -\dfrac{\pi}{3}\right)$; O ; $-\dfrac{\pi}{3}$

29. O $(-2, -\pi)$; $-\pi$ **31.** $\left(5, \dfrac{2\pi}{3}\right)$; $\dfrac{2\pi}{3}$; O **(a)** $\left(5, -\dfrac{4\pi}{3}\right)$ **(b)** $\left(-5, \dfrac{5\pi}{3}\right)$ **(c)** $\left(5, \dfrac{8\pi}{3}\right)$ **33.** 3π ; O $(-2, 3\pi)$ **(a)** $(2, -2\pi)$ **(b)** $(-2, \pi)$ **(c)** $(2, 2\pi)$

35. $\left(1, \dfrac{\pi}{2}\right)$; $\dfrac{\pi}{2}$; O **37.** $\left(-3, -\dfrac{\pi}{4}\right)$; O ; $-\dfrac{\pi}{4}$

(a) $\left(1, -\dfrac{3\pi}{2}\right)$

(b) $\left(-1, \dfrac{3\pi}{2}\right)$

(c) $\left(1, \dfrac{5\pi}{2}\right)$

(a) $\left(3, -\dfrac{5\pi}{4}\right)$

(b) $\left(-3, \dfrac{7\pi}{4}\right)$

(c) $\left(3, \dfrac{11\pi}{4}\right)$

39. $(0, 3)$ **41.** $(-2, 0)$ **43.** $(-3\sqrt{3}, 3)$ **45.** $(\sqrt{2}, -\sqrt{2})$ **47.** $\left(-\dfrac{1}{2}, \dfrac{\sqrt{3}}{2}\right)$ **49.** $(2, 0)$

51. $(-2.57, 7.05)$ **53.** $(-4.98, -3.85)$ **55.** $(3, 0)$ **57.** $(1, \pi)$ **59.** $\left(\sqrt{2}, -\dfrac{\pi}{4}\right)$ **61.** $\left(2, \dfrac{\pi}{6}\right)$

63. $(2.47, -1.02)$ **65.** $(9.30, 0.47)$ **67.** $r^2 = \dfrac{3}{2}$ or $r = \dfrac{\sqrt{6}}{2}$ **69.** $r^2\cos^2\theta - 4r\sin\theta = 0$

71. $r^2\sin 2\theta = 1$ **73.** $r\cos\theta = 4$ **75.** $x^2 + y^2 - x = 0$ or $\left(x - \dfrac{1}{2}\right)^2 + y^2 = \dfrac{1}{4}$

77. $(x^2 + y^2)^{3/2} - x = 0$ **79.** $x^2 + y^2 = 4$ **81.** $y^2 = 8(x + 2)$

83. (a) $(-10, 36)$ **(b)** $\left(2\sqrt{349}, 180° + \tan^{-1}\left(-\dfrac{18}{5}\right)\right) \approx (37.36, 105.5°)$ **(c)** $(-3, -35)$ **(d)** $\left(\sqrt{1234}, 180° + \tan^{-1}\left(\dfrac{35}{3}\right)\right) \approx (35.13, 265.1°)$

9.2 Assess Your Understanding (page 579)

7. polar equation **8.** False **9.** $-\theta$ **10.** $\pi - \theta$ **11.** True **12.** $2n$; n

13. $x^2 + y^2 = 16$; circle, radius 4, center at pole

15. $y = \sqrt{3}x$; line through pole, making an angle of $\dfrac{\pi}{3}$ with polar axis

17. $y = 4$; horizontal line 4 units above the pole

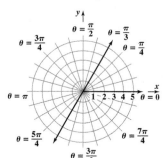
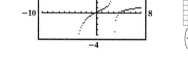
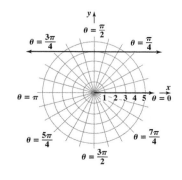

19. $x = -2$; vertical line 2 units to the left of the pole

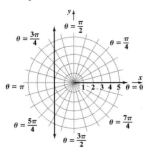

21. $(x - 1)^2 + y^2 = 1$; circle, radius 1, center $(1, 0)$ in rectangular coordinates

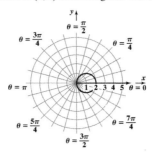

23. $x^2 + (y + 2)^2 = 4$; circle, radius 2, center at $(0, -2)$ in rectangular coordinates

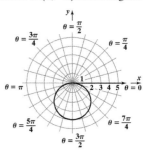

25. $(x - 2)^2 + y^2 = 4$, $x \neq 0$; circle, radius 2, center at $(2, 0)$ in rectangular coordinates, hole at $(0, 0)$

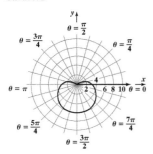

27. $x^2 + (y + 1)^2 = 1$, $x \neq 0$; circle, radius 1, center at $(0, -1)$ in rectangular coordinates, hole at $(0, 0)$

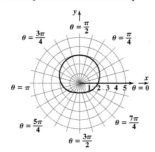

29. E **31.** F **33.** H **35.** D
37. Cardioid

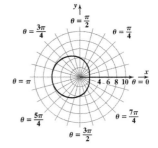

39. Cardioid

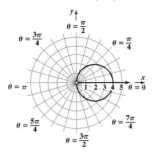

41. Limaçon without inner loop

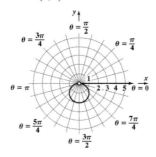

43. Limaçon without inner loop

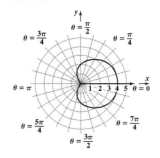

45. Limaçon with inner loop

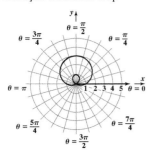

47. Limaçon with inner loop

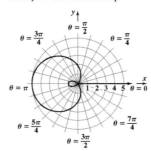

49. Rose

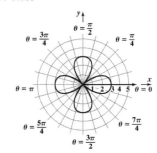

51. Rose

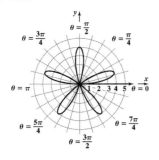

53. Lemniscate

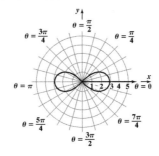

55. Spiral

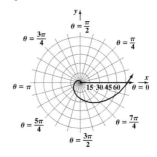

57. Cardioid

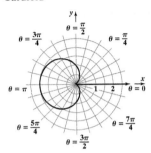

59. Limaçon with inner loop

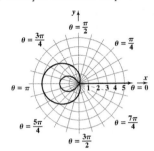

61.

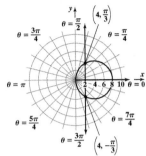

63.

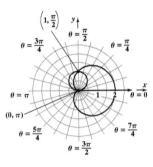

65.

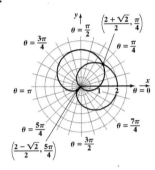

67. $r = 3 + 3\cos\theta$ **69.** $r = 4 + \sin\theta$

71.

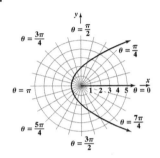

73.

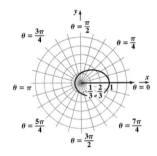

75.

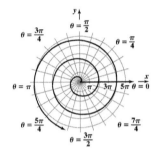

77.

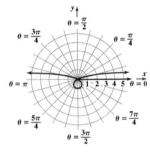

79.

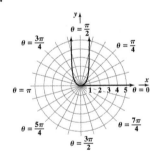

81. $r\sin\theta = a$
$y = a$

83.
$$r = 2a\sin\theta$$
$$r^2 = 2ar\sin\theta$$
$$x^2 + y^2 = 2ay$$
$$x^2 + y^2 - 2ay = 0$$
$$x^2 + (y - a)^2 = a^2$$
Circle, radius a, center at $(0, a)$
in rectangular coordinates

85.
$$r = 2a\cos\theta$$
$$r^2 = 2ar\cos\theta$$
$$x^2 + y^2 = 2ax$$
$$x^2 - 2ax + y^2 = 0$$
$$(x - a)^2 + y^2 = a^2$$
Circle, radius a, center at $(a, 0)$
in rectangular coordinates

87. (a) $r^2 = \cos\theta; r^2 = \cos(\pi - \theta)$
$r^2 = -\cos\theta$
Not equivalent; test fails.
$(-r)^2 = \cos(-\theta)$
$r^2 = \cos\theta$
New test works.

(b) $r^2 = \sin\theta; r^2 = \sin(\pi - \theta)$
$r^2 = \sin\theta$
Test works.
$(-r)^2 = \sin(-\theta)$
$r^2 = -\sin\theta$
Not equivalent; new test fails.

Historical Problems *(page 587)*
1. (a) $1 + 4i, 1 + i$ **(b)** $-1, 2 + i$

9.3 Assess Your Understanding *(page 588)*

5. real; imaginary   **6.** magnitude; modulus; argument   **7.** $r_1 r_2$; $\theta_1 + \theta_2$; $\theta_1 + \theta_2$ **8.** r^n; $n\theta$; $n\theta$ **9.** three   **10.** True

11.

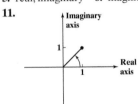

$\sqrt{2}(\cos 45° + i\sin 45°)$

13.

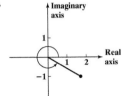

$2(\cos 330° + i\sin 330°)$

15.

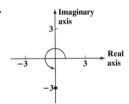

$3(\cos 270° + i\sin 270°)$

17.

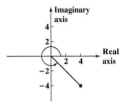

$4\sqrt{2}(\cos 315° + i \sin 315°)$

19.

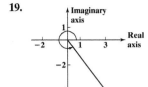

$5(\cos 306.9° + i \sin 306.9°)$

21.

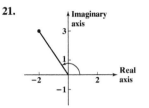

$\sqrt{13}(\cos 123.7° + i \sin 123.7°)$

23. $-1 + \sqrt{3}i$ **25.** $2\sqrt{2} - 2\sqrt{2}i$ **27.** $-3i$ **29.** $-0.035 + 0.197i$ **31.** $1.970 + 0.347i$

33. $zw = 8(\cos 60° + i \sin 60°); \dfrac{z}{w} = \dfrac{1}{2}(\cos 20° + i \sin 20°)$ **35.** $zw = 12(\cos 40° + i \sin 40°); \dfrac{z}{w} = \dfrac{3}{4}(\cos 220° + i \sin 220°)$

37. $zw = 4\left(\cos \dfrac{9\pi}{40} + i \sin \dfrac{9\pi}{40}\right); \dfrac{z}{w} = \cos \dfrac{\pi}{40} + i \sin \dfrac{\pi}{40}$ **39.** $zw = 4\sqrt{2}(\cos 15° + i \sin 15°); \dfrac{z}{w} = \sqrt{2}(\cos 75° + i \sin 75°)$

41. $-32 + 32\sqrt{3}i$ **43.** $32i$ **45.** $\dfrac{27}{2} + \dfrac{27\sqrt{3}}{2}i$ **47.** $-\dfrac{25\sqrt{2}}{2} + \dfrac{25\sqrt{2}}{2}i$ **49.** $-4 + 4i$ **51.** $-23 + 14.142i$

53. $\sqrt[6]{2}(\cos 15° + i \sin 15°), \sqrt[6]{2}(\cos 135° + i \sin 135°), \sqrt[6]{2}(\cos 255° + i \sin 255°)$

55. $\sqrt[4]{8}(\cos 75° + i \sin 75°), \sqrt[4]{8}(\cos 165° + i \sin 165°), \sqrt[4]{8}(\cos 255° + i \sin 255°), \sqrt[4]{8}(\cos 345° + i \sin 345°)$

57. $2(\cos 67.5° + i \sin 67.5°), 2(\cos 157.5° + i \sin 157.5°), 2(\cos 247.5° + i \sin 247.5°), 2(\cos 337.5° + i \sin 337.5°)$

59. $\cos 18° + i \sin 18°, \cos 90° + i \sin 90°, \cos 162° + i \sin 162°, \cos 234° + i \sin 234°, \cos 306° + i \sin 306°$

61. $1, i, -1, -i$

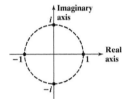

63. Look at formula (8); $|z_k| = \sqrt[n]{r}$ for all k.

65. Look at formula (8). The z_k are spaced apart by an angle of $\dfrac{2\pi}{n}$.

67. (a)

$z = a_0$	a_1	a_2	a_3	a_4	a_5	a_6
$0.1 - 0.4i$	$-0.05 - 0.48i$	$-0.13 - 0.35i$	$-0.01 - 0.31i$	$0.004 - 0.395i$	$-0.06 - 0.0i$	$-0.06 - 0.35i$
$0.5 + 0.8i$	$0.11 + 1.6i$	$-2.05 + 1.15i$	$3.37 - 3.92i$	$-3.52 - 25.6i$	$-641.7 + 180.0i$	$379073 - 232071i$
$-0.9 + 0.7i$	$-0.58 - 0.56i$	$-0.88 + 1.35i$	$-1.95 - 1.67i$	$0.13 + 7.21i$	$-52.88 + 2.56i$	$2788.5 - 269.6i$
$-1.1 + 0.1i$	$0.1 - 0.12i$	$-1.10 + 0.76i$	$0.11 - 0.068i$	$-1.09 + 0.085i$	$0.085 - 0.85i$	$-1.10 + 0.086i$
$0 - 1.3i$	$-1.69 - 1.3i$	$1.17 + 3.09i$	$-8.21 + 5.92i$	$32.46 - 98.47i$	$-8643.6 - 6393.7i$	$33833744 + 110529134.4i$
$1 + 1i$	$1 + 3i$	$-7 + 7i$	$1 - 97i$	$-9407 - 193i$	$88454401 + 3631103i$	$7.8 \times 10^{15} + 6.4 \times 10^{14}i$

(b) z_1 and z_4 are in the Mandlebrot set. a_6 for the complex numbers not in the set have very large components.

(c)

z	$|z|$	$|a_6|$
$0.1 - 0.4i$	0.4	0.4
$0.5 + 0.8i$	0.9	444470
$-0.9 + 0.7i$	1.1	2802
$-1.1 + 0.1i$	1.1	1.1
$0 - 1.3i$	1.3	115591573
$1 + 1i$	1.4	7.8×10^{15}

The numbers that are in the Mandlebrot set satisfy the condition $|a_n| \le 2$.

9.4 Assess Your Understanding *(page 600)*

1. vector **2.** 0 **3.** unit **4.** position **5.** horizontal; vertical **6.** resultant **7.** True **8.** False

9.

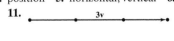

11.

$3v$

13.

15.

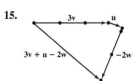

17. T   **19.** F   **21.** F   **23.** T   **25.** 12   **27.** $\mathbf{v} = 3\mathbf{i} + 4\mathbf{j}$ **29.** $\mathbf{v} = 2\mathbf{i} + 4\mathbf{j}$ **31.** $\mathbf{v} = 8\mathbf{i} - \mathbf{j}$ **33.** $\mathbf{v} = -\mathbf{i} + \mathbf{j}$ **35.** 5   **37.** $\sqrt{2}$ **39.** $\sqrt{13}$ **41.** $-\mathbf{j}$

43. $\sqrt{89}$ **45.** $\sqrt{34} - \sqrt{13}$ **47.** $\mathbf{i}$ **49.** $\dfrac{3}{5}\mathbf{i} - \dfrac{4}{5}\mathbf{j}$ **51.** $\dfrac{\sqrt{2}}{2}\mathbf{i} - \dfrac{\sqrt{2}}{2}\mathbf{j}$ **53.** $\mathbf{v} = \dfrac{8\sqrt{5}}{5}\mathbf{i} + \dfrac{4\sqrt{5}}{5}\mathbf{j}$ or $\mathbf{v} = -\dfrac{8\sqrt{5}}{5}\mathbf{i} - \dfrac{4\sqrt{5}}{5}\mathbf{j}$

55. $\{-2 + \sqrt{21}, -2 - \sqrt{21}\}$ **57.** $\mathbf{v} = \dfrac{5}{2}\mathbf{i} + \dfrac{5\sqrt{3}}{2}\mathbf{j}$ **59.** $\mathbf{v} = -7\mathbf{i} + 7\sqrt{3}\mathbf{j}$ **61.** $\mathbf{v} = \dfrac{25\sqrt{3}}{2}\mathbf{i} - \dfrac{25}{2}\mathbf{j}$ **63.** 45°   **65.** 150°   **67.** 333.4°   **69.** 258.7°

71. (a) $(-1, 4)$

(b)
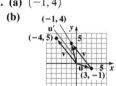

73. $\mathbf{F} = 20\sqrt{3}\mathbf{i} + 20\mathbf{j}$ **75.** $\mathbf{F} = (20\sqrt{3} + 30\sqrt{2})\mathbf{i} + (20 - 30\sqrt{2})\mathbf{j}$

91.

77. (a) $\mathbf{v}_a = 550\mathbf{j}$; $\mathbf{v}_w = 50\sqrt{2}\mathbf{i} + 50\sqrt{2}\mathbf{j}$ **(b)** $\mathbf{v}_g = 50\sqrt{2}\mathbf{i} + (550 + 50\sqrt{2})\mathbf{j}$
(c) $\|\mathbf{v}_g\| = 624.7$ mph; N6.5°E
79. $\mathbf{v} = (250\sqrt{2} - 30)\mathbf{i} + (250\sqrt{2} + 30\sqrt{3})\mathbf{j}$; 518.8 km/h; N38.6°E
81. Approximately 4031 lb   **83.** 8.6° left of direct heading across the river; 1.52 min
85. Tension in right cable: 1000 lb; tension in left cable: 845.2 lb   **87.** Tension in right part:
1088.4 lb; tension in left part: 1089.1 lb   **89.** The truck must pull with a force of 4635.2 lb.

Historical Problem *(page 608)*

$(a\mathbf{i} + b\mathbf{j}) \cdot (c\mathbf{i} + d\mathbf{j}) = ac + bd$
Real part $[(\overline{a + bi})(c + di)] = $ real part$[(a - bi)(c + di)] = $ real part$[ac + adi - bci - bdi^2] = ac + bd$

9.5 Assess Your Understanding *(page 609)*

2. dot product   **3.** orthogonal   **4.** parallel   **5.** T   **6.** F   **7. (a)** 0   **(b)** 90°   **(c)** orthogonal   **9. (a)** 0   **(b)** 90°   **(c)** orthogonal
11. (a) $\sqrt{3} - 1$ **(b)** 75°   **(c)** neither   **13. (a)** -50 **(b)** 180°   **(c)** parallel   **15. (a)** 0   **(b)** 90°   **(c)** orthogonal
17. $\dfrac{2}{3}$ **19.** $\mathbf{v}_1 = \dfrac{5}{2}\mathbf{i} - \dfrac{5}{2}\mathbf{j}$, $\mathbf{v}_2 = -\dfrac{1}{2}\mathbf{i} - \dfrac{1}{2}\mathbf{j}$ **21.** $\mathbf{v}_1 = -\dfrac{1}{5}\mathbf{i} - \dfrac{2}{5}\mathbf{j}$, $\mathbf{v}_2 = \dfrac{6}{5}\mathbf{i} - \dfrac{3}{5}\mathbf{j}$ **23.** $\mathbf{v}_1 = \dfrac{14}{5}\mathbf{i} + \dfrac{7}{5}\mathbf{j}$, $\mathbf{v}_2 = \dfrac{1}{5}\mathbf{i} - \dfrac{2}{5}\mathbf{j}$ **25.** 9 ft-lb
27. (a) $\|\mathbf{I}\| \approx 0.022$; the intensity of the sun's rays is approximately 0.022 W/cm^2. $\|\mathbf{A}\| = 500$; the area of the solar panel is 500 cm^2.
(b) $W = 10$; ten watts of energy is collected.   **(c)** Vectors $\mathbf{I}$ and $\mathbf{A}$ should be parallel with the solar panels facing the sun.
29. Force required to keep Sienna from rolling down the hill: 737.6 lb; force perpendicular to the hill: 5248.4 lb
31. Timmy must exert 85.5 lb.   **33.** 60°   **35.** Let $\mathbf{v} = a\mathbf{i} + b\mathbf{j}$. Then $\mathbf{0} \cdot \mathbf{v} = 0a + 0b = 0$.
37. $\mathbf{v} = \cos \alpha\mathbf{i} + \sin \alpha\mathbf{j}, 0 \le \alpha \le \pi$; $\mathbf{w} = \cos \beta\mathbf{i} + \sin \beta\mathbf{j}, 0 \le \beta \le \pi$. If θ is the angle between $\mathbf{v}$ and $\mathbf{w}$, then $\mathbf{v} \cdot \mathbf{w} = \cos\theta$, since $\|\mathbf{v}\| = 1$ and $\|\mathbf{w}\| = 1$.
Now $\theta = \alpha - \beta$ or $\theta = \beta - \alpha$. Since the cosine function is even, $\mathbf{v} \cdot \mathbf{w} = \cos(\alpha - \beta)$. Also, $\mathbf{v} \cdot \mathbf{w} = \cos \alpha \cos \beta + \sin \alpha \sin \beta$. So $\cos(\alpha - \beta)$
  $= \cos \alpha \cos \beta + \sin \alpha \sin \beta$.
39. (a) If $\mathbf{u} = a_1\mathbf{i} + b_1\mathbf{j}$ and $\mathbf{v} = a_2\mathbf{i} + b_2\mathbf{j}$, then, since $\|\mathbf{u}\| = \|\mathbf{v}\|, a_1^2 + b_1^2 = \|\mathbf{u}\|^2 = \|\mathbf{v}\|^2 = a_2^2 + b_2^2$,
  $(\mathbf{u} + \mathbf{v}) \cdot (\mathbf{u} - \mathbf{v}) = (a_1 + a_2)(a_1 - a_2) + (b_1 + b_2)(b_1 - b_2) = (a_1^2 + b_1^2) - (a_2^2 + b_2^2) = 0$.
  (b) The legs of the angle can be made to correspond to vectors $\mathbf{u} + \mathbf{v}$ and $\mathbf{u} - \mathbf{v}$.
41. $(\|\mathbf{w}\|\mathbf{v} + \|\mathbf{v}\|\mathbf{w}) \cdot (\|\mathbf{w}\|\mathbf{v} - \|\mathbf{v}\|\mathbf{w}) = \|\mathbf{w}\|^2\mathbf{v} \cdot \mathbf{v} - \|\mathbf{w}\|\|\mathbf{v}\|\mathbf{v} \cdot \mathbf{w} + \|\mathbf{v}\|\|\mathbf{w}\|\mathbf{w} \cdot \mathbf{v} - \|\mathbf{v}\|^2\mathbf{w} \cdot \mathbf{w} = \|\mathbf{w}\|^2\mathbf{v} \cdot \mathbf{v} - \|\mathbf{v}\|^2\mathbf{w} \cdot \mathbf{w} = \|\mathbf{w}\|^2\|\mathbf{v}\|^2 - \|\mathbf{v}\|^2\|\mathbf{w}\|^2 = 0$
43. $\|\mathbf{u} + \mathbf{v}\|^2 - \|\mathbf{u} - \mathbf{v}\|^2 = (\mathbf{u} + \mathbf{v}) \cdot (\mathbf{u} + \mathbf{v}) - (\mathbf{u} - \mathbf{v}) \cdot (\mathbf{u} - \mathbf{v}) = (\mathbf{u} \cdot \mathbf{u} + \mathbf{u} \cdot \mathbf{v} + \mathbf{v} \cdot \mathbf{u} + \mathbf{v} \cdot \mathbf{v}) - (\mathbf{u} \cdot \mathbf{u} - \mathbf{u} \cdot \mathbf{v} - \mathbf{v} \cdot \mathbf{u} + \mathbf{v} \cdot \mathbf{v})$
  $= 2(\mathbf{u} \cdot \mathbf{v}) + 2(\mathbf{v} \cdot \mathbf{u}) = 4(\mathbf{u} \cdot \mathbf{v})$

9.6 Assess Your Understanding *(page 618)*

2. xy-plane   **3.** components   **4.** 1   **5.** F   **6.** T   **7.** All points of the form $(x, 0, z)$ **9.** All points of the form $(x, y, 2)$
11. All points of the form $(-4, y, z)$ **13.** All points of the form $(1, 2, z)$ **15.** $\sqrt{21}$ **17.** $\sqrt{33}$ **19.** $\sqrt{26}$
21. $(2, 0, 0); (2, 1, 0); (0, 1, 0); (2, 0, 3); (0, 1, 3); (0, 0, 3)$ **23.** $(1, 4, 3); (3, 2, 3); (3, 4, 3); (3, 2, 5); (1, 4, 5); (1, 2, 5)$
25. $(-1, 2, 2); (4, 0, 2); (4, 2, 2); (-1, 2, 5); (4, 0, 5); (-1, 0, 5)$ **27.** $\mathbf{v} = 3\mathbf{i} + 4\mathbf{j} - \mathbf{k}$ **29.** $\mathbf{v} = 2\mathbf{i} + 4\mathbf{j} + \mathbf{k}$ **31.** $\mathbf{v} = 8\mathbf{i} - \mathbf{j}$ **33.** 7   **35.** $\sqrt{3}$
37. $\sqrt{22}$ **39.** $-\mathbf{j} - 2\mathbf{k}$ **41.** $\sqrt{105}$ **43.** $\sqrt{38} - \sqrt{17}$ **45.** $\mathbf{i}$ **47.** $\dfrac{3}{7}\mathbf{i} - \dfrac{6}{7}\mathbf{j} - \dfrac{2}{7}\mathbf{k}$ **49.** $\dfrac{\sqrt{3}}{3}\mathbf{i} + \dfrac{\sqrt{3}}{3}\mathbf{j} + \dfrac{\sqrt{3}}{3}\mathbf{k}$ **51.** $\mathbf{v} \cdot \mathbf{w} = 0; \theta = 90°$
53. $\mathbf{v} \cdot \mathbf{w} = -2, \theta \approx 100.3°$ **55.** $\mathbf{v} \cdot \mathbf{w} = 0; \theta = 90°$ **57.** $\mathbf{v} \cdot \mathbf{w} = 52; \theta = 0°$
59. $\alpha \approx 64.6°; \beta \approx 149.0°; \gamma \approx 106.6°; \mathbf{v} = 7(\cos 64.6°\mathbf{i} + \cos 149.0°\mathbf{j} + \cos 106.6°\mathbf{k})$
61. $\alpha = \beta = \gamma \approx 54.7°; \mathbf{v} = \sqrt{3}(\cos 54.7°\mathbf{i} + \cos 54.7°\mathbf{j} + \cos 54.7°\mathbf{k})$ **63.** $\alpha = \beta = 45°; \gamma = 90°; \mathbf{v} = \sqrt{2}(\cos 45°\mathbf{i} + \cos 45°\mathbf{j} + \cos 90°\mathbf{k})$
65. $\alpha \approx 60.9°; \beta \approx 144.2°; \gamma \approx 71.1°; \mathbf{v} = \sqrt{38}(\cos 60.9°\mathbf{i} + \cos 144.2°\mathbf{j} + \cos 71.1°\mathbf{k})$ **67. (a)** $\mathbf{d} = \mathbf{a} + \mathbf{b} + \mathbf{c} = \ <7, 1, 5>$ **(b)** 8.66 ft
69. $(x - 3)^2 + (y - 1)^2 + (z - 1)^2 = 1$ **71.** Radius = 2, center $(-1, 1, 0)$ **73.** Radius = 3, center $(2, -2, -1)$
75. Radius = $\dfrac{3\sqrt{2}}{2}$, center $(2, 0, -1)$ **77.** 2 newton-meters = 2 joules   **79.** 9 newton-meters = 9 joules

9.7 Assess Your Understanding *(page 624)*

1. T   **2.** T   **3.** T   **5.** F   **4.** F   **6.** T   **7.** 2   **9.** 4   **11.** $-11A + 2B + 5C$ **13.** $-6A + 23B - 15C$ **15. (a)** $5\mathbf{i} + 5\mathbf{j} + 5\mathbf{k}$ **(b)** $-5\mathbf{i} - 5\mathbf{j} - 5\mathbf{k}$
(c) 0   **(d)** 0   **17. (a)** $\mathbf{i} - \mathbf{j} - \mathbf{k}$ **(b)** $-\mathbf{i} + \mathbf{j} + \mathbf{k}$ **(c)** 0   **(d)** 0   **19. (a)** $-\mathbf{i} + 2\mathbf{j} + 2\mathbf{k}$ **(b)** $\mathbf{i} - 2\mathbf{j} - 2\mathbf{k}$ **(c)** 0   **(d)** 0   **21. (a)** $3\mathbf{i} - \mathbf{j} + 4\mathbf{k}$
(b) $-3\mathbf{i} + \mathbf{j} - 4\mathbf{k}$ **(c)** 0   **(d)** 0   **23.** $-9\mathbf{i} - 7\mathbf{j} - 3\mathbf{k}$ **25.** $9\mathbf{i} + 7\mathbf{j} + 3\mathbf{k}$ **27.** 0   **29.** $-27\mathbf{i} - 21\mathbf{j} - 9\mathbf{k}$ **31.** $-18\mathbf{i} - 14\mathbf{j} - 6\mathbf{k}$ **33.** 0   **35.** -25
37. 25   **39.** 0   **41.** Any vector of the form $c(-9\mathbf{i} - 7\mathbf{j} - 3\mathbf{k})$, where c is a nonzero scalar   **43.** Any vector of the form $c(-\mathbf{i} + \mathbf{j} + 5\mathbf{k})$, where c is a
nonzero scalar   **45.** $\sqrt{166}$ **47.** $\sqrt{555}$ **49.** $\sqrt{34}$ **51.** $\sqrt{998}$ **53.** $\dfrac{11\sqrt{19}}{57}\mathbf{i} + \dfrac{\sqrt{19}}{57}\mathbf{j} + \dfrac{7\sqrt{19}}{57}\mathbf{k}$ or $-\dfrac{11\sqrt{19}}{57}\mathbf{i} - \dfrac{\sqrt{19}}{57}\mathbf{j} - \dfrac{7\sqrt{19}}{57}\mathbf{k}$

57. $\mathbf{u} \times \mathbf{v} = \begin{vmatrix} \mathbf{i} & \mathbf{j} & \mathbf{k} \\ a_1 & b_1 & c_1 \\ a_2 & b_2 & c_2 \end{vmatrix} = (b_1c_2 - b_2c_1)\mathbf{i} - (a_1c_2 - a_2c_1)\mathbf{j} + (a_1b_2 - a_2b_1)\mathbf{k}$

$\|\mathbf{u} \times \mathbf{v}\|^2 = \left(\sqrt{(b_1c_2 - b_2c_1)^2 + (a_1c_2 - a_2c_1)^2 + (a_1b_2 - a_2b_1)^2}\right)^2$

$= b_1^2c_2^2 - 2b_1b_2c_1c_2 + b_2^2c_1^2 + a_1^2c_2^2 - 2a_1a_2c_1c_2 + a_2^2c_1^2 + a_1^2b_2^2 - 2a_1a_2b_1b_2 + a_2^2b_1^2$

$\|\mathbf{u}\|^2 = a_1^2 + b_1^2 + c_1^2, \|\mathbf{v}\|^2 = a_2^2 + b_2^2 + c_2^2$

$\|\mathbf{u}\|^2\|\mathbf{v}\|^2 = (a_1^2 + b_1^2 + c_1^2)(a_2^2 + b_2^2 + c_2^2) = a_1^2a_2^2 + a_1^2b_2^2 + a_1^2c_2^2 + b_1^2a_2^2 + b_1^2b_2^2 + b_1^2c_2^2 + a_2^2c_1^2 + b_2^2c_1^2 + c_1^2c_2^2$

$(\mathbf{u} \cdot \mathbf{v})^2 = (a_1a_2 + b_1b_2 + c_1c_2)^2 = (a_1a_2 + b_1b_2 + c_1c_2)(a_1a_2 + b_1b_2 + c_1c_2)$

$= a_1^2a_2^2 + a_1a_2b_1b_2 + a_1a_2c_1c_2 + b_1b_2c_1c_2 + b_1b_2a_1a_2 + b_1^2b_2^2 + b_1b_2c_1c_2 + a_1a_2c_1c_2 + c_1^2c_2^2$

$= a_1^2a_2^2 + b_1^2b_2^2 + c_1^2c_2^2 + 2a_1a_2b_1b_2 + 2b_1b_2c_1c_2 + 2a_1a_2c_1c_2$

$\|\mathbf{u}\|^2\|\mathbf{v}\|^2 - (\mathbf{u} \cdot \mathbf{v})^2 = a_1^2b_2^2 + a_1^2c_2^2 + b_1^2a_2^2 + a_2^2c_1^2 + b_2^2c_1^2 + b_1^2c_2^2 - 2a_1a_2b_1b_2 - 2b_1b_2c_1c_2 - 2a_1a_2c_1c_2$, which equals $\|\mathbf{u} \times \mathbf{v}\|^2$.

59. By Problem 58, since $\mathbf{u}$ and $\mathbf{v}$ are orthogonal, $\|\mathbf{u} \times \mathbf{v}\| = \|\mathbf{u}\|\|\mathbf{v}\|$. If, in addition, $\mathbf{u}$ and $\mathbf{v}$ are unit vectors, $\|\mathbf{u} \times \mathbf{v}\| = 1 \cdot 1 = 1$.

61. Assume that $\mathbf{u} = a\mathbf{i} + b\mathbf{j} + c\mathbf{k}, \mathbf{v} = d\mathbf{i} + e\mathbf{j} + f\mathbf{k}$, and $\mathbf{w} = l\mathbf{i} + m\mathbf{j} + n\mathbf{k}$. Then $\mathbf{u} \times \mathbf{v} = (bf - ec)\mathbf{i} - (af - dc)\mathbf{j} + (ae - db)\mathbf{k}$,

$\mathbf{u} \times \mathbf{w} = (bn - mc)\mathbf{i} - (an - lc)\mathbf{j} + (am - lb)\mathbf{k}$, and $\mathbf{v} + \mathbf{w} = (d + l)\mathbf{i} + (e + m)\mathbf{j} + (f + n)\mathbf{k}$. Therefore,

$(\mathbf{u} \times \mathbf{v}) + (\mathbf{u} \times \mathbf{w}) = (bf - ec + bn - mc)\mathbf{i} - (af - dc + an - lc)\mathbf{j} + (ae - db + am - lb)\mathbf{k}$ and $\mathbf{u} \times (\mathbf{v} + \mathbf{w})$

$= [b(f + n) - (e + m)c]\mathbf{i} - [a(f + n) - (d + l)c]\mathbf{j} + [a(e + m) - (d + l)b]\mathbf{k}$

$= (bf - ec + bn - mc)\mathbf{i} - (af - dc + an - lc)\mathbf{j} + (ae - db + am - lb)\mathbf{k}$, which equals $(\mathbf{u} \times \mathbf{v}) + (\mathbf{u} \times \mathbf{w})$.

Review Exercises *(page 626)*

1. $\left(\dfrac{3\sqrt{3}}{2}, \dfrac{3}{2}\right)$

3. $(1, \sqrt{3})$

5. $(0, 3)$

7. $\left(3\sqrt{2}, \dfrac{3\pi}{4}\right), \left(-3\sqrt{2}, -\dfrac{\pi}{4}\right)$

9. $\left(2, -\dfrac{\pi}{2}\right), \left(-2, \dfrac{\pi}{2}\right)$

11. $(5, 0.93), (-5, 4.07)$

13. (a) $x^2 + (y - 1)^2 = 1$ **(b)** circle, radius 1, center $(0, 1)$ in rectangular coordinates

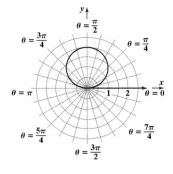

15. (a) $x^2 + y^2 = 25$ **(b)** circle, radius 5, center at pole

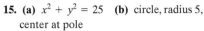
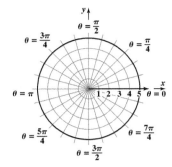

17. (a) $x + 3y = 6$ **(b)** line through $(6, 0)$ and $(0, 2)$ in rectangular coordinates

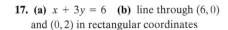
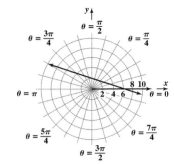

19. Circle; radius 2, center at $(2, 0)$ in rectangular coordinates; symmetric with respect to the polar axis

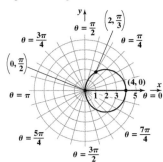

21. Cardioid; symmetric with respect to the line $\theta = \dfrac{\pi}{2}$

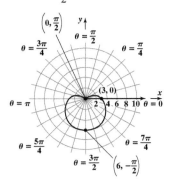

23. Limaçon without inner loop; symmetric with respect to the polar axis

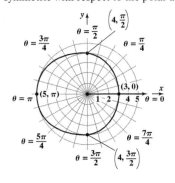

25. $\sqrt{2}(\cos 225° + i \sin 225°)$ **27.** $5(\cos 323.1° + i \sin 323.1°)$

29. $-\sqrt{3} + i$

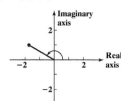

31. $-\dfrac{3}{2} + \dfrac{3\sqrt{3}}{2}i$

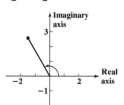

33. $0.10 - 0.02i$

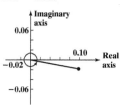

35. $zw = \cos 130° + i \sin 130°;\ \dfrac{z}{w} = \cos 30° + i \sin 30°$ **37.** $zw = 6(\cos 0 + i \sin 0) = 6;\ \dfrac{z}{w} = \dfrac{3}{2}\left(\cos \dfrac{8\pi}{5} + i \sin \dfrac{8\pi}{5}\right)$

39. $zw = 5(\cos 5° + i \sin 5°);\ \dfrac{z}{w} = 5(\cos 15° + i \sin 15°)$ **41.** $\dfrac{27}{2} + \dfrac{27\sqrt{3}}{2}i$ **43.** $4i$ **45.** 64 **47.** $-527 - 336i$

49. $3, 3(\cos 120° + i \sin 120°), 3(\cos 240° + i \sin 240°)$ or $3, -\dfrac{3}{2} + \dfrac{3\sqrt{3}}{2}i, -\dfrac{3}{2} - \dfrac{3\sqrt{3}}{2}i$

51.
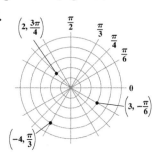
53.
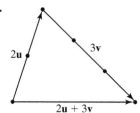

55. $\mathbf{v} = 2\mathbf{i} - 4\mathbf{j};\ \|\mathbf{v}\| = 2\sqrt{5}$ **57.** $\mathbf{v} = -\mathbf{i} + 3\mathbf{j};\ \|\mathbf{v}\| = \sqrt{10}$ **59.** $2\mathbf{i} - 2\mathbf{j}$ **61.** $-20\mathbf{i} + 13\mathbf{j}$

63. $\sqrt{5}$ **65.** $\sqrt{5} + 5 \approx 7.24$ **67.** $-\dfrac{2\sqrt{5}}{5}\mathbf{i} + \dfrac{\sqrt{5}}{5}\mathbf{j}$ **69.** $\mathbf{v} = \dfrac{3}{2}\mathbf{i} + \dfrac{3\sqrt{3}}{2}\mathbf{j}$ **71.** $120°$

73. $\sqrt{43} \approx 6.56$ **75.** $\mathbf{v} = 3\mathbf{i} - 5\mathbf{j} + 3\mathbf{k}$ **77.** $21\mathbf{i} - 2\mathbf{j} - 5\mathbf{k}$ **79.** $\sqrt{38}$

81. 0 **83.** $3\mathbf{i} + 9\mathbf{j} + 9\mathbf{k}$ **85.** $\dfrac{3\sqrt{14}}{14}\mathbf{i} + \dfrac{\sqrt{14}}{14}\mathbf{j} - \dfrac{\sqrt{14}}{7}\mathbf{k};\ -\dfrac{3\sqrt{14}}{14}\mathbf{i} - \dfrac{\sqrt{14}}{14}\mathbf{j} + \dfrac{\sqrt{14}}{7}\mathbf{k}$

87. $\mathbf{v} \cdot \mathbf{w} = -11;\ \theta \approx 169.7°$ **89.** $\mathbf{v} \cdot \mathbf{w} = -4;\ \theta \approx 153.4°$ **91.** $\mathbf{v} \cdot \mathbf{w} = 1;\ \theta \approx 70.5°$

93. $\mathbf{v} \cdot \mathbf{w} = 0;\ \theta = 90°$ **95.** Parallel **97.** Parallel **99.** Orthogonal **101.** $\mathbf{v}_1 = \dfrac{4}{5}\mathbf{i} - \dfrac{3}{5}\mathbf{j};\ \mathbf{v}_2 = \dfrac{6}{5}\mathbf{i} + \dfrac{8}{5}\mathbf{j}$ **103.** $\mathbf{v}_1 = \dfrac{9}{10}(3\mathbf{i} + \mathbf{j});\ \mathbf{v}_2 = -\dfrac{7}{10}\mathbf{i} + \dfrac{21}{10}\mathbf{j}$

105. $a \approx 56.1°;\ \beta \approx 138°;\ \gamma \approx 68.2°$ **107.** $2\sqrt{83}$ **109.** $-2\mathbf{i} + 3\mathbf{j} - \mathbf{k}$ **111.** $\sqrt{29} \approx 5.39$ mi/hr; 0.4 mi

113. Left cable: 1843.21 lb; right cable: 1630.41 lb **115.** A force of 697.2 lb is needed to keep the van from rolling down the hill. The magnitude of the force on the hill is 7969.6 lb.

Chapter Test *(page 629)*

1–3.
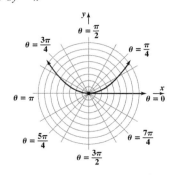

4. $\left(4, \dfrac{\pi}{3}\right)$ **5.** $x^2 + y^2 = 49$ **6.** $\dfrac{y}{x} = 3$ or $y = 3x$

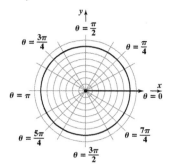

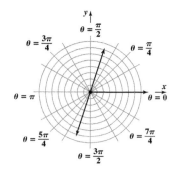

7. $8y = x^2$

8. $r^2 \cos \theta = 5$ is symmetric about the pole, the polar axis, and the line $\theta = \dfrac{\pi}{2}$.

9. $r = 5 \sin \theta \cos^2 \theta$ is symmetric about the line $\theta = \dfrac{\pi}{2}$. The tests for symmetry about the pole and the polar axis fail, so the graph of $r = 5 \sin \theta \cos^2 \theta$ may or may not be symmetric about the pole or polar axis.

10. $z \cdot w = 6(\cos 107° + i \sin 107°)$ **11.** $\dfrac{w}{z} = \dfrac{3}{2}(\cos 297° + i \sin 297°)$ **12.** $w^5 = 243(\cos 110° + i \sin 110°)$

13. $z_0 = 2\sqrt[3]{2}(\cos 40° + i \sin 40°),\ z_1 = 2\sqrt[3]{2}(\cos 160° + i \sin 160°),\ z_2 = 2\sqrt[3]{2}(\cos 280° + i \sin 280°)$

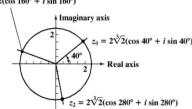

14. $\mathbf{v} = \langle 5\sqrt{2}, -5\sqrt{2} \rangle$ **15.** $\|\mathbf{v}\| = 10$ **16.** $\mathbf{u} = \dfrac{\mathbf{v}}{\|\mathbf{v}\|} = \left\langle \dfrac{\sqrt{2}}{2}, -\dfrac{\sqrt{2}}{2} \right\rangle$ **17.** $315°$ off the positive x-axis   **18.** $\mathbf{v} = 5\sqrt{2}\mathbf{i} - 5\sqrt{2}\mathbf{j}$

19. $\mathbf{v}_1 + 2\mathbf{v}_2 - \mathbf{v}_3 = \langle 6, -10 \rangle$ **20.** Vectors $\mathbf{v}_1$ and $\mathbf{v}_4$ are parallel.   **21.** Vectors $\mathbf{v}_2$ and $\mathbf{v}_3$ are orthogonal.   **22.** $172.87°$ **23.** $-9\mathbf{i} - 5\mathbf{j} + 3\mathbf{k}$

24. $\alpha \approx 57.7°, \beta \approx 143.3°, \gamma \approx 74.5°$ **25.** $\sqrt{115}$ **26.** The cable must be able to endure a tension of approximately 670.82 lb.

Cumulative Review *(page 629)*

1. $\{-3, 3\}$ **2.** $y = \dfrac{\sqrt{3}}{3}x$ **3.** $x^2 + (y - 1)^2 = 9$ **4.** $\left\{ x \mid x < \dfrac{1}{2} \right\}$ or $\left(-\infty, \dfrac{1}{2} \right)$ **5.** Symmetry with respect to the y-axis   **6.**

7.   **8.**   **9.** $-\dfrac{\pi}{6}$ **10.**   **11.** 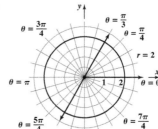   **12.** Amplitude: 4; period: 2

CHAPTER 10 Analytic Geometry

10.2 Assess Your Understanding *(page 639)*

6. parabola   **7.** (c)   **8.** $(3, 2)$ **9.** $(3, 6)$ **10.** $y = -2$ **11.** B   **13.** E   **15.** H   **17.** C

19. $y^2 = 16x$

21. $x^2 = -12y$
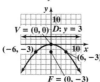

23. $y^2 = -8x$
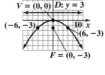

25. $x^2 = 2y$

27. $x^2 = \dfrac{4}{3}y$
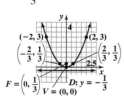

29. $(x - 2)^2 = -8(y + 3)$
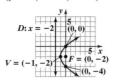

31. $(y + 2)^2 = 4(x + 1)$
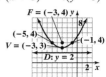

33. $(x + 3)^2 = 4(y - 3)$
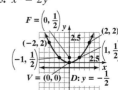

35. $(y + 2)^2 = -8(x + 1)$
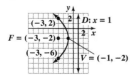

37. Vertex: $(0, 0)$; focus: $(0, 1)$; directrix: $y = -1$

39. Vertex: $(0, 0)$; focus: $(-4, 0)$; directrix: $x = 4$

41. Vertex: $(-1, 2)$; focus: $(1, 2)$; directrix: $x = -3$

43. Vertex: $(3, -1)$; focus: $\left(3, -\dfrac{5}{4} \right)$; directrix: $y = -\dfrac{3}{4}$
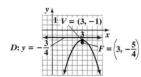

45. Vertex: $(2, -3)$; focus: $(4, -3)$; directrix: $x = 0$
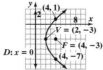

47. Vertex: $(0, 2)$; focus: $(-1, 2)$; directrix: $x = 1$
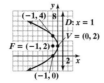

49. Vertex: $(-4, -2)$; focus: $(-4, -1)$; directrix: $y = -3$
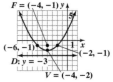
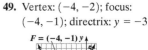

51. Vertex: $(-1, -1)$; focus: $\left(-\dfrac{3}{4}, -1\right)$;

directrix: $x = -\dfrac{5}{4}$

53. Vertex: $(2, -8)$; focus: $\left(2, -\dfrac{31}{4}\right)$;

directrix: $y = -\dfrac{33}{4}$

55. $(y - 1)^2 = x$ **57.** $(y - 1)^2 = -(x - 2)$

59. $x^2 = 4(y - 1)$ **61.** $y^2 = \dfrac{1}{2}(x + 2)$

63. 1.5625 ft from the base of the dish, along the axis of symmetry

65. 1 in. from the vertex, along the axis of symmetry

67. 20 ft   **69.** 0.78125 ft

71. 4.17 ft from the base, along the axis of symmetry

73. 24.31 ft, 18.75 ft, 7.64 ft

75. (a) $y = -\dfrac{625}{(299)^2}x^2 + 625$

(b) 567 ft: 63.12 ft; 478 ft: 225.67 ft; 308 ft: 459.2 ft   **(c)** No

77. $Cy^2 + Dx = 0, C \neq 0, D \neq 0$

$Cy^2 = -Dx$

$y^2 = -\dfrac{D}{C}x$

This is the equation of a parabola with vertex at $(0, 0)$ and axis of symmetry the x-axis.

The focus is $\left(-\dfrac{D}{4C}, 0\right)$; the directrix is the line $x = \dfrac{D}{4C}$. The parabola opens to the right if

$-\dfrac{D}{C} > 0$ and to the left if $-\dfrac{D}{C} < 0$.

79. $Cy^2 + Dx + Ey + F = 0, C \neq 0$

$Cy^2 + Ey = -Dx - F$

$y^2 + \dfrac{E}{C}y = -\dfrac{D}{C}x - \dfrac{F}{C}$

$\left(y + \dfrac{E}{2C}\right)^2 = -\dfrac{D}{C}x - \dfrac{F}{C} + \dfrac{E^2}{4C^2}$

$\left(y + \dfrac{E}{2C}\right)^2 = -\dfrac{D}{C}x + \dfrac{E^2 - 4CF}{4C^2}$

(a) If $D \neq 0$, then the equation may be written as

$\left(y + \dfrac{E}{2C}\right)^2 = -\dfrac{D}{C}\left(x - \dfrac{E^2 - 4CF}{4CD}\right)$.

This is the equation of a parabola with vertex at $\left(\dfrac{E^2 - 4CF}{4CD}, -\dfrac{E}{2C}\right)$

and axis of symmetry parallel to the x-axis.

(b)–(d) If $D = 0$, the graph of the equation contains no points if $E^2 - 4CF < 0$, is a single horizontal line if $E^2 - 4CF = 0$, and is two horizontal lines if $E^2 - 4CF > 0$.

10.3 Assess Your Understanding *(page 649)*

7. ellipse   **8.** major   **9.** $(0, -5)$; $(0, 5)$ **10.** 5; 3; x **11.** $(-2, -3)$; $(6, -3)$ **12.** $(1, 4)$ **13.** C   **15.** B

17. Vertices: $(-5, 0), (5, 0)$

Foci: $(-\sqrt{21}, 0), (\sqrt{21}, 0)$

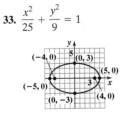

19. Vertices: $(0, -5), (0, 5)$

Foci: $(0, -4), (0, 4)$

21. $\dfrac{x^2}{4} + \dfrac{y^2}{16} = 1$

Vertices: $(0, -4), (0, 4)$

Foci: $(0, -2\sqrt{3}), (0, 2\sqrt{3})$

23. $\dfrac{x^2}{8} + \dfrac{y^2}{2} = 1$

Vertices: $\left(-2\sqrt{2}, 0\right), \left(2\sqrt{2}, 0\right)$

Foci: $\left(-\sqrt{6}, 0\right), \left(\sqrt{6}, 0\right)$

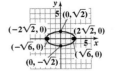

25. $\dfrac{x^2}{16} + \dfrac{y^2}{16} = 1$

Vertices: $(-4, 0), (4, 0)$, $(0, -4), (0, 4)$; Focus: $(0, 0)$

27. $\dfrac{x^2}{25} + \dfrac{y^2}{16} = 1$

29. $\dfrac{x^2}{9} + \dfrac{y^2}{25} = 1$

31. $\dfrac{x^2}{9} + \dfrac{y^2}{5} = 1$

33. $\dfrac{x^2}{25} + \dfrac{y^2}{9} = 1$

35. $\dfrac{x^2}{4} + \dfrac{y^2}{13} = 1$

37. $x^2 + \dfrac{y^2}{16} = 1$

39. $\dfrac{(x + 1)^2}{4} + (y - 1)^2 = 1$

41. $(x - 1)^2 + \dfrac{y^2}{4} = 1$

43. Center: (3, −1); vertices: (3, −4), (3, 2); foci: $\left(3, -1 - \sqrt{5}\right), \left(3, -1 + \sqrt{5}\right)$

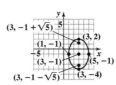

45. $\dfrac{(x + 5)^2}{16} + \dfrac{(y - 4)^2}{4} = 1$

Center: (−5, 4); vertices: (−9, 4), (−1, 4); foci: $\left(-5 - 2\sqrt{3}, 4\right), \left(-5 + 2\sqrt{3}, 4\right)$

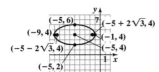

47. $\dfrac{(x + 2)^2}{4} + (y - 1)^2 = 1$

Center: (−2, 1); vertices: (−4, 1), (0, 1); foci: $\left(-2 - \sqrt{3}, 1\right), \left(-2 + \sqrt{3}, 1\right)$

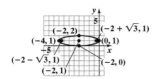

49. $\dfrac{(x - 2)^2}{3} + \dfrac{(y + 1)^2}{2} = 1$

Center: (2, −1); vertices: $\left(2 - \sqrt{3}, -1\right)$; $\left(2 + \sqrt{3}, -1\right)$; foci: (1, −1), (3, −1)

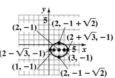

51. $\dfrac{(x - 1)^2}{4} + \dfrac{(y + 2)^2}{9} = 1$

Center: (1, −2); vertices: (1, −5), (1, 1); foci: $\left(1, -2 - \sqrt{5}\right), \left(1, -2 + \sqrt{5}\right)$

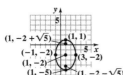

53. $x^2 + \dfrac{(y + 2)^2}{4} = 1$

Center: (0, −2); vertices: (0, −4), (0, 0); foci: $\left(0, -2 - \sqrt{3}\right), \left(0, -2 + \sqrt{3}\right)$

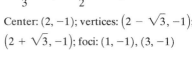

55. $\dfrac{(x - 2)^2}{25} + \dfrac{(y + 2)^2}{21} = 1$

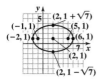

57. $\dfrac{(x - 4)^2}{5} + \dfrac{(y - 6)^2}{9} = 1$

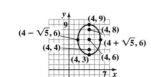

59. $\dfrac{(x - 2)^2}{16} + \dfrac{(y - 1)^2}{7} = 1$

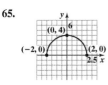

61. $\dfrac{(x - 1)^2}{10} + (y - 2)^2 = 1$

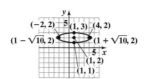

63. $\dfrac{(x - 1)^2}{9} + \dfrac{(y - 2)^2}{9} = 1$

65.

67.

69. $\dfrac{x^2}{100} + \dfrac{y^2}{36} = 1$ **71.** 43.3 ft **73.** 24.65 ft, 21.65 ft, 13.82 ft **75.** 30 ft **77.** The elliptical hole will have a major axis of length $2\sqrt{41}$ in. and a minor axis of length 8 in. **79.** 91.5 million mi; $\dfrac{x^2}{(93)^2} + \dfrac{y^2}{8646.75} = 1$

81. Perihelion: 460.6 million mi; mean distance: 483.8 million mi; $\dfrac{x^2}{(483.8)^2} + \dfrac{y^2}{233,524.2} = 1$

83. (a) $Ax^2 + Cy^2 + F = 0$ If A and C are of the same sign and F is of opposite sign, then the equation takes the form

$Ax^2 + Cy^2 = -F$ $\dfrac{x^2}{\left(-\dfrac{F}{A}\right)} + \dfrac{y^2}{\left(-\dfrac{F}{C}\right)} = 1$, where $-\dfrac{F}{A}$ and $-\dfrac{F}{C}$ are positive. This is the equation of an ellipse with center at (0, 0).

(b) If $A = C$, the equation may be written as $x^2 + y^2 = -\dfrac{F}{A}$.

This is the equation of a circle with center at (0, 0) and radius equal to $\sqrt{-\dfrac{F}{A}}$.

10.4 Assess Your Understanding *(page 662)*

7. hyperbola **8.** transverse axis **9.** b
10. $(2, 4); (2, -2)$ **11.** $(2, 6); (2, -4)$
12. 4 **13.** $2; 3; x$
14. $y = -\dfrac{4}{9}x; y = \dfrac{4}{9}x$ **15.** B **17.** A

19. $x^2 - \dfrac{y^2}{8} = 1$

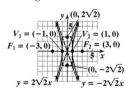

21. $\dfrac{y^2}{16} - \dfrac{x^2}{20} = 1$

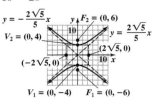

23. $\dfrac{x^2}{9} - \dfrac{y^2}{16} = 1$

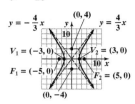

25. $\dfrac{y^2}{36} - \dfrac{x^2}{9} = 1$

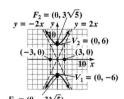

27. $\dfrac{x^2}{8} - \dfrac{y^2}{8} = 1$

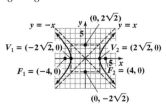

29. $\dfrac{x^2}{25} - \dfrac{y^2}{9} = 1$
Center: $(0, 0)$
Transverse axis: x-axis
Vertices: $(-5, 0), (5, 0)$
Foci: $\left(-\sqrt{34}, 0\right), \left(\sqrt{34}, 0\right)$
Asymptotes: $y = \pm\dfrac{3}{5}x$

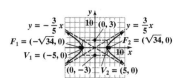

31. $\dfrac{x^2}{4} - \dfrac{y^2}{16} = 1$
Center: $(0, 0)$
Transverse axis: x-axis
Vertices: $(-2, 0), (2, 0)$
Foci: $\left(-2\sqrt{5}, 0\right), \left(2\sqrt{5}, 0\right)$
Asymptotes: $y = \pm 2x$

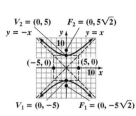

33. $\dfrac{y^2}{9} - x^2 = 1$
Center: $(0, 0)$
Transverse axis: y-axis
Vertices: $(0, -3), (0, 3)$
Foci: $\left(0, -\sqrt{10}\right), \left(0, \sqrt{10}\right)$
Asymptotes: $y = \pm 3x$

35. $\dfrac{y^2}{25} - \dfrac{x^2}{25} = 1$
Center: $(0, 0)$
Transverse axis: y-axis
Vertices: $(0, -5), (0, 5)$
Foci: $\left(0, -5\sqrt{2}\right), \left(0, 5\sqrt{2}\right)$
Asymptotes: $y = \pm x$

37. $x^2 - y^2 = 1$

39. $\dfrac{y^2}{36} - \dfrac{x^2}{9} = 1$

41. $\dfrac{(x - 4)^2}{4} - \dfrac{(y + 1)^2}{5} = 1$

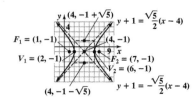

43. $\dfrac{(y + 4)^2}{4} - \dfrac{(x + 3)^2}{12} = 1$

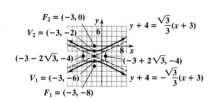

45. $(x - 5)^2 - \dfrac{(y - 7)^2}{3} = 1$

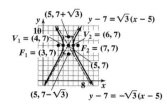

47. $\dfrac{(x-1)^2}{4} - \dfrac{(y+1)^2}{9} = 1$

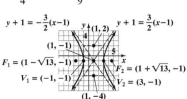

49. $\dfrac{(x-2)^2}{4} - \dfrac{(y+3)^2}{9} = 1$

Center: $(2, -3)$

Transverse axis: parallel to x-axis

Vertices: $(0, -3), (4, -3)$

Foci: $(2 - \sqrt{13}, -3), (2 + \sqrt{13}, -3)$

Asymptotes: $y + 3 = \pm\dfrac{3}{2}(x - 2)$

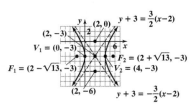

51. $\dfrac{(y-2)^2}{4} - (x+2)^2 = 1$

Center: $(-2, 2)$

Transverse axis: parallel to y-axis

Vertices: $(-2, 0), (-2, 4)$

Foci: $(-2, 2 - \sqrt{5}), (-2, 2 + \sqrt{5})$

Asymptotes: $y - 2 = \pm 2(x + 2)$

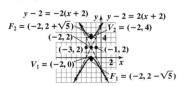

53. $\dfrac{(x+1)^2}{4} - \dfrac{(y+2)^2}{4} = 1$

Center: $(-1, -2)$

Transverse axis: parallel to x-axis

Vertices: $(-3, -2), (1, -2)$

Foci: $(-1 - 2\sqrt{2}, -2), (-1 + 2\sqrt{2}, -2)$

Asymptotes: $y + 2 = \pm(x + 1)$

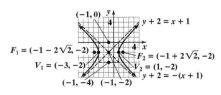

55. $(x-1)^2 - (y+1)^2 = 1$

Center: $(1, -1)$

Transverse axis: parallel to x-axis

Vertices: $(0, -1), (2, -1)$

Foci: $(1 - \sqrt{2}, -1), (1 + \sqrt{2}, -1)$

Asymptotes: $y + 1 = \pm(x - 1)$

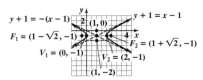

57. $\dfrac{(y-2)^2}{4} - (x+1)^2 = 1$

Center: $(-1, 2)$

Transverse axis: parallel to y-axis

Vertices: $(-1, 0), (-1, 4)$

Foci: $(-1, 2 - \sqrt{5}), (-1, 2 + \sqrt{5})$

Asymptotes: $y - 2 = \pm 2(x + 1)$

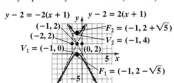

59. $\dfrac{(x-3)^2}{4} - \dfrac{(y+2)^2}{16} = 1$

Center: $(3, -2)$

Transverse axis: parallel to x-axis

Vertices: $(1, -2), (5, -2)$

Foci: $(3 - 2\sqrt{5}, -2), (3 + 2\sqrt{5}, -2)$

Asymptotes: $y + 2 = \pm 2(x - 3)$

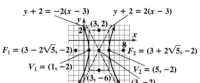

61. $\dfrac{(y-1)^2}{4} - (x+2)^2 = 1$

Center: $(-2, 1)$

Transverse axis: parallel to y-axis

Vertices: $(-2, -1), (-2, 3)$

Foci: $(-2, 1 - \sqrt{5}), (-2, 1 + \sqrt{5})$

Asymptotes: $y - 1 = \pm 2(x + 2)$

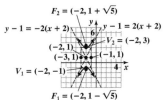

63.

65.

67. Center: $(3, 0)$

Transverse axis: parallel to x-axis

Vertices: $(1, 0), (5, 0)$

Foci: $(3 - \sqrt{29}, 0), (3 + \sqrt{29}, 0)$

Asymptotes: $y = \pm\dfrac{5}{2}(x - 3)$

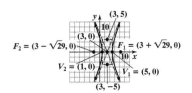

69. Vertex: $(0, 3)$; focus: $(0, 7)$;

directrix: $y = -1$

71. $\dfrac{(x-5)^2}{9} + \dfrac{y^2}{25} = 1$

Center: $(5, 0)$; vertices: $(5, 5), (5, -5)$;

foci: $(5, -4), (5, 4)$

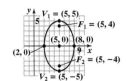

73. $(x-3)^2 = 8(y + 5)$

Vertex: $(3, -5)$; focus: $(3, -3)$;

directrix: $y = -7$

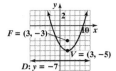

75. The fireworks display is 50,138 ft north of the person at point A.   **77.** The tower is 592.4 ft tall.   **79. (a)** $y = \pm x$ **(b)** $\dfrac{x^2}{100} - \dfrac{y^2}{100} = 1, x \geq 0$

81. If the eccentricity is close to one, the "opening" of the hyperbola is very small. As e increases, the opening gets bigger.

83. $\dfrac{x^2}{4} - y^2 = 1$; asymptotes $y = \pm\dfrac{1}{2}x$

    $y^2 - \dfrac{x^2}{4} = 1$; asymptotes $y = \pm\dfrac{1}{2}x$

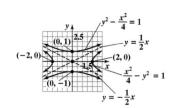

85. $Ax^2 + Cy^2 + F = 0$ If A and C are of opposite sign and $F \neq 0$, this equation may be written as $\dfrac{x^2}{\left(-\dfrac{F}{A}\right)} + \dfrac{y^2}{\left(-\dfrac{F}{C}\right)} = 1$,

     $Ax^2 + Cy^2 = -F$ where $-\dfrac{F}{A}$ and $-\dfrac{F}{C}$ are opposite in sign. This is the equation of a hyperbola with center $(0, 0)$.

                       The transverse axis is the x-axis if $-\dfrac{F}{A} > 0$; the transverse axis is the y-axis if $-\dfrac{F}{A} < 0$.

10.5 Assess Your Understanding *(page 671)*

5. $\cot(2\theta) = \dfrac{A - C}{B}$ **6.** Parabola   **7.** $B^2 - 4AC < 0$ **8.** T   **9.** T   **10.** F   **11.** Parabola   **13.** Ellipse   **15.** Hyperbola

17. Hyperbola   **19.** Circle   **21.** $x = \dfrac{\sqrt{2}}{2}(x' - y')$, $y = \dfrac{\sqrt{2}}{2}(x' + y')$ **23.** $x = \dfrac{\sqrt{2}}{2}(x' - y')$, $y = \dfrac{\sqrt{2}}{2}(x' + y')$

25. $x = \dfrac{1}{2}(x' - \sqrt{3}y')$, $y = \dfrac{1}{2}(\sqrt{3}x' + y')$ **27.** $x = \dfrac{\sqrt{5}}{5}(x' - 2y')$, $y = \dfrac{\sqrt{5}}{5}(2x' + y')$ **29.** $x = \dfrac{\sqrt{13}}{13}(3x' - 2y')$, $y = \dfrac{\sqrt{13}}{13}(2x' + 3y')$

31. $\theta = 45°$ (see Problem 21)

$x'^2 - \dfrac{y'^2}{3} = 1$

Hyperbola

Center at origin

Transverse axis is the x'-axis.

Vertices at $(\pm 1, 0)$

33. $\theta = 45°$ (see Problem 23)

$x'^2 + \dfrac{y'^2}{4} = 1$

Ellipse

Center at $(0, 0)$

Major axis is the y'-axis.

Vertices at $(0, \pm 2)$

35. $\theta = 60°$ (see Problem 25)

$\dfrac{x'^2}{4} + y'^2 = 1$

Ellipse

Center at $(0, 0)$

Major axis is the x'-axis.

Vertices at $(\pm 2, 0)$

37. $\theta \approx 63°$ (see Problem 27)

$y'^2 = 8x'$

Parabola

Vertex at $(0, 0)$

Focus at $(2, 0)$

39. $\theta \approx 34°$ (see Problem 29)

$\dfrac{(x' - 2)^2}{4} + y'^2 = 1$

Ellipse

Center at $(2, 0)$

Major axis is the x'-axis.

Vertices at $(4, 0)$ and $(0, 0)$

41. $\cot(2\theta) = \dfrac{7}{24}$;

$\theta = \sin^{-1}\left(\dfrac{3}{5}\right) \approx 37°$

$(x' - 1)^2 = -6\left(y' - \dfrac{1}{6}\right)$

Parabola

Vertex at $\left(1, \dfrac{1}{6}\right)$

Focus at $\left(1, -\dfrac{4}{3}\right)$

43. Hyperbola   **45.** Hyperbola   **47.** Parabola   **49.** Ellipse   **51.** Ellipse

53. Refer to equation (6): $A' = A\cos^2\theta + B\sin\theta\cos\theta + C\sin^2\theta$

                         $B' = B(\cos^2\theta - \sin^2\theta) + 2(C - A)(\sin\theta\cos\theta)$

                         $C' = A\sin^2\theta - B\sin\theta\cos\theta + C\cos^2\theta$

                         $D' = D\cos\theta + E\sin\theta$

                         $E' = -D\sin\theta + E\cos\theta$

                         $F' = F$

55. Use Problem 53 to find $B'^2 - 4A'C'$. After much cancellation, $B'^2 - 4A'C' = B^2 - 4AC$.

57. The distance between P_1 and P_2 in the $x'y'$-plane equals $\sqrt{(x_2' - x_1')^2 + (y_2' - y_1')^2}$.
Assuming that $x' = x \cos\theta - y \sin\theta$ and $y' = x \sin\theta + y \cos\theta$, then

$(x_2' - x_1')^2 = (x_2 \cos\theta - y_2 \sin\theta - x_1 \cos\theta + y_1 \sin\theta)^2$

$\qquad = \cos^2\theta(x_2 - x_1)^2 - 2\sin\theta\cos\theta(x_2 - x_1)(y_2 - y_1) + \sin^2\theta(y_2 - y_1)^2$, and

$(y_2' - y_1')^2 = (x_2 \sin\theta + y_2 \cos\theta - x_1 \sin\theta - y_1 \cos\theta)^2 = \sin^2\theta(x_2 - x_1)^2 + 2\sin\theta\cos\theta(x_2 - x_1)(y_2 - y_1) + \cos^2\theta(y_2 - y_1)^2$.

Therefore, $(x_2' - x_1')^2 + (y_2' - y_1')^2 = \cos^2\theta(x_2 - x_1)^2 + \sin^2\theta(x_2 - x_1)^2 + \sin^2\theta(y_2 - y_1)^2 + \cos^2\theta(y_2 - y_1)^2$

$\qquad\qquad = (x_2 - x_1)^2(\cos^2\theta + \sin^2\theta) + (y_2 - y_1)^2(\sin^2\theta + \cos^2\theta) = (x_2 - x_1)^2 + (y_2 - y_1)^2$.

10.6 Assess Your Understanding (page 677)

3. conic; focus; directrix **4.** 1; <1; >1 **5.** T **6.** T **7.** Parabola; directrix is perpendicular to the polar axis 1 unit to the right of the pole.

9. Hyperbola; directrix is parallel to the polar axis $\dfrac{4}{3}$ units below the pole.

11. Ellipse; directrix is perpendicular to the polar axis $\dfrac{3}{2}$ units to the left of the pole.

13. Parabola; directrix is perpendicular to the polar axis 1 unit to the right of the pole; vertex is at $\left(\dfrac{1}{2}, 0\right)$.

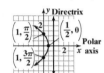

15. Ellipse; directrix is parallel to the polar axis $\dfrac{8}{3}$ units above the pole; vertices are at $\left(\dfrac{8}{7}, \dfrac{\pi}{2}\right)$ and $\left(8, \dfrac{3\pi}{2}\right)$.

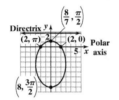

17. Hyperbola; directrix is perpendicular to the polar axis $\dfrac{3}{2}$ units to the left of the pole; vertices are at $(-3, 0)$ and $(1, \pi)$.

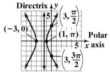

19. Ellipse; directrix is parallel to the polar axis 8 units below the pole; vertices are at $\left(8, \dfrac{\pi}{2}\right)$ and $\left(\dfrac{8}{3}, \dfrac{3\pi}{2}\right)$.

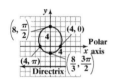

21. Ellipse; directrix is parallel to the polar axis 3 units below the pole; vertices are at $\left(6, \dfrac{\pi}{2}\right)$ and $\left(\dfrac{6}{5}, \dfrac{3\pi}{2}\right)$.

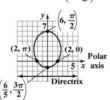

23. Ellipse; directrix is perpendicular to the polar axis 6 units to the left of the pole; vertices are at $(6, 0)$ and $(2, \pi)$.

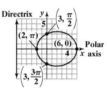

25. $y^2 + 2x - 1 = 0$ **27.** $16x^2 + 7y^2 + 48y - 64 = 0$ **29.** $3x^2 - y^2 + 12x + 9 = 0$ **31.** $4x^2 + 3y^2 - 16y - 64 = 0$

33. $9x^2 + 5y^2 - 24y - 36 = 0$ **35.** $3x^2 + 4y^2 - 12x - 36 = 0$ **37.** $r = \dfrac{1}{1 + \sin\theta}$ **39.** $r = \dfrac{12}{5 - 4\cos\theta}$ **41.** $r = \dfrac{12}{1 - 6\sin\theta}$

43. Use $d(D, P) = p - r \cos\theta$ in the derivation of equation (a) in Table 5.

45. Use $d(D, P) = p + r \sin\theta$ in the derivation of equation (a) in Table 5.

10.7 Assess Your Understanding (page 688)

2. plane curve; parameter **3.** ellipse **4.** cycloid **5.** F **6.** T

7.

$x - 3y + 1 = 0$

9.

$y = \sqrt{x - 2}$

11.

$y = x - 8$

13.

$x = 3(y - 1)^2$

15.

$2y = 2 + x$

17.

$y = x^3$

19.

$\dfrac{x^2}{4} + \dfrac{y^2}{9} = 1$

21.

$\dfrac{x^2}{4} + \dfrac{y^2}{9} = 1$

23.

$x^2 - y^2 = 1$

25.

back and forth twice

$x + y = 1$

27. $x = t$ or $x = \dfrac{t+1}{4}$
$y = 4t - 1$ $y = t$

29. $x = t$ or $x = t^3$
$y = t^2 + 1$ $y = t^6 + 1$

31. $x = t$ or $x = \sqrt[3]{t}$
$y = t^3$ $y = t$

33. $x = t$ or $x = t^3$
$y = t^{2/3}, t \geq 0$ $y = t^2, t \geq 0$

35. $x = t + 2, y = t, 0 \leq t \leq 5$ **37.** $x = 3\cos t, y = 2\sin t, 0 \leq t \leq 2\pi$

39. $x = 2\cos(\pi t), y = -3\sin(\pi t), 0 \leq t \leq 2$

41. $x = 2\sin(2\pi t), y = 3\cos(2\pi t), 0 \leq t \leq 1$

43.

45.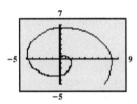

47.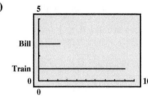

49. (a) $x = 3$
$y = -16t^2 + 50t + 6$
(b) 3.24 s
(c) 1.56 s; 45.06 ft
(d)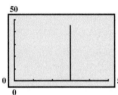

51. (a) Train: $x_1 = t^2, y_1 = 1$;
Bill: $x_2 = 5(t - 5), y_2 = 3$
(b) Bill won't catch the train.
(c)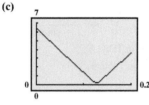

53. (a) $x = (145\cos 20°)t$
$y = -16t^2 + (145\sin 20°)t + 5$
(b) 3.20 s (c) 435.61 ft
(d) 1.55 s; 43.43 ft
(e)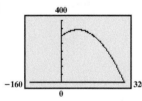

55. (a) $x = (40\cos 45°)t$
$y = -4.9t^2 + (40\sin 45°)t + 300$
(b) 11.23 s (c) 317.52 m
(d) 2.89 s; 340.82 m
(e)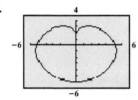

57. (a) Camry: $x = 40t - 5, y = 0$; Chevy Impala: $x = 0, y = 30t - 4$
(b) $d = \sqrt{(40t - 5)^2 + (30t - 4)^2}$
(c)
(d) 0.2 mi; 7.68 min
(e) Turn axes off to see the graph:

59. (a) $x = \dfrac{\sqrt{2}}{2} v_0 t, y = -16t^2 + \dfrac{\sqrt{2}}{2} v_0 t + 3$ (b) Maximum height is 139.1 ft. (c) The ball is 272.25 ft from home plate. (d) Yes, the ball will clear the wall by about 99.5 ft. **61.** The orientation is from (x_1, y_1) to (x_2, y_2).

Review Exercises *(page 692)*

1. Parabola; vertex $(0,0)$, focus $(-4, 0)$, directrix $x = 4$ **3.** Hyperbola; center $(0,0)$, vertices $(5, 0)$ and $(-5, 0)$, foci $\left(\sqrt{26}, 0\right)$ and $\left(-\sqrt{26}, 0\right)$, asymptotes $y = \dfrac{1}{5}x$ and $y = -\dfrac{1}{5}x$ **5.** Ellipse; center $(0,0)$, vertices $(0, 5)$ and $(0, -5)$, foci $(0, 3)$ and $(0, -3)$ **7.** $x^2 = -4(y - 1)$: Parabola; vertex $(0, 1)$, focus $(0, 0)$, directrix $y = 2$ **9.** $\dfrac{x^2}{2} - \dfrac{y^2}{8} = 1$: Hyperbola; center $(0,0)$, vertices $\left(\sqrt{2}, 0\right)$ and $\left(-\sqrt{2}, 0\right)$, foci $\left(\sqrt{10}, 0\right)$ and $\left(-\sqrt{10}, 0\right)$, asymptotes $y = 2x$ and $y = -2x$ **11.** $(x - 2)^2 = 2(y + 2)$: Parabola; vertex $(2, -2)$, focus $\left(2, -\dfrac{3}{2}\right)$, directrix $y = -\dfrac{5}{2}$

13. $\dfrac{(y-2)^2}{4} - (x-1)^2 = 1$: Hyperbola; center $(1,2)$, vertices $(1,4)$ and $(1,0)$, foci $\left(1, 2 + \sqrt{5}\right)$ and $\left(1, 2 - \sqrt{5}\right)$, asymptotes $y - 2 = \pm 2(x - 1)$

15. $\dfrac{(x-2)^2}{9} + \dfrac{(y-1)^2}{4} = 1$: Ellipse; center $(2,1)$, vertices $(5,1)$ and $(-1,1)$, foci $\left(2 + \sqrt{5}, 1\right)$ and $\left(2 - \sqrt{5}, 1\right)$

17. $(x-2)^2 = -4(y+1)$: Parabola; vertex $(2,-1)$, focus $(2,-2)$, directrix $y = 0$

19. $\dfrac{(x-1)^2}{4} + \dfrac{(y+1)^2}{9} = 1$: Ellipse; center $(1,-1)$, vertices $(1,2)$ and $(1,-4)$, foci $\left(1, -1 + \sqrt{5}\right)$ and $\left(1, -1 - \sqrt{5}\right)$

21. $y^2 = -8x$

23. $\dfrac{y^2}{4} - \dfrac{x^2}{12} = 1$

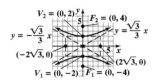

25. $\dfrac{x^2}{16} + \dfrac{y^2}{7} = 1$

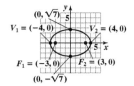

27. $(x-2)^2 = -4(y+3)$

29. $(x+2)^2 - \dfrac{(y+3)^2}{3} = 1$

31. $\dfrac{(x+4)^2}{16} + \dfrac{(y-5)^2}{25} = 1$

33. $\dfrac{(x+1)^2}{9} - \dfrac{(y-2)^2}{7} = 1$

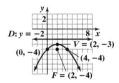

35. $\dfrac{(x-3)^2}{9} - \dfrac{(y-1)^2}{4} = 1$

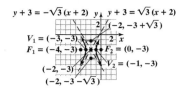

37. Parabola **39.** Ellipse

41. Parabola **43.** Hyperbola

45. Ellipse

47. $x'^2 - \dfrac{y'^2}{9} = 1$
Hyperbola
Center at the origin
Transverse axis the x'-axis
Vertices at $(\pm 1, 0)$

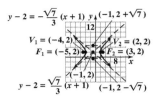

49. $\dfrac{x'^2}{2} + \dfrac{y'^2}{4} = 1$
Ellipse
Center at origin
Major axis the y'-axis
Vertices at $(0, \pm 2)$

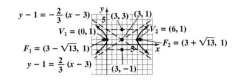

51. $y'^2 = -\dfrac{4\sqrt{13}}{13} x'$
Parabola
Vertex at the origin
Focus on the x'-axis at $\left(-\dfrac{\sqrt{13}}{13}, 0\right)$

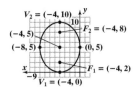

53. Parabola; directrix is perpendicular to the polar axis 4 units to the left of the pole; vertex is $(2, \pi)$.

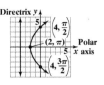

55. Ellipse; directrix is parallel to the polar axis 6 units below the pole; vertices are $\left(6, \dfrac{\pi}{2}\right)$ and $\left(2, \dfrac{3\pi}{2}\right)$.

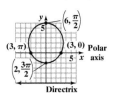

57. Hyperbola; directrix is perpendicular to the polar axis 1 unit to the right of the pole; vertices are $\left(\dfrac{2}{3}, 0\right)$ and $(-2, \pi)$.

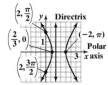

59. $y^2 - 8x - 16 = 0$ **61.** $3x^2 - y^2 - 8x + 4 = 0$

63.

$x + 4y = 2$

65.

$$\frac{x^2}{9} + \frac{(y - 2)^2}{16} = 1$$

67.

$1 + y = x$

69. $x = t, y = -2t + 4, -\infty < t < \infty$ **71.** $x = 4\cos\left(\frac{\pi}{2}t\right), y = 3\sin\left(\frac{\pi}{2}t\right), 0 \le t \le 4$ **73.** $\frac{x^2}{5} - \frac{y^2}{4} = 1$ **75.** The ellipse $\frac{x^2}{16} + \frac{y^2}{7} = 1$

$x = \frac{t - 4}{-2}, y = t, -\infty < t < \infty$

77. $\frac{1}{4}$ ft or 3 in.   **79.** 19.72 ft, 18.86 ft, 14.91 ft   **81.** 450 ft

83. (a) $x = (80 \cos 35°)t$

$y = -16t^2 + (80 \sin 35°)t + 6$

(b) 2.9932 s
(c) 1.4339 s; 38.9 ft
(d) 196.15 ft

(e)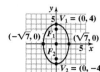

Chapter Test *(page 694)*

1. Hyperbola; center: $(-1, 0)$; vertices: $(-3, 0)$ and $(1, 0)$; foci: $\left(-1 - \sqrt{13}, 0\right)$ and $\left(-1 + \sqrt{13}, 0\right)$; asymptotes: $y = -\frac{3}{2}(x + 1)$ and $y = \frac{3}{2}(x + 1)$

2. Parabola; vertex: $\left(1, -\frac{1}{2}\right)$; focus: $\left(1, \frac{3}{2}\right)$; directrix: $y = -\frac{5}{2}$

3. Ellipse; center: $(-1, 1)$; foci: $\left(-1 - \sqrt{3}, 1\right)$ and $\left(-1 + \sqrt{3}, 1\right)$; vertices: $(-4, 1)$ and $(2, 1)$

4. $(x + 1)^2 = 6(y - 3)$

5. $\frac{x^2}{7} + \frac{y^2}{16} = 1$

6. $\frac{(y - 2)^2}{4} - \frac{(x - 2)^2}{8} = 1$

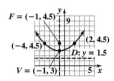

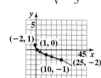

7. Hyperbola   **8.** Ellipse   **9.** Parabola

10. $x'^2 + 2y'^2 = 1$. This is the equation of an ellipse with center at $(0, 0)$ in the $x'y'$-plane. The vertices are at $(-1, 0)$ and $(1, 0)$ in the $x'y'$-plane.

11. Hyperbola; $(x + 2)^2 - \frac{y^2}{3} = 1$ **12.** $y = 1 - \sqrt{\frac{x + 2}{3}}$

13. The microphone should be located $\frac{2}{3}$ ft from the base of the reflector, along its axis of symmetry.

Cumulative Review *(page 694)*

1. $-6x + 5 - 3h$ **2.** $\left\{-5, -\frac{1}{3}, 2\right\}$ **3.** $\{x | -3 \le x \le 2\}$ or $[-3, 2]$ **4. (a)** Domain: $(-\infty, \infty)$; range: $(2, \infty)$

(b) $y = \log_3 (x - 2)$; domain: $(2, \infty)$; range: $(-\infty, \infty)$ **5. (a)** $\{18\}$ **(b)** $(2, 18]$ **6. (a)** $y = 2x - 2$ **(b)** $(x - 2)^2 + y^2 = 4$ **(c)** $\frac{x^2}{9} + \frac{y^2}{4} = 1$

(d) $y = 2(x - 1)^2$ **(e)** $y^2 - \frac{x^2}{3} = 1$ **(f)** $y = 4^x$ **7.** $\theta = \frac{\pi}{12} \pm \pi k, k$ is any integer; $\theta = \frac{5\pi}{12} \pm \pi k, k$ is any integer   **8.** $\theta = \frac{\pi}{6}$

9. $r = 8 \sin \theta$

10. $\left\{x \mid x \ne \frac{3\pi}{4} \pm \pi k, k \text{ is an integer}\right\}$ **11.** $\{22.5°\}$ **12.** $y = \frac{x^2}{5} + 5$

CHAPTER 11 Systems of Equations and Inequalities

11.1 Assess Your Understanding (page 708)

3. inconsistent **4.** consistent; independent **5.** $(3, -2)$ **6.** consistent; dependent

7. $\begin{cases} 2(2) - (-1) = 5 \\ 5(2) + 2(-1) = 8 \end{cases}$ **9.** $\begin{cases} 3(2) - 4\left(\frac{1}{2}\right) = 4 \\ \frac{1}{2}(2) - 3\left(\frac{1}{2}\right) = -\frac{1}{2} \end{cases}$ **11.** $\begin{cases} 4 - 1 = 3 \\ \frac{1}{2}(4) + 1 = 3 \end{cases}$ **13.** $\begin{cases} 3(1) + 3(-1) + 2(2) = 4 \\ 1 - (-1) - 2 = 0 \\ 2(-1) - 3(2) = -8 \end{cases}$ **15.** $\begin{cases} 3(2) + 3(-2) + 2(2) = 4 \\ 2 - 3(-2) + 2 = 10 \\ 5(2) - 2(-2) - 3(2) = 8 \end{cases}$

17. $x = 6, y = 2; (6, 2)$ **19.** $x = 3, y = -6; (3, -6)$ **21.** $x = 8, y = -4; (8, -4)$ **23.** $x = \frac{1}{3}, y = -\frac{1}{6}; \left(\frac{1}{3}, -\frac{1}{6}\right)$ **25.** Inconsistent

27. $x = \frac{3}{2}, y = 3; \left(\frac{3}{2}, 3\right)$ **29.** $\{(x, y)| x = 4 - 2y, y \text{ is any real number}\}$ or $\left\{(x, y)\middle| y = \frac{4 - x}{2}, x \text{ is any real number}\right\}$ **31.** $x = 1, y = 1; (1, 1)$

33. $x = \frac{3}{2}, y = 1; \left(\frac{3}{2}, 1\right)$ **35.** $x = 4, y = 3; (4, 3)$ **37.** $x = \frac{4}{3}, y = \frac{1}{5}; \left(\frac{4}{3}, \frac{1}{5}\right)$ **39.** $x = \frac{1}{5}, y = \frac{1}{3}; \left(\frac{1}{5}, \frac{1}{3}\right)$ **41.** $x = 8, y = 2, z = 0; (8, 2, 0)$

43. $x = 2, y = -1, z = 1; (2, -1, 1)$ **45.** Inconsistent **47.** $\{(x, y, z)| x = 5z - 2, y = 4z - 3; z \text{ is any real number}\}$ **49.** Inconsistent

51. $x = 1, y = 3, z = -2; (1, 3, -2)$ **53.** $x = -3, y = \frac{1}{2}, z = 1; \left(-3, \frac{1}{2}, 1\right)$ **55.** Length 30 ft; width 15 ft

57. There were 18 commercial launches and 37 noncommercial launches in 2005. **59.** 22.5 lb

61. Average wind speed 25 mph; average airspeed 175 mph **63.** 80 $25 sets and 120 $45 sets **65.** $9.96

67. Mix 50 mg of first compound with 75 mg of second. **69.** $a = \frac{4}{3}, b = -\frac{5}{3}, c = 1$ **71.** $Y = 9000, r = 0.06$ **73.** $I_1 = \frac{10}{71}, I_2 = \frac{65}{71}, I_3 = \frac{55}{71}$

75. 100 orchestra, 210 main, and 190 balcony seats **77.** 1.5 chicken, 1 corn, 2 milk

79. If x = price of hamburgers, y = price of fries, and z = price of colas, then

$x = 2.75 - z, y = \frac{41}{60} + \frac{1}{3}z, \$0.60 \le z \le \$0.90.$

There is not sufficient information:

x	$2.13	$2.01	$1.86
y	$0.89	$0.93	$0.98
z	$0.62	$0.74	$0.89

81. It will take Beth 30 hr, Bill 24 hr, and Edie 40 hr.

11.2 Assess Your Understanding (page 723)

1. matrix **2.** augmented **3.** third; fifth **4.** T

5. $\begin{bmatrix} 1 & -5 & | & 5 \\ 4 & 3 & | & 6 \end{bmatrix}$ **7.** $\begin{bmatrix} 2 & 3 & | & 6 \\ 4 & -6 & | & -2 \end{bmatrix}$ **9.** $\begin{bmatrix} 0.01 & -0.03 & | & 0.06 \\ 0.13 & 0.10 & | & 0.20 \end{bmatrix}$ **11.** $\begin{bmatrix} 1 & -1 & 1 & | & 10 \\ 3 & 3 & 0 & | & 5 \\ 1 & 1 & 2 & | & 2 \end{bmatrix}$ **13.** $\begin{bmatrix} 1 & 1 & -1 & | & 2 \\ 3 & -2 & 0 & | & 2 \\ 5 & 3 & -1 & | & 1 \end{bmatrix}$ **15.** $\begin{bmatrix} 1 & -1 & -1 & | & 10 \\ 2 & 1 & 2 & | & -1 \\ -3 & 4 & 0 & | & 5 \\ 4 & -5 & 1 & | & 0 \end{bmatrix}$

17. $\begin{cases} x - 3y = -2 & (1) \\ 2x - 5y = 5 & (2) \end{cases}$ $\begin{bmatrix} 1 & -3 & | & -2 \\ 0 & 1 & | & 9 \end{bmatrix}$ **19.** $\begin{cases} x - 3y + 4z = 3 & (1) \\ 3x - 5y + 6z = 6 & (2); \\ -5x + 3y + 4z = 6 & (3) \end{cases}$ $\begin{bmatrix} 1 & -3 & 4 & | & 3 \\ 0 & 4 & -6 & | & -3 \\ 0 & -12 & 24 & | & 21 \end{bmatrix}$

21. $\begin{cases} x - 3y + 2z = -6 & (1) \\ 2x - 5y + 3z = -4 & (2); \\ -3x - 6y + 4z = 6 & (3) \end{cases}$ $\begin{bmatrix} 1 & -3 & 2 & | & -6 \\ 0 & 1 & -1 & | & 8 \\ 0 & -15 & 10 & | & -12 \end{bmatrix}$ **23.** $\begin{cases} 5x - 3y + z = -2 & (1) \\ 2x - 5y + 6z = -2 & (2); \\ -4x + y + 4z = 6 & (3) \end{cases}$ $\begin{bmatrix} 1 & 7 & -11 & | & 2 \\ 2 & -5 & 6 & | & -2 \\ 0 & -9 & 16 & | & 2 \end{bmatrix}$

25. $\begin{cases} x = 5 \\ y = -1 \end{cases}$
Consistent; $x = 5, y = -1$ or $(5, -1)$

27. $\begin{cases} x = 1 \\ y = 2 \\ 0 = 3 \end{cases}$
Inconsistent

29. $\begin{cases} x + 2z = -1 \\ y - 4z = -2 \\ 0 = 0 \end{cases}$
Consistent:
$\begin{cases} x = -1 - 2z \\ y = -2 + 4z \\ z \text{ is any real number or} \end{cases}$
$\{(x, y, z) \mid x = -1 - 2z,$
$y = -2 + 4z, z \text{ is any real}$
number$\}$

31. $\begin{cases} x_1 = 1 \\ x_2 + x_4 = 2 \\ x_3 + 2x_4 = 3 \end{cases}$
Consistent:
$\begin{cases} x_1 = 1, x_2 = 2 - x_4 \\ x_3 = 3 - 2x_4 \\ x_4 \text{ is any real number or} \end{cases}$
$\{(x_1, x_2, x_3, x_4) \mid x_1 = 1,$
$x_2 = 2 - x_4, x_3 = 3 - 2x_4,$
$x_4 \text{ is any real number}\}$

33. $\begin{cases} x_1 + 4x_4 = 2 \\ x_2 + x_3 + 3x_4 = 3 \\ 0 = 0 \end{cases}$
Consistent:
$\begin{cases} x_1 = 2 - 4x_4 \\ x_2 = 3 - x_3 - 3x_4 \\ x_3, x_4 \text{ are any real numbers or} \end{cases}$
$\{(x_1, x_2, x_3, x_4) \mid x_1 = 2 - 4x_4,$
$x_2 = 3 - x_3 - 3x_4, x_3, x_4 \text{ are}$
any real numbers$\}$

35. $\begin{cases} x_1 + x_4 = -2 \\ x_2 + 2x_4 = 2 \\ x_3 - x_4 = 0 \\ 0 = 0 \end{cases}$
Consistent:
$\begin{cases} x_1 = -2 - x_4 \\ x_2 = 2 - 2x_4 \\ x_3 = x_4 \\ x_4 \text{ is any real number or} \end{cases}$
$\{(x_1, x_2, x_3, x_4) \mid x_1 = -2 - x_4,$
$x_2 = 2 - 2x_4, x_3 = x_4, x_4 \text{ is any}$
real number$\}$

37. $x = 6, y = 2; (6, 2)$ **39.** $x = \dfrac{1}{2}, y = \dfrac{3}{4}; \left(\dfrac{1}{2}, \dfrac{3}{4}\right)$ **41.** $x = 4 - 2y$, y is any real number; $\{(x, y) \mid x = 4 - 2y, y$ is any real number$\}$

43. $x = \dfrac{3}{2}, y = 1; \left(\dfrac{3}{2}, 1\right)$ **45.** $x = \dfrac{4}{3}, y = \dfrac{1}{5}; \left(\dfrac{4}{3}, \dfrac{1}{5}\right)$ **47.** $x = 8, y = 2, z = 0; (8, 2, 0)$ **49.** $x = 2, y = -1, z = 1; (2, -1, 1)$

51. Inconsistent **53.** $x = 5z - 2, y = 4z - 3$, where z is any real number; $\{(x, y, z) \mid x = 5z - 2, y = 4z - 3, z$ is any real number$\}$

55. Inconsistent **57.** $x = 1, y = 3, z = -2; (1, 3, -2)$ **59.** $x = -3, y = \dfrac{1}{2}, z = 1; \left(-3, \dfrac{1}{2}, 1\right)$ **61.** $x = \dfrac{1}{3}, y = \dfrac{2}{3}, z = 1; \left(\dfrac{1}{3}, \dfrac{2}{3}, 1\right)$

63. $x = 1, y = 2, z = 0, w = 1; (1, 2, 0, 1)$ **65.** $y = 0, z = 1 - x$, x is any real number; $\{(x, y, z) \mid y = 0, z = 1 - x, x$ is any real number$\}$

67. $x = 2, y = z - 3$, z is any real number; $\{(x, y, z) \mid x = 2, y = z - 3, z$ is any real number$\}$ **69.** $x = \dfrac{13}{9}, y = \dfrac{7}{18}, z = \dfrac{19}{18}; \left(\dfrac{13}{9}, \dfrac{7}{18}, \dfrac{19}{18}\right)$

71. $x = \dfrac{7}{5} - \dfrac{3}{5}z - \dfrac{2}{5}w, y = -\dfrac{8}{5} + \dfrac{7}{5}z + \dfrac{13}{5}w$, where z and w are any real numbers; $\left\{(x, y, z, w) \,\middle|\, x = \dfrac{7}{5} - \dfrac{3}{5}z - \dfrac{2}{5}w, y = -\dfrac{8}{5} + \dfrac{7}{5}z + \dfrac{13}{5}w,\right.$

z and w are any real numbers$\bigg\}$ **73.** $y = -2x^2 + x + 3$ **75.** $f(x) = 3x^3 - 4x^2 + 5$ **77.** 1.5 salmon steak, 2 baked eggs, 1 acorn squash

79. \$4000 in Treasury bills, \$4000 in Treasury bonds, \$2000 in corporate bonds **81.** 8 Deltas, 5 Betas, 10 Sigmas **83.** $I_1 = \dfrac{44}{23}, I_2 = 2, I_3 = \dfrac{16}{23}, I_4 = \dfrac{28}{23}$

85. (a)

Amount Invested At		
7%	**9%**	**11%**
0	10,000	10,000
1000	8000	11,000
2000	6000	12,000
3000	4000	13,000
4000	2000	14,000
5000	0	15,000

(b)

Amount Invested At		
7%	**9%**	**11%**
12,500	12,500	0
14,500	8500	2000
16,500	4500	4000
18,750	0	6250

(c) All the money invested at 7% provides \$2100, more than what is required.

87.

First Supplement	Second Supplement	Third Supplement
50 mg	75 mg	0 mg
36 mg	76 mg	8 mg
22 mg	77 mg	16 mg
8 mg	78 mg	24 mg

11.3 Assess Your Understanding (page 734)

1. $ad - bc$ **2.** $\begin{vmatrix} 5 & 3 \\ -3 & -4 \end{vmatrix}$ **3.** F **4.** F **5.** F **6.** F **7.** 22 **9.** -2 **11.** 10 **13.** -26 **15.** $x = 6, y = 2; (6, 2)$ **17.** $x = 3, y = 2; (3, 2)$

19. $x = 8, y = -4; (8, -4)$ **21.** $x = 4, y = -2; (4, -2)$ **23.** Not applicable **25.** $x = \dfrac{1}{2}, y = \dfrac{3}{4}; \left(\dfrac{1}{2}, \dfrac{3}{4}\right)$ **27.** $x = \dfrac{1}{10}, y = \dfrac{2}{5}; \left(\dfrac{1}{10}, \dfrac{2}{5}\right)$

29. $x = \dfrac{3}{2}, y = 1; \left(\dfrac{3}{2}, 1\right)$ **31.** $x = \dfrac{4}{3}, y = \dfrac{1}{5}; \left(\dfrac{4}{3}, \dfrac{1}{5}\right)$ **33.** $x = 1, y = 3, z = -2; (1, 3, -2)$ **35.** $x = -3, y = \dfrac{1}{2}, z = 1; \left(-3, \dfrac{1}{2}, 1\right)$

37. Not applicable **39.** $x = 0, y = 0, z = 0; (0, 0, 0)$ **41.** Not applicable **43.** -4 **45.** 12 **47.** 8 **49.** 8 **51.** -5 **53.** $\dfrac{13}{11}$ **55.** 0 or -9

57. $(y_1 - y_2)x - (x_1 - x_2)y + (x_1 y_2 - x_2 y_1) = 0$ **59.** The triangle has an area of 5 square units.

$$(y_1 - y_2)x + (x_2 - x_1)y = x_2 y_1 - x_1 y_2$$
$$(x_2 - x_1)y - (x_2 - x_1)y_1 = (y_2 - y_1)x + x_2 y_1 - x_1 y_2 - (x_2 - x_1)y_1$$
$$(x_2 - x_1)(y - y_1) = (y_2 - y_1)x - (y_2 - y_1)x_1$$
$$y - y_1 = \frac{y_2 - y_1}{x_2 - x_1}(x - x_1)$$

61. If $a = 0$, we have

$$by = s$$
$$cx + dy = t$$

Thus, $y = \dfrac{s}{b}$ and

$$x = \frac{t - dy}{c} = \frac{tb - ds}{bc}$$

Using Cramer's Rule, we get

$$x = \frac{sd - tb}{-bc} = \frac{tb - sd}{bc}$$
$$y = \frac{-sc}{-bc} = \frac{s}{b}$$

If $b = 0$, we have

$$ax = s$$
$$cx + dy = t$$

Since $D = ad \neq 0$, then $a \neq 0$ and $d \neq 0$.

Thus, $x = \dfrac{s}{a}$ and

$$y = \frac{t - cx}{d} = \frac{ta - cs}{ad}$$

Using Cramer's Rule, we get

$$x = \frac{sd}{ad} = \frac{s}{a}$$
$$y = \frac{ta - cs}{ad}$$

If $c = 0$, we have

$$ax + by = s$$
$$dy = t$$

Since $D = ad \neq 0$, then $a \neq 0$ and $d \neq 0$.

Thus, $y = \dfrac{t}{d}$ and

$$x = \frac{s - by}{a} = \frac{sd - bt}{ad}$$

Using Cramer's Rule, we get

$$x = \frac{sd - bt}{ad}$$
$$y = \frac{at}{ad} = \frac{t}{d}$$

If $d = 0$, we have

$$ax + by = s$$
$$cx = t$$

Since $D = -bc \neq 0$, then $b \neq 0$ and $c \neq 0$.

Thus, $x = \dfrac{t}{c}$ and

$$y = \frac{s - ax}{b} = \frac{sc - at}{bc}$$

Using Cramer's Rule, we get

$$x = \frac{-tb}{-bc} = \frac{t}{c}$$
$$y = \frac{at - sc}{-bc} = \frac{sc - at}{bc}$$

63. $\begin{vmatrix} a_{11} & a_{12} & a_{13} \\ ka_{21} & ka_{22} & ka_{23} \\ a_{31} & a_{32} & a_{33} \end{vmatrix} = -ka_{21}(a_{12}a_{33} - a_{32}a_{13}) + ka_{22}(a_{11}a_{33} - a_{31}a_{13}) - ka_{23}(a_{11}a_{32} - a_{31}a_{12})$

$$= k[-a_{21}(a_{12}a_{33} - a_{32}a_{13}) + a_{22}(a_{11}a_{33} - a_{31}a_{13}) - a_{23}(a_{11}a_{32} - a_{31}a_{12})] = k\begin{vmatrix} a_{11} & a_{12} & a_{13} \\ a_{21} & a_{22} & a_{23} \\ a_{31} & a_{32} & a_{33} \end{vmatrix}$$

65. $\begin{vmatrix} a_{11} + ka_{21} & a_{12} + ka_{22} & a_{13} + ka_{23} \\ a_{21} & a_{22} & a_{23} \\ a_{31} & a_{32} & a_{33} \end{vmatrix} = (a_{11} + ka_{21})(a_{22}a_{33} - a_{32}a_{23}) - (a_{12} + ka_{22})(a_{21}a_{33} - a_{31}a_{23}) + (a_{13} + ka_{23})(a_{21}a_{32} - a_{31}a_{22})$

$$= a_{11}a_{22}a_{33} - a_{11}a_{32}a_{23} + \overline{ka_{21}a_{22}a_{33}} - \overline{ka_{21}a_{32}a_{23}} - a_{12}a_{21}a_{33} + a_{12}a_{31}a_{23}$$
$$\quad - \overline{ka_{22}a_{21}a_{33}} + \overline{ka_{22}a_{31}a_{23}} + a_{13}a_{21}a_{32} - a_{13}a_{31}a_{22} + \overline{ka_{23}a_{21}a_{32}} - \overline{ka_{23}a_{31}a_{22}}$$
$$= a_{11}a_{22}a_{33} - a_{11}a_{32}a_{23} - a_{12}a_{21}a_{33} + a_{12}a_{31}a_{23} + a_{13}a_{21}a_{32} - a_{13}a_{31}a_{22}$$
$$= a_{11}(a_{22}a_{33} - a_{32}a_{23}) - a_{12}(a_{21}a_{33} - a_{31}a_{23}) + a_{13}(a_{21}a_{32} - a_{31}a_{22})$$
$$= \begin{vmatrix} a_{11} & a_{12} & a_{13} \\ a_{21} & a_{22} & a_{23} \\ a_{31} & a_{32} & a_{33} \end{vmatrix}$$

Historical Problems *(page 750)*

1. (a) $2 - 5i \longleftrightarrow \begin{bmatrix} 2 & -5 \\ 5 & 2 \end{bmatrix}$, $1 + 3i \longleftrightarrow \begin{bmatrix} 1 & 3 \\ -3 & 1 \end{bmatrix}$ **(b)** $\begin{bmatrix} 2 & -5 \\ 5 & 2 \end{bmatrix}\begin{bmatrix} 1 & 3 \\ -3 & 1 \end{bmatrix} = \begin{bmatrix} 17 & 1 \\ -1 & 17 \end{bmatrix}$ **(c)** $17 + i$ **(d)** $17 + i$

2. $\begin{bmatrix} a & b \\ -b & a \end{bmatrix}\begin{bmatrix} a & -b \\ b & a \end{bmatrix} = \begin{bmatrix} a^2 + b^2 & 0 \\ 0 & b^2 + a^2 \end{bmatrix}$; the product is a real number.

3. (a) $x = k(ar + bs) + l(cr + ds) = r(ka + lc) + s(kb + ld)$ **(b)** $A = \begin{bmatrix} ka + lc & kb + ld \\ ma + nc & mb + nd \end{bmatrix}$
$\qquad y = m(ar + bs) + n(cr + ds) = r(ma + nc) + s(mb + nd)$

11.4 Assess Your Understanding *(page 750)*

1. square **2.** T **3.** columns; rows **4.** F **5.** inverse **6.** singular **7.** T **8.** $A^{-1}B$

9. $\begin{bmatrix} 4 & 4 & -5 \\ -1 & 5 & 4 \end{bmatrix}$ **11.** $\begin{bmatrix} 0 & 12 & -20 \\ 4 & 8 & 24 \end{bmatrix}$ **13.** $\begin{bmatrix} -8 & 7 & -15 \\ 7 & 0 & 22 \end{bmatrix}$ **15.** $\begin{bmatrix} 28 & -9 \\ 4 & 23 \end{bmatrix}$ **17.** $\begin{bmatrix} 1 & 14 & -14 \\ 2 & 22 & -18 \\ 3 & 0 & 28 \end{bmatrix}$ **19.** $\begin{bmatrix} 15 & 21 & -16 \\ 22 & 34 & -22 \\ -11 & 7 & 22 \end{bmatrix}$ **21.** $\begin{bmatrix} 25 & -9 \\ 4 & 20 \end{bmatrix}$

23. $\begin{bmatrix} -13 & 7 & -12 \\ -18 & 10 & -14 \\ 17 & -7 & 34 \end{bmatrix}$ **25.** $\begin{bmatrix} -2 & 4 & 2 & 8 \\ 2 & 1 & 4 & 6 \end{bmatrix}$ **27.** $\begin{bmatrix} 5 & 14 \\ 9 & 16 \end{bmatrix}$ **29.** $\begin{bmatrix} 9 & 2 \\ 34 & 13 \\ 47 & 20 \end{bmatrix}$ **31.** $\begin{bmatrix} 1 & -1 \\ -1 & 2 \end{bmatrix}$ **33.** $\begin{bmatrix} 1 & -\dfrac{5}{2} \\ -1 & 3 \end{bmatrix}$ **35.** $\begin{bmatrix} 1 & -\dfrac{1}{a} \\ -1 & \dfrac{2}{a} \end{bmatrix}$

37. $\begin{bmatrix} 3 & -3 & 1 \\ -2 & 2 & -1 \\ -4 & 5 & -2 \end{bmatrix}$ **39.** $\begin{bmatrix} -\dfrac{5}{7} & \dfrac{1}{7} & \dfrac{3}{7} \\ \dfrac{9}{7} & \dfrac{1}{7} & -\dfrac{4}{7} \\ \dfrac{3}{7} & -\dfrac{2}{7} & \dfrac{1}{7} \end{bmatrix}$ **41.** $x = 3, y = 2; (3, 2)$ **43.** $x = -5, y = 10; (-5, 10)$ **45.** $x = 2, y = -1; (2, -1)$

47. $x = \dfrac{1}{2}, y = 2; \left(\dfrac{1}{2}, 2\right)$ **49.** $x = -2, y = 1; (-2, 1)$ **51.** $x = \dfrac{2}{a}, y = \dfrac{3}{a}; \left(\dfrac{2}{a}, \dfrac{3}{a}\right)$ **53.** $x = -2, y = 3, z = 5; (-2, 3, 5)$

55. $x = \dfrac{1}{2}, y = -\dfrac{1}{2}, z = 1; \left(\dfrac{1}{2}, -\dfrac{1}{2}, 1\right)$ **57.** $x = -\dfrac{34}{7}, y = \dfrac{85}{7}, z = \dfrac{12}{7}; \left(-\dfrac{34}{7}, \dfrac{85}{7}, \dfrac{12}{7}\right)$ **59.** $x = \dfrac{1}{3}, y = 1, z = \dfrac{2}{3}; \left(\dfrac{1}{3}, 1, \dfrac{2}{3}\right)$

61. $\begin{bmatrix} 4 & 2 & | & 1 & 0 \\ 2 & 1 & | & 0 & 1 \end{bmatrix} \rightarrow \begin{bmatrix} 1 & \dfrac{1}{2} & | & \dfrac{1}{4} & 0 \\ 2 & 1 & | & 0 & 1 \end{bmatrix} \rightarrow \begin{bmatrix} 1 & \dfrac{1}{2} & | & \dfrac{1}{4} & 0 \\ 0 & 0 & | & -\dfrac{1}{2} & 1 \end{bmatrix}$ **63.** $\begin{bmatrix} 15 & 3 & | & 1 & 0 \\ 10 & 2 & | & 0 & 1 \end{bmatrix} \rightarrow \begin{bmatrix} 1 & \dfrac{1}{5} & | & \dfrac{1}{15} & 0 \\ 10 & 2 & | & 0 & 1 \end{bmatrix} \rightarrow \begin{bmatrix} 1 & \dfrac{1}{5} & | & \dfrac{1}{15} & 0 \\ 0 & 0 & | & -\dfrac{2}{3} & 1 \end{bmatrix}$

65. $\begin{bmatrix} -3 & 1 & -1 & | & 1 & 0 & 0 \\ 1 & -4 & -7 & | & 0 & 1 & 0 \\ 1 & 2 & 5 & | & 0 & 0 & 1 \end{bmatrix} \rightarrow \begin{bmatrix} 1 & 2 & 5 & | & 0 & 0 & 1 \\ 1 & -4 & -7 & | & 0 & 1 & 0 \\ -3 & 1 & -1 & | & 1 & 0 & 0 \end{bmatrix} \rightarrow \begin{bmatrix} 1 & 2 & 5 & | & 0 & 0 & 1 \\ 0 & -6 & -12 & | & 0 & 1 & -1 \\ 0 & 7 & 14 & | & 1 & 0 & 3 \end{bmatrix}$

$$\rightarrow \begin{bmatrix} 1 & 2 & 5 & | & 0 & 0 & 1 \\ 0 & 1 & 2 & | & 0 & -\dfrac{1}{6} & \dfrac{1}{6} \\ 0 & 1 & 2 & | & \dfrac{1}{7} & 0 & \dfrac{3}{7} \end{bmatrix} \rightarrow \begin{bmatrix} 1 & 2 & 5 & | & 0 & 0 & 1 \\ 0 & 1 & 2 & | & 0 & -\dfrac{1}{6} & \dfrac{1}{6} \\ 0 & 0 & 0 & | & \dfrac{1}{7} & \dfrac{1}{6} & \dfrac{11}{42} \end{bmatrix}$$

67. $\begin{bmatrix} 0.01 & 0.05 & -0.01 \\ 0.01 & -0.02 & 0.01 \\ -0.02 & 0.01 & 0.03 \end{bmatrix}$ **69.** $\begin{bmatrix} 0.02 & -0.04 & -0.01 & 0.01 \\ -0.02 & 0.05 & 0.03 & -0.03 \\ 0.02 & 0.01 & -0.04 & 0.00 \\ -0.02 & 0.06 & 0.07 & 0.06 \end{bmatrix}$ **71.** $x = 4.57, y = -6.44, z = -24.07$ or $(4.57, -6.44, -24.07)$

73. $x = -1.19, y = 2.46, z = 8.27$ or $(-1.19, 2.46, 8.27)$ **75.** $x = -5, y = 7; (-5, 7)$ **77.** $x = -4, y = 2, z = \dfrac{5}{2}; \left(-4, 2, \dfrac{5}{2}\right)$

79. Inconsistent; $\varnothing$ **81.** $x = -\dfrac{1}{5}z + \dfrac{1}{5}, y = \dfrac{1}{5}z - \dfrac{6}{5}$, where z is any real number; $\left\{(x, y, z) \,\middle|\, x = -\dfrac{1}{5}z + \dfrac{1}{5}, y = \dfrac{1}{5}z - \dfrac{6}{5}, z \text{ is any real number}\right\}$

83. (a) $A = \begin{bmatrix} 6 & 9 \\ 3 & 12 \end{bmatrix}; B = \begin{bmatrix} 80.00 \\ 277.80 \end{bmatrix}$ **(b)** $AB = \begin{bmatrix} 2980.20 \\ 3573.60 \end{bmatrix}$; Nikki's total tuition is $2980.20, and Joe's total tuition is $3573.60.

85. (a) $\begin{bmatrix} 500 & 350 & 400 \\ 700 & 500 & 850 \end{bmatrix}; \begin{bmatrix} 500 & 700 \\ 350 & 500 \\ 400 & 850 \end{bmatrix}$ **(b)** $\begin{bmatrix} 15 \\ 8 \\ 3 \end{bmatrix}$ **(c)** $\begin{bmatrix} 11,500 \\ 17,050 \end{bmatrix}$ **(d)** $[0.10 \quad 0.05]$ **(e)** $2002.50

87. (a) $K^{-1} = \begin{bmatrix} 1 & 0 & -1 \\ -1 & 1 & 1 \\ 0 & -1 & 1 \end{bmatrix}$ **(b)** $M = \begin{bmatrix} 13 & 1 & 20 \\ 8 & 9 & 19 \\ 6 & 21 & 14 \end{bmatrix}$ **(c)** Math is fun.

89. If $D = ad - bc \neq 0$, then $a \neq 0$ and $d \neq 0$, or $b \neq 0$ and $c \neq 0$. Assuming the former,

$$\begin{bmatrix} a & b & | & 1 & 0 \\ c & d & | & 0 & 1 \end{bmatrix} \rightarrow \begin{bmatrix} 1 & \dfrac{b}{a} & | & \dfrac{1}{a} & 0 \\ c & d & | & 0 & 1 \end{bmatrix} \rightarrow \begin{bmatrix} 1 & \dfrac{b}{a} & | & \dfrac{1}{a} & 0 \\ 0 & \dfrac{D}{a} & | & -\dfrac{c}{a} & 1 \end{bmatrix} \rightarrow \begin{bmatrix} 1 & \dfrac{b}{a} & | & \dfrac{1}{a} & 0 \\ 0 & 1 & | & -\dfrac{c}{D} & \dfrac{a}{D} \end{bmatrix} \rightarrow \begin{bmatrix} 1 & 0 & | & \dfrac{d}{D} & -\dfrac{b}{D} \\ 0 & 1 & | & -\dfrac{c}{D} & \dfrac{a}{D} \end{bmatrix}$$

$$R_1 = \dfrac{1}{a}r_1 \qquad R_2 = -cr_1 + r_2 \qquad R_2 = \dfrac{a}{D}r_2 \qquad R_1 = -\dfrac{b}{a}r_2 + r_1$$

11.5 Assess Your Understanding (page 760)

5. Proper **7.** Improper; $1 + \dfrac{9}{x^2 - 4}$ **9.** Improper; $5x + \dfrac{22x - 1}{x^2 - 4}$ **11.** Improper; $1 + \dfrac{-2(x - 6)}{(x + 4)(x - 3)}$ **13.** $\dfrac{-4}{x} + \dfrac{4}{x - 1}$ **15.** $\dfrac{1}{x} + \dfrac{-x}{x^2 + 1}$

17. $\dfrac{-1}{x - 1} + \dfrac{2}{x - 2}$ **19.** $\dfrac{\frac{1}{4}}{x + 1} + \dfrac{\frac{3}{4}}{x - 1} + \dfrac{\frac{1}{2}}{(x - 1)^2}$ **21.** $\dfrac{\frac{1}{12}}{x - 2} + \dfrac{-\frac{1}{12}(x + 4)}{x^2 + 2x + 4}$ **23.** $\dfrac{\frac{1}{4}}{x - 1} + \dfrac{\frac{1}{4}}{(x - 1)^2} + \dfrac{-\frac{1}{4}}{x + 1} + \dfrac{\frac{1}{4}}{(x + 1)^2}$

25. $\dfrac{-5}{x + 2} + \dfrac{5}{x + 1} + \dfrac{-4}{(x + 1)^2}$ **27.** $\dfrac{\frac{1}{4}}{x} + \dfrac{1}{x^2} + \dfrac{-\frac{1}{4}(x + 4)}{x^2 + 4}$ **29.** $\dfrac{\frac{2}{3}}{x + 1} + \dfrac{\frac{1}{3}(x + 1)}{x^2 + 2x + 4}$ **31.** $\dfrac{\frac{2}{7}}{3x - 2} + \dfrac{\frac{1}{7}}{2x + 1}$ **33.** $\dfrac{\frac{3}{4}}{x + 3} + \dfrac{\frac{1}{4}}{x - 1}$

35. $\dfrac{1}{x^2 + 4} + \dfrac{2x - 1}{(x^2 + 4)^2}$ **37.** $\dfrac{-1}{x} + \dfrac{2}{x - 3} + \dfrac{-1}{x + 1}$ **39.** $\dfrac{4}{x - 2} + \dfrac{-3}{x - 1} + \dfrac{-1}{(x - 1)^2}$ **41.** $\dfrac{x}{(x^2 + 16)^2} + \dfrac{-16x}{(x^2 + 16)^3}$

43. $\dfrac{-\frac{8}{7}}{2x + 1} + \dfrac{\frac{4}{7}}{x - 3}$ **45.** $\dfrac{-\frac{2}{9}}{x} + \dfrac{-\frac{1}{3}}{x^2} + \dfrac{\frac{1}{6}}{x - 3} + \dfrac{\frac{1}{18}}{x + 3}$

Historical Problem (page 766)

$x = 6$ units, $y = 8$ units

11.6 Assess Your Understanding (page 766)

5.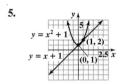

7.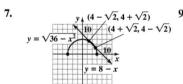

9.

11.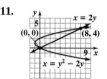

13.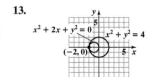

15.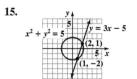

17.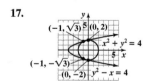

19.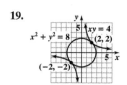

21. No points of intersection

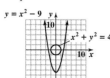

23.

25. $x = 1, y = 4; x = -1, y = -4; x = 2\sqrt{2}, y = \sqrt{2}; x = -2\sqrt{2}, y = -\sqrt{2}$ or $(1, 4), (-1, -4), (2\sqrt{2}, \sqrt{2}), (-2\sqrt{2}, -\sqrt{2})$

27. $x = 0, y = 1; x = -\dfrac{2}{3}, y = -\dfrac{1}{3}$ or $(0, 1), \left(-\dfrac{2}{3}, -\dfrac{1}{3}\right)$ **29.** $x = 0, y = -1; x = \dfrac{5}{2}, y = -\dfrac{7}{2}$ or $(0, -1), \left(\dfrac{5}{2}, -\dfrac{7}{2}\right)$

31. $x = 2, y = \dfrac{1}{3}; x = \dfrac{1}{2}, y = \dfrac{4}{3}$ or $\left(2, \dfrac{1}{3}\right), \left(\dfrac{1}{2}, \dfrac{4}{3}\right)$ **33.** $x = 3, y = 2; x = 3, y = -2; x = -3, y = 2; x = -3, y = -2$ or

$(3, 2), (3, -2), (-3, 2), (-3, -2)$ **35.** $x = \dfrac{1}{2}, y = \dfrac{3}{2}; x = \dfrac{1}{2}, y = -\dfrac{3}{2}; x = -\dfrac{1}{2}, y = \dfrac{3}{2}; x = -\dfrac{1}{2}, y = -\dfrac{3}{2}$ or $\left(\dfrac{1}{2}, \dfrac{3}{2}\right), \left(\dfrac{1}{2}, -\dfrac{3}{2}\right), \left(-\dfrac{1}{2}, \dfrac{3}{2}\right), \left(-\dfrac{1}{2}, -\dfrac{3}{2}\right)$

37. $x = \sqrt{2}, y = 2\sqrt{2}; x = -\sqrt{2}, y = -2\sqrt{2}$ or $(\sqrt{2}, 2\sqrt{2}), (-\sqrt{2}, -2\sqrt{2})$ **39.** No real solution exists.

41. $x = \dfrac{8}{3}, y = \dfrac{2\sqrt{10}}{3}; x = -\dfrac{8}{3}, y = \dfrac{2\sqrt{10}}{3}; x = \dfrac{8}{3}, y = -\dfrac{2\sqrt{10}}{3}; x = -\dfrac{8}{3}, y = -\dfrac{2\sqrt{10}}{3}$ or $\left(\dfrac{8}{3}, \dfrac{2\sqrt{10}}{3}\right), \left(-\dfrac{8}{3}, \dfrac{2\sqrt{10}}{3}\right), \left(\dfrac{8}{3}, -\dfrac{2\sqrt{10}}{3}\right), \left(-\dfrac{8}{3}, -\dfrac{2\sqrt{10}}{3}\right)$

43. $x = 1, y = \dfrac{1}{2}; x = -1, y = \dfrac{1}{2}; x = 1, y = -\dfrac{1}{2}; x = -1, y = -\dfrac{1}{2}$ or $\left(1, \dfrac{1}{2}\right), \left(-1, \dfrac{1}{2}\right), \left(1, -\dfrac{1}{2}\right), \left(-1, -\dfrac{1}{2}\right)$ **45.** No real solution exists.

47. $x = \sqrt{3}, y = \sqrt{3}; x = -\sqrt{3}, y = -\sqrt{3}; x = 2, y = 1; x = -2, y = -1$ or $(\sqrt{3}, \sqrt{3}), (-\sqrt{3}, -\sqrt{3}), (2, 1), (-2, -1)$

49. $x = 0, y = -2; x = 0, y = 1; x = 2, y = -1$ or $(0, -2), (0, 1), (2, -1)$ **51.** $x = 2, y = 8$ or $(2, 8)$ **53.** $x = 81, y = 3$ or $(81, 3)$

55.

57. $x = 0.48, y = 0.62$ **59.** $x = -1.65, y = -0.89$

61. $x = 0.58, y = 1.86; x = 1.81, y = 1.05; x = 0.58, y = -1.86; x = 1.81, y = -1.05$

63. $x = 2.35, y = 0.85$

65.

67.

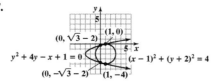

69.

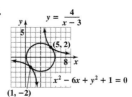

71. 3 and 1; −1 and −3 **73.** 2 and 2; −2 and −2 **75.** $\dfrac{1}{2}$ and $\dfrac{1}{3}$ **77.** 5 **79.** 5 in. by 3 in. **81.** 2 cm and 4 cm **83.** tortoise: 7 m/hr, hare: $7\dfrac{1}{2}$ m/hr

85. 12 cm by 18 cm **87.** $x = 60$ ft; $y = 30$ ft **89.** $l = \dfrac{P + \sqrt{P^2 - 16A}}{4}; w = \dfrac{P - \sqrt{P^2 - 16A}}{4}$ **91.** $y = 4x - 4$ **93.** $y = 2x + 1$

95. $y = -\dfrac{1}{3}x + \dfrac{7}{3}$ **97.** $y = 2x - 3$ **99.** $r_1 = \dfrac{-b + \sqrt{b^2 - 4ac}}{2a}; r_2 = \dfrac{-b - \sqrt{b^2 - 4ac}}{2a}$ **101. (a)** 4.274 ft by 4.274 ft or 0.093 ft by 0.093 ft

11.7 Assess Your Understanding (page 775)

7. dashes; solid **8.** half-planes **9.** F **10.** unbounded

11.

13.

15.

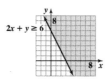

17.

19.

21.

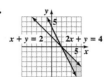

23.

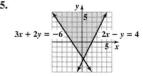

25.

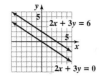

27.

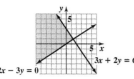

29.

31.

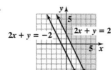

33. No solution

35.

37.

39.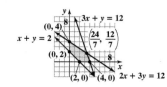

41.

43. Bounded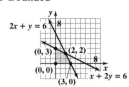

45. Unbounded

47. Bounded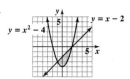

49. Bounded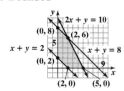

51. Bounded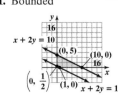

53. $\begin{cases} x \le 4 \\ x + y \le 6 \\ x \ge 0 \\ y \ge 0 \end{cases}$

55. $\begin{cases} x \le 20 \\ y \ge 15 \\ x + y \le 50 \\ x - y \le 0 \\ x \ge 0 \end{cases}$

57. (a) $\begin{cases} x + y \le 50{,}000 \\ x \ge 35{,}000 \\ y \le 10{,}000 \\ y \ge 0 \end{cases}$

(b)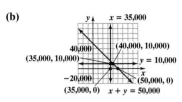

59. (a) $\begin{cases} x \ge 0 \\ y \ge 0 \\ x + 2y \le 300 \\ 3x + 2y \le 480 \end{cases}$

(b)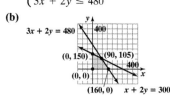

61. (a) $\begin{cases} 3x + 2y \le 160 \\ 2x + 3y \le 150 \\ x \ge 0 \\ y \ge 0 \end{cases}$

(b)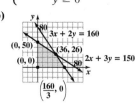

11.8 Assess Your Understanding *(page 782)*

1. objective function   **2.** T   **3.** Maximum value is 11; minimum value is 3.   **5.** Maximum value is 65; minimum value is 4.   **7.** Maximum value is 67; minimum value is 20.   **9.** The maximum value of z is 12, and it occurs at the point $(6, 0)$.   **11.** The minimum value of z is 4, and it occurs at the point $(2, 0)$.   **13.** The maximum value of z is 20, and it occurs at the point $(0, 4)$.   **15.** The minimum value of z is 8, and it occurs at the point $(0, 2)$.
17. The maximum value of z is 50, and it occurs at the point $(10, 0)$.   **19.** Produce 8 downhill and 24 cross-country; \$1760; \$1920 which is the profit when producing 16 downhill and 16 cross-country.   **21.** Rent 15 rectangular tables and 16 round tables for a minimum cost of \$1252.
23. (a) \$10,000 in a junk bond and \$10,000 in Treasury bills   **(b)** \$12,000 in a junk bond and \$8000 in Treasury bills   **25.** 100 lb of ground beef should be mixed with 50 lb of pork.   **27.** Manufacture 10 racing skates and 15 figure skates.   **29.** Order 2 metal samples and 4 plastic samples; \$34
31. (a) Configure with 10 first class seats and 120 coach seats.   **(b)** Configure with 15 first class seats and 120 coach seats.

Review Exercises *(page 785)*

1. $x = 2, y = -1$ or $(2, -1)$ **3.** $x = 2, y = \dfrac{1}{2}$ or $\left(2, \dfrac{1}{2}\right)$ **5.** $x = 2, y = -1$ or $(2, -1)$ **7.** $x = \dfrac{11}{5}, y = -\dfrac{3}{5}$ or $\left(\dfrac{11}{5}, -\dfrac{3}{5}\right)$ **9.** Inconsistent

11. $x = 2, y = 3$ or $(2, 3)$ **13.** Inconsistent   **15.** $x = -1, y = 2, z = -3$ or $(-1, 2, -3)$

17. $x = \dfrac{7}{4}z + \dfrac{39}{4},\ y = \dfrac{9}{8}z + \dfrac{69}{8}$, where z is any real number or $\left\{(x, y, z) \,\middle|\, x = \dfrac{7}{4}z + \dfrac{39}{4},\ y = \dfrac{9}{8}z + \dfrac{69}{8}, z \text{ is any real number}\right\}$

19. $\begin{cases} 3x + 2y = 8 \\ x + 4y = -1 \end{cases}$

21. $\begin{bmatrix} 4 & -4 \\ 3 & 9 \\ 4 & 4 \end{bmatrix}$

23. $\begin{bmatrix} 6 & 0 \\ 12 & 24 \\ -6 & 12 \end{bmatrix}$

25. $\begin{bmatrix} 4 & -3 & 0 \\ 12 & -2 & -8 \\ -2 & 5 & -4 \end{bmatrix}$

27. $\begin{bmatrix} 8 & -13 & 8 \\ 9 & 2 & -10 \\ 22 & -13 & -4 \end{bmatrix}$

29. $\begin{bmatrix} \dfrac{1}{2} & -1 \\[2mm] -\dfrac{1}{6} & \dfrac{2}{3} \end{bmatrix}$

31. $\begin{bmatrix} -\dfrac{5}{7} & \dfrac{9}{7} & \dfrac{3}{7} \\[2mm] \dfrac{1}{7} & \dfrac{1}{7} & -\dfrac{2}{7} \\[2mm] \dfrac{3}{7} & -\dfrac{4}{7} & \dfrac{1}{7} \end{bmatrix}$

33. Singular   **35.** $x = \dfrac{2}{5}, y = \dfrac{1}{10}$ or $\left(\dfrac{2}{5}, \dfrac{1}{10}\right)$ **37.** $x = 9, y = \dfrac{13}{3}, z = \dfrac{13}{3}$ or $\left(9, \dfrac{13}{3}, \dfrac{13}{3}\right)$

39. $x = -\dfrac{1}{2}, y = -\dfrac{2}{3}, z = -\dfrac{3}{4}$, or $\left(-\dfrac{1}{2}, -\dfrac{2}{3}, -\dfrac{3}{4}\right)$

41. $z = -1, x = y + 1$, where y is any real number or $\{(x, y, z) \mid x = y + 1, z = -1, y \text{ is any real number}\}$

43. $x = 4, y = 2, z = 3, t = -2$ or $(4, 2, 3, -2)$ **45.** 5 **47.** 108 **49.** -100 **51.** $x = 2, y = -1$ or $(2, -1)$ **53.** $x = 2, y = 3$ or $(2, 3)$

55. $x = -1, y = 2, z = -3$ or $(-1, 2, -3)$ **57.** 16 **59.** $\dfrac{-\frac{3}{2}}{x} + \dfrac{\frac{3}{2}}{x - 4}$ **61.** $\dfrac{-3}{x - 1} + \dfrac{3}{x} + \dfrac{4}{x^2}$ **63.** $\dfrac{-\frac{1}{10}}{x + 1} + \dfrac{\frac{1}{10}x + \frac{9}{10}}{x^2 + 9}$

65. $\dfrac{x}{x^2 + 4} + \dfrac{-4x}{(x^2 + 4)^2}$ **67.** $\dfrac{\frac{1}{2}}{x^2 + 1} + \dfrac{\frac{1}{4}}{x - 1} + \dfrac{-\frac{1}{4}}{x + 1}$ **69.** $x = -\dfrac{2}{5}, y = -\dfrac{11}{5}; x = -2, y = 1$ or $\left(-\dfrac{2}{5}, -\dfrac{11}{5}\right), (-2, 1)$

71. $x = 2\sqrt{2}, y = \sqrt{2}; x = -2\sqrt{2}, y = -\sqrt{2}$ or $(2\sqrt{2}, \sqrt{2}), (-2\sqrt{2}, -\sqrt{2})$ **73.** $x = 0, y = 0; x = -3, y = 3; x = 3, y = 3$ or

$(0, 0), (-3, 3), (3, 3)$ **75.** $x = \sqrt{2}, y = -\sqrt{2}; x = -\sqrt{2}, y = \sqrt{2}; x = \dfrac{4}{3}\sqrt{2}, y = -\dfrac{2}{3}\sqrt{2}; x = -\dfrac{4}{3}\sqrt{2}, y = \dfrac{2}{3}\sqrt{2}$ or

$(\sqrt{2}, -\sqrt{2}), (-\sqrt{2}, \sqrt{2}), \left(\dfrac{4}{3}\sqrt{2}, -\dfrac{2}{3}\sqrt{2}\right), \left(-\dfrac{4}{3}\sqrt{2}, \dfrac{2}{3}\sqrt{2}\right)$ **77.** $x = 1, y = -1$ or $(1, -1)$

79.
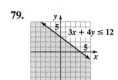

81.
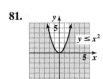

83. Unbounded
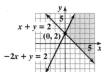

85. Bounded
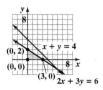

87. Bounded
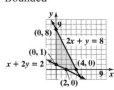

89.

91.

93. The maximum value is 32 when $x = 0$ and $y = 8$. **95.** The minimum value is 3 when $x = 1$ and $y = 0$. **97.** 10

99. $y = -\dfrac{1}{3}x^2 - \dfrac{2}{3}x + 1$ **101.** Mix 70 lb of $6.00 coffee and 30 lb of $9.00 coffee. **103.** Buy 1 small, 5 medium, and 2 large.

105. Speedboat: 36.67 km/hr; Aguarico River: 3.33 km/hr **107.** Bruce: 4 hr; Bryce: 2 hr; Marty: 8 hr

109. Produce 35 gasoline engines and 15 diesel engines; the factory is producing an excess of 15 gasoline engines and 0 diesel engines.

Chapter Test *(page 789)*

1. $x = 3, y = -1$ or $(3, -1)$ **2.** Inconsistent **3.** $x = -z + \dfrac{18}{7}, y = z - \dfrac{17}{7}$, where z is any real number or

$\left\{(x, y, z) \mid x = -z + \dfrac{18}{7}, y = z - \dfrac{17}{7}, z \text{ is any real number}\right\}$ **4.** $x = \dfrac{1}{3}, y = -2, z = 0$ or $\left(\dfrac{1}{3}, -2, 0\right)$ **5.** $\begin{bmatrix} 4 & -5 & 1 & | & 0 \\ -2 & -1 & 0 & | & -25 \\ 1 & 5 & -5 & | & 10 \end{bmatrix}$

6. $\begin{cases} 3x + 2y + 4z = -6 \\ 1x + 0y + 8z = 2 \\ -2x + 1y + 3z = -11 \end{cases}$ or $\begin{cases} 3x + 2y + 4z = -6 \\ x + 8z = 2 \\ -2x + y + 3z = -11 \end{cases}$ **7.** $\begin{bmatrix} 6 & 4 \\ 1 & -11 \\ 5 & 12 \end{bmatrix}$ **8.** $\begin{bmatrix} -11 & -19 \\ -3 & 5 \\ 6 & -22 \end{bmatrix}$ **9.** $\begin{bmatrix} 4 & 10 & 26 \\ 1 & -11 & 2 \\ -1 & 26 & 3 \end{bmatrix}$

10. $\begin{bmatrix} 16 & 17 \\ 3 & -10 \end{bmatrix}$ **11.** $\begin{bmatrix} 2 & -1 \\ -\dfrac{5}{2} & \dfrac{3}{2} \end{bmatrix}$ **12.** $\begin{bmatrix} 3 & 3 & -4 \\ -2 & -2 & 3 \\ -4 & -5 & 7 \end{bmatrix}$ **13.** $x = \dfrac{1}{2}, y = 3$ or $\left(\dfrac{1}{2}, 3\right)$ **14.** $x = -\dfrac{1}{4}y + 7$, where y is any real number or

$\left\{(x, y) \mid x = -\dfrac{1}{4}y + 7, y \text{ is any real number}\right\}$ **15.** $x = 1, y = -2, z = 0$ or $(1, -2, 0)$ **16.** Inconsistent **17.** -29 **18.** -12

19. $x = -2, y = -5$ or $(-2, -5)$ **20.** $x = 1, y = -1, z = 4$ or $(1, -1, 4)$ **21.** $(1, -3)$ and $(1, 3)$ **22.** $(3, 4)$ and $(1, 2)$

23.
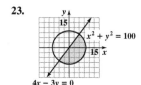

24. $\dfrac{3}{x + 3} + \dfrac{-2}{(x + 3)^2}$

25. $\dfrac{-\dfrac{1}{3}}{x} + \dfrac{\dfrac{1}{3}x}{(x^2 + 3)} + \dfrac{5x}{(x^2 + 3)^2}$

26. Unbounded
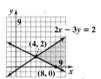

27. The maximum value of z is 64, and it occurs at the point $(0, 8)$. **28.** Flare jeans cost $24.50, camisoles cost $8.50, and T-shirts cost $6.00.

Cumulative Review (page 790)

1. $\left\{0, \frac{1}{2}\right\}$ **2.** $\{5\}$ **3.** $\left\{-1, -\frac{1}{2}, 3\right\}$ **4.** $\{-2\}$ **5.** $\left\{\frac{5}{2}\right\}$ **6.** $\left\{\frac{1}{\ln 3}\right\}$ **7.** Odd; symmetric with respect to the origin

8. Center: $(1, -2)$; radius $= 4$

9. Domain: all real numbers
Range: $\{y | y > 1\}$
Horizontal asymptote: $y = 1$

10. $f^{-1}(x) = \frac{5}{x} - 2$
Domain of f: $\{x | x \neq -2\}$
Range of f: $\{y | y \neq 0\}$
Domain of f^{-1}: $\{x | x \neq 0\}$
Range of f^{-1}: $\{y | y \neq -2\}$

11. (a)

(b)

(c)

(d)
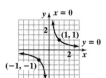
(e)

(f)

(g)

(h)

(i)
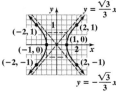
(j)

12. (a)
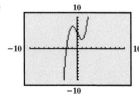
; -2.28
(b) Local maximum of 7 at $x = -1$;
local minimum of 3 at $x = 1$
(c) $(-\infty, -1), (1, \infty)$

CHAPTER 12 Sequences; Induction; the Binomial Theorem

12.1 Assess Your Understanding (page 799)

3. sequence   **4.** True   **5.** $n(n-1) \cdots 3 \cdot 2 \cdot 1$ **6.** recursive   **7.** summation   **8.** True   **9.** 3,628,800   **11.** 504   **13.** 1260   **15.** $s_1 = 1, s_2 = 2, s_3 = 3,$
$s_4 = 4, s_5 = 5$ **17.** $a_1 = \frac{1}{3}, a_2 = \frac{1}{2}, a_3 = \frac{3}{5}, a_4 = \frac{2}{3}, a_5 = \frac{5}{7}$ **19.** $c_1 = 1, c_2 = -4, c_3 = 9, c_4 = -16, c_5 = 25$ **21.** $s_1 = \frac{1}{2}, s_2 = \frac{2}{5}, s_3 = \frac{2}{7}, s_4 = \frac{8}{41}, s_5 = \frac{8}{61}$

23. $t_1 = -\frac{1}{6}, t_2 = \frac{1}{12}, t_3 = -\frac{1}{20}, t_4 = \frac{1}{30}, t_5 = -\frac{1}{42}$ **25.** $b_1 = \frac{1}{e}, b_2 = \frac{2}{e^2}, b_3 = \frac{3}{e^3}, b_4 = \frac{4}{e^4}, b_5 = \frac{5}{e^5}$ **27.** $a_n = \frac{n}{n+1}$ **29.** $a_n = \frac{1}{2^{n-1}}$

31. $a_n = (-1)^{n+1}$ **33.** $a_n = (-1)^{n+1}n$ **35.** $a_1 = 2, a_2 = 5, a_3 = 8, a_4 = 11, a_5 = 14$ **37.** $a_1 = -2, a_2 = 0, a_3 = 3, a_4 = 7, a_5 = 12$

39. $a_1 = 5, a_2 = 10, a_3 = 20, a_4 = 40, a_5 = 80$ **41.** $a_1 = 3, a_2 = \frac{3}{2}, a_3 = \frac{1}{2}, a_4 = \frac{1}{8}, a_5 = \frac{1}{40}$ **43.** $a_1 = 1, a_2 = 2, a_3 = 2, a_4 = 4, a_5 = 8$

45. $a_1 = A, a_2 = A + d, a_3 = A + 2d, a_4 = A + 3d, a_5 = A + 4d$

47. $a_1 = \sqrt{2}, a_2 = \sqrt{2 + \sqrt{2}}, a_3 = \sqrt{2 + \sqrt{2 + \sqrt{2}}},$ **49.** $3 + 4 + \cdots + (n+2)$ **51.** $\frac{1}{2} + 2 + \frac{9}{2} + \cdots + \frac{n^2}{2}$ **53.** $1 + \frac{1}{3} + \frac{1}{9} + \cdots + \frac{1}{3^n}$
$a_4 = \sqrt{2 + \sqrt{2 + \sqrt{2 + \sqrt{2}}}},$
$a_5 = \sqrt{2 + \sqrt{2 + \sqrt{2 + \sqrt{2 + \sqrt{2}}}}}$ **55.** $\frac{1}{3} + \frac{1}{9} + \cdots + \frac{1}{3^n}$ **57.** $\ln 2 - \ln 3 + \ln 4 - \cdots + (-1)^n \ln n$ **59.** $\sum_{k=1}^{20} k$

61. $\sum_{k=1}^{13} \frac{k}{k+1}$ **63.** $\sum_{k=0}^{6} (-1)^k \left(\frac{1}{3^k}\right)$ **65.** $\sum_{k=1}^{n} \frac{3^k}{k}$ **67.** $\sum_{k=0}^{n} (a + kd)$ or $\sum_{k=1}^{n+1} [a + (k-1)d]$ **69.** 200   **71.** 820   **73.** 1110   **75.** 1560   **77.** 3570

79. 44,000   **81.** \$2930   **83.** \$18,058.03   **85.** 21 pairs   **87.** Fibonacci sequence   **89. (a)** 3.630170833   **(b)** 3.669060828   **(c)** 3.669296668   **(d)** 12

91. (a) $a_1 = 0.4; a_2 = 0.7; a_3 = 1; a_4 = 1.6; a_5 = 2.8; a_6 = 5.2; a_7 = 10; a_8 = 19.6$
(b) Except for term 5, which has no match, Bode's formula provides excellent approximations for the mean distances of the planets from the Sun.
(c) The mean distance of Ceres from the Sun is approximated by $a_5 = 2.8$ and that of Uranus is $a_8 = 19.6$.
(d) $a_9 = 38.8; a_{10} = 77.2$ **(e)** Pluto's distance is approximated by a_9, but no term approximates Neptune's mean distance from the Sun.
(f) According to Bode's Law, the mean orbital distance of Eris will be 154 AU from the Sun.

93. $a_0 = 2; a_5 = 2.236067977; 2.236067977$ **95.** $a_0 = 4; a_5 = 4.582575695; 4.582575695$ **97.** 1, 3, 6, 10, 15, 21, 28

99. $u_n = 1 + 2 + 3 + \cdots + n = \sum_{k=1}^{n} k = \frac{n(n+1)}{2}$, and from Problem 98, $u_{n+1} = \frac{(n+1)(n+2)}{2}$.

Thus, $u_{n+1} + u_n = \frac{(n+1)(n+2)}{2} + \frac{n(n+1)}{2} = \frac{(n+1)[(n+2) + n]}{2} = (n+1)^2$.

12.2 Assess Your Understanding (page 807)

1. arithmetic **2.** F **3.** 17 **4.** T **5.** $s_n - s_{n-1} = (n + 4) - [(n - 1) + 4] = n + 4 - (n + 3) = n + 4 - n - 3 = 1$, a constant;
$d = 1; s_1 = 5, s_2 = 6, s_3 = 7, s_4 = 8$

7. $a_n - a_{n-1} = (2n - 5) - [2(n - 1) - 5] = 2n - 5 - (2n - 2 - 5) = 2n - 5 - (2n - 7) = 2n - 5 - 2n + 7 = 2$, a constant;
$d = 2; a_1 = -3, a_2 = -1, a_3 = 1, a_4 = 3$

9. $c_n - c_{n-1} = (6 - 2n) - [6 - 2(n - 1)] = 6 - 2n - (6 - 2n + 2) = 6 - 2n - (8 - 2n) = 6 - 2n - 8 + 2n = -2$, a constant;
$d = -2; c_1 = 4, c_2 = 2, c_3 = 0, c_4 = -2$

11. $t_n - t_{n-1} = \left(\dfrac{1}{2} - \dfrac{1}{3}n\right) - \left[\dfrac{1}{2} - \dfrac{1}{3}(n - 1)\right] = \dfrac{1}{2} - \dfrac{1}{3}n - \left(\dfrac{1}{2} - \dfrac{1}{3}n + \dfrac{1}{3}\right) = \dfrac{1}{2} - \dfrac{1}{3}n - \left(\dfrac{5}{6} - \dfrac{1}{3}n\right) = \dfrac{1}{2} - \dfrac{1}{3}n - \dfrac{5}{6} + \dfrac{1}{3}n = -\dfrac{1}{3}$, a constant;
$d = -\dfrac{1}{3}; t_1 = \dfrac{1}{6}, t_2 = -\dfrac{1}{6}, t_3 = -\dfrac{1}{2}, t_4 = -\dfrac{5}{6}$

13. $s_n - s_{n-1} = \ln 3^n - \ln 3^{n-1} = n \ln 3 - (n - 1) \ln 3 = n \ln 3 - (n \ln 3 - \ln 3) = n \ln 3 - n \ln 3 + \ln 3 = \ln 3$, a constant;
$d = \ln 3; s_1 = \ln 3, s_2 = 2 \ln 3, s_3 = 3 \ln 3, s_4 = 4 \ln 3$

15. $a_n = 3n - 1; a_{51} = 152$ **17.** $a_n = 8 - 3n; a_{51} = -145$ **19.** $a_n = \dfrac{1}{2}(n - 1); a_{51} = 25$ **21.** $a_n = \sqrt{2}n; a_{51} = 51\sqrt{2}$ **23.** 200 **25.** -266 **27.** $\dfrac{83}{2}$

29. $a_1 = -13; d = 3; a_n = a_{n-1} + 3; a_n = -16 + 3n$ **31.** $a_1 = -53; d = 6; a_n = a_{n-1} + 6; a_n = -59 + 6n$

33. $a_1 = 28; d = -2; a_n = a_{n-1} - 2; a_n = 30 - 2n$ **35.** $a_1 = 25; d = -2; a_n = a_{n-1} - 2; a_n = 27 - 2n$ **37.** n^2 **39.** $\dfrac{n}{2}(9 + 5n)$ **41.** 1260

43. 324 **45.** 30,919 **47.** 10,036 **49.** 6080 **51.** -1925 **53.** 15,960 **55.** $-\dfrac{3}{2}$ **57.** 24 terms **59.** 1185 seats

61. 210 beige and 190 blue **63.** $\{T_n\} = \{-5.5n + 67\}; T_5 = 39.5°F$ **65.** The amphitheater has 1647 seats. **67.** 8 yr

Historical Problem (page 816)

1. $1\dfrac{2}{3}$ loaves, $10\dfrac{5}{6}$ loaves, 20 loaves, $29\dfrac{1}{6}$ loaves, $38\dfrac{1}{3}$ loaves

12.3 Assess Your Understanding (page 817)

3. geometric **4.** $\dfrac{a}{1 - r}$ **5.** divergent series **6.** T **7.** F **8.** T **9.** $r = 3; s_1 = 3, s_2 = 9, s_3 = 27, s_4 = 81$

11. $r = \dfrac{1}{2}; a_1 = -\dfrac{3}{2}, a_2 = -\dfrac{3}{4}, a_3 = -\dfrac{3}{8}, a_4 = -\dfrac{3}{16}$ **13.** $r = 2; c_1 = \dfrac{1}{4}, c_2 = \dfrac{1}{2}, c_3 = 1, c_4 = 2$ **15.** $r = 2^{1/3}; e_1 = 2^{1/3}, e_2 = 2^{2/3}, e_3 = 2, e_4 = 2^{4/3}$

17. $r = \dfrac{3}{2}; t_1 = \dfrac{1}{2}, t_2 = \dfrac{3}{4}, t_3 = \dfrac{9}{8}, t_4 = \dfrac{27}{16}$ **19.** $a_5 = 162; a_n = 2 \cdot 3^{n-1}$ **21.** $a_5 = 5; a_n = 5 \cdot (-1)^{n-1}$ **23.** $a_5 = 0; a_n = 0$

25. $a_5 = 4\sqrt{2}; a_n = (\sqrt{2})^n$ **27.** $a_7 = \dfrac{1}{64}$ **29.** $a_9 = 1$ **31.** $a_8 = 0.00000004$ **33.** $a_n = 7 \cdot 2^{n-1}$ **35.** $a_n = -3 \cdot \left(-\dfrac{1}{3}\right)^{n-1} = \left(-\dfrac{1}{3}\right)^{n-2}$

37. $a_n = -(-3)^{n-1}$ **39.** $a_n = \dfrac{7}{15}(15)^{n-1} = 7 \cdot 15^{n-2}$ **41.** $-\dfrac{1}{4}(1 - 2^n)$ **43.** $2\left[1 - \left(\dfrac{2}{3}\right)^n\right]$ **45.** $1 - 2^n$

47.
```
(1/4)sum(seq(2^n
,n,0,14,1))
        8191.75
```

49.
```
sum(seq((2/3)^n,
n,1,15,1))
       1.995432683
```

51.
```
-1sum(seq(2^n,n,
0,14,1))
            -32767
```

53. Converges; $\dfrac{3}{2}$ **55.** Converges; 16 **57.** Converges; $\dfrac{8}{5}$ **59.** Diverges **61.** Converges; $\dfrac{20}{3}$ **63.** Diverges **65.** Converges; $\dfrac{18}{5}$ **67.** Converges; 6

69. Arithmetic; $d = 1; 1375$ **71.** Neither **73.** Arithmetic; $d = -\dfrac{2}{3}; -700$ **75.** Neither **77.** Geometric; $r = \dfrac{2}{3}; 2\left[1 - \left(\dfrac{2}{3}\right)^{50}\right]$

79. Geometric; $r = -2; -\dfrac{1}{3}[1 - (-2)^{50}]$ **81.** Geometric; $r = 3^{1/2}; -\dfrac{\sqrt{3}}{2}(1 + \sqrt{3})(1 - 3^{25})$ **83.** -4 **85.** \$21,879.11 **87.** **(a)** 0.775 ft **(b)** 8th

(c) 15.88 ft **(d)** 20 ft **89.** \$349,496.41 **91.** \$96,885.98 **93.** \$305.10 **95.** 1.845×10^{19} **97.** 10 **99.** \$72.67 per share **101.** December 20, 2010;
\$9999.92 **103.** Option B results in more money (\$524,287 versus \$500,500). **105.** Total pay: \$41,943.03; pay on day 22: \$20,971.52

12.4 Assess Your Understanding (page 823)

1. (I) $n = 1: 2(1) = 2$ and $1(1 + 1) = 2$
  (II) If $2 + 4 + 6 + \cdots + 2k = k(k + 1)$, then $2 + 4 + 6 + \cdots + 2k + 2(k + 1) = (2 + 4 + 6 + \cdots + 2k) + 2(k + 1)$
    $= k(k + 1) + 2(k + 1) = k^2 + 3k + 2 = (k + 1)(k + 2) = (k + 1)[(k + 1) + 1]$.

3. (I) $n = 1: 1 + 2 = 3$ and $\dfrac{1}{2}(1)(1 + 5) = \dfrac{1}{2}(6) = 3$

  (II) If $3 + 4 + 5 + \cdots + (k + 2) = \dfrac{1}{2}k(k + 5)$, then $3 + 4 + 5 + \cdots + (k + 2) + [(k + 1) + 2]$

    $= [3 + 4 + 5 + \cdots + (k + 2)] + (k + 3) = \dfrac{1}{2}k(k + 5) + k + 3 = \dfrac{1}{2}(k^2 + 7k + 6) = \dfrac{1}{2}(k + 1)(k + 6) = \dfrac{1}{2}(k + 1)[(k + 1) + 5]$.

5. (I) $n = 1$: $3(1) - 1 = 2$ and $\frac{1}{2}(1)[3(1) + 1] = \frac{1}{2}(4) = 2$

(II) If $2 + 5 + 8 + \cdots + (3k - 1) = \frac{1}{2}k(3k + 1)$, then $2 + 5 + 8 + \cdots + (3k - 1) + [3(k + 1) - 1]$

$= [2 + 5 + 8 + \cdots + (3k - 1)] + (3k + 2) = \frac{1}{2}k(3k + 1) + (3k + 2) = \frac{1}{2}(3k^2 + 7k + 4) = \frac{1}{2}(k + 1)(3k + 4)$

$= \frac{1}{2}(k + 1)[3(k + 1) + 1].$

7. (I) $n = 1$: $2^{1-1} = 1$ and $2^1 - 1 = 1$

(II) If $1 + 2 + 2^2 + \cdots + 2^{k-1} = 2^k - 1$, then $1 + 2 + 2^2 + \cdots + 2^{k-1} + 2^{(k+1)-1} = (1 + 2 + 2^2 + \cdots + 2^{k-1}) + 2^k$

$= 2^k - 1 + 2^k = 2(2^k) - 1 = 2^{k+1} - 1.$

9. (I) $n = 1$: $4^{1-1} = 1$ and $\frac{1}{3}(4^1 - 1) = \frac{1}{3}(3) = 1$

(II) If $1 + 4 + 4^2 + \cdots + 4^{k-1} = \frac{1}{3}(4^k - 1)$, then $1 + 4 + 4^2 + \cdots + 4^{k-1} + 4^{(k+1)-1} = (1 + 4 + 4^2 + \cdots + 4^{k-1}) + 4^k$

$= \frac{1}{3}(4^k - 1) + 4^k = \frac{1}{3}[4^k - 1 + 3(4^k)] = \frac{1}{3}[4(4^k) - 1] = \frac{1}{3}(4^{k+1} - 1).$

11. (I) $n = 1$: $\frac{1}{1 \cdot 2} = \frac{1}{2}$ and $\frac{1}{1 + 1} = \frac{1}{2}$

(II) If $\frac{1}{1 \cdot 2} + \frac{1}{2 \cdot 3} + \frac{1}{3 \cdot 4} + \cdots + \frac{1}{k(k + 1)} = \frac{k}{k + 1}$, then $\frac{1}{1 \cdot 2} + \frac{1}{2 \cdot 3} + \frac{1}{3 \cdot 4} + \cdots + \frac{1}{k(k + 1)} + \frac{1}{(k + 1)[(k + 1) + 1]}$

$= \left[\frac{1}{1 \cdot 2} + \frac{1}{2 \cdot 3} + \frac{1}{3 \cdot 4} + \cdots + \frac{1}{k(k + 1)}\right] + \frac{1}{(k + 1)(k + 2)} = \frac{k}{k + 1} + \frac{1}{(k + 1)(k + 2)} = \frac{k(k + 2) + 1}{(k + 1)(k + 2)}$

$= \frac{k^2 + 2k + 1}{(k + 1)(k + 2)} = \frac{(k + 1)^2}{(k + 1)(k + 2)} = \frac{k + 1}{k + 2} = \frac{k + 1}{(k + 1) + 1}.$

13. (I) $n = 1$: $1^2 = 1$ and $\frac{1}{6} \cdot 1 \cdot 2 \cdot 3 = 1$

(II) If $1^2 + 2^2 + 3^2 + \cdots + k^2 = \frac{1}{6}k(k + 1)(2k + 1)$, then $1^2 + 2^2 + 3^2 + \cdots + k^2 + (k + 1)^2$

$= (1^2 + 2^2 + 3^2 + \cdots + k^2) + (k + 1)^2 = \frac{1}{6}k(k + 1)(2k + 1) + (k + 1)^2 = \frac{1}{6}(2k^3 + 9k^2 + 13k + 6)$

$= \frac{1}{6}(k + 1)(k + 2)(2k + 3) = \frac{1}{6}(k + 1)[(k + 1) + 1][2(k + 1) + 1].$

15. (I) $n = 1$: $5 - 1 = 4$ and $\frac{1}{2}(1)(9 - 1) = \frac{1}{2} \cdot 8 = 4$

(II) If $4 + 3 + 2 + \cdots + (5 - k) = \frac{1}{2}k(9 - k)$, then $4 + 3 + 2 + \cdots + (5 - k) + [5 - (k + 1)]$

$= [4 + 3 + 2 + \cdots + (5 - k)] + 4 - k = \frac{1}{2}k(9 - k) + 4 - k = \frac{1}{2}(9k - k^2 + 8 - 2k) = \frac{1}{2}(-k^2 + 7k + 8)$

$= \frac{1}{2}(k + 1)(8 - k) = \frac{1}{2}(k + 1)[9 - (k + 1)].$

17. (I) $n = 1$: $1 \cdot (1 + 1) = 2$ and $\frac{1}{3} \cdot 1 \cdot 2 \cdot 3 = 2$

(II) If $1 \cdot 2 + 2 \cdot 3 + 3 \cdot 4 + \cdots + k(k + 1) = \frac{1}{3}k(k + 1)(k + 2)$, then $1 \cdot 2 + 2 \cdot 3 + 3 \cdot 4 + \cdots + k(k + 1)$

$+ (k + 1)[(k + 1) + 1] = [1 \cdot 2 + 2 \cdot 3 + 3 \cdot 4 + \cdots + k(k + 1)] + (k + 1)(k + 2)$

$= \frac{1}{3}k(k + 1)(k + 2) + \frac{1}{3} \cdot 3(k + 1)(k + 2) = \frac{1}{3}(k + 1)(k + 2)(k + 3) = \frac{1}{3}(k + 1)[(k + 1) + 1][(k + 1) + 2].$

19. (I) $n = 1$: $1^2 + 1 = 2$, which is divisible by 2.

(II) If $k^2 + k$ is divisible by 2, then $(k + 1)^2 + (k + 1) = k^2 + 2k + 1 + k + 1 = (k^2 + k) + 2k + 2$. Since $k^2 + k$ is divisible by 2 and $2k + 2$ is divisible by 2, $(k + 1)^2 + (k + 1)$ is divisible by 2.

21. (I) $n = 1$: $1^2 - 1 + 2 = 2$, which is divisible by 2.

(II) If $k^2 - k + 2$ is divisible by 2, then $(k + 1)^2 - (k + 1) + 2 = k^2 + 2k + 1 - k - 1 + 2 = (k^2 - k + 2) + 2k$. Since $k^2 - k + 2$ is divisible by 2 and $2k$ is divisible by 2, $(k + 1)^2 - (k + 1) + 2$ is divisible by 2.

23. (I) $n = 1$: If $x > 1$, then $x^1 = x > 1$.

(II) Assume, for an arbitrary natural number k, that if $x > 1$ then $x^k > 1$. Multiply both sides of the inequality $x^k > 1$ by x. If $x > 1$, then $x^{k+1} > x > 1$.

25. (I) $n = 1$: $a - b$ is a factor of $a^1 - b^1 = a - b$.

(II) If $a - b$ is a factor of $a^k - b^k$, then $a^{k+1} - b^{k+1} = a(a^k - b^k) + b^k(a - b)$. Since $a - b$ is a factor of $a^k - b^k$ and $a - b$ is a factor of $a - b$, then $a - b$ is a factor of $a^{k+1} - b^{k+1}$.

27. (I) $n = 1: (1 + a)^1 = 1 + a \geq 1 + 1 \cdot a$

(II) Assume that there is an integer k for which the inequality holds. So $(1 + a)^k \geq 1 + ka$. We need to show that $(1 + a)^{k+1} \geq 1 + (k + 1)a$.
$(1 + a)^{k+1} = (1 + a)^k (1 + a) \geq (1 + ka)(1 + a) = 1 + ka^2 + a + ka = 1 + (k + 1)a + ka^2 \geq 1 + (k + 1)a$.

29. If $2 + 4 + 6 + \cdots + 2k = k^2 + k + 2$, then $2 + 4 + 6 + \cdots + 2k + 2(k + 1)$
$= (2 + 4 + 6 + \cdots + 2k) + 2k + 2 = k^2 + k + 2 + 2k + 2 = k^2 + 3k + 4 = (k^2 + 2k + 1) + (k + 1) + 2$
$= (k + 1)^2 + (k + 1) + 2$.
But $2 \cdot 1 = 2$ and $1^2 + 1 + 2 = 4$. The fact is that $2 + 4 + 6 + \cdots + 2n = n^2 + n$, not $n^2 + n + 2$ (Problem 1).

31. (I) $n = 1: [a + (1 - 1)d] = a$ and $1 \cdot a + d\dfrac{1 \cdot (1 - 1)}{2} = a$.

(II) If $a + (a + d) + (a + 2d) + \cdots + [a + (k - 1)d] = ka + d\dfrac{k(k - 1)}{2}$, then

$a + (a + d) + (a + 2d) + \cdots + [a + (k - 1)d] + [a + ((k + 1) - 1)d] = ka + d\dfrac{k(k - 1)}{2} + a + kd$

$= (k + 1)a + d\dfrac{k(k - 1) + 2k}{2} = (k + 1)a + d\dfrac{(k + 1)(k)}{2} = (k + 1)a + d\dfrac{(k + 1)[(k + 1) - 1]}{2}$.

33. (I) $n = 3$: The sum of the angles of a triangle is $(3 - 2) \cdot 180° = 180°$.

(II) Assume for some $k \geq 3$ that the sum of the angles of a convex polygon of k sides is $(k - 2) \cdot 180°$. A convex polygon of $k + 1$ sides consists of a convex polygon of k sides plus a triangle (see the illustration). The sum of the angles is
$(k - 2) \cdot 180° + 180° = (k - 1) \cdot 180° = [(k + 1) - 2] \cdot 180°$.

k sides

$k + 1$ sides

12.5 Assess Your Understanding (page 829)

1. Pascal's triangle   **2.** $1; n$ **3.** F   **4.** Binomial Theorem   **5.** 10   **7.** 21   **9.** 50   **11.** 1   **13.** $\approx 1.8664 \times 10^{15}$ **15.** $\approx 1.4834 \times 10^{13}$
17. $x^5 + 5x^4 + 10x^3 + 10x^2 + 5x + 1$ **19.** $x^6 - 12x^5 + 60x^4 - 160x^3 + 240x^2 - 192x + 64$ **21.** $81x^4 + 108x^3 + 54x^2 + 12x + 1$
23. $x^{10} + 5x^8y^2 + 10x^6y^4 + 10x^4y^6 + 5x^2y^8 + y^{10}$ **25.** $x^3 + 6\sqrt{2}x^{5/2} + 30x^2 + 40\sqrt{2}x^{3/2} + 60x + 24\sqrt{2}x^{1/2} + 8$
27. $a^5x^5 + 5a^4bx^4y + 10a^3b^2x^3y^2 + 10a^2b^3x^2y^3 + 5ab^4xy^4 + b^5y^5$ **29.** 17,010   **31.** $-101,376$ **33.** 41,472   **35.** $2835x^3$
37. $314,928x^7$ **39.** 495   **41.** 3360   **43.** 1.00501

45. $\dbinom{n}{n - 1} = \dfrac{n!}{(n - 1)! [n - (n - 1)]!} = \dfrac{n!}{(n - 1)! 1!} = \dfrac{n \cdot (n - 1)!}{(n - 1)!} = n; \dbinom{n}{n} = \dfrac{n!}{n! (n - n)!} = \dfrac{n!}{n!0!} = \dfrac{n!}{n!} = 1$

47. $2^n = (1 + 1)^n = \dbinom{n}{0}1^n + \dbinom{n}{1}(1)^{n-1}(1) + \cdots + \dbinom{n}{n}1^n = \dbinom{n}{0} + \dbinom{n}{1} + \cdots + \dbinom{n}{n}$ **49.** 1

Review Exercises (page 831)

1. $a_1 = -\dfrac{4}{3}, a_2 = \dfrac{5}{4}, a_3 = -\dfrac{6}{5}, a_4 = \dfrac{7}{6}, a_5 = -\dfrac{8}{7}$ **3.** $c_1 = 2, c_2 = 1, c_3 = \dfrac{8}{9}, c_4 = 1, c_5 = \dfrac{32}{25}$ **5.** $a_1 = 3, a_2 = 2, a_3 = \dfrac{4}{3}, a_4 = \dfrac{8}{9}, a_5 = \dfrac{16}{27}$

7. $a_1 = 2, a_2 = 0, a_3 = 2, a_4 = 0, a_5 = 2$ **9.** $6 + 10 + 14 + 18 = 48$ **11.** $\displaystyle\sum_{k=1}^{13} (-1)^{k+1}\dfrac{1}{k}$ **13.** Arithmetic; $d = 1; S_n = \dfrac{n}{2}(n + 11)$ **15.** Neither

17. Geometric; $r = 8; S_n = \dfrac{8}{7}(8^n - 1)$ **19.** Arithmetic; $d = 4; S_n = 2n(n - 1)$ **21.** Geometric; $r = \dfrac{1}{2}; S_n = 6\left[1 - \left(\dfrac{1}{2}\right)^n\right]$ **23.** Neither

25. 3825   **27.** 1125   **29.** $\dfrac{1093}{2187} \approx 0.49977$ **31.** 35   **33.** $\dfrac{1}{10^{10}}$ **35.** $9\sqrt{2}$ **37.** $\{a_n\} = \{5n - 4\}$ **39.** $\{a_n\} = \{n - 10\}$ **41.** Converges; $\dfrac{9}{2}$

43. Converges; $\dfrac{4}{3}$ **45.** Diverges   **47.** Converges; 8

49. (I) $n = 1: 3 \cdot 1 = 3$ and $\dfrac{3 \cdot 1}{2}(1 + 1) = 3$

(II) If $3 + 6 + 9 + \cdots + 3k = \dfrac{3k}{2}(k + 1)$, then $3 + 6 + 9 + \cdots + 3k + 3(k + 1) = (3 + 6 + 9 + \cdots + 3k) + (3k + 3)$

$= \dfrac{3k}{2}(k + 1) + (3k + 3) = \dfrac{3k^2}{2} + \dfrac{3k}{2} + \dfrac{6k}{2} + \dfrac{6}{2} = \dfrac{3}{2}(k^2 + 3k + 2) = \dfrac{3}{2}(k + 1)(k + 2) = \dfrac{3(k + 1)}{2}[(k + 1) + 1]$.

51. (I) $n = 1: 2 \cdot 3^{1-1} = 2$ and $3^1 - 1 = 2$

(II) If $2 + 6 + 18 + \cdots + 2 \cdot 3^{k-1} = 3^k - 1$, then $2 + 6 + 18 + \cdots + 2 \cdot 3^{k-1} + 2 \cdot 3^{(k+1)-1} = (2 + 6 + 18 + \cdots + 2 \cdot 3^{k-1}) + 2 \cdot 3^k$
$= 3^k - 1 + 2 \cdot 3^k = 3 \cdot 3^k - 1 = 3^{k+1} - 1$.

53. (I) $n = 1: (3 \cdot 1 - 2)^2 = 1$ and $\dfrac{1}{2} \cdot 1 \cdot [6(1)^2 - 3(1) - 1] = 1$

(II) If $1^2 + 4^2 + 7^2 + \cdots + (3k - 2)^2 = \dfrac{1}{2}k(6k^2 - 3k - 1)$, then $1^2 + 4^2 + 7^2 + \cdots + (3k - 2)^2 + [3(k + 1) - 2]^2$

$= [1^2 + 4^2 + 7^2 + \cdots + (3k - 2)^2] + (3k + 1)^2 = \dfrac{1}{2}k(6k^2 - 3k - 1) + (3k + 1)^2 = \dfrac{1}{2}(6k^3 - 3k^2 - k) + (9k^2 + 6k + 1)$

$= \dfrac{1}{2}(6k^3 + 15k^2 + 11k + 2) = \dfrac{1}{2}(k + 1)(6k^2 + 9k + 2) = \dfrac{1}{2}(k + 1)[6(k + 1)^2 - 3(k + 1) - 1]$.

55. 10 **57.** $x^5 + 10x^4 + 40x^3 + 80x^2 + 80x + 32$ **59.** $32x^5 + 240x^4 + 720x^3 + 1080x^2 + 810x + 243$ **61.** 144 **63.** 84

65. (a) 8 bricks **(b)** 1100 bricks **67. (a)** $20\left(\dfrac{3}{4}\right)^3 = \dfrac{135}{16}$ ft **(b)** $20\left(\dfrac{3}{4}\right)^n$ ft **(c)** 13 times **(d)** 140 ft **69.** \$244,129.08

Chapter Test *(page 833)*

1. $0, \dfrac{3}{10}, \dfrac{8}{11}, \dfrac{5}{4}, \dfrac{24}{13}$ **2.** $4, 14, 44, 134, 404$ **3.** $2 - \dfrac{3}{4} + \dfrac{4}{9} = \dfrac{61}{36}$ **4.** $-\dfrac{1}{3} - \dfrac{14}{9} - \dfrac{73}{27} - \dfrac{308}{81} = -\dfrac{680}{81}$ **5.** $\displaystyle\sum_{k=1}^{10}(-1)^k\left(\dfrac{k+1}{k+4}\right)$ **6.** Neither

7. Geometric; $r = 4$; $S_n = \dfrac{2}{3}(1 - 4^n)$ **8.** Arithmetic: $d = -8$; $S_n = n(2 - 4n)$ **9.** Arithmetic; $d = -\dfrac{1}{2}$; $S_n = \dfrac{n}{4}(27 - n)$

10. Geometric; $r = \dfrac{2}{5}$ $S_n = \dfrac{125}{3}\left[1 - \left(\dfrac{2}{5}\right)^n\right]$ **11.** Neither **12.** Converges; $\dfrac{1024}{5}$ **13.** $243m^5 + 810m^4 + 1080m^3 + 720m^2 + 240m + 32$

14. First we show that the statement holds for $n = 1$. $\left(1 + \dfrac{1}{1}\right) = 1 + 1 = 2$. The equality is true for $n = 1$, so Condition I holds. Next we assume that

$\left(1 + \dfrac{1}{1}\right)\left(1 + \dfrac{1}{2}\right)\left(1 + \dfrac{1}{3}\right)\cdots\left(1 + \dfrac{1}{n}\right) = n + 1$ is true for some k, and we determine whether the formula then holds for $k + 1$. We assume that

$\left(1 + \dfrac{1}{1}\right)\left(1 + \dfrac{1}{2}\right)\left(1 + \dfrac{1}{3}\right)\cdots\left(1 + \dfrac{1}{k}\right) = k + 1$. Now we need to show that $\left(1 + \dfrac{1}{1}\right)\left(1 + \dfrac{1}{2}\right)\left(1 + \dfrac{1}{3}\right)\cdots\left(1 + \dfrac{1}{k}\right)\left(1 + \dfrac{1}{k+1}\right)$

$= (k + 1) + 1 = k + 2$. We do this as follows:

$\left(1 + \dfrac{1}{1}\right)\left(1 + \dfrac{1}{2}\right)\left(1 + \dfrac{1}{3}\right)\cdots\left(1 + \dfrac{1}{k}\right)\left(1 + \dfrac{1}{k+1}\right) = \left[\left(1 + \dfrac{1}{1}\right)\left(1 + \dfrac{1}{2}\right)\left(1 + \dfrac{1}{3}\right)\cdots\left(1 + \dfrac{1}{k}\right)\right]\left(1 + \dfrac{1}{k+1}\right)$

$= (k + 1)\left(1 + \dfrac{1}{k+1}\right)$(induction assumption) $= (k + 1)\cdot 1 + (k + 1)\cdot\dfrac{1}{k+1} = k + 1 + 1 = k + 2$

Condition II also holds. Thus, the formula holds true for all natural numbers.
15. After 10 years, the Durango will be worth \$6103.11. **16.** The weightlifter will have lifted a total of 8000 pounds after 5 sets.

Cumulative Review *(page 833)*

1. $\{-3, 3, -3i, 3i\}$ **2. (a)**

(b) $\left\{\left(\sqrt{\dfrac{-1 + \sqrt{3601}}{18}}, \dfrac{-1 + \sqrt{3601}}{6}\right), \left(-\sqrt{\dfrac{-1 + \sqrt{3601}}{18}}, \dfrac{-1 + \sqrt{3601}}{6}\right)\right\}$

(c) The circle and the parabola intersect at

$\left(\sqrt{\dfrac{-1 + \sqrt{3601}}{18}}, \dfrac{-1 + \sqrt{3601}}{6}\right), \left(-\sqrt{\dfrac{-1 + \sqrt{3601}}{18}}, \dfrac{-1 + \sqrt{3601}}{6}\right)$.

3. $\left\{\ln\left(\dfrac{5}{2}\right)\right\}$ **4.** $y = 5x - 10$ **5.** $(x + 1)^2 + (y - 2)^2 = 25$ **6. (a)** 5 **(b)** 13 **(c)** $\dfrac{6x + 3}{2x - 1}$ **(d)** $\left\{x \middle| x \ne \dfrac{1}{2}\right\}$ **(e)** $\dfrac{7x - 2}{x - 2}$ **(f)** $\{x | x \ne 2\}$

(g) $g^{-1}(x) = \dfrac{1}{2}(x - 1)$; all reals **(h)** $f^{-1}(x) = \dfrac{2x}{x - 3}$; $\{x | x \ne 3\}$ **7.** $\dfrac{x^2}{7} + \dfrac{y^2}{16} = 1$ **8.** $(x + 1)^2 = 4(y - 2)$

9. $r = 8\sin\theta$; $x^2 + (y - 4)^2 = 16$ **10.** $\left\{\dfrac{3\pi}{2}\right\}$ **11.** $\dfrac{2\pi}{3}$ **12. (a)** $-\dfrac{\sqrt{15}}{4}$ **(b)** $-\dfrac{\sqrt{15}}{15}$ **(c)** $-\dfrac{\sqrt{15}}{8}$ **(d)** $\dfrac{7}{8}$ **(e)** $\sqrt{\dfrac{1 + \dfrac{\sqrt{15}}{4}}{2}} = \dfrac{\sqrt{4 + \sqrt{15}}}{2\sqrt{2}}$

CHAPTER 13 Counting and Probability

13.1 Assess Your Understanding *(page 840)*

5. subset; $\subseteq$ **6.** finite **7.** $n(A) + n(B) - n(A \cap B)$ **8.** T **9.** $\varnothing, \{a\}, \{b\}, \{c\}, \{d\}, \{a, b\}, \{a, c\}, \{a, d\}, \{b, c\}, \{b, d\}, \{c, d\}, \{a, b, c\}, \{b, c, d\}, \{a, c, d\},$
$\{a, b, d\}, \{a, b, c, d\}$ **11.** 25 **13.** 40 **15.** 25 **17.** 37 **19.** 18 **21.** 5 **23.** 15 different arrangements **25.** 9000 numbers **27.** 175; 125
29. (a) 15 **(b)** 15 **(c)** 15 **(d)** 25 **(e)** 40 **31. (a)** 11,923 thousand **(b)** 75,241 thousand **33.** 480 portfolios

13.2 Assess Your Understanding *(page 847)*

3. permutation **4.** combination **5.** $\dfrac{n!}{(n - r)!}$ **6.** $\dfrac{n!}{(n - r)!r!}$ **7.** 30 **9.** 24 **11.** 1 **13.** 1680 **15.** 28 **17.** 35 **19.** 1 **21.** 10,400,600

23. $\{abc, abd, abe, acb, acd, ace, adb, adc, ade, aeb, aec, aed, bac, bad, bae, bca, bcd, bce, bda, bdc, bde, bea, bec, bed, cab, cad, cae, cba, cbd, cbe, cda,$
$cdb, cde, cea, ceb, ced, dab, dac, dae, dba, dbc, dbe, dca, dcb, dce, dea, deb, dec, eab, eac, ead, eba, ebc, ebd, eca, ecb, ecd, eda, edb, edc\}$; 60

25. $\{123, 124, 132, 134, 142, 143, 213, 214, 231, 234, 241, 243, 312, 314, 321, 324, 341, 342, 412, 413, 421, 423, 431, 432\}$; 24

27. $\{abc, abd, abe, acd, ace, ade, bcd, bce, bde, cde\}$; 10 **29.** $\{123, 124, 134, 234\}$; 4 **31.** 16 **33.** 8 **35.** 24 **37.** 60 **39.** 18,278 **41.** 35
43. 1024 **45.** 120 **47.** 132,860 **49.** 336 **51.** 90,720 **53. (a)** 63 **(b)** 35 **(c)** 1 **55.** 1.157×10^{76} **57.** 362,880 **59.** 660 **61.** 15
63. (a) 125,000; 117,600 **(b)** A better name for a *combination* lock would be a *permutation* lock because the order of the numbers matters.

Historical Problem *(page 857)*

1. (a) $\{AAAA, AAAB, AABA, AABB, ABAA, ABAB, ABBA, ABBB, BAAA, BAAB, BABA, BABB, BBAA, BBAB, BBBA, BBBB\}$

(b) $P(A \text{ wins}) = \dfrac{C(4,2) + C(4,3) + C(4,4)}{2^4} = \dfrac{6+4+1}{16} = \dfrac{11}{16}; \ P(B \text{ wins}) = \dfrac{C(4,3) + C(4,4)}{2^4} = \dfrac{4+1}{16} = \dfrac{5}{16}$

13.3 Assess Your Understanding *(page 857)*

1. equally likely   **2.** complement   **3.** F   **4.** T   **5.** $0, 0.01, 0.35, 1$ **7.** Probability model   **9.** Not a probability model

11. $S = \{HH, HT, TH, TT\}; P(HH) = \dfrac{1}{4}, P(HT) = \dfrac{1}{4}, P(TH) = \dfrac{1}{4}, P(TT) = \dfrac{1}{4}$ **13.** $S = \{HH1, HH2, HH3, HH4, HH5, HH6, HT1, HT2, HT3,$
$HT4, HT5, HT6, TH1, TH2, TH3, TH4, TH5, TH6, TT1, TT2, TT3, TT4, TT5, TT6\}$; each outcome has the probability of $\dfrac{1}{24}$.

15. $S = \{HHH, HHT, HTH, HTT, THH, THT, TTH, TTT\}$; each outcome has the probability of $\dfrac{1}{8}$.

17. $S = \{1 \text{ Yellow}, 1 \text{ Red}, 1 \text{ Green}, 2 \text{ Yellow}, 2 \text{ Red}, 2 \text{ Green}, 3 \text{ Yellow}, 3 \text{ Red}, 3 \text{ Green}, 4 \text{ Yellow}, 4 \text{ Red}, 4 \text{ Green}\}$; each outcome has the probability
of $\dfrac{1}{12}$; thus, $P(2 \text{ Red}) + P(4 \text{ Red}) = \dfrac{1}{12} + \dfrac{1}{12} = \dfrac{1}{6}$.

19. $S = \{1 \text{ Yellow Forward}, 1 \text{ Yellow Backward}, 1 \text{ Red Forward}, 1 \text{ Red Backward}, 1 \text{ Green Forward}, 1 \text{ Green Backward}, 2 \text{ Yellow Forward}, 2 \text{ Yellow}$
$\text{Backward}, 2 \text{ Red Forward}, 2 \text{ Red Backward}, 2 \text{ Green Forward}, 2 \text{ Green Backward}, 3 \text{ Yellow Forward}, 3 \text{ Yellow Backward}, 3 \text{ Red Forward}, 3 \text{ Red}$
$\text{Backward}, 3 \text{ Green Forward}, 3 \text{ Green Backward}, 4 \text{ Yellow Forward}, 4 \text{ Yellow Backward}, 4 \text{ Red Forward}, 4 \text{ Red Backward}, 4 \text{ Green Forward}, 4 \text{ Green}$
$\text{Backward}\}$; each outcome has the probability of $\dfrac{1}{24}$; thus, $P(1 \text{ Red Backward}) + P(1 \text{ Green Backward}) = \dfrac{1}{24} + \dfrac{1}{24} = \dfrac{1}{12}$.

21. $S = \{11 \text{ Red}, 11 \text{ Yellow}, 11 \text{ Green}, 12 \text{ Red}, 12 \text{ Yellow}, 12 \text{ Green}, 13 \text{ Red}, 13 \text{ Yellow}, 13 \text{ Green}, 14 \text{ Red}, 14 \text{ Yellow}, 14 \text{ Green}, 21 \text{ Red}, 21 \text{ Yellow}, 21 \text{ Green},$
$22 \text{ Red}, 22 \text{ Yellow}, 22 \text{ Green}, 23 \text{ Red}, 23 \text{ Yellow}, 23 \text{ Green}, 24 \text{ Red}, 24 \text{ Yellow}, 24 \text{ Green}, 31 \text{ Red}, 31 \text{ Yellow}, 31 \text{ Green}, 32 \text{ Red}, 32 \text{ Yellow}, 32 \text{ Green}, 33 \text{ Red},$
$33 \text{ Yellow}, 33 \text{ Green}, 34 \text{ Red}, 34 \text{ Yellow}, 34 \text{ Green}, 41 \text{ Red}, 41 \text{ Yellow}, 41 \text{ Green}, 42 \text{ Red}, 42 \text{ Yellow}, 42 \text{ Green}, 43 \text{ Red}, 43 \text{ Yellow}, 43 \text{ Green}, 44 \text{ Red},$
$44 \text{ Yellow}, 44 \text{ Green}\}$; each outcome has the probability of $\dfrac{1}{48}$; thus, $E = \{22 \text{ Red}, 22 \text{ Green}, 24 \text{ Red}, 24 \text{ Green}\}; P(E) = \dfrac{n(E)}{n(S)} = \dfrac{4}{48} = \dfrac{1}{12}$.

23. A, B, C, F   **25.** B   **27.** $P(H) = \dfrac{4}{5}; \ P(T) = \dfrac{1}{5}$ **29.** $P(1) = P(3) = P(5) = \dfrac{2}{9}; \ P(2) = P(4) = P(6) = \dfrac{1}{9}$ **31.** $\dfrac{3}{10}$ **33.** $\dfrac{1}{2}$ **35.** $\dfrac{1}{6}$ **37.** $\dfrac{1}{8}$

39. $\dfrac{1}{4}$ **41.** $\dfrac{1}{6}$ **43.** $\dfrac{1}{18}$ **45.** 0.55 **47.** 0.70 **49.** 0.30 **51.** 0.87 **53.** 0.66 **55.** 0.95 **57.** $\dfrac{17}{20}$ **59.** $\dfrac{11}{20}$ **61.** $\dfrac{1}{2}$ **63.** $\dfrac{3}{10}$ **65.** $\dfrac{2}{5}$

67. (a) 0.57 **(b)** 0.95 **(c)** 0.83 **(d)** 0.38 **(e)** 0.29 **(f)** 0.05 **(g)** 0.78 **(h)** 0.71 **69. (a)** $\dfrac{25}{33}$ **(b)** $\dfrac{25}{33}$ **71.** 0.167 **73.** 0.000033069

Review Exercises *(page 861)*

1. $\varnothing, \{Dave\}, \{Joanne\}, \{Erica\}, \{Dave, Joanne\}, \{Dave, Erica\}, \{Joanne, Erica\}, \{Dave, Joanne, Erica\}$
3. 17   **5.** 29   **7.** 7   **9.** 25   **11.** 336   **13.** 56   **15.** 60   **17.** 128   **19.** 3024   **21.** 1680   **23.** 91   **25.** 1,600,000   **27.** 216,000   **29.** 1260
31. (a) 381,024   **(b)** 1260   **33. (a)** $8.634628387 \times 10^{45}$ **(b)** 0.6531 **(c)** 0.3469 **35. (a)** 0.058 **(b)** 0.942 **37.** $\dfrac{4}{9}$ **39.** $0.2; 0.26$

Chapter Test *(page 862)*

1. 22   **2.** 3   **3.** 8   **4.** 45   **5.** 5040   **6.** 151,200   **7.** 462   **8.** There are 54,264 ways to choose 6 different colors from the 21 available colors.
9. There are 840 distinct arrangements of the letters in the word REDEEMED.   **10.** There are 56 different exacta bets for an 8-horse race.
11. There are 155,480,000 possible license plates using the new format.   **12. (a)** 0.95 **(b)** 0.30 **13. (a)** 0.25 **(b)** 0.55 **14.** 0.19

15. $P(\text{win on \$1 play}) = \dfrac{1}{120,526,770} \approx 0.0000000083$ **16.** $P(\text{exactly 2 fours}) = \dfrac{1250}{7776} \approx 0.1608$

Cumulative Review *(page 863)*

1. $\left\{\dfrac{1}{3} - \dfrac{\sqrt{2}}{3}i, \dfrac{1}{3} + \dfrac{\sqrt{2}}{3}i\right\}$ **2.** 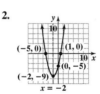   **3.** 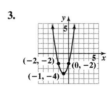   **4.** $\{x | 3.99 \le x \le 4.01\}$ or $[3.99, 4.01]$

5. $\left\{-\dfrac{1}{2} + \dfrac{\sqrt{7}}{2}i, -\dfrac{1}{2} - \dfrac{\sqrt{7}}{2}i, -\dfrac{1}{5}, 3\right\}$ **6.** 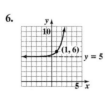   **7.** 2   **8.** $\left\{\dfrac{8}{3}\right\}$ **9.** $x = 2, y = -5, \ z = 3$ **10.** $125; 700$

11. 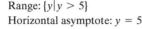   **12.** $a \approx 6.09, B \approx 31.9°, C \approx 108.1°$; area ≈ 14.46 square units

Domain: all real numbers
Range: $\{y | y > 5\}$
Horizontal asymptote: $y = 5$

CHAPTER 14 A Preview of Calculus: The Limit, Derivative, and Integral of a Function

14.1 Assess Your Understanding (page 869)

3. $\lim_{x \to c} f(x)$ **4.** does not exist   **5.** T   **6.** F   **7.** 32   **9.** 1   **11.** 4   **13.** 2   **15.** 0   **17.** 3   **19.** 4   **21.** Does not exist

23.

$\lim_{x \to 4} f(x) = 13$

25.

$\lim_{x \to 2} f(x) = -3$

27.

$\lim_{x \to -3} f(x) = 6$

29.

$\lim_{x \to \pi/2} f(x) = 1$

31.

$\lim_{x \to 0} f(x) = 1$

33.

$\lim_{x \to -1} f(x) = -1$

35.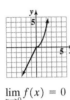

$\lim_{x \to 0} f(x) = 0$

37.

$\lim_{x \to 1} f(x)$ does not exist.

39.

$\lim_{x \to 0} f(x) = 0$

41.

$\lim_{x \to 0} f(x) = 0$

43. 0.67   **45.** 1.6   **47.** 0

14.2 Assess Your Understanding (page 877)

1. product   **2.** b **3.** c **4.** T   **5.** F   **6.** F   **7.** 5   **9.** 4   **11.** -10 **13.** 80   **15.** 8   **17.** 8   **19.** -1 **21.** 8   **23.** 3   **25.** -1 **27.** 32   **29.** 2   **31.** $\dfrac{7}{6}$
33. 3   **35.** 0   **37.** $\dfrac{2}{3}$ **39.** $\dfrac{8}{5}$ **41.** 0   **43.** 5   **45.** 6   **47.** 0   **49.** 0   **51.** -1 **53.** 1   **53.** $\dfrac{3}{4}$

14.3 Assess Your Understanding (page 883)

7. one-sided   **8.** $\lim_{x \to c^+} f(x) = R$ **9.** continuous; c **10.** F   **11.** T   **12.** T   **13.** $\{x | -8 \le x < -6 \text{ or } -6 < x < 4 \text{ or } 4 < x \le 6\}$ **15.** $-8, -5, -3$
17. $f(-8) = 0; f(-4) = 2$ **19.** ∞ **21.** 2   **23.** 1   **25.** Limit exists; 0   **27.** No   **29.** Yes   **31.** No   **33.** 5   **35.** 7   **37.** 1   **39.** 4   **41.** $-\dfrac{2}{3}$ **43.** $\dfrac{3}{2}$

45. Continuous   **47.** Continuous   **49.** Not continuous   **51.** Not continuous   **53.** Not continuous   **55.** Continuous   **57.** Not continuous
59. Continuous   **61.** Continuous for all real numbers   **63.** Continuous for all real numbers   **65.** Continuous for all real numbers

67. Continuous for all real numbers except $x = \dfrac{k\pi}{2}$, where k is an odd integer   **69.** Continuous for all real numbers except $x = -2$ and $x = 2$

71. Continuous for all positive real numbers except $x = 1$

73. Discontinuous at $x = -1$ and $x = 1$;

$\lim_{x \to 1} R(x) = \dfrac{1}{2}$: Hole at $\left(1, \dfrac{1}{2}\right)$

$\lim_{x \to -1^-} R(x) = -\infty; \ \lim_{x \to -1^+} R(x) = \infty$;

vertical asymptote at $x = -1$

75. Discontinuous at $x = -1$ and $x = 1$;

$\lim_{x \to -1} R(x) = \dfrac{1}{2}$: Hole at $\left(-1, \dfrac{1}{2}\right)$

$\lim_{x \to 1^-} R(x) = -\infty; \ \lim_{x \to 1^+} R(x) = \infty$;

vertical asymptote at $x = 1$

77. $x = -\sqrt[3]{2}$: Asymptote; $x = 1$: Hole   **79.** $x = -3$: Asymptote; $x = 2$: Hole   **81.** $x = -\sqrt[3]{2}$: Asymptote; $x = -1$: Hole

83.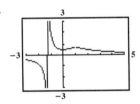

85.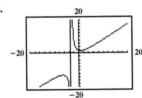

87.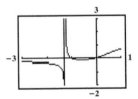

14.4 Assess Your Understanding (page 890)

3. tangent line   **4.** derivative   **5.** velocity   **6.** T   **7.** T   **8.** T

9. $m_{\tan} = 3$

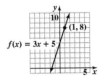

$f(x) = 3x + 5$

11. $m_{\tan} = -2$

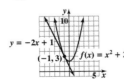

$y = -2x + 1$

$f(x) = x^2 + 2$

13. $m_{\tan} = 12$

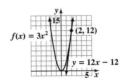

$f(x) = 3x^2$

$y = 12x - 12$

15. $m_{\tan} = 5$

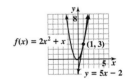

$f(x) = 2x^2 + x$

$y = 5x - 2$

17. $m_{\tan} = -4$

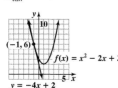

$f(x) = x^2 - 2x + 3$
$(-1, 6)$
$y = -4x + 2$

19. $m_{\tan} = 13$

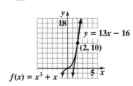

$y = 13x - 16$
$(2, 10)$
$f(x) = x^3 + x$

21. -4 **23.** 0 **25.** 7 **27.** 7 **29.** 3 **31.** 1 **33.** 60 **35.** -0.8587776956
37. 1.389623659 **39.** 2.362110222 **41.** 3.643914112 **43.** 18π ft^3/ft
45. 16π ft^3/ft   **47. (a)** 6 sec   **(b)** 64 ft/sec   **(c)** $(-32t + 96)$ ft/sec
(d) 32 ft/sec   **(e)** 3 sec   **(f)** 144 ft   **(g)** -96 ft/sec
49. (a) $-23\frac{1}{3}$ ft/sec   **(b)** -21 ft/sec   **(c)** -18 ft/sec
(d) $s(t) = -2.631t^2 - 10.269t + 999.933$ **(e)** Approximately -15.531 ft/sec

14.5 Assess Your Understanding *(page 897)*

3. $\int_a^b f(x)\,dx$ **4.** $\int_a^b f(x)\,dx$ **5.** 3 **7.** 56

9. (a)

(b) 36 **(c)** 72
(d) 45 **(e)** 63 **(f)** 54

11. (a)

(b) 18 **(c)** 9
(d) $\frac{63}{4}$ **(e)** $\frac{45}{4}$ **(f)** $\frac{27}{2}$

13. (a)

(b) 22 **(c)** $\frac{51}{2}$
(d) $\int_0^4 (x^2 + 2)\,dx$ **(e)** $\frac{88}{3}$

15. (a)
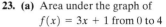

(b) 36 **(c)** 49
(d) $\int_0^4 x^3\,dx$ **(e)** 64

17. (a)

(b) $\frac{25}{12}$ **(c)** $\frac{4609}{2520}$
(d) $\int_1^5 \frac{1}{x}\,dx$ **(e)** 1.609

19. (a)

(b) 11.475 **(c)** 15.197
(d) $\int_{-1}^3 e^x\,dx$ **(e)** 19.718

21. (a)

(b) 1.896 **(c)** 1.974
(d) $\int_0^\pi \sin x\,dx$ **(e)** 2

23. (a) Area under the graph of
$f(x) = 3x + 1$ from 0 to 4
(b)

(c) 28

25. (a) Area under the graph of $f(x) = x^2 - 1$
from 2 to 5
(b)

(c) 36

27. (a) Area under the graph of $f(x) = \sin x$
from 0 to $\frac{\pi}{2}$
(b)

(c) 1

29. (a) Area under the graph of $f(x) = e^x$
from 0 to 2
(b)

(c) 6.389

31. Using left endpoints: $n = 2$: $0 + 0.5 = 0.5$;
$n = 4$: $0 + 0.125 + 0.25 + 0.375 = 0.75$;
$n = 10$: $0 + 0.02 + 0.04 + 0.06 + \cdots + 0.18 = \frac{10}{2}(0 + 0.18) = 0.9$;
$n = 100$: $0 + 0.0002 + 0.0004 + 0.0006 + \cdots + 0.0198$
$= \frac{100}{2}(0 + 0.0198) = 0.99$;

Using right endpoints:
$n = 2$: $0.5 + 1 = 1.5$; $n = 4$: $0.125 + 0.25 + 0.375 + 0.5 = 1.25$;
$n = 10$: $0.02 + 0.04 + 0.06 + \cdots + 0.20 = \frac{10}{2}(0.02 + 0.20) = 1.1$;
$n = 100$: $0.0002 + 0.0004 + 0.0006 + \cdots + 0.02$
$= \frac{100}{2}(0.0002 + 0.02) = 1.01$

Review Exercises *(page 899)*

1. 9 **3.** 25 **5.** 4 **7.** 0 **9.** 64 **11.** $-\frac{1}{4}$ **13.** $\frac{1}{3}$ **15.** $\frac{6}{7}$ **17.** 0 **19.** $\frac{3}{2}$ **21.** $\frac{28}{11}$ **23.** Continuous   **25.** Not continuous   **27.** Not continuous
29. Continuous   **31.** $\{x \mid -6 \le x < 2 \text{ or } 2 < x < 5 \text{ or } 5 < x \le 6\}$ **33.** $1, 6$ **35.** $f(-6) = 2; f(-4) = 1$ **37.** 4 **39.** -2 **41.** $-\infty$
43. Does not exist   **45.** No   **47.** No   **49.** Yes
51. R is discontinuous at $x = -4$ and $x = 4$.

$\lim_{x \to -4} R(x) = -\frac{1}{8}$: Hole at $\left(-4, -\frac{1}{8}\right)$
$\lim_{x \to 4^-} R(x) = -\infty$; $\lim_{x \to 4^+} R(x) = \infty$:
The graph of R has a vertical asymptote at
$x = 4$.

$x = 4$

53. Undefined at $x = 2$ and $x = 9$; R has a hole at
$x = 2$ and a vertical asymptote at $x = 9$.

55. $m_{\tan} = 12$

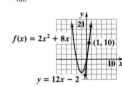

$f(x) = 2x^2 + 8x$ (1, 10)

$y = 12x - 2$

57. $m_{\tan} = 0$

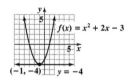

$f(x) = x^2 + 2x - 3$

$(-1, -4)$ $y = -4$

59. $m_{\tan} = 16$

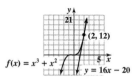

$(2, 12)$

$f(x) = x^3 + x^2$ $y = 16x - 20$

61. -24 **63.** -3 **65.** 7 **67.** -158 **69.** 0.6662517653 **71. (a)** 7 sec **(b)** 6 sec **(c)** 64 ft/sec **(d)** $(-32t + 96)$ ft/sec **(e)** 32 ft/sec
(f) At $t = 3$ sec **(g)** -96 ft/sec **(h)** -128 ft/sec **73. (a)** $61.29/watch **(b)** $71.31/watch **(c)** $81.40/watch
(d) $R(x) = -0.25x^2 + 100.01x - 1.24$ **(e)** Approximately $87.51/watch

75. (a)

(b) 24 **(c)** 32
(d) 26 **(e)** 30 **(f)** 28

77. (a)

(b) 10 **(c)** $\dfrac{77}{8}$

(d) $\displaystyle\int_{-1}^{2} (4 - x^2)\,dx$ **(e)** 9

79. (a)

(b) $\dfrac{49}{36} \approx 1.36$ **(c)** 1.02

(d) $\displaystyle\int_{1}^{4} \dfrac{1}{x^2}\,dx$ **(e)** 0.75

81. (a) Area under the graph of
$f(x) = 9 - x^2$ from -1 to 3
(b)

(c) $\dfrac{80}{3}$

83. (a) Area under the graph of $f(x) = e^x$ from -1 to 1 **(b)**

(c) 2.35

Chapter Test (page 902)

1. -5 **2.** $\dfrac{1}{3}$ **3.** 5 **4.** -2 **5.** 135 **6.** $\dfrac{2}{3}$ **7.** -1 **8.** -3 **9.** 5 **10.** 2 **11.** Limit exists; 2

12. (a) Yes **(b)** No; $\lim\limits_{x \to 1} f(x) \neq f(1)$ **(c)** No; $\lim\limits_{x \to 3^-} f(x) \neq f(3)$ **(d)** Yes **13.** $x = -7$: asymptote; $x = 2$: hole

14. (a) 5
(b) $y = 5x - 19$
(c)

$f(x) = 4x^2 - 11x - 3$
$y = 5x - 19$
$(2, -9)$

15. (a)

(graph)

(b) 13.359
(c) $4\pi \approx 12.566$

16. $\displaystyle\int_{1}^{4} (-x^2 + 5x + 3)\,dx$ **17.** $35\dfrac{1}{3}$ ft/sec

APPENDIX A Review

A.1 Assess Your Understanding (page A10)

1. variable **2.** origin **3.** strict **4.** base; exponent or power **5.** T **6.** T **7.** F **8.** F **9.** {1, 2, 3, 4, 5, 6, 7, 8, 9} **11.** {4} **13.** {1, 3, 4, 6}
15. {0, 2, 6, 7, 8} **17.** {0, 1, 2, 3, 5, 6, 7, 8, 9} **19.** {0, 1, 2, 3, 5, 6, 7, 8, 9} **21.** (number line: -2.5, -1, 0, $\frac{3}{4}$, 1, 0.25, $\frac{5}{2}$) **23.** > **25.** >

27. > **29.** = **31.** < **33.** $x > 0$ **35.** $x < 2$ **37.** $x \leq 1$ **39.** (number line: -2) **41.** (number line: -1) **43.** 1 **45.** 2 **47.** 6 **49.** 4

51. -28 **53.** $\dfrac{4}{5}$ **55.** 0 **57.** 1 **59.** 5 **61.** 1 **63.** 22 **65.** 2 **67.** $x = 0$ **69.** $x = 3$ **71.** None **73.** $x = 0, x = 1, x = -1$ **75.** $\{x \mid x \neq 5\}$

77. $\{x \mid x \neq -4\}$ **79.** 0°C **81.** 25°C **83.** 16 **85.** $\dfrac{1}{16}$ **87.** $\dfrac{1}{9}$ **89.** 9 **91.** 5 **93.** 4 **95.** $64x^6$ **97.** $\dfrac{x^4}{y^2}$ **99.** $\dfrac{x}{y}$ **101.** $-\dfrac{8x^3z}{9y}$ **103.** $\dfrac{16x^2}{9y^2}$ **105.** -4

107. 5 **109.** 4 **111.** 2 **113.** $\sqrt{5}$ **115.** $\dfrac{1}{2}$ **117.** 10; 0 **119.** 81 **121.** 304,006.671 **123.** 0.004 **125.** 481.890 **127.** 0.000 **129.** $A = lw$

131. $C = \pi d$ **133.** $A = \dfrac{\sqrt{3}}{4}x^2$ **135.** $V = \dfrac{4}{3}\pi r^3$ **137.** $V = x^3$ **139. (a)** $6000 **(b)** $8000 **141.** $|x - 4| \geq 6$ **143. (a)** $2 \leq 5$ **(b)** $6 > 5$

145. (a) Yes **(b)** No **147.** No; $\dfrac{1}{3}$ is larger; 0.000333... **149.** No

A.2 Assess Your Understanding (page A19)

1. right; hypotenuse **2.** $A = \frac{1}{2}bh$ **3.** $C = 2\pi r$ **4.** similar **5.** T **6.** T **7.** F **8.** T **9.** T **10.** F **11.** 13 **13.** 26 **15.** 25 **17.** Right triangle; 5
19. Not a right triangle **21.** Right triangle; 25 **23.** Not a right triangle **25.** 8 in.^{2} **27.** 4 in.^{2} **29.** $A = 25\pi$ m^2; $C = 10\pi$ m
31. $V = 224$ ft^3; $S = 232$ ft^2 **33.** $V = \frac{256}{3}\pi$ cm^3; $S = 64\pi$ cm^2 **35.** $V = 648\pi$ in.^{3}; $S = 306\pi$ in.^{2} **37.** π square units **39.** 2π square units
41. $x = 4$ units; $A = 90°$; $B = 60°$; $C = 30°$ **43.** $x = 67.5$ units; $A = 60°$; $B = 95°$; $C = 25°$ **45.** About 16.8 ft **47.** 64 ft^2
49. $24 + 2\pi \approx 30.28$ ft^2; $16 + 2\pi \approx 22.28$ ft **51.** 160 paces **53.** About 5.477 mi **55.** From 100 ft: 12.2 mi; From 150 ft: 15.0 mi

A.3 Assess Your Understanding (page A30)

1. 4; 3 **2.** $x^4 - 16$ **3.** $x^3 - 8$ **4.** F **5.** F **6.** quotient; divisor; remainder **7.** $3x(x - 2)(x + 2)$ **8.** add; $\frac{25}{4}$ **9.** T **10.** F **11.** Monomial; variable: x;
coefficient: 2; degree: 3 **13.** Not a monomial; the exponent of the variable is not a nonnegative integer **15.** Not a monomial; it has more than one term
17. Not a monomial; the exponent of one of the variables is not a nonnegative integer **19.** Not a monomial; it has more than one term **21.** Yes; 2
23. Yes; 0 **25.** No; the variable of one of the terms is not a nonnegative integer **27.** Yes; 3 **29.** No; the polynomial of the denominator has a
degree greater than 0 **31.** $x^2 + 7x + 2$ **33.** $x^3 - 4x^2 + 9x + 7$ **35.** $-2x^3 + 18x^2 - 18$ **37.** $15y^2 - 27y + 30$ **39.** $x^3 + x^2 - 4x$
41. $x^2 + 6x + 8$ **43.** $2x^2 + 9x + 10$ **45.** $x^2 - 49$ **47.** $4x^2 - 9$ **49.** $x^2 + 8x + 16$ **51.** $4x^2 - 12x + 9$ **53.** $x^3 - 6x^2 + 12x - 8$
55. $8x^3 + 12x^2 + 6x + 1$ **57.** $4x^2 - 11x + 23$; remainder -45 **59.** $4x - 3$; remainder $x + 1$ **61.** $5x^2 - 13$; remainder $x + 27$
63. $2x^2$; remainder $-x^2 + x + 1$ **65.** $x^2 - 2x + \frac{1}{2}$; remainder $\frac{5}{2}x + \frac{1}{2}$ **67.** $-4x^2 - 3x - 3$; remainder -7 **69.** $x^2 - x - 1$; remainder $2x + 2$
71. $x^2 + ax + a^2$; remainder 0 **73.** $(x + 6)(x - 6)$ **75.** $2(1 + 2x)(1 - 2x)$ **77.** $(x + 1)(x + 10)$ **79.** $(x - 7)(x - 3)$ **81.** $4(x^2 - 2x + 8)$
83. Prime **85.** $-(x - 5)(x + 3)$ **87.** $3(x + 2)(x - 6)$ **89.** $y^2(y + 5)(y + 6)$ **91.** $(2x + 3)^2$ **93.** $2(3x + 1)(x + 1)$
95. $(x - 3)(x + 3)(x^2 + 9)$ **97.** $(x - 1)^2(x^2 + x + 1)^2$ **99.** $x^5(x - 1)(x + 1)$ **101.** $(4x + 3)^2$ **103.** $-(4x - 5)(4x + 1)$
105. $(2y - 5)(2y - 3)$ **107.** $-(3x - 1)(3x + 1)(x^2 + 1)$ **109.** $(x + 3)(x - 6)$ **111.** $(x + 2)(x - 3)$ **113.** $(3x - 5)(9x^2 - 3x + 7)$
115. $(x + 5)(3x + 11)$ **117.** $(x - 1)(x + 1)(x + 2)$ **119.** $(x - 1)(x + 1)(x^2 - x + 1)$ **121.** 25; $(x + 5)^2$ **123.** 9; $(y - 3)^2$
125. $\frac{1}{16}$; $\left(x - \frac{1}{4}\right)^2$ **127.** $2(3x + 4)(9x + 13)$ **129.** $2x(3x + 5)$ **131.** $5(x + 3)(x - 2)^2(x + 1)$ **133.** $3(4x - 3)(4x - 1)$
135. $6(3x - 5)(2x + 1)^2(5x - 4)$ **137.** The possibilities are $(x \pm 1)(x \pm 4) = x^2 \pm 5x + 4$ or $(x \pm 2)(x \pm 2) = x^2 \pm 4x + 4$, none of which
equals $x^2 + 4$.

A.4 Assess Your Understanding (page A35)

1. quotient; divisor; remainder **2.** $-3\overline{)2\ 0\ -5\ 1}$ **3.** T **4.** T **5.** $x^2 + x + 4$; remainder 12 **7.** $3x^2 + 11x + 32$; remainder 99
9. $x^4 - 3x^3 + 5x^2 - 15x + 46$; remainder -138 **11.** $4x^5 + 4x^4 + x^3 + x^2 + 2x + 2$; remainder 7 **13.** $0.1x^2 - 0.11x + 0.321$; remainder -0.3531
15. $x^4 + x^3 + x^2 + x + 1$; remainder 0 **17.** No **19.** Yes **21.** Yes **23.** No **25.** Yes **27.** -9

A.5 Assess Your Understanding (page A42)

1. lowest terms **2.** least common multiple **3.** T **4.** F **5.** $\frac{3}{x - 3}$ **7.** $\frac{x}{3}$ **9.** $\frac{4x}{2x - 1}$ **11.** $\frac{y + 5}{2(y + 1)}$ **13.** $\frac{3}{5x(x - 2)}$ **15.** $\frac{2x(x^2 + 4x + 16)}{x + 4}$
17. $\frac{4}{5(x - 1)}$ **19.** $-\frac{(x - 4)^2}{4x}$ **21.** $\frac{(x - 2)(x + 2)}{2x - 3}$ **23.** $\frac{2(x^2 - 2)}{x(x - 2)(x + 2)}$ **25.** $\frac{5x}{(x - 6)(x - 1)(x + 4)}$ **27.** $\frac{2(2x^2 + 5x - 2)}{(x - 2)(x + 2)(x + 3)}$
29. $\frac{5x + 1}{(x - 1)^2(x + 1)^2}$ **31.** $\frac{x + 1}{x - 1}$ **33.** $\frac{-2x(x^2 - 2)}{(x + 2)(x^2 - x - 3)}$ **35.** $\frac{19}{(3x - 5)^2}$ **37.** $\frac{(x + 1)(x - 1)}{(x^2 + 1)^2}$ **39.** $\frac{x(3x + 2)}{(3x + 1)^2}$ **41.** $-\frac{(x + 3)(3x - 1)}{(x^2 + 1)^2}$
43. $f = \frac{R_1 \cdot R_2}{(n - 1)(R_1 + R_2)}$; $\frac{2}{15}$ m

A.6 Assess Your Understanding (page A51)

5. F **6.** identity **7.** F **8.** T **9.** add; $\frac{25}{4}$ **10.** discriminant; negative **11.** F **12.** F **13.** 7 **15.** -3 **17.** 4 **19.** $\frac{5}{4}$ **21.** -1 **23.** -18 **25.** -3
27. -16 **29.** 0.5 **31.** 2 **33.** 2 **35.** 3 **37.** $\{0, 9\}$ **39.** $\{0, 9\}$ **41.** 21 **43.** $\{-2, 2\}$ **45.** 6 **47.** $\{-3, 3\}$ **49.** $\{-4, 1\}$ **51.** $\left\{-1, \frac{3}{2}\right\}$ **53.** $\{-4, 4\}$
55. 2 **57.** No real solution **59.** $\{-2, 2\}$ **61.** $\{-1, 3\}$ **63.** $\{-2, -1, 0, 1\}$ **65.** $\{0, 4\}$ **67.** $\{-6, 2\}$ **69.** $\left\{-\frac{1}{2}, 3\right\}$ **71.** $\{3, 4\}$ **73.** $\frac{3}{2}$
75. $\left\{-\frac{2}{3}, \frac{3}{2}\right\}$ **77.** $\left\{-\frac{3}{4}, 2\right\}$ **79.** $\{-5, 5\}$ **81.** $\{-1, 3\}$ **83.** $\{-3, 0\}$ **85.** $\{-7, 3\}$ **87.** $\left\{-\frac{1}{4}, \frac{3}{4}\right\}$ **89.** $\left\{\frac{-1 - \sqrt{7}}{6}, \frac{-1 + \sqrt{7}}{6}\right\}$
91. $\{2 - \sqrt{2}, 2 + \sqrt{2}\}$ **93.** $\left\{\frac{5 - \sqrt{29}}{2}, \frac{5 + \sqrt{29}}{2}\right\}$ **95.** $\left\{1, \frac{3}{2}\right\}$ **97.** No real solution **99.** $\left\{\frac{-1 - \sqrt{5}}{4}, \frac{-1 + \sqrt{5}}{4}\right\}$
101. $\left\{\frac{-\sqrt{3} - \sqrt{15}}{2}, \frac{-\sqrt{3} + \sqrt{15}}{2}\right\}$ **103.** No real solution **105.** Repeated real solution **107.** Two unequal real solutions **109.** $x = \frac{b + c}{a}$
111. $x = \frac{abc}{a + b}$ **113.** $x = a^2$ **115.** $R = \frac{R_1 R_2}{R_1 + R_2}$ **117.** $R = \frac{mv^2}{F}$ **119.** $r = \frac{S - a}{S}$ **121.** $\frac{-b + \sqrt{b^2 - 4ac}}{2a} + \frac{-b - \sqrt{b^2 - 4ac}}{2a} = \frac{-2b}{2a} = \frac{-b}{a}$
123. $k = -\frac{1}{2}$ or $\frac{1}{2}$ **125.** The solutions of $ax^2 - bx + c = 0$ are $\frac{b + \sqrt{b^2 - 4ac}}{2a}$ and $\frac{b - \sqrt{b^2 - 4ac}}{2a}$. **127.** (b)

A.7 Assess Your Understanding (page A60)

1. T **2.** 5 **3.** F **4.** real; imaginary; imaginary unit **5.** $\{-2i, 2i\}$ **6.** F **7.** T **8.** F **9.** $8 + 5i$ **11.** $-7 + 6i$ **13.** $-6 - 11i$

15. $6 - 18i$ **17.** $6 + 4i$ **19.** $10 - 5i$ **21.** 37 **23.** $\frac{6}{5} + \frac{8}{5}i$ **25.** $1 - 2i$ **27.** $\frac{5}{2} - \frac{7}{2}i$ **29.** $-\frac{1}{2} + \frac{\sqrt{3}}{2}i$ **31.** $2i$ **33.** $-i$ **35.** i **37.** -6 **39.** $-10i$

41. $-2 + 2i$ **43.** 0 **45.** 0 **47.** $2i$ **49.** $5i$ **51.** $5i$ **53.** $\{-2i, 2i\}$ **55.** $\{-4, 4\}$ **57.** $\{3 - 2i, 3 + 2i\}$ **59.** $\{3 - i, 3 + i\}$ **61.** $\left\{\frac{1}{4} - \frac{1}{4}i, \frac{1}{4} + \frac{1}{4}i\right\}$

63. $\left\{\frac{1}{5} - \frac{2}{5}i, \frac{1}{5} + \frac{2}{5}i\right\}$ **65.** $\left\{-\frac{1}{2} - \frac{\sqrt{3}}{2}i, -\frac{1}{2} + \frac{\sqrt{3}}{2}i\right\}$ **67.** $\{2, -1 - \sqrt{3}i, -1 + \sqrt{3}i\}$ **69.** $\{-2, 2, -2i, 2i\}$ **71.** $\{-3i, -2i, 2i, 3i\}$

73. Two complex solutions that are conjugates of each other **75.** Two unequal real solutions **77.** A repeated real solution

79. $2 - 3i$ **81.** 6 **83.** 25 **85.** $2 + 3i$ ohms **87.** $z + \overline{z} = (a + bi) + (a - bi) = 2a; z - \overline{z} = (a + bi) - (a - bi) = 2bi$

89. $\overline{z + w} = \overline{(a + bi) + (c + di)} = \overline{(a + c) + (b + d)i} = (a + c) - (b + d)i = (a - bi) + (c - di) = \overline{z} + \overline{w}$

A.8 Assess Your Understanding (page A69)

1. mathematical modeling **2.** interest **3.** uniform motion **4.** F **5.** T **6.** $100 - x$ **7.** $A = \pi r^2; r = $ radius, $A = $ area **9.** $A = s^2; A = $ area,
$s = $ length of a side **11.** $F = ma; F = $ force, $m = $ mass, $a = $ acceleration **13.** $W = Fd; W = $ work, $F = $ force, $d = $ distance **15.** $C = 150x;$
$C = $ total variable cost, $x = $ number of dishwashers **17.** Invest \$31,250 in bonds and \$18,750 in CDs. **19.** \$11,600 was loaned out at 8%. **21.** Mix 75 lb
of Earl Grey tea with 25 lb of Orange Pekoe tea. **23.** Mix 160 lb of cashews with the almonds. **25.** The speed of the current is 2.286 mi/hr.
27. The speed of the current is 5 mi/hr. **29.** Karen walked at 4.05 ft/sec. **31.** A doubles tennis court is 78 feet long and 36 feet wide.
33. Working together, it takes 12 min. **35. (a)** The dimensions are 10 ft by 5 ft. **(b)** The area is 50 sq ft. **(c)** The dimensions would be 7.5 ft by 7.5 ft.
(d) The area would be 56.25 sq ft. **37.** The defensive back catches up to the tight end at the tight end's 45-yd line. **39.** Add $\frac{2}{3}$ gal of water.
41. Evaporate $10\frac{2}{3}$ oz of water. **43.** 40 g of 12-karat gold should be mixed with 20 g of pure gold. **45.** Mike passes Dan $\frac{1}{3}$ mile from the start,
2 min from the time Mike started to race. **47.** The latest the auxiliary pump can be started is 9:45 AM. **49.** The tub will fill in 1 hr. **51.** Run: 12 miles;
bicycle: 75 miles. **53.** Lewis would beat Burke by 16.75 m. **55.** The dimensions should be 4 ft by 4 ft. **57.** Set the original price at \$40. At 50% off, there
will be no profit. **61.** The tail wind was 91.47 knots.

A.9 Assess Your Understanding (page A78)

5. negative **6.** closed interval **7.** $-5, 5$ **8.** $-5 < x < 5$ **9.** T **10.** T **11.** $[0, 2]; 0 \le x \le 2$ **13.** $[2, \infty); x \ge 2$ **15.** $[0, 3); 0 \le x < 3$
17. (a) $6 < 8$ **(b)** $-2 < 0$ **(c)** $9 < 15$ **(d)** $-6 > -10$ **19. (a)** $7 > 0$ **(b)** $-1 > -8$ **(c)** $12 > -9$ **(d)** $-8 < 6$ **21. (a)** $2x + 4 < 5$
(b) $2x - 4 < -3$ **(c)** $6x + 3 < 6$ **(d)** $-4x - 2 > -4$

23. $[0, 4]$

25. $[4, 6)$

27. $[4, \infty)$

29. $(-\infty, -4)$

31. $2 \le x \le 5$

33. $-3 < x < -2$

35. $x \ge 4$

37. $x < -3$

39. $<$ **41.** $>$ **43.** $\ge$ **45.** $<$ **47.** $\le$ **49.** $>$ **51.** $\ge$

53. $\{x | x < 4\}$ or $(-\infty, 4)$

55. $\{x | x \ge -1\}$ or $[-1, \infty)$

57. $\{x | x > 3\}$ or $(3, \infty)$

59. $\{x | x \ge 2\}$ or $[2, \infty)$

61. $\{x | x > -7\}$ or $(-7, \infty)$

63. $\left\{x \middle| x \le \frac{2}{3}\right\}$ or $\left(-\infty, \frac{2}{3}\right]$

65. $\{x | x < -20\}$ or $(-\infty, -20)$

67. $\left\{x \middle| x \ge \frac{4}{3}\right\}$ or $\left[\frac{4}{3}, \infty\right)$

69. $\{x | 3 \le x \le 5\}$ or $[3, 5]$

71. $\left\{x \middle| \frac{2}{3} \le x \le 3\right\}$ or $\left[\frac{2}{3}, 3\right]$

73. $\left\{x \middle| -\frac{11}{2} < x < \frac{1}{2}\right\}$ or $\left(-\frac{11}{2}, \frac{1}{2}\right)$

75. $\{x | -6 < x < 0\}$ or $(-6, 0)$

77. $\{x | x < -5\}$ or $(-\infty, -5)$

79. $\{x | x \ge -1\}$ or $[-1, \infty)$

81. $\left\{x \middle| \frac{1}{2} \le x < \frac{5}{4}\right\}$ or $\left[\frac{1}{2}, \frac{5}{4}\right)$

83. $\left\{x \middle| x < -\frac{1}{2}\right\}$ or $\left(-\infty, -\frac{1}{2}\right)$

85. $\left\{x \middle| x > \frac{10}{3}\right\}$ or $\left(\frac{10}{3}, \infty\right)$

87. $\{x | x > 3\}$ or $(3, \infty)$

89. $\{x | -4 < x < 4\}; (-4, 4)$

91. $\{x | x < -4 \text{ or } x > 4\}; (-\infty, -4) \cup (4, \infty)$

93. $\{x | 0 \le x \le 1\}; [0, 1]$ **95.** $\{x | x < -1 \text{ or } x > 2\}; (-\infty -1) \cup (2, \infty)$ **97.** $\{x | -1 \le x \le 1\}; [-1, 1]$ **99.** $\{x | x \le -2 \text{ or } x \ge 2\}; (-\infty, -2] \cup [2, \infty)$

101. $|x - 2| < \frac{1}{2}$; $\left\{ x \middle| \frac{3}{2} < x < \frac{5}{2} \right\}$ **103.** $|x + 3| > 2$; $\{x | x < -5 \text{ or } x > -1\}$ **105.** $\{x | x \geq -2\}$ **107.** $21 < \text{Age} < 30$ **109. (a)** Male ≥ 76.60 years
(b) Female ≥ 81.03 years **(c)** A female can expect to live 4.43 years longer. **111.** The agent's commission ranges from \$45,000 to \$95,000, inclusive.
As a percent of selling price, the commission ranges from 5% to 8.6%, inclusive. **113.** The amount withheld varies from \$84.10 to \$134.10, inclusive.
115. The usage varies from 675 kW · hr to 2500 kW · hr, inclusive. **117.** The dealer's cost varies from \$15,254.24 to \$16,071.43, inclusive.
119. (a) You need at least a 74 on the fifth test. **(b)** You need at least a 77 on the fifth test.

121. $\dfrac{a + b}{2} - a = \dfrac{a + b - 2a}{2} = \dfrac{b - a}{2} > 0$; therefore, $a < \dfrac{a + b}{2}$.

$b - \dfrac{a + b}{2} = \dfrac{2b - a - b}{2} = \dfrac{b - a}{2} > 0$; therefore, $b > \dfrac{a + b}{2}$.

123. $(\sqrt{ab})^2 - a^2 = ab - a^2 = a(b - a) > 0$; thus $(\sqrt{ab})^2 > a^2$ and $\sqrt{ab} > a$.

$b^2 - (\sqrt{ab})^2 = b^2 - ab = b(b - a) > 0$; thus $b^2 > (\sqrt{ab})^2$ and $b > \sqrt{ab}$.

125. $h - a = \dfrac{2ab}{a + b} - a = \dfrac{ab - a^2}{a + b} = \dfrac{a(b - a)}{a + b} > 0$; thus $h > a$.

$b - h = b - \dfrac{2ab}{a + b} = \dfrac{b^2 - ab}{a + b} = \dfrac{b(b - a)}{a + b} > 0$; thus $h < b$.

127. Since $0 < a < b$, then $a - b < 0$ and $\dfrac{a - b}{ab} < 0$.

So $\dfrac{a}{ab} - \dfrac{b}{ab} < 0$, or $\dfrac{1}{b} - \dfrac{1}{a} < 0$. Therefore, $\dfrac{1}{b} < \dfrac{1}{a}$. And $0 < \dfrac{1}{b}$ because $b > 0$.

A.10 Assess Your Understanding *(page A87)*

3. index **4.** T **5.** cube root **6.** F **7.** 3 **9.** -2 **11.** $2\sqrt{2}$ **13.** $-2x\sqrt[3]{x}$ **15.** $x^3 y^2$ **17.** $x^2 y$ **19.** $6\sqrt{x}$ **21.** $6x\sqrt{x}$ **23.** $15\sqrt[3]{3}$ **25.** $12\sqrt{3}$
27. $7\sqrt{2}$ **29.** $\sqrt{2}$ **31.** $2\sqrt{3}$ **33.** $-\sqrt[3]{2}$ **35.** $x - 2\sqrt{x} + 1$ **37.** $(2x - 1)\sqrt[3]{2x}$ **39.** $(2x - 15)\sqrt{2x}$ **41.** $-(x + 5y)\sqrt[3]{2xy}$ **43.** $\dfrac{\sqrt{2}}{2}$
45. $-\dfrac{\sqrt{15}}{5}$ **47.** $\dfrac{(5 + \sqrt{2})\sqrt{3}}{23}$ **49.** $\dfrac{8\sqrt{5} - 19}{41}$ **51.** $\dfrac{5\sqrt[3]{4}}{2}$ **53.** $\dfrac{2x + h - 2\sqrt{x^2 + xh}}{h}$ **55.** $\left\{ \dfrac{9}{2} \right\}$ **57.** $\{3\}$ **59.** 4 **61.** -3 **63.** 64 **65.** $\dfrac{1}{27}$
67. $\dfrac{27\sqrt{2}}{32}$ **69.** $\dfrac{27\sqrt{2}}{32}$ **71.** $x^{7/12}$ **73.** xy^2 **75.** $x^{2/3}y$ **77.** $\dfrac{8x^{5/4}}{y^{3/4}}$ **79.** 1.41 **81.** 1.59 **83.** 4.89 **85.** 2.15 **87.** $\dfrac{3x + 2}{(1 + x)^{1/2}}$ **89.** $\dfrac{x(3x^2 + 2)}{(x^2 + 1)^{1/2}}$
91. $\dfrac{22x + 5}{10\sqrt{x} - 5\sqrt{4x + 3}}$ **93.** $\dfrac{2 + x}{2(1 + x)^{3/2}}$ **95.** $\dfrac{4 - x}{(x + 4)^{3/2}}$ **97.** $\dfrac{1}{x^2(x^2 - 1)^{1/2}}$ **99.** $\dfrac{1 - 3x^2}{2\sqrt{x}(1 + x^2)^2}$ **101.** $\dfrac{1}{2}(5x + 2)(x + 1)^{1/2}$
103. $2x^{1/2}(3x - 4)(x + 1)$ **105.** $(x^2 + 4)^{1/3}(11x^2 + 12)$ **107.** $(3x + 5)^{1/3}(2x + 3)^{1/2}(17x + 27)$ **109.** $\dfrac{3(x + 2)}{2x^{1/2}}$

111. (a) 15,660.4 gal **(b)** 390.7 gal **113.** $2\sqrt{2}\pi \approx 8.89$ sec **115.** $\dfrac{\pi\sqrt{3}}{6} \approx 0.91$ sec

APPENDIX B Graphing Utilities

B.1 Exercises *(page B2)*

1. $(-1, 4)$; II **3.** $(3, 1)$; I **5.** $X\text{min} = -6, X\text{max} = 6, X\text{scl} = 2, Y\text{min} = -4, Y\text{max} = 4, Y\text{scl} = 2$
7. $X\text{min} = -6, X\text{max} = 6, X\text{scl} = 2, Y\text{min} = -1, Y\text{max} = 3, Y\text{scl} = 1$ **9.** $X\text{min} = 3, X\text{max} = 9, X\text{scl} = 1, Y\text{min} = 2, Y\text{max} = 10, Y\text{scl} = 2$
11. $X\text{min} = -11, X\text{max} = 5, X\text{scl} = 1, Y\text{min} = -3, Y\text{max} = 6, Y\text{scl} = 1$
13. $X\text{min} = -30, X\text{max} = 50, X\text{scl} = 10, Y\text{min} = -90, Y\text{max} = 50, Y\text{scl} = 10$
15. $X\text{min} = -10, X\text{max} = 110, X\text{scl} = 10, Y\text{min} = -10, Y\text{max} = 160, Y\text{scl} = 10$

B.2 Exercises *(page B4)*

1. (a)
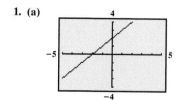
(b)
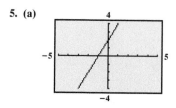
3. (a)
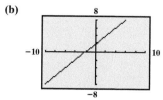
(b)
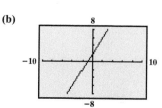

5. (a)
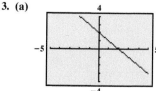
(b)
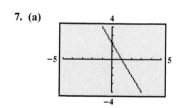
7. (a)
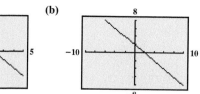
(b)
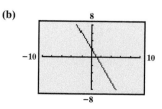

9. (a) 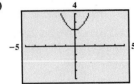 **(b)** 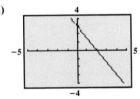 **11. (a)** 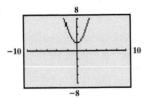 **(b)**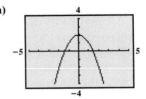

13. (a) **(b)** **15. (a)** **(b)**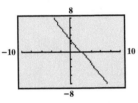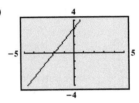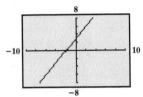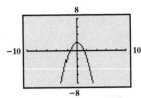

17. Y₁=X+2

19. Y₁=-X+2

21. Y₁=2X+2

23. Y₁=-2X+2

25. Y₁=X²+2

27. Y₁=-X²+2

29. Y₁=-(3/2)X+3

31. Y₁=(3/2)X+3

B.3 Exercises *(page B6)*

1. −3.41   **3.** −1.71   **5.** −0.28   **7.** 3.00   **9.** 4.50   **11.** 1.00, 23.00

B.5 Exercises *(page B8)*

1. Yes   **3.** Yes   **5.** No   **7.** Yes   **9.** Answers may vary. A possible answer is $Y\text{min} = 4$, $Y\text{max} = 12$, and $Y\text{scl} = 1$.

Index

CONICS

Parabola

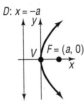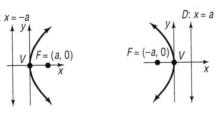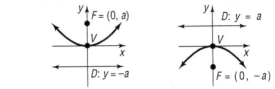

$$y^2 = 4ax \qquad y^2 = -4ax \qquad x^2 = 4ay \qquad x^2 = -4ay$$

Ellipse

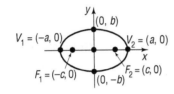 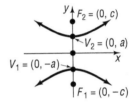

$$\frac{x^2}{a^2} + \frac{y^2}{b^2} = 1, \quad a > b, \quad c^2 = a^2 - b^2 \qquad\qquad \frac{x^2}{b^2} + \frac{y^2}{a^2} = 1, \quad a > b, \quad c^2 = a^2 - b^2$$

Hyperbola

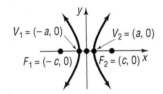

$$\frac{x^2}{a^2} - \frac{y^2}{b^2} = 1, \quad c^2 = a^2 + b^2$$

$$\text{Asymptotes:} \quad y = \frac{b}{a}x, \quad y = -\frac{b}{a}x$$

$$\frac{y^2}{a^2} - \frac{x^2}{b^2} = 1, \quad c^2 = a^2 + b^2$$

$$\text{Asymptotes:} \quad y = \frac{a}{b}x, \quad y = -\frac{a}{b}x$$

PROPERTIES OF LOGARITHMS

$$\log_a(MN) = \log_a M + \log_a N$$

$$\log_a\left(\frac{M}{N}\right) = \log_a M - \log_a N$$

$$\log_a M^r = r\log_a M$$

$$\log_a M = \frac{\log M}{\log a} = \frac{\ln M}{\ln a}$$

$$a^x = e^{x \ln a}$$

PERMUTATIONS/COMBINATIONS

$$0! = 1 \qquad 1! = 1$$
$$n! = n(n-1)\cdot \ldots \cdot (3)(2)(1)$$

$$P(n,r) = \frac{n!}{(n-r)!}$$

$$C(n,r) = \binom{n}{r} = \frac{n!}{(n-r)!\,r!}$$

BINOMIAL THEOREM

$$(a+b)^n = a^n + \binom{n}{1}ba^{n-1} + \binom{n}{2}b^2 a^{n-2}$$
$$+ \cdots + \binom{n}{n-1}b^{n-1}a + b^n$$

ARITHMETIC SEQUENCE

$$a_1 + (a_1 + d) + (a_1 + 2d) + \cdots + [a_1 + (n-1)d]$$
$$= \frac{n}{2}[2a_1 + (n-1)d] = \frac{n}{2}[a_1 + a_n]$$

GEOMETRIC SEQUENCE

$$a_1 + a_1 r + a_1 r^2 + \cdots + a_1 r^{n-1} = a_1 \cdot \frac{1 - r^n}{1 - r}$$

GEOMETRIC SERIES

$$\text{If } |r| < 1, a_1 + a_1 r + a_1 r^2 + \cdots = \sum_{k=1}^{\infty} a_1 r^{k-1}$$
$$= \frac{a_1}{1 - r}$$

LIBRARY OF FUNCTIONS

Identity Function
$f(x) = x$

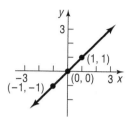

Square Function
$f(x) = x^2$

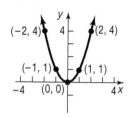

Cube Function
$f(x) = x^3$

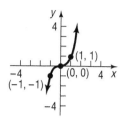

Square Root Function
$f(x) = \sqrt{x}$

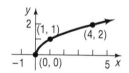

Reciprocal Function
$f(x) = \dfrac{1}{x}$

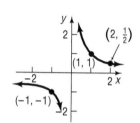

Cube Root Function
$f(x) = \sqrt[3]{x}$

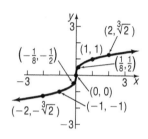

Absolute Value Function
$f(x) = |x|$

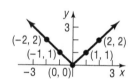

Exponential Function
$f(x) = e^x$

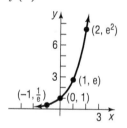

Natural Logarithm Function
$f(x) = \ln x$

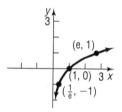

Sine Function
$f(x) = \sin x$

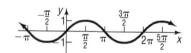

Cosine Function
$f(x) = \cos x$

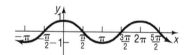

Tangent Function
$f(x) = \tan x$

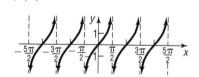

Cosecant Function
$f(x) = \csc x$

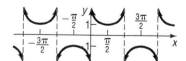

Secant Function
$f(x) = \sec x$

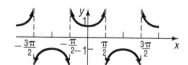

Cotangent Function
$f(x) = \cot x$

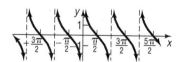

FORMULAS/EQUATIONS

Distance Formula

If $P_1 = (x_1, y_1)$ and $P_2 = (x_2, y_2)$, the distance from P_1 to P_2 is

$$d(P_1, P_2) = \sqrt{(x_2 - x_1)^2 + (y_2 - y_1)^2}$$

Standard Equation of a Circle

The standard equation of a circle of radius r with center at (h, k) is

$$(x - h)^2 + (y - k)^2 = r^2$$

Slope Formula

The slope m of the line containing the points $P_1 = (x_1, y_1)$ and $P_2 = (x_2, y_2)$ is

$$m = \frac{y_2 - y_1}{x_2 - x_1} \qquad \text{if } x_1 \neq x_2$$

$$m \text{ is undefined} \qquad \text{if } x_1 = x_2$$

Point–Slope Equation of a Line

The equation of a line with slope m containing the point (x_1, y_1) is

$$y - y_1 = m(x - x_1)$$

Slope–Intercept Equation of a Line

The equation of a line with slope m and y-intercept b is

$$y = mx + b$$

Quadratic Formula

The solutions of the equation $ax^2 + bx + c = 0, a \neq 0$, are

$$x = \frac{-b \pm \sqrt{b^2 - 4ac}}{2a}$$

If $b^2 - 4ac > 0$, there are two unequal real solutions.
If $b^2 - 4ac = 0$, there is a repeated real solution.
If $b^2 - 4ac < 0$, there are two complex solutions that are not real.

GEOMETRY FORMULAS

Circle

$r = $ Radius, $\quad A = $ Area, $\quad C = $ Circumference
$$A = \pi r^2 \qquad C = 2\pi r$$

Triangle

$b = $ Base, $\quad h = $ Altitude (Height), $\quad A = $ area
$$A = \tfrac{1}{2}bh$$

Rectangle

$l = $ Length, $\quad w = $ Width, $\quad A = $ area, $\quad P = $ perimeter
$$A = lw \qquad P = 2l + 2w$$

Rectangular Box

$l = $ Length, $\quad w = $ Width, $\quad h = $ Height, $\quad V = $ Volume, $\quad S = $ Surface area
$$V = lwh \qquad S = 2lw + 2lh + 2wh$$

Sphere

$r = $ Radius, $\quad V = $ Volume, $\quad S = $ Surface area
$$V = \tfrac{4}{3}\pi r^3 \qquad S = 4\pi r^2$$

Right Circular Cylinder

$r = $ Radius, $\quad h = $ Height, $\quad V = $ Volume, $\quad S = $ Surface area
$$V = \pi r^2 h \qquad S = 2\pi r^2 + 2\pi rh$$